Marc Honigsberg

BIOLOGY

BIOLOGY

BY HELENA CURTIS

BIOLOGY

ILLUSTRATIONS BY SHIRLEY BATY

PICTURE EDITOR: ANNE FELDMAN

DESIGNED BY MALCOLM GREAR / GORDON BRETT

TYPE SET IN PALATINO BY CONNECTICUT PRINTERS, INC.

PRINTED BY CONNECTICUT PRINTERS, INC.

ON S. D. WARREN'S BOOKMAN THIN

BOUND BY J. F. TAPLEY COMPANY

WORTH PUBLISHERS, INC.

171 MADISON AVENUE

NEW YORK, NEW YORK 10016

This book is dedicated to C. P. Rhoads, M. D.

PREFACE

This book is the result of an unusually broad cooperative venture. There were several essential factors in this venture. My own contribution was my long experience as a professional writer in the field of biology and a desire to communicate my interests and enthusiasms about the subject. Second, and more important, was the arrival on the publishing scene of a vigorous young company with fresh ideas and initiative. The third and by far the most important factor was the willingness of a large number of teachers and experts in all fields of biology to lend their assistance at every stage of the planning, writing, and innumerable revisions of the manuscript and illustrations.

Our purpose was to write a book for students who are taking biology as their first science course in college. This is a particularly interesting group of students from the point of view of one concerned with science and with education. For a great many of them, it will be their only exposure to science in their academic career. What is it we want them to learn within this short period of time, and how can we best achieve this purpose? I personally feel that there is no reason to present an "easier" or less challenging course in science to the student who will major in the humanities or the social sciences than to the student who will go on to be a biology or physics major. In fact, I could present a case for the opposite approach. I think we all agree, however, that the emphasis should be somewhat different. There is no point, for example, in stressing the acquisition of a large amount of detailed data or, in particular, an exhaustive technical vocabulary unless the student is going to continue to use this material, since it will be, at best, memorized and forgotten. On the other hand, new ideas and new ways of looking at things tend to endure, and nothing tugs so persistently at the strings of memory as an interesting unanswered question. So, therefore, we have tried to deal with broad ideas, to remind the student, and ourselves, of the fundamental questions and concerns of biology, and also to show them how biologists themselves ask questions and seek answers.

The unifying theme of the book is evolution, which is, of course, a unifying concept of all biology. The Introduction, which discusses the background and the essential ideas of Darwinian evolution, provides a perspective that will be useful to the student throughout his study of biology. The rest of the book is designed as a series of movements from past to present, from simpler to more complex, from the cell considered in isolation to the biosphere.

Each teacher will adapt the book to his own particular needs and interests and those of his class. Although it is true that high schools are offering more and more in the way of science teaching, most students now entering college have not had a thorough grounding in either biology or chemistry. The first half of the book, the three sections covering Cells, Organisms, and Genetics, was planned with such students in mind. For students with a better background in the sciences, the chapters on cell chemistry, for instance, or taxonomy, or classical genetics, may be used as reviews, with teaching emphasis placed upon the more recent material.

In the second half of the book, we have covered areas of biology in which much new and exciting work is being done: Development, Behavior, and Population Biology and Ecology. These draw upon information offered from a different point of view in the early chapters, and particularly in the last section, we have attempted to bring together many of the previous themes of the story and to leave the student with a sense of his place in the world of living things. The teacher who has limited time at his disposal may want to select only one of these sections, or isolated chapters from each, to give a flavor of the work in these different fields. I would hope that at least one of them could be pursued in depth.

We have tried throughout to illustrate and illuminate the ideas of biology with concrete examples, not only in words but in the many drawings and photographs that accompany the text. Some topics such as cell chemistry, concepts of molecular biology, mitosis and meiosis, and alternation of generations can be particularly difficult to understand and so have been given special attention and have been illustrated more extensively for additional clarity. Many illustrations are accompanied by measurement scales in order to awaken the student's realization that he is looking at a living organism which exists outside of a biology text.

Although we have not hesitated to make use of new and sometimes complicated material when it seemed pertinent, we have tried in such cases to give the student special assistance with it. For example, each electron micrograph is accompanied by a labeled diagram to aid the student in picking out the elements in the micrograph. Unfamiliar terms and, in particular, new and crucial concepts are defined in the unusually ample glossary. At the end of each section, we have provided a bibliography which includes both sources of additional information on special subjects for the more ambitious student and books that can be read for pleasure by any interested amateur. We have not included *Scientific American* reprints in the bibliographies, since complete lists of articles are generally available, but we do recommend them highly.

In addition to the principal consultants to the book, whose names are listed on page x and to whom my indebtedness is unlimited, I express my thanks to the many teachers throughout the country who gave their opinions about what they considered the most important topics to be studied by general biology students and what features should be emphasized, thus helping greatly in the formulation of the original plan for the book. I also record my particular appreciation to the following teachers, writers, and investigators, who helped me by reviewing various sections of the book during its many stages of development.

Jay Martin Anderson, Bryn Mawr College; Daniel Arnon, University of California, Berkeley; Andrew S. Bajer, University of Oregon; Edwin M. Banks, University of Illinois; Alan P. Brockway, University of Colorado, Denver; John Buettner-Janusch, Duke University School of Medicine; Allison L. Burnett, Case Western Reserve University; A. G. W. Cameron, Institute for Space Studies; Sir Wilfrid Le Gros Clark, Oxford University; Mary E. Clutter, Yale University; Carleton S. Coon, University of Pennsylvania; Thomas Eisner, Cornell University; B. E. Frye, University of Michigan; J. Woodland Hastings, Harvard University; Harold Hempling, Cornell University School of Medicine; W. W. Howells, Harvard University; Lionel Jaffe, University of Pennsylvania; Ursula Johnson, Harvard University; Bostwick H. Ketchum, Woods Hole Oceanographic Institute; Donald L. Kimmel, Jr., Brown University; John H. Law, University of Chicago; Monte Lloyd, University of Chicago; Charles F. Lytle, Pennsylvania State University; Everett Mendelsohn, Harvard University; Thomas R. Mertens, Ball State University; Roger Milkman, Syracuse University; Ingirth Deyrup-Olsen, University of Washington, Seattle; Lee D. Peachey, University of Pennsylvania; Shepherd K. Roberts, Temple University; Arnold Ross, American Museum of Natural History; Roberts Rugh, Columbia Presbyterian Medical Center; Joseph Schwab, University of Chicago; Malcolm S. Steinberg, Princeton University; Mary E. Townes, North Carolina College; Charles A. West, University of California, Los Angeles, John S. Willis, University of Illinois; Emil Witschi, Universität Basel.

I would like to acknowledge my debt to the staff of Worth Publishers, who organized this large undertaking, and in particular, to Walter Meagher, who aided and encouraged me through every stage of the book. I was greatly assisted by Mrs. Jean Ely, who provided editorial assistance and supplied captions and summaries.

I feel particularly privileged to be writing for young people; I like their curiosity, their energies, their imaginativeness, and their dislike of the pompous and the pedantic. I hope I serve them well.

HELENA CURTIS

Woods Hole, Massachusetts
December, 1967

CONSULTANTS

SECTION 1   CELLS

KEITH R. PORTER
Harvard University

ALBERT L. LEHNINGER
Johns Hopkins School of Medicine

SECTION 2   ORGANISMS

PETER H. RAVEN
Stanford University

SECTION 3   GENETICS

WALTER F. BODMER
Stanford University

SECTION 4   DEVELOPMENT

CLIFFORD L. GROBSTEIN
University of California, La Jolla

SECTION 5   BEHAVIOR

EDWARD O. WILSON
Harvard University

SECTION 6   POPULATION BIOLOGY AND ECOLOGY

RICHARD C. LEWONTIN
University of Chicago

ROBERT H. MacARTHUR
Princeton University

TABLE OF CONTENTS

PREFACE   vii

INTRODUCTION   1

SECTION 1

CELLS

CHAPTER 1–1

ORIGIN OF CELLS   15

The Formation of Our Solar System   15

Dating the Past   17

The Beginning of Life   21

The Development of Photosynthesis   23

The Coming of Oxygen   24

Summary   26

CHAPTER 1–2

CELLS AS ORGANISMS:
THE ONE-CELLED PLANTS AND ANIMALS   27

ESSAY: *Measuring the Microscopic World*   28

Chlamydomonas   29

Euglena   29

Amoeba   30

Paramecium   32

Euplotes   34

Summary   36

CHAPTER 1–3

CELL STRUCTURE AND PROCESSES   37

Some Basic Cell Processes   37

Diffusion   41

Osmosis   41

ESSAY: *How the Cell Theory Developed*   42

Active Transport   43

The Anatomy of Cells   43

Cilia and Flagella   43

The Cell Wall   45

The Cell Membrane   46

The Cytoplasm   47

The Organelles   47

Summary   55

CHAPTER 1–4

THE CELL NUCLEUS   56

The Nucleolus   56

Chromatin   56

Nuclear Functions   57

Replication of Nuclear Material   59

Mitosis   59

Meiosis   65

Summary   69

CHAPTER 1–5

SOMATIC CELLS 70

Plant Cells 71

Specialists in Photosynthesis 71

Protector Cells 72

Conducting Cells 72

Support Cells 74

Cells for Growth 74

Animal Cells 75

Protector Cells 75

Chemist Cells 77

Connective and Supporting Cells 77

Muscle 80

The Bloodstream 84

The Nervous System 86

Summary 91

CHAPTER 1–6

THE CHEMISTRY OF THE LIVING CELL 93

The Fundamental Particles 94

The Structure of the Atom 94

Energy and the Electron 96

Valence 97

Electrolytes in Living Cells 98

Chemical Bonds 100

Molecular Bonds 100

Weak Bonds 105

ESSAY: *Quantitative Measurements in Chemical Reactions* 106

Chemical Reactions 108

Types of Reactions 108

The Energy Factor 109

Chemical Equilibrium 110

Acids and Bases 111

Summary 115

CHAPTER 1–7

BIOLOGICAL MOLECULES 117

Carbohydrates 117

Lipids 120

Informational Macromolecules 123

Proteins 123

Nucleic Acids 132

Summary 136

CHAPTER 1–8

THE FLOW OF ENERGY 138

Energy Laws 138

Energy Flow in Living Systems 140

Energy Transfer in Cells 149

Photosynthesis 150

Summary 155

SECTION 2

ORGANISMS

CHAPTER 2–1

THE NAMING OF LIVING ORGANISMS 159

John Ray and the Catalog of Nature 159

Binomials: the "Two-name" System 162

The Major Categories of Living Things 163

A Question of Kingdoms 166

Summary 167

CHAPTER 2–2

BACTERIA, VIRUSES, AND BLUE-GREEN ALGAE 169

The Bacteria 169

The Viruses 172

The Blue-green Algae 174

Summary 176

CHAPTER 2–3

THE FIRST PLANTS: THE THALLOPHYTES 177

The Algae 177
The Chlorophyta 178
Other Algae Groups 184

The Fungi 189
The Fungi and Man 189
Biology of the Fungi 191
Classes of Fungi 193

The Lichens 195

The Slime Molds 197
Summary 198

CHAPTER 2–4

THE TRANSITION TO LAND 200

The Bryophyta: Mosses and Liverworts 201
Sexual Cycles in the Bryophyta 201

The Tracheophyta: The Vascular Plants 202
The Psilopsida 203
The Lycopsida 204
The Sphenopsida 205
The Pteropsida 205
ESSAY: *Modes of Pollination* 216
Summary 218

CHAPTER 2–5

THE LIFE OF THE PLANT 220
Growth 220
Conducting Systems 225
Regulatory Systems in Plants 229
Growth Cycles and Dormancy 235
Circadian Rhythms in Plants 240
Summary 243

CHAPTER 2–6

THE LOWER INVERTEBRATES 245
Introduction 245

Classification of Animals 247
The Protozoa 247
Sponges 251
The Coelenterates 253
The Flatworms 259
The Annelids 262
The Mollusks 268
The Echinoderms 273
Summary 276

CHAPTER 2–7

THE HIGHER ANIMALS: ARTHROPODS AND CHORDATES 278
Arthropods 278
ESSAY: *Termites* 289
Chordates 291

Evolutionary History 293
How Animals May Have Originated 293
The Coelomates 295
The Evolution of the Chordates 296
Summary 302

CHAPTER 2–8

HOW ANIMALS LIVE 307
Respiration and Breathing 307
Digestion 308
Circulation 310
Excretion, Chemical Regulation, and Water Balance 314
ESSAY: *Special Problems in Water Balance* 318
Reproduction 321

Regulatory Systems 326
Endocrine System: The Hormones 326

ESSAY: *Temperature Regulation*   327

Interactions of the Endocrine and Nervous Systems   332

The Nervous System   332

Biological Clocks   339

Summary   341

SECTION 3

GENETICS

PART I

CLASSICAL GENETICS

CHAPTER 3–1

CONCEPTS OF HEREDITY   347

Early Ideas About Heredity   348

The First Experiments   349

ESSAY: *Spontaneous Generation*   350

The Cell Theory   352

Mendel's Experiments   353

Summary   359

CHAPTER 3–2

THE PHYSICAL BASIS OF HEREDITY   360

The Discovery of Chromosomes   360

The Mechanism of Heredity   361

ESSAY: *Mitosis and Meiosis*   362

Cytology and Genetics Meet: Sutton's Hypothesis   362

Exceptions to Mendel's Principles   368

Genes in Populations: The Hardy-Weinberg Law   369

Mendelian Inheritance in Man   374

Summary   379

CHAPTER 3–3

CHROMOSOME MAPS   381

Sex Chromosomes   381

The Famous Fruit Fly   382

Sex-linked Characteristics   383

Linkage and Crossing-over   386

Mapping the Chromosome   388

Giant Chromosomes   391

Sex Determination   392

Human Autosomal Abnormalities   396

Summary   398

PART II

MOLECULAR GENETICS

CHAPTER 3–4

MOLDS AND MICROBES   400

Gene-Enzyme Relationships   400

One Gene, One Protein   406

The Chemistry of the Gene: DNA vs. Protein   408

The Nature of DNA   409

Summary   412

CHAPTER 3–5

DEOXYRIBONUCLEIC ACID   413

The Role of DNA in Viral Infection   413

Further Evidence for DNA   417

ESSAY: *How Scientists Investigate the Atomic Structure of a Molecule*   418

The Hypothesis is Confirmed   418

The Watson-Crick Model   419

Support for the Watson-Crick Structure   424

Summary   425

CHAPTER 3–6

THE MAKING OF PROTEINS   427

The Genetic Code   427

The RNAs   428

The RNAs in Protein Biosynthesis: A Summary 432

"Breaking the Code" 434

Summary 438

CHAPTER 3–7

MAPPING MOLECULES 439

Maps of E. coli 439

The Structure of the Gene 444

ESSAY: *The Molecular Basis of Recombination* 449

T4 Bacteriophage 452

Turning the Genes On and Off 454

Colinearity 456

Summary 458

Work in Progress 459

SECTION 4

DEVELOPMENT

CHAPTER 4–1

SIMPLE COMPONENTS OF DEVELOPMENT 463

Introduction 463

One-celled Organisms: Growth and Replication 463

Cellular Slime Molds: Multicellularity 465

ESSAY: *Differentiation and Morphogenesis* 466

Sponges 472

Hydras: Constancy and Change 473

ESSAY: *Polarity and Differentiation in Hydra: An Hypothesis* 476

Summary 479

CHAPTER 4–2

INTERACTIONS IN DEVELOPMENT 481

Nuclear Determinants 482

Cytoplasmic Determinants 483

Biography of a Sea Urchin 486

Summary 494

CHAPTER 4–3

CONTINUOUS DEVELOPMENT—THE SKIN 495

The Skin Surface 495

The Skin in Cross Section 498

Morphogenesis: The Formation of Hair 499

The Epidermis: A Turnover System 501

Cell Differentiation: Tissue Interactions 505

Dedifferentiation and New Growth 506

Summary 509

CHAPTER 4–4

DEVELOPMENT IN VERTEBRATES: FOCUS ON THE MOUSE 510

Gametogenesis 510

Fertilization 514

Implantation 515

Embryology and Evolution 516

ESSAY: *Embryology and Evolution* 519

Interpretation of the Mouse Embryo 528

Organogenesis 531

Summary 537

CHAPTER 4–5

HEREDITY AND ITS MODIFICATION 538

Tracking the Germ Cells 539

Proving Weismann's Hypothesis 540

Sex Determination 542

Summary 545

SECTION 5

BEHAVIOR

INTRODUCTION 549

CHAPTER 5–1

BEGINNINGS OF BEHAVIOR: THE LOWER INVERTEBRATES 552

The Basic Responses of Living Creatures 552
ESSAY: *Learning in Paramecia* 557
The Development of the Nerve System 557
The Coming of the Brain 559
The Simpler Mollusks 561
The Octopus 563
Summary 569

CHAPTER 5–2

ORGANIZATION OF ARTHROPOD BEHAVIOR 570

Arthropod Nervous Systems 570
Arthropod Vision 572
Touch 575
Hearing 577
Smell and Taste 578
Communication 581
Built-in Behavior 586
Summary 587

CHAPTER 5–3

BASES OF VERTEBRATE BEHAVIOR 589

The Brain 591
The Hindbrain 591
The Midbrain 592
The Forebrain 592
The Special Senses 596

The Vertebrate Eye 596
Chemoreceptors 600
Phonoreceptors 603
Other Sensory Organs 608
The Endocrine System 610
Hormones and Behavior 610
Endocrine Activity and Behavior in Birds 610
Summary 613

CHAPTER 5–4

INSTINCT, LEARNING AND MEMORY 614

Instinct 614
Criteria of Instinctive Behavior 615
Analysis of Instinct 617
Learning 624
Categories of Learning 624
Imprinting 626
Learning in the Laboratory 628
Memory 631
The Search for the Engram 631
The Molecule-code Theory of Memory 634
Summary 636

CHAPTER 5–5

SOCIAL BEHAVIOR 638

Mating Rituals 638
Care of the Young 641
Animal Colonies 643
Social Dominance 644
Territoriality 645
Fighting Among Animals 647
Population Control 650
Insect Societies 650
Affectional Systems 656
Summary 660

SECTION 6

POPULATION BIOLOGY AND
ECOLOGY

| INTRODUCTION | 665 |

CHAPTER 6-1

POPULATION GENETICS	668
Modern Evolutionary Theory	668
Stability and Variation	671
Maintaining Variation	679
Summary	690

CHAPTER 6-2

THE PROCESSES OF EVOLUTION	691
The Ratio of Increase	691
Evolution in a Man-Made Environment	692
Speciation	698
Geographic Isolation	699
Other Factors in Speciation	704
How Species Are Maintained	706
Hybrids	709
Speciation by Chromosomal Changes	709
Differences between Plants and Animals	711
Macroevolution	712
Extinction	715
Summary	715

CHAPTER 6-3

THE NUMBERS OF PLANTS AND ANIMALS	717
Reproduction and Mortality	717
Reproductive Rates	717
Reproductive Success	721
Mortality Rates	721
Environmental Resistance	722
Food Supply	723
Predation	723

Disease	734
Self-regulation of Animal Populations	737
The Number of Species	740
Ecological Niches	740
The Niche and Interspecies Competition	744
Why Are There So Many Species?	746
Summary	747

CHAPTER 6-4

THE PLANTS AND ANIMALS AT HOME	749
The Biosphere	749
Seascapes and Landscapes: The Biomes	750
The Sea	750
The Land	758
The Inland Waters	771
ESSAY: *The World's Oldest Lake*	771
Biological Regulation of the Community	774
Ecological Succession	774
Energy Flow in Ecosystems	778
Summary	783

CHAPTER 6-5

THE EVOLUTION OF MAN	785
The First Mammals	786
The Early Primates	788
The Prosimians	790
The Anthropoidea	792
The Road to Modern Man	796
Present Courses of Evolution	805
Summary	808

APPENDIX 1: CLASSIFICATION OF ORGANISMS	812
APPENDIX 2: GEOLOGICAL ERAS	822
GLOSSARY	823
INDEX	843

xvii   *Table of Contents*

"Afterwards, on becoming very intimate with Fitz-Roy [the captain of the Beagle], I heard that I had run a very narrow risk of being rejected on account of the shape of my nose! He . . . was convinced that he could judge of a man's character by the outline of his features; and he doubted whether anyone with my nose could possess sufficient energy and determination for the voyage. But I think he was afterwards well satisfied that my nose had spoken falsely." (Radio Times Hulton Picture Library)

INTRODUCTION

In 1831, a young Englishman, Charles Darwin, sailed from Devonport on what was to prove the most consequential voyage in the history of biology. Not yet twenty-three, Darwin had already abandoned a proposed career in medicine—he describes himself as fleeing a surgical theater in which an operation was being performed on an unanesthetized child—and was a reluctant candidate for the clergy, a profession deemed more suitable for the younger son of an English gentleman. An indifferent student, Darwin was an ardent hunter and fisherman, a collector of beetles, mollusks, and shells, and an amateur botanist and geologist. When the captain of the surveying ship *Beagle,* himself only a little older than Darwin, offered passage and a berth in his own cabin to any young man who would volunteer to go without pay as a naturalist, Darwin eagerly seized the opportunity to escape from Cambridge. This voyage, which lasted five years, shaped the course of Darwin's future work. He returned to an inherited fortune, an estate in the English countryside, and a lifetime of work and study.

The Road to Evolutionary Theory

That Darwin was the founder of the modern theory of evolution is well known. In order to understand the meaning of his theory, however, it is useful to look briefly at the intellectual climate in which it was formulated.

THE LADDER OF LIFE

Aristotle, the first great biologist, believed that all living things could be arranged in a hierarchy. This hierarchy became known as the *Scala Naturae,* or ladder of nature, in which the simplest creatures had a humble position on the bottommost rung, man occupied the top, and all other organisms had their proper places between. European biologists of more modern times also believed in a "ladder of life," as it was sometimes called. But whereas to Aristotle, living organisms had always existed, the later

Europeans, in harmony with the teachings of the Scriptures, believed that all living things were the products of a divine creation. In either case, the concept that prevailed for 2,000 years was that all the kinds, or species (*species* simply means "kinds"), of animals had come into existence in their present form. Even those who believed in spontaneous generation (toads forming from the mud and snakes from a lady's hair dropped in a rain barrel) did not believe that any species had a historical relationship to any other one—any common ancestry, so to speak.

One of the more famous biologists who believed in original creation was Carolus Linnaeus of Sweden, the great eighteenth century systematist who established a method of classifying the plants and animals. All the time that Linnaeus was at work on his encyclopedic *Systema Naturae* and *Species Plantarum*, explorers of the New World were continuing to return to Europe with new species of plants and animals and even new kinds of human beings. Linnaeus revised edition after edition to accommodate these findings, but he did not change his opinions on the fixity of species. He was sometimes criticized by his contemporaries, who felt that his classifications were too artificial. Few, however, questioned his belief in a special creation.

PREEVOLUTIONISTS

Among the first to suggest that species might undergo some changes in the course of time was the French scientist Georges-Louis Leclerc de Buffon (1707–1788). Buffon believed that these changes took place by a process of degeneration. He suggested that, in addition to the numerous creatures that were the product of the special creation at the beginning of the world, "There are lesser families conceived by Nature and produced by Time." In fact, as he summed it up, ". . . improvement and degeneration are the same thing, for both imply an alteration of the original constitution." If you are familiar with classical philosophy, you will see that Buffon was influenced by the Platonic concept of the ideal, or true form, of which all worldly expressions are merely imperfect copies.

Another early doubter of the fixity of species was Erasmus Darwin (1731–1802), Charles Darwin's grandfather. Erasmus Darwin was a physician, a gentleman naturalist, and a prolific and discursive writer, often in verse, on both botany and zoology. Erasmus Darwin suggested, largely in asides and footnotes, that species had historical connections with one another, that competition played a role in the development of different species, that animals might change in response to their environment, and that their offspring might inherit these changes. For instance, a polar bear, he maintained, is an "ordinary" bear which has become modified by living in the Arctic and which passes these modifications along to its cubs. These ideas were never clearly formulated; what Erasmus Darwin thought is of interest largely because of its possible effects on Charles Darwin, although the latter, who was born after his grandfather died, did not hold his grandfather's views in high esteem.

THE AGE OF THE EARTH

It was the geologists far more than the biologists who paved the way for evolutionary theory. One of the most influential of these was James Hutton (1726–1797). Hutton proposed that the earth had been molded not by sudden, violent events but by slow and gradual processes—wind, weather, and the flow of water—the same processes that can be seen at work in the world today. This theory of Hutton's was known as *uniformitarianism*, and it was important because it implied that the earth had a long history. This was a new idea. Christian theologians, by counting the successive generations since Adam (as recorded in the Bible), had calculated the maximum life-span of the world at about 6,000 years. No one had ever thought in terms of a longer period. And 6,000 years was not enough time for any form of evolution to have taken place.

THE FOSSIL RECORD

During the late eighteenth century, there was a revival of interest in fossils. In previous centuries, fossils had been collected as curiosities, but they had generally been regarded either as accidents of nature—stones that somehow looked like shells—or as evidence of great natural catastrophes, such as proof of Noah's Flood. The English surveyor William Smith (1769–1839) was the first to make a systematic study of fossils. Whenever his work took him down into a mine or along canals or across country, he carefully noted the order of the different layers of rock, the *strata*, and collected the fossils from each layer. He eventually established that each stratum, no matter where he came across it in England, contained a characteristic group of specimens and that these fossils were actually the best means of identifying a particular stratum. (The use of fossils to identify strata is still widely practiced.) Smith did not interpret his findings, but the implication that the earth had been formed layer by layer over the course of time was an unavoidable one.

Like Hutton's world, the world seen and reported by William Smith was clearly a very ancient one. A revolution in geology was beginning; earth science was becoming a study of time and change rather than a mere cataloging of types of rocks. As a consequence, the history of the earth became inseparable from the history of living organisms, as revealed in the fossil record.

CATASTROPHISM

Although the way was being prepared, the time was not yet ripe for a parallel revolution in biology. The dominating force in European science at the end of the eighteenth century was Georges Cuvier (1769–1832). Cuvier was the founder of paleontology, the scientific study of the fossil record. An expert in anatomy and zoology, he applied his special knowledge of the way in which animals are constructed to the study of fossil animals, and he was able to make brilliant deductions about the form of an entire animal from a few fragments of bone. We think of paleontology and evolution as so closely connected that it is surprising to learn that Cuvier was a staunch and powerful opponent of evolutionary theories. He recognized the fact that many species that had once existed no longer did. (In fact, according to modern estimates, considerably less than 1 percent of all species that have ever lived are represented on the earth today.) He explained the extinction of species by postulating a series of catastrophes. After each catastrophe, the most recent of which was the Flood, the species that remained alive repopulated the world.

The proponents of catastrophism were of two schools of thought: the *deluvianists* held that all the great upheavals which had destroyed extinct species were floods, while the *vulcanists* believed that the world had periodically been inundated with lava. According to both theories, however, the fossil record was simply the remains of those species of once living things which the violence of nature had eliminated. Time and nature, the catastrophists believed, acted not to create but to eliminate.

The Theories of Lamarck

The first scientist to work out a systematic theory of evolution was Jean Baptiste Lamarck (1744–1829). "This justly celebrated naturalist," as Darwin himself referred to him, boldly proposed in 1801 that all species, including man, are descended from other species. Lamarck, unlike most of the other zoologists of his time, was particularly interested in the protozoans and other invertebrates, and it is undoubtedly his long study of these "simpler" forms of life that led him to think of living things in terms of constantly increasing complexity, each form leading from the other.

Like Cuvier and others, Lamarck noted that the older the rocks, the simpler the forms of life they contained, but unlike Cuvier, he interpreted this as meaning that the higher forms had risen from the simpler forms by a kind of progression. According to his hypothesis, this progression, or evolution, to use the modern term, was dependent on two main forces. The first was the inheritance of acquired characteristics. Organs in animals become stronger or weaker, more or less important, through use or disuse, and these changes, according to Lamarck's theory, are transmitted from the parents to the progeny. His most famous example, and the one that Cuvier used most often to ridicule him, was that of the giraffe which stretched its neck longer and longer to reach the leaves on the higher trees and transmitted this longer neck to its offspring, who again stretched their necks, and so on.

The second important factor in Lamarck's theory of evolution was a universal creative principle, an unconscious striving upward on the *Scala Naturae* that moved every living creature toward greater complexity. Every amoeba was on its way to man. Some might get waylaid—the orangutan, for instance, by being caught in an unfavorable environment had been diverted off its course—but the will was always present. Life in its simplest forms was constantly emerging by spontaneous generation to fill the void left at the bottom of the ladder. In Lamarck's formulation, the ladder of life of the ancients had been transformed into a steadily ascending escalator, powered by a universal will.

This concept, the inheritance of acquired characteristics, as it is generally known, is an attractive one. Darwin borrowed from it consciously and unconsciously, and in fact, successive editions of *The Origin of Species* show that he was maneuvered into this particular Lamarckian point of view by some of his critics and by his own inability (owing to the primitive state of the science of genetics at that time) to explain some of the ways in which animals changed. Lamarck's theories persisted into the twentieth century in the work of the Russian biologist Lysenko.

Lamarck's contemporaries did not object to his ideas about the inheritance of acquired characteristics, as we would today with our more advanced knowledge of the mechanics of inheritance, nor did they criticize his belief in a metaphysical force, which was actually a common element in all the theories of the time. But these vague, unprovable postulates provided a very shaky foundation for so radical a proposal. Lamarck's championship of evolution was damaging not only to his own career but to the concept of evolution itself. The result of his theories was that both scientists and the public became even less prepared for an evolutionary doctrine.

Darwin's Theory

THE EARTH HAS A HISTORY

The person who most influenced Darwin, it is generally agreed, was Charles Lyell (1797–1875), a geologist who was Darwin's senior by only ten years. One of the few books that Darwin took with him on his voyage was the first volume of Lyell's newly published *Principles of Geology*, and the second volume was sent to him while he was on the *Beagle*. On the basis of his own observations and those of his predecessors, Lyell opposed the theory of catastrophes. Instead, he produced new evidence in support of Hutton's earlier theory of uniformitarianism. According to Lyell, the slow, steady, and cumulative effect of natural forces had produced continuous change in the course of the earth's history. Since this process was demonstrably slow, its results being barely visible in a single lifetime, it must have been going on for a very long time. In his earlier works, Lyell did not discuss the biological implications of his theory, but apparently they were clear to Darwin. If the earth had a long continuous history and if no forces other than outside physical agencies were needed to explain the events as they were recorded in the geologic record, might not living organisms have had a similar history? What Darwin's theory needed, as he knew very well, was time, and it was time that Lyell gave him.

THE VOYAGE OF THE *Beagle*

This then, was the intellectual equipment with which Charles Darwin set sail from Devonport. As the *Beagle* moved down the Atlantic coast of South America, through the Straits of Magellan, and up the Pacific coast, Darwin traveled the interior, fished, hunted, and rode horseback. He explored the rich fossil beds of South America (with the theories of Lyell fresh in his mind), and collected specimens of the many new kinds of plant and animal life he encountered. One of the points brought home to him most strongly by his long, slow trip down the coast and up again was the constantly changing varieties of organisms that he encountered. The birds and other animals on the west coast, for example, were very different from those on the east coast, and even as he moved slowly up the western coast, one species would give way to another one.

Most interesting to Darwin were the animals and plants that inhabited a small barren group of islands, the Galapagos, that lie some 580 miles off the coast of Ecuador. The Galapagos were named after the islands' most striking inhabitants, the tortoises (*galápagos* in Spanish), some of which weigh as much as 200 pounds or more. Each island has its own type of tortoise; the fishermen who frequented the islands and hunted the tortoises for food could readily tell which island any particular tortoise had come from. Then there was a group of finchlike birds, 13 species in all, which differed from one another in size and in the shapes and sizes of their beaks. The Galapagos finches, by modifying their beaks, had diversified their eating habits, assuming feeding habits customarily preempted by other types of birds on the mainland. The woodpeckerlike finch, for example, had taken on the woodpecker's role in routing insects out of the bark of trees. It was not fully equipped for this, however, lacking the long tongue with which the woodpecker flicks out insects from under the bark. In compensation, the woodpecker finch carries with it a small stick to pry the insects loose.

From his knowledge of geology, Darwin knew that these islands, clearly of volcanic origin, were much younger than the mainland. Yet the plants and animals of the islands were different from those of the mainland, and in fact, the inhabitants of different islands in the archipelago differed from one another. Were the living things on each island the product of a separate special creation? "One might really fancy," Darwin mused at a later date, "that from an original paucity of birds in this archipelago one species had been taken and modified for different ends." For years after his return, this problem continued, in his own word, to "haunt" him.

DEVELOPMENT OF THE THEORY

Not long after Darwin's return, he came across a book by the Reverend Thomas Malthus that had first appeared in 1798. In this book, Malthus warned, as economists have warned frequently ever since, that the human population was increasing so rapidly that it not only would soon outstrip the food supply but would leave "standing room only" on the earth. Darwin saw that this conclusion—that food supply and other factors hold populations in check—was true for all species, not just the human one. For example, a single breeding pair of elephants, which are the slowest breeders of all animals, could produce 19 million elephants in 750 years, yet the average number of elephants generally remains the same over the years. Where there might have been 19 million elephants in theory, there are, in fact, only two. The process by which the two survivors were "chosen" was termed by Darwin *natural selection*. He saw it as a process analogous to the type of selection exercised by breeders of cattle, horses, or dogs—which, as a country squire, he was very familiar with. In the case of artificial selection, man chooses variants for breeding on the basis of characteristics which seem to him to be desirable. In the case of natural selection, environmental conditions are the principal active force, operating on the variations continually produced in all species to "favor" some variants and "discourage" or eliminate others.

Where do the variations come from? According to Darwin's theory, variations occur absolutely at random. They are not produced by the environment, by a "creative force," or by the unconscious striving of the organism. In themselves, they have no direction; *direction is imposed entirely by natural selection.* A variation that gives an animal even a slight advantage makes that animal more likely to leave surviving offspring. Thus, to return to Lamarck's giraffe, an animal with a slightly longer neck has an advantage in feeding and so is apt to leave more offspring than one with a shorter neck. If the longer neck is an inherited trait, some of these offspring will also have long necks, and since the animals with longer necks are always favored, the next generation will have even longer necks. Finally, the population of short-necked giraffes will give way to a population of long-necked ones.

The Origin of Species, which Darwin pondered for more than 20 years before its publication in 1859, is, in his own words, "one long argument."

No experiments are performed. No new information is revealed. Fact after fact, observation after observation, culled from the remotest Pacific island to the neighbor's pasture, is recorded, analyzed, and commented upon. Every objection is anticipated and countered. The hypothesis is not tested and proved; since the process of evolution is so slow, Darwin did not believe that proof was possible (although the twentieth century has produced evidence of evolution in progress). Yet *The Origin of Species* made it impossible to believe anything else. Indeed, since its publication, few intelligent people have questioned the fact that evolution actually occurs, although Darwin's theory has sometimes been modified or misinterpreted.

The influence of the theory of evolution on every aspect of human thought can best be appreciated by reflecting for a moment on how logical and even unexciting Darwin's ideas seem to us today and how "odd" those of his predecessors. Yet little more than a hundred years ago, these "odd" theories were supported by the great majority of both scientists and laymen. It would be difficult to find an area of intellectual activity that has not been influenced by the publication of *The Origin of Species*.

There is no longer any serious religious conflict over the acceptance of evolutionary theory. The real difficulty in accepting Darwin's theory has always been that it seems to diminish man's significance. The new astronomy had made it clear that the earth was not the center of the universe or even of our own solar system. Now the new biology was asking man to accept the fact that he was a product of a random process and that, as far as science could show him, he was not created for any special purpose or as a part of any universal design. We are still dealing with this problem today.

IMPORTANCE OF THE THEORY IN MODERN BIOLOGY

What is the importance of this theory to modern biologists, a majority of whom are concerned with such areas of investigation as the chemistry of heredity—a phrase that would have been meaningless in Darwin's time—or the interpretation of subcellular structures newly revealed by the electron microscope? Perhaps the clearest answer to this question is that recently formulated by Ernst Mayr of Harvard University:*

The theory of evolution is quite rightly called the greatest unifying theory in biology. The diversity of organisms, similarities and differences between kinds of organisms, patterns of distribution and behavior, adaptation and interaction, all this was merely a bewildering chaos of facts until given meaning by the evolutionary theory. There is no area in biology in which that theory has not served as an ordering principle.

*Ernst Mayr, *Animal Species and Evolution*, Harvard University Press, Cambridge, Mass., 1963.

Because they are of particular importance in this book, we shall single out for mention three of the many ways in which Darwin's theory has "served as an ordering principle" in biology. The first involves the kinds of living organisms, the plants and animals that fill the world about us. Because of the evolutionary theory, we can understand, as Linnaeus could not, the resemblances and differences among families of plants and animals.

Second, we begin to understand the seeming purposefulness of living things and their activities. Why do bees visit flowers? Why do flowers often have sweet odors and bright colors? Why does our heart pump blood through our lungs? If we answer that the heart pumps blood through our lungs in order to oxygenate it, we imply that the heart has a purpose, that it knows what it is doing—which is, of course, not true. Yet in another sense, this sort of explanation is the correct one. Flowers and their insect pollinators evolved together; brightly colored flowers were more apt to be pollinated and, therefore, left more offspring. As you can see, within the framework of evolutionary theory, "why" and "what for" questions become interesting and meaningful.

The third point, closely related to the second, is that evolutionary theory emphasizes the dynamic relationship between structure and function. Anatomy, on the one hand, and physiology or behavior, on the other, cannot logically be studied or understood apart from one another. The two have necessarily evolved together, the function shaping the structure and the structure directing and guiding the activity.

As you will see, we can say with equal truthfulness that man can use his hands for grasping because he has an opposable thumb and that man has an opposable thumb because he uses his hands for grasping. This does not imply perfection; the wisdom of nature is a sentimental notion. Your body will automatically reject a skin graft from another person—unless the person happens to be your identical twin—even if you are dying of an extensive burn and the graft could save your life. Evolution has imposed a number of clumsy burdens of this sort. The human vertebral column is a good example. An engineer could devise a much better structural support for modern man if he were permitted to start from the beginning. The point is, however, that our backbone and our pelvis have been molded by time—by variation and natural selection—into their present form, and their structure and function are inseparable.

Levels of Organization

As we look at evolution through a modern perspective, we can see it not merely as a slow pattern of gradual change but also as a process of ever-increasing organization.

During the seventeenth century, a school of biologists called *mechanists* arose, of which the French philosopher René Descartes (1596–1650) was an exponent. The mechanists set about proving that the body worked essentially like a machine; the arms and legs moved like levers and pulleys, the heart like a pump, the lungs like a bellows, and the stomach like a mortar and pestle. Opposing them were a group known as the *vitalists*, who contended that living things were qualitatively different from inanimate objects, containing within them a "vital spirit" which enabled them to perform activities that could not possibly be carried out outside of the living organism or fully described by chemistry or physics.

By the nineteenth century, simple mechanical models of living organisms had been abandoned, and the argument now centered around whether or not the chemistry of living organisms was governed by the same principles as the chemistry performed in the laboratory by man. The vitalists claimed that man could not carry out the same chemical operations as those performed by living tissues. The *reductionists*, as their opponents were now called (since they believed that the complex operations of living systems could be reduced to simpler and more readily understandable ones) achieved a partial victory when the German chemist Friedrich Wöhler (1800–1882) converted an "inorganic" substance (ammonium cyanate) into a familiar organic substance (urea). The claims of the vitalists were supported by the fact that as chemical knowledge improved, many new compounds were found in living tissues that were never seen in the nonliving, or inorganic, world. In spite of many advances in biochemistry, this phase of the controversy lasted until 1898. Until this time, the chemical processes involved in turning fruit juice to alcohol had been carried out only in the presence of living yeast cells. Finally, however, the German chemist Eduard Buchner (1860–1917) showed that a substance extracted from the yeast cells could produce fermentation outside of the living cell. This substance was given the name enzyme, from *zyme*, the Greek word meaning "yeast" or "ferment."

Today it is clear that the vitalists were wrong; organic chemistry "obeys the rules" of inorganic chemistry. The mechanists were wrong, too, of course—the body is not merely a simple machine—just as the reductionists were somewhat foolish when they claimed in "Believe It or Not" columns or in some textbooks that the human body is nothing more than 98 cents worth of chemicals. It is, of course, much more, as water is more than its component parts—hydrogen and oxygen atoms do not have any of the special properties by which we identify water. What then is the difference between 98 cents worth of chemicals and the human body, or between free hydrogen and oxygen and water? The difference is one of organization. The long, slow movement of evolution can be described as the gradual imposition of order and of organization. And, as is the case with hydrogen, oxygen, and water, when we move from one level of organization to another, we move to something qualitatively different. An atom is one level of organization, a molecule another.

We know now that living things are made up of a relatively few elements, all of which can be found in simple forms in the thin film of earth and atmosphere in which we live. But when these elements become organized into a cell, we have an entity with properties quite different from those of the molecules alone. We progress from single cells to many-celled organisms. This occurred in the course of evolution, and it occurs over and over again as each many-celled plant or animal develops from a single cell, the fertilized egg, and in so doing, becomes something more than and different from the egg. Finally, the organisms, in turn, are organized into populations, communities, and societies, in which the behavior of any individual organism is not the same as the behavior of the organism in isolation. All these different levels of organization, from cells to societies, are the subjects of biology. Science is man's way of seeking principles of order in the natural world, and biology is that branch of science that seeks order in the living world at all these different levels. In this book, we shall move along the course once taken by evolution from the single-celled organism to man, from the sparsely populated primitive earth to the crowded modern world, looking for the evidence of order and trying to understand how and why evolution moved in this direction and perhaps even to glimpse where it is going now.

One final word: In our enthusiasm for telling you all that biology has discovered, do not let us convince you that all is known. Many questions are still unanswered. More important, many good questions have not yet been asked. Perhaps you may be the one to ask them.

SUGGESTIONS FOR FURTHER READING

DARWIN, CHARLES: *The Origin of Species by Means of Natural Selection, or The Preservation of Favored Races in the Struggle for Life*, Doubleday & Company, Inc., Garden City, N.Y. 1960.*

Darwin's "long argument." Every student of biology should, at the very least, browse through this book to catch its special flavor and to begin to understand its extraordinary force.

———: *The Voyage of the Beagle*, Natural History Library, Doubleday & Company, Inc., Garden City, N.Y., 1962.*

Darwin's own chronicle of the expedition on which he made the discoveries and observations that eventually led him to his theory of evolution. This is the best introduction both to the man and to his work.

GROBSTEIN, CLIFFORD: *The Strategy of Life,* W. H. Freeman and Company, San Francisco, 1965.*

A brief, provocative introduction to the fundamental ideas of modern biology.

MAZZEO, JOSEPH A.: *The Design of Life,* Pantheon Books, Random House, Inc., New York, 1967.

An analysis of the major themes in the development of biological thought, from the Greeks to the present day.

TOULMIN, STEPHEN, AND JUNE GOODFIELD: *The Discovery of Time,* Harper & Row, Publishers, Inc., New York, 1965.*

An enjoyable account of the historical development of our ideas of time as they relate to nature, human nature, and human society.

*Available in paperback.

CELLS

Chapter 1–1

Origin of Cells

The Formation of Our Solar System

THE SUN

Sagittarius, the archer, is a constellation that is visible in our fall skies. If you look toward Sagittarius on a clear moonless night, you are looking toward the center of the Milky Way, the galaxy of which our sun and planet are a part. There are 100 billion stars in our own galaxy, and within the range of our most powerful telescopes are about 100 million more such galaxies.

The Milky Way was some 10 billion years old, the astronomers calculate, when the sun was formed. Like other stars, the sun formed from a condensation of particles of ice and dust and gases whirling in space among the older stars. You can see such clouds of particles and gases as dark patches in the starlit sky. These materials gradually condensed, about 4.5 billion years ago, in a series of contractions and fragmentations that took place over several million years. The heat and energy stored in the sun as a result of this condensation raised the internal temperature until it was high enough to drive a thermonuclear reaction. From these thermonuclear reactions come the light and heat on which present-day life on earth depends.

THE PLANETS

According to the most widely held current theory, the nine planets formed after the sun from the remaining ice and dust and gas moving around the newborn star. Each planet began as a series of chance encounters of interstellar debris, and as the accumulated matter whirled, other, smaller lumps of matter became embedded in it. Probably many such masses accumulated, only to be disintegrated by collisions with larger debris.

15 *Origin of Cells*

(*Courtesy of Harvard College Observatory*)

1–1 *Because man has never been able to penetrate more than a tiny fraction of the earth's crust, all theories about the interior of our planet have developed from indirect information. Although there is no direct proof for the structure of the earth as shown here in cross section—it has been pieced together from seismological data collected over a number of years—most scientists today regard it as correct. Underneath the crust, which is rarely over 40 miles thick, is the plastic mantle, extending down some 1,800 miles. The outer core, of molten nickle-iron, is 1,300 miles thick, and the dense inner core has a radius of 860 miles. The nickle-iron of the inner core is probably compressed solid by the immense weight of all the materials above it. At the bottom of the mantle, for example, the pressure is believed to be about 17 million pounds per square inch, and the temperature is 7,000°F!*

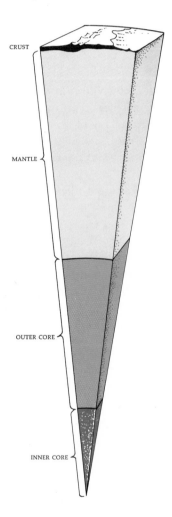

CRUST

MANTLE

OUTER CORE

INNER CORE

At first, in the planets-to-be, particles were collected merely at random, but as each mass grew larger, other particles began to be attracted by the gravity of the central mass. The whirling dust and forming spheres continued to revolve around the sun until finally each planet had swept its own path clean, picking up loose matter like a giant snowball. The orbit nearest the sun was swept clean by Mercury, the next by Venus, the third by Earth, the fourth by Mars, and so on out to Pluto.

This theory of how the planets were formed differs from the one generally accepted a little more than a decade ago. At that time, it was thought by most astronomers that the planets formed as the result of a wandering star passing too close to the sun and sucking chunks of matter out of its fiery mass. The decline of this theory, on the basis of new evidence and new calculations by physicists, geologists, and astronomers, has important implications for the question of whether life exists on other planets. In the vastness of the universe, it is highly unlikely that one star will enter the gravitational field of another, and so it is even more unlikely that planets like Earth will be formed. If we assume, however, as many scientists now do, that all stars condense from interstellar matter and that many, in condensing, give rise to a family of satellite planets, it is clear that other solar systems such as ours must exist, many with planets similar to Earth. At a recent meeting of the National Academy of Sciences, it was estimated that right in our own galaxy there are a billion planets capable of supporting life. Some scientists believe, however, that the events by which life must have arisen are so complicated that there is little chance that they occurred more than once.

During the time Earth and the other planets were being formed, the constant bombardment of their surfaces by fresh building materials may have helped to keep their bodies very hot. When Earth was still hot, the heavier materials collected in a dense core whose diameter is about half that of the earth. As soon as the supply of stellar dust, stones, and larger rocks was exhausted, the planet ceased to grow and began to cool. As the earth's surface cooled, lower-density materials from the interior burst through from under the surface, wrinkling into mountains and forming the pits which are now the basins of the oceans. This outer crust, a skin as thin by comparison as the skin of an apple, was formed over a billion years after the formation of the earth itself; the oldest rocks known are about 3.3 billion years old, while the age of the earth is estimated at 4.5 billion years.

Between the thin crust of the earth and its dense interior is a thick layer, known as the *mantle*, made of hot compressed rock. The mantle is slightly plastic, so it "gives" a little. The portions of the mantle on which the continents rest curve slightly under their weight. Only 30 miles below us, the earth is still hot—a small fraction of it is even still molten. We see evidence of this in the occasional volcanic eruption that forces lava through weak points in the earth's skin or in the geyser which spews up boiling water that has wandered down to the earth's interior through some underground stream. Very little is known about what lies just beneath the surface of the earth.

Dating the Past

How do scientists date events so remote in time and circumstance from the world of today? In Darwin's time, the earth was estimated to be only about 100 million years old. This may seem old enough on a human scale, but Darwin was troubled by this estimate because it did not seem long enough for the slow trial-and-error process of evolution by natural selection that he had proposed. In the last 100 years, geochemists have added some 4,400 million years to the earth's estimated age!

RADIOACTIVE ISOTOPES

The new data are largely based on an ingenious and extremely valuable technique known as *radioactive dating*. To understand radioactive dating, we shall have to review some principles of atomic structure which may already be familiar to you. As you may know, the nucleus of an atom contains one or more protons, which are positively charged particles. The number of protons in an atom determines its chemical character. Chemical elements consist of atoms of only one kind. Hydrogen consists of atoms

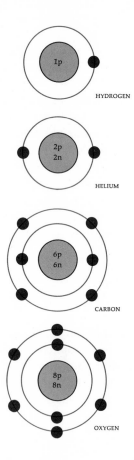

1–2 *Atomic models of four common elements. The dark spheres represent the electrons in orbit outside the nucleus.*

HYDROGEN

HELIUM

CARBON

OXYGEN

with one proton each; helium consists of atoms with two protons. The carbon atom has six protons; nitrogen, seven; oxygen, eight; and so on up to an as yet unnamed element which has 104. Sometimes an atom loses a proton. This can be caused by natural radiations, or it can be induced artificially in atomic reactors. When an atom loses or gains a proton, it changes its chemical identity.

In addition to protons, which are positively charged, the nucleus of the atom contains neutrons, which have no charge but which each have a mass equal to that of a proton. While atoms of the same element always contain the same number of protons, they vary in their neutron content and therefore in their atomic weights. Atoms which have the same atomic number but different atomic weights are known as *isotopes*. In nature, the most common isotope of hydrogen is H^1 which contains one proton in the nucleus and no neutrons. Another isotope of hydrogen is deuterium, or heavy hydrogen (H^2), which contains one proton and one neutron. A third hydrogen isotope, tritium (H^3), contains one proton and two neutrons. Tritium is unstable, however, which means that it tends to emit high-energy particles from its nucleus until it reaches a stable form. Such unstable forms are known as *radioactive isotopes*. Both deuterium and tritium have nearly the same chemical properties as the more common isotope of hydrogen (H^1), and either can substitute for it in chemical reactions. If hydrogen gains a proton, however, as contrasted with a neutron, it is no longer hydrogen but helium.*

Many naturally occurring isotopes are radioactive. All the heavier elements—atoms that have 84 or more protons in their nucleus—are unstable and therefore radioactive. All radioactive elements emit nuclear particles at a fixed rate, undergoing decay and eventually reaching a stable state. This rate is measured in terms of *half-life*; the half-life of a radioactive element is defined as the time in which half the atoms in a sample of the element lose their radioactivity and become stable. If the half-life of an element is known, it is possible to calculate the fraction of decay which takes place in any given time.

Half-lives vary widely, depending on the isotope. The radioactive nitrogen isotope N^{13} has a half-life of 10 minutes. Tritium has a half-life of 12 1/4 years. The most common isotope of uranium (U^{238}) has a half-life of 4 1/2 billion years. As the uranium atom undergoes a series of decays, the uranium turns to lead 206.

---

* The sun is made up almost entirely of a mixture of hydrogen and helium gases, with hydrogen predominating. Within the core of the sun, which is estimated to have a temperature equivalent to 16 million°C, hydrogen atoms are constantly fusing with one another to form helium, with a concomitant tremendous release of energy. The fusion of the heavier isotopes of hydrogen (deuterium and tritium) to form helium is the source of energy of the hydrogen bomb.

The origins of radioactive dating can be traced back to 1905, when a geologist pointed out the universal presence of lead in uranium-bearing rock and observed that the ratio between lead and uranium was surprisingly constant in samples of rock from the same region. Subsequent work has shown that by comparing the relative amounts of uranium 238 and lead 206, it is possible to tell when a particular rock was formed. Fortunately, the lead formed from uranium decay (lead 206) is a different isotope from the lead (lead 204) originally present in rock, so that the two can be distinguished.

The use of the rate of radioactive decay as a timing device requires the assumption, of course, that the radioactive clock has been running at the same speed for millions of years. Many tests have been made to see if changes in temperature, pressure, or other conditions affect the rate of decay; all have had negative results. Furthermore, traces in the surrounding rock, produced by the discharge of particles from the radioactive nucleus, indicate that the amount of energy released by the uranium atom in its radioactive decay has not changed over the ages, and the amount of energy released and the rate of its release are known to be very closely correlated.

Rock samples as old as the Earth itself have never been found,

1–3 *Radioactive isotopes, such as those listed here, emit nuclear particles at a fixed rate and gradually decay into other elements. Each isotope has a characteristic rate of decay, measured in terms of half-life (the time required for half the atoms in a sample to disintegrate). A specimen can therefore be dated quite accurately by measuring the proportion of isotopes left in it.*

RADIOACTIVE ISOTOPE	MATERIAL TESTED	RANGE OF ACCURACY (YEARS)	HALF-LIFE (YEARS)
CARBON 14	CHARCOAL, WOOD, SHELL	70,000	5,730
PROTACTINIUM 231	DEEP-SEA SEDIMENT	120,000	32,000
THORIUM 230	DEEP-SEA SEDIMENT, CORAL, SHELL	400,000	75,000
URANIUM 234	CORAL	1,000,000	250,000
CHLORINE 36	IGNEOUS AND VOLCANIC ROCKS	500,000	300,000
BERYLLIUM 10	DEEP-SEA SEDIMENT	8,000,000	4.5 million
HELIUM 4	CORAL, SHELL	...	12.5 billion
POTASSIUM 40 — ARGON 40	VOLCANIC ASH, LAVA	...	1.3 billion

|————2.5mm————|*

1–4 *Sphecomyrma freyi, a worker ant preserved in amber, recently discovered at the base of a seaside bluff in New Jersey. Radioactive dating methods show that the amber was formed in the lower part of the Upper Cretaceous period. As you can see, it is quite wasp-like, with a narrow waist and a stinger (seen protruding from the abdominal tip, on the left). Scientists believe that this ant clearly represents an evolutionary link between the wasps and the ants. Moreover, since this ant is a worker (a sterile female) its discovery reveals that social life in insects has existed for at least 100 million years. (Courtesy of Museum of Comparative Zoology, Harvard University)*

* *In this and other figures in the book, the size is indicated by a short horizontal line indicating the scale of the figure. The ant, for example, is slightly less than 6 millimeters long (or almost ¹/₄ inch).*

but many scientists believe that meteorites, which contain lead, have the same age as Earth and the rest of the solar system. The estimated age of 4¹/₂ billion years is based on studies of these meteorites. As you can see, these present estimates, like past ones, are built on hypotheses, and although there is general agreement that these hypotheses are valid, they, too, are subject to modification with increasing knowledge.

CARBON–14 DATING

The dates of more recent events can be calculated because of the presence in the atmosphere of the radioactive isotope, carbon 14. Carbon 14 is produced as a result of bombardment by high-energy particles from outer space and occurs in small amounts as heavy carbon dioxide. Plant cells use carbon dioxide to make glucose and other organic molecules. All animals are directly or indirectly dependent upon this carbon process for food, thus a fixed proportion of carbon atoms in the tissues of all living things is radioactive carbon 14. After death, no more carbon is ingested, so the proportions shift, with the radioactive carbon 14 decaying slowly and the carbon 12 remaining the same. Carbon 14 has a half-life of 5,730 years, so a fossil that old should contain just half the C^{14} of a living animal. By measuring the ratio of C^{14} to C^{12} in a fossil or even in a man-made structure of wood or some other once-living material, the objects can be dated quite accurately. Carbon-14 dating is particularly useful for studying archaeological remains, most of which lie within its time span. This dating method depends on the assumption that the proportion of C^{14} to C^{12} has remained constant in the atmosphere within the time span under study.

ESTIMATING THE AGE OF FOSSILS

Within the last decade, improvements in radioactive dating have come about through analysis of the radioactive decay of potassium 40 to argon 40 and rubidium 87 to strontium 87. The use of these minerals has widely expanded the possibilities for dating fossil materials since they are more likely to be present in rocks, such as shale and sandstone, in which fossils are usually found. The oldest known fossils are bacterialike organisms embedded in specimens of sedimentary rock found in 1965 in South Africa. Radioactive dating indicates that these specimens are 3 billion years old. In 1967, scientists at Harvard University announced the discovery, in Kenya, of the oldest specimen yet found of a bone identified as belonging to the human genus. This find, consisting of the lower end of an upper arm bone (the humerus), was determined by the potassium-argon technique to be 2 1/2 million years old (plus or minus 200,000 years). These recent fossil discoveries, combined with more precise radioactive-dating methods, have shown that both the first living cells and the first manlike creatures appeared on earth far earlier than scientists had previously believed.

The Beginning of Life

WHY ON EARTH

In our solar system, Earth among all the planets was greatly favored for the production of life. At very low temperatures, the chemical reactions on which life—any form of life—depends must virtually cease. At high temperatures, compounds are too unstable for life to form or survive. The planets most distant from the sun, such as Pluto, are too cold. Mercury, the closest to the sun, is too hot. Also, planets much smaller than Earth cannot hold an adequate atmosphere, while any planet much larger than Earth might hold so dense an atmosphere that radiations from the sun could not reach its surface. Of all the planets in this solar system, life can theoretically exist only on three: Mars, Earth, and Venus.

THE PRIMITIVE ATMOSPHERE

Sometime between the time the earth formed and the date of the earliest fossils discovered so far—an interval of 1 1/2 billion years—life began. The chief raw materials for life were to be found in the atmosphere of the young earth. In 1923, the Russian biochemist A. I. Oparin suggested that the complex molecules associated with living things* could have arisen only in a world with little free oxygen. Most biochemists now agree with Oparin that the early atmosphere of the earth was probably deficient in free oxygen, consisting mainly of water vapor, carbon dioxide, nitrogen, and some hydrogen-containing compounds (ammonia and methane, primarily). The formula for ammonia is NH_3, which means that each molecule of ammonia contains one atom of nitrogen and three of hydrogen. Methane is CH_4, water is H_2O, and carbon dioxide is CO_2. Combinations of these four elements available in the primitive atmosphere—hydrogen, oxygen, carbon, and nitrogen—make up more than 99 percent of the tissues of all living things.

In order to break apart the simple gases of the atmosphere and reform them into organic molecules, energy was required. And energy abounded on the young earth. First there was heat, both boiling (moist) heat and baking (dry) heat. Water vapor spewed out of the primitive seas, cooled in the upper atmosphere, collected into clouds, fell back on the crust of the earth, and steamed up again. Violent rainstorms were accompanied by

---

* The complex molecules of living things are generally referred to as *organic molecules*. The term "organic chemistry" was first applied to substances made by plants and animals, and by extension it came to include all compounds which contain both carbon and hydrogen, since these are the chief constituents of such compounds. Now many such compounds are made routinely in the laboratory, and some of them, like synthetic fibers and plastics, are never found in organisms. The laboratories in which these compounds are made are still referred to as laboratories of organic chemistry. The term "organic molecules" will be used in this book to mean the relatively complex carbon-containing molecules found in living systems.

lightning, which provided electrical energy. The sun bombarded the earth's surface with high-energy particles and ultraviolet light. Radioactive elements within the earth released particles into the atmosphere. These conditions can be simulated in the laboratory, and scientists have now shown that under such conditions, organic molecules are produced.

In the 1950s, Stanley Miller conducted a series of experiments in the University of Chicago laboratories. When he discharged a high-frequency electric spark into a "primeval" atmosphere or bombarded it with ultraviolet rays, he found that amino acids formed. These experiments are particularly interesting because amino acids are the subunits from which proteins are formed, and proteins are extremely important molecules in the structures and functions of living things.

AGGREGATIONS OF CHEMICALS

As biochemists reconstruct these events, the compounds that were formed in the atmosphere tended to be washed out by the driving rains and to collect in the oceans, which grew as the earth cooled. These compounds were relatively stable—that is, once formed, they did not break apart readily—and so the ocean became an increasingly rich mixture of organic molecules.

Before life could have arisen, these chemicals must have aggregated in groups. The groups may have taken the form of droplets, such as the droplets formed by oil or by soap molecules in water, which gradually grew larger as they accumulated other chemicals within them. Laboratory experiments have shown that under conditions simulating those hypothesized to exist during the earth's first billion years, organic molecules aggregate into groups and that around these groups a slight film tends to form. These aggregates, known as *coacervates*, superficially resemble modern cells in appearance. Another possibility, suggested by some biochemists, is that chemicals may have aggregated as a film on underwater rocks and clay rather than as free-floating droplets. As we shall see, surfaces play an important role in facilitating reactions between organic molecules.

Droplets of oil or soap tend to break in two as they reach a certain size, and so will the more complex coacervates, although these can become larger than the oil or soap droplets. Eventually, however, a system must have evolved by which one of these aggregates, instead of just breaking apart, was able to divide into two *identical* parts; in other words, the aggregate was able to make copies of itself. This is the property of *self-replication*, and the acquisition of this property was the most important event in the evolution of life.

In Section 3, we shall find that all known organisms have the same method of self-replication. Does this mean that a chemical system capable of self-replication developed only once? Did all life begin by some single chance event? This is an awesome thought, and many biologists believe that it may be true. On the other hand, it is possible that the same system came into being many different times and in many different places, or it is even possible that several different forms of replicating systems once existed but, under the pressures of natural selection, only one prevailed. One of the reasons that scientists are interested in finding life on other planets is to see whether such life is based on the same chemical system as our own.

WHAT IS LIFE?

It may be many years before scientists can determine when life first appeared, and it is possible that we shall never know. Indeed, even if we did know exactly when each event in the sequence took place, few of us would be able to agree on exactly which step marked the beginning of life. For instance, do you think life is a self-replicating molecule? Or maybe something more complicated and more elusive? We can agree, at least, on one point: Once a cell-like unit came into existence that was capable of making more cell-like units very much like itself, life was well on its way.

The Development of Photosynthesis

The primitive cells or cell-like structures that first formed, it is generally believed, were *heterotrophs. Hetero* means "other," and *troph* comes from the Greek word *trophos,* "one that feeds." A heterotrophic organism is one that cannot make all the complex organic molecules needed by living things from simple molecules like CO_2, H_2O, H_2, and CH_4 but must receive them from other sources. Modern heterotrophs, including man, get such organic molecules from other living things. The early heterotrophs, however, could not depend on other organisms, since these were, for all practical purposes, nonexistent. They must have received their nourishment from the rich organic soup in which they arose. At first, presumably, these cells used the most complex molecules, the ones most like themselves and requiring the least modification. These molecules, which had taken millions of years to accumulate, would soon have been used up, however. The primitive cells that required the most complex organic substances could then no longer multiply, while cells able to make more complex chemicals out of slightly simpler ones had a selective advantage in this changing environment. As the medium in which they lived became increasingly depleted, the less competent cell-like systems were weeded out. So in the course of time there evolved cells which were able to make organic molecules out of very simple materials. Such cells are called *autotrophs,* from *auto,* meaning "self." These cells are believed to have been very simple in structure, perhaps somewhat resembling modern bacteria.

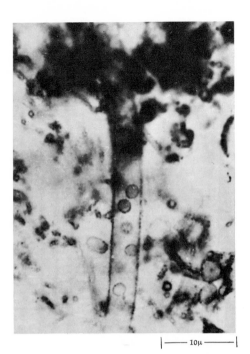

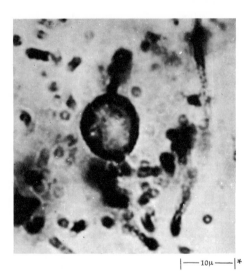

1–5 *Photomicrographs of fossil cells of blue-green algae, discovered some years ago on the Canadian shore of Lake Superior. Although these cell remains are some 2 billion years old, they are remarkably similar to existing organisms. (Dr. Elso S. Barghoorn)*

* *The symbol μ (the Greek letter mu) is the abbreviation for micron. A micron is 1/1000 of a millimeter.*

Embedded in rock that solidified 2.7 billion years ago, fossil remains have been found of organisms that resemble the simplest of the modern one-celled algae. This is evidence that sometime in the second billion years of the earth's history, another crucial event occurred—the development of photosynthesis.

Photosynthesis is the process by which organisms that possess chlorophyll or chlorophyll-like pigments can trap the energy of the sun and use it to make glucose from carbon dioxide and water. Glucose, which is a type of sugar, is the starting point for the manufacture of most of the other compounds needed by living organisms. In addition, glucose is the major source of energy for modern heterotrophs, providing the "fuel" they require for their cellular activities. Today, all the "fuel" for running living systems has stored within it energy from the sun, captured by green plants. Man, at the far end of the food chain, either eats the plants themselves or eats other animals that have eaten them.

Photosynthetic organisms are autotrophs since they are able to synthesize the nutritive substances they require from simple, inorganic materials and so can feed themselves. At one time, scientists believed that the photosynthetic organisms must have been the first to develop since, under present-day conditions, heterotrophs could not exist without these autotrophs. This is a difficult theory to maintain, however, since photosynthesis is a very complicated process and must itself be the product of many millions of years of evolution of living cells. Probably the photosynthetic autotrophs evolved from simpler, chemosynthetic autotrophs. Both can use simple molecules to make complicated ones, but the photosynthetic autotroph uses energy from sunlight, whereas the chemosynthetic autotroph derives energy from the conversion of one small molecule to another. Although photosynthesis is complex, the reaction for the formation of glucose is deceptively simple:

$$6CO_2 + 6H_2O \rightarrow C_6H_{12}O_6 + 6O_2$$

Six molecules of carbon dioxide and six molecules of water form one glucose molecule and six molecules of oxygen.

The Coming of Oxygen

Look at the equation for making glucose once more. As a by-product of photosynthesis, oxygen is released. You will remember that there probably was no free oxygen in the primitive atmosphere; in fact, chemists have found that if there had been, the reactions necessary for the formation of organic molecules probably could not have taken place. Some scientists believe that oxygen appeared as the result of the breakdown of molecules of H_2O in the atmosphere. The sun's energy frees the hydrogen from the water vapor in the upper atmosphere, and because of the low mass of hydrogen (only one proton), the earth loses the hydrogen to outer space, leaving free oxygen. Others believe that the accumulation of oxygen came about largely as a consequence of the evolution of photosynthesis. As photosynthetic cells multiplied in the oceans, more and more free oxygen was released into the atmosphere. In either case, the appearance of oxygen had profound effects on the further development of life:

1   The appearance of oxygen made it possible for cells to use oxygen for breaking down organic molecules for energy. Rapid uncontrolled oxidation in the presence of oxygen is the phenomenon we know as *burning;* when an organic compound, such as glucose, wood, or gas, is burned, carbon dioxide and water are formed and oxygen is consumed. In cells, oxidation of glucose takes place, yielding the same end products—carbon dioxide and water. However, oxidation does not take place in cells in an uncontrolled, violent fashion, leading to outright burning; rather, the glucose oxidation occurs in a highly controlled manner, so that the chemical energy of the glucose is released in a series of small steps, making it available to the cell for work. Simple heat energy such as is produced by burning is not useful to the cell except to maintain its temperature. Energy to do cellular work must be made available in a chemical form. Ninety percent of the energy of the modern cell comes from the oxidation of carbon-containing compounds. It is probable that none of these more complex cells nor any of the multicelled organisms, with their high energy requirements, could ever have developed in an oxygen-free atmosphere.

2   As oxygen collected in the upper atmosphere, it formed a shield against the more harmful wavelengths of radiant energy from the sun. Since oxygen can absorb these wavelengths, it removed one of the forces that had helped life to form but had also made survival more difficult. The earliest cells probably escaped the destructive effects of ultraviolet light by remaining below the surface of the water. With the increasing accumulation of oxygen in the atmosphere, they could rise to the surface and, eventually, evolve into forms which could live on the land. Without free oxygen, this would not have been possible.

3   Ironically, the presence of free oxygen may have poisoned and destroyed most of the early photosynthetic cells, making way for the development of other organisms better adapted to the new environment. Even today, we oxygenate our water supply to poison certain types of microorganisms that cannot live in the presence of free oxygen.

With the coming of photosynthesis and of respiration, cells were able to develop that were probably not very different from some of the cell forms we know today.

SUMMARY

The chain of circumstances leading to the first appearance of life on Earth begins with the formation of the solar system. The sun and its planets were formed about 4.5 billion years ago—the sun probably from the condensation and contraction of the solar nebula, and the planets as accumulations of interstellar debris. The earth's crust, the thin outer skin on which we live, formed over a billion years after the earth itself was formed.

Scientists are able to approximate the dates of these and other early events by radioactive-dating techniques.

Only three planets (Mars, Venus, and Earth) in the solar system theoretically can support life, and most scientists now believe that of these, only Earth has an environment favorable to life. The chief raw materials of life existed in the primitive atmosphere of Earth—hydrogen, oxygen, carbon, and nitrogen, combined in water vapor and gases. The energy required to break apart the simple gases in the atmosphere and reform them into organic molecules was supplied by heat, lightning, radioactivity, and high-energy particles and ultraviolet rays from the sun.

After the initial formation of the organic molecules, two further steps were taken toward the beginning of life: (1) Organic molecules began to aggregate in groups, and (2) some groups of chemicals developed which could self-replicate.

The first cells that formed were probably *heterotrophs*. But as the complex organic molecules on which these cells fed became depleted, a type of cell developed which could synthesize complex molecules from simpler ones; this was the *chemosynthetic autotroph*. And from these cells evolved, sometime in the second billion years of the earth's history, cells capable of *photosynthesis*.

The by-product of photosynthesis is oxygen, and as the photosynthetic cells multiplied, more and more free oxygen was released into the atmosphere. The appearance of free oxygen had several important effects: (1) Cells could oxidize organic compounds for energy. (2) Free oxygen in the upper atmosphere provided a shield against ultraviolet rays from the sun, allowing cells to rise to the surface of the ocean and, eventually, live on land. (3) Certain earlier cells, adapted to an oxygen-free environment, were gradually destroyed, making way for cells that were probably not very different from those of today.

Chapter 1–2

Cells as Organisms: The One-celled Plants and Animals

The exact point of demarcation between living and nonliving matter is not easy to define. For example, certain combinations of nonliving chemicals can "grow," can change in response to the environment, and can even reproduce themselves, although in a rudimentary, haphazard way—and growth, response, and replication are the phenomena we usually call upon when we try to state what we mean by living. However, these processes become organized and predictable, persisting through many generations, only when they take place within the living cell. Most plants and animals begin life as one cell, and as we shall see, some quite complicated organisms spend their entire lives within the seemingly small boundaries of a single cell. And once the cell is broken apart, life vanishes. For this reason, we are going to begin this study of biology—which is the study of life—with the study of the cell.

In the following chapters, we shall explore the physiology of cells, their structures and functions, but first let us look at some of the one-celled plants and animals, the organisms of which their discoverer, Antony van Leeuwenhoek, wrote some 300 years ago: "This was for me, among all the marvels that I have discovered in nature, the most marvelous of all; and I must say, for my part, that no more pleasant sight has come before my eye than these many thousands of living creatures seen all alive in a drop of water, moving among one another, each several creatures having its own proper motion." These "marvelous creatures" are not more alive than any other cell, but because of their ceaseless activity and obvious self-sufficiency, they impress upon us with particular force the fact that cells are *living* organizations.

MEASURING THE MICROSCOPIC WORLD

Cells vary greatly in size. The largest is the ostrich egg, which, by virtue of the yolk it contains, is several inches in diameter and so can easily be described in terms of a familiar scale of measurement, as can the egg cells of most birds and reptiles (although, in these cases, the large, visible portion of the egg is only storage material). The majority of cells, however, can be seen only with the aid of a microscope, and some bacterial cells (which are the smallest) cannot be clearly visualized by even the finest light microscope. The units of measurement generally used for describing cells are microns, millimicrons, and angstroms:

1 inch = 25.4 millimeters

1 millimeter = 1,000 microns

1 micron = 1,000 millimicrons

1 millimicron = 10 angstroms

The unaided human eye has a resolving power of about 1/10 millimeter, or 1/254 inch. This means that if you look at two lines that are less than 100 microns apart, they merge into a single line. Similarly, two dots less than 100 microns apart look like a single blurry dot. To separate structures closer than this, optical instruments such as microscopes are used. The best light microscope has a resolving power of 0.2 micron, or 200 millimicrons, or 2,000 angstroms, and so improves on the naked eye about 500 times. It is theoretically impossible to build a light microscope that will do better than this. Notice that resolving power and magnification are two different things; if you take a picture through the best light microscope of two lines that are less than 0.2 micron, or 200 millimicrons, apart, you can enlarge that photograph indefinitely, but the two lines will still blur together. By using more powerful lenses, you can increase magnification, but this will not improve resolution.

With the electron microscope, resolving power has been increased almost 400 times over that provided by the light microscope. This is achieved by using "illumination" consisting of electron beams instead of light rays. Electron microscopy at present affords a resolving power of about 5 angstroms, roughly 200,000 times greater than that of the human eye. The electron microscope has one great disadvantage, however. Electrons have a very small mass and must travel in a vacuum; electron beams can only pass through specimens that are exceedingly thin. To prepare them for the electron microscope, specimens must, therefore, be killed and embedded in hard materials so they can be sliced by special cutting instruments. This means, of course, that the high resolving powers of the electron microscope can only be applied to tissues that are no longer alive.

The human egg cell is 1/10 millimeter in diameter, right on the edge of visibility for the unaided eye. Somatic cells, the cells that make up the tissues of the body (soma) of multicelled plants and animals, are generally several times smaller than egg cells, averaging about 20 microns in diameter. The largest bacterial cells are about 5 microns in length, and the smallest are beyond the limits of light resolution. A few kinds of cells, almost all viruses, and many of the structures within cells can be seen only with the electron microscope.

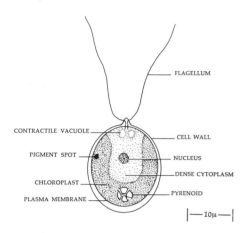

FLAGELLUM

CONTRACTILE VACUOLE

CELL WALL

PIGMENT SPOT

NUCLEUS

DENSE CYTOPLASM

CHLOROPLAST

PLASMA MEMBRANE

PYRENOID

|—10μ—|

1–6 *This one-celled green alga, Chlamydomonas, darts through the water by rapid movements of its flagella. It is photosynthetic, containing chlorophyll in its single cup-shaped chloroplast, which almost fills the cell, and like the green land plants, it stores food in the form of starch.*

Chlamydomonas

If you take a drop of water from the sunlit surface of a pond or even from the bright corner of a home aquarium, one of the cells you will be most likely to encounter is *Chlamydomonas*. *Chlamydomonas* is small (about 15 microns long), oval in shape and grass-green. It moves very rapidly, with a characteristic darting motion imparted by the beating of the two *flagella* ("whips") that protrude from its larger, anterior end. The green is caused by the pigment chlorophyll. The chlorophyll is contained within a structure known as the *chloroplast*. In *Chlamydomonas*, a single chloroplast fills almost the entire cell. As the presence of chlorophyll reveals, *Chlamydomonas* is a photosynthetic autotroph, using the sun's energy to convert carbon dioxide and water to glucose. Within the green chloroplast that fills most of the body of the cell, you may, with a light microscope, be able to detect a light-colored spherical body, the *pyrenoid*. The exact way in which the pyrenoid functions is not known, but this body is associated with the conversion of glucose to starch for food storage, and starch deposits can be detected surrounding the pyrenoid body. Above the pyrenoid, you may be able to see the nucleus, the central controlling structure of the cell. The entire cell body is surrounded by a plasma membrane and a thin and flexible outer cell wall. *Chlamydomonas* is of special interest because it is believed to be a representative of the ancient cell line from which the higher plants, and perhaps the higher animals, developed, an hypothesis that will be discussed in more detail in chapters to come.

Euglena

Euglena, like *Chlamydomonas*, is a phytoflagellate, that is, a cell that possesses both a flagellum and chlorophyll. *Euglena* is somewhat larger than *Chlamydomonas* (from 35 to 100 microns in length, depending on the species) and is elongated in shape, like the hull of a submarine. It is one of the chief contributors to the scum that covers the surface of slow-moving waters, and it is a persistent annoyance to the owners of outdoor swimming pools.

29 *Cells as Organisms: The One-celled Plants and Animals*

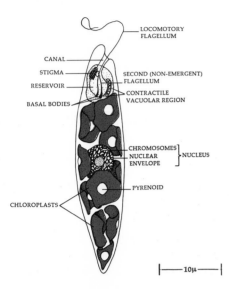

LOCOMOTORY
FLAGELLUM

CANAL

STIGMA

RESERVOIR

BASAL BODIES

SECOND (NON-EMERGENT)
FLAGELLUM

CONTRACTILE
VACUOLAR REGION

CHROMOSOMES
NUCLEAR
ENVELOPE } NUCLEUS

PYRENOID

CHLOROPLASTS

|— 10μ —|

1–7 *Euglena is one of the most versatile of all one-celled organisms. As you can see in the diagram, it contains a number of chloroplasts, and it uses these to synthesize its food from sunlight, carbon dioxide, and water. The swelling at the base of the motile flagellum is believed to be the photoreceptor. This light-sensitive area is shielded by the reddish eyespot (stigma) overlying the reservoir. Euglena moves by means of a single flagellum.*

Euglena moves by means of a single flagellum, which is extended forward and to the side. The whiplike beat of this flagellum rotates the body of *Euglena* and moves it forward simultaneously. The flagellum is attached to the base of a flask-shaped opening, the *reservoir*, at the anterior end of the cell. Next to the long free flagellum can be seen a very short flagellum, which serves no apparent purpose; presumably *Euglena* is derived from an ancestral cell which was biflagellated, like *Chlamydomonas*.

Right beside the reservoir and emptying into it is the *contractile vacuole*. This vacuole collects excess water from all parts of the cell, swelling like a bubble, and then contracts so quickly that it seems to disappear as it discharges into the reservoir. The body behind the reservoir is filled with multiple chloroplasts, small green packages of chlorophyll, that catch the light as *Euglena* rotates through the water. The body is surrounded by an outer coat, or *pellicle*, made up of small, fine scales, or plates, which is more flexible than the cell wall of *Chlamydomonas*. The flexible pellicle permits *Euglena* to wriggle, providing an alternative means of locomotion for mud-dwelling forms.

If you leave a culture of *Euglena* near a sunny window, a clearly visible green cloud will form in the water, and this will move as the light changes, always finding itself a spot which is bright but not too bright. *Euglena* is able to move toward the light because of a pair of special organelles—the *stigma* and the *photoreceptor*—which function as an eye. The stigma, or eyespot, is a speck of orange pigment, one of a group known as the *carotenoids*. Carotenoids, as their name implies, are the pigments that color the cells of carrots. Similar pigments are found in the eyes of man and other vertebrates. The stigma lies over the reservoir, shading a segment of the free flagellum. The section of the flagellum that lies beneath the stigma is slightly thickened. This has been hypothesized to be the light-sensitive area, the photoreceptor. When the light is shining from one side of *Euglena*, as from a window, this photoreceptor is alternately shielded and exposed by the stigma to the light rays as *Euglena* rotates. If the animal is headed directly toward or directly away from the light, the photoreceptor is constantly exposed. *Euglena* orients itself directly toward or directly away from light like an airplane orienting itself on a radio beam. Apparently, the light acting on the photoreceptor directs the angle of beat of the flagellum and so determines the direction of motion of the entire creature.

Amoeba

Amoeba, in contrast to the finely formed green flagellates, has no color, no constant shape, and no special organelles for locomotion. The name "amoeba" is from the Greek word for "change." The most familiar species

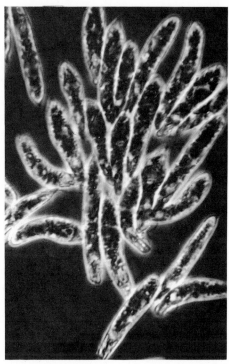

|— 20μ —|

is *Amoeba proteus,* named after Proteus, the sea-god of Greek mythology who eluded capture by constantly changing his form.

Viewed from above, the usual vantage point of the microscopist, the cell moves like a slowly traveling inkblot, spreading tentatively forward and erasing itself behind. This unusual form of locomotion is possible only when the amoeba has a surface below it to grip. The cytoplasm of the cell is able to assume two different consistencies. One, the *gel,* is quite rigid, like a well-set gelatin dessert; the other, the *sol,* is a thick liquid. In the advancing "foot," or *pseudopodium* ("false foot"), of the amoeba, the innermost contents, in the form of sol, flow forward through the semirigid tube or cylinder formed by the outermost contents, the gel. The gel contracts at the rear of the amoeba, and the sol then turns back, fountainlike, on the gel and stiffens, itself becoming a part of the rigid outer layer. The internal structure of the amoeba—its organelles—flow along with the sol. Food, fat droplets, and a large number of small gray crystalline particles (whose function is not known) are also circulated by these cytoplasmic currents. These movements, called *protoplasmic streaming,* are frequently seen also in somatic cells of both plants and animals. In somatic cells, however, the movement often does not serve to change the position of the cell, as in *Amoeba,* but primarily to distribute cell nutrients and other substances. The question of how the flowing cytoplasm of *Amoeba* actually produces amoeboid motion is still a matter of debate.

1–8 *Photomicrograph of a colony of Euglena gracilis moving toward light. The light source is at the lower left. (Eric V. Gravé)*

1–9 *The body of Amoeba consists of an almost clear mass of gelatinous cytoplasm. According to one theory of amoeboid motion, the amoeba moves by pushing out temporary cytoplasmic projections (pseudopodia), into which additional cytoplasm flows until the whole animal has moved forward. A stable gel layer surrounds the core of liquid, flowing cytoplasm. As the liquid cytoplasm (sol) reaches the tip of the pseudopodium, it is pushed to the sides by the cytoplasm behind and is converted to gel. At the same time, the gel at the posterior end becomes sol and flows forward.*

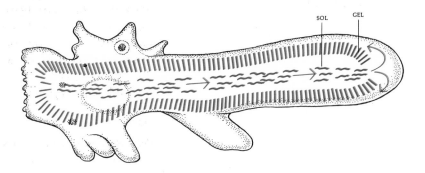

31 *Cells as Organisms: The One-celled Plants and Animals*

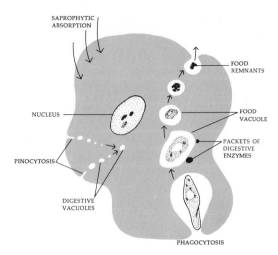

SAPROPHYTIC
ABSORPTION

FOOD
REMNANTS

NUCLEUS

FOOD
VACUOLE

PINOCYTOSIS

PACKETS OF
DIGESTIVE
ENZYMES

DIGESTIVE
VACUOLES

PHAGOCYTOSIS

1–10 *The three ways in which Amoeba feeds. In saprophytic nutrition, dissolved materials seep in through the cell membrane. In phagocytosis, the amoeba extends pseudopodia to capture an organism (see Figure 1–11). The engulfed food is surrounded by a food vacuole, and the encircling cytoplasm secretes digestive enzymes to break down the food for absorption. As digestion proceeds, nutrients and water are absorbed from the food and the vacuole gradually shrinks. Indigestible remnants are expelled from the body. Pinocytosis (cell drinking) is like phagocytosis except that the nutrients are in solution and the vacuoles are smaller.*

The amoeba, which has no chlorophyll, is heterotrophic, depending on other organisms to synthesize its food. It feeds in three ways: (1) saprophytically, that is, on liquid materials passing through the cell membrane; (2) by phagocytosis, which means "cell eating"; and (3) by pinocytosis, which means "cell drinking."

1   In *saprophytic nutrition*, dissolved materials having nutrient values seep in through the cell membrane. This is the chief form of nourishment for the cells that make up the bodies of plants and animals, and even autotrophs like the phytoflagellates absorb vitamins, minerals, and other substances in this way.

2   In *phagocytosis*, the cell extends pseudopodia around its prey, which is often another protozoan or an alga. If you watch carefully, you can see that the pseudopodia are formed especially for the particular prey; for example, a small algal cell will cause an amoeba to extend small pseudopodia, while a larger or more active cell will call forth larger and more extensive pincerlike projections. When the pseudopodia surround the prey, they meet and fuse, and the body of the amoeba flows over the prey, engulfing it. Then the portion of the amoeba cell membrane surrounding the captive pinches off from the outer membrane, forming a food vacuole. As this vacuole moves through the body of the amoeba, the animal secretes digestive juice into it and nutrients digested from the prey are released through the surface of the vacuole into the cytoplasm. Once the contents of the vacuole have been digested, the remains are discarded, vacuole and all, through the cell membrane. The feeding behavior of *Amoeba* is described in more detail in Section 5.

3   *Pinocytosis* closely resembles phagocytosis except that the nutrients digested are in solution rather than in solid form and the vacuoles are generally smaller. Sometimes, long pinocytic channels can be seen running down from the surface toward the center of the cell.

All cells, both independent and somatic, absorb some of their nutrients saprophytically. Phagocytosis is characteristic of a number of different types of Protozoa, of digestive cells in some invertebrates, and of white blood cells in man and other vertebrates. Electron microscopy has now shown that pinocytosis, once thought a rare phenomenon, occurs with surprising frequency among somatic as well as independent cells. It is possible that much cell nutrition formerly believed to be saprophytic actually is a result of pinocytosis.

Paramecium

Paramecium, because of its shape, was the "slipper animalcule" of the early microscopists. The dark area in the body of the animal that looks

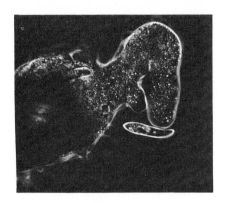
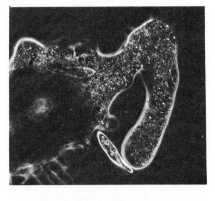
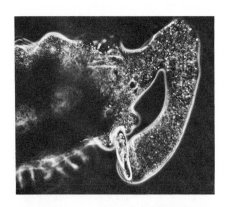
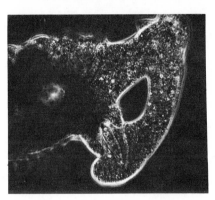
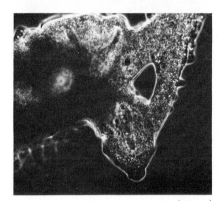

1–11 *The giant amoeba Chaos chaos captures a paramecium. (Eric V. Gravé)*

|–100μ–|

like the arch of the slipper is the oral groove that funnels food into its *cytostome.* Although the cytostome is sometimes referred to as the mouth, it is not an opening, like the mouth of a higher animal, but rather a thin spot in the pellicle where the inrushing food particles press against the membrane to form a vacuole.

Paramecia are covered with short hairlike structures called *cilia,* a name which comes from the Latin word for "eyelash." There is no clear distinction between cilia and flagella, although "cilia" is the term generally applied to shorter structures occurring in greater numbers. *Paramecium caudatum* has some 2,500 cilia, which arise from rows of small cylinder-shaped basal bodies lying beneath the pellicle. (See Figure 1–12.) Their beating is coordinated. They do not all stroke at the same time, like the oars of a well-trained crew, but their stroking motion runs in waves down the animal's body, giving the same effect as stems of grain in a wheat field blown by the wind. These waves travel at a slightly oblique angle, causing the paramecium to rotate as it swims.

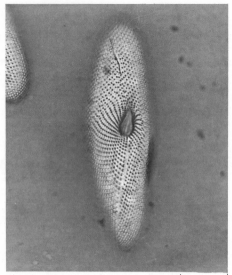

| ⊢—10μ—⊣ |

1–12 *Photomicrograph of Paramecium*
aurelia, treated by a silver-staining
method to show the rows of granules
marking the bases of the cilia. The dark
spot in the center is the opening to the
animal's "mouth," or cytostome, where
ingested food is formed into vacuoles.
(*Dr. T. M. Sonneborn*)

In open water, the paramecium swims swiftly, at least on a microscopic scale, but it slows down in the presence of bacteria, which compose its usual diet. When the animal is swimming slowly, the cilia around its oral groove beat more strongly than do those on the rest of its body. This creates currents in the water which draw in nearby particles and cause them to flow down the funnel-like groove to the cytostome. Some particles are rejected by a reverse flick of a cilium,* but the majority collect at the base, pressing against the thin membrane there until it balloons in, forming a food vacuole, and seals off. A single paramecium can consume up to 5,000 bacteria a day. The food vacuoles move through the body of the cell, while the contents are digested, releasing soluble nutrients. Finally any indigestible remains are excreted through a special pore in the pellicle.

Like the other ciliated protozoans, paramecia have two kinds of nuclei: a large (macro) nucleus and one or more small (micro) nuclei. The comparatively large size and great complexity of these protozoans seem to require a division of nuclear labor.

Euplotes

Euplotes, also one of the common one-celled animals, belongs to a group of protozoans known as the Hypotricha, which are the most structurally complicated of all cells. In the hypotrichs, the cilia are fused into *cirri* and *membranelles*. Each cirrus is a tapering bundle of cilia pulled out from a rounded base into a point, like the hairs of an artist's brush. The membranelles, on the other hand, resemble more the brush of a housepainter. Each membranelle is made up of clumps of cilia two or three rows thick and 20 to 25 cilia long, all adhering to one another. The row of membranelles, of which there are about 40, starts anteriorly, sweeping down clockwise along the ventral surface and finally terminating in the funnel-like cavity leading to the cytostome. Membranelles are connected with one another by a root system and beat in a regular undulating motion, carrying food particles into the cytostome and often aiding in locomotion. Cirri, assisted by the powerful membranelles, may be used like paddles for swimming, but usually they are used for walking, which gives the hypotrichs a highly characteristic busy, jerky, scurrying motion.

Viewed from the side, *Euplotes* looks decidedly buglike, with its nimble, swiftly moving "legs." It has the advantage (to the observer) of a very transparent pellicle and cytoplasm, so that many of its structures can be seen at the same time. Its pellicle is rigid, concave on the dorsal surface, and flat on the bottom. From its undersurface, the cirri protrude—17 or more, depending on the species. Most of the undersurface on the forward

* Whether there is any element of selection in this rejecting motion of *Paramecium* is not at present known. We do know that another ciliate, *Stentor*, can selectively reject (see Chapter 5–1).

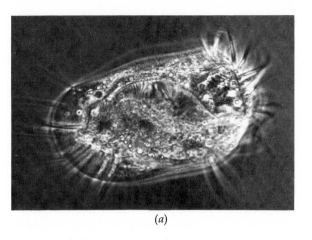

(a)

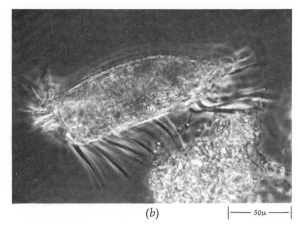

(b) |——— 50μ ———|

1–13 *Euplotes patella, viewed from the top*
(a) and side (b). As you can see, the cilia
on the animal's lower surface, are fused
together in groups to form heavy cirri.
These cirri do not beat rhythmically
like ordinary cilia but instead move in
rapid jerks. They are used by Euplotes
as legs, enabling it to crawl about on
vegetation. (Eric V. Gravé)

left side (*Euplotes*' left, that is) is taken up by a large scoop-shaped depression, which leads to the cytostome. In addition, it is possible to see within the body of the cell, which is about 90 microns long, the large C-shaped macronucleus, with the smaller micronucleus lying to its side, the contractile vacuole, which collects water from fixed channels that radiate through the animal's body, and a series of food vacuoles moving from the cytostome to the anal pore.

All the many cirri and membranelles of *Euplotes* are coordinated in their movements. Whether the animal is scurrying, paddling, or spiraling through the water, they move in synchrony. Furthermore, and even more difficult to explain, they can work one at a time; the cirri can remain motionless while the membranelles beat, or some cirri can move while others are still. Fast and slow, forward and backward motions are maneuvered with great facility. Microscopists have been able to trace, within the body of *Euplotes*, a system of interconnecting fibrils apparently linking the cirri with one another and with the membranelles and converging near the cytostome. If one takes a glass needle and makes a cut in the side of *Euplotes* which severs these fibrils, the rear cirri, those behind the cut, lose their coordination with the organelles in the forepart of the body. A similar cut on the other side of the cell, where there are no fibrils, has no such effect. This has been taken as evidence that these fibrils act as a sort of nervous system, although we do not know, of course, what other structures might have been affected.

Euplotes, which is far more varied in its structures and coordinated in its activities than a number of many-celled animals, is a good representative of the limits of complexity of a single cell.

SUMMARY

The basic unit of life is the cell. All living things are composed of cells, and many organisms begin life as one cell. From this beginning, some grow into complex organizations of billions of cells, but some remain single-celled all their lives. We have introduced our study of cells by examining some representative types of these one-celled organisms.

Two phytoflagellates (cells possessing both flagella and chlorophyll) were considered first: *Chlamydomonas* and *Euglena.* The green chlorophyll that fills most of the body of the phytoflagellate cell gives it the ability to use the sun's energy in the conversion of carbon dioxide and water to glucose. The pyrenoid, a spherical body within the chloroplast of *Chlamydomonas,* is associated with the conversion of this glucose to starch. The flagella provide these cells with the power of locomotion. *Euglena* also possesses a pair of special organelles—a stigma and photoreceptor—which function as an eye, enabling the cell to orient itself toward light.

Protoplasmic streaming is exemplified by the relative movements of the sol and gel forms of the cytoplasm in *Amoeba.* This movement serves both as a means of locomotion (the amoeba has no organelles for locomotion) and as the method by which the cell forms pseudopodia to capture prey. The amoeba feeds in three ways: (1) saprophytically, (2) by phagocytosis, and (3) by pinocytosis.

Paramecium is representative of the ciliated protozoans. The cilia which cover the outer coat of the paramecium perform two functions: (1) their synchronized beating moves the cell through the water, and (2) the beating of the cilia around the cell's oral groove draws food particles into the groove and down to the cytostome. Ciliated protozoans have a macronucleus and one or more micronuclei.

Euplotes is a hypotrich, a group of protozoans which includes the most structurally complicated of all cells. In *Euplotes,* the cilia are fused into cirri and membranelles. Membranelles are used for swimming and for carrying food particles to the cytostome, while cirri are used primarily for walking. The movements of all these groups of cilia are coordinated, apparently by a system of interconnecting fibrils.

Cell Processes and Structure

A newborn baby is made up of 2,000 billion (2×10^{12}) cells. The cells that make up the tissues of a many-celled animal, such as a baby, or of a many-celled plant appear superficially to be very different from the "marvelous creatures" of Leeuwenhoek. These external differences reflect the fact that somatic cells are often less complex and more specialized. In other words, they have given over certain functions, such as locomotion—which is one of the more spectacular achievements of the protozoa—to specialize in others, such as producing a hormone or conducting a nerve impulse. Somatic cells live an interdependent existence, in contrast to the independence of most single-celled organisms. Yet they retain a surprising degree of autonomy. Almost every type of somatic cell can be isolated and maintained in a test tube if the appropriate nutrient medium is provided, and the nutrient medium for a somatic cell turns out to contain precisely the same components as those required by a ciliated protozoan such as *Paramecium*.

Figures 1–14 to 1–16 show electron micrographs of the one-celled organism *Chlamydomonas* and of representative somatic cells from a plant and from an animal. In this chapter and the next, we shall explore some of the structures and functions that these cells have in common. In Chapter 1–5, we shall survey some of the different types of cells that make up the tissues of higher animals and plants.

SOME BASIC CELL PROCESSES

Certain basic activities are common to all cells, whether they are somatic cells or Protozoa. In Chapter 1–2, we described the ways in which nutrients get into cells. Here we shall examine some of the principles that govern the movement of substances through cells and across cell membranes.

1–14 *Electron micrograph and diagram of Chlamydomonas. At the top of the micrograph, on the right, are the bases of the organism's two flagella. Two mitochondria are seen just below the flagella. A single chloroplast fills most of the cell. Within the chloroplast starch is stored. Around the outside of the cell are both a cell membrane and a cell wall. (Dr. Ursula Johnson)*

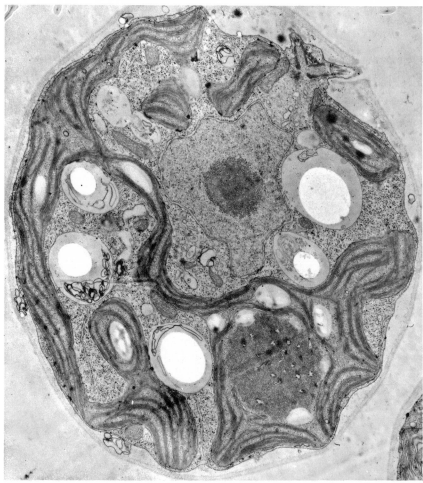

|———2μ———|

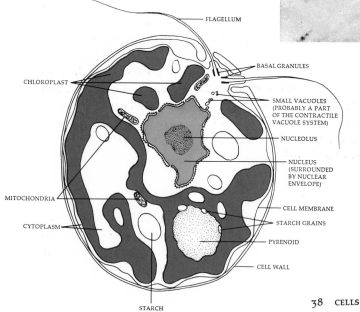

FLAGELLUM

CHLOROPLAST

BASAL GRANULES

SMALL VACUOLES
(PROBABLY A PART
OF THE CONTRACTILE
VACUOLE SYSTEM)

NUCLEOLUS

NUCLEUS
(SURROUNDED
BY NUCLEAR
ENVELOPE)

MITOCHONDRIA

CELL MEMBRANE

CYTOPLASM

STARCH GRAINS

PYRENOID

CELL WALL

STARCH

1–15 *Electron micrograph and diagram of a "typical" plant cell. A maturing cell, like the one from a tobacco leaf shown here, usually contains several vacuoles in different parts of the cell. These vacuoles will swell as the cell reaches maturity, stretching the flexible cell wall, until most of the interior of the cell is taken up by a single large, centralized vacuole. In the mature cell, the cellulose cell wall becomes thick and inflexible. The chloroplasts are the largest bodies in the cytoplasm. Within the chloroplasts, you can see chlorophyll-containing grana, and also several starch grains in which the plant stores its reserve supplies of food. (Dr. E. H. Newcomb)*

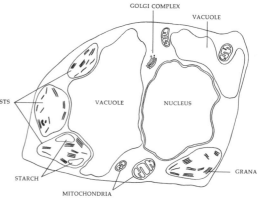

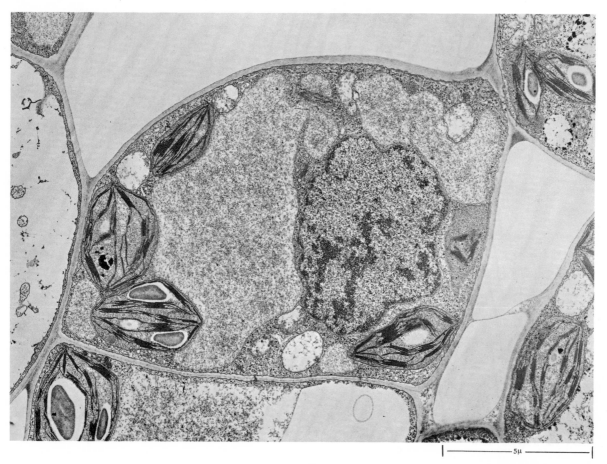

1–16 *A rat-liver cell, representing a "typical"
animal cell. The cytoplasm surrounding
the nucleus is filled with mitochondria
and endoplasmic reticulum. In many
places, the endoplasmic reticulum has
granules on it, but the agranular form
can also be seen in the lower right
corner. Three lysosomes appear as dark
circles on the upper right side, and to
their left, indicated by an arrow, is
the Golgi complex. The dark globules are fat droplets and the dark
granules are glycogen. (Dr. Keith R.
Porter)*

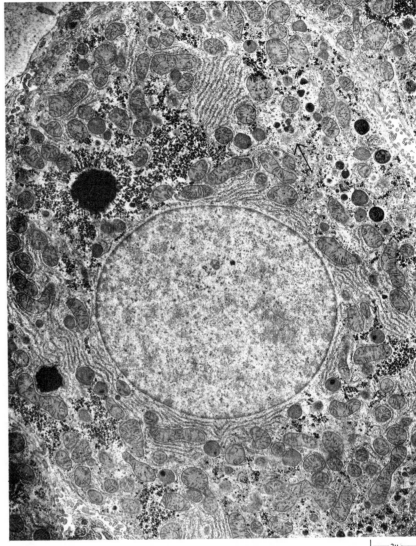

— 2μ —

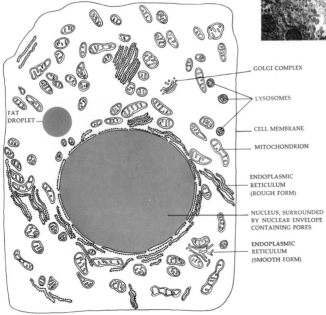

GOLGI COMPLEX

LYSOSOMES

FAT
DROPLET

CELL MEMBRANE

MITOCHONDRION

ENDOPLASMIC
RETICULUM
(ROUGH FORM)

NUCLEUS, SURROUNDED
BY NUCLEAR ENVELOPE
CONTAINING PORES

ENDOPLASMIC
RETICULUM
(SMOOTH FORM)

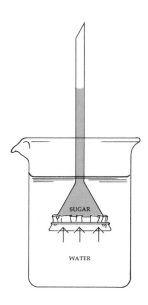

1–17 *A demonstration of osmosis. The glass funnel is filled with a sugar solution, covered with cellophane, and placed in a beaker of water. The water molecules, moving from the area of higher water concentration (the 100 percent water in the beaker) to the area of lower concentration in the funnel will pass through the cellophane, which is analogous to the cell membrane, into the funnel. As osmosis occurs, the solution will rise in the glass tube and will become more and more diluted. Eventually, the weight of the solution in the tube will exert a pressure that just counterbalances the tendency of water to enter the funnel. At this point the water will stop entering by osmosis, and the system is in osmotic equilibrium.*

Diffusion

The molecules in a gas or a liquid are in constant motion. These molecular motions are responsible for the familiar phenomenon known as *diffusion*. As you know, if a drop of perfume evaporates in one corner of a room, the entire room is soon equally permeated with scent. The volatile molecules of the perfume are dispersed by their own random movements and by the bombardment of other molecules. Similarly, a teaspoonful of salt in a saucepan of water will diffuse throughout the water so that every drop is equally salty. In moving from an area of greater concentration of perfume or salt molecules to an area of lesser concentration, the substances are said to move along a *concentration gradient*.

In cells, substances diffuse through the cytoplasmic fluid or the surrounding medium. Diffusion of some of these substances is limited by the outer cell membrane or by the membranes within the cell, just as the walls of the room may limit the diffusion of the perfume. Other substances pass back and forth through the membrane. Diffusion through a nonliving membrane generally depends on the size of the pores in the membrane, with smaller molecules sifting through and larger ones being excluded. In the case of the cell membrane, however, the size of the molecules does not seem to be the only governing factor. Only a few substances, including oxygen, carbon dioxide, and water, pass through all cell membranes. Most other molecules may or may not diffuse through, depending on the type of cell and on its physiological condition. A membrane such as the cell membrane is said to be *selectively permeable*.

Osmosis

Osmosis (which is from the Greek word for "push") is the movement of water between two solutions separated by a membrane which is permeable to water and less permeable or impermeable to the substance in solution. Under such circumstances, the water will, in nearly every case, follow its own concentration gradient, moving from areas of higher water concentration to areas of lower concentration. In a solution of salt in water, for instance, the water molecules are less concentrated than they are in pure water. Therefore, molecules of water will move across the membrane, or toward the more concentrated salt solution from the less concentrated solution.

Osmosis was long assumed to be simply the diffusion of water molecules. Recent observations indicate, however, that the movement of water in osmosis is more rapid than can be explained on the basis of diffusion and that osmosis also involves a bulk flow of water through pores in membranes. This flow presumably results from a hydrostatic pressure difference which causes water to flow toward the higher salt concentration.

Osmosis is associated with nonliving as well as living membranes. If

HOW THE CELL THEORY DEVELOPED

The seventeenth century microscopist Robert Hooke noticed that cork and other plant tissues are made up of small cavities separated by walls. He called these cavities cells, *meaning "little rooms." The word did not take on its present meaning, however, until 1839, when the German biologist Theodor Schwann proposed that all living organisms are composed of cells. For Hooke, cells were empty containers; for Schwann and the biologists who have followed him, cells are the functional units of all living things. Organisms are composed either of one cell or of many cells, and there is no life apart from the life of cells.*

In 1858, cell theory took on a broader significance when the great pathologist Rudolf Virchow generalized that cells can arise only from preexisting cells: "Where a cell exists, there must have been a preexisting cell, just as the animal arises only from an animal and the plant only from a plant. . . . Throughout the whole series of living forms, whether entire animal or plant organisms or their component parts, there rules an eternal law of continuous development."

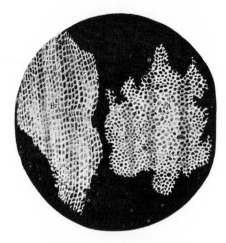

Robert Hook's drawings of two slices of a piece of cork, reproduced from his Micrographia *(1665). (The Bettman Archive)*

you make a pouch out of some material such as cellophane (which is permeable to water but less permeable to sugar), fill it half full of a concentrated sugar solution, and immerse it in a beaker of distilled water, the water outside the pouch will push its way inside, to the region of lower water concentration, seeking a point of equilibrium at which the water concentration will be the same on both sides. The pouch will swell and may even be burst open by the increased volume of water. The same effect can be produced in a red blood cell by removing it from the salty blood plasma which is its normal environment and placing it in distilled water. Conversely, if a pouch full of plain water or a red blood cell is immersed in a solution containing an even greater amount of a substance other than water, both the pouch and the red blood cell will shrink in size as the water pushes out of them into the area of lower water concentration.

Cells that live in fresh water, such as the one-celled organisms that we surveyed in the last chapter, have salts and other materials in solution in their cytoplasmic liquids, which therefore have a lower water concentration than the surrounding medium. For this reason, such cells must work actively to keep from being flooded with water, like the cellophane bag filled with sugar solution. Freshwater protozoans solve this problem by means of their contractile vacuoles, which act like miniature bilge pumps, rhythmically ejecting the excess water. Some saltwater protozoans, even those closely related to the freshwater forms, do not have contractile vacuoles; in other species, they are retained but are relatively inactive.

Osmosis plays an important role in the life of the green plant. As you can see in Figure 1–18, the typical immature plant cell possesses a number of vacuoles (fluid-containing compartments) surrounded by membranes. As the plant grows, these vacuoles grow larger and coalesce. Eventually the vacuole takes up most of the volume of the cell, with cytoplasm and nucleus crowded against the cell membrane and cell wall. Waste materials, materials being held in reserve, and other solutes collect in the vacuoles so that the concentration of molecules in solution within the cell increases and the concentration of pure water decreases. Therefore water tends to move into the cell by osmosis and so the cell may become distended. The firm cell wall keeps the cell from expanding indefinitely or rupturing. The pressure produced within the cell by the osmotic entry of water is known as *turgor*. Turgor gives support to the plant. When plant cells lose water and so lose turgor, the plant wilts.

Active Transport

A particularly important property associated with cell membranes (but not with nonliving membranes) is active transport. Active transport is the process by which a cell can move a substance from a point of lower concentration to a point of higher concentration, that is, against the diffusion gradient. The membrane of the nerve cell, for example, keeps 14 times as much sodium outside as inside and 30 times as much potassium inside as out, a fact on which the conduction of the nerve impulse depends, as we shall see. The properties of active transport and selective permeability are not well understood, but it seems clear that they must be associated with the chemical properties of different areas of the cell membrane. Active transport requires chemical energy.

THE ANATOMY OF CELLS

Cilia and Flagella

With the increasing refinement of the techniques of microscopy, it has become clear that despite differences in external appearance and in various specialized functions, the internal structures of cells are remarkably similar. A cilium or flagellum, as shown in Figure 1–19, offers one of the most striking examples of this. Cilia and flagella appear throughout the animal world. For many of the small water-dwelling animals, such as the flatworms, the cilia are the means for propelling the organism through the water. In larger animals, the organism stays still and the beating cilia move the water across its surfaces; in the case of the clam, for example, motion of the cilia on the gills is responsible for bringing in a steady current of

1–18 *Because soluble materials collect in plant-cell vacuoles, water from the more dilute external solutions (the area of greater water concentration) will tend to move into the vacuoles. As the vacuole becomes distended, it pushes the cytoplasm against the cell wall. As long as the wall is extensible, as shown here, water uptake will continue and the cell will grow larger until the wall is unable to expand further. It is believed that the cell elongates rather than widens because of the arrangement of the cellulose fibers in the cell wall.*

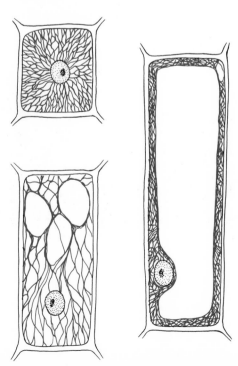

1–19 *Electron micrograph of cilia of Tetrahymeria pyriformis, a common protozoa, and diagram showing the structure of a cilium or flagellum. All cilia and flagella appear to have the same basic structure. Inside the membrane is an outer ring of nine pairs of fibrils surrounding two additional fibrils in the center. This structure can be seen clearly in the lower part of the micrograph, which shows a number of cilia in cross section. Above these are two cilia in longitudinal section. As you can see, the outer fibrils grow out of the basal body, while the two inner fibrils originate just above the basil plate. Some scientists believe that ciliary and flagellar motion is the result of the outer fibrils moving against the two inner ones somewhat like a tractor tread. Others postulate that the outer fibrils are contractile. (Dr. Richard D. Allen)*

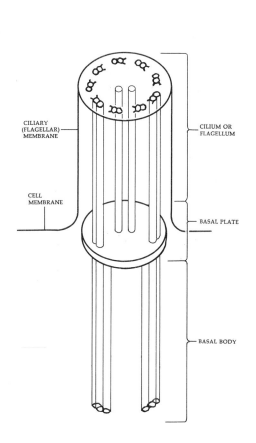

CILIARY
(FLAGELLAR)
MEMBRANE

CILIUM OR
FLAGELLUM

CELL
MEMBRANE

BASAL PLATE

BASAL BODY

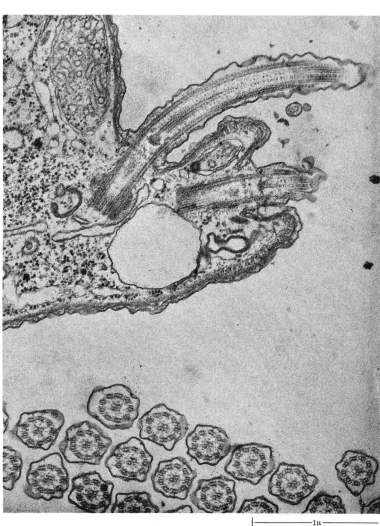

1μ

waterborne food particles. Within our own bodies, the constant beating of the cilia on the inner surfaces of the respiratory tract moves lubricating, protective fluids across the delicate surfaces and helps prevent particles of soot and tobacco tar from lodging directly on the membrane. In the human female, the egg cell is transported from ovary to uterus by the coordinated beat of the cilia that line the Fallopian tubes, and if a sperm cell produced by a human male reaches that egg cell, it is as a result of the forceful beating of the single flagellum, or "tail," of the sperm. You will notice that we have not identified the cell that is the source of Figure 1–19. It is not necessary to do so. Every cilium or flagellum, regardless of the organism on which it is found, has this same internal structure.*

Studies with isolated cilia and flagella have shown that the beat originates within the structure itself; in other words, the sperm cell, for example, does not "wag" its tail, as a dog does, but the tail beats independently. The exact way in which this beating comes about is not known, but if one imagines that the nine pairs of tubules forming the outer circle of the typical "nine-plus-two" structure (see Figure 1–19) are contractile and that each pair can contract individually, it is possible to explain any type of ciliary or flagellar motion. Alternatively, some investigators believe that ciliary motion is caused by the creeping, tractor-fashion, of the outside tubules along the center pair.

How did this one structure come to be distributed so universally through all living things? Does it represent the best possible solution to the problem of ciliary and flagellar beat? This would seem likely, or otherwise it would surely have been modified under the pressures of evolution. Was this solution arrived at separately by many different varieties of living organisms? The structure is so complex that this is hard to believe. Was it, instead, found by some remote one-celled organism—ancestral both to *Chlamydomonas* and to us—and passed down a long, unbroken hereditary sequence? These questions are impossible to answer now, and may always be, but it is difficult not to ask them.

The Cell Wall

As you can see in Figure 1–15, our typical plant cell has a stiff cell wall. This wall is constructed by the cell, using glucose as its starting material. Once the wall is constructed, however, it is no longer dependent on the cell; if the cell dies, the wall remains in place. Nor can glucose, once deposited (as cellulose) in the cell wall, ever again be used by the plant for nourishment. The wall provides protection and support to the cell but prevents the entry of food particles by phagocytosis; plants must absorb

* Bacterial cilia are the single exception.

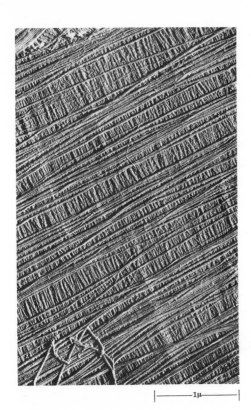

|———1μ———|

1–20 *Electron micrograph of the cell-wall surface of an alga (Chaetomorpha). The wall is made up of layers of tough cellulose fibrils, closely packed in parallel array. The layers are oriented in different directions, so that the fibrils of one layer are approximately perpendicular to those of the layer below. (Dr. R. D. Preston)*

their nutrients in solution. The cell wall in the typical cell of multicellular plants is perforated by holes through which strands of cytoplasm are threaded; these connect the plant cell to adjacent cells.

The principal component of the cell wall is cellulose, which is composed of glucose spun into long microfibrils. These microfibrils wind together to form fine threads, and the threads, in turn, coil around one another like strands in a cable. (See Figure 1–20.) Each "cable" contains about a billion cellulose molecules. Cellulose wound in this fashion is as strong as an equivalent thickness of steel.

As the cell grows in volume, it enlarges the wall along with it, stretching the wall by exerting pressure against it and adding a new layer inside the outer one. In growing plant cells, the Golgi complexes (see below) produce vesicles which appear to contain certain components of the wall. These vesicles move to the cell surface, where their contents become incorporated with the growing wall. Once the cell ceases its expansion, the wall stiffens and hardens. In many types of fibrous and woody plants—trees, for instance—most of the cells die, leaving only the rigid wall, which then forms the supporting structure for the plant. These empty chambers were the "cells" seen by Robert Hooke in 1665.

The Cell Membrane

Limiting the cytoplasm of all cells, both plant and animal, is a delicate structure known as the *plasma membrane*. This membrane, which is only about 10 millimicrons thick, could not be seen clearly before the development of the electron microscope. Now, as you can see in Figure 1–21, electron microscopy reveals that the membrane has a characteristic structure consisting of two dense layers making the whole not unlike a sandwich. The outer layers are believed to be composed of protein, and the inner layer of lipid, a fatty material. This three-layer structure is also often called the *unit membrane* since it represents the basic design of most biological membranes. Often a number of unit membranes are found together in stacks or folds, an arrangement particularly common in structures absorbing light energy.

In plant cells, which have an outer cell wall, the plasma membrane lies just within the wall. In the somatic cells of animals, adjacent membranes form regular borders, marking off the boundaries of the cells within the tissues. The two membranes of adjoining cells do not lie right against one another but are always separated by a space of about 15 to 20 millimicrons. The invisible material occupying the space is sometimes referred to as the *cement substance* since it would appear to be responsible for holding the somatic cells in close contact. Presumably, it is associated with the outer surface of the membrane.

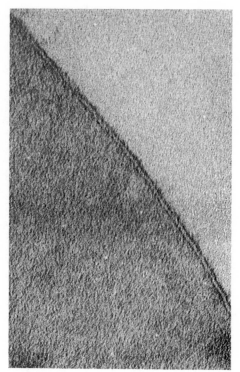

|——— 0.1μ ———|

1–21 *Electron micrograph of the cell membrane of a red blood cell. The three-layered structure of the membrane, plainly visible in this picture, is believed to consist of a layer of lipid material coated on each side with a layer of protein. The lipid is the clear center and the protein the darker, outer lines. Between a cell and its surroundings, there is a continuous exchange of water and dissolved materials, and this two-way traffic is controlled by the membrane, which allows some molecules to pass in or out of the cell and prevents others from doing so. (Dr. J. David Robertson)*

The Cytoplasm

The cytoplasm consists for the most part of a viscous liquid which, although not visible in most light micrographs, plays an important role in the life of the cell. This liquid contains a great number and variety of small and large molecules. The smaller molecules are in solution, dispersed among the water molecules of which the liquid is largely composed. The larger molecules, or assemblies of them, are suspended in the liquid, forming what is known as a *colloid*. These suspended particles do not settle out because they are in a state of constant motion, like dust particles in the air, and the consistency of the cytoplasmic liquid depends on their density, shape, and interactions. The reversible sol and gel states of *Amoeba*, for example, depend on the coming together and separating of suspended particles.

The Organelles

Also present in the cytoplasm, and larger by far than the suspended molecules, are the organelles ("little organs"), which are special structures found within cells.

THE MITOCHONDRIA

Mitochondria are found in both plant and animal cells and are the chief power sources of the cells; some 90 percent of the chemical energy required by the cell comes from reactions which take place in the mitochondria. Mitochondria, which are usually about half a micron in diameter and vary greatly in length, can be seen by the light microscope. In some cells, they appear to be moving constantly and are perhaps carried by cytoplasmic currents. They wiggle and twist and even appear to make journeys from one part of the cell to another. In other cells, such as muscle cells, they are fixed in location. They tend to congregate where energy is required. In *Chlamydomonas*, for example, you can often see a number of mitochondria near the bases of the flagella, which require the energy generated by them. Those cells which are most active in terms of motion or the synthesis of complex molecules contain the greatest number of mitochondria. An "average" cell—the liver cell, shown in Figure 1–16 for example —contains about 1,000 mitochondria.

Since mitochondria can be separated undamaged from the rest of the cell and can be isolated and purified, it is possible to identify the enzyme systems associated with them and to make quite precise correlations between mitochondrial structures and functions.

The mitochondrion was one of the first parts of the cell to be studied by the electron microscope. As you can see in Figure 1–22, it is surrounded by two unit membranes; the outer one serves to enclose the organelle, while

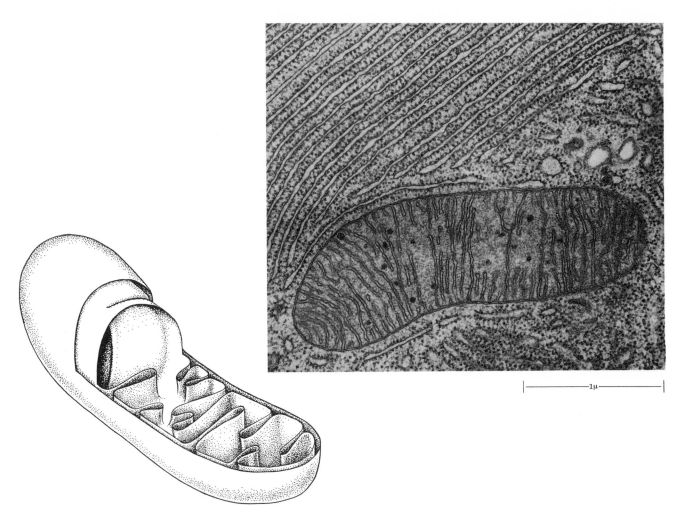

1μ

1–22 *Electron micrograph and cutaway drawing of a mitochondrion from a bat-pancreas cell. The outer wall of the mitochondrion is a unit membrane. A second unit membrane folds back and forth across the interior increasing the working surface of the organelle. The function of the mitochondrion is to convert the food absorbed by the cell into energy in a form that can be used by the cell for its various life processes. The conversion takes place within the folds and on the surfaces of the inner membrane. Scattered among these folds are spherical granules (shown as small, dark spots in the micrograph) which are believed to represent collections of calcium and phosphate (and possibly magnesium) needed for the mitochondrion's work. Above the mitochondrion in the micro-graph are the membrane and flattened sacs of the endoplasmic reticulum. (Dr. Keith R. Porter)*

the inner one is convoluted into folds, pleats, or shelflike projections known as *cristae*. Some of the energy-producing reactions of the cell take place in the dense liquid which fills the mitochondrion, but most of the cellular energy is produced on the surfaces of the cristae. These surfaces contain groups of enzymes that form a part of the actual structure of the cristae; they are woven into the membrane just as threads might be woven into a fabric. Even isolated fragments of mitochondrial membrane are able to carry out the enzymatic reactions described in Chapter 1–8.

Not all mitochondria are identical though they are all constructed on the same plan. In the mitochondria of most Protozoa, the infoldings of the mitochondrial inner wall take the form of tubules rather than cristae, but these tubules serve the same function, that is, to increase the membrane surface. Some insect flight muscles and cells of the adrenal gland also have the tubular type of mitochondrion. The greater the energy requirements of the cell, the greater is the internal membrane area of the mitochondrion and the more complex and numerous are the cristae.

The cytological literature contains some interesting speculations concerning the possible evolutionary origin of mitochondria. Bacterial cells do not possess mitochondria. In fact, they could not since they themselves are only about the same size as a mitochondrion. The chemical reactions which take place on the inner surfaces of the mitochondria in larger cells are known to take place on the inner surface of the plasma membrane in the bacterial cell.

Early cells were probably no bigger than bacteria, but as cells grew larger and more complex in the course of evolution, they undoubtedly required more energy, and in order to produce more energy, they needed more membrane surface. Also, as cells grew larger, distances between the outer membrane, where chemical energy was being produced, and the inner structures where it was required, became greater. One can imagine that perhaps certain areas of the cell membrane became specialized, folding inward into the cell, and then pinched off completely to form separate organelles, which gradually, under the pressures of natural selection, developed into mitochondria. Alternatively, some scientists suggest that mitochondria may have had a completely independent origin, starting as bacterialike organisms which moved into the cytoplasm of larger cells and took up a parasitic existence there. This hypothesis is discussed in more detail in Chapter 1–4.

CHLOROPLASTS

The chloroplast is a prominent structure in both *Chlamydomonas* and the photosynthetic plant cell. As you can see in Figures 1–14 and 1–15, the chloroplasts of the two types of cells are superficially different. *Chlamydomonas* contains only one large irregular chloroplast, surrounded by one

1–23 *Several views of chloroplasts: (a) Electron micrograph of a maize-cell chloro-*
plast, (b) electron micrograph showing details of several grana within the
chloroplast, and (c) diagram of the chloroplast structure of a higher plant. As
you can see in (a), the chloroplast of a higher plant, such as maize, is enclosed in
two unit membranes and is made up of grana, stacks of membranous chloro-
phyll envelopes. Photosynthesis, the process by which plant cells use sunlight
to transform carbon dioxide and water into chemical energy, begins in the light-
trapping chlorophyll molecules within the chloroplast. (Dr. A. E. Vatter)

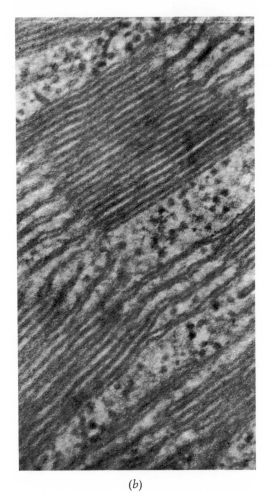

(b)

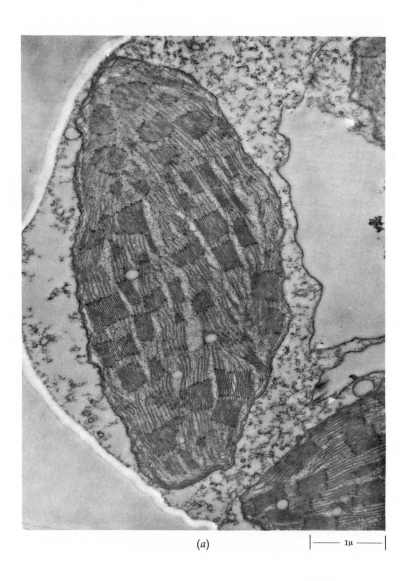

(a) $\mid$ —— 1μ —— $\mid$

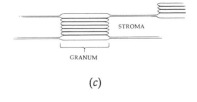

(c)

double membrane. *Chlamydomonas* contains a pyrenoid body within the chloroplast, a feature found only in single-celled photosynthetic organisms. The loose arrangement of the inner structure of the chloroplast of *Chlamydomonas* is also typical of one-celled forms. The chlorophyll within the chloroplasts of both cell types is the same in chemical structure, however, and serves the same essential function, which is the capture of energy from the sun.

The green cells of the "higher" plants often contain large numbers of relatively simple chloroplasts; a single cell from the leaf of a spinach plant, for example, has about fifty. Pyrenoid bodies are not found within these chloroplasts, although the chloroplasts may contain grains of starch.

The chloroplast is far more than just a container of chlorophyll. Chlorophyll isolated in a test tube cannot capture solar energy. Its capacity for photosynthesis depends upon its arrangement in the structure of the chloroplast. According to one theory, the chlorophyll is packaged in small "envelopes," a layer of green pigment within the unit membranes. In the multicelled plants, these chlorophyll envelopes are stacked in piles known as *grana,* so called because they appear as small green grains under the light microscope. Under the electron microscope, however, it can be seen that each granum is composed of many different layers. The material surrounding the grana is called the *stroma*. The grana are connected with one another by sheets of membranes which pass through the stroma.

Light is captured in the grana by the layered arrangement of chlorophyll and membranes. The so-called "dark reactions," in which some of the energy captured in the grana is used in the biosynthesis of glucose, presumably take place in the stroma. As we pointed out in Chapter 1–1, glucose is used by all living things. Plants and animals use glucose as a starter material to build the molecules from which cellular structures are made, and they break down glucose to release the energy required to drive cellular reactions.

The chloroplast belongs to a group of organelles known as *plastids*. This group includes, besides the chloroplast, the leucoplast and the chromoplast. *Leucoplasts* are plant organelles similar in shape to chloroplasts but without chlorophyll. Starch, oil, or protein is formed in the leucoplast; cells containing leucoplasts make up the edible part of a potato, for instance. *Chromoplasts* are the pigment-containing organelles which give color to the cells of flower petals. All these plastids develop from smaller, colorless bodies known as *proplastids*.

THE ENDOPLASMIC RETICULUM

The endoplasmic reticulum, the existence of which was first established by electron microscopy, looks flat or sheetlike in the typical cell pictures. As

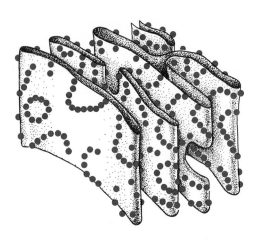

1–24 *The endoplasmic reticulum consists of a system of hollow sacs and connecting channels which spread in networks through the cytoplasm serving to separate it into compartments and also perhaps to provide for the movement of materials from one part of the cell to another. Shown in the drawing is a "rough" form, in which the outer membrane surfaces are heavily coated with ribosomes. In "smooth" endoplasmic reticulum, surfaces of the membrane are free of ribosomal particles.*

shown in Figure 1–24, however, it is actually a system of tiny interconnecting vesicles and channels. These thin membrane-bound cavities vary considerably in size and shape in different types of cells and under different physiological conditions. In some cells, the network consists of fine tubules of 50 to 100 millimicrons in diameter. In other cells, the cavities may be much larger, forming flattened sacs called *cisternae*. The endoplasmic reticulum divides the cytoplasm into various chambers or compartments which serve to separate different groups of chemical reactions from one another, providing a series of "laboratories" in which the chemical work of the cell is carried out.

On the surfaces of the canals and vesicles are areas where enzyme reactions take place, as on the mitochondrial surfaces. The endoplasmic reticulum can be seen to connect with the nuclear envelope, which is, in fact, a part of this complex membrane system. The reticulum, it is believed, may form a communication system for the transport of substances through the cytoplasm.

RIBOSOMES

Ribosomes are small spherical bodies only about 15 to 20 millimicrons in diameter. They form different patterns in different types of cells. In very rapidly growing cells, such as embryonic cells and cancer cells, they are scattered in small clusters of five or ten throughout the cytoplasm; while in other cells many of the ribosomes are attached to the membranes of the endoplasmic reticulum, as shown in Figure 1–24.

George Palade, who was one of the first to call attention to these particles and their varying patterns, wrote of them in 1958: "Sometimes while looking at these intriguing patterns, I believe that I feel very much like the French explorers who, during Napoleon's expedition to Egypt, found themselves face to face with hieroglyphs. Like some of them, I am recording the patterns and I am waiting hopefully for a biochemical Champollion to decipher their meaning."

Owing to the efforts of a number of biochemical Champollions, the function of the ribosome has now become somewhat less obscure. These studies, which are described in Section 3, have shown that ribosomes are the sites at which amino acids are assembled into protein molecules. The number of ribosomes that can be found within any cell reflects its activity in protein production, and the patterns of the ribosomes appear to be related to the kinds of proteins the cell produces.

Cells in which the great majority of ribosomes are attached to the endoplasmic reticulum are generally cells that are making proteins, such as digestive enzymes, which need to be kept segregated from the other parts of the cell or proteins to be used outside the cell, such as those of the intercellular cement. Cells in which the ribosomes are scattered throughout the

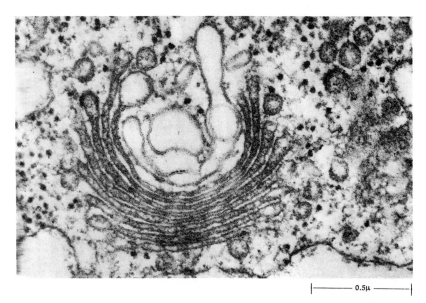

1–25 *The diagram below shows a typical Golgi complex, which consists of stacked membrane sacs, vesicles and vacuoles. Protein from the rough-surfaced endoplasmic reticulum plus sugar-rich components collect in these hollow sacs, where they are packaged into secretion granules for release from the cell. The Golgi complexes are not uniform in shape, and it often takes careful study to find and identify them. (Dr. Ursula Johnson)*

|————— 0.5μ —————|

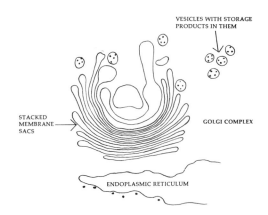

VESICLES WITH STORAGE
PRODUCTS IN THEM

STACKED
MEMBRANE
SACS

GOLGI COMPLEX

ENDOPLASMIC RETICULUM

cytoplasm are making structural proteins, needed for rapid growth, or other, special proteins, such as hemoglobin.

When ribosomes were first discovered, in the 1950s, they could only be visualized as clusters of blurry dots. Now, improved techniques have shown that each ribosome is composed of two subunits, one slightly smaller than the other, which fit together to form the functional unit.

THE GOLGI COMPLEX

The Golgi complex has long been a subject of dispute. It was first described about 70 years ago by Camillo Golgi, who found it in brain cells from an owl. It could only be seen, however, under the light microscope in cells that were stained by special and rather difficult techniques. Furthermore, it often looked different from cell to cell, so questions soon arose as to whether it existed at all or whether it was merely an *artifact*. (Artifacts—as in "artificial"—are findings that are the products of the technique or experimental procedure rather than of nature.) The electron microscope proved that Golgi complexes do indeed exist, and now the controversy is focused on the question of their function.

As you can see in the electron micrograph shown in Figure 1–25, the Golgi complex is an accumulation of stacked membranes, vesicles, and vacuoles. It characteristically occupies a site near the cell center. The membranes of which it is composed are smooth; that is, no ribosomes are attached to them. The Golgi complex appears to function as a packaging center for the cell. Enzymes and other proteins made in the cisternae of the endoplasmic reticulum bud off the membrane in little vesicles and travel to the Golgi

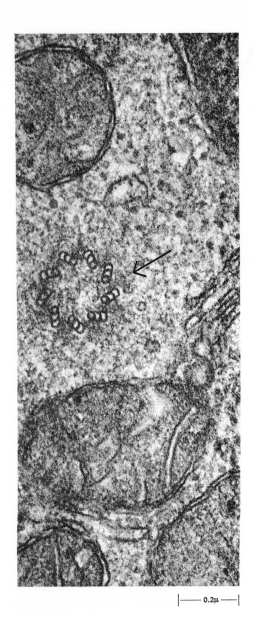

|—— 0.2µ ——|

1–26 *Electron micrograph of a centriole. Note the similarity between this structure and that of a cilium or flagellum. (Dr. Etienne de Harven)*

complex. There they are repackaged in larger sacs made up of membranes of the Golgi complex, and in these vesicles they travel to other parts of the cell or to the plasma membrane. When they reach the plasma membrane, the membranes of the vesicle fuse with this outer cell membrane, opening the vesicle and dumping out its contents. This process is the reverse of phagocytosis, in which a portion of the plasma membrane is pinched off to make an intracellular vesicle.

LYSOSOMES

Lysosomes (see Figure 1–16) are spherical membrane-enclosed organelles, about 500 millimicrons in diameter, although their sizes vary widely. As revealed by special staining techniques, they contain digestive enzymes. They are particularly prominent in the phagocytic protozoans, in which they fuse with the food vacuoles and empty their contents into them.

It is now generally believed that lysosomes are packages of digestive enzymes formed on ribosomes in compartments of the endoplasmic reticulum. The enzymes are transferred from the endoplasmic reticulum to the Golgi complex, where they are packaged within membranes. The enzyme-filled sacs fuse with food vacuoles in phagocytic cells. Similar sacs may also enclose and digest cellular structures, such as mitochondria, making the components of the mitochondrion available again to the cell.

The Belgian investigator Christian de Duve, who discovered lysosomes, has referred to them as "suicide bags" since if lysosomes are ruptured, the digestive juices they contain are capable of destroying the cell itself. This might be injurious to the organism, or it might serve to dispose of cells which are no longer useful—cells that have died, for example. In some cases, lysosomes seem to be the means for the orderly destruction—or *autolysis*—of entire cells or groups of cells, such as those in the tail of the tadpole that is undergoing metamorphosis to a frog.

CENTRIOLES

Centrioles are small cylinder-shaped organelles which appear to play an important role in the division of the nuclear material in animal cells. They are 300 to 400 millimicrons long and about 150 millimicrons in diameter. Centrioles are often found in pairs, with each member of the pair lying at right angles to its partner. As you can see in Figure 1–26 the centriole is structured somewhat like the cilia and flagella, but it has nine triplets instead of doublets around the outside and it lacks the two central fibers.

The centriole has two different functions: It has a role in cell division and it also may serve as the basal body from which a cilium or flagellum originates. The same centriole may serve both functions: In the human spermatid (the cell which matures to form the sperm), the sperm flagellum arises from one of the centrioles.

SUMMARY

There are many apparent differences between somatic cells and the one-celled organisms we examined in the last chapter. Somatic cells lead an interdependent existence, while most one-celled organisms are independent. Somatic cells are less complex than many of the independent cells and are more specialized, and this specialization results in great differences in cellular organelles and function. Yet, despite these differences, all cells are remarkably alike in internal structure. In this chapter, we have studied those properties which represent the *unity* of cells—the structural components and basic activities common to all cells.

Materials pass in and out of the cell by diffusion through the cell membrane, which possesses the property of *selective permeability*. Osmosis, which is the movement of water across a membrane, is important in cell function and the growth of plant cells. In *active transport*, materials pass through the cell membrane against the concentration gradient. In some cells, materials are taken in by the process of phagocytosis or pinocytosis.

Cilia and *flagella* appear throughout the living world, and except for bacterial cilia, every cilium or flagellum, regardless of the plant or animal on which it is located and regardless of its particular function within the organization of that plant or animal, has the same internal structure.

Not every cell has a wall, but all cells possess a membrane (the plasma membrane), which surrounds the cytoplasm. In cells that have an outer wall, the membrane lies within the wall. The internal structures (organelles) of the cell are contained in the cytoplasm.

A prominent cell organelle is the *mitochondrion*. Chemical reactions taking place in mitochondria form the principal source of energy for the cell. *Chloroplasts* are found in many protozoans and in plant cells; they contain the cell's supply of chlorophyll and carry out the process of photosynthesis. Most cells possess an *endoplasmic reticulum*, which is a complex system of vesicles connected in an elaborate network. The endoplasmic reticulum serves to divide the cell into functional compartments for the production of enzymes and other proteins. It may also form a communication system for the transport of substances through the cytoplasm.

Other cell organelles are ribisomes, centrioles, lysosomes, and the Golgi complex. *Ribosomes* are associated with the production of protein molecules in the cell. The *Golgi* complex appears to function as a kind of packaging center for the cell, enclosing in membranes the enzymes and other proteins made in the compartments of the endoplasmic reticulum. Digestive enzymes are packaged in *lysosomes*, which fuse with food vacuoles and also, in some cases, carry out the orderly destruction of cell structures and groups of cells. *Centrioles* appear to play an important part in the division of animal cells.

Chapter 1–4

The Cell Nucleus

The nucleus is usually the most prominent organelle in the cell. As you can see in Figure 1–27, it is surrounded by a double layer of unit membrane. The nuclear membrane is often referred to as the *nuclear envelope* because it is not a single membrane but a thin, flattened sac. The envelope, as you can see in the electron micrograph, looks as if it has holes in it; these are not actually holes but membrane-covered *pores*. The nucleus may send its information-bearing molecules out into the cytoplasm through these pores.

The Nucleolus

The only structure ordinarily visible within the nucleus is a nearly spherical body known as the *nucleolus*, the "little nucleus." A nucleus usually contains more than one nucleolus. This organelle plays an important part in supplying materials for the formation of the ribosomes.

Chromatin

If the cell is treated by special staining techniques, thin strands and grains can be discerned within the nuclear boundaries. These are collectively known as *chromatin*, which is the Greek word for "color" and refers to the appearance of the nuclear material when stained. At the time of cell division, the chromatin condenses to reveal the rodlike structures known as *chromosomes*. Different organisms differ in the numbers of chromosomes present in their cells: A mosquito has 6; a cabbage, 18; corn, 20; a frog, 26; a sunflower, 34; a cat, 38; a man, 46; a plum, 48; a dog, 78; and a goldfish, 94. The number of chromosomes commonly present in the cells of higher plants and animals is known as the *diploid number*, and this number is generally constant in all cells except the sperm and egg cells, which are

1–27 *The nucleus of a cell from the spinal cord of a bat fills the lower part of this electron micrograph. Within the nucleus can be seen scattered chromatin and a nucleolus, the large dense body slightly to the right of center. Separating the nucleus from the cytoplasm (above), is the double membrane of the nuclear envelope in which the characteristic pores are clearly visible. (One pore is pointed out by an arrow.) Running almost parallel to the nuclear envelope is a plasma membrane and above that a small portion of the cytoplasm of an adjacent cell. (Dr. Keith R. Porter)*

haploid cells, meaning that they have a single set of chromosomes, that is, half as many chromosomes as the somatic cells of the same organism. Thus, when sperm and egg come together, the diploid number is restored.

Nuclear Functions

The nucleus exercises a continuing control over the cytoplasm. For example, if you take an amoeba and cut it in two, the half that retains the nucleus is normal in function, indistinguishable from any other amoeba. But the half that is left with no nucleus, although it may live for as long as two weeks, loses its capacity to form pseudopodia and so can neither move nor eat. If, however, the nucleus is removed from the first amoeba half within two or three days and transplanted into the nonnucleated half, this half immediately regains both its mobility and its capacity for phagocytosis. It will also soon be able to divide into two new amoebas.

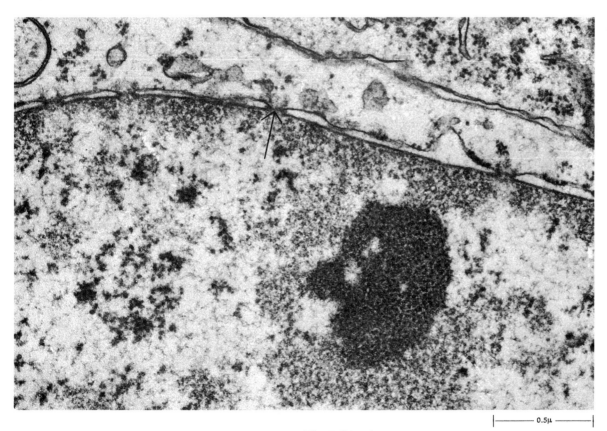

|———— 0.5μ ————|

57   *The Cell Nucleus*

The nucleus exercises control over structure as well as function. Figure 1–28 illustrates a famous experiment that was done a number of years ago on a single-celled plant known as *Acetabularia*. This one-celled alga is composed of a cap, a chloroplast-containing stalk, and a rootlike structure which contains the nucleus. The cap varies according to the species. In the diagram, two species of *Acetabularia* are shown, one with a compact umbrella-shaped cap and the other with a cap composed of loose petal-like structures. If the cap is removed from either cell, a new cap will form which resembles the previous one. However, if both caps are removed and the nuclei are exchanged, each cap that reforms will somewhat resemble the original cap of the other cell, the cell that contributed the nucleus. If

1–28 *The control which the nucleus exercises over cell structures was illustrated some years ago by an experiment performed with the one-celled plant Acetabularia. Two species of the plant were used, Acetabularia mediterranea (top left) and Acetabularia crenulata (top right). The two species differ in the shape of their caps. In either species, as shown at the top of the drawing, if the cap is removed, the cell will grow another one just like it. If the cap and nucleus are removed from A. mediterranea and a nucleus from A. crenulata grafted on to the cell, as shown at the bottom, the new cap that forms will somewhat resemble that of the A. crenulata species. If that cap is removed, another cap will grow which is identical to the A. crenulata cap. Can you suggest an explanation?*

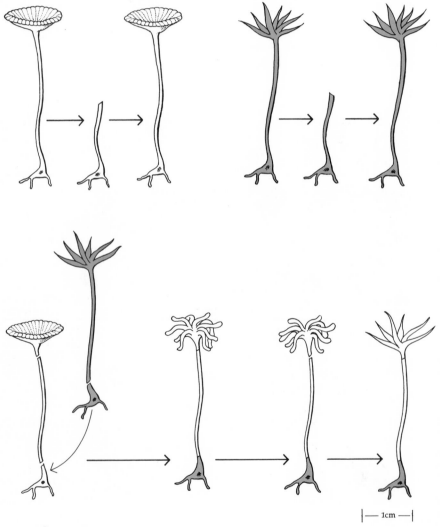

|— 1cm —|

these caps, in turn, are removed, the caps that then form will each be identical to that of the species from which the new nucleus was derived. The investigator who performed this experiment interpreted these results as meaning that certain cap-shaping substances are produced under the direction of the nucleus. These cap-shaping substances may accumulate in the cytoplasm, which is why the first cap that formed after nuclear transplantation was of an intermediate type. By the time the second cap formed, however, the cap-shaping substances already in the cytoplasm had been exhausted and the form of the cap was completely under the control of the new nucleus. When two nuclei, each from a different species, were transplanted into a cell which had had its cap removed, the cap that subsequently formed was intermediate between those of the two species. When two nuclei from one species and one nucleus from another species were implanted in one cell, the cap was more like that of the species which had contributed the two nuclei than like the cap of the species which had contributed one nucleus.

The relationship between nucleus and cytoplasm is not so simple, however, as these experiments might indicate. Some of the cytoplasmic structures have considerable autonomy, or "self-government." Furthermore, while the nucleus controls the cytoplasm, the cytoplasm also regulates the nucleus, just as information fed into the central office of a factory will presumably alter its activities and modify the orders issuing from it.

REPLICATION OF NUCLEAR MATERIAL

The nucleus is able to exercise control over the cytoplasm because it contains the instructions for making proteins, the materials on which all cellular structure and functions depend. When a cell divides, these instructions must be replicated and a duplicate copy passed to each daughter cell. Consider, for example, that it may have taken a billion years for *Acetabularia* to evolve; all this accumulation of precisely organized chemicals could be lost, perhaps irrevocably, if the hereditary material—the directions, so to speak, for being this particular small cell—were not precisely copied and transmitted.

Mitosis

Most cells ensure the precise division and distribution of their genetic material by a process known as *mitosis*. The process of mitosis is conventionally divided into four major sequences: prophase, metaphase, anaphase, and telophase. During the period before and after mitosis, the cell is in interphase. It is important to remember, however, that cell growth and division is a continuous, uninterrupted flow of events and that these so-called "phases" are merely convenient man-made designations. Although

1–29 *Most cells reproduce by mitosis, the process in which a cell divides into two identical daughter cells. Shown here are several stages in the mitosis of cells from young seeds of the South African blood lily. The diagrams are idealized representations of the mitotic stages, and they are simplified by showing only a few chromosomes. The clock time of each stage was recorded as it was photographed. The entire mitotic sequence in these plants—from early prophase until nucleoli appear in the daughter nuclei—lasts between 8 and 20 hours; only the middle stages are included here. These photographs were taken with the new Nomarski interference contrast system. They are not three-dimensional, but their "relief effect" is characteristic of this special technique. (Dr. Andrew S. Bajer)*

| — 20μ — |

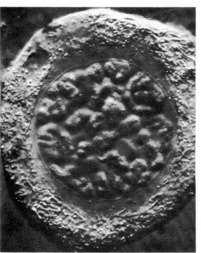

1 *8:08 Late prophase. The chromosomes, which have already duplicated, are becoming condensed. The nuclear membrane is still visible. (The thickness of the nuclear membrane is about 10 millimicrons which is below the resolution limit of the light microscope. Therefore, it can be seen but not resolved.)*

2 *8:46 Metaphase begins. The nuclear membrane has just disappeared, and the spindle has formed. The chromosomes have become more condensed. Each now consists of two chromatids held together by a centromere (shown in the drawing as a white dot). The chromosomes are beginning to move toward the equatorial plane of the cell.*

5 *10:12 Middle anaphase. The chromosomes have moved halfway toward the poles. Each centromere is attached to a spindle fiber. The spindle fibers appear to pull the chromosomes to the poles of the dividing cell.*

6 *10:37 Early telophase. The chromosomes have reached the opposite poles of the cell. The small structures along the equator of the cell indicate that the cell plate is beginning to form. This cell plate will eventually become the new cell walls that separate the two daughter cells.*

3 *9:00 Early metaphase. The centromeres, which have not yet divided, have been guided to the equatorial plane of the cell by spindle fibers to which they are attached. The chromatid arms are still held together, and the shorter arms, as shown in the diagram, have lined up along the equator. You can make out the spindle fibers and some long, thin mitochondria are also visible.*

4 *10:05 Early anaphase. The centromeres have begun to divide, and the daughter chromosomes are moving toward the opposite ends of the cell.*

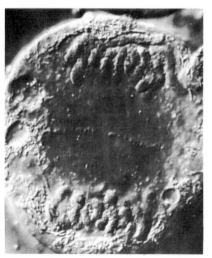

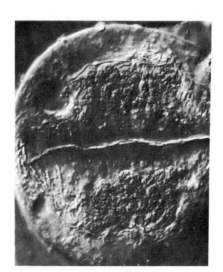

7 *10:42 Telophase. The small structures along the equator of the cell, which were just visible in the previous photograph, have now begun to fuse, and the cell plate is partly formed.*

8 *11:12 Late telophase. This is the end of mitosis and almost the end of cell division. A new nuclear membrane has formed and the chromosomes are once more becoming diffuse. The new cell walls are completed and the two daughter cells will soon be separated.*

61   *The Cell Nucleus*

there are some differences in detail between mitosis in plant cells and mitosis in animal cells, the fundamental process of mitosis is remarkably the same in all cells.

First, we should consider what happens to the genetic material, since this is the heart of the phenomenon. In interphase, before mitosis begins, the chromatin replicates. This replication cannot be seen, but chemical measurements have proved that a duplication of the material takes place during this stage. At the beginning of prophase, the chromatin threads coil tighter and tighter until they become the compact structures called *chromosomes*, or "colored bodies," a name given them by microscopists of the last century since they could best be seen when treated with certain stains. When the forming chromosomes first come into view, it can be seen that they consist of two separate strands, the chromatids. There are, then, three words to remember, all beginning with *chrom: chromatin*, the diffused nuclear material seen in the cell in the interphase; *chromosomes*, the dense bodies seen in the cell during mitosis, which (we know now) are condensations of the chromatin; and *chromatids*, the two strands of the double-stranded chromosome, as seen in the early stages of mitosis.

On each chromosome, there is a special area known as the *centromere*, which holds together the two chromatids. The centromere may be located at the center of the chromosome, as its name implies, or it may be off-center; in either case, it has a location characteristic of the particular chromosome.

During metaphase, the chromosomes are maneuvered to the center of the dividing cell and lined up along the equator (the center line of the cell), in preparation for the apportionment of one identical chromatid to each new cell. During anaphase, the centromeres divide and the chromatid pairs are separated, with one chromatid moving to each side of the dividing line. When the two chromatids separate, each becomes a daughter chromosome. Then half of the daughter chromosomes move to one end of the cell, and half to the other. Telophase begins as the nuclear envelope reforms.

As you can see, the function of mitosis has been accomplished; each new cell has received one of each chromatid pair, or in other words, each cell has an identical set of chromosomes. As telophase ends, the chromosomes resume their extended state, become increasingly indistinct, and finally disappear from view, although the genetic material persists in the form of chromatin.

THE SPINDLE

As shown in Figure 1–30, a new and dominating structure appears in the cell at the time of mitosis. This structure is called the *spindle*. The spindle seems to provide the machinery for the movement of the chromosomes, although the way in which this is accomplished is not yet understood.

1–30 *Spindle apparatus in a living egg of the marine worm Chaetopterus pergamentaceous. The prominent bright streaks are the spindle fibers. The chromosomes appear as indistinct gray bodies near the equator of the spindle. The smooth curved line at the right is part of the cell membrane. (S. Inoué, Polarization Optical Studies of the Mitotic Spindle, I. The Demonstration of Spindle Fibers in Living Cells, Chromosome Bd. 5: 487–500, Springer, 1953)*

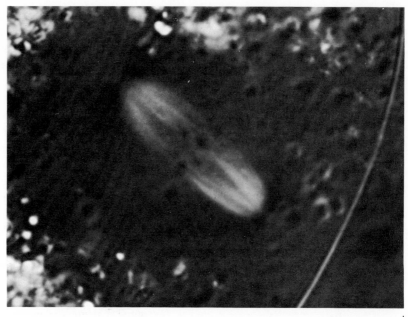

|———— 10μ ————|

In animal cells, the formation of the spindle seems to be related to the centrioles and their movements. At cell division, each daughter cell usually receives one pair of centrioles. At or near the beginning of prophase, the centrioles begin to move apart as if they repelled one another. A group of fibers then appears, which radiate out from each centriole like spokes from the hub of a wheel. This configuration is known as the *aster,* from the Latin word for "star." Some of the fibers reach from one centriole to the other, stretching as the pair separates. The centrioles continue to migrate until they lie at opposite sides of the nucleus. Their positions mark the *poles* toward which the chromosomes move. When the nuclear envelope breaks down at the end of prophase, the region between the centrioles becomes clearly demarcated as a transparent football-shaped area; this is the spindle. As the centrioles take up their positions at the poles, some of the spindle fibers extend to reach from pole to pole, like the longitudinal lines on a globe.

Other spindle fibers attach to the centromeres of the chromosomes and appear to guide them toward the equator. When all the centromeres are lined up exactly along the equator, the centromeres divide and the chromatids separate and move toward the opposite poles. They appear to be tugged along by the spindle fibers; the centromeres, to which the fibers are attached, move first, while the two "arms" of the chromosome drag behind. The centrioles replicate at this time.

The composition of the spindle fibers is not known; they appear to form by the aggregation of protein molecules. Under the electron microscope, these fibers appear as fine straight hollow tubules, like the fibers of flagella, all arranged in the same direction. Although they lengthen and then shorten during mitosis, they do not appear to get thicker or thinner. This suggests that they do not stretch or contract but that new material is added to the fiber or removed from it as the spindle changes shape. In a recent experiment, a small mark was made at one point on a moving spindle fiber by "branding" it with ultraviolet light. The mark could be seen to move from a point near the equator to the pole and off the end of the fiber, indicating that protein is added at the equator and removed at the pole. The spindle and the asters disappear at telophase.

OTHER CHANGES AT MITOSIS

The nucleolus and the nuclear membrane usually disappear at the end of prophase and form again at telophase. The nucleolus is formed at a specific point, the *nucleolus organizer*, on a particular chromosome. At the time the nucleolus first appears, it can be seen to be attached to this chromosome. The nuclear membrane does not disappear during mitosis in all cells; in some, such as certain protozoans, it remains nearly intact, pulling apart in a sort of dumbbell shape as the cell divides, until the two nuclei, each with a complete set of chromosomes, pinch apart and go to each daughter cell.

During telophase in animal cells, the cell elongates and the cellular membrane begins to constrict at the line of the equator. This ring of constriction tightens until the original cell is divided in two.

MITOSIS IN PLANT CELLS

There are two main points of difference between mitosis in some of the higher plants and mitosis in animals. First, the plants apparently do not have centrioles, although a spindle forms which is similar in other respects to the spindle in animal cells. Some biologists think that centrioles or some analogous structures may yet be found in plant cells; they are, in fact, present in some plant cells, such as the flagellated spermatozoan of the fern.

The second difference cannot be seen until telophase, when a new structure, the *division plate*, appears at the point previously occupied by the equator of dividing cells. This division plate of plant cells is a partition of cellulose which, beginning at the center, extends until it reaches the opposite walls of the dividing cell, completing the separation into two cells. Structures similar to division plates are also seen at the time of division of animal cells with more pronounced cell walls, such as oocytes, the cells from which the ova arise.

Chloroplasts and mitochondria—and possibly centrioles as well—are not made solely under the direction of the nucleus, like the cap of *Acetabularia*. Each of these organelles, like each cell, can only be replicated from a previously existing organelle. Both chloroplasts and mitochondria, and perhaps centrioles, contain genetic material similar to the sort found in the nucleus; such material (which is known as DNA and which you will hear a great deal more about in subsequent chapters) has not been found elsewhere in the cytoplasm.

The discovery that these organelles are self-replicating has led some investigators to speculate that they may have had their origin as parasites which invaded cells early in the course of evolution and developed a *symbiotic* ("living together") relationship with them. Cells which had these symbionts would have had an adaptive advantage over less favored cell lines.

Symbiotic relationships are common in nature. For example, many animals live symbiotically with algae. Several species of ciliated Protozoa, including a type of *Paramecium* (*Paramecium bursaria*), contain large numbers of very small algal cells, which live in the comparative safety of their cytoplasms and contribute the benefits of photosynthesis to the cellular economy. The corals, the animals that build the coral reefs, have symbiotic algae; the rate of coral formation is much slower in the absence of the algae, although both algae and coral can be grown independently. So far, however, this proposal is only speculative, since there is no direct evidence that chloroplasts, mitochondria, or centrioles ever had an independent existence or that they can form or even exist apart from the whole cell.

Meiosis

Meiosis, or reduction division, is the special process of cell division by which sex cells, such as the egg and the sperm, are formed. It has two stages: the first meiotic division and the second meiotic division. In the course of reduction division, the number of chromosomes in the cell is reduced to one-half. Biologists refer to the chromosome set of the diploid, somatic cell as $2n$ and to that of the haploid, germ cell as $1n$—meaning that, for any given organism, there are half as many chromosomes in the germ cell as in a representative somatic cell.

The process by which this reduction division takes place superficially resembles mitosis since much of the same cellular machinery is used, but actually the results are quite different. We shall concentrate here on describing those features of meiosis that result in the number of chromosomes being halved. Some other important events that take place during meiosis will be examined in detail in Chapter 3–3.

1–31 *Meiosis and spore formation in the royal fern Osmunda regalis. The diploid (2n) number of chromosomes in this organism is 22. Each spore has 11 chromosomes. For clarity only six (2n) chromosomes are shown in the drawings. Micrographs 1 to 10 show "squash preparations" in which the cells have been flattened and the chromosomes spread out and stained. Meiosis takes place in two stages, I, shown here in the upper row, and II, below. (Dr. Mary E. Clutter)*

|— 10μ —|

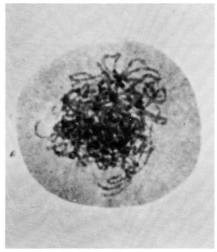

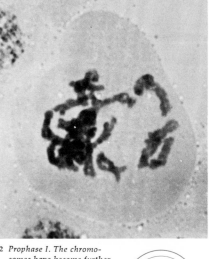

1 *Early prophase I. The chromosomes have become visible. Each still appears as a single strand.*

2 *Prophase I. The chromosomes have become further condensed. Homologous chromosomes are beginning to pair, forming bivalents. Each chromosome now consists of two chromatids and each bivalent is made up of four chromatids.*

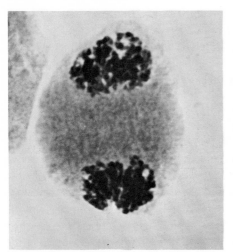

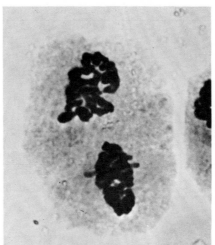

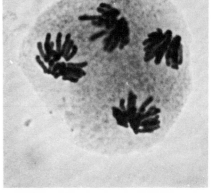

6 *Prophase II. The chromosomal material, which became diffuse when the first meiotic division was completed, is beginning to condense again.*

7 *Metaphase II. Two spindles have formed and the chromosomes are lining up along the equatorial plate of the spindle. Note that each chromosome consists of two chromatids and that each set of chromosomes now contains the haploid (1n) number.*

8 *Anaphase II. The centromeres have divided and the daughter chromosomes (previously each a chromatid) are moving to the opposite poles of the spindle.*

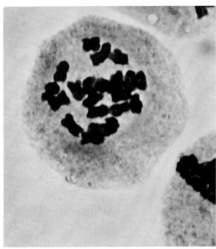

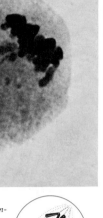

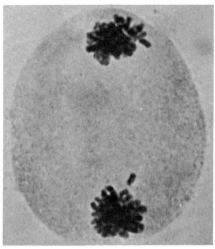

3 *Metaphase I. The nuclear membrane has disappeared and the spindle has formed The bivalents are now aligned along the equatorial plate so that their centromeres lie on either side. (Photograph shows polar view, and diagram shows equatorial view.)*

4 *Anaphase I. Homologous chromosomes, each still consisting of a pair of chromatids, move to opposite poles. Note the crucial difference between what is occurring here and what happens during the corresponding stage of mitosis. (See Figure 1–29.)*

5 *Telophase I. The homologous chromosomes are completely separated. The spindles now disappear and, in most organisms, the nuclear membranes reform before Meiosis II.*

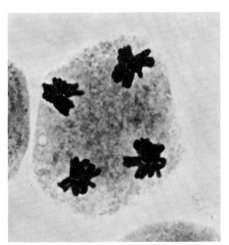

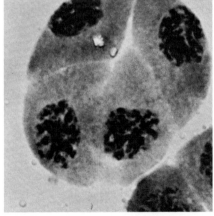

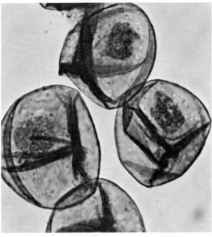

9 *Telophase II. The daughter chromosomes have separated completely. Four haploid sets of chromosomes have now been produced. The first meiotic division is sometimes referred to as the reduction division and the second as the equational division. Can you explain why?*

10 *The cell walls have begun to form. The original diploid mother cell has become four haploid spore cells.*

11 *The spores are now completely separated. Although the end-products are strikingly different, the processes by which sperm cells and egg cells in animals are formed are remarkably the same as those shown here.*

Before meiosis, as before mitosis, the genetic material replicates, the chromatin threads coil and tighten into the rodlike chromosomes, and the spindle apparatus begins to appear. It is at this point that the crucial difference between mitosis and meiosis occurs. In meiosis, the chromosomes come together in pairs. These pairs are known as *homologues.* In each pair, one of the homologues was originally of paternal origin and one originally of maternal origin.

It was not until the beginning of the twentieth century that cytologists came to understand that in any somatic cell, half of the chromosomes are from the organism's maternal parent and half from the organism's paternal parent and that for every maternal chromosome, there is a matching paternal chromosome, and vice versa. When the homologous chromosomes pair, their entire lengths are parallel. This pairing is known as *synapsis,* and it occurs only in meiosis, not in mitosis.

At about the time of synapsis, it can be seen that each chromosome consists of two chromatids. The chromosome pairs are known as *bivalents.* Each bivalent is then actually made up of four chromatids.

At metaphase, when typically the spindle apparatus has formed and the nuclear membrane dissolved, the bivalents orient themselves on the equator of the spindle for the first meiotic division. In the course of this division, the homologous chromosomes are separated, with one chromosome (two chromatids) of each pair apportioned to each of the two daughter cells. This is another important difference between mitosis and meiosis. In mitotic division, the chromosomes of the two daughter cells are exactly alike, while the chromosomes of the two daughter cells produced by the first meiotic division *cannot* be exactly alike. Remember that while the chromatid pairs which separate during mitosis are replicas of one another, the homologues which separate during the first division of meiosis are not replicas, nor are they exactly alike in the hereditary information they contain, since one was originally of maternal origin and one of paternal origin.

THE SECOND MEIOTIC DIVISION

Between the first and second meiotic divisions, no replication of genetic material occurs. The chromosomes, as you will recall, are already in the form of chromatids. The second meiotic division is actually exactly like mitosis. At prophase, the chromosomes in haploid number appear as chromatid pairs. When the centromere divides, one chromatid of each pair goes to each daughter cell. Since the genetic material has been replicated only once (before the first meiotic division) and has been divided up twice, the total amount has been reduced by one-half. More important, this reduction has taken place in an orderly way, so that each cell has received a copy of one of the two homologues. You will notice that either homologue, whether maternal or paternal, may go to either of the cells at the first meiotic division; thus there has been not only a reduction of the genetic material, and a separation of the homologues, but also a random reassortment of maternal and paternal chromosomes.

SUMMARY

The principal cell organelle is the *nucleus,* which directs both the activity and the structure of the cell as a whole. The membrane which surrounds the nucleus, the *nuclear envelope,* contains pores through which large molecules may pass to the cytoplasm. The *nucleolus,* a spherical body within the nucleus, is the site of the synthesis of ribosomal material. Also within the nucleus is the *chromatin,* the thin strands which condense into chromosomes at the time of cell division.

Without the nucleus, the cell is not able to perform those activities normal to it and necessary for its survival. The nucleus also controls the structure of the cell. In turn, the cytoplasm regulates nuclear activities as information is exchanged between nucleus and cytoplasm.

New cells are formed by cell division, or *mitosis,* in which the hereditary material is divided equally between two daughter cells, each receiving an identical set of chromosomes. At the start of mitosis, the chromatin condenses into chromosomes. Each chromosome is visible as two identical strands, the chromatids. The spindle apparatus appears, and in metaphase, the chromosomes line up along the equator. The centromere of each chromosome then divides, and the chromatids, which become the daughter chromosomes, separate. Apparently pulled along by the spindle fibers, the daughter chromosomes move to opposite poles in the cell. In telophase, the separation of the chromosomes is complete, new nuclei are formed, and the cell constricts in the middle, forming two new cells.

Certain cell organelles—chloroplasts and mitochondria—are not made under the direction of the nucleus but form from preexisting organelles.

Meiosis, or reduction division, is the special type of cell division by which the sex cells are formed. This process takes place in two stages, the first meiotic division and the second meiotic division and in the sex cells that are formed, the number of chromosomes is reduced to one-half the number in the parent cell. During the first meiotic division, homologous chromosomes (one of paternal origin and one of maternal origin) are paired and then separated. Since the homologous chromosomes are not identical in terms of the genetic information they contain, the two daughter cells which result from this division are not alike. The second meiotic division resembles mitosis, with the two daughter nuclei each dividing into two haploid nuclei.

Somatic Cells

In the preceding chapters, we examined a variety of structures and functions that are common to all cells. In this chapter, we shall look at some of the ways in which somatic cells differ from the one-celled organisms and from one another. From this you will get at least a glimpse of the great diversity of cells found in organisms and of the many ways in which membranes, organelles, and activities can be modified to serve new purposes: The flagellum of the protozoan, for example, reappears as the exquisitely sensitive photoreceptor of the retina, and the feeding activities of the amoeba are seemingly adapted to the bacteria-destroying capacities of the white blood cell.

The somatic cells of the many-celled organism are specialists. In the course of evolution, plants and animals solved certain problems by becoming larger and more complex, but this created a number of new problems. Some of these problems result simply from the requirements of the individual cells. Every single living cell, whether a skin cell, a heart cell, or a cell that stores fat or makes bone, has the same fundamental requirements for food, water, and oxygen as an amoeba or a paramecium has. In the single cell (or even the very small organism) living in a watery environment, these essentials can come directly from the outside world, but in the larger plant or animal, they must be transported to the individual cell. Plants have solved this problem one way, animals another, and both use specialized cells to do so.

Another, related problem is how to keep from losing these essential components, especially water, which easily evaporates to the outside environment. This, too, has led to the evolution of a group of specialized cells. Other problems—those of coordination, locomotion, and reproduction—are quite different from the problems faced by the single-celled organisms and are imposed by the multicellularity itself.

1–32 *The structure of a sugar maple leaf. The outer surface of the leaf is made up of epidermal cells, which are coated with a waxy substance which retards evaporation of water. Under this "skin" are two layers of chlorophyll-containing parenchyma cells. The cells just beneath this transparent epidermis in the palisade layer are crowded on end, exposing the greatest possible number of chloroplasts to the sun. Beneath this layer, the cells are packed loosely, forming a spongy layer. Running through the middle of the leaf are veins, which support the leaf and also transport materials between the leaf and the rest of* **the tree.**

In Section 2, these problems and their solutions will be discussed in more detail. This chapter will give only a brief overview of some representative specialized somatic cells, laying the foundations for the discussions in Section 2 and broadening our concept of what is meant by that deceptively simple word "cell."

PLANT CELLS

Let us look at the cells of one of the higher plants—such as a tree, grass, or a shrub—and see how they work together to supply the requirements of the organism. One of the first questions we are interested in is photosynthesis, since this is the process that supplies the energy for the life of the cell.

Specialists in Photosynthesis

In the case of the one-celled plants, each cell contains chlorophyll in one or more chloroplasts, but in the higher plants, the chlorophyll is found mostly in certain cells within the leaves and sometimes within the stems. These cells are of a general type known as *parenchyma cells*.

Figure 1–32 shows the structure of a sugar maple leaf. As you can see, the chloroplast-containing parenchyma cells are relatively large, and most of them have large central vacuoles. Usually they are partly separated from one another, forming a loose, spongy tissue. The spaces between the cells inside the leaf are filled with gases, including carbon dioxide, oxygen, and water vapor.

Parenchyma cells are also found in the tissue of trunks, stems, and roots. These parenchyma cells, which usually contain leucoplasts, are specially adapted for the storage of water and of starch or other food reserves.

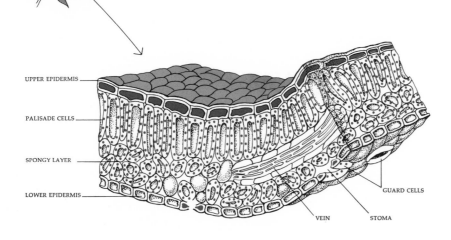

UPPER EPIDERMIS

PALISADE CELLS

SPONGY LAYER

LOWER EPIDERMIS

GUARD CELLS

VEIN   STOMA

71   *Somatic Cells*

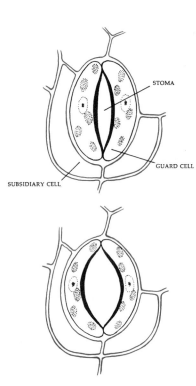

Protector Cells

The thin-walled, loosely packed parenchyma cells would soon dry out if they were exposed. They, and the other inner tissues of plants, are protected by layers of *epidermal cells*. Epidermal cells usually line the outer surfaces of roots, stems, and leaves. They have flattened surfaces and are almost always covered by a layer of water-proofing material, frequently a waxy cuticle, on their outer surface, which aids in the conservation of water. In Figure 1–32, you can see the epidermal cells on the outer surfaces of a leaf.

Among the epidermal cells are highly specialized cells known as *guard cells*, which occur in pairs. Between each pair of guard cells, there is an opening, or *stoma*, into the interior of the leaf. The stomata open and close, regulating the flow of oxygen and carbon dioxide into and out of the leaf and the flow of water vapor out of it. The openings and closings are controlled by the turgor pressure of the guard cells. The inner walls of these guard cells, which enclose the stoma (Figure 1–33), are much thicker than the outer ones. Thus, when a guard cell is under pressure, the weaker outer wall will balloon out, pulling the two inner walls apart and opening the stoma. When the guard cells are flaccid, the thick elastic inner walls are relaxed, closing the stoma. In hot dry weather, the stomata of many plants are open only in the early mornings, when it is somewhat cooler and damper. When the sun approaches its height, they close to preserve water.

Conducting Cells

One of the crucial problems that had to be solved by plants in their transition from water to land was that of water supply. In an aquatic plant, no cell is far from water, but the roots of the land plant must often reach deep into the ground to find a water supply, and then the water must somehow be transported above ground to the photosynthesizing surfaces. And, in turn, the glucose produced by photosynthesis must be transported to the rest of the plant body, including the roots, since this is the only energy source for the entire organism. The success with which these problems have been solved is demonstrated by trees like the redwood, in which water and nutrients are transported over distances measured in hundreds of feet. The conducting cells of the plant make up what is known as its *vascular system*. The way in which this system works—or, at least, what we now believe to be the way—will be examined in detail in Section 2; at this time, we shall limit our discussion to some of its cellular components.

There are two types of vascular tissue in higher plants: *xylem* and *phloem*. Xylem conducts water and minerals from the ground to the leaves, while phloem conducts sugar compounds, the products of photosynthesis,

1–33 *Tiny openings, or stomata, into the interior of the leaf regulate the flow of carbon dioxide and oxygen into and out of the leaf and the evaporation of water. Each stoma is flanked by two sausage-shaped guard cells, which control its openings and closings. When adequate moisture is available, water pressure (turgor) within the cells causes the outer walls to balloon out, pulling the thick inner walls apart and opening the stoma.*

1–34 *Some conducting cells of xylem and phloem. The three types of xylem cells shown (a to c) form tubes through which water can move from the roots of the tree to its leaves, as indicated by the arrows in the drawing. In addition, these thick-walled non-living cells serve as the support system for the tree. Unlike xylem cells, the sieve cells (d) which make up the phloem, contain living protoplasm. They are interconnected end to end, forming tubes through which nutrient materials from the leaves are conducted to the stem and roots. The nuclear functions of these cells appear to be carried out by the companion cells.*

down from the leaves to the rest of the plant. Both xylem and phloem consist of elongated cells stacked end to end.

Figure 1–34 traces three stages in the evolution of xylem cells: (1) In the pine tree, cells known as *tracheids* pass water from one cell to another through small holes or pits on their lateral surfaces. (2) In the birch are cells known as *vessel elements,* in which the end walls are partially dissolved at maturity. (3) In the oak, more specialized vessel elements, in which end walls are completely absent, fit together to form long, relatively wide, rigid tubes (the vessels). Once these connecting systems form, the cells die. Thus the woody tissue of trees and shrubs is made up of dead xylem cells.

The nutrient material passes down through the phloem, the conducting elements of which are the *sieve cells.* Unlike the xylem cells, sieve cells are alive and contain metabolizing protoplasm. The walls at the tops and bottoms of these cells are thickened but have specialized perforations by which the cells are interconnected. These interconnections, or *plasmodesmata,* are threads of cytoplasm which are limited by a plasma membrane continuous with that of the adjacent cells.

As the sieve cells mature, the number of mitochondria and ribosomes in them decreases. In the flowering plants (the "highest" plants), the mature sieve cell has no nucleus. The metabolic activities of these cells appear to be continued by shorter, narrower, thin-walled cells, known as *com-*

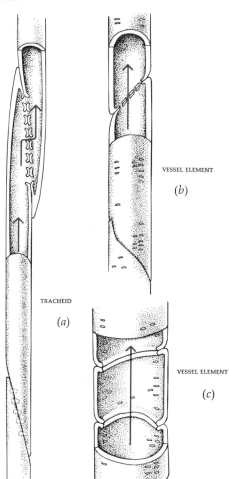

VESSEL ELEMENT

(b)

TRACHEID

(a)

VESSEL ELEMENT

(c)

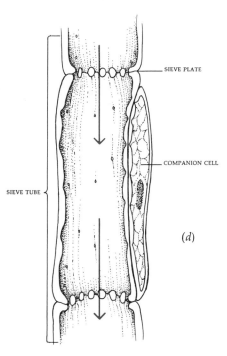

SIEVE PLATE

COMPANION CELL

SIEVE TUBE

(d)

73   *Somatic Cells*

panion cells, that lie alongside them and are connected to them by strands of cytoplasm.

This two-way conducting system, the lifeline of the plant, runs through the plant body from every root tip to the slender veins throughout every leaf.

Support Cells

Among the parenchyma cells and the vascular tissues can be found the supporting cells, such as *fibers*, which are conspicuously elongated cells, and *stone cells*. These give mechanical support to the other tissues of the plant. At maturity, fibers very commonly die and remain as strands or cylinders of tightly joined cells. Stone cells may occur in compact masses, but unlike the fibers, they also can be found in isolation.

Cells for Growth

Plants, unlike most animals, grow until they die, constantly forming new leaves and roots and branches. The sources of these new tissues are the *meristematic cells*, which are found at crucial locations throughout the plant body, such as at the apex or growing tip of the shoot, at the root tip, and in a thin layer around the trunks of trees. A meristematic cell is essentially embryonic; that is, it consists of undifferentiated, rapidly dividing cells that can develop into any of the specialized cells required by the plant.

1–35 *Photomicrograph of meristematic cells in the tip of an onion root. Many of these cells are in mitosis. Can you identify the various mitotic stages shown? (Courtesy of General Biological Supply House)*

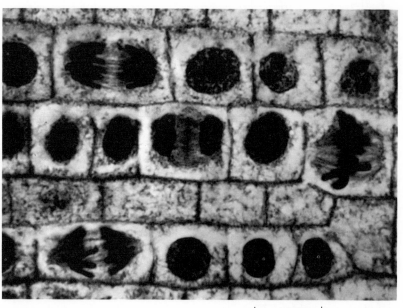

|——— 30μ ———|

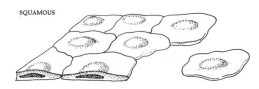

SQUAMOUS

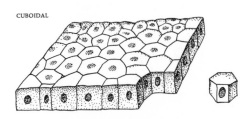

CUBOIDAL

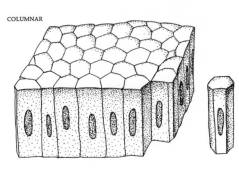

COLUMNAR

1–36 *The three types of epithelial cells which cover the inner and outer surfaces of the body. Squamous cells, which usually perform a protective function, make up the outer layers of the skin and the lining of the mouth and other mucous membranes. Cuboidal and columnar cells generally protect internal surfaces and also perform much of the chemical work of the body.*

The light micrograph (Figure 1–35) shows a section of meristematic cells from a growing onion-root tip. The nuclei have been stained to show the chromosomes. Many of these cells are in mitosis. You can probably identify the various mitotic stages in some of these cells. As you can see, the cells are small and cubical in shape, thin-walled and densely packed, with comparatively large nuclei. As these cells mature, they can develop into parenchyma cells, epidermal cells, vascular elements, or supporting cells, depending on the immediate local needs of the developing organism.

ANIMAL CELLS

The individual cells of animals have the same basic requirements as the cells of plants and Protozoa; that is, they require oxygen, water, and nutrients. Animals as organisms, however, face problems which are quite different from those of plants. Since animals are heterotrophs, rather than autotrophs, they need complicated systems for breaking down nutrients into forms which can be transmitted to the individual cells to meet their energy requirements. Animals, particularly land animals, also need supporting systems; but since animals are mobile while plants only move by growing or in minor responses to light, these supporting systems need to be far more complicated. Also, perhaps as a corollary of their mobility, animals have evolved a complex group of cells—the nervous system—by which they keep in touch with the outer and inner environment. Finally, instead of maintaining a continuous flow of water up the body and out into the atmosphere, as plants do, animals recirculate their water, using this circulating fluid, or plasma, as the medium for carrying oxygen, carbon dioxide, and nutrients. Many types of cells are involved in these various activities. We shall look at a representative few of them.

Protector Cells

Like the epidermal cells in plants, *epithelial cells* cover the body surface, protecting the body against injury and guarding it against water loss. They secrete protective materials, including mucus, keratin (the fibrous protein which forms a thin film over the outer surfaces of our own bodies), and chitin, which is contained in the exoskeleton of insects. A type of epithelial cell that performs a primarily protective function is the *squamous cell*. Squamous cells are thin and flattened, like tiles. They make up the outer layers, or epidermis, of the skin and line the mouth and other mucous membranes.

Epithelial cells also line and protect the inner surfaces of the body. In Figure 1–37 are shown the cells that line the trachea, the upper respiratory tract. Projecting from the surfaces of these cells are cilia. These cilia are structurally identical to the cilia of paramecia and the other protozoans,

75 *Somatic Cells*

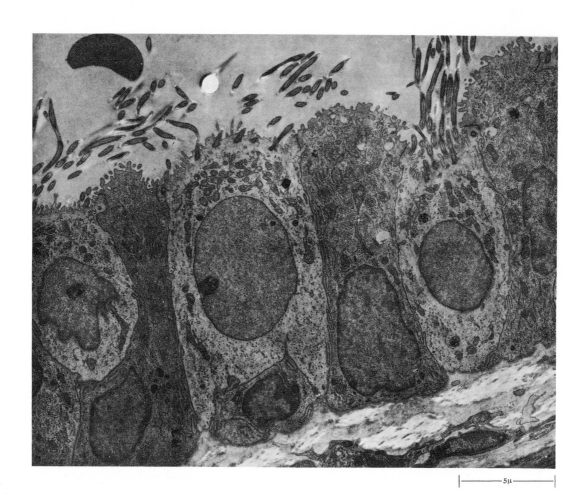

1–37 *Electron micrograph and diagram of epithelial cells from the trachea (or windpipe) of a bat. As you can see, ciliated cells (marked "C" in the drawing) and mucus-secreting cells (M) alternate in a regular pattern. The beating of the cilia removes foreign particles from the trachea and distributes a protective coating of mucus. In the micrograph, the white circles in the cytoplasm of the middle (M) cell are secretion droplets of mucus. (Dr. Keith R. Porter)*

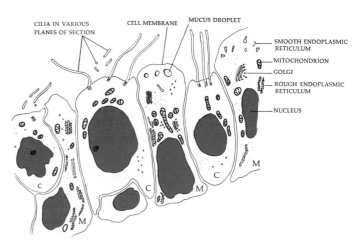

CILIA IN VARIOUS PLANES OF SECTION

CELL MEMBRANE

MUCUS DROPLET

SMOOTH ENDOPLASMIC RETICULUM

MITOCHONDRION

GOLGI

ROUGH ENDOPLASMIC RETICULUM

NUCLEUS

76 CELLS

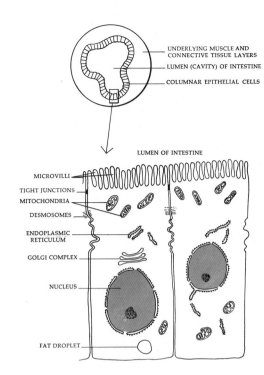

UNDERLYING MUSCLE AND
CONNECTIVE TISSUE LAYERS

LUMEN (CAVITY) OF INTESTINE

COLUMNAR EPITHELIAL CELLS

LUMEN OF INTESTINE

MICROVILLI

TIGHT JUNCTIONS

MITOCHONDRIA

DESMOSOMES

ENDOPLASMIC
RETICULUM

GOLGI COMPLEX

NUCLEUS

FAT DROPLET

1–38 *Diagram of columnar epithelial cells from the small intestine of a mouse. At the top is a cross section of the intestine, as seen with a light microscope. Intestine linings are composed primarily of cells of this columnar, absorptive type. Materials passing through the lumen of the intestine are absorbed by the cells through the microvilli, finger-like cytoplasmic projections of the cells' outer surface. Tight junctions near the lumen surface connect adjacent cells and prevent materials undergoing digestion from entering the intercellular space. Desmosomes provide physical adhesion between cells.*

and like the cilia of paramecia, these cilia keep up a steady, rhythmic beating. In the case of the tracheal cells, this beating distributes a protective coating of mucus and helps propel foreign matter, such as specks of soot or tobacco-smoke condensate, along the epithelial surface and out of the lungs. Interspersed among these ciliated epithelial cells are mucus-secreting cells containing droplets of mucus.

Chemist Cells

In addition to their protective functions, epithelial cells perform much of the chemical work of the body, absorbing materials from the external environment through the digestive and respiratory tracts and excreting waste products into the environment through the lungs, skin, and kidney tubules. They form the secretory cells of glands and digestive organs, producing hormones and enzymes which are released into the bloodstream, the stomach or the small intestine. Cells that perform these functions are classified as *cuboidal* (cuboidal cells, despite their name, are hexagonal, as you can see in Figure 1–36) or *columnar*. Although the designations are convenient, the different types of epithelial cells actually form a continuum from the tile-shaped squamous cells through the taller cuboidal cells to the columnar cells; in general, the more chemically active an epithelial cell is, the more columnar it is.

Cuboidal cells are found in such glands as the thyroid and in the walls of kidney tubules. Egg and sperm cells are produced from cuboidal epithelial cells in the ovaries and testes. Columnar cells make up the lining of the stomach and the intestines.

Figure 1–38 shows a schematic drawing of columnar epithelial cells from the small intestine of a mouse. Note, in particular, the numerous small projections along the free surface of the cells. These are the *microvilli*. The microvilli greatly increase the surface area for absorption or intake of nutrients. As in the mitochondria, certain enzymes are a part of the fabric of the membrane surface. Each cell has some 3,000 individual microvilli, and a square millimeter of the intestine may have as many as 200 million. Soluble nutrients are taken in through the surfaces of the microvilli and, to a lesser extent, through pinocytic channels which form at their bases. Typically, the mitochondria of these cells tend to gather near the cell surface, where the most active work of the cell is being performed.

Connective and Supporting Cells

These cells and the tissues they compose support the body and bind together its component parts. In plants, as we have seen, most of the supporting tissue is made up of dead cells with thick cellulose walls. In animals, the bulk of connective tissue is often not part of the living cells them-

77 *Somatic Cells*

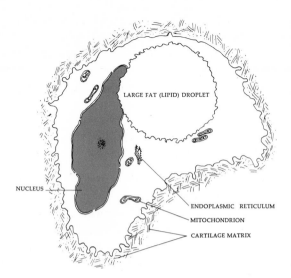

LARGE FAT (LIPID) DROPLET

NUCLEUS

ENDOPLASMIC RETICULUM

MITOCHONDRION

CARTILAGE MATRIX

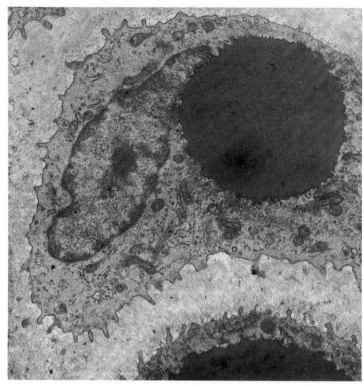

|—1μ—|

1–39 *Electron micrograph and diagram of a cartilage cell (*chondrocyte*) from the trachea of a bat. The cell is embedded in a dense, nonliving material, consisting of tiny fibrils and a jellylike material known as* ground substance *both of which are produced by the chondrocyte. These cells have an unusually large supply of stored food on hand in the form of large lipid droplets in the cytoplasm. (Dr. Keith R. Porter)*

selves but is composed of deposits of material secreted by the cells and surrounding them. A major part of this is the fibrous protein collagen.

FIBROUS CONNECTIVE TISSUE

Fibrous connective tissue is found everywhere throughout the body. It forms a supportive layer under the skin, holds and anchors the organs of the body, makes up the tough outer walls of arteries and veins, and forms sheaths around muscle fibers and nerve cells, binding them together. Tendons and ligaments are made up of fibrous connective tissue; tendons connect muscle to muscle or muscle to bone, and ligaments connect one bone to another. Fibrous tissue is composed of spindle-shaped cells called *fibrocytes*, which are wide in the middle and taper toward both ends—and the fibrous protein collagen, which is secreted by the immature fibrocytes (*fibroblasts*).

About one-third of the protein of the human body is collagen. The collagenous fibers are bound in bundles. These bundles may be arranged at approximate right angles to one another in a strong fabriclike weave, or they may be arranged parallel to one another, as in the tendons and liga-

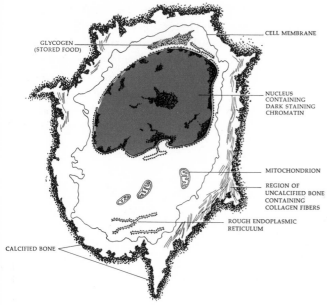

GLYCOGEN
(STORED FOOD)

CELL MEMBRANE

NUCLEUS
CONTAINING
DARK STAINING
CHROMATIN

MITOCHONDRION

REGION OF
UNCALCIFIED BONE
CONTAINING
COLLAGEN FIBERS

ROUGH ENDOPLASMIC
RETICULUM

CALCIFIED BONE

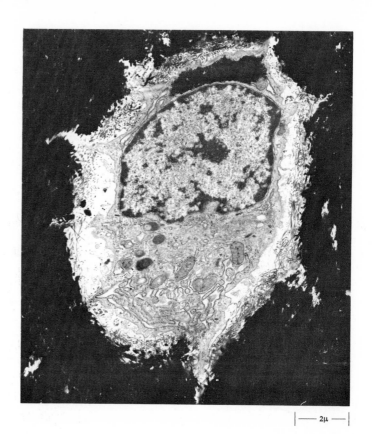

|— 2µ —|

1–40 *Electron micrograph and diagram of a rat osteocyte. Young bone cells (osteoblasts) produce the intercellular bone matrix, an organic material consisting of collagen fibers and an amorphous ground substance. This matrix gradually mineralizes (calcifies), becoming the hard, dense tissue which we call bone. When the osteocyte has finally become encased in calcified tissue, it can make no further contribution to the growth of the bone. (Dr. Keith R. Porter)*

ments. Connective tissues also have extracellular fluids which lubricate the moving parts of the body.

CARTILAGE

Cartilage makes up the skeletons of all vertebrates in their embryonic stage, persisting in the adult in a few places such as joints, the ends of ribs, and the ear. In some animals—for example, the shark—cartilage forms the permanent skeleton. It is a tough, gristly substance; you can determine the texture of it very readily by feeling the tip of your nose. It is made by a special type of cell, the *chondrocyte*, that produces both the fibers and a sort of cement, a jellylike material known as *ground substance*, which fills the interstices between the fibers and binds them together.

BONE

In most vertebrates, including man, bone replaces cartilage at maturity, forming the permanent supporting tissue of the body. Bone is a dense, hard material composed largely of collagen and calcium salts. It is produced by young bone cells, the *osteoblasts*, which become surrounded by and

79   *Somatic Cells*

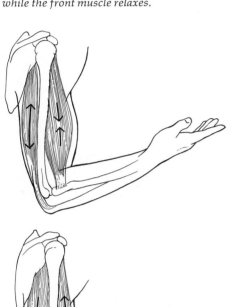

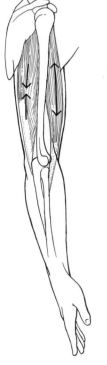

1–41 *Every muscle in the body has a counterpart, or opposing muscle, and the two work as a team. While one muscle contracts, the other relaxes. When you move your hand toward your shoulder, as shown here, the front muscle of the upper arm contracts and the rear muscle relaxes. When you move your hand down again, the rear muscle contracts while the front muscle relaxes.*

trapped in their own secretion. (*Blast* comes from the Greek word for "germ" and is applied to many types of immature cells.) The *osteocytes,* or mature bone cells, are scattered through the dense bony tissue, maintaining contact with one another by thin strands of cytoplasm weaving through the bone. These cytoplasmic strands also connect the cells with the fine network of blood vessels that bring them nourishment and oxygen and carry off wastes. Also present in bone are *osteolytic cells,* which serve to break bone down so that it can be remodeled and reshaped in the process of growth.

FAT CELLS

Fat cells are classified as part of the connective tissues, although they do not perform a connective function. Unlike other connective-tissue cells, fat cells are characterized by their deposits of intracellular rather than extracellular substance. Each fat cell contains one or more relatively huge oily droplets, often so large that the nucleus and other cellular structures are crowded off to one edge of the cell. Fat provides energy reserves for the body; if your intake of food is less than your requirements, the fat will be mobilized from these depots and released into the bloodstream.

Muscle

Muscle is the tissue that moves the various organs and appendages of the animal body. Muscles move by contraction. When you flex your arm, you can feel the muscles in your upper arm contract as you pull your fist toward your shoulder. As you stretch your arm out again, you may think that these same muscles are pushing it, but this is not so. Your arm extends because of the contraction of opposing muscles leading from elbow to shoulder along the back of the upper arm. All muscular movements are based on alternate contraction and relaxation of muscles. By use of the electron microscope, this contraction and relaxation can be visualized in terms of the cellular structures that make it possible.

Vertebrates have muscles of three main types: *striated,* or voluntary; *smooth,* or involuntary; and *cardiac,* the special muscular tissue of the heart. Striated muscles also occur in insects and some other animals without backbones. These types of muscle are related to the functions they perform.

STRIATED MUSCLE

The principal striated muscles of the body are the skeletal muscles that move the arms, legs, hands, paws, wings, or other appendages. They are known as *voluntary muscles* because they can be moved intentionally, unlike the muscles of the heart or the intestinal tract.

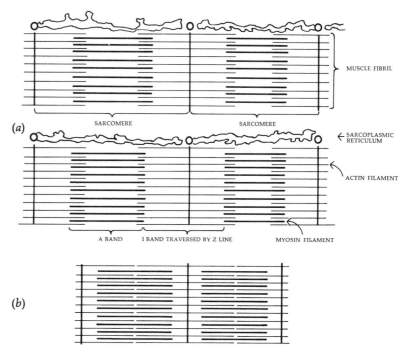

(a)

MUSCLE FIBRIL

SARCOMERE   SARCOMERE

← SARCOPLASMIC
RETICULUM

ACTIN FILAMENT

A BAND   I BAND TRAVERSED BY Z LINE   MYOSIN FILAMENT

(b)

|——————1μ——————|

1–42 *Electron micrograph and diagrams of*
striated-muscle fibrils. A single striated
muscle may be made up of many hun-
dreds of thousands of muscle cells, ar-
ranged to form a kind of living cable.
Each cell, in turn, contains some 1,000
to 2,000 smaller strands, or fibrils, in
parallel array. The fibrils, which are the
contracting elements, are composed of
units of alternating thick and thin fila-
ments. In the diagram, the arrangement
of filaments is shown with the fibril
relaxed (a) *and with the fibril contracted*
(b). *Notice that the filaments do not*
become shorter as the fibril contracts
but seem, instead, to slide together.
(Dr. Keith R. Porter)

Striated muscles are made up of cells which are usually 50 to 100 microns in diameter and which may be as long as several centimeters. Each of these unusually large cells has many nuclei, which are crowded out of the body of the cell by the contractile materials and can be found near the cell surface, just under the plasma membrane. The body of the cell is filled with small contractile fibers, the *myofibrils*, which form a regular repeating pattern that gives the cell its characteristic striped, or striated, appearance.

Each unit of the pattern is called a *sarcomere*. Figure 1–42 shows the sarcomere as seen in a longitudinal section of muscle. Each sarcomere is about 2 or 3 microns in length. The Z line is the dense black line seen in the electron micrograph; the I band is the relatively clear, broad stripe which the Z band bisects; and the A band is the dense stripe. As the diagram shows, each sarcomere is composed of two types of filaments running parallel to one another. The thicker filaments in the central portion of the sarcomere are composed of a protein known as myosin; the thinner filaments are of actin. The Z line is made up of the interweaving of actin filaments from adjacent sarcomeres. In Figure 1–42, you can see the alternating thin and thick filaments, actin and myosin, respectively, arranged in a regular pattern. In very active muscles, such as the flight muscles of the hummingbird and of certain insects, the mitochondria are relatively enormous and are located exactly opposite the junction of A and I bands.

81   *Somatic Cells*

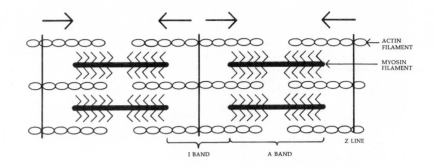

1–43 The most generally accepted theory of muscle contraction is shown here. When the muscle fiber is stimulated to contract, the actin filaments, which are protein chains composed of globular subunits, slide past the myosin filaments in the direction indicated by the arrows. This causes each sarcomere to shorten, and thus the fibril as a whole contracts. The force "pulling" each actin filament toward the center of the sarcomere is thought to be developed at the crossbridges (represented by arrowheads) on the myosin filament. Like a ratchet, the crossbridges interact with successive sites along the actin protein chain. Since the cross-bridges face in opposite directions on each side of the sarcomere, the actin chains can move toward one another until they meet or even overlap.

A complex network of tubules and sacs, the *sarcoplasmic reticulum*, runs parallel to the myofibrils in the spaces between them. The roles of this system in the muscle cell are not completely known. Another system of tubules is formed by transverse invaginations of the cell surfaces, and this is known to serve as a communication system enabling all the myofibrils in the depth of the fiber to contract simultaneously. This transverse tubular system also provides for the distribution in muscle cells of the chemicals needed for muscle action.

The diagram in Figure 1–43 shows what happens when a striated-muscle cell contracts. Shortening takes place when the actin filaments slide in between the myosin filaments of the A band. The way in which these two types of filaments react with one another to cause this sliding is not known, but it is believed that the filaments are linked to each other in such a way that the actin filaments can move along the myosin filaments.

CARDIAC MUSCLE

The heart is the organ that circulates the blood through the animal body. It is composed entirely of striated muscle, but whereas skeletal-muscle fibers are single long cells arranged in end-to-end alignments, cardiac-muscle fibers tend to branch and form a network of connections. Cardiac-muscle cells have numerous large mitochondria. Because of this and other special adaptations, the heart muscle is able to work slowly but constantly, in contrast to voluntary muscle, which can contract and relax much more rapidly than heart muscle but must pause to "catch its breath," that is, to restore its oxygen supply and eliminate wastes.

SMOOTH MUSCLE

Smooth muscle is found in the walls of the intestinal tract, uterus, and bladder and in the lining of the blood vessels. The cells of smooth muscle are usually very long and thin and are traversed by what appears to be only a single type of filament running longitudinally through the cells. Cells within a bundle or layer are usually oriented in the same direction,

1–44 *Electron micrograph of cardiac muscle from the heart of a bat. In this micrograph, portions of the cytoplasm of three muscle cells can be seen, one at the right and two, one above the other, at the left. The cell at the right is separated from those on the left by a thin layer of connective tissue, within which can be seen the dark outline of a red blood cell lodged within a capillary. The striated-muscle pattern of the fibrils is clearly shown. Note the size and number of mitochondria. Presumably, these are needed by the hardworking cardiac muscle to supply its unusual energy requirements. (Dr. Keith R. Porter)*

├─────────5μ─────────┤

1–45 *Electron micrograph of smooth muscle from the trachea of a bat. Smooth muscle is made up of long, spindle-shaped cells containing contractile proteins. Portions of a number of these can be seen in the picture. Part of the nucleus of one cell, distinguishable by its dark color and granular texture, can be seen in the left half of the micrograph. Very thin filaments run lengthwise through the cells and make up the bulk of the cytoplasm. The plasma membranes are indicated by the fine lines which appear to be encrusted with tiny vesicles. These vesicles are actually invaginations, or pits, in the membranes. They are found in all smooth-muscle cells, but what role they play in the cell is not known. (Dr. Keith R. Porter)*

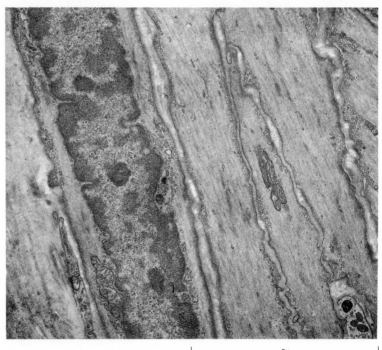

├─────────5μ─────────┤

but neighboring bundles and layers may be at varying angles to one another. For example, the two muscle layers of the intestinal wall lie at right angles to each other, making possible the wormlike contractile motions necessary to churn the food and move it through the digestive tract.

The Bloodstream

The bloodstream is the means by which materials are circulated through the animal body. The fluid part of the blood is called *plasma*. A filtrate of plasma bathes all the cells of the body, seeping out between the cells of the capillary walls, flowing into the tissue spaces of the body, and returning to the bloodstream through the walls of small blood vessels. The whole plasma within the circulation system carries soluble nutrients and wastes and also the white cells, called *leucocytes*, and the red cells, or *erythrocytes*.

WHITE CELLS

The chief function of the white cells is the defense of the body against invaders such as viruses, bacteria, and various foreign particles. They accomplish this function in two ways:

1 By taking part in the manufacture of special protein substances known as *antibodies*, which combine with disease-causing agents and inactivate them.
2 By phagocytosis. Phagocytosis is accomplished in the white blood cells in much the same way as in the amoeba; that is, the cell extends pseudopodia around the foreign substance, incorporates it within a food vacuole, and destroys it with the help of enzymes from the lysosomes.

White cells are often destroyed in the course of fighting infection. Pus is composed largely of white blood cells. New white cells are formed constantly in the spleen, bone marrow, and certain other tissues to take the place of those cells that are sacrificed.

White blood cells are unusual among somatic cells because of their active locomotion. They travel by amoeboid movement and are attracted to sites of infection, probably by the chemical substances diffused from such sites. They are quite capable of moving against the bloodstream, migrating through the walls of small blood vessels, and making their way into damaged or infected tissues.

RED CELLS

Figure 1–46 shows an electron micrograph of mammalian erythrocytes, perhaps the most highly specialized of all cells. As the picture demonstrates, there is not very much to see in this structure. The function of the erythrocyte is the transportation of oxygen to the various cells of the body,

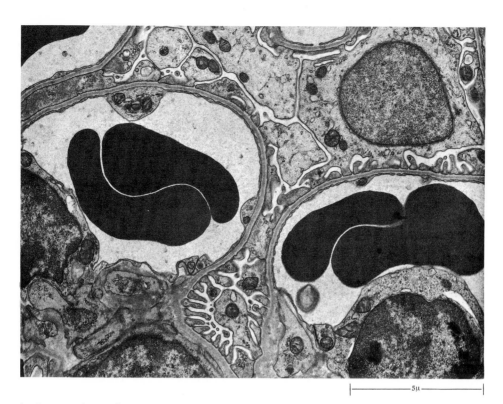

|—————5µ—————|

1–46 *Electron micrograph of mammalian red blood cells. Four cells—the dark shapes in the middle, two on the left and two on the right—are shown in the picture. These are mature cells from which nuclei and organelles have been lost, and they are little more than masses of hemoglobin enclosed in membranes. (Dr. Keith R. Porter)*

and it is extraordinarily well adapted to this purpose. Seen from the side, it is biconcave. This enables it to move easily with the flow of the bloodstream and to bend or twist to slip through tiny blood vessels smaller than itself. This shape also provides it with a large surface, which facilitates its exchange of oxygen and carbon dioxide with other cells.

The entire volume of the red blood cell is filled with hemoglobin. Hemoglobin is a protein molecule with a core of iron in its center; a mature red blood cell contains 265 million molecules of hemoglobin. These molecules, combining loosely with oxygen, enable our bloodstreams to carry about 60 times as much oxygen as could be transported by an equal volume of water or plasma. Erythrocytes are manufactured in the bone marrow, with some 2 1/2 million made every second as an equal number "wear out."

The young cell, or *erythroblast* still possesses a nucleus, some mitochondria, and clusters of ribosomes, on which hemoglobin is manufactured. In a very short time, this cell will become mature. It will extrude its nucleus; its mitochondria and other cellular structures will dissolve; and, fully differentiated, it will spend its remaining days—an average of 127—transporting oxygen to other cells.

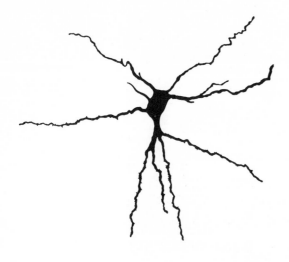

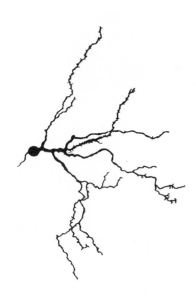

1–47 *Nerve cells, or neurons, are highly specialized. Since each is designed to do a single, particular job and no other, individual neurons vary greatly in structure. Shown here are four neurons which carry messages within the central nervous system. (Dr. Raymond C. Truex)*

The Nervous System

The nervous system serves to integrate the activities of the animal and coordinate them with the outside environment.

NEURONS

Of all the cells in the body, nerve cells, or *neurons,* are the most diverse and the most morphologically spectacular. Figure 1–47 shows the form of a number of different nerve cells. These drawings were made from tissues treated with a silver stain, which is picked up selectively by the nerve cells. The stain travels along the many intricately branching nerve fibers, tracing out their delicate patterns.

The typical nerve cell consists of three components: the body of the cell, which has a large central nucleus, and two branching systems, the dendrites and the axon. The *dendrites* receive nerve impulses from other nerve cells; the dendrite characteristically consists of many small, fine branches. The *axon* is a single long branch that transmits the impulses. The axon is also sometimes referred to as the *nerve fiber.* Near its end, the axon may divide into fine ramifications that terminate at the dendrites or in a special unfolded region of a muscle cell.

Nerve cells may reach astonishing lengths. For example, the axon of one motor neuron—the nerve cell that activates motor tissues—may extend from the spinal cord down the whole length of the leg right to the toe. Or a sensory nerve—one that transmits sensations to the brain—that is based on the spinal cord may send one fiber down to the toe and another fiber up the entire length of the spinal cord to terminate in the lower part of the brain. In a full-grown giraffe, such a nerve cell would be 15 feet long!

NERVE IMPULSES

Nerve signals travel through a single cell as *electric impulses* running the entire length of the cell. These impulses cease abruptly when they come to the point at which the axon's terminal fibers make contact with other nerve

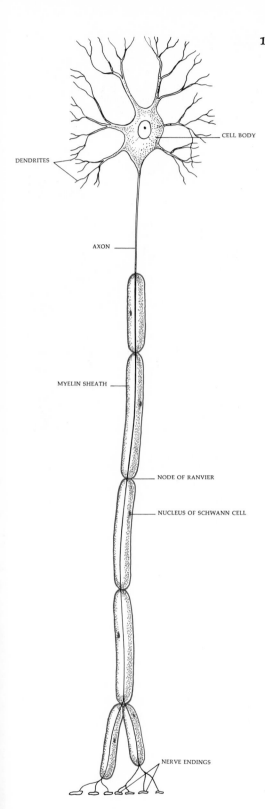

DENDRITES

CELL BODY

AXON

MYELIN SHEATH

NODE OF RANVIER

NUCLEUS OF SCHWANN CELL

NERVE ENDINGS

1–48 *A typical motor neuron. The stimulus is received by the dendrites, which conduct it to the cell body and to the axon. The axon is a sheathed filament which acts as a self-powered transmission cable. Its power is in the form of a minute voltage difference, derived from a chemical exchange between the axon and its surroundings. Any disturbance of the axon initiates a momentary reversal of this voltage difference, and the resulting impulse travels along the axon until it comes to the nerve endings. (See Figure 1–57). The nodes of Ranvier are gaps in the axon sheath which occur at the junctions of adjacent Schwann cells. The nerve endings shown here are tiny unsheathed filaments terminating in bulbous "feet." Different types of neurons have differently shaped endings.*

cells. These junction points between two neurons are known as *synapses*. The impulse is relayed across these synapses, it is believed, by the action of chemical substances. As you can see in Figure 1–49, the synaptic knob contains many tiny vesicles or sacs. These are presumed to contain the transmitter chemicals. Golgi complexes are prominent in nerve cells and may be involved in the production and packaging of these transmitter substances. Electric impulses can pass along the axon in either direction, laboratory experiments have shown, but synaptic transmission can occur in only one direction.

SCHWANN CELL

Axons are insulated by a type of cell known as a Schwann cell, which has been adapted for this specific purpose. A single Schwann cell may sheath many fibers. The fibers do not actually penetrate the cytoplasm of the Schwann cell; rather they nestle into its surface and become enwrapped by it. Some fibers are completely surrounded by many layers of Schwann-cell membranes; these are generally the larger nerve fibers with fast conduction rates. In these cases, the Schwann cell, as it grows, moves around and around the axon, leaving a layer of membrane each time. Collectively, these layers comprise myelin, and nerve fibers surrounded by a Schwann cell are said to be *myelinated*. Such fibers generally transmit impulses more rapidly than unmyelinated nerve fibers. The diagram in Figure 1–50 shows the process by which a Schwann-cell membrane is wrapped around an axon.

RODS AND CONES

Of all the many senses, vision is the one that is the most important to man and the other primates. Vision depends on the perception of light. The

87   *Somatic Cells*

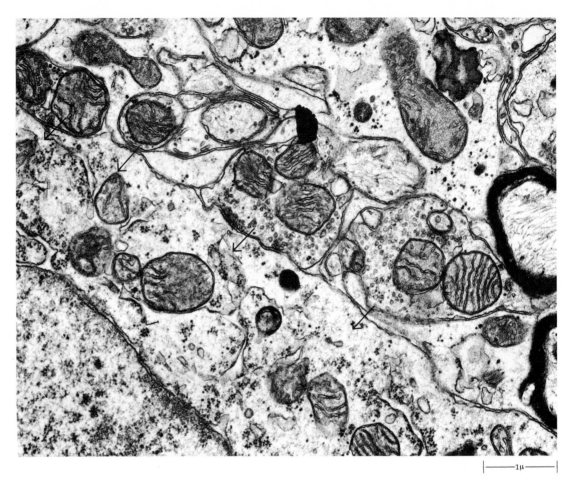

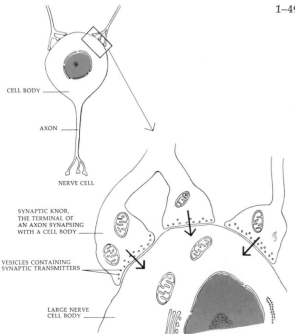

CELL BODY

AXON

NERVE CELL

SYNAPTIC KNOB,
THE TERMINAL OF
AN AXON SYNAPSING
WITH A CELL BODY

VESICLES CONTAINING
SYNAPTIC TRANSMITTERS

LARGE NERVE
CELL BODY

1–49 *Electron micrograph of a synaptic area in the spinal cord of **a bat, and a diagram** of a synapse. In the micrograph, part of a motor neuron occupies the left side of the picture. Its nucleus fills the lower left corner. Several nerve terminals are clustered at the cell surface just outside the cell. These are characterized by numerous synaptic vesicles, which appear in the picture as small, grayish granules, most numerous near the plasma membranes adjoining the motor neuron. In the synaptic region (the area of contact between the nerve terminal in the center of the picture and the motor neuron), the plasma membranes of the two cells are intact and clearly separated from one another by a gap about 10 millimicrons wide. Apparently, the vesicles, triggered by an electric impulse in the axon, release their chemical contents across this gap. The chemicals, known as synaptic transmitters, stimulate the adjacent neuron and thus relay the impulse from one nerve cell to another, but in one direction only, as indicated by the arrows. (Dr. Keith R. Porter)*

88 CELLS

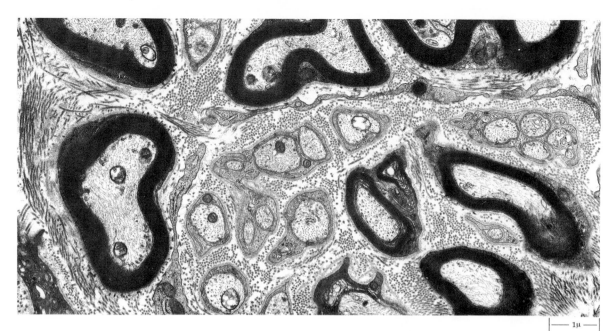

—— 1μ ——

1–50 *In the electron micrograph the large, irregular shapes with the broad dark borders are cross sections of fast-conduction nerve fibers enclosed in myelin sheaths. Schwann-cell cytoplasm can be seen on the outer edges of some of the myelin sheaths. Bundles of smaller, non-myelinated, "slow" fibers are enclosed by the cytoplasm of other Schwann cells. The spaces between the fibers are laced with collagen fibrils. The diagram shows how the myelin sheath develops. A nerve axon is surrounded by a Schwann cell. When the Schwann cell meets itself, the two facing plasma membranes form a unit known as the* mesaxon. *As this grows and becomes elongated, it extends itself around and around the axon and gradually excludes the cytoplasm of the Schwann cell from between the layers. (Dr. Keith R. Porter)*

NUCLEUS

SCHWANN CELL

AXON — AXON — AXON

MESAXON   SCHWANN CELL MEMBRANE

cells in the eye which are concerned with photoreception are the *rods* and *cones*, which derive their names from their shapes. They are sensitive to light, and when they are stimulated by light, they transmit signals to other neurons, which relay the signals to the brain. The cones, which number some 7 million in the human eye, are stimulated by light of relatively high intensity. Cones are responsible for sharp vision and for color discrimination. The rods, of which the human eye has an estimated 100 million, react to low intensities of light. They serve in the twilight, which is why everything begins to look colorless as light fades, and for night vision.

Figure 1–51 shows an electron micrograph of rod cells. The dense portion is made up of disk-shaped double-layered membranes piled one on top of the other like a high stack of coins. The efficient absorption of light seems to be dependent on this particular layered arrangement. It is interesting to compare the human eye with the eye of an invertebrate. Figure 1–52 shows the photosensitive area of the eye of a scallop. The scallop's eye evolved separately from that of man and other vertebrates, and as you can see, it appears in some respects to be quite different from the vertebrate eye. The light-receiving portion is not a stack of membranes but consists rather of one membrane folded tightly inside another, like a head of cabbage. However, although superficially different, the two types of eye are actually very similar, since each presents a closely layered membrane surface to the incoming light waves.

89   *Somatic Cells*

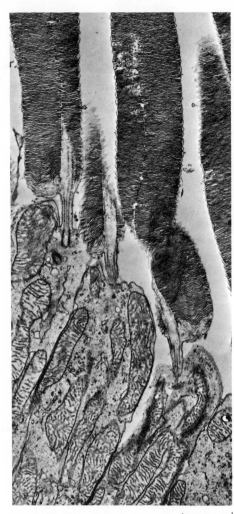

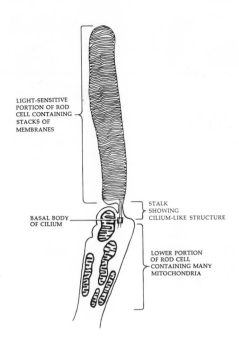

|——1μ——|

1–51 *Electron micrograph of the outer segments of rod cells from the retina of a
kangaroo rat. The diagram identifies the
structures shown in the micrograph. The
stack of thin, membranous sacs is enclosed in plasma membrane, which is
continuous with the rest of the rod cell
by way of a slender connecting stalk.
The pigments involved in the biochemistry of vision are built into the membranes of these sacs. (Dr. Keith R.
Porter)*

The light-receiving portions of the rods and cones are connected with
the cell body by a narrow stalk. A cross section of this stalk reveals, surprisingly, that it has the same basic structure as the cilium and flagellum,
lacking only the two central fibers. In the electron micrograph of the eye
of the scallop, for instance, it can be seen that each leaf of the "cabbage"
is played out from a single cilium. Similarly, a cilium (including its limiting membrane) is the only physical connection linking the membranous
layers of the vertebrate eye with the body of the cell and its axon, which
transmits information to the brain. The way in which this structure is able
to carry sensory information is not known, neither for *Euglena* nor for the
vertebrate eye. However, many—perhaps half—of the sensory organs of
both vertebrates and invertebrates are derived from cilia, including the
chemoreceptors of insects, the touch receptors on the suckers of the octopus, and the mechanoreceptors of the rabbit nose.

The light-receiving unit of rods and cones contains a single-coiled molecule of a substance known as *retinene*, a carotenelike chemical. The smallest measurable quantity of light is the *quantum*, which is the light energy
contained in one single particle, or photon, of light. When a molecule of
retinene is exposed to light, the molecule unfolds. It is this unfolding of
the molecule that presumably triggers the sensation that is passed through
the ciliary structures into the body of the nerve cell and on to the brain. As
few as 5 quanta of light, enough to activate five photoreceptors, produce

1–52 *Electron micrograph of the light-sensitive portion of the eye of a scallop. Concentric layers of membrane are continuous with stalks of cilia, seen on the left. Compare this arrangement with the coinlike stacks and connecting cilia of the vertebrate eye, Figure 1–51. (Dr. W. H. Miller)*

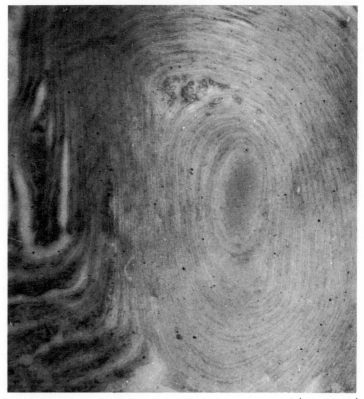

|—— 0.5μ ——|

the sensation of light in the human eye. Somehow the cilium, whose basic structure must have evolved more than a billion years ago with the first green flagellates, has been slowly shaped over the course of time to play this new, intricate, and highly specialized role.

SUMMARY

In this chapter, we looked at some representative cases of the great diversity that exists among somatic cells. This diversity arises from the variety of functions that somatic cells must perform. Somatic cells are specialists, and each kind of cell, in adapting to its own specialized function, becomes differentiated from all other kinds of cells. In the course of the evolution of larger plants and animals, the cell components that we examined in Chapters 1–3 and 1–4 have been modified in various ways to serve new purposes.

The specialized cells of the higher plants perform many different functions: (1) Photosynthesis is carried out in the *parenchyma cells* of the leaf. These cells, forming the bulk of the plant tissue, also serve for the storage of energy reserves. (2) *Epidermal cells* waterproof the outer surfaces of leaves and stems and, in the form of *guard cells,* control the opening and closing of stomata. (3) Conducting cells form *xylem tissue* for conducting water and minerals up from the ground to the leaves and *phloem tissue* for conducting the products of photosynthesis down from the leaves to the rest of the plant. (4) Support cells, including *fibers* and *stone cells,* give mechanical support to the other tissues of the plant. (5) *Meristematic cells,* which are essentially undifferentiated, or embryonic, can develop into any of the specialized cells required by the plant. The presence of meristematic tissue makes it possible for plants, unlike animals, to grow all during their lives.

Animal cells perform six major functions for the organism:

1 *Protection.* Epithelial cells protect the inner and outer surfaces of the body from injury and guard the body against water loss. These functions are primarily performed by *squamous cells.*

2 *Chemistry.* Epithelial cells also perform the chemical work of the body —absorbing and excreting materials and manufacturing enzymes and hormones. These cells are classified as *cuboidal* or *columnar.*

3 *Connection and support.* Various cells form the bone, cartilage, and fibrous connective tissue that support the body and bind together its component parts.

4 *Movement.* The appendages and organs of the animal body are moved by alternate contractions and relaxations of muscle tissue. Muscle tissue includes striated (voluntary) muscle, cardiac muscle, and smooth (involuntary) muscle.

5 *Circulation.* Materials are circulated through the animal body by means of the bloodstream. The chief function of the white blood cells is to defend the body against foreign particles. Unlike most other somatic cells, white cells are capable of self-locomotion. The red blood cells carry oxygen to the various cells of the body. To adapt to this function, the maturing cell extrudes its nucleus and dissolves its mitochondria and other cellular substances; the entire volume of the mature cell is filled with hemoglobin.

6 *Communication.* Nerve cells typically consist of three components: the body of the cell, the *dendrites,* and the *axon.* The great variety of nerve cells indicates the highly specialized functions which they perform. Dendrites receive nerve impulses from other cells, and axons transmit the impulses. The junction points of nerve cells are *synapses.* Impulses can pass along a nerve fiber in either direction, but synaptic transmission is one-way. Axons which are sheathed by Schwann-cell membrane are *myelinated;* such nerve fibers generally transmit impulses more rapidly than unmyelinated nerve fibers.

Chapter 1–6

The Chemistry of the Living Cell

Albert Szent-Györgyi is an American biochemist who received a Nobel Prize for his work on the chemistry of living systems. In a recent reminiscence about his career in science, he recalled that in his "hunt for the secret of life," he had begun by working with rabbits, had shifted to bacteria, and then had turned from bacteria to molecules and, finally, from molecules to electrons. "But electrons are just electrons, and have no life at all. Evidently on the way I lost life; it had run out between my fingers."

In this chapter, which begins with electrons and atoms, we shall try not to let life slip from between our fingers. Electrons, atoms, and molecules are not life any more than a pile of bricks is a home. But though they will not tell us the "secret" of life, they do much, as Szent-Györgyi and others have shown, to illuminate its nature. Studies of the chemistry of living things, comparatively recent in the history of biology, have established two important concepts that are profoundly influencing all biology:

1 Living systems obey the same chemical and physical laws as nonliving systems. This does not mean that we understand all the chemical and physical activities of the cell, but it does mean that we work on the premise that these activities can be understood—that they are knowable.

2 Living cells, no matter how diverse in appearance and function, are remarkably the same.

The more we know about the biochemistry of cells, the more we have "evidence for the great fundamental unity of living Nature," as Szent-Györgyi said, speaking at a different time and, perhaps, in a different mood. "There is no real difference between cabbages and kings; we are all recent leaves on the old tree of life."

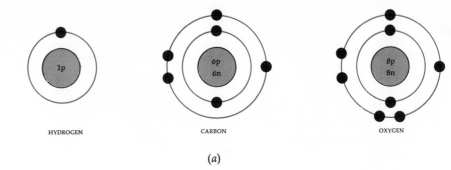

HYDROGEN CARBON OXYGEN

(a)

1–53 *Two ways of representing the structure of atoms. The models in (a) picture electrons as moving in planetary orbits around the nucleus which contains protons (p) and neutrons (n). An alternative concept of the atom is shown in (b), in which the electrons are not specifically located but are shown in terms of their wave functions, or orbitals. The sphere at the top represents the space in which the hydrogen electron is more likely to be found at any given time. The three dumbbell-shaped orbitals of the oxygen atom are the areas in which the electrons of the outer shell are most likely to be found.*

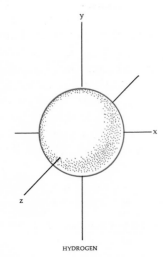

HYDROGEN

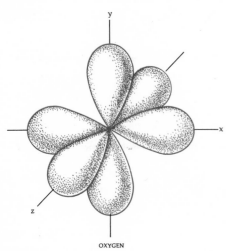

OXYGEN

(b)

THE FUNDAMENTAL PARTICLES

The Structure of the Atom

Matter is composed of elements, and atoms are the irreducible units of elements. This does not mean that an atom cannot be broken apart but rather that the parts of the atom have quite different properties from the properties of the atom itself. Table 1–1 lists some of the elements known to be necessary for life and gives their symbols and their atomic numbers.

The atomic number of an element represents the number of protons in its nucleus. Protons, as you will recall from our brief discussion in Chapter 1–1, are positively charged. Neutrons, also found in the nucleus, have no charge. Therefore, the nucleus of any atom has a net positive charge, and the strength of this charge can be determined from the atomic number. This net positive charge of the nucleus is offset by electrons, negative particles which move about the nucleus at varying distances from it, traveling at a high velocity. The negative charge of one electron is sufficient to balance out the positive charge of one proton. Therefore, for an atom to be electrically neutral, the number of electrons circling the nucleus must equal the number of protons within it. Notice in Table 1–1 that the atomic number equals the sum of all the electrons in the shells surrounding the nucleus of the electrically stable atom. An atom which lacks one of its orbital electrons has a charge of $+1$, one which lacks two electrons has a charge of $+2$, while an atom which has gained an electron will have a charge of -1.

Figure 1–53 shows two ways of representing atoms. At the top are three examples of the model first proposed in 1913 by Niels Bohr. In this model, negatively charged electrons are pictured as moving in planetary orbits around the nucleus. The relative sizes of electrons and nucleus are not meant to be accurately represented. Electrons are much, much smaller and lighter than atomic nuclei. When you weigh yourself on a scale, only 1 or 2 ounces of your total weight are made up of electrons; all the rest is protons and neutrons. In any representational picture, if the nucleus of an atom were depicted as the size of a period on this piece of paper, the electron, in proportion, could not be represented at all, since it would be much too small to be visible. Furthermore, this invisible speck would not lie near the nucleus or even on the page; on this scale, it would be found somewhere outside the room in which you are sitting and probably all the way across the street.

The simple Bohr, or planetary, model, which we follow in this text has been replaced for some purposes by the representation diagrammed at the bottom of Figure 1–53. Here the positions of the electrons are represented in terms of their so-called "wave functions," or orbitals. An *orbital* is the region in which we are likely to find a given electron most of the time. The electron of a single hydrogen atom, for example, will most probably be

Table 1–1 *Some Elements Present in Living Matter*

Element	Symbol	Atomic number	Number of electrons			
			Shell 1	Shell 2	Shell 3	Shell 4
Hydrogen	H	1	1	0	0	0
Carbon	C	6	2	4	0	0
Nitrogen	N	7	2	5	0	0
Oxygen	O	8	2	6	0	0
Sodium	Na	11	2	8	1	0
Magnesium	Mg	12	2	8	2	0
Silicon	Si	14	2	8	4	0
Phosphorus	P	15	2	8	5	0
Sulfur	S	16	2	8	6	0
Chlorine	Cl	17	2	8	7	0
Potassium	K	19	2	8	8	1
Calcium	Ca	20	2	8	8	2
Iron	Fe	26	2	8	8	8

found somewhere in the sphere shown. The regions in which there is a high probability (95 percent) of finding electrons of the outer shell of the oxygen atom are three dumbbell-shaped orbitals which are perpendicular to each other.

You may wonder why scientists speak of electron positions only in terms of probabilities. Is it impossible to determine exactly the pathway of a given electron around a nucleus? The answer, according to the *Heisenberg Uncertainty Principle,* is yes. You would have to know both the position and the velocity of that electron, and physicists have found that the energy involved in the process of measuring an electron's position changes its velocity and, in the same way, measuring its velocity changes its position. In other words, the experimental measurements themselves change the original conditions of the experiment.

Energy and the Electron

ELECTRON ENERGY LEVELS

As you can see in Figure 1–53, electrons tend to be found at certain fixed distances from the nucleus, arranged in *electron shells,* which have different energy levels. In order to understand how such a minute particle as an electron can possess energy and why it is that the distance from the nucleus determines its energy level, it may be helpful to begin with an analogy. A boulder sitting still on flat ground has no energy. If you push it up a hill, it gains *potential* energy. So long as it sits on the peak of the hill, it neither gains nor loses energy. If it is permitted to roll down the hill, it loses energy as it rolls toward level ground (Figure 1–54). Similarly, a rocket poised on the launching pad has no energy. The chemical energy of rocket fuel is required to blast it away from earth, but no input energy is required for its return flight to earth.

The electron is like the rocket in that an input of energy can raise it to a higher level, further away from the nucleus. So long as it remains in this higher level, it possesses potential energy. When it returns to a lower level, its potential energy is released. (Note that the electron never comes to rest at the nucleus, however, in the way that the rocket returns to earth. The first energy level, or electron shell, is "ground zero" for electrons.) An atom or group of atoms in which one or more electrons have been pushed to a higher energy level is known as an *excited* atom. Electrons which have been forced to a higher energy level possess potential energy.

OXIDATION-REDUCTION REACTIONS

An electron may be completely lost by an atom, just as a rocket may escape from the earth's gravitational field. The loss of an electron is known as *oxidation* because, as we shall see, the electron is often (not necessarily always) accepted by an oxygen atom, resulting in a new combination involving oxygen and the atom or molecule that has lost the electron. The gain of an electron is known as *reduction*. Oxidation and reduction take place simultaneously since an electron that is lost by one atom is accepted by another. Oxidation-reduction reactions are an important means of energy transfer within living systems.

Valence

Positive charges and negative charges attract one another. For this reason, the atomic nucleus tends to attract as many electrons as there are protons in the nucleus. Another principle is also at work, however, in determining the pattern of electrons. Each shell can accommodate only a fixed number of electrons. The first shell can hold two, and the second eight. Every outer shell similarly can hold no more than eight, although if the fourth shell is filled, the third shell can hold as many as eighteen. Atoms with as many as seven shells are known. Only atoms with a large number of protons, such as uranium, with an atomic number of 92, can attract enough electrons to fill so many shells. As you can see in Table 1–1, most of the elements involved in life processes are elements with relatively few protons, so for our purposes, we need only be concerned with the first two or three shells.

1–54 *An electron raised to a higher energy level is analogous to a boulder that has been pushed uphill. Both contain potential energy, which is lost as they return to ground state.*

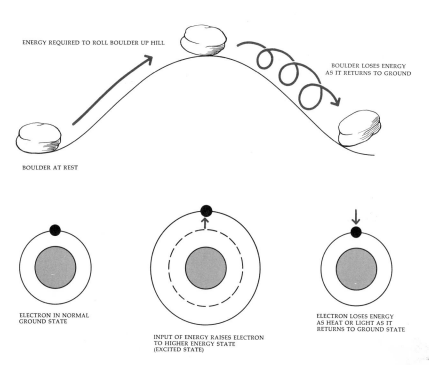

ENERGY REQUIRED TO ROLL BOULDER UP HILL

BOULDER LOSES ENERGY AS IT RETURNS TO GROUND

BOULDER AT REST

ELECTRON IN NORMAL GROUND STATE

INPUT OF ENERGY RAISES ELECTRON TO HIGHER ENERGY STATE (EXCITED STATE)

ELECTRON LOSES ENERGY AS HEAT OR LIGHT AS IT RETURNS TO GROUND STATE

97   *The Chemistry of the Living Cell*

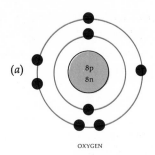

(a)

OXYGEN

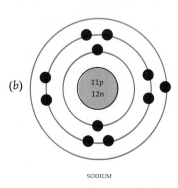

(b)

SODIUM

1–55 *To obtain a full outer shell (eight electrons), oxygen must gain two electrons. Therefore, its valence is —2. Sodium, which needs to lose one electron to have a full outer shell (eight electrons), has a valence of +1. In losing an electron, sodium acquires a positive charge and becomes the sodium ion Na+.*

Atoms tend to stabilize, or complete their shells. Figure 1–55a diagrams the oxygen atom. As we know from Table 1–1, oxygen needs eight electrons to achieve a neutral charge. Two of these electrons are in the inner shell, leaving six for the outer shell. Thus oxygen needs to gain two electrons to stabilize its outer shell at eight. (The gain of electrons, you will recall, is called *reduction*.) Sodium (Figure 1–55b) has an atomic number of 11 and so, as you can predict, has two electrons in its inner shell, eight in its second shell, and one in its third shell. As a consequence, the sodium atom has a tendency to lose this odd electron—or become *oxidized*—achieving a stable electron configuration of eight in what then becomes its outer shell. The loss of this electron gives sodium a net positive charge of 1. In chemical symbols, sodium is Na and sodium which has been oxidized is Na^+. Magnesium, with an atomic number of 12, needs to lose two electrons in order to gain a stable outer shell. It then becomes Mg^{++}. Chlorine, which has an atomic number of 17, needs to gain an electron in order to stabilize its outer shell. In gaining an electron, it acquires a negative charge and becomes Cl^-.

The number of electrons an atom or molecule must gain or lose to attain a stable configuration in its outer shell is its *valence*. Magnesium is said to have a valence of +2 since it needs to lose two electrons, chlorine to have a valence of –1 since it needs to gain one. In general, atoms with less than four electrons in the outer shell tend to lose electrons, or become oxidized, thereby achieving a net positive charge; those with more than four electrons tend to gain electrons, or become reduced.

Electrically charged atoms or groups of atoms are known as *ions*. They are also sometimes called *electrolytes* since solutions that contain ions can conduct electric current, which is carried by the charged particles. (See Figure 1–56.)

Electrolytes in Living Cells

Many of the inorganic chemical components of the living organism are found in the form of ions, or electrolytes, in the interior fluids of the cells or in the blood or other extracellular fluids. These same elements—sodium, chlorine, potassium, calcium, magnesium—are also found in solution in seawater. The concentration of these elements in seawater is about three times greater than in our body fluids, but the proportions in which they appear are almost the same, offering us a reminder of our watery origins.

Only very slight changes in the concentrations of these salts in the body fluids can be tolerated. They affect the functioning of the living organism in very subtle and unexpected ways. For instance, if the Mg^{++} concentration in a cell is lowered only a fraction, the two halves of the ribosome

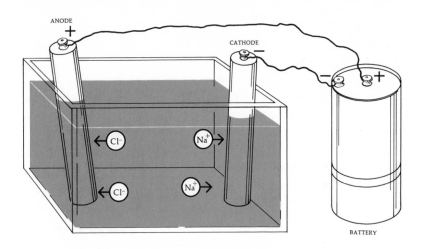

1–56 *How solutions that contain ions conduct electric current. Negatively charged chloride ions (Cl^-) migrate to the positively charged electrode (the anode) and give up their electrons, to become chlorine gas (Cl_2). Positively charged sodium ions (Na^+) migrate to the negative electrode (the cathode) and become metallic sodium, which is deposited on the electrode.*

separate and all protein synthesis stops. K^+ relaxes muscle cells, while a slight excess of Ca^{++} can produce muscular contractions and even convulsions.

Figure 1–57 shows how electrolytes are thought to function in the propagation of an impulse along an axon. The inside of the axon, which is rich in K^+ but low in Na^+, is negatively charged in relation to its surroundings. This difference in charge is known as the *electric potential*. The membrane of the axon, by a process of active transport, pumps Na^+ out of the cell and K^+ into the cell. Approximately 14 times more sodium is outside than inside the cell, and 30 times more potassium inside than out.

The passage of a nerve impulse is initiated by a momentary change in the permeability of a small area of the axon membrane. Such a change can be triggered by a synaptic transmission from another nerve cell or by heat, touch, or a wide range of other stimuli. The change in permeability permits sodium to pour in; and because of the positive charge of sodium, the inner surface of the membrane becomes momentarily positive and the outer surface negative, reversing the potential. This transitory negative charge, which progresses along the outer surface of the membrane like a burning fuse, is actually the nerve impulse.

The flow of sodium into the axon is followed, almost instantaneously, by a return to the original permeability. The Na^+ is then pumped out, and so the local negative charge of the inside of the axon is restored at this point. This change in electric potential of the membrane, which propagates the impulse, requires the exchange of only a relatively few sodium and potassium ions, so that the overall internal composition of the axon is scarcely affected. In living organisms, nerve cells are maintained in continuous firing condition.

99   *The Chemistry of the Living Cell*

1–57 *Nerve signals are thought to travel along the axon as pulses of reversed electric potential. In its resting state, the interior of the axon is negative in relation to the surrounding fluid. A change in the permeability of a small area of the axon membrane, triggered by a stimulus from the nerve dendrites, permits sodium ions (Na$^+$) to pass to the inside of the fiber, converting its standing negative charge to positive. After half a millisecond or less, the membrane begins to regain its resting property of excluding or pushing out sodium ions. At the same time, potassium ions (K$^+$) leak out, restoring the status quo. This can happen up to a thousand times a second, transmitting spikes of potential along the nerve.*

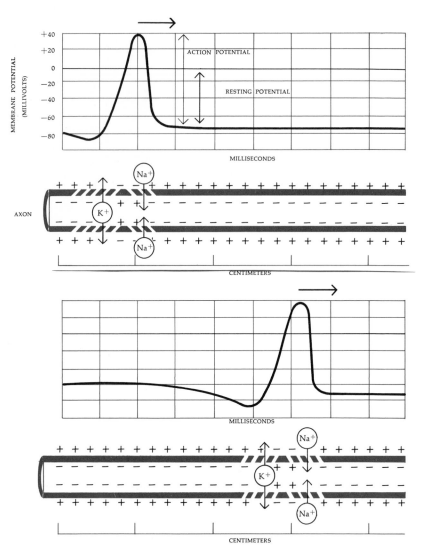

CHEMICAL BONDS

Molecular Bonds

Atoms may be held to one another by forces known as *chemical bonds*, and an assembly of atoms held together by chemical bonds is called a *molecule*. A molecule is made of two or more atoms; these atoms may be the same, as in the case of the oxygen molecule, which is composed of two atoms of oxygen, or they may be different. A molecule made of two or more kinds of atoms is known as a *compound*. Molecules may have quite different properties from those of their constituent atoms, just as atoms are quite different from protons, neutrons, or electrons. For example, wa-

100 CELLS

ter is very different from either hydrogen or oxygen; its component elements and its properties could not easily be deduced from those of the two elements.

There are two general types of chemical bonds which bind atoms into molecules: ionic bonds and covalent bonds.

IONIC BONDS

The most common type of bond in inorganic molecules is the ionic bond. Ionic bonds are formed between electropositive and electronegative atoms or groups of atoms. Sodium ions and chlorine ions, for example, are mutually attracted to one another, producing crystalline sodium chloride, NaCl (table salt). Ionic bonds may be formed between atoms that are already ionized, or the ions may be produced by electron exchanges between atoms. Sodium may lose an electron to chlorine, leaving sodium with a valence of $+1$ and chlorine with a valence of -1 (Figure 1–58a). The two oppositely charged particles then attract one another. In this process, you will note, sodium becomes oxidized and chlorine reduced. Magnesium tends to lose two electrons; since it then has a charge of $+2$, it has enough attractive force to hold two chlorine ions. Sodium chloride and other ionic salts crystallize in a lattice made up of alternating electropositive and electronegative ions, which gives the crystal great stability. (See Figure 1–58b.) When crystalline salts are dissolved in water, they tend to dissociate as ions.

COVALENT BONDS

Covalent bonds figure prominently in organic chemistry, which is essentially the chemistry of the first four elements listed in Table 1–1. This type of bond results from the sharing of a pair of electrons. Let us look at some of these covalent bonds. Each hydrogen atom, for instance, has one proton and one electron. The hydrogen atom needs one more electron to complete its outer shell. Each oxygen atom has eight protons and eight electrons. Two of the electrons are in the first shell, and six in the second shell; so oxygen needs two more electrons to stabilize its outer shell. If two hydrogen atoms share their electrons with one oxygen atom, this satisfies the requirements of all three, as shown in Figure 1–59. A nitrogen atom has seven protons, and so an uncharged atom of nitrogen has seven electrons, two in the inner shell and five in the outer shell. Nitrogen needs three electrons to fill its outer shell; hence it combines with three hydrogen atoms to make NH_3, which is ammonia (Figure 1–60). (As you may remember, ammonia was one of the gases in the primitive atmosphere.)

Notice that there is no sharp dividing line between ionic and covalent bonds. In most ionic bonds, there is some sharing of the electron or electrons donated from one atom to another; and many covalent bonds have some ionic (or polarized) character.

1–58 *How ionic bonds are formed. (a) When sodium and chlorine react, sodium loses the single electron in its outer shell and chlorine gains an electron to fill its outer shell so that the outer shell of each atom now has eight electrons. Sodium thus acquires a positive charge and chlorine a negative charge. (b) The oppositely charged Na$^+$ and Cl$^-$ ions attract each other strongly. Crystalline sodium chloride is made up of a lattice of alternating Na$^+$ and Cl$^-$ ions held together by their opposing charges.*

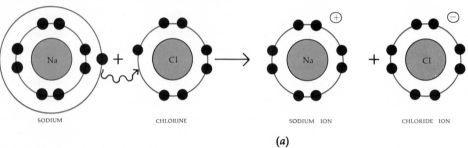

SODIUM   CHLORINE   SODIUM ION   CHLORIDE ION

(a)

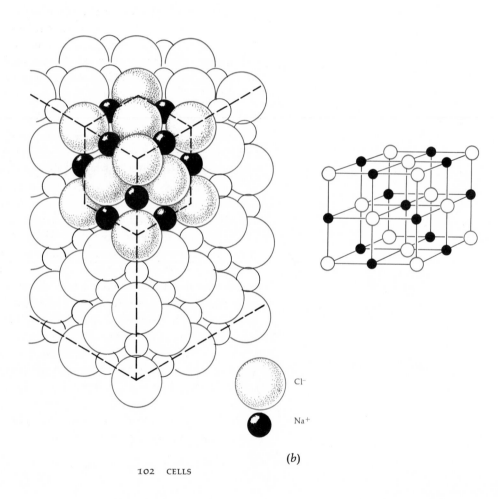

Cl$^-$

Na$^+$

(b)

1–59 *Covalent bonds result from the sharing of electrons. When two hydrogen atoms combine with an oxygen atom, they share their electrons with the un-filled outer orbital of the oxygen atom. In this way, all three atoms complete their outer shells.*

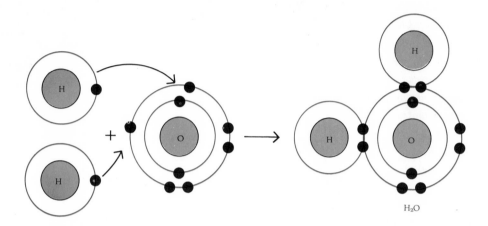

H_2O

1–60 *Hydrogen and nitrogen combine by covalent bonds to make ammonia.*

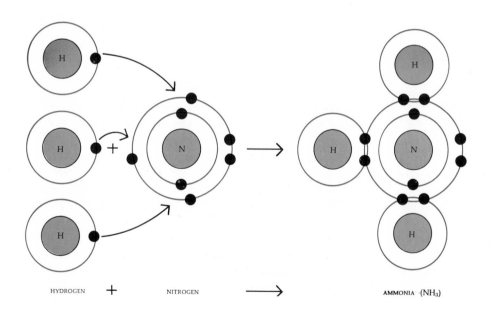

HYDROGEN + NITROGEN $\longrightarrow$ AMMONIA (NH_3)

1–61 (a) *The carbon atom, with four electrons in its outer shell, can form four covalent bonds simultaneously. For example, it combines with four hydrogen atoms to make methane. (b) The methane molecule forms the outline of a solid, four-sided pyramid known as a tetrahedron. The bond angles between the four hydrogen atoms are each 109° 28′. Shown here are three ways of representing this three-dimensional structure. This type of representation is very important in the chemistry of living things since reactions between molecules depend in large part on molecular configurations and bond angles. (c) Two-dimensional representations of other hydrocarbons formed by the electron-sharing tendency of carbon atoms.*

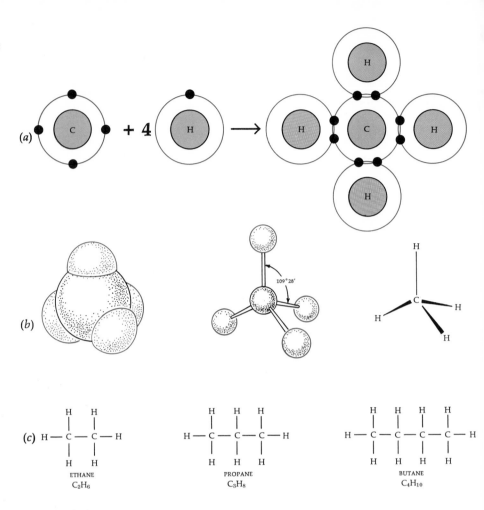

(a)

(b)

(c)

ETHANE
C_2H_6

PROPANE
C_3H_8

BUTANE
C_4H_{10}

1–62 *Some functional groups which play important roles as building blocks in organic compounds.*

— OH   HYDROXYL GROUP

— NH₂   AMINO GROUP

$-C-CH_3$ ACETYL GROUP
  $\parallel$
  O

$-C-OH$ CARBOXYL GROUP
  $\parallel$
  O

  OH
  |
$-O-P-OH$ PHOSPHATE GROUP
  $\parallel$
  O

CARBON-ATOM COMBINATIONS

A carbon atom has six protons and six electrons, two in the inner shell and four in the outer shell. This means that carbon does not tend either to gain or to lose electrons but usually forms covalent bonds. Since it is neither strongly electropositive nor strongly electronegative, it can combine both with electronegative elements such as oxygen, nitrogen, phosphorus, and sulfur and with the electropositive element hydrogen. Also, it can form four covalent bonds simultaneously. For these reasons, a tremendous variety of compounds can be built up from carbon atoms. Figure 1–61 shows a few of the combinations that carbon atoms can make with hydrogen atoms to form methane, ethane, propane, and butane; these are called *hydrocarbons*. Furthermore, carbon atoms can combine with each other to form very long chains or rings, which are the backbones of most organic molecules.

The only possible rival for carbon is silicon. Silicon has an atomic number of 14, so it, too, has four electrons in its outer shell. Because of its greater size and weight, however, silicon cannot form a gas with oxygen, and for this reason, it could not substitute for carbon in living systems as we know them. As we shall see, the flow of energy through the living world is dependent upon the capacity of plants and animals to exchange carbon dioxide with the atmosphere.

Functional Groups

Sometimes clusters of atoms joined by covalent bonds tend to move or react together as a group, as if they were a single atom. One class of such atomic clusters is represented by complex ions. Water, for example, has a slight tendency to dissociate into H^+ and the hydroxyl ion OH^- which behaves as a unit in acid-base reactions. A second class is represented by organic radicals, or functional groups, which play important roles as building units in organic compounds. Figure 1–62 shows some functional groups which occur repeatedly in organic molecules.

Weak Bonds

Certain types of weak bonds are important in biochemistry precisely because of their weakness. Since weak bonds are easily broken—in contrast to covalent bonds, which are much stronger—making and breaking such bonds require very little energy and may take place very rapidly. Yet weak bonds in large numbers can provide unions of great stability. Some types of weak bonds are based upon attractions between opposite electrical charges. Characteristically, such bonds do not bind atoms into molecules but serve as links between different molecules or between various areas in the same molecule. The most important weak bonds in biological systems are the hydrogen bond, the hydrophobic interaction, and the van der Waals bond.

HYDROGEN BONDS

The characteristic three-dimensional shape of some very important compounds, such as nucleic acids and proteins, results from hydrogen bonding. Hydrogen bonding is essentially an electrostatic bonding, and perhaps the easiest way to understand it is to look at a three-dimensional model of a molecule of water. As you can see in Figure 1–63, the oxygen atom and the two hydrogen atoms form a triangle. Since the electrons are more strongly attracted by the oxygen atom than by the hydrogen atoms, they tend to be located near the oxygen atom. As a result, the two hydrogen atoms of the water molecule carry a local positive charge and the oxygen atom a local negative charge, although the molecule as a whole is electrically neutral. Molecules which, like water, are positive at one end

1–63 *In the water molecule, the single electrons of the hydrogen atoms are shared with the oxygen atom and are located near the latter. As you can see in (a), this results in zones of local positive and negative charge, although the molecule as a whole is electrically neutral. The three-dimensional model in (b) shows the dipolar nature of the water molecule.*

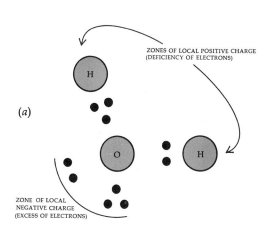

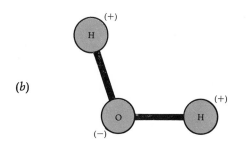

QUANTITATIVE MEASUREMENT IN CHEMICAL REACTIONS

The principal unit of measure used for defining quantities of substances involved in chemical reactions is the mole. *The number of particles in 1 mole of any substance (whether atoms, ions, or molecules) is always the same: 6.023×10^{23}. For example, 1 mole of water (H_2O) contains 6.023×10^{23} water molecules, and 1 mole of glucose ($C_6H_{12}O_6$) contains 6.023×10^{23} glucose molecules. This constant is known as the Avogadro number.*

The variable here is, obviously, the amount *of substance that constitutes 1 mole, and this is based on the molecular weight of the substance, which is, in turn, determined by the atomic weights of the constituent atoms. A few more definitions will help to explain what we mean:*

1 *Molecular weight is the sum of the atomic weights of all the atoms in a molecule.*

2 *The* atomic weight *of an atom is approximately equal to the number of its protons and neutrons, counting each as 1. Actually, atomic weights are based on physical measurements of the elements, relative to some one element which is taken as a standard. Today, the standard generally used is carbon (C^{12}), with an atomic weight of 12 (six protons and six neutrons). Hypothetically, an element exactly twice as heavy as carbon would have an atomic weight of 24; an element one-half as heavy, 6.*

3 *Since atoms are much too small to be weighed individually, they are measured in amounts called* gram atoms. *One gram atom of an element is that amount of the element which equals, in grams, its atomic weight. For example, 1 gram atom of carbon is that amount of carbon that weighs 12 grams, and 1 gram atom of hydrogen weighs about 1 gram (actually 1.008 gram).*

4 *A* gram molecule *is the amount of a substance which equals, in grams, its molecular weight. One gram molecule of oxygen gas (O_2) weighs 32 grams, and one gram molecule of hydrogen gas (H_2) weighs about 2 grams.*

It should now be clear that 1 mole of any substance equals 1 gram molecule of that substance and contains 6.023×10^{23} molecules.

In order to make water, one would combine 2 moles of hydrogen (4 grams) with 1 mole of oxygen (32 grams); in other words, four hydrogen atoms for every two oxygen atoms. Two moles of water would be produced, each weighing 18 grams. Similarly, to make table salt (NaCl), one would add 1 gram atom of sodium (about 23 grams) and 1 gram atom of chlorine (about 35.5 grams).

and negative at the other are said to be *polar*. Polar molecules are generally soluble in water since the electrostatic attraction of opposite charges tends to align the water molecules around them.

When the positively charged hydrogen atom of the water molecule comes in juxtaposition with an atom carrying a sufficiently strong electronegative charge—such as the oxygen atom in another water molecule —the force of the attraction forms a bond between them which is known as the *hydrogen bond*.

As shown in Figure 1–64, the molecules in water are held together in a shifting latticework by the interaction of many hydrogen bonds, any one of which has only an exceedingly short lifetime (about 10^{-11} second). This makes it possible for water to show strong intermolecular attractions and yet not be very viscous, an arrangement that is responsible for many of its unusual properties. For instance, water has a relatively high boiling point for a liquid. As a consequence, it is a liquid at ordinary temperatures. Yet, it is very fluid, capable of spreading thin on surfaces, of making its way through minute cracks in the earth where it can be found by plant roots, and of traveling through the fine capillaries of plant and animal tissues.

Hydrogen bonds tend to form between any hydrogen atom which is covalently bonded to oxygen or to nitrogen and any strongly electronegative atom, usually oxygen or nitrogen, in another molecule or in another part of the same molecule. An important feature of the hydrogen bond is that it always has a specific length and a specific direction. If the bond is stable at all, its geometry is really very precise, as you can see in Figure 1–64. Bond lengths differ from one hydrogen-bonding system to another, depending on the structural geometry and electron distribution of the molecules involved. For example, in ice, the length of the hydrogen bond is 1.77 angstroms and the average distance between oxygen atoms is 2.76 angstroms; in liquid water, the average oxygen–oxygen distance is 3.05 angstroms at 83°C. The direction of the bond is determined by the specific location of the bonding orbitals around the electronegative acceptor atoms (oxygen or nitrogen).

HYDROPHOBIC INTERACTIONS

Some of the molecular components of cells, tissues, and body fluids are only slightly soluble in water, yet these hydrophobic ("water-fearing") compounds can be "dissolved" in the aqueous solutions of organisms and transported in and out of cells. This is due to a weak association, known as *hydrophobic interaction*, which forms between hydrophobic substances in water.

In hydrophobic interactions, the insoluble substance is dispersed in the water in the form of small particles called *micelles*. The polar groups in

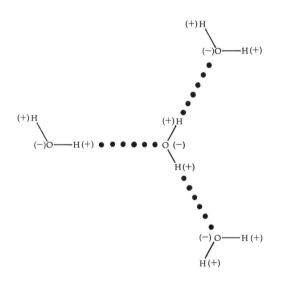

1–64 *Water molecules are held together in a shifting latticework by the interaction of many hydrogen bonds, indicated by black dots. These bonds are produced by the electrostatic attraction between the positively charged zone on the hydrogen atom of one molecule and the negatively charged zone on the oxygen atom of another. The fact that each individual hydrogen bond is very short-lived, lasting only about 10^{-11} second, gives water its unique property of being very fluid and yet stable, with a relatively high boiling point and low vapor pressure.*

the substance remain on the outer surface of the micelle, exposed to the water and forming hydrogen bonds with it. The nonpolar, hydrophobic parts are tucked inside the micelle, hidden from contact with the water. The hydrophobic association is a consequence of the tendency of the surrounding water molecules to hydrogen-bond with each other more readily than they will interact with the nonpolar structures.

Sodium stearate, for example, is a soap which has very little tendency to dissolve in water. However, it does, in fact, go into apparent solution in water in the form of micelles. In each micelle, the highly polar carboxyl groups are on the outside and the nonpolar, insoluble chains are hidden within the micelle structure.

Unlike hydrogen bonds, hydrophobic interactions have relatively little specificity and directionality. They do, however, produce systems of very high stability, such as the cell membranes.

VAN DER WAALS BONDS

Van der Waals bonds are weaker than hydrogen bonds and only act between molecules that are brought very close together. The bonds result not from any permanent charge separations (as in hydrogen bonds) but from the fluctuating charges caused by the nearness of the molecules; they therefore operate between all types of molecules, both polar and nonpolar. If the molecules are brought too close to each other, the attraction forces are overcome by repulsion forces, caused by the overlapping of the outer shells of the atoms involved. For this reason, the strongest van der Waals bond occurs when one of the molecules contains a cavity which exactly complements a protruding group on the other molecule. Van der Waals bonds are the attractive forces in enzyme-substrate combinations (page 130).

CHEMICAL REACTIONS

Chemical compounds, as we have seen, are formed by bonds which result from the giving over or the sharing of electrons. All chemical reactions involve the breaking of such bonds and the formation of new bonds.

Types of Reactions

All chemical reactions can be classified into a few general types. One type can be represented by the formula $A + B \rightarrow AB$. An example of this sort of reaction is the combination of hydrogen gas with oxygen gas to produce water. Hydrogen gas is H_2, and oxygen gas is O_2. However, we know that each molecule of water contains 2 atoms of hydrogen and one of oxygen. We can, therefore, write the following balanced equation:

$$2H_2 + O_2 \rightarrow 2H_2O$$

The principle of balancing equations is familiar to you from elementary algebra. The advantage of the balanced equation in chemistry is that it shows not only the components of the reaction but how much of each component is required to complete the reaction.

A reaction may also take the form $AB \rightarrow A + B$. For example, the equation above showing the formation of water can be reversed:

$$2H_2O \rightarrow 2H_2 + O_2.$$

This means that from water you can obtain hydrogen and oxygen. The fact that a reaction is reversible can be indicated by double arrows:

$$2H_2 + O_2 \rightleftharpoons 2H_2O$$

A reaction may also involve an exchange, taking the form:

$$AB + CD \rightarrow AD + CB$$

An example of such a reaction is the combination of hydrochloric acid and sodium hydroxide to make table salt and water:

$$HCl + NaOH \rightarrow H_2O + NaCl$$

Hydrochloric acid can also react with magnesium hydroxide. In this case, magnesium chloride and water are produced. Can you write the equation for this reaction in a balanced form?

One of the most important reactions in biology, and one which we have already mentioned, is the combination of carbon dioxide and water to yield glucose and free oxygen, a reaction which takes place in the green plant. Glucose is $C_6H_{12}O_6$. With a little experimenting, we find that the equation for this reaction balances if we begin with six molecules of carbon dioxide and six of water:

$$6CO_2 + 6H_2O \rightarrow C_6H_{12}O_6 + 6O_2$$

The Energy Factor

Although the equations as written above are balanced in terms of their chemical components, one crucial factor is missing from each of them. This factor is *energy*. All chemical reactions involve changes in energy. More specifically, chemical reactions generally proceed in such a way as to cause a loss of energy to the surroundings. The end products of chemical reactions that proceed spontaneously contain less energy than was present in the starting molecules. For example, the combination of hydrogen and oxygen molecules to make water liberates energy. On the other hand, the separation of water into hydrogen and oxygen requires energy and hence does not proceed by itself. Similarly, the oxidation of glucose or any other carbon compound to carbon dioxide and water liberates energy. We know this from everyday experience: If we touch a match to many

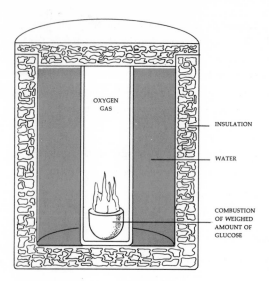

1–65 *A calorimeter is a device for measuring the amount of heat produced by biochemical reactions. A known amount of glucose is placed in the crucible and burned. The heat released causes the temperature of the surrounding water to rise. From the known weight of the water and the rise in its temperature, the heat of combustion of the glucose can be calculated in terms of calories. A calorie is the amount of heat required to raise the temperature of 1 gram of water 1° C.*

OXYGEN GAS

INSULATION

WATER

COMBUSTION OF WEIGHED AMOUNT OF GLUCOSE

carbon compounds, such as natural gas, petroleum, or coal, we start a reaction in which large amounts of energy are liberated in the form of heat.

The heat changes taking place during chemical or biochemical reactions can be measured very precisely by means of a *calorimeter*. In the calorimeter, as shown in Figure 1–65, energy released by the reaction is transferred to the water jacket surrounding the flask and measured in the terms of *calories*. A calorie is by definition the amount of heat necessary to raise the temperature of 1 gram of water 1°C. As we shall see, the living cell is organized so that this loss of energy through heat is kept to a minimum.

ENDERGONIC AND EXERGONIC REACTIONS

A reaction that requires energy is known as *endergonic* (from the Greek *endon*, meaning "within," and *ergon*, meaning "work") since energy must be put into it. A reaction that liberates energy is an *exergonic* reaction. To return to our analogy of the boulder and the hill, an endergonic reaction is an "uphill" reaction and an exergonic reaction is a "downhill" reaction. Only exergonic (downhill) reactions can proceed spontaneously. Endergonic reactions do not occur by themselves; they must be coupled to some downhill process in such a way that the energy released by the downhill process is larger than the energy required for the uphill process. In living systems, the uphill and downhill movements are often accomplished in very small stages, so that large amounts of energy are not required or released all at once.

Even in a downhill reaction, a certain amount of energy is needed to start the reaction. The lighting of a match by friction provides the energy of activation for the rapid oxidation of carbon compounds, and a slight push is the energy of activation required by the boulder perched on top of the hill. In chemical laboratories, energy of activation is usually supplied by heat, which serves to set the molecules in motion so they can begin to interact with one another. Once the interaction begins, an exergonic reaction often becomes self-sustaining by the heat energy it produces.

Chemical Equilibrium

All chemical reactions that are reversible will go on so long as the molecules of reactant and product are present in the system. This is because reversible reactions reach a point of *dynamic equilibrium*, at which no further net chemical change takes place. When that point is reached, the rate of forward reaction is equal to the rate of reverse reaction; thereafter, the reaction will continue in both directions until some other process intervenes. For example, in the reaction:

$$A \rightarrow B$$

the point of equilibrium is reached when as many molecules of B are being converted to molecules of A as molecules of A are being converted to molecules of B. This is expressed as:

$$A \rightleftharpoons B$$

The concentration of reactant (A) does *not* have to equal the concentration of product (B) in order for equilibrium to be established; only the rates of the forward and reverse reactions must be the same. Consider the reaction:

$$A + B \rightleftharpoons C + D$$

The different lengths of the arrows indicate that the conversion of A + B to C + D occurs more readily than the conversion of C + D to A + B. In other words, less energy is required for A and B to interact than for C and D to interact in a given period of time and at the same concentrations. At first, then, the reaction occurs primarily to the right, with many more (A + B) molecules converting to (C + D) molecules. Figure 1–66 shows the relative changes in concentration as the reaction continues. As C and D accumulate, the rate of the reverse reaction increases, and at the same time, the rate of the forward reaction decreases because of the decreasing concentrations of A and B. At about time 6, the rates of the forward and reverse reactions equalize and no further changes in concentration take place. The proportions of A + B and C + D will remain the same, but there will always be more C and D molecules in the system.

Nearly all biochemical reactions are reversible and so could exist in a state of dynamic equilibrium. But a living system requires a continuous one-way production and breakdown of molecules in order to carry out its activities; if all metabolic processes were to attain equilibrium, death would result. Biochemical reactions generally take place in a series of steps; from original reactant to final product, a number of intermediate reactions and products are almost always involved. The overall reactions are kept going in one direction because the product from each individual reaction is used as the reactant for the next reaction in the series. This can be represented as:

$$A \rightleftharpoons B \rightleftharpoons C \rightleftharpoons D \rightleftharpoons E \text{ (End product)}$$

Acids and Bases

The terms "acid" and "base" were used long before the chemistry of these properties was known. Acids taste sour, like sour milk, citrus fruits, and vinegar. Bases taste bitter and flat, like milk of magnesia, and feel slippery and soapy in solution.

1–66 *The changes in concentration of products and reactants in a reversible reaction. At first, only molecules of A and B are present. The reaction begins when A and B start to yield products C and D. At the end of two minutes, the concentrations of A + B and C + D are equal. Because the energy required for the forward reaction is less than that required for the reverse reaction, the concentration of C + D will continue to increase to the point of chemical equilibrium (at about the sixth minute) and will thereafter remain greater than the concentration of A + B. This is the proportion at which the rates of forward and reverse reactions are the same.*

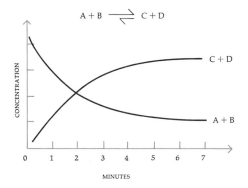

$$A + B \rightleftharpoons C + D$$

CONCENTRATION

C + D

A + B

0   1   2   3   4   5   6   7

MINUTES

To understand "acid" and "base" in chemical terms, we shall first look at water. Water, as you know, consists of two atoms of hydrogen and one of oxygen held together by covalent bonds. Water molecules also have a slight tendency to ionize, separating into H^+ and OH^- In any given volume of pure water, a very small but constant number of water molecules will be dissociated in this form. The number is constant because the tendency of water to dissociate is exactly offset by the tendency of the ions to reunite; thus even as some are ionizing, an equal number of others are forming covalent bonds. This is a state of dynamic equilibrium.

In pure water, the number of H^+ ions exactly equals the number of OH^- ions. This is necessarily the case since neither ion can be formed without the other when only H_2O molecules are present. A solution acquires the properties we recognize as acid when the number of H^+ ions exceeds the number of OH^- ions; conversely, a solution is basic when the OH^- ions exceed the H^+ ions. There is always an inverse relationship between the concentration of H^+ and OH^- ions; when H^+ is high, OH^- is low, and vice versa. This is because the product of their concentrations is a constant.

$$H^+ \times OH^- = 1 \times 10^{-14} \qquad \text{at } 25°C$$

DEFINITIONS

We can now define our terms chemically:

1   An *acid* is a substance which donates H^+ ions to a solution. Since an H^+ ion is really a proton, acids can also be defined as *proton donors.*

2   A *base* is a substance which decreases the number of H^+ ions, or protons. More specifically, a base is a *proton acceptor.* The OH^- ion is a base because it can accept a proton and thus be neutralized:

$$H^+ + OH^- \rightarrow H_2O$$

3   In any acid-base reaction, there is always a proton donor and a proton acceptor.

STRONG AND WEAK ACIDS AND BASES

Hydrochloric acid (HCl) is an example of a common acid. It is a strong acid, meaning that it tends to be almost completely ionized. Sodium hydroxide (NaOH) is a common strong base; it exists entirely as Na^+ and OH^-. Weak acids and weak bases are those which ionize only slightly. Compounds which contain the carboxyl group (COOH) are weak acids since some of the COOH compound (R–COOH) dissociates to yield hydrogen ions when dissolved in water:

$$R\text{–}COOH \rightleftharpoons R\text{–}COO^- + H^+$$

Compounds which contain the amino group $-NH_2$ act as weak bases since the NH_2 has a weak tendency to accept hydrogen ions, thereby forming NH_3^+:

$$R-NH_2 + H^+ \rightleftharpoons R-NH_3^+$$

Because of the strong tendency of H^+ and OH^- to combine and the weak tendency of water to ionize, the product of their concentrations is a very small and constant number, as we noted previously; therefore the concentration of H^+ ions will always decrease as the concentration of OH^- increases, and vice versa. If HCl is added to a solution in which NaOH is present, the following reaction will take place:

$$Na^+ + OH^- + H^+ + Cl^- \rightarrow H_2O + Na^+ + Cl^-$$

If the acid and base are added in equivalent amounts, the solution will once more be neutral. This is another characteristic of acids and bases: Added together, they produce a salt and water.

THE pH SCALE

Chemists define degrees of acidity by means of the pH scale. The Danish biochemist Sören Sörensen, who originated the expression "pH," meant the p to stand for "power" and the H to stand for the hydrogen ion.

In a liter of pure water, 1/10,000,000 mole of hydrogen ions can be detected. For convenience, this is written in terms of a power, 10^{-7}; and in terms of the pH scale, this is referred to simply as pH 7 (see Table 1–2). At pH 7, the concentrations of free H^+ and OH^- ions are exactly the same, and thus pure water is "neutral." Any pH below 7 is acidic, and any pH above 7 is basic. The lower the pH number, the higher the concentration of hydrogen ions. Thus pH 2 means 10^{-2} mole of hydrogen ions per liter of water, or 1/100 mole per liter—which is, of course, a much larger figure than 1/10,000,000.

BUFFERS

It is possible to get solutions more acidic than pH 1 or more basic than pH 14, but these are not included in the scale because they are almost never encountered in biological systems. In fact, almost all the chemistry of living things takes place at a pH of between 6 and 8, with the notable exception of the chemical processes in the stomach of man and other animals, which have a pH of about 2, and in food vacuoles. The blood, for instance, maintains an almost constant pH of 7.4 despite the fact that it is the vehicle for a large number and variety of nutrients and other chemicals being delivered to the cells and for the removal of wastes, many of which are acids or bases. Organisms resist strong sudden changes in the pH of blood and the fluids, both intracellular and extracellular, by means of *buffer systems*.

1–67 *Some weak acids and bases.*

SOME WEAK ACIDS (PROTON DONORS)

$$HCOOH \longrightarrow HCOO^- + H^+$$
FORMIC ACID — FORMATE ION — PROTON

$$CH_3COOH \longrightarrow CH_3COO^- + H^+$$
ACETIC ACID — ACETATE ION

$$CH_3-CH-COOH \longrightarrow CH_3CHCOO^- + H^+$$
$$\quad\quad |\quad\quad\quad\quad\quad\quad\quad\quad |$$
$$\quad\quad OH\quad\quad\quad\quad\quad\quad\quad OH$$
LACTIC ACID — LACTATE ION

SOME WEAK BASES (PROTON ACCEPTORS)

$$NH_3 + H^+ \longrightarrow NH_4^+$$
AMMONIA — PROTON — AMMONIUM ION

$$CH_3NH_2 + H^+ \longrightarrow CH_3NH_3^+$$
METHYLAMINE — METHYLAMMONIUM ION

Table 1–2 *The pH Scale*

	Concentration of H$^+$ ions (moles per liter)		pH	Concentration of OH$^-$ ions (moles per liter)	
	1.0	10^0	0	10^{-14}	
	0.1	10^{-1}	1	10^{-13}	
	0.01	10^{-2}	2	10^{-12}	
Acidic	0.001	10^{-3}	3	10^{-11}	
	0.0001	10^{-4}	4	10^{-10}	
	0.00001	10^{-5}	5	10^{-9}	
	0.000001	10^{-6}	6	10^{-8}	
Neutral	0.0000001	10^{-7}	7	10^{-7}	Neutral
		10^{-8}	8	10^{-6}	0.000001
		10^{-9}	9	10^{-5}	0.00001
		10^{-10}	10	10^{-4}	0.0001
Basic		10^{-11}	11	10^{-3}	0.001
		10^{-12}	12	10^{-2}	0.01
		10^{-13}	13	10^{-1}	0.1
		10^{-14}	14	10^0	1.0

A buffer is a combination of the proton-donor and proton-acceptor forms of weak acids or bases. The capacity of a buffer system to resist changes in pH is greatest when the concentrations of proton-donor and proton-acceptor are equal. As the ratio changes in either direction, the buffer becomes less effective.

The major buffer system of vertebrate blood plasma is the acid-base pair H_2CO_3–HCO_3^-. The weak acid H_2CO_3 (carbonic acid) dissociates into H^+ and bicarbonate ions as follows:

$$H_2CO_3 \text{ (proton donor)} \rightleftharpoons H^+ + HCO_3^- \text{ (proton acceptor)}$$

The H_2CO_3–HCO_3^- buffer system resists the changes in pH that might result from the addition of small amounts of acid or base by "soaking" up the acid or base. If a small amount of H^+ in the form of HCl is added to the system, it combines with the proton acceptor HCO_3^- to form H_2CO_3. If a small amount of OH^- is added, it combines with the H^+ to form H_2O; more H_2CO_3 tends to ionize to replace the H^+ as it is used.

Control of the pH of the blood is rendered even "tighter" by the fact that the H_2CO_3 is in equilibrium with dissolved CO_2 in the blood:

$$H_2O + CO_2 \rightleftharpoons H_2CO_3$$

Dissolved CO_2 in the blood is, in turn, in equilibrium with the CO_2 of the air in the lungs. Retention or loss of the CO_2 in the lungs, by change in the rate of breathing, can change the H_2CO_3 concentration in the blood and thus help control pH.

Obviously, if the blood should be flooded with a very large excess of acid or base, the buffer will fail, but normally it is able to adjust continuously and instantaneously to the constant small additions of acid or base which normally occur in body fluids.

SUMMARY

Studies of the chemistry of living things have shown that living systems obey the same physical and chemical laws as nonliving systems. We began this discussion of cell chemistry with electrons and atoms because the principles which govern these basic units of matter explain a great deal about the nature of life.

The nucleus of any atom contains one or more protons, which are positively charged, and neutrons, which have no charge. The net positive charge of the nucleus (which is the same as the atomic number of that element) is offset by the negatively charged electrons that surround it. For an atom to be electrically neutral, the number of electrons surrounding the nucleus must equal the number of protons within it.

Electrons can be found at fixed distances from the nucleus; these distances constitute *electron shells,* which have different energy levels. Each shell can accommodate only a fixed number of electrons—the first shell, two; the second, eight; and every outer shell, no more than eight. Atoms tend to stabilize, or complete their shells, and the number of electrons an atom (or molecule) must gain or lose to accomplish this is its *valence.* In general, atoms with less than four electrons in the outer shell lose these electrons (oxidation), thus acquiring a positive charge, and atoms with more than four gain electrons (reduction), acquiring a negative charge. Electrically charged atoms or groups of atoms are called *ions* or *electrolytes,* and many of the inorganic chemical components of the living organism are in this state.

Molecules are formed of two or more atoms bound together by chemical bonds. The two general types of chemical bonds which bind atoms into molecules are ionic bonds, which are formed between atoms of opposite electrical charges, and covalent bonds, which result from the sharing of electrons. The carbon atom, which usually forms covalent bonds, is extremely important in living systems because (1) it can combine with both electropositive and electronegative elements; (2) it can form four covalent bonds simultaneously, making possible a tremendous number of compounds; and (3) it can combine with other carbon atoms to form long chains or rings.

Weak bonds are based on attractions between electrical charges. Generally, weak bonds do not bind atoms to one another but serve as links between molecules or between various areas in the molecule. The most important weak bonds are the hydrogen bonds, the hydrophobic interactions, and the van der Waals bonds.

All *chemical reactions* involve the breaking of bonds and the formation of new bonds, and all involve changes in energy. An *endergonic* reaction requires energy; an *exergonic* reaction liberates energy. Reversible reactions may reach a point of *dynamic equilibrium*, at which the rates of forward and reverse reaction are equal and no further net chemical change takes place. In most biological systems, however, the products of any one reaction are removed by a further reaction, so reactions proceed in sequence.

An *acid* is a substance which donates H^+ ions to a solution; a *base* is a substance which decreases the proportion of H^+ ions (adds OH^- ions) to a solution. The degree of acidity of a solution is measured in terms of the pH scale. In living systems, only very slight changes in the pH of the intracellular and extracellular fluids and of the blood can be tolerated. The almost constant pH of these substances is achieved by means of buffer systems, which are combinations of the proton-donor and proton-acceptor forms of weak acids or bases.

Biological Molecules

In this chapter, we shall discuss some of the organic compounds which cells manufacture and use. Organic compounds are the principal materials from which cell structures are formed and which cells use in their metabolic functions. (The word "metabolism" means the sum of all chemical activities within a living organism.) These "materials of life," which all contain the element carbon, are of four basic types: (1) *Carbohydrates* serve as the primary chemical-energy source for almost every form of life. (2) *Lipids* (fats and fatlike substances) are another important source of energy and also of structural materials for the cell. (3) *Proteins* serve both as structural elements and as regulators or catalysts in cell processes. (4) *Nucleic acids*, directly or indirectly, build the proteins.

Because their energy-supplying functions are basically the same in all living systems, one organism's carbohydrates and lipids are much like those of any other organism. The proteins and nucleic acids of each species, on the other hand, are probably unique—just as the organism itself is unique. Coded in the long sequences of molecular building blocks that make up these macromolecules (*macro* means "large") is the genetic information specific for species and for function. For this reason, proteins and nucleic acids are sometimes called *informational macromolecules*.

Carbohydrates

Carbohydrates are compounds which contain carbon combined with hydrogen and oxygen in the proportion of one carbon atom to two hydrogen atoms to one oxygen atom. The simplest carbohydrates are the *monosaccharides* ("single" sugars), made up of a chain of carbon atoms to which H and O atoms are attached. Monosaccharides with three carbon atoms are trioses, four-carbon sugars are tetroses, five-carbon sugars are pentoses,

1–68 *Some important monosaccharides. The five- and six-carbon sugars, as shown here, are found in both chain and ring forms. In the latter, the heavy bonds of the ring project forward of the plane of the page; the light bonds of the ring project behind the page. By convention, the carbon atoms in the ring forms are not labeled.*

1–69 *Sugar molecules are asymmetrical and can exist either in "left-handed" or "right-handed" forms, which are mirror images of one another. Two ways of depicting the three-dimensional structures of the two forms of glyceraldehyde are shown.*

	GLYCERALDEHYDE $C_3H_6O_3$	RIBOSE $C_5H_{10}O_5$	GLUCOSE $C_6H_{12}O_6$	FRUCTOSE $C_6H_{12}O_6$
OPEN-CHAIN STRUCTURE	(structure shown)	(structure shown)	(structure shown)	(structure shown)
PROJECTIONS OF THE STRUCTURE OF THE RING FORMS		(ring structure)	(ring structure)	(ring structure)

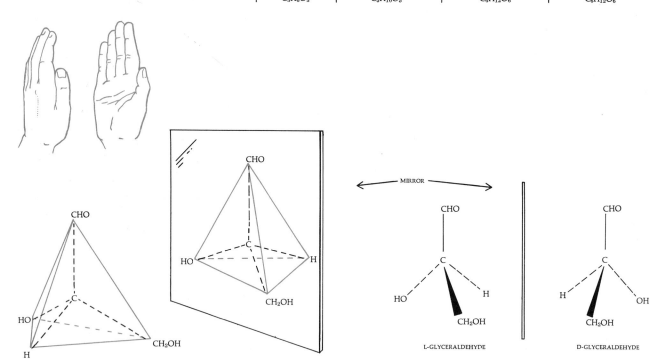

L-GLYCERALDEHYDE   D-GLYCERALDEHYDE

MIRROR

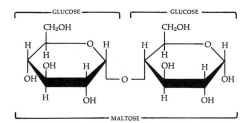

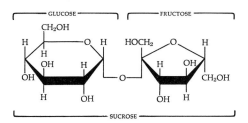

1–70 *Monosaccharides are the basic carbo-hydrate structural units from which the larger carbohydrates are built. The joining of two monosaccharide molecules yields a double sugar, or disaccharide. Two molecules of glucose, for example, combine to form maltose, and glucose and fructose form ordinary table sugar, sucrose.*

and six-carbon sugars are hexoses. Examples of some common monosaccharides are shown in Figure 1–68. As the figure indicates, the five- and six-carbon sugars can also exist in ring form; in fact, they are normally found in this form when they are dissolved in water.

Sugar molecules are asymmetrical, as can be seen in the simple example of glyceraldehyde shown in Figure 1–69. Asymmetrical compounds can exist in either a "left-handed" or a "right-handed" form, known as L form and D form, respectively. If glucose is synthesized in the laboratory, both left-handed and right-handed forms will be produced. In nature, however, only the right-handed form of glucose is found. Why did living things "decide" on one type instead of the other? Is this again evidence that all life derived from one common source? Or did all organisms making left-handed sugars somehow get weeded out in the process of evolution? In either case, the end result is an economic one. If plants made two types of sugars in photosynthesis, living things would have to have two separate metabolic systems in order to utilize both of them.

GLUCOSE

Sugar is generally transported through plant and animal systems as a monosaccharide or a disaccharide. In vertebrates, the principal monosaccharide is glucose. Two molecules of glucose and other monosaccharides can combine to form disaccharides (Figure 1–70); larger numbers of molecules combine to form polysaccharides (Figure 1–71). As you can see in Figure 1–70, the union is accomplished by the removal of a molecule of water from each pair of sugar molecules joined. Polysaccharides are a general storage form for sugar molecules; such molecules can be broken apart again by *hydrolysis*, the addition of a molecule of water at each linkage, to form monosaccharide units again.

1–71 *Linkage of D-glucose units in glycogen, a polysaccharide. The glycogen molecule may contain several hundred glucose units, which form long, branching chains as shown below.*

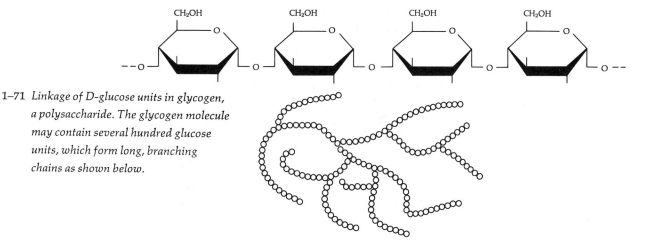

A combination of two glucose units forms the disaccharide maltose (malt sugar); a combination of glucose and fructose forms sucrose (cane sugar), which is our common table sugar. The most common polysaccharides are glycogen, starch, and cellulose, all of which are made of different arrangements of the glucose molecule in long chains. Glycogen is the chief storage form of carbohydrates in animals, and starch is the chief storage form in plants.

Lipids

Lipids are a diverse group of compounds which are generally insoluble in water.

FATS

One of the principal lipids is natural fat, which is used as a storage compound. Fat can be taken in directly in the diet, or glucose or other nutrient molecules can be converted into fat in the cell. Fat consists of fatty acids joined to a glycerol molecule (Figure 1–72). Fatty acids are made up of long hydrocarbon chains which carry a terminal carboxyl group, giving them the characteristics of a weak acid. The glycerol forms a link with the carboxyl group, releasing a molecule of water. (Like the polysaccharides and the proteins, fats are broken down by hydrolysis.) The glycerol thus serves as a binder or carrier for the fatty acids. The physical nature of the fat is determined by the chain lengths of the fatty acids and by whether the acids are *saturated* or *unsaturated*. Unsaturated fatty acids contain carbon atoms linked together by covalent bonds involving two pairs of shared electrons. Such bonds are known as *double bonds*. Carbon atoms linked by double bonds are able to form additional bonds with other atoms (hence the term "unsaturated"). Unsaturated fats tend to be oily liquids at body temperature; an example is olive oil. Fats, such as lard, containing saturated fatty acids usually have higher melting temperatures.

PHOSPHOLIPIDS

Closely related to the fats are various compounds in which glycerol is attached to only two fatty acids, with the third space occupied by a molecule containing phosphorus and nitrogen. Such compounds are known as *phospholipids*. They are very important in cellular structure, particularly in the membranes of cells.

The polar phosphate ends of the molecule are soluble in water, while the fatty acids are not (Figure 1–73). If phospholipids are added to water, they tend to form a film along its surface, with their polar heads under the water and the insoluble fatty acid chains protruding above the surface (Figure 1–74a). In the watery interior of the cell, the phospholipids tend to align themselves in rows, with the insoluble fatty acids oriented toward one another and the phosphate ends directed outward (Figure 1–74b). It is

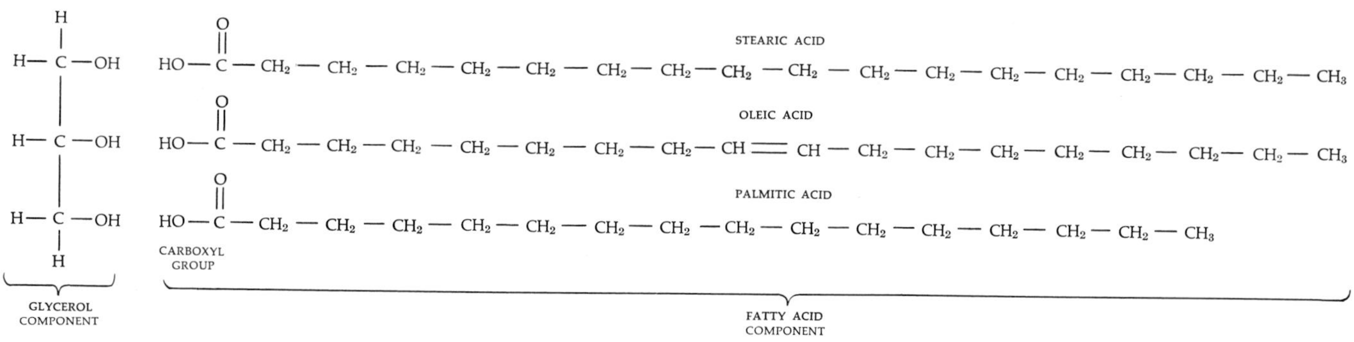

H—C—OH   O‖   STEARIC ACID
         HO—C—CH₂—CH₂—CH₂—CH₂—CH₂—CH₂—CH₂—CH₂—CH₂—CH₂—CH₂—CH₂—CH₂—CH₂—CH₂—CH₂—CH₃

H—C—OH   O‖   OLEIC ACID
         HO—C—CH₂—CH₂—CH₂—CH₂—CH₂—CH₂—CH₂—CH══CH—CH₂—CH₂—CH₂—CH₂—CH₂—CH₂—CH₂—CH₃

H—C—OH   O‖   PALMITIC ACID
         HO—C—CH₂—CH₂—CH₂—CH₂—CH₂—CH₂—CH₂—CH₂—CH₂—CH₂—CH₂—CH₂—CH₂—CH₂—CH₃
   H
        CARBOXYL
        GROUP

GLYCEROL COMPONENT   FATTY ACID COMPONENT

1–72 *A fat molecule consists of fatty acids joined to a glycerol molecule. The long hydrocarbon chains of which the fatty acids are composed terminate in carboxyl groups, which link with the glycerol molecule. The physical nature of the fat is determined by the lengths of the chains and by whether its component fatty acids are saturated or unsaturated. Three different fatty acids are shown here. Stearic acid is saturated, and oleic acid is unsaturated, as you can see by the double bond in its structure.*

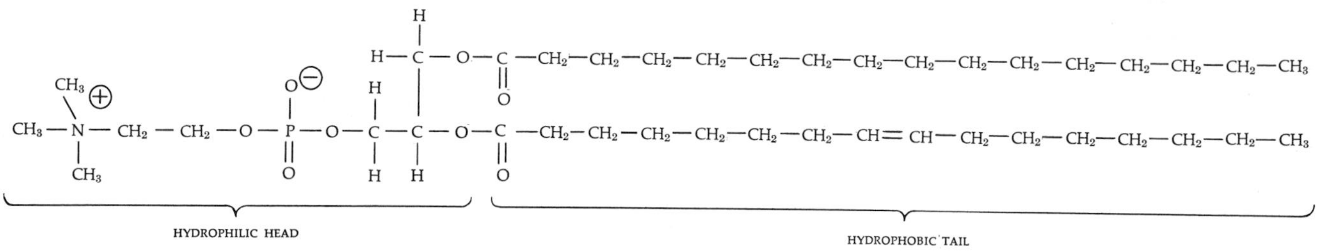

CH₃⊕
 \
CH₃—N—CH₂—CH₂—O—P—O—C—C—O—C—CH₂—CH₂—CH₂—CH₂—CH₂—CH₂—CH══CH—CH₂—CH₂—CH₂—CH₂—CH₂—CH₂—CH₃
 |
CH₃

HYDROPHILIC HEAD   HYDROPHOBIC TAIL

1–73 *A phospholipid molecule, showing its polar, or hydrophilic, head and its non-polar, or hydrophobic, tail. The glycerol molecule is attached to two fatty acids (instead of three, as in fats), with the third space occupied by a phosphate group attached to a nitrogenous compound.*

this configuration that is believed to form the inner layer of the three-ply unit-membrane structure characteristic of all cellular membranes. The outer layers are composed of globular proteins and polysaccharides.

CAROTENOIDS

The carotenoids, an important group of red and yellow plant pigments, are classified with the lipids since they, too, are oily and insoluble in water. Carotenoids are found in all plant cells, including one-celled plants such as *Euglena*. They are generally associated with *phototropism*, the orientation of plants toward light.

121   *Biological Molecules*

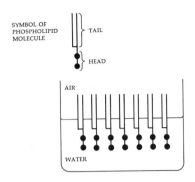

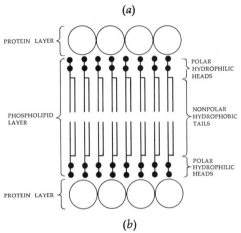

1–74 *Phospholipid molecules tend to form a film on the surface of water* (a), *with their polar "heads" under the surface of the water and their nonpolar "tails" protruding above the surface. In the cell, they tend to align themselves in rows, with the tails oriented toward one another and the heads pointing outward. This configuration is believed to form the middle layer of the three-ply unit membrane, as shown in* (b).

Carotene

The structure of the most common of the carotenoids, carotene, is shown at the top of Figure 1–75. From one molecule of beta carotene two molecules of the compound we call vitamin A can be formed. Vitamin A, like other vitamins, is a substance that is very important to the function of an organism (although it is needed in only small amounts) and that must be taken in from outside sources. Carotene is the compound which gives carrots their orange color.

Retinene

Figure 1–75 also shows the structure of retinene, the molecule found in the photoreceptor of the eye. As you can see, retinene is formed from vitamin A. In fact, the structure of retinene was first suspected when the dramatic effects of vitamin A in the treatment of night blindness were discovered. The eye has developed three separate times in the course of evolution—once in mollusks, such as the octopus and the scallop, once in insects, and once in vertebrates. These organisms have no common evolutionary ancestor; in other words, these three types of eyes had no common forerunner. Yet each of these eyes contains retinene. In this instance, this extraordinary biochemical unity would appear to be the result not of a common beginning but of the unusual and perhaps unique "fitness" of this particular molecule for its purpose.

STEROIDS

The steroids are a group of solid, fatlike substances which include the hormones secreted by the sex glands and by the outer cortex of the adrenal gland, including testosterone, the estrogens, and the cortisonelike hormones. How these substances perform their varied and complex activities in controlling bodily activities is not yet known. As fatty substances, steroid hormones may act on the fatty molecules of the cell membrane to govern the passage of materials through the cell membrane, thus controlling what the cell produces. By allowing certain materials to enter particular cells and keeping others out, a single hormone can have profound and diverse effects on the body's metabolism.

Steroids are formed from a substance known as *cholesterol*. Food, especially butter and eggs, is a major source of cholesterol; it also can be synthesized within the body. Cholesterol circulates in the bloodstream and is picked up from the blood by specialized cells of the sex and adrenal glands, which perform the chemical steps necessary to change cholesterol into the steroid hormones. Cholesterol is also found in many membranes, particularly in the fatty sheaths formed around nerves by the Schwann cells.

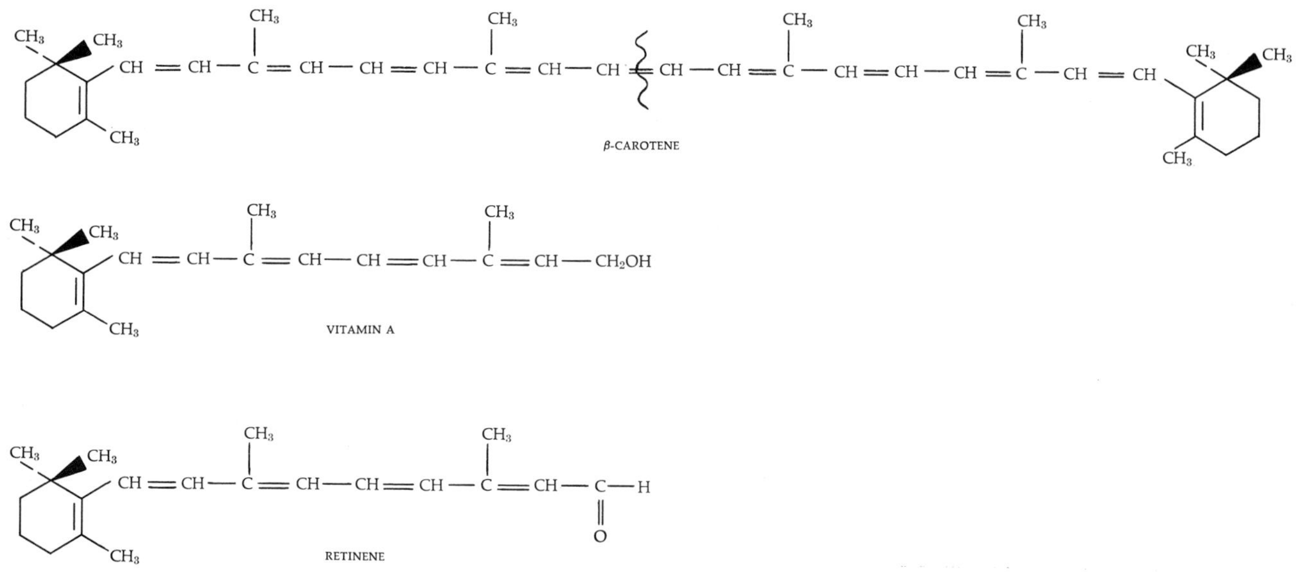

β-CAROTENE

VITAMIN A

RETINENE

1–75 *Related carotenoids. Cleavage of the β-carotene molecule at the point shown yields two molecules of vitamin A. Oxidation of vitamin A yields retinene.*

INFORMATIONAL MACROMOLECULES

Proteins

Proteins consist of chains of nitrogen-containing molecules known as *amino acids*. Living systems contain 20 amino acids, which constitute the universal alphabet of protein structure. Just as arranging the letters of the alphabet in different ways spells different words, so different arrangements of these 20 building blocks form different proteins. Even a single variation in sequence in a chain involving hundreds of amino acid molecules may change the properties of the resulting protein molecule. And since protein molecules are large and complex—some with thousands of amino acids—the number of different amino acid sequences, and therefore the possible variety of protein molecules, is enormous. In a single complex organism such as man, for example, there are thousands, possibly hundreds of thousands, of different proteins. Each has a special job to do, and by its unique chemical nature each is specifically fitted for that job.

Fibrous proteins, which are among the simplest of the proteins, provide the structural framework of the body for complex animals, just as cellulose serves as the framework of plants. The scales of fish and reptiles and hair, feathers, horns, hoofs, and claws are made up mainly of the protein keratin. The internal supporting tissues—cartilage, ligaments, tendons—are largely composed of protein molecules such as collagen and elastin. Muscle consists mainly of a complex fibrous protein called actomyosin.

123 *Biological Molecules*

1–76 The general structural formula of an
amino acid. Every amino acid contains
an amino group and a carboxyl group
bonded to a carbon atom. The identity
of any particular amino acid is determined by the radical group, indicated
by the "R" in the diagram.

1–77 The 20 amino acids found in proteins.

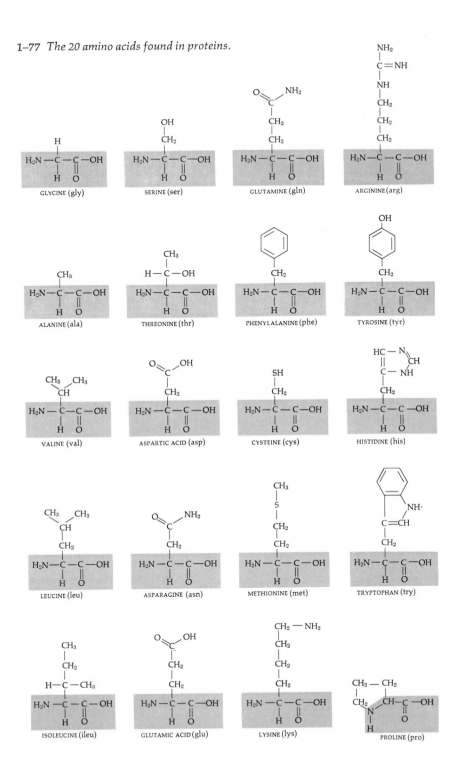

1–78 Like sugars, amino acids can occur in
"left-handed" (L) and "right-handed"
(R) forms, but all amino acids occurring
in the proteins are L.

Globular proteins, on the other hand, have more subtle and complicated functions; they play important dynamic or metabolic roles in living systems. For example, enzymes, which are specialized to serve as specific catalysts in the various chemical reactions of the body, are globular proteins. Many of the hormones are also globular proteins.

Another way to classify proteins is as *simple* and *conjugated*. Simple proteins contain nothing but amino acids arranged in chains. Conjugated proteins are simple proteins combined with some other molecular group.

AMINO ACIDS

Figure 1–76 shows the basic structure of an amino acid; it consists of an amino group and a carboxyl group bonded to a carbon atom, the so-called "alpha" carbon. The R stands for a radical, a chemical grouping which varies in structure; it is the R group that determines the identity of any particular amino acid. Some 70 amino acids are known, but only 20 are encountered in proteins. Figure 1–77 shows the full structure of these 20 amino acids. Most animal cells can make only some of these amino acids. Those that the organism cannot make for itself are known as *essential* amino acids, since these must be supplied in the diet. Amino acids formed in the cell are made largely from breakdown products of glucose. Like sugars, amino acids can occur in "right-handed" and "left-handed" forms (Figure 1–78), but all the amino acids occurring in proteins are "left-handed," or L-forms.

POLYPEPTIDE CHAINS

Amino acids may be joined to one another in a long chain known as a *polypeptide*. (See Figure 1–79.) As in the case of polysaccharides, a molecule of water must be removed to create each link. (The amino acids are

1–79 *Polypeptides are chains of amino acids linked together by peptide bonds, the amino group of one acid joining the carboxyl group of its neighbor, as shown in the colored boxes in the drawing. The polypeptide chain shown here contains six different amino acids, but some chains may contain as many as 300 linked amino acids. Proteins, the substances that play such important and complicated roles in living systems, are made up of one or more polypeptide chains. In these chains, the sequence in which the amino acids are arranged determines the biological character of the protein molecule; even one small variation in this sequence may alter or destroy its function.*

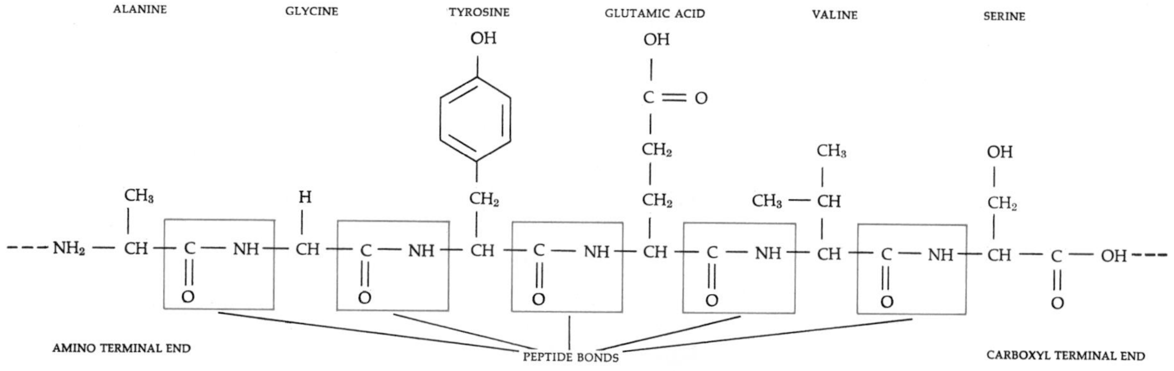

then commonly called *amino acid residues*.) The amino group of one amino acid always links to the carboxyl group of the other; this bond is known as the *peptide bond*. Proteins are extremely large molecules, with molecular weights ranging from 10,000 to 10,000,000 or more—in comparison with water, which has a molecular weight of 18, and glucose, which has a molecular weight of 180. Protein molecules consist of one or more long peptide chains, in which there may be as many as 300 amino acids per chain.

LEVELS OF PROTEIN ORGANIZATION

In some proteins, the polypeptide chains line up end-to-end to form one very long molecule. In others, they line up side by side, with connecting chemical bonds. More complex geometric patterns involve a twisting and folding of the polypeptide chain. The principal levels of protein organization are (1) the amino acid sequence (*primary structure*); (2) the coiling of the polypeptide chain into the alpha helix or the interaction of two polypeptides to produce the beta configuration (*secondary structure*); and (3) the folding of the alpha helix into various shapes to produce a more or less globular protein molecule (*tertiary structure*).

Primary Structure

The primary structure of a proteinlike substance was first identified in 1954 by Frederick Sanger, when he analyzed the hormone insulin, a relatively small polypeptide consisting of 51 amino acid units. Sanger was able to accomplish this difficult feat because of the existence of enzymes that hydrolyze peptide bonds at only particular spots—pepsin, for instance, hydrolyzes bonds only between tyrosine or phenylalanine and other amino acids—and because of a special property of the compound known as dinitrofluorobenzene. This latter compound can attach to the end, or terminal, amino group of a peptide, converting it to a bright yellow derivative (Figure 1–80). Sanger was able to break up the insulin molecule in a variety of different ways. The amino-end acid of each fragment could be identified since it would be marked with the yellow "marker" group. From each such analysis, he was able to get a little more information. Finally, he put all the various pieces together and identified the amino acid sequence of insulin. The whole process took more than five years.

As you can see in Figure 1–81, insulin proved to consist of two polypeptide chains linked together by disulfide bonds forming between two molecules of cysteine. The formation of such disulfide bonds between cysteine molecules has since been found to play an important role in determining the structures of many proteins. Since 1954, the amino acid sequence of many proteins, having from 100 to 300 amino acids per chain, has been analyzed.

1-80 *A technique used in analyzing the primary structure of a protein. The amino end of a peptide chain can be identified by labeling it with Sanger's reagent (dinitrofluorobenzene), which has the property of attaching to this terminal group and converting it to a bright yellow derivative. The process is illustrated in (a) and (b) for the tripeptide alanine-tyrosine-serine. The peptide chain can then be hydrolized to its building blocks (c). The amino acid previously at the amino-terminal of the peptide is easily identified since it is the one which contains the yellow labeling group.*

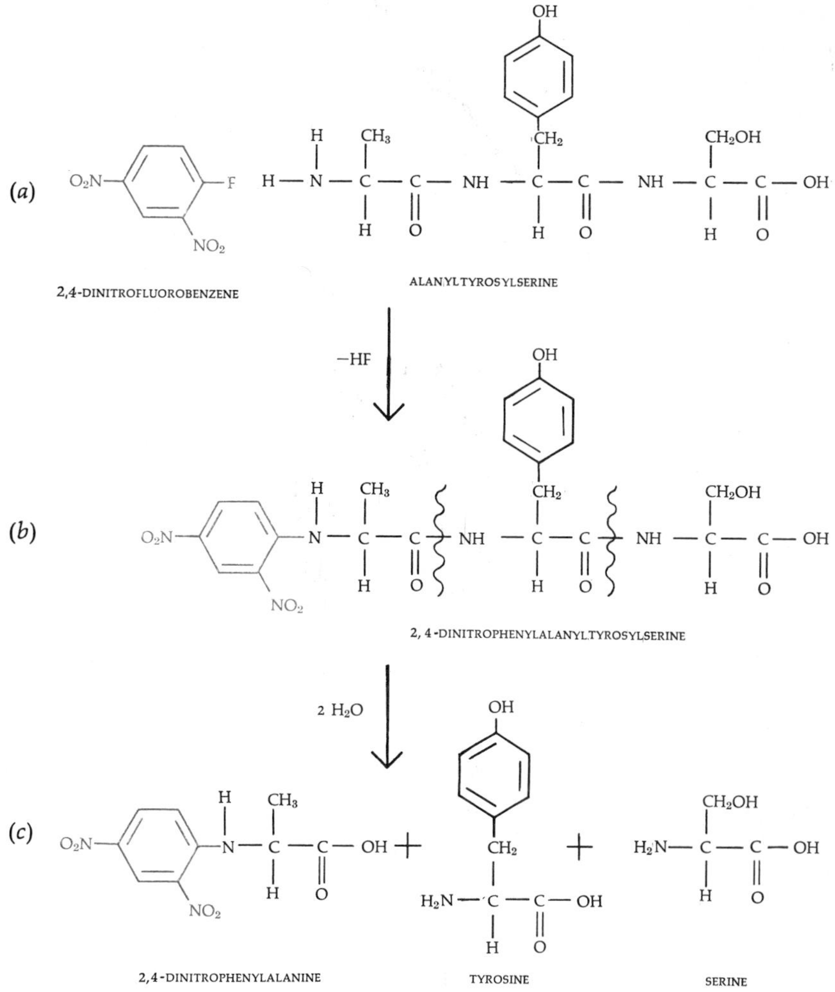

(a)

2,4-DINITROFLUOROBENZENE

ALANYLTYROSYLSERINE

−HF

(b)

2, 4 -DINITROPHENYLALANYLTYROSYLSERINE

2 H$_2$O

(c)

2,4-DINITROPHENYLALANINE   TYROSINE   SERINE

1-81 *The structure of beef insulin.*

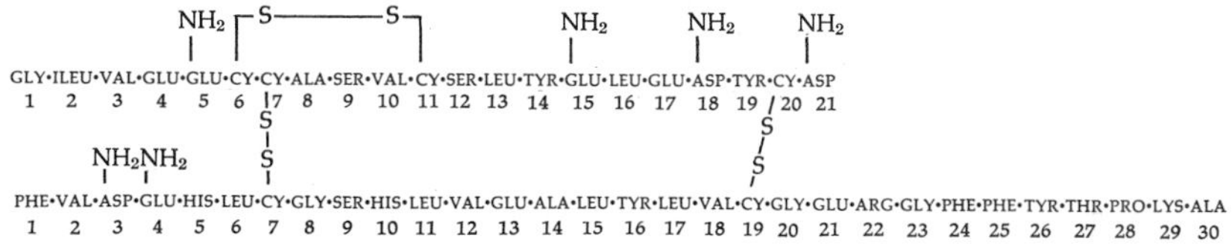

GLY·ILEU·VAL·GLU·GLU·CY·CY·ALA·SER·VAL·CY·SER·LEU·TYR·GLU·LEU·GLU·ASP·TYR·CY·ASP
1   2   3   4   5   6   7   8   9   10   11 12   13   14   15   16   17   18 19 20 21

PHE·VAL·ASP·GLU·HIS·LEU·CY·GLY·SER·HIS·LEU·VAL·GLU·ALA·LEU·TYR·LEU·VAL·CY·GLY·GLU·ARG·GLY·PHE·PHE·TYR·THR·PRO·LYS·ALA
1   2   3   4   5   6   7   8   9   10 11 12 13 14 15 16 17 18 19 20 21 22 23 24 25 26 27 28 29 30

1–82 *The alpha helix arrangement is the most common secondary structure of polypeptide chains. The configuration is very regular in its geometry, with a turn occurring every 3.6 amino acids, as shown in (a). The successive turns of the helix are held together by hydrogen bonds, represented in (b) by the dotted lines connecting the C–O with the N–H groups.*

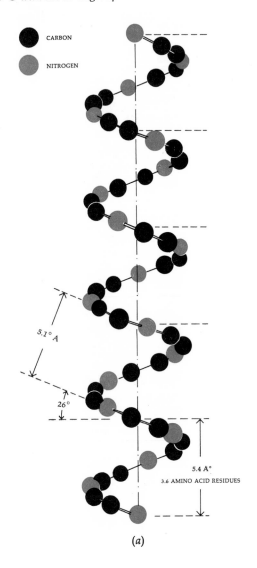

- ● CARBON
- ● NITROGEN

5.1° A

26°

5.4 A°
3.6 AMINO ACID RESIDUES

(a)

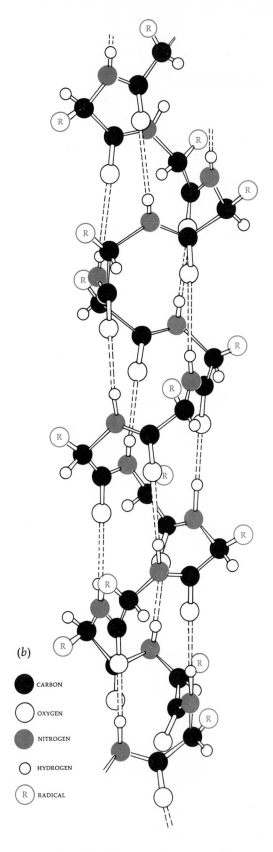

(b)

- ● CARBON
- ○ OXYGEN
- ● NITROGEN
- ○ HYDROGEN
- Ⓡ RADICAL

In the cell, polypeptide chains do not lie out flat—as diagrammed in Figure 1–79 but they spontaneously assume regular coiled structures in three dimensions. The coiled arrangement of the polypeptide chain is called its *secondary structure*. The most common secondary structure is the *alpha helix*, which resembles a spiral staircase. The alpha helix is very uniform in its geometry, with a turn of the helix occurring every 3.6 amino acids. The helix structure is maintained by hydrogen bonds across successive turns of the spiral, with the hydrogen atom in the amino group of one amino acid bonded to an oxygen atom of the carboxyl group of another amino acid in the next coil (Figure 1–82). The alpha-helical arrangement is found in native wool and hair and in other fibrous proteins.

Another secondary structure, the *beta configuration*, occurs when hydrogen bonds form between adjacent polypeptide chains. Silk, for example, is formed by long filamentous chains cross-linked to one another by hydrogen bonds; this arrangement is called a *pleated sheet*.

A third type of secondary structure is exemplified by collagen, another fibrous protein, which first forms a triple helix, each element being a single polypeptide chain. This helix then becomes coiled together with other collagen helices until a long, thick, ropelike structure—like a tendon—is built up (Figure 1–83).

Tertiary Structure

Peptide chains may also fold up to form globular structures, composed of straight sections of alpha helix separated by bends (Figure 1–84). This is called the *tertiary structure* of protein. Most biologically active proteins, such as enzymes and hormones, are globular. Globular proteins are soluble in cytoplasm and in other body fluids, with the molecule folding back on itself, often with many complex convolutions.

The tertiary structure is maintained mostly by hydrogen bonds and hydrophobic interactions. These bonds are relatively weak and can be broken quite easily by physical or chemical changes in the environment such as heat or increased acidity. For example, only a small amount of heat is required to change the globular, soluble proteins of raw egg white (albumen) into the fibrous, insoluble proteins of cooked egg white. Such a change is called *denaturation*; in principle, the tightly coiled peptide chains are unfolded to a randomly disposed configuration, causing a loss of the biological activity of the protein.

ENZYMES

Enzymes are globular proteins which are specialized to serve as catalysts. Over 1,000 enzymes are now known, each of them capable of catalyzing some specific chemical reaction.

1–83 *Three types of secondary structure of polypeptide chains, as seen in different fibrous proteins.*

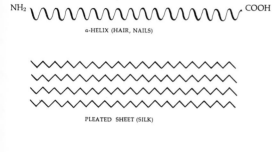

NH₂ ∿∿∿∿∿∿∿∿∿∿∿ COOH

α-HELIX (HAIR, NAILS)

PLEATED SHEET (SILK)

COLLAGEN HELIX

1–84 *The tertiary structure of a globular protein. Only the backbone of the peptide chain is shown here; the R groups would fill most of the space within the molecule.*

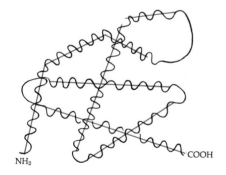

NH₂   COOH

1–85 *The enzyme invertase is specific for hydrolyzing sucrose to yield a molecule of glucose and a molecule of fructose. As you can see in (a), the active site of the enzyme fits the opposing surface of the sucrose molecule almost exactly. When the two combine (b), the small difference in surface configuration pushes the active site slightly out of shape and places a strain on the substrate molecule, rendering it susceptible to attack by hydrolysis. In this way, the substrate molecule is converted to its products (c). The enzyme-substrate complex then dissociates, and the enzyme returns to its original shape.*

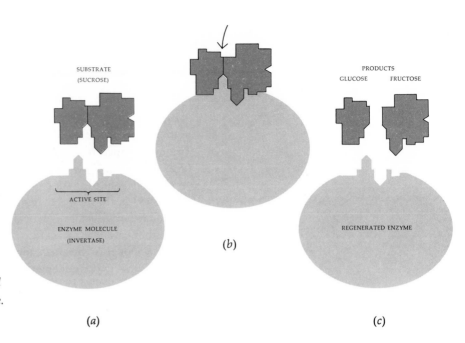

SUBSTRATE
(SUCROSE)

ACTIVE SITE

ENZYME MOLECULE
(INVERTASE)

(a)

(b)

PRODUCTS
GLUCOSE   FRUCTOSE

REGENERATED ENZYME

(c)

Because of enzymes, cells are able to perform reactions at great speed and at body temperature; without enzymes, such reactions would require the input of considerable heat or other forms of energy. Each enzymatic reaction is a reaction which would take place spontaneously within the cell but at a rate so slow that the product accumulation would be negligible. Enzymes speed up rates of reaction by bringing various molecules in alignment with one another. Figure 1–85 diagrams the hydrolysis of sucrose by a specific enzyme to yield a molecule of glucose and a molecule of fructose. As you can see, the enzyme itself remains unchanged in this reaction.

The chemical, or chemicals, upon which an enzyme acts is known as its *substrate*. The site on the surface of the globular enzyme molecule into which the substrate fits is the *active*, or catalytic, site; usually there is only one active site in each enzyme molecule. In the enzyme-substrate complex, the active site is made to order, so to speak, for the particular substrate. In other words, the substrate fits the active site as a key fits into a lock. The remarkable specificity of enzymes is due to this geometrical relationship of chemical groups; an enzyme will only accept a molecule that has a complementary fit.

Like other catalysts, enzymes lower the amount of energy needed to start a reaction. When an enzyme combines with a substrate, the enzyme molecule is deformed somewhat, placing some strain on the geometry of the substrate molecule. This renders the substrate molecule susceptible to attack by H$^+$ or OH$^-$ ions or by specific functional groups of the enzyme. In this manner, the substrate molecule is converted to its products, which now diffuse away from the active site. The enzyme molecule returns to its native shape, combines with another substrate molecule, and repeats the cycle. The substrate is held at the active site by weak bonds for the split second required for the catalytic action to take place. In one minute, a single enzyme molecule may carry out as many as several million catalytic cycles.

Only a few amino acid molecules are involved in any particular active site; some of these may be adjacent to one another in the primary structure, but often they are brought into proximity to one another by the intricate foldings of the chains involved in the tertiary structure.

Figure 1–86 shows a model of chymotrypsinogen, an enzyme precursor which is made in the cells of the pancreas and released into the small intestine, where it is converted by an enzyme into chymotrypsin. This seemingly extra step is necessary because, in the form of the digestive enzyme chymotrypsin, the substance would digest the pancreatic cells that make it. The primary structure of chymotrypsinogen has been analyzed and has been found to contain 246 amino acid residues. When the peptide bond between amino acids 15 and 16 is catalytically split, the molecule converts to chymotrypsin and becomes catalytically active. Three of the amino acids—two histidines and one serine, occupying numbers 40, 57, and 195 in the long polypeptide chain—are required for the catalytic action of chymotrypsin. Therefore, the chain must be bent to bring these amino acids together at the combining site.

1–86 *A schematic diagram of the chymotrypsinogen molecule. The numbers represent the positions of particular amino acids in the peptide chain, which is held together in a three-dimensional arrangement by disulfide bonds (S–S). When the peptide bond between amino acids 15 and 16 is split, the molecule becomes the catalytically active digestive enzyme chymotrypsin. Evidence that amino acids 40, 57, and 195 are required for this catalytic activity indicates that the chain is folded so that these amino acids are brought together. (After Watson, 1965)*

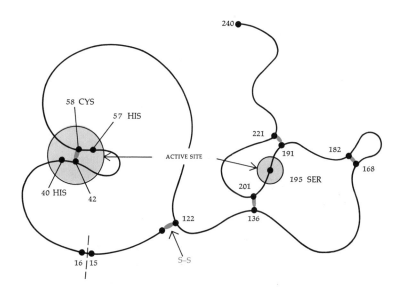

1–87 *The heme group of hemoglobin. It contains an iron atom (Fe) coordinated to the porphyrin ring. The porphyrin ring consists of four nitrogen-containing rings, the pyrroles, which are numbered in the diagram.*

1–88 *The magnesium-porphyrin group of chlorophyll a. The "tail" portion consists of a long side chain of carbon and hydrogen atoms. Chlorophyll b differs in having a —CHO group in place of the —CH₃ group circled in the diagram.*

As a consequence of their dependence on their tertiary structures, enzymes are very sensitive to slight changes in heat. Sometimes enzymes within the same organism have different heat tolerances. If you have ever seen a Siamese cat, you have probably noticed that its coat is darker on its ears, nose, and feet and on the tip of its tail. This is because in the Siamese cat the enzyme controlling pigmentation is active only in these cooler peripheral regions of the body.

Porphyrins

Porphyrin-containing compounds such as hemoglobin and chlorophyll are of central importance in the life processes of animals and plants. In these compounds, four smaller rings known as *pyrroles*, each containing a nitrogen atom, are linked to form a larger ring structure, the porphyrin ring. In the center of the porphyrin ring, attached to each of the four nitrogens, is a metal. In heme, which is the porphyrin group of hemoglobin, the metal is iron. The heme is combined with special proteins to form hemoglobin, the oxygen-carrying pigment that fills red blood cells. (A substance such as protein in which the protein is combined with some other type of molecular group is known as a *conjugated protein*.)

The chlorophylls also have a porphyrin ring as their central structure but in these compounds the central core is magnesium and the porphyrin ring is combined with a lipid rather than a protein. The higher plants contain chlorophylls *a* and *b*.

Other porphyrin compounds, the *cytochromes*, are present in the chloroplasts of cells and in the mitochondria, both of which are crucial in the capture of energy by the cell. Their function will be described in more detail in the next chapter.

Nucleic Acids

In the same way that proteins are composed of long chains of amino acids, nucleic acids consist of significant sequences of building blocks known as *nucleotides*. A nucleotide is a molecule made up of three subunits: (1) a phosphate group, (2) a five-carbon (or pentose) sugar, and (3) a nitrogen base, so-called because its ring structure contains nitrogen as well as carbon. Nucleotides contain two types of nitrogen bases: *pyrimidines*, which have a single ring, and *purines*, which have two fused rings. The three biologically important pyrimidines are thymine, cytosine, and uracil, and the two important purines are adenine and guanine.

There are two different series of nucleotides, one characterized by a ribose sugar and the other by a deoxyribose sugar; *deoxy* means "minus one oxygen," and as you can see in Figure 1–89, this is the only difference between these two pentose sugars. In the deoxyribose forms, nucleotides

1–89 *The building blocks of ribonucleic acid (RNA) and deoxyribonucleic acid (DNA). Molecules of RNA and DNA are made up of long chains of these nucleotides, each containing a phosphate group, a five-carbon sugar, and a nitrogen base. As you can see, one RNA nucleotide contains uracil, while its DNA counterpart contains thymine. What is the only other difference between the two nucleotide series?*

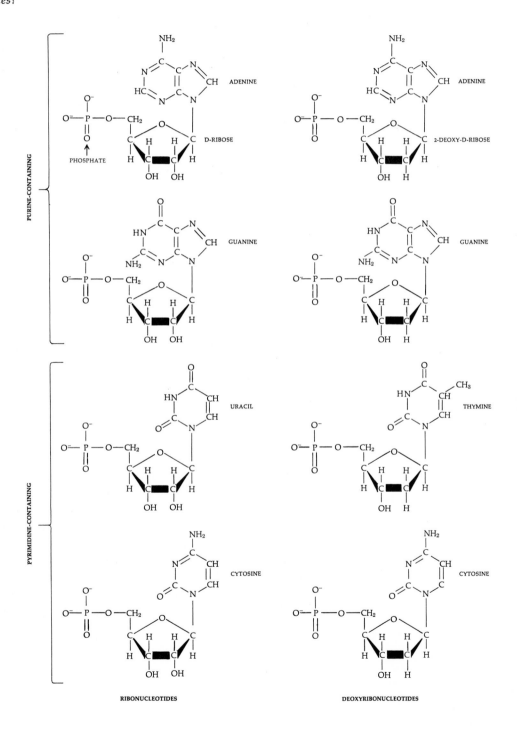

PURINE-CONTAINING

PYRIMIDINE-CONTAINING

ADENINE

D-RIBOSE

PHOSPHATE

GUANINE

URACIL

CYTOSINE

RIBONUCLEOTIDES

ADENINE

2-DEOXY-D-RIBOSE

GUANINE

THYMINE

CYTOSINE

DEOXYRIBONUCLEOTIDES

are linked together in long chains to form deoxyribonucleic acid (DNA), which is found in the chromosomes of cells and also, in much smaller amounts, in certain organelles, such as the mitochondria and chloroplasts. In the ribose forms, nucleotides make up RNA (ribonucleic acid). The bulk of RNA is found in the ribosomes and in the nucleolus, but smaller amounts are also present in solution in the cytoplasm.

DNA

As we shall see in Section 3, it is in the DNA molecule that genetic information is transmitted from one generation to the next. The two major strands of the double-stranded helix structure of DNA are composed of sugar-phosphate units, alternating. (See Figure 1–89.) These form the outer, acidic part of the molecule. Two pyrimidines (thymine and cytosine) and two purines (adenine and guanine) make up the rungs of this "spiral staircase." Each rung consists of two bases joined in the center by hydrogen bonds. The four bases are complementary—that is, adenine will hydrogen-bond only with thymine, and guanine only with cytosine. The order in which the bases occur along the strands spells out the "genetic code."

RNA

The components of RNA are almost exactly the same as those of DNA except that its sugar component is ribose instead of deoxyribose and it contains uracil in place of thymine. The function of RNA is to build the proteins specified by the nucleotide sequences of the DNA molecules. By a process explained in detail in Section 3, various RNA molecules function together to bring into line the proper amino acids, following the exact order laid down by the DNA code, and to form them into strands of protein.

NUCLEOTIDES

ATP

ATP, adenosine triphosphate, is a common and important mononucleotide. It is composed of one unit of adenine, a ribose sugar, and as its name implies, three phosphate groups (Figure 1–90). You will notice that the last two phosphates are linked to the molecule by a wavy line. This line signifies the presence of a so-called "high-energy" bond. A high-energy bond is one from which large amounts of energy are released when it is hydrolyzed. The energy released is not really in the bond (which requires energy to be broken) but arises because the hydrolysis products (ADP and a phosphate group) have much less energy than ATP. As you will see in the next chapter, most of the available chemical energy of the cell is packaged for ready use in the form of ATP molecules. The energy of the ATP is released when a phosphate group is transferred from ATP

1–90 *The structure of adenosine triphosphate (ATP). The symbol ~ designates the so-called "high-energy" bonds.*

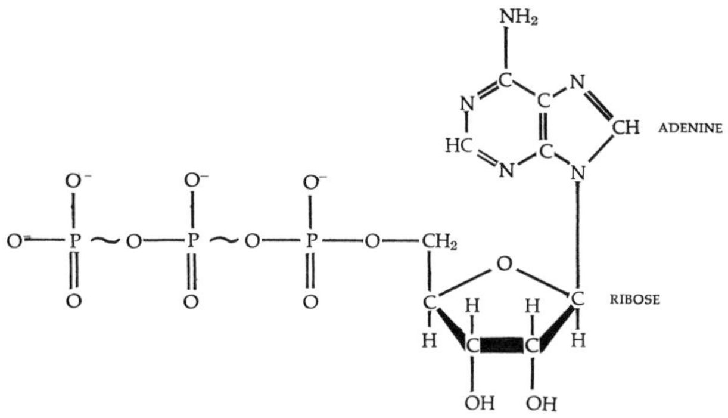

to some other molecule. Many of the cell's enzymes are specifically "tooled" for the energy-releasing transfer of phosphate groups from ATP to other molecules. The phosphate group is restored to the ADP, at the expense, if necessary, of foodstuff energy, to "recharge" the ADP into ATP.

NAD

Another compound which is a nucleotide of adenine is nicotinamide adenine dinucleotide, usefully abbreviated as NAD. This large and complicated molecule is formed of a submolecule of the vitamin nicotinamide attached to a ribose sugar and a phosphate, which are attached, in turn, to a nucleotide of adenine. (See Figure 1–91.) The NAD molecule is important because it can act as a hydrogen and electron acceptor in reactions involving energy transfers in cells. NAD can accept two hydrogen atoms from a food molecule, becoming NAD_{red} (NAD reduced). NAD in the oxidized form is also written as NAD_{ox}. Two other closely related compounds, abbreviated as NADP and FAD, also contain a nucleotide of adenine and perform similar functions in the cells.

Coenzymes

NAD, NADP, and FAD belong to a group of compounds known as *coenzymes*. Coenzymes always act in conjunction with specific enzymes. NAD, NADP and FAD act in conjunction with enzymes that transfer the hydrogen atoms or electrons back and forth in the course of cellular oxidation reactions. In these cases, the nucleotides function as electron or hydrogen carriers. One reason that they provide such an efficient vehicle is that, unlike CO_2 and O_2 and other small molecules, they cannot diffuse in and out through the cell membrane, so that the energy captured in the phosphate bond of ATP or in the form of electrons or hydrogen atoms of NAD_{red} cannot escape from the cell.

1–91 *Nicotinamide adenine dinucleotide (NAD) in its oxidized form (a) and reduced form (b). In the reduced form (NAD$_{red}$), the nicotinamide ring has accepted two hydrogen atoms, at the points shown by the colored dots. One of the hydrogen atoms is then released and becomes an H$^+$ ion.*

SUMMARY

In Chapter 1–6, we described the basic units of matter and the principles governing their interactions. In this chapter, we used these generalities to examine some compounds that are vitally important in life processes.

Carbohydrates serve as a primary source of chemical energy for most living systems. The simplest carbohydrates are the monosaccharides ("single sugars"). In most animal systems, glucose is the most important of the monosaccharides. Glucose and other molecules can be combined to form disaccharides ("two sugars") and polysaccharides (chains of many submolecules of sugar). These molecules can be broken apart again by hydrolysis.

Lipids are another source of energy and also of structural materials for cells. Compounds in this group are generally insoluble in water. The group includes fats, phospholipids, carotenoids, and steroids. Among the steroids are the sex and adrenocortical hormones, which have important regulatory functions in the body's metabolism. Steroids are formed from cholesterol. Carotenoids are the red and yellow pigments found in many plant cells. Carotene, the compound which gives carrots their orange color, and retinene, the molecule found in the photoreceptor of the eye, are the most common carotenoids.

Proteins and *nucleic acids* are referred to as *informational macromolecules* because the specific arrangements of their component groups code the individual properties of organisms. Proteins are very large molecules composed of long chains of amino acids known as *polypeptide chains*. There are 20 different amino acids in proteins, and from these, an enormous number of different protein molecules are built. Fibrous proteins serve as structural elements, and globular proteins play important dynamic and metabolic roles. The principal levels of protein organization are (1) primary structure, the amino acid sequence; (2) secondary structure, the coiling or spiraling of the polypeptide chain; and (3) tertiary structure, the folding of the coiled chain into various shapes. Most biologically active proteins, such as enzymes and hormones, fold back on themselves to form tertiary structures, which are globular.

Because of *enzymes*, cells are able to catalyze reactions at high speed and at body temperature. The specificity of enzymes is due to the "key-and-lock" fit of the active site on the enzyme with the substrate molecule.

Hemoglobin and chlorophyll are porphyrin-containing compounds. In the former, the porphyrin has a central core of iron. In chlorophyll, the metal in the central core is magnesium.

Nucleic acids consist of *nucleotides* linked together in long chains. Nucleotides are composed of three submolecules: a nitrogen base, a phosphate group, and a five-carbon sugar. Nucleotides containing deoxyribose sugar form *DNA;* those containing ribose sugar form *RNA.* Genetic information is transmitted in the DNA molecule, coded in the sequence of the nitrogen bases. The function of RNA is to build the proteins specified by the nucleotide sequence of the DNA molecules.

ATP (adenosine triphosphate) is a mononucleotide which holds and transfers the cell's chemical energy. Other nucleotides include the coenzymes NAD, NADP, and FAD.

The Flow of Energy

In Chapters 1–3 to 1–5, we described cells in terms of their structures and their overall activities. In Chapters 1–6 and 1–7, you were introduced to some of the principal chemical constituents of living cells. Yet, as Szent-Györgyi noted, it seems difficult to reconcile these lifeless formulas with the bustling, scurrying activity of *Euplotes* or the surging growth of the burrowing root tip of a plant.

What acts upon these chemicals to "bring them to life"? At one time, scientists postulated that the "vital force" must be some sort of power not comprehensible by science. Now, however, we can define this vital force in scientific terms and measure it very exactly. It is *energy* that drives the many processes we recognize as living. Life itself, in fact, is the ceaseless flow of energy through cells and from cell to cell and organism to organism, generation after generation.

Energy exists either as potential energy or as kinetic energy. Potential energy is energy which is stored, or inactive. A stick of dynamite is a good example of this kind of energy. Kinetic energy, on the other hand, is energy in action.

There are many different forms of potential and kinetic energy. The energy possessed by chemical compounds is *chemical energy*. Gasoline, for example, contains potential chemical energy. The small electric currents that flow along nerve membranes and the large electric charges built up by the electric eel are examples of *electrical energy*. *Mechanical energy* is the energy involved in motion. Energy which travels in waves, such as heat, light, radio waves, and x-rays, is *radiant energy*.

Energy Laws

No machine or living system can produce energy out of nothing. It can only change energy from one form to another. A gasoline engine, for example, produces energy in the form of motion. In order to produce this motion, it must use up energy in another form—the potential chemical energy in the gasoline. By burning the gasoline as fuel, the engine changes the chemical energy to heat and then changes the heat to motion. In all systems, animate and inanimate, the transformations of different kinds of energy are governed by two quite simple principles, the *first* and *second laws of thermodynamics*. Heat is often the most convenient form in which to measure energy, which is why the study of energy is called *thermodynamics* ("heat" dynamics).

THE FIRST LAW OF THERMODYNAMICS

Energy can be neither created nor destroyed but can only be transformed, so that the total energy of any system plus that of its surroundings remains constant regardless of the physical or chemical changes it may undergo. Our previous example of the boulder on the hill will help to make this statement clear. The energy required to push the boulder up the hill is the sum of the potential energy in the boulder and the energy needed to overcome the friction between the ground and the boulder. As the boulder rolls down the hill, the potential energy in the system becomes kinetic—matter is being moved and a small amount of heat is being dissipated into the surroundings. When the boulder reaches the bottom, it has converted all its potential energy into kinetic energy and all the frictional energy has been dissipated as heat. The total kinetic energy expended equals the total energy required to get the boulder back up the hill, which is the total potential energy present in the system at the start.

Notice that the frictional energy—the energy required during the uphill push to overcome the friction between the boulder and the ground—is lost to the surroundings as heat during the downhill movement. The energy is not actually lost in the sense of being unaccounted for; it is merely converted into a useless form that cannot do work. No transformation of energy from a useful form to another is ever 100 percent efficient. Some energy is always lost in a useless form—as heat into the atmosphere or simply by not being used. An electric motor converts only between 25 and 50 percent of the electrical energy into mechanical energy. The rest of the energy is lost as heat in the surroundings and is no longer readily available to be used again. The sum of the heat so formed plus the mechanical energy recovered is exactly equal to the electrical energy input.

THE SECOND LAW OF THERMODYNAMICS

All processes take place so as to increase entropy. In order to understand this statement, we must first define what we mean by *entropy*. When a system proceeds from an organized state to a less organized one, it increases its entropy, which is a measure of disorder, or randomness of state. The greater the state of disorganization, the greater the entropy. A completely random distribution of molecules and atoms in a system is a state of maximum entropy.

In every energy transformation, there is almost always a loss of some energy as heat dissipated to the surroundings. Since heat involves the random motion of molecules, each such loss increases the entropy in the surroundings. During the course of many different sequential transformations of energy, the amount of energy lost as entropy at each step accumulates, and thus the total entropy steadily increases.

Living organisms, because they are highly organized, have very little entropy, but this low-entropy state is preserved by increasing the entropy of the surroundings. For example, a large increase in the entropy of the surroundings occurs when animals take in glucose for energy and return the end products CO_2 and water to the surroundings.

WORK

Energy is useful when it is available to do work; the boulder in our example released useful energy as it rolled downhill. If it is difficult to visualize a rushing boulder as having the capacity to do work, remember that boulders are not conventionally harnessed for this purpose. Substitute water, for which the first law of thermodynamics applies equally well. Suppose that, instead of the boulder, we transport water to the top of our imaginary hill and let it rush down again. We know from experience that the water could be used to turn a series of paddle wheels and that such wheels could be used to grind corn or do other work useful in human terms.

Similarly, in the cell, it is not just a question of making energy available for work; this energy must be harnessed in order to be useful. In the course of evolution, cells have developed methods for harnessing energy which act with a precision and an efficiency far exceeding that of any man-made machine. Cells, moreover, are specialists in energy transformations; they cannot use heat energy or mechanical energy or electrical energy. Almost all their energy exchanges involve chemical energy because this is the only form that can do work in the watery environment of the cell. In effect, cells are chemical factories, breaking down complex chemicals into smaller and simpler parts and rearranging and combining simple chemicals into more complex parts.

Energy Flow in Living Systems

Figure 1–92 diagrams the flow of energy in the living world. All biological energy arises from the sun. Two important steps in the process of making this energy available for cellular work are carried out by the chloroplast and the mitochondrion (Figure 1–92). The chloroplast in the green plant

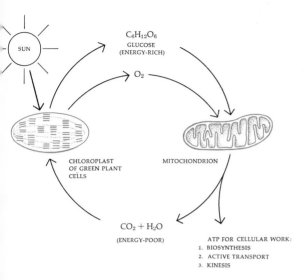

C₆H₁₂O₆
GLUCOSE
(ENERGY-RICH)

O₂

SUN

CHLOROPLAST
OF GREEN PLANT
CELLS

MITOCHONDRION

CO₂ + H₂O

(ENERGY-POOR)

ATP FOR CELLULAR WORK:
1. BIOSYNTHESIS
2. ACTIVE TRANSPORT
3. KINESIS

1–92 *The flow of biological energy. The radiant energy of sunlight is produced by the fusion of hydrogen atoms to form helium. Chloroplasts of green plant cells capture this energy and use it to convert water and carbon dioxide into glucose, starch, and other foodstuff molecules. Oxygen is released into the air as a by-product of the chemical reactions. The mitochondria of animals break down these compounds and capture their stored energy in ATP molecules. This process also produces carbon dioxide and water, completing the cycle.*

cell captures the energy of sunlight, which is used in the biosynthesis of the glucose molecule from carbon dioxide and water. This glucose is then oxidized or "burned" as fuel by the mitochondria of the same green cell in which the glucose was generated, by other cells of the plant that contain no chlorophyll and thus cannot photosynthesize, or by the cells of animals which eat the plants. During oxidation of the glucose, energy is released to carry out work and CO_2 and H_2O are formed.

First we shall examine energy recovery during the oxidation of glucose since this process is better understood than photosynthesis. The molecule is broken down gradually in small steps in two distinct overall stages: The first stage is *glycolysis,* which occurs in the cytoplasm. The second stage is *respiration,* which takes place within the mitochondrion. As the glucose is oxidized, the energy packed into it by the biosynthetic reactions that take place in the chloroplast is extracted in a series of small discrete steps, each catalyzed by an enzyme, and packaged in the form of ATP. The entire process ends just where it began, with carbon dioxide and water, at the bottom of the hill.

Let us look at each of these separate stages, beginning with glycolysis.

GLYCOLYSIS

Glycolysis, the first phase in the breakdown of glucose in animal cells, is an *anaerobic process;* that is, it requires no oxygen. Figure 1–93 looks complicated, but the overall process is easy to see. The energy-rich glucose is broken down into two simpler, energy-poorer molecules of pyruvic acid.* The overall reaction can be represented by:

$$C_6H_{12}O_6 \text{ (glucose)} \rightarrow 2CH_3COCOOH \text{ (pyruvic acid)} + 4H$$

As you can see, the breakdown of glucose is accomplished by a series of separate steps, each of which is catalyzed by a different enzyme. (It is not important to memorize the details of the chemical structure of the various compounds that are formed. These are included only to show you that the glycolytic enzymes work in an ordered series, like workmen on an assembly line.) The chemical modification that occurs at each step is very small: The molecule literally falls apart, a little at a time. The whole point of glycolysis is to release the energy of glucose in small, separate steps. If the energy of the molecule were liberated all at once, it would produce heat. A sudden burst of heat would be of little use to the cell and could be destructive. By releasing the energy in a series of small steps, the cell loses only a little of it as heat and is able to conserve or recover a sizable proportion in the form of useful chemical energy.

* The terms pyruvic acid and pyruvate are commonly used interchangeably. Chemically, pyruvate refers to the negatively-charged ion (shown in Figure 1-93). As you can see, this ion, in solution, will tend to attract protons (hydrogen atoms minus their electrons) to become pyruvic acid.

141   *The Flow of Energy*

1–93 *Glycolysis, the first phase in the breakdown of glucose. In a series of separate steps, each controlled by a specific enzyme, the 6-carbon glucose molecule is split into two 3-carbon molecules.*

GLUCOSE → HEXO-KINASE → GLUCOSE 6-PHOSPHATE → HEXOSE PHOSPHATE ISOMERASE → FRUCTOSE 6-PHOSPHATE → PHOSPHO-FRUCTO-KINASE → FRUCTOSE 1, 6-DIPHOSPHATE

What happens to the energy released during glycolysis? Some of it is held momentarily by the coenzyme NAD, two molecules of which are reduced in the course of the glycolytic sequence. We shall set these aside for the moment since they do not reach their ultimate destination until completion of the respiratory cycle. Four molecules of ATP are formed during glycolysis, but, as you can see in Figure 1–93, these are not net gain. Two molecules of ATP are put into the reaction, one at the first and one at the third enzymatic step. The two ingoing ATP's provide the energy for this rearrangement and for "priming" the subsequent steps in the reaction.

The second half of the glycolytic sequence begins with the breaking in half of the six-carbon sugar fructose, 1, 6-diphosphate, to form two three-carbon sugar phosphates. Two ATP molecules are formed in the course of the breakdown of each half of the original molecule to provide a total of four. This is a net gain of two.

In order to write the complete equation of glycolysis, we must take into account not only the carbon compounds but also NAD, ATP, the inorganic phosphates P_i, and ADP:

$$C_6H_{12}O_6 + 2ATP + 2ADP + 2P_i + 2NAD_{ox} \rightarrow$$
$$2C_3H_4O_3 + 4ATP + 2NAD_{red}$$

We may simplify this to:

$$C_6H_{12}O_6 + 2ADP + 2P_i + 2NAD_{ox} \rightarrow$$
$$2C_3H_4O_3 + 2ATP + 2NAD_{red}*$$

The fact that glycolysis does not require oxygen suggests that the glycolytic sequence evolved early, before free oxygen was available, and

* This equation is for the major components in the reaction and does not include changes in the water or acidity in the medium and, therefore, does not balance.

PYRUVIC ACID (FROM GLYCOLYSIS) $CH_3C\,COOH$ → CO_2 → ACETALDEHYDE CH_3-C-H → NAD_{red} (FROM GLYCOLYSIS) → NAD_{ox} → ETHANOL CH_3CH_2OH

1–94 *The steps by which pyruvic acid, formed by glycolysis, is converted to ethyl alcohol (ethanol). Ethanol is produced only in the absence of oxygen. Compared with respiration, which uses oxygen to derive energy in the form of ATP from the pyruvic acid, fermentation is very inefficient. Most of the energy of the glucose remains in the alcohol, which is the end product of the sequence.*

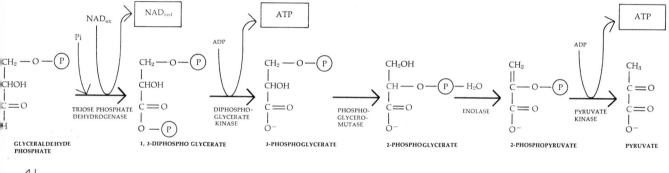

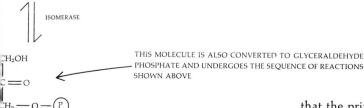

ISOMERASE

THIS MOLECULE IS ALSO CONVERTED TO GLYCERALDEHYDE PHOSPHATE AND UNDERGOES THE SEQUENCE OF REACTIONS SHOWN ABOVE

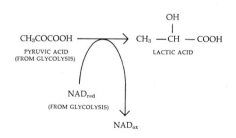

1–95 *The enzymatic reaction that produces lactic acid from pyruvic acid in muscle cells. In the course of this reaction the coenzyme NAD is oxidized; that is, it loses hydrogen atoms.*

that the primitive heterotrophs used glycolysis, or something very much like it, to extract energy from the organic compounds which they absorbed from their watery surroundings. Let us look briefly at what happens to cells when oxygen is not present.

The Anaerobic Pathway

Yeast cells can live without oxygen. Under anaerobic (oxygenless) conditions, they convert glucose to pyruvic acid by the glycolysis sequence shown in Figure 1–93. The pyruvic acid so formed is then converted to alcohol by the steps shown in Figure 1–94.

When the glucose-filled juices of grapes and other fruit are extracted and stored in airtight kegs, the yeast cells, present as a bloom on the skin of the fruit, turn the fruit juice to wine by converting glucose into ethyl alcohol. Yeast, like all living things, has a limited tolerance for alcohol, and when a certain concentration (about 12 percent) is reached, the yeast cells die and fermentation ceases.

Because of the economic importance of the wine industry, alcoholic fermentation was the first enzymatic process to be intensively studied. The word "enzyme" comes from *zyme*, the Greek word for "leaven," and for many years enzymes were commonly referred to as *ferments,* although the scope of their activities is so broad that this word is inappropriate in the light of present-day knowledge and is being abandoned. Louis Pasteur worked on problems of fermentation for many years and was the first to recognize that the process depended upon the presence of living yeast cells.

Cells of higher animals do not form alcohol from pyruvic acid; instead, they form lactic acid. (See Figure 1–95.) Lactic acid production during

143 *The Flow of Energy*

glycolysis has been studied in particular in muscle cells. When muscle works hard, the cells need to produce extra energy. The richest source of energy, as we shall see, is respiration. Therefore, during muscular exertion, we breathe hard, increasing our intake of oxygen, and our heart pumps more rapidly, increasing the flow of hemoglobin to the muscle cells. If this supply is inadequate to meet the extra demands, the pyruvic acid in the muscle cell accumulates as lactic acid, which is toxic to the cell and produces the sensation we experience as muscle fatigue. You will notice that each time a molecule of pyruvic acid is reduced to lactic acid or to alcohol, a molecule of NAD_{red} is oxidized to NAD_{ox}, thereby renewing the limited supply of NAD_{ox} in the cell.

Now we can write the complete balanced equation for the anaerobic breakdown of glucose in yeast:

$$C_6H_{12}O_6 + 2ADP + 2P_i \rightarrow 2CH_3CH_2OH \text{ (ethyl alcohol)} + 2CO_2 + 2ATP$$

and in muscle cells:

$$C_6H_{12}O_6 + 2ADP + 2P_i \rightarrow 2CH_3CHOHCOOH \text{ (lactic acid)} + 2ATP$$

In either case, two molecules of ATP are generated from ADP and P_i as each molecule of glucose is broken down. This represents a recovery of about 7 percent of the total available energy of the glucose molecule. Anaerobic glycolysis does not yield much of the energy of glucose and is therefore, in a sense, wasteful. The remaining 93 percent of the available energy of glucose can, however, be extracted from the two molecules of pyruvic acid formed in glycolysis.

Only a few types of organisms which depend solely on anaerobic glycolysis still exist on our planet. One of these, as an example, is the bacterium that causes tetanus. This is why this dangerous and sometimes fatal disease develops in puncture wounds, such as those made by nails, where no oxygen can reach the growing cells.

THE RESPIRATORY SEQUENCE

Krebs Cycle

In the presence of free oxygen, the pyruvic acid formed in glycolysis enters into another enzyme sequence, which completes the oxidation of glucose. This sequence, which takes place in the mitochondrion, is known as the *Krebs cycle*, in honor of Sir Hans Krebs, who first postulated its existence in 1937. It is diagrammed in Figure 1–97.

Pyruvic acid must first be prepared for the Krebs cycle. This takes place in several steps, only the end results of which are shown in Figure 1–97. The three-carbon pyruvic acid is oxidized forming the two-carbon acetyl group (CH_3CO) and releasing CO_2, electrons, and protrons. Two electrons and one proton are accepted by NAD. Simultaneously, the acetyl group

$$CH_3C-S-CoA$$
$$\overset{\|}{O}$$

1–96 *Acetyl-CoA. The pyruvate molecule formed in glycolysis is oxidized to acetic acid and linked to coenzyme A in preparation for entry into the Krebs cycle.*

144   CELLS

1–97 *Pyruvic acid, formed in glycolysis, is converted to acetyl-CoA. It then enters the Krebs cycle where the breakdown of the molecule is completed. This enzymatic sequence is known as a cycle because one of its components (oxaloacetic acid) is constantly regenerated. Energy released in the Krebs cycle is captured by the coenzymes NAD and FAD.*

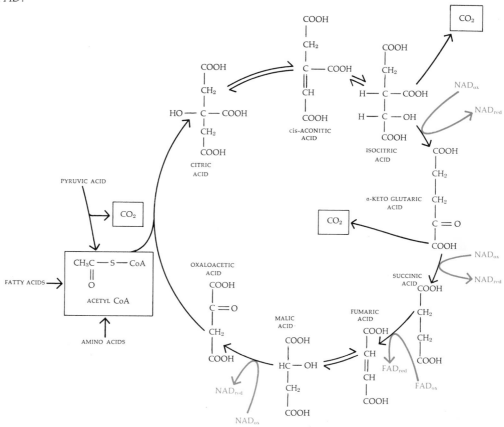

is linked by a high-energy bond to a compound known as *coenzyme A.* Coenzyme A serves as a carrier of acetyl groups in much the same way as NAD acts as a carrier of hydrogen. This complex, *acetyl-CoA* as it is called, is the principal form in which substances can enter the Krebs cycle.

In the first step of the Krebs cycle, the acetyl group is released from coenzyme A and combined with oxaloacetic acid to form citric acid. Since citric acid is always the starting point, the Krebs cycle is also sometimes known as the *citric acid cycle.* By the last step of the cycle, the two-carbon acetyl group has been oxidized to two molecules of CO_2 and oxaloacetic acid and has been regenerated, which is why this series is literally a cycle. Each turn around the cycle uses up one acetyl group and regenerates a molecule of oxaloacetic acid, which is left ready to serve as a vehicle for

Electrons extracted during the Krebs cycle are fed into a series of electron-carrier enzymes, or cytochromes (indicated by black circles), which make up the respiratory chain. The cytochromes are coupled to an enzyme system that packages the energy emitted by the electron flow into ATP, a process known as oxidative phosphorylation. At the end of the chain, the electrons combine with oxygen atoms, which can then attract hydrogen ions to form water. For every glucose molecule, 38 ATP molecules are produced in the overall glycolysis-respiration sequence.

the next acetyl group. In effect, all these steps are ways of trapping the energy released by the oxidation of the carbons in the acetyl groups.

Most of the energy produced by the oxidation of the acetyl group is stored in the four pairs of removed electrons. These electrons are accepted by the coenzymes NAD and flavin nucleotide (FAD). At each turn of the cycle, three molecules of NAD_{red} and one of FAD_{red} are formed.

The acetyl-CoA used by the Krebs cycle is a pivotal substance at a busy intersection in the biochemical pathways of the cell, because it is in this form that fats and amino acids may also enter the energy-releasing Krebs cycle, as shown in Figure 1–97. These two types of compounds can also be converted to acetyl-CoA by a series of reactions appropriate to each type of compound. If you remember the general structure of the fatty acids, you can form an impression of the large number of acetyl groups that can be processed from a single molecule of fat, which is why fat is such an efficient product for long-term storage of energy.

The pathways leading to the acetyl-CoA intersection are not necessarily one-way streets. A molecule of glucose which has been broken down to pyruvic acid by glycolysis may, instead of entering the Krebs cycle, change its course and, by a different series of reactions, end up as a fat molecule or as an amino acid in any one of a thousand cellular structures. There is a constant interaction of factors in the life of a cell to determine which of several alternative routes a particular "all-purpose" molecule such as acetyl-CoA may take.

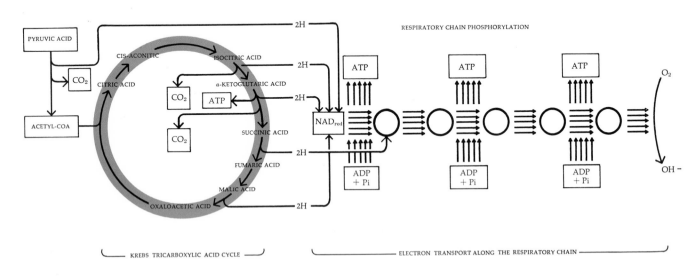

Electron Transport Chain

Figure 1–98 diagrams the final and crucial stage of the respiratory sequence. The coenzymes that have accepted electrons from the glycolytic sequence, from the conversion of pyruvic acid to acetyl-CoA, and from the Krebs cycle now donate them—two each—to the first of a chain of electron-carrying enzymes. These electrons all have a relatively high energy content—they are all still very close to the top of the hill, to return to our first analogy. The electron carriers are a series of cytochromes, each with a central core of iron.

Each successive cytochrome in this chain exerts a slightly greater pull on the electrons than the preceding one, so the electrons, in effect, move downhill, losing a certain proportion of their energy at each step in the chain, as water might in flowing over a series of paddle wheels. At the bottom of the electron-transport hill is free oxygen. Without oxygen as an acceptor of the electrons, their downhill flow cannot be completed. The oxygen combines with the spent electrons from the electron transport chain and with the hydrogen ions released in the course of the reduction reactions that have taken place to form water.

Just as a paddle wheel might be coupled to a piece of machinery within the water mill, the cytochrome series is coupled to an enzyme system which packages the energy emitted by the electron flow into ATP. These *coupling enzymes*, as they are called, have not yet been identified. The process by which ATP is produced by the cytochromes in the presence of oxygen is known as *oxidative phosphorylation*.

Each time a pair of electrons passes down the electron-transport chain from NAD_{red} to oxygen, three molecules of ATP are formed from ADP and phosphate.

THE BALANCE SHEET

How can we account for all the energy liberated as the glucose molecule is oxidized to CO_2 and H_2O? In the first stage, glycolysis, glucose was broken down to pyruvic acid and two molecules of ATP were formed directly. Also, as you will remember, this reaction yielded two molecules of NAD_{red}, each carrying two electrons. These four electrons, as they pass along the electron transport chain in the mitochondrion, contribute enough additional energy to make a total of six molecules of ATP from ADP and P_i. So the yield from the first phase of glucose oxidation is a total of eight ATP's per molecule of glucose.

The oxidation of each of the two molecules of pyruvic acid to acetyl-CoA produces an additional NAD_{red}. Passage of its two electrons to oxygen yields three ATP's. Since each molecule of glucose provides two molecules of pyruvic acid, the total yield from this step is six ATP's per molecule of glucose.

In each revolution of the Krebs cycle, four pairs of electrons are produced, yielding a total of 12 ATP's for each acetyl-CoA and thus 24 ATP's per molecule of glucose.

If we add all these together, we can see that each molecule of glucose results in the formation of a total of 38 molecules of ATP from ADP. Only two of these are actually formed in the glycolytic sequence; the other 36 are formed by oxidative phosphorylation. In this way, an estimated 60 per cent of the energy of the glucose molecule ends up recovered or conserved in the form of useful energy available to the cell for work, with only 40 percent lost as heat and entropy in the process. In a gasoline engine, only 25 percent of the energy liberated during the combustion of the fuel is converted into work.

Energy Transfer in Cells
THE ATP CYCLE

Figure 1–99 shows the complete energy-transfer cycle in heterotrophic cells. ATP is the charged, or energy-rich, form of the energy-carrying system, and ADP and phosphate are the discharged form. The energy of the foodstuff molecules, released by the processes of glycolysis and respiration, continuously regenerates ATP in the mitochondria. The regenerated ATP diffuses to other parts of the cell, where the chemical energy it carries is used to perform the mechanical, osmotic, and chemical work of the cell. As the ATP energy is used, ADP and phosphate are formed—the spent end products, so to speak—and these return to the mitochondria to be recharged again to form ATP. Thus the energy-carrier system of the cell functions in a continuous dynamic cycle.

USES OF ATP ENERGY
Kinesis

The energy released from glucose and stored in ATP can be used for the contraction of muscle cells and so can be converted into kinetic energy. You will recall that muscle cells contain large and numerous mitochondria. The muscle proteins actin and myosin, in a complex called *actomyosin*, can be found to contract in the test tube in the presence of ATP; in fact, it was this reaction that provided the first evidence for the role of ATP as an energy carrier. It is now believed that ATP facilitates the sliding of actin and myosin filaments along each other to shorten the sarcomere, the basic contractile unit of muscle. In this process ATP is broken down to ADP. (See Figure 1–43.)

ATP also provides the energy for the movement of flagella and cilia. The flagellum of a sperm cell has long mitochondria wound helically around its base. It has been found that isolated flagella hydrolyze ATP to

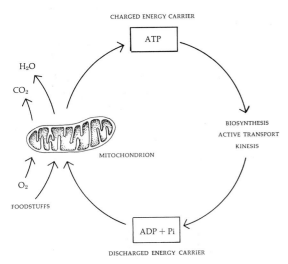

CHARGED ENERGY CARRIER

ATP

H_2O

CO_2

MITOCHONDRION

BIOSYNTHESIS
ACTIVE TRANSPORT
KINESIS

O_2

FOODSTUFFS

ADP + Pi

DISCHARGED ENERGY CARRIER

1–99 *In the energy-carrying system of the cell, ATP is the charged, or energy-rich, form produced in the mitochondrion by the energy extracted from foodstuff molecules. The ATP diffuses to other parts of the cell, where the energy it carries is used to perform the mechanical and chemical work of the cell. As the ATP energy is used, ADP and phosphate are formed, and these return to the mitochondrion to be regenerated into ATP.*

ADP and phosphate and that, as a consequence of this hydrolysis, the flagella move.

Active Transport

The energy of ATP is also used for active transport of substances across the cell membrane, as evidenced by the massing of mitochondria near the membranes of intestinal cells and other cells involved in pumping substances back and forth across cell membranes. By this process, the energy of ATP can be converted to electrical energy since, as you will recall, the unequal distribution of ions across the axon membrane is responsible for the movement of the nerve impulse. This conversion of chemical energy to electrical energy reaches its culmination in the electric eel; by means of active transport, the eel is able to build up enough electrical potential to deliver a shock of over 200 volts.

A striking example of active transport across a layer of cells is the formation of gastric hydrochloric acid from blood plasma. Gastric juice is the most acid of all body fluids, with a pH of about 1. Since blood plasma has a pH of 7.4, the H^+ ions are about 10^6 more concentrated in gastric juice than in blood plasma. Gastric HCl is formed along one side of a layer of specialized epithelial cells from the components of the blood which bathes the other side of the cell layer. To form an extremely acidic solution from a weakly acidic one in this way requires that hydrogen ions be transported from a region of low concentration to a region of high concentration. This is "going against the current," and a large amount of energy is needed for the process.

Biosynthesis

A chief use of the energy of ATP is the biosynthesis from small precursor molecules of the many different types of larger molecules needed by the cell—the amino acids, fatty acids, phospholipids, nucleotides, and other building blocks that make up the internal structures of the cell—and, in particular, the assembly of biological macromolecules such as protein. In fact, the synthesis of proteins from amino acids in rapidly growing cells, as in a bacterial culture, may require 85 percent of the total ATP energy generated by the respiration of the cell.

Biosynthesis of cell material is a never-ending, dynamic process; so long as life continues, the cell is constantly wearing out and rebuilding its machinery, growing and preparing to divide, disassembling large molecules into smaller ones, reprocessing some, pumping out breakdown products, and capturing and using energy. The biosynthetic processes are among the most complex of all the energy-requiring activities of living organisms. (Some of the details of one biosynthetic process, the assembly of amino acids into proteins, are given in Section 3.) Although the proc-

1–100 *Ribulose diphosphate is a five-carbon sugar with two ("di-") phosphate groups. Melvin Calvin and coworkers at the University of California, using radioactive carbon as a tracer, discovered that this sugar-phosphate is the compound that serves as the carbon dioxide acceptor in the "dark reactions" of photosynthesis.*

esses may differ in many respects, depending on the product being synthesized, the underlying principle is the same, however, in all biosynthetic processes: In coupled enzymatic reactions, the terminal phosphate groups of ATP are used, directly or indirectly, to activate a building-block (precursor) molecule so that it can link with the next building-block molecule. Once activated, parts are fitted together and assembled into molecules with astonishing precision and speed. The bacterial cell, for example, can assemble over 1,000 molecules of cell proteins *per second!*

Photosynthesis

Now that we have examined the energy transformations in the heterotrophic cell, we should consider how solar energy, which is the prime source of all biological energy, is harnessed by green plant cells in the process of photosynthesis.

Photosynthesis is the essential link in the flow of energy from the sun to the biosphere, and it is the first step in the energy-recovery process. We have chosen to discuss it last because it is a somewhat more complicated process than the oxidation of glucose and will be easier to understand in the light of the processes that we have just described.

The overall effect of photosynthesis is to reverse the process of respiration: energy is stored, carbon dioxide is reduced to organic compounds, and oxygen is liberated.

There are two steps in photosynthesis. The first is *photoelectron transport*, sometimes referred to as the "light reactions." Photoelectron transport resembles electron transport along the respiratory chain, with formation of ATP, which we just described—but in reverse. This "reverse" electron flow from water to NADP requires an input of energy. The energy

1–101 *Calvin and his collaborators briefly exposed photosynthesizing algae to radioactive carbon dioxide ($C^{14}O_2$). They found that the radioactive carbon is first incorporated into ribulose diphosphate which then immediately splits to form two molecules of phosphoglycerate (PGA). The radioactive carbon atom, indicated in color, next appears in one of the two molecules of PGA.*

comes from the absorption of sunlight by the plant's pigments. The second stage of photosynthesis is *reductive synthesis,* in which carbon dioxide is reduced to energy-rich organic compounds. Reductive synthesis is sometimes known as the "dark reactions" since the process can be carried out in the absence of light. Dark reactions are driven in the chloroplast, however, by $NADP_{red}$ and ATP from photoelectron transport produced by light energy.

PHOTOELECTRON TRANSPORT

We have seen that in the electron transport of the respiratory sequence, electrons move "downhill" in energy as they are passed along by electron carriers, cytochromes, which hold the electrons successively more tightly. Eventually the electrons are passed to oxygen, which holds electrons very strongly, and water is formed. As energy is released along the path, it is stored in the bonds of ATP.

In photoelectron transport, electrons are stripped from the oxygen of water and ultimately given to NADP, which holds electrons less tightly. To return to our analogy, they move "uphill." The energy to accomplish this comes from the sunlight which is absorbed by chlorophyll and other plant pigments.

Photoelectron transport begins when a photon, a particle of light, is absorbed by a molecule of chlorophyll or another pigment such as carotene. The energy level of the electrons in the molecule is increased by the absorption of the photon, and the molecule is "excited." In isolation, the excited pigment molecule would quickly remit the energy and the molecule would return to its ground state. In the membranes of the chloroplast, pigment molecules are organized into units made up of several hundred chlorophyll molecules plus carotenes, cytochromes, and other electron carriers. The pigment molecules are so close to each other in these units that an excited molecule can pass its energy to another molecule before the energy is reemitted as light energy.

In the array of pigment molecules, the packet of energy is passed around until it reaches a special energy-trapping center. At this trapping center, the energy is used to boost an electron "uphill" from a molecule that holds electrons tightly to a carrier that holds electrons loosely.

TWO LIGHT REACTIONS

There is now much evidence that there are two such steps in the photo-electron-transport sequence. In one of these, the molecule produced by removal of its tightly held electron is such a strong oxidant that it oxidizes water, producing O_2. The electron carrier receiving the electron passes it "downhill" to other carriers, including cytochromes. As it passes "down-

1–102 *The Calvin Cycle. In each complete cycle, three CO_2 molecules are added to three five-carbon sugar-phosphate molecules (RuDP). These first split and then are converted, using energy from ATP and $NADP_{red}$, to six three-carbon sugar-phosphates (glyceraldehyde phosphate). One of these is used for biosynthesis of carbohydrates, amino acids and other compounds essential to plant and animal life. The other five are rearranged to give three molecules of RuDP, thus completing the cycle.*

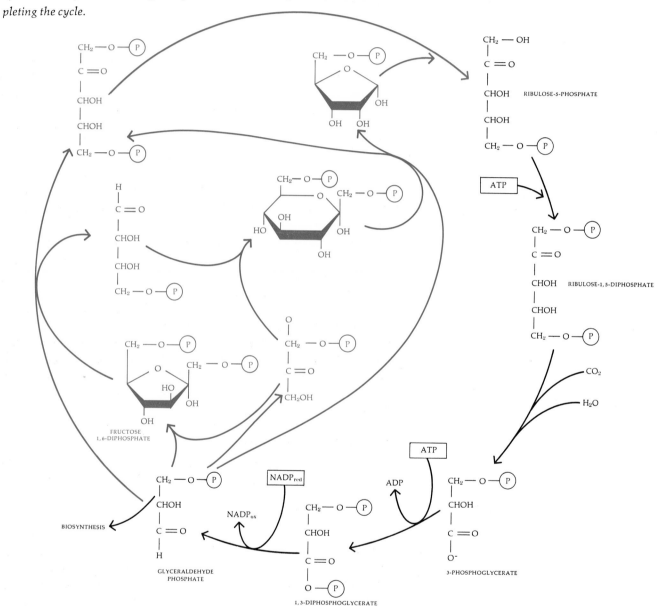

hill," enzymes convert its energy into ATP. This process is known as *photophosphorylation*.

When the electron has lost some of its energy, it is again boosted in energy by a second photochemical reaction. This reaction depends upon an array of pigments and carriers slightly different from those of the other light reaction. This time, the resulting reduced carrier is a strong reducing agent, an iron-protein complex called *ferredoxin*. Reduced ferredoxin can act directly as a reducing agent or can serve to reduce $NADP_{ox}$.

The exact number of ATP molecules produced for each pair of electrons that move from water to $NADP_{ox}$ is not known, but it appears to be one or two. Additional ATP may be produced by *cyclic photophosphorylation*. In cyclic photophosphorylation, electrons from reduced ferredoxin are cycled back through a phosphorylation step.

Although the scheme in Figure 1–103 accounts for most of the experimental observations on the light reactions of photosynthesis, it has recently been postulated that the two photochemical reactions may function independently of each other and thus share no common electron carriers.

REDUCTIVE SYNTHESIS

The $NADP_{red}$ and ATP formed during photoelectron transport provide the electrons and energy for the fixation of CO_2 and the reduction of bound CO_2 to carbohydrates and other products, such as fatty acids and amino acids. The formation of amino acids requires the reduction of the nitrates and sulfate taken up by the plants through their roots. At least part of these reduction reactions are directly dependent on $NADP_{red}$ and reduced ferredoxin from photoelectron transport.

Most of the $NADP_{red}$ and ATP are used to run the carbon-reduction cycle, or *Calvin cycle*, which incorporates CO_2 and produces sugar phosphates. The first step in this cycle is the addition of CO_2 and water to a five-carbon sugar diphosphate, ribulose diphosphate (Figure 1–100). The product splits, giving two molecules of 3-phosphoglycerate (PGA). The next four steps, leading to fructose 6-phosphate, are an almost exact reversal of glycolysis (Figure 1–93). Notice that glycolysis *produces* ATP and NAD_{red} and the Calvin cycle *uses* ATP and $NADP_{red}$.

In order to keep the cycle running, it is necessary for the plant to regenerate the CO_2 acceptor, RuDP. To accomplish this, the carbon chains of the sugar phosphates are rearranged so that five molecules of the three-carbon sugar phosphate glyceraldehyde phosphate are converted to three molecules of the five-carbon compound RuDP. The conversion of each of the three ribulose phosphate molecules to ribulose diphosphate, the step which completes the cycle, uses another ATP molecule (three in all).

For each complete turn of this cycle, the three ribulose diphosphate molecules gain three CO_2 molecules to make six molecules of 3-phosphoglycerate. Reduction of each of these with ATP and $NADP_{red}$ produces six glyceraldehyde phosphate molecules, one more than is required to regenerate the ribulose diphosphate molecules:

$$6\,NADP_{red} + 9\,ATP + 3\,CO_2 \rightarrow$$
$$C_3H_5O_3 - P + 6\,NADP_{ox} + 9\,ADP + 8\,P_i$$

The "extra" glyceraldehyde phosphate produced by the cycle is the starting point for the synthesis of carbohydrates, amino acids, and many other organic compounds made in green plant cells. Free glucose is not an important product of photosynthesis. Fructose 6-phosphate is converted

1–103 *The photoelectron transport reactions of photosynthesis. Light energy, absorbed in two pigment arrays as electromagnetic energy, migrates to traps where it is converted to chemical energy. This energy boosts electrons from chlorophyll, which holds electrons tightly, to acceptor molecules that hold them loosely. These electrons now pass "downhill" along a chain of carriers. The released energy is used to form ATP from ADP and inorganic phosphorus. The identities of some electron carriers are known, but not their precise sequence.*

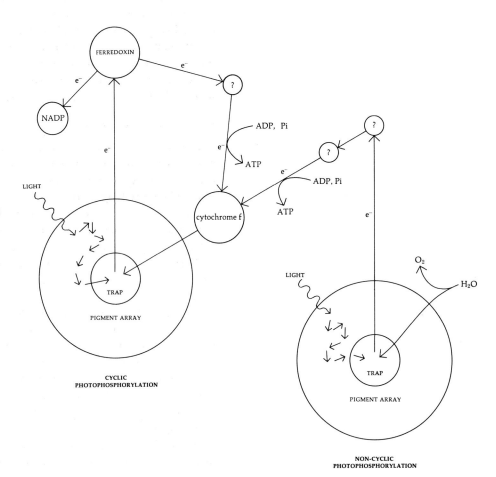

to glucose 6-phosphate, and these and other sugar phosphates are used directly by the chloroplasts for the synthesis of sucrose, starch, and other disaccharides and polysaccharides.

These compounds provide the stored energy which is released by glycolysis and the respiratory sequence of the mitochondrion and on which the cellular work of plant and animal cells depends.

SUMMARY

The force that drives the many processes of living is energy. Energy is either *potential* (inactive) or *kinetic* (active), and some of its different forms are chemical, electrical, mechanical, and radiant. Two principles govern all energy transformations: the *first law of thermodynamics*, that energy cannot be created or destroyed, only transformed; and the *second law of thermodynamics*, that entropy, or useless energy, steadily increases. Energy is useful when it is available to do work.

All biological energy arises from the sun; the energy of sunlight is used in the biosynthesis of energy-rich carbohydrate molecules from carbon dioxide and water. These molecules are then oxidized—"burned" as fuel—by the cell which produced it or by heterotrophic cells.

The first stage of the energy-flow sequence is *photosynthesis*. This process has two phases:

1   *Photoelectron transport*. This phase begins when a photon is absorbed by a molecule of chlorophyll or another plant pigment. The energy is trapped and converted to ATP and NAD_{red}.

2   *Reductive synthesis*. In this phase, carbon dioxide from the atmosphere is reduced to carbohydrates and other organic compounds using energy from photoelectron transport.

The breakdown of energy-rich carbohydrate molecules occurs in three phases:

1   *Glycolysis*. The glucose molecule is broken down into two molecules of pyruvic acid. The glycolytic process is anaerobic (oxygenless).

2   *Krebs cycle*. The pyruvic acid is oxidized to CO_2 and water by a cyclic enzyme system. Because this stage and the following one require free oxygen, they are together called the *respiratory sequence*.

3   *Electron-transport chain*. The high energy content of the electrons released during the preceding stages is accepted by a series of cytochromes, which form this emitted energy into ATP by a process known as *oxidative phosphorylation*.

The energy released from the glucose molecule and stored in ATP can be (1) converted into kinetic energy, (2) used for the active transport of substances across the cell membrane, or (3) used in the biosynthesis of molecules needed by the cell.

SUGGESTIONS FOR FURTHER READING

AFZELIUS, BJORN: *Anatomy of the Cell,* The University of Chicago Press, Chicago, 1966.*

A good brief discussion of the functional anatomy of the cell, with emphasis on those specific areas of cell biology in which the functional organization is best known.

GIESE, ARTHUR C.: *Cell Physiology,* 2d ed., W. B. Saunders Company, Philadelphia, 1962.

A description of the major problems in cell physiology; intended for the more advanced student.

KENNEDY, DONALD (ED.): *The Living Cell: Readings from the Scientific American,* W. H. Freeman and Company, San Francisco, 1965.*

A collection of articles and photographs which have appeared in the Scientific American, with some new material; lively and readable.

LEHNINGER, ALBERT L.: *Bioenergetics: The Molecular Basis of Biological Energy Transformations,* W. A. Benjamin, Inc., New York, 1965.*

A clear, well-written account of the flow of energy in living systems.

PORTER, K. R., AND M. A. BONNEVILLE: *An Introduction to the Fine Structure of Cells and Tissues,* 2d ed., Lea & Febiger, Philadelphia, 1965. (Available in loose-leaf form.)

A collection of many superb electron micrographs accompanied by text which is both concise and informative.

SWANSON, CARL: *The Cell,* 2d ed., Prentice-Hall, Inc., Englewood Cliffs, N.J., 1964.*

A discussion of the cell for the layman; nicely illustrated and particularly good in the area of chromosomal mechanics.

VROMAN, LEO: *Blood,* The Natural History Press, Garden City, N.Y., 1967.

An informal account of one man's work that shows the intimate relationships between biology, biochemistry, and medicine.

WILSON, E. B.: *The Cell in Development and Inheritance,* 3d ed., Macmillan and Company, New York, 1925.

Although this book is now more than 40 years old, it is still the best introduction to the vast classical literature on the cell.

* Available in paperback.

ORGANISMS

(Dr. Ross E. Hutchins)

The Naming of Living Organisms

Chapter 2–1

All of us have names for things that are important to us. If you like saltwater fishing, you are very likely able to tell a mackerel from a bluefish from a striped bass without a moment's hesitation, while others may know the name only of something spectacular, like a shark. On the other hand, the person who cannot tell a snapper from a flounder may know the names of all the local flowers. Gauchos, the cowboys of Argentina who are famous for their horsemanship, have some two hundred names for different colors of horses but divide all the plants known to them into four groups: *pasto*, or fodder; *paja*, or bedding; *cardo*, wood; and *yuyos*, everything else.

Once we get beyond the range of common plants and animals and perhaps a few uncommon ones that are of special interest to us, we usually run out of names. Some 700,000 different kinds of insects, for instance, have been named and classified. How many of these can you identify exactly? Are you even sure a particular "bug" is an insect?

John Ray and the Catalog of Nature

Suppose you set out to catalog all the organisms in the world and to arrange them systematically, that is, in some order that makes sense. An Englishman, John Ray, set out to do just that in the middle of the seventeenth century. If you had been Ray, you would have faced two problems. First, how do you decide what you mean by a *kind* of individual? How similar do two individuals have to be before you decide they are the same kind, or *species*? How different do they have to be before you decide they are two different kinds? This is a particularly difficult problem for plants since individuals in different situations may be drastically modified by the environment. Ray used the word "species" to describe a morpho-

159   *The Naming of Living Organisms*

logically (*morphe* means "shape" in Greek) distinct type that can reproduce its own kind from seed. Whatever was reproduced from a seed was also a member of that species, no matter how different the offspring of a particular individual might look. In other words, he tied the concept of species to the concept of heredity, which fits in, of course, with our experience about kinds of organisms—that a cat, for instance, may have an unusual or abnormal kitten but that it will never give birth to a rabbit.

The other question that you would have faced was how to group the kinds, or species, of organisms. Aristotle had been concerned with this problem. He recognized that you could not choose any single characteristic and end up with groups that made sense. For instance, suppose you decided to group all the animals into those that fly and those that do not. You would end up with one category that included most insects, most birds, bats, and even an occasional squirrel, and you would have to separate some obviously close relations, such as the winged and the wingless ants which occur as members of the same colony. Ray and Aristotle both understood that one had to look not just at one criterion, but at the overall "plan" of a

2–1 *From left to right, the arm and hand of a man, the flipper of a whale, and the wing of a bird. As you can see, these organs, although superficially different, are built on the same basic plan. They are therefore known as* homologous. *Organs that serve similar purposes but are different in the essentials of their structure, such as the wings of an insect and a bat, are* analagous. *Today it is known that homology reflects a common ancestry while analogy reveals only a common function.*

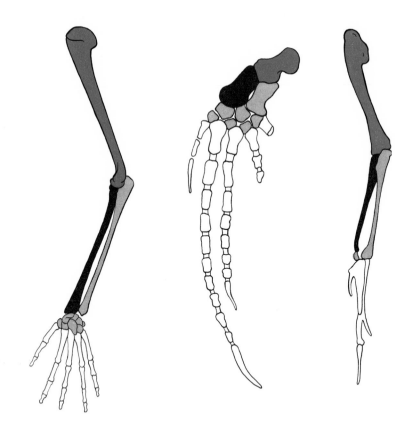

2–2 *Strawberry plant from a French herbal dated about 550 A.D. The picture has obviously been drawn from another picture and not from the plant itself. The leaves are incorrectly shown in groups of four and five instead of in groups of three, and the "runners" are too numerous. (Courtesy of the University of Leiden Library)*

plant or animal before assigning it a place in the scheme of nature. On the basis of overall similarities, an organism could be grouped with other forms in some more inclusive entity: "fish," "bird," "warbler," and so forth.

As you know from your studies of history, Aristotle and John Ray were separated by 2,000 years. During most of this period, interest in science and in the natural world languished. The one exception was the plants, which were cataloged because of their use in medicine. In these medieval catalogs, called *herbals*, plants were arranged alphabetically or, more likely, by what they were supposed to be good for. The lists were accompanied by drawings, but as these drawings were copied from text to text and as the individual artists tended to lend their own embellishments, the drawings became more decorative and more stylized and bore less and less resemblance to any living organism.

In the fifteenth and sixteenth centuries, several new developments stimulated a revival of the study of nature. From the voyages of discovery, the inhabitants of England and the Continent began to hear intriguing tales of

161   *The Naming of Living Organisms*

2–3 *Acorn and leaves of the stalked oak (Quercus robur) from one of the notebooks of Leonardo da Vinci. Leonardo was fascinated by the world around him, and his notebooks are filled with close observations. "The leaf always turns its upper side toward the sky," he noted, ". . . and these leaves are arranged on the plants in such a way that one covers another as little as possible." (Reproduced by permission of Her Majesty Queen Elizabeth, Royal Library, Windsor)*

strange and varied forms of life from distant lands and even to see some specimens of exotic flora and fauna. This stirred great interest in the natural world and opened many eyes to a fresh view of what was around them. Secondly, there was a revolution in art. Artists became interested in depicting the world as it actually appeared to them. They, too, looked at nature with a fresh and curious eye and even, as in the case of Leonardo da Vinci, dissected plants, animals, flowers, eyes, and hands and tried to understand how they functioned. Artists were scientists, and scientists, artists. In Botticelli's famous *Primavera*, painted in 1478, over 30 different species of plants are depicted in exquisite detail. And, as a corollary, the work of Vesalius, the great sixteenth century anatomist, is illustrated with drawings still treasured by art collectors. John Ray, a clergyman in the Church of England, began by looking about him and cataloging the plants in the vicinity of Cambridge, the first complete catalog of one locality ever to be made. Then, traveling through England and the Continent, he worked his way, astonishingly, through all the plants that he could learn about (almost 19,000) and the birds, the fishes, and the four-footed animals.

Binomials: The "Two-name" System

At the time of Ray and for a number of years thereafter, plants and animals were designated by cumbersome phrase names, or *polynomials*. These polynomials were brief descriptive phrases concerning the plant or animal to which they were applied. The first word in the polynomial had come, by the close of the seventeenth century, to designate the *genus*, an inclusive group of similar species. Thus, the numerous kinds of rose were grouped in the genus *Rosa*, many butterflies in the genus *Papilio*, and cats and catlike animals in the genus *Felis*. This grouping into genera simplified the system a great deal, since there are far fewer genera than species. Once a genus was described, its attributes could be expected to apply to all the included species. Thus the house cat and the lion share certain distinguishing features by which they are grouped together in the genus, *Felis*, but they also have distinctive features which place them as different species of this genus.

A very important advance in the system of classifying living things was made by the eighteenth century Swedish encyclopedist Carolus Linnaeus, whose ambition was to prepare books that listed all the known kinds of plants and animals (and even minerals!) under their genera. In 1753, he published a two-volume work, *Species Plantarum* ("the kinds of plants"), which contained brief analytical descriptions of every known species of plant, with references to the earlier works about each one. He used the familiar polynomial designations for all species, in some cases changing them so that they would fit better into his system. He regarded these polynomials as the proper names for species, but he also made a very important innovation. In the margin of his book, opposite the "proper" name of each species, he included a single word which, taken together with the generic name, would form a convenient "shorthand" designation for the species. The convenience of this system, by which every species of plant and animal would have a simple two-part name, was so obvious that Linnaeus and subsequent authors soon replaced the "proper" name with the "shorthand" one. The resulting *binomial* ("two-name") system has persisted to the present day.

Linnaeus followed his work on the species of plants with a synoptical treatment of the genera of plants—*Genera Plantarum* (1754)—and these two works have been taken as the starting point for the modern names of plants. No names published earlier, or not published in accordance with the binomial system, are in use today. In 1758, Linnaeus published the tenth edition of his monumental descriptive catalog of known animals—*Systema Naturae*—and here he brought the names for animals into conformity with his increasingly popular binomial system.

In some cases, Linnaeus found it convenient to subdivide species into varieties—elements classed together as a single species but differing in one or a group of important respects and hence given a distinctive name. Subsequent authors have divided species into subspecies, with the result that some names of plants and animals consist of three parts, but the binomial name is still the basis of classification. As we have seen, the name of a species consists of two parts, the genus and the specific epithet (which is never written alone but is always preceded by the name of the genus). By convention, these names are written in italics; thus the brown house rat, or Norway rat, is *Rattus norvegicus* and the black rat, also known as the roof rat, is *Rattus rattus*. The California live oak is *Quercus agrifolia*, and the Eastern red oak is *Quercus rubra*. For precise citation, the name of the author who first applied this name is added, and sometimes other information, such as the date of publication, but these details need not concern us here.

The Major Categories of Living Things

Linnaeus (and earlier scientists) recognized the plant, animal, and mineral kingdoms, and the *kingdom* is still the major division used in biological classification. Between the level of genus and the level of kingdom, however, subsequent authors in the nineteenth and twentieth centuries have added a number of categories. Thus, genera are grouped into *families*, families into *orders*, orders into *classes*, and classes into *phyla* (singular: phylum). In botanical classification, *division* is conventionally used instead of phylum. These categories may be subdivided or aggregated into a number of less important categories.

Table 2–1 shows how this works out for a plant, for an insect, and for man. Do not bother to memorize the details, but notice how much you know about an organism when you know its place in the system. For instance, once you were able to identify the insect in your garden as a beetle, you would, if you knew the characteristics of the group in which it was included, know not only how it was put together but a great deal about its life history.

Table 2–1 *Biological Classifications*

1 RED MAPLE

Category	Name	Description
Kingdom	Plantae	Organisms which usually have rigid cell walls and which usually possess chlorophyl
Subkingdom	Embryophyta	Plants forming embryos
Division	Tracheophyta	Vascular plants
Subdivision	Pteropsida	Generally large conspicuous leaves, complex vascular pattern
Class	Angiospermae	Flowering plants, seed enclosed in ovary
Subclass	Dicotyledonae	Embryo with two seed leaves (cotyledons)
Order	Sapindales	Soapberry order; trees and shrubs
Family	Aceraceae	Maple family; trees of temperate regions
Genus	*Acer*	Maples and box elder
Species	*Acer rubrum*	Red maple

Category	Name	Description
Kingdom	Animalia	Multicellular organisms requiring organic plant and animal substances for food
Phylum	Arthropoda	Segmented animals with external skeleton and jointed legs
Class	Insecta	Arthropods with three pairs of legs, one pair of antennae, compound eyes, and body divided into three sections
Order	Coleoptera	Beetles; insects that undergo complete metamorphosis, have chewing mouth parts and hardened front wings that meet in a straight line down the middle of the back
Family	Lampyridae	Fireflies and glowworms; nocturnal beetles, often with phosphorescent organs
Genus	*Microphotus*	Glowworms; sexes dimorphic, the females larvalike
Species	*Microphotus angustus*	Pink glowworm

3 MAN

Category	Name	Description
Kingdom	Animalia	Multicellular organisms requiring organic plant and animal substances for food
Phylum	Chordata	Animals with notochord, dorsal hollow nerve cord, gills in pharynx at some stage of life cycle
Subphylum	Vertebrata	Spinal cord enclosed in a vertebral column, body basically segmented; skull enclosing brain
Superclass	Tetrapoda	Land vertebrates, four-legged
Class	Mammalia	Young nourished by milk glands; breathing by lungs; skin with hair or fur; body cavity divided by diaphragm; red corpuscles without nuclei; constant body temperature
Order	Primata	Tree dwellers, usually with fingers and flat nails, sense of smell reduced
Family	Hominidae	Flat face, eyes forward, color vision, upright, two-legged, with hands and feet differently specialized
Genus	*Homo*	Large brain, speech, long childhood
Species	*Homo sapiens*	Prominent chin, high forehead, sparse body hair

A hundred years after the publication of Linnaeus's great work, *The Origin of Species* appeared, and the classifications of Linnaeus took on a new meaning. Linnaeus treated the kinds of organisms as if each had existed since the beginning of time. Some had become extinct, as revealed by the fossil record, but those still alive were assumed to have always been more or less constant in appearance and other characteristics. Similarities between organisms—the properties by which individuals might be grouped into species or species into genera, for example—were left unexplained.

The theory of evolution demonstrated that these resemblances were the result of a common origin, representing the effects of a process that had happened and indeed was still happening. Today the species is seen as a population of similar individuals, varying from one to another and flowing and changing as a group through time and space. Evolutionary theory has thus provided a theoretical basis for the logical grouping of living things even though it did not change the existing system of classification.

A Question of Kingdoms

The eighteenth century taxonomists, as we mentioned previously, divided all living things into two kingdoms, the plants and the animals. In recent years, there has been increasing dissatisfaction with this simple division into two main categories. In the case of the higher forms, this does not present any problems, but for the more primitive types (those that evolved earlier), the distinction is not meaningful or useful. For example, studies of the structure and biochemistry of the bacteria and the blue-green algae have revealed that these two groups are very like each other and quite different from either the plants or the animals. Therefore, some biologists put the bacteria and the blue-green algae in a different kingdom, the Monera (from the Greek *monos*, meaning "alone"), a practice which we shall follow in this book. Many scientists also group the one-celled animals and the algae into a separate Kingdom, the Protista, a system which we do not follow.

Problems such as this about classification are the concern of professional taxonomists and not the proper subject of this book. We have mentioned them here both to explain why we are using a system with which you may not be familiar and to emphasize the fact that the purpose of classifying plants and animals is not so much to fit everything into its own pigeonhole as to provide useful ways for people to think and communicate about the world of nature.

2–4 *The three kingdoms in which most biologists classify all living things. As you can see, the plants and animals evolved from eucaryotic cells (cells with nuclear membranes), while bacteria and blue-green algae evolved separately, from procaryotic cells (without nuclear membranes). Can you explain what the question marks indicate about the slime molds and fungi?*

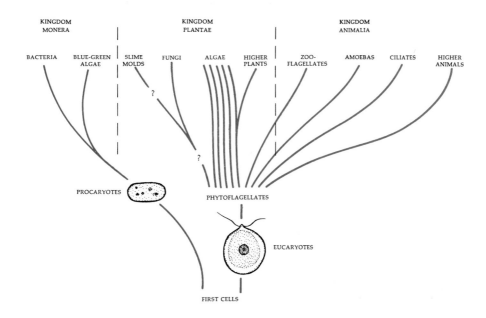

KINGDOM
MONERA

KINGDOM
PLANTAE

KINGDOM
ANIMALIA

BACTERIA   BLUE-GREEN   SLIME   FUNGI   ALGAE   HIGHER   ZOO-   AMOEBAS   CILIATES   HIGHER
            ALGAE   MOLDS   PLANTS   FLAGELLATES   ANIMALS

?

?

PROCARYOTES

PHYTOFLAGELLATES

EUCARYOTES

FIRST CELLS

SUMMARY

In this chapter, we traced the history of our present methods for naming living organisms and for grouping them together in orderly and logical ways. *Systematics,* as this field is called, had its beginnings in the fifteenth and sixteenth centuries as a part of the renewed general interest in the natural world.

In the eighteenth century, the binomial ("two-name") system, which has persisted until the present day, was introduced. The binomial consists of two parts, the name of the genus and that of the species. Additional categories of classification were added in the nineteenth and twentieth cen-

167   *The Naming of Living Organisms*

turies. Genera are now grouped into *families*; families into *orders*; orders into *classes*, and classes into *phyla* or, in the case of plants, into *divisions*; and phyla and divisions into *kingdoms*.

This method of naming and classifying living things permits the biologist to designate very precisely the particular organism with which he is working, an essential factor in scientific communication. To the trained biologist, the classification of an organism also reveals in a convenient shorthand form many details of its structure and function. Evolutionary theory—which states that organisms are related to one another by heredity and that some are more closely related than others—provides the theoretical basis for classification of living things.

Bacteria, Viruses, and Blue-green Algae

The bacteria and blue-green algae that make up the Kingdom Monera are the simplest of the one-celled organisms in terms of organization and structure and probably bear the closest resemblance of any modern organisms to the earliest forms of life on earth. The most striking difference between the Monera and the cells we examined in Section 1 is that the Monera lack any membrane around the nucleus; they are therefore known as *procaryotic*. (This is a word composed of *pro*, meaning "before," and *karyon*, which means "nut" or "kernel" in Greek, just as *nucleus* means "nut" or "kernel" in Latin.) Cells which have a nuclear membrane are known as *eucaryotic*, or "truly nucleated." The hereditary material of the Monera is DNA, as it is in all cells, but in the procaryotic cell the DNA is not organized into chromosomes but is found in pools within the cytoplasm. For convenience, these pools of DNA are also called *nuclei*, although some authorities feel that the term should be reserved for eucaryotic cells. The procaryotic cell contains ribosomes, but it does not have the complex endoplasmic reticulum of eucaryotic cells, nor does it have mitochondria.

The Bacteria

Bacteria are the smallest cellular organisms. Most of them measure less than 8 microns in length. Figure 2–5 shows the structure of a generalized bacterial cell; that is, it shows the features usually found in all bacteria, although it does not exactly resemble any one cell. As you can see, the organization is comparatively simple.

The relatively unstructured cytoplasm is surrounded by a cell membrane and then by a cell wall which is a combination of sugars and protein woven together in a macromolecular mesh. Outside the bacterial cell wall is often found a slimy sheath of polysaccharides secreted by the cell.

Bacterial cells do not divide mitotically, but rather each cell simply gets larger and then finally splits in two. In a thriving colony of bacteria, two to four nuclei are commonly present in each cell; apparently, nuclear division proceeds more rapidly than cell division.

Many bacteria, particularly bacilli, can form thick-walled dry spores, in which they may stay dormant for years. Some of these spores can remain viable even when boiled for as long as two hours, although fortunately this is not true of most common disease-causing (pathogenic) forms.

Figure 2–6 shows representatives of the three major groups of bacteria. The rod-shaped forms are known as *bacilli*, the spherical forms are *cocci*, and the spiral-shaped bacteria are *spirilli*. As the picture shows, the cocci tend to remain together when they divide—in pairs, long chains, flat plates, or cubical packets, depending on the plane of division, which is typical of a species. For instance, the cocci that cause pneumonia remain in pairs (each pair is a diplococcus); the chainlike forms are streptococcus; and the grapelike clusters are staphylococcus.

The rod-shaped bacilli are more commonly found alone. When they do remain together, they spread out end to end, in filaments, since they always divide transversely. Because these filaments are funguslike in appearance, the combining form *myco* (from the Greek word for fungus) is often a part of the name of these organisms and is a clue to their appearance. *Mycobacterium tuberculosis*, for instance, is a rod-shaped bacterium that forms a filamentous growth, or *mycelium*.

The total amount of bacteria by weight in the world exceeds that of all other organisms, and bacteria can survive in environments that support no other form of life. The chief reasons for their success, in these biological terms, are their rapid rate of cell division and the fact that the bacteria, more than any other group of organisms, have a wide variety of means for eking out a living. They use glucose as their chief energy source, as do the eucaryotic cells, whose metabolism was previously described, but they have an extraordinary number of ways for making or obtaining glucose. Unlike animal and many plant cells, many bacteria can survive in the absence of organic materials. Some of them are photosynthetic, although their photosynthetic pigments, which appear in small granules, do not resemble the chlorophyll in the cells of plants. Also, unlike plants, their photosynthesis is always carried out in the absence of oxygen, which leads one to speculate that these bacteria may be the descendants of a larger group that thrived in the oxygenless atmosphere of our young planet. Some of the photosynthetic bacteria perform their photosynthesis "in the dark," that is, in the presence of light (infrared) not visible to us. Other bacteria are chemosynthetic; these cells are able to oxidize inorganic substances to obtain energy for synthesizing glucose. The best known of the chemosynthetic types are the sulfur bacteria, which oxidize hydrogen sulfide first

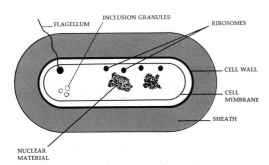

2–5 *Diagram showing the general structure of a bacterial cell. Bacteria are the smallest of living cells and have fewer special parts than other living things. The cytoplasm and the fibrillar nuclear material are surrounded by a cell membrane and cell wall. Some bacteria secrete a slimy material, which accumulates around the outside of the cell wall, forming a capsule, or sheath. The inclusion granules shown in the cytoplasm are reserve foods and pigments. What particular characteristic of these cells classifies them as procaryotic?*

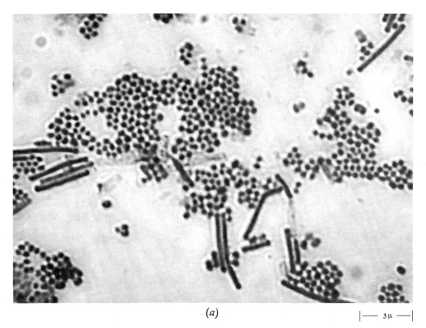

(a) |— 3μ —|

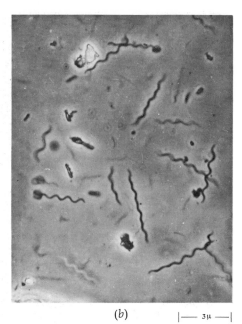

(b) |— 3μ —|

2–6 *The three major groups of bacteria. In (a) are shown rodlike bacilli and round cocci; and in (b) are shown spiral-shaped spirilli. (Eric V. Gravé)*

into free sulfur, which is stored as droplets, and then into sulfate (–SO₄) compounds as further energy may be needed.

Most bacteria, however, live on organic substances produced by other organisms. Parasitic bacteria are the kind that we are the most familiar with since they are the ones that derive their energy from living organisms, often at the expense of their hosts. These are the disease-causing bacteria.

Despite their bad reputation, most bacteria are harmless. The most common bacterial inhabitant of our digestive tract, for example, is *Escherichia coli,* a rod-shaped bacterium which, although it shares our nourishment, does us no harm and, in fact, is believed to serve the useful function of crowding out the disease-causing species. In the cow and other grass-eating animals, bacteria (and protozoans as well) are absolutely necessary elements of the digestive system. The cow has no means of digesting cellulose, which is the chief material in its diet. In the first two stomachs of the cow, the bacteria digest the cellulose, releasing some of it in the form of digestible fatty acids and using the rest for their own multiplication. Then, in the next two stomachs of the cow, the bacteria themselves are digested, providing the cow with its needed proteins. This association is an example of *symbiosis.* Organisms are said to be symbiotic when the association between them benefits both. Although many individ-

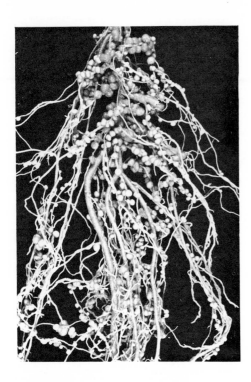

2–7 *Nitrogen fixation by legumes is illustrated by the roots of birdsfoot trefoil (Lotus corniculatus). The swellings, or nodules, on the roots are caused by specialized bacteria, which penetrate the root hairs and stimulate the cells to divide. Using sugar or other compounds obtained from the plant as a source of energy, the symbiotic bacteria reduce the nitrogen of the air to ammonia, forming nitrate fertilizer. This benefits not only the bacteria and the legumes but also any other plant in the neighborhood. (Courtesy of The Nitragin Company, Inc.)*

ual bacteria are sacrificed in stomachs three and four, the species flourishes —warm, wet, protected, and well nourished—in stomachs one and two.

Another important service performed by bacteria is nitrification, which is carried out by certain soil-dwelling species. These bacteria have the ability to oxidize the ammonia released into the soil from decaying organic material into nitrogen-containing salts, nitrates, and nitrites. As a result, the nitrogen is not lost from the soil in the form of gas but remains there for use in the making of proteins by plant bodies.

Bacteria of the genus *Rhizobium* ("root dweller") infect the roots of leguminous plants, such as alfalfa, clover, and beans, forming nodules. The root hairs and the bacteria in combination are able to use free nitrogen (that is, nitrogen as it is present in the air) for their metabolism, although neither can use free nitrogen if it is not in association with the other. When crops are rotated to conserve soil fertility, one of the crops is always a leguminous plant, since these plants enrich rather than deplete the nitrogen content of a field.

A striking example of the capacity of the nitrogen-fixing bacteria to improve the fertility of the soil was seen in an experiment carried out by the U.S. Forest Service near Athens, Ohio. A planting of cedar trees was set out in an area of very poor soil. In one part of the area, a number of locust trees were set among the cedars. Locusts, which are legumes, carry nitrogen-fixing bacteria on their roots. Eleven years later, the cedar trees that had been planted alone averaged 30 inches high, while those planted among the locusts had grown to an average of 7 feet.

In the overall economy of nature, however, it is the saprophytic bacteria that make the greatest contribution. Saprophytes are organisms which live on dead organic materials. The characteristic dank smell of rich soil, or humus, is caused by the bacteria which live in the soil. These bacteria break down dead plant and animal matter and, by thus enriching the soil, return the material to the food chain.

The Viruses

Until we know more about the origin of the viruses, it is convenient to classify them in the Monera kingdom. If viruses can be said to be alive, they are the simplest forms of living things. They are not cells; they consist only of a strand of nucleic acid surrounded by a coat of protein. The largest, the pox virus, is on the borderline of visibility with the light microscope. Many viruses have been visualized for the first time only in the last few years as a result of advances in the techniques of electron microscopy.

Outside of living cells, viruses are lifeless chemicals; many of them can, in fact, be crystallized. Once in a living cell, the viral nucleic acid, freed of its protein coat, uses the metabolic machinery of the cell to produce hun-

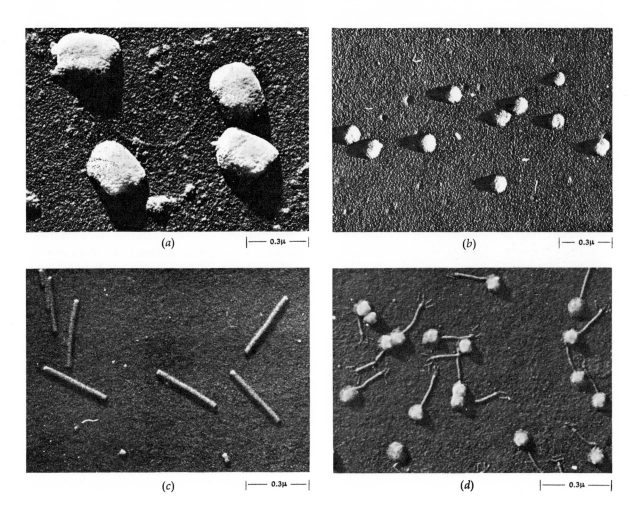

(a) |— 0.3μ —|

(b) |— 0.3μ —|

(c) |— 0.3μ —|

(d) |— 0.3μ —|

2–8 *Electron micrographs of a few of the many different kinds of viruses: (a) Vaccinia virus, prepared from a small-pox vaccine. (b) Human influenza virus, strain PR-8. (c) Rods of tobacco mosaic virus. (d) A bacterial virus (T5 bacteriophage), showing the head, tail, and short tail fibers. (Courtesy of the Virus Laboratory, University of California, Berkeley)*

dreds, and sometimes thousands, of new virus particles, complete with protein jackets, which are then released from the cell. The type of cell that a particular virus can infect depends primarily on its protein outercoating, which sticks to the surface of a susceptible cell and not to that of an unsusceptible one. Different types of viruses are usually very specific as to the cells they can infect. For example, the virus that causes chicken pox multiplies in the cells of the skin, while viruses that cause the common cold specialize in the cells lining the upper respiratory tract. Almost all plant and animal cells, and even the bacteria, are susceptible to particular viruses.

A few of the many different kinds of viruses are shown in Figure 2–8. Some scientists believe that viruses may resemble the earliest beginnings

173   *Bacteria, Viruses, and Blue-green Algae*

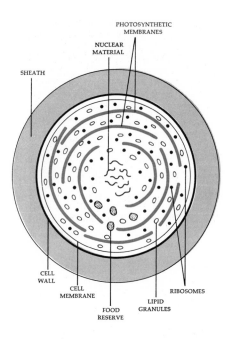

PHOTOSYNTHETIC
MEMBRANES

NUCLEAR
MATERIAL

SHEATH

CELL
WALL

CELL
MEMBRANE

FOOD
RESERVE

LIPID
GRANULES

RIBOSOMES

2–9 *Diagram showing the general structure of the blue-green algae. Unlike bacteria, blue-green algae contain chlorophyll. In other ways, however, this cell resembles the bacterial cell. Both possess an abundance of ribosomes, both are procaryotic —that is, the nuclear material, consisting of DNA fibrils, is not surrounded by a nuclear membrane—and both are enclosed by a cell membrane, a cell wall, and often a mucilaginous sheath.*

of life, but since viruses can live and multiply only as parasites, it seems more reasonable to suppose that they originated as bacterialike organisms which lost their metabolic faculties or perhaps even as particles of cells which took up an independent existence. This last possibility will be considered in more detail in the chapters on genetics (Section 3), a science to which the viruses have made a large contribution.

The Blue-green Algae

The blue-green algae, like the bacteria but unlike all other cells, are procaryotic. They have no nuclear membrane, no mitochondria, and no endoplasmic reticulum. Like all photosynthetic organisms, they contain chlorophyll and two other types of pigments, a carotene and a xanthophyll, both of which are also light absorbers. In addition, the blue-green algae have two unusual pigments, the *phycobilins*, one of which is blue and the other red. The phycobilins give the blue-greens their characteristic colors. The photosynthetic pigments, although associated with membranes, are not packed neatly into chloroplasts, as they are in the eucaryotic cells, but are scattered through the cytoplasm. Also like the bacteria but unlike all other cells, the blue-green algae have cell walls which contain protein. They store their food in the form of glycogen, rather than starch as do almost all the higher plants. Like many of the bacteria, the cell has an outer mucilaginous sheath or coating. (See Figure 2–9.)

About 1,500 species of blue-green algae are known. Some characteristic types are shown in Figure 2–10. Each cell is a bright-colored sphere, about 10 microns in diameter. A few of the blue-greens live as individual cells, but usually the cells are strung together in long filaments, which can sometimes be seen by the unaided eye as a soft floating mat on the water or as a damp mosslike growth on the land. Any cell within the filament may divide, and as the delicate threads grow longer as a result of cell division, they fragment into new filaments. The cells are attached to one another only by their outer walls, and each cell leads an independent existence. The filaments move through the water with a slow gliding motion, although how this is done is not known, since the cells lack flagella or any other visible means of locomotion.

Despite their name, only about half of these algae are actually bluegreen. The outer sheath is often deeply pigmented, particularly in species that spread up onto the land, and their colors include a light golden yellow, brown, red, emerald green, blue, violet, and blue-black. Almost all of them need only oxygen, light, and inorganic substances to survive. Like the bacteria, they are adaptable to extremely inhospitable environments, from the near-boiling water of hot springs to the melting ice floes of the Arctic. Some species can fix nitrogen, as can some species of bacteria. In South-

2–10 *While some blue-green algae occur as single cells, most form colonies, usually filamentous in structure. Shown here are two common types of algal filaments. Oscillatoria (a) is probably the most widely distributed. It derives its name from the fact that the filaments move through the water with a slow, oscillating movement. In the Nostoc genus (b), the cells are cylindrical, giving the filament the appearance of a string of beads. Notice the larger, oblong shapes. These are thick-walled spores, known as resting spores, which are resistant to heat and drying and which contain accumulated food materials. (Eric V. Gravé (a), Dr. M. S. Fuller (b))*

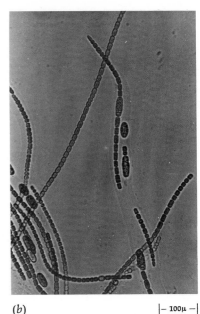

(a) |——— 100μ ———| (b) |— 100μ —|

east Asia, rice can be grown on the same land for years without the addition of fertilizers because of the rich growth of blue-green algae in the waterlogged rice paddies.

The chief methods of reproduction among the blue-green algae are (1) simple cell division and (2) the production of *spores*. Spores are single cells from which a whole organism can be produced. They are often surrounded by tough outer walls, which are resistant to dryness or to temperature extremes. Blue-green algae often lie dormant in the form of spores during the winter or when the pond or stream in which they are living dries up.

The blue-greens are often the first organisms to colonize bare areas of rock and soil. A dramatic example of such colonization was seen on the island of Krakatoa in Indonesia, which was denuded of all visible plant life by its cataclysmic volcanic explosion of 1883. Filamentous blue-green algae were the first living things to appear on the pumice and volcanic ash; within a few years they had formed a dark-green gelatinous growth. The layer of blue-green algae eventually became thick enough to provide a soil for the growth of higher plants. The algae further contributed to soil formation by acting to break down the surface of the rock.

The many structural, chemical, and metabolic resemblances between the bacteria and the blue-green algae have only recently been recognized. These affinities have been further emphasized by discoveries of very early fossils, reaching back 3 1/2 billion years into the past, long before life was once thought to have existed. These fossils show microscopic traces of cells that closely resemble both the bacteria and the blue-greens. In addition, certain modern filamentous, gliding organisms, once generally regarded as bacteria, have now been identified on the basis of their structure as colorless derivatives of filamentous blue-green algae. One of the most common of this group is *Beggiatoa,* a form that can be found in nature wherever hydrogen sulfide is in contact with the atmosphere. It is usually found near sulfur springs and on the surface of black mud. Now there is general agreement that both bacteria and blue-green algae probably sprang from one procaryotic ancestral line.

SUMMARY

The Monera kingdom includes the bacteria and the blue-green algae. These one-celled organisms are *procaryotic* ("pre-nucleated"). They differ from other, *eucaryotic* ("well-nucleated") cells in that their hereditary material is not organized into chromosomes.

Bacteria are best known for their pathogenic forms. The majority are not harmful to man, however, and many of them play important ecological roles. Nitrifying bacteria convert nitrogen to a form in which it can be used by plants, and saprophytic bacteria break down the bodies of dead plants and animals, returning the organic materials to the food chain.

Viruses are composed of nucleic acids surrounded by a protective protein coating. They can multiply only within a living cell, which is often damaged or destroyed by the parasitic relationship. It is believed that viruses may have originated as bacteria-like organisms, which subsequently lost many of their structures and functions in their adaptation to parasitism.

The blue-green algae, of which about 1,500 species are known, are procaryotic, like bacteria, but they contain chlorophyll and are photosynthetic. They also contain special pigments, the phycobilins, which give them their characteristic colors. Widely distributed in nature, they are found on both fresh and salt water and on damp ground. They are among the first organisms to colonize bare rock, which they may help to make suitable for growth of higher plants.

Chapter 2—3

The First Plants: The Thallophytes

Plants can be divided naturally into two general groups. The first includes the algae and the fungi, which are sometimes referred to as *lower plants.* These comparatively simple plants, well adapted to life in the water, preceded the more complex forms, the true land plants, which we shall discuss in Chapter 2–4. All fossil evidence supports this concept.

The "lower" plants are also sometimes known as *thallophytes.* A thallus is a plant body without roots, stems, and leaves that possess water-conducting tissue, or xylem, and in which the egg does not develop in a complex multicellular structure such as an ovary. A thallus may be composed of a single cell or many billions of cells. The two principal groups of thallophytes are the photosynthetic algae and the nonphotosynthetic fungi.

THE ALGAE

The algae make up the first six divisions of the plant kingdom* and comprise thousands of different kinds of organisms. They inhabit fresh and salt waters from the tropics to the Poles and from the melting ice of the glaciers to the near-boiling water of hot springs. More than 90 percent of the photosynthesis of the world is carried out by the marine algae, "the great meadow of the sea." In size, they range from the delicate single-celled desmids to the giant kelps, which reach 100 feet or more in length.

Algae are classified on the basis of a number of characteristics, such as the structure of the individual cells, the presence or absence of a cell wall, the form in which energy reserves are stored, and in particular, the pigments the cell contains. The pigments of the algae are light-absorbent and determine the depths at which photosynthesis takes place. Water filters

* See Appendix 1.

2–11 *Desmids are free-floating green algae, commonly found in ponds and lakes. They usually occur as single cells, although sometimes the cells are found linked end to end in filamentlike colonies. Most desmids, like the one shown here, are divided into two equal halves by a constriction across the middle of the cell. Each half contains one or two large chloroplasts. (Eric V. Gravé)*

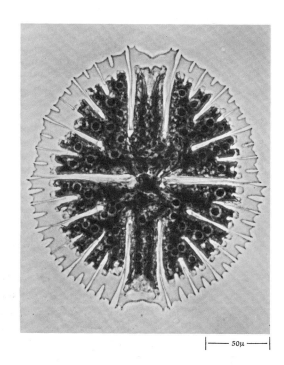

|——— 50μ ———|

out light, removing first the longer wavelengths—the reds and the oranges. These are the wavelengths used primarily by the green algae. (Their greenness is caused by the fact that they absorb the longer wavelengths and transmit, or reflect back, green.) The red algae, which absorb green and blue light and do not depend on red light, can live at the greater depths, where only these lights penetrate.

The clear-cut differences among the major groups of algae make it evident that their evolutionary relationships are not close.

The Chlorophyta

Of all the algae, the most interesting to us are the Chlorophyta, or green algae, since these seem to be the group from which the land plants evolved. Both the chlorophytes and the land plants, but not the other groups of algae, contain chlorophylls *a* and *b* as their photosynthetic pigments. Only a few species are marine, the majority being freshwater forms.

Green algae are usually small and simple in structure. *Chlamydomonas*, which we examined briefly in Chapter 1–2, is a member of this division. *Chlamydomonas* has a cellulose wall, like that of the higher plants, two flagella, a photoreceptor that enables it to move toward light, and a single

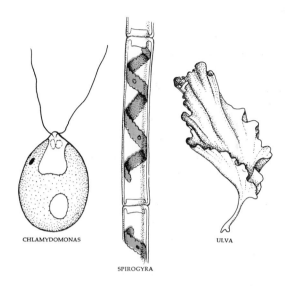

CHLAMYDOMONAS

SPIROGYRA

ULVA

2–12 *Three types of chlorophytes, or green algae.*

chloroplast within which is contained the pyrenoid body, the storage depot for starch. The ancestral cells from which the chlorophytes arose probably resembled *Chlamydomonas.* Many biologists believe that the first eucaryotic cells were green phytoflagellates, that is, chlorophyll-bearing flagellates, and that all the modern plants, and probably the modern animals as well, descended from these primitive phytoflagellates.

Chlamydomonas reproduces both sexually and asexually. Figure 2–13 shows the sexual cycle. Mating can only occur between individuals of different mating strains, which are conventionally designated *plus* and *minus* ($+$ and $-$). Higher organisms form specialized cells, the gametes, which unite to form the zygote, or fertilized cell, from which the new individual will develop. In *Chlamydomonas*, however, the organism itself functions as a gamete. Each cell is haploid ($1n$); that is, it contains only one set of chromosomes, like the gametes of higher organisms. As shown in the diagram, the two cells meet "head on," apparently attracted by a chemical diffused into the water. They fuse, and their nuclei merge, forming a diploid ($2n$) cell, which then undergoes reduction division to produce four new

2–13 *Chlamydomonas usually reproduces asexually, by mitotic division, but under certain conditions, it may reproduce sexually, as shown here. Cells of different mating strains* (a) *are attracted to each other* (b)*, and their cytoplasms slowly fuse. Finally, their nuclei unite in the process of fertilization, which produces a single diploid cell, the zygote* (c)*. The zygote sheds its flagella* (d)*, sinks to the bottom, and develops a thick protective coat* (e)*. The zygote is able to survive through periods of unfavorable conditions, such as the drying up of the pond or the cold of winter. When conditions again become favorable, the zygote germinates, dividing by meiosis to produce four haploid cells* (f)*. The new cells quickly mature* (g)*, and the sexual reproductive cycle is completed.*

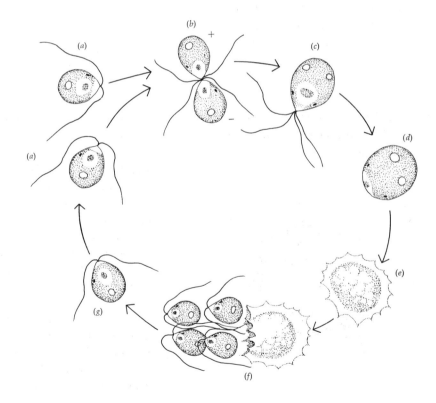

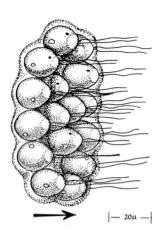

2–14 *Gonium is made up of 4 to 16 cells (depending on the species), each of which is morphologically similar to Chlamydomonas. The cells are embedded in a mucilaginous matrix and are arranged in a flat or slightly curved disk. The flagella of all the cells point in the same direction so the colony can swim as a unit.*

2–15 *Pandorina usually consists of 16 cells tightly packed in a sphere, with the flagella of each cell pointing outward.*

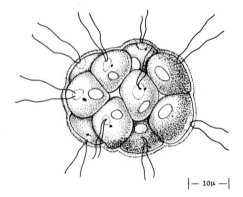

cells with the haploid (1*n*) number. These swim away. They may or may not divide mitotically before the next sexual fusion.

In most species of *Chlamydomonas*, the + and − cells are identical in size and structure. This arrangement is known as *isogamy*—from *iso*, meaning "equal." In some species, however, the cells of one of the strains are smaller than the other (*anisogamy*), and in others, only the + strain is motile. Mating in which one of the sex cells is motile and the other, nearly always the larger one, is immotile is known as *oogamy*. Isogamy is usually found in very primitive forms, while oogamy is, of course, characteristic of the higher plants and animals. Thus, in a single genus, we see a range of evolutionary stages.

In asexual reproduction, which is most common in *Chlamydomonas*, the cell divides into two to eight daughter cells within the cell wall of the parent. These daughter cells then form their own cell walls and flagella. The original cellulose wall becomes a gelatinous mass from which the daughter cells can escape. It is not uncommon to find fully formed daughter cells still glued together in this jellylike bed. In ancient phytoflagellates, such aggregations of daughter cells may have been the forerunners of multicelled organisms.

THE VOLVOCINES

The chlorophytes evolved in a number of different directions. One of the pathways led to the volvocines, some of which are described below.

Gonium, Pandorina, and Pleodorina

The simplest member of this group in its organization, *Gonium* is a colony of separate cells held together in a gelatinlike matrix. Each colony is made up of 4 to 16 cells (depending on the species) arranged in a flat disk, or shield. The individual cells are very small—only about 10 microns in diameter—and are green, flagellated, and cellulose-walled, like *Chlamydomonas*. Their flagella are all pointed in the same direction, at right angles to the surface of the shield. Each cell beats its flagella separately, and as a result, the entire shield is pulled forward. From time to time, the colony seems to lose its balance entirely, tumbles, somersaults once or twice, and then rights itself. Each cell in *Gonium* divides to produce an entire new colony.

A closely related colony is *Pandorina*, which forms a tightly packed sphere of 16 cells embedded in a clear mucilage. Each cell has two flagella, and since all the flagella point outward, *Pandorina* rolls through the water like a ball. When the cells attain their maximum size, the colony sinks to the bottom and each one of the cells divides four times, forming a subcolony of 16 cells. The subcolonies remain together until each one is com-

|— 400µ —|

2–16 *Volvox is shaped like a hollow sphere. The outer surface of the sphere is made up of from 500 to as many as 50,000 individual cells, connected by cytoplasmic strands. The interior is filled with a watery mucilage, and the whole colony is surrounded by a gelatinous sheath. Within many of these large spheres, you can see daughter colonies forming which will be released when the mother colony disintegrates. (Courtesy of General Biological Supply House, Inc.)*

pleted, and then the parent breaks open like Pandora's box, from which it gets its name, releasing 16 new daughter colonies.

Pleodorina is also a spherical colony made up of green flagellates, 32 in the most common species. It differs from *Gonium* and *Pandorina* in one interesting particular: 4 of its cells, cells which are smaller than the other 28, are incapable of reproducing to form new colonies. Here we see a beginning of specialization of function.

Volvox

The most spectacular of the volvocine line, and the one from which the group gets its name, is *Volvox*, a hollow sphere made up, according to age and species, of 500 to 50,000 tiny cells. The individual cells in *Volvox*, like those of *Gonium*, closely resemble *Chlamydomonas*—small and bright green, with two equal flagella and a tiny red eyespot. They are held together not only by a clear mucilage but also by fine protoplasmic strands that form a hexagonal pattern over the surface of the sphere. Actually, these connections between the cells usually cannot be seen, and so when *Volvox* whirls through the water, it appears like a spinning universe of individual stars fixed in an invisible firmament.

Volvox has a definite polarity—that is, it has a top and bottom, permanent north and south poles. The flagella of each cell beat sideways in such a way as to spin the entire colony around this north-south axis. *Volvox* orients toward the light but moves away from strong light. The entire sphere can stop, reverse itself, and spin off in the opposite direction. This movement to or away from light is possible because the cells on the too light or too dark side give an extra little kick with their flagella, a backward thrust that pushes the colony forward even as it spins.

If a single cell is cut loose from the colony by severing the threads that hold it to its neighbors, it is able to swim around alone like any other green flagellate, but with one important exception: It cannot reproduce. Reproduction takes place only within the colony and, for reasons which are not entirely understood, only within the cells in the southern hemisphere. These cells, which appear identical in the young colony, become larger and greener, morphologically distinct, as the colony matures.

Reproduction is usually asexual. One of the southern cells enlarges and then begins to divide. As it divides, the daughter cells are held together by a sticky matrix and by protoplasmic threads, remaining attached to the original reproductive cell in the mother colony. A little pouch or balloon is thus formed on the inner surface of the original sphere. At this stage, all the newly formed cells are facing inward, their anterior ends turned toward the center of the sphere. At the point at which the daughter sphere is attached to the mother cell, there is a small hole. When the new colony is completed, it is held to the mother cell only by a few remaining mucilag-

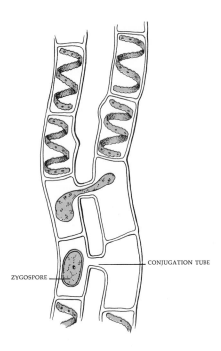

ZYGOSPORE   CONJUGATION TUBE

2–17 *Sexual reproduction in Spirogyra involves the formation of a conjugation tube between two cells from filaments of different mating strains. The entire contents of one cell move through the tube and fuse with the contents of the other cell to form a zygospore.*

inous threads. Suddenly, and with remarkable coordination, it turns itself completely inside out, through the hole, like the finger of a glove. Then, with the heads of the cells all pointing outward, each cell sprouts flagella and the daughter is ready for independent existence. Daughter colonies remain inside the mother colony until the latter breaks apart to let them loose, and it is not unusual to see daughters with a third generation forming, or sometimes already completed, within them.

Volvox may also produce mating cells, or gametes; these, too, form only in the southern hemisphere. The gametes are of unequal size. Depending on the species, some colonies produce only male (smaller) gametes, some only female gametes, and some both. The individual cells and the gametes of *Volvox* are both haploid ($1n$).

Sperm cells are produced in much the same way as the asexual daughter colonies. One cell begins to enlarge and then to divide, developing into an inward bulge of small cells, which eventually turns inside out. The colony of sperm cells pushes its way out of the parent colony, and then the individual cells separate. The female cells, which are considerably larger, remain attached to the parent colony until they are fertilized by the male cell to form the $2n$ zygote. The zygote develops a hard spiny outercoat and drops to the bottom of the pond. It is in this form that *Volvox* survives the winter.

SPIROGYRA AND ULVA

Other evolutionary lines in the Chlorophyta are represented by *Spirogyra* and *Ulva*, both common forms. In *Spirogyra* (Figure 2–17), the cells are strung together in long fine filaments in which the chloroplasts form spirals which look like strips of green tape within each cell. Usually, the individual cells divide mitotically, producing longer and longer strands, which eventually fragment. In sexual reproduction, two filaments of opposite mating strains line up alongside each other, and cytoplasmic connections—conjugation tubes—form between them. The protoplasmic contents (the protoplast) of one cell slide over into the adjacent cell through the tube, and the two protoplasts combine to form a zygospore. As in *Volvox*, mating in *Spirogyra* takes place with the coming of drought or cold weather, the zygote developing tough protective walls in which it lies dormant. The cells of *Spirogyra* are haploid; only the zygote is diploid.

In *Ulva*, which is commonly known as sea lettuce, the thallus consists of two cell sheets back to back. *Ulva* has a reproductive pattern that is characteristic of many of the algae and of all the higher plants. This pattern is known as *alternation of generations*.

ALTERNATION OF GENERATIONS

In alternation of generations, one generation reproduces sexually and the

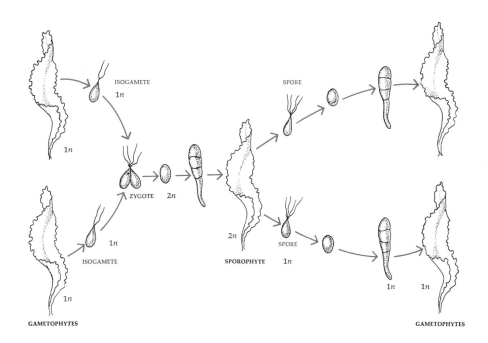

Labels in figure: ISOGAMETE 1*n*, 1*n*, 1*n*, ISOGAMETE, 1*n*, ZYGOTE 2*n*, SPORE, SPORE, 2*n*, SPOROPHYTE, 1*n*, 1*n*, 1*n*, GAMETOPHYTES, GAMETOPHYTES

2–18 *In the sea lettuce,* Ulva, *we can see the reproductive pattern known as alternation of generations, in which one generation produces spores, the other gametes. The haploid (1n) gametophyte produces haploid gametes, and the gametes fuse to form a diploid (2n) zygote. The zygote develops into a plant in which all of the cells are diploid. This plant, known as a sporophyte, produces haploid spores by meiosis. The haploid spores develop into haploid gametophytes, and the cycle begins again.*

next one reproduces asexually. The plant that produces gametes is known as the *gametophyte,* or gamete plant. The individual cells of the plant are haploid (1*n*), and so are the gametes that it produces. The gametes fuse to form a diploid (2*n*) zygote. The zygote develops into a plant in which all the cells are diploid. This plant is known as the *sporophyte,* or spore-producing plant. Spores, which are produced by meiosis, are haploid.

Spores differ from gametes in that a spore germinates directly to form a new organism, while a gamete must unite with another gamete. The gametophyte and the sporophyte are always different since one is composed of haploid cells and one of diploid cells. Sometimes the two generations look alike, however. In *Ulva,* for example, two small flagellated isogametes fuse to make one zygote, which for a period of time may have four flagella. These flagella disappear, and the zygote divides by mitosis to become a mature plant, the sporophyte. Any cell in the mature plant may then begin to divide by meiosis to form spores, which all have four flagella, like the zygote. The spores soon settle down, lose their flagella, and without mating, develop into complete new plants, the gametophytes.

In other Chlorophyta, the sporophyte and the gametophyte do not resemble one another. In fact, in some cases, the two generations of the same plant were considered to be two entirely different species until the life

2–19 *In some plants the alternating generations are so different that they were believed to be of different genera. The gametophyte of the plant shown was once called Halicystis, and the sporophyte Derbesia.*

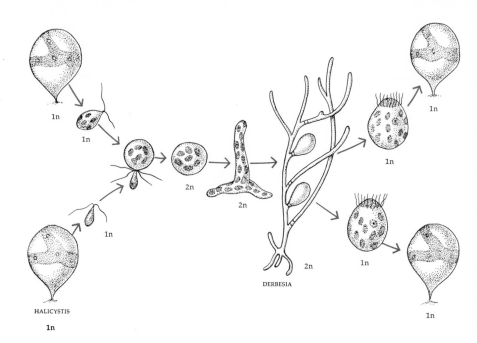

HALICYSTIS

1n

DERBESIA

2–20 *The euglenoid Peranema looks very much like Euglena, as you will see if you compare this drawing with Figure 1–7. Unlike Euglena and most other euglenoids, however, it does not contain chlorophyll and is therefore clearly "animal," with no plantlike characteristics whatsoever.*

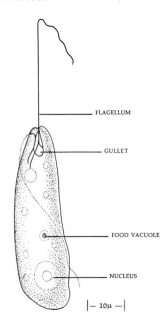

FLAGELLUM

GULLET

FOOD VACUOLE

NUCLEUS

|— 10μ —|

cycles were studied in the laboratory. Figure 2–19 shows such a plant, which was called *Derbesia* in its sporophyte (2n) form and *Halicystis* in its gametophyte (1n) form. The flagellated spores produced by the *Derbesia* side of its character are unusual in that they have a whole circlet of small flagella. After a brief free-swimming period, these spores settle down and grow into the spherical *Halicystis* stage, the gametophyte. The gametes, one of which is much larger than the other, each have two flagella. After fertilization, the zygote develops into a typical *Derbesia*. In the higher plants, there is an increasing divergence in form and size between the two generations.

Other Algae Groups

THE EUGLENOIDS

The euglenoids are one-celled freshwater organisms which usually have one or two flagella and which lack a cellulose cell wall. They store their food in the form of a special carbohydrate known as *paramylum*, which is not found elsewhere in the plant kingdom. Most of the euglenoids contain chlorophyll, but some do not. One species that does not is *Peranema*, which, as you can see in Figure 2–20, looks very much like *Euglena*, although it lacks the bright green chloroplasts of the latter genus. It has all

184 ORGANISMS

the other identifying characteristics of the division, but it is clearly "animal," with no plantlike characteristics whatsoever.

If *Euglena* is kept in a rich medium in which it divides very rapidly, it may reproduce itself faster than its chloroplasts can reproduce, and literally outrunning them, it may lose its powers of photosynthesis. In fact, there are some strains of *Euglena* and *Euglena*-like flagellates which, having done just that, are permanently without chloroplasts. These can survive indefinitely in a suitable medium. It seems reasonable to speculate that forms such as *Peranema* arose from other euglenoids by this process or some similar one and even perhaps that the animal-like organisms arose from the phytoflagellates in this same way.

THE CHRYSOPHYTA

The Chrysophytes are the "golden" algae. Almost 17,000 species are known, most of which are diatoms. Diatoms are the principal component of phytoplankton, the plant life that floats on the surface of the waters and is the primary source of food for all the animals that live in the water and for some land animals as well. Members of this group have several identifying characteristics: (1) their photosynthetic pigments are chlorophylls *a* and *c*, (2) they have outer shells of silicon, and (3) they store their food in the form of oil rather than as starch. Because of these oil reserves, which may be more useful than starch for plants that float, fresh water in which large amounts of these algae are growing may have an unpleasant, oily taste.

Diatoms are enclosed in a fine double shell, the two halves of which fit together, one on top of the other, like a carved pillbox. The delicate markings of these shells, by which the species are identified, were traditionally used by microscopists to test the excellence of their lenses. Despite their lack of locomotor organelles, many species of diatoms are motile. They are believed to be powered by the streaming of protoplasm along a slit in the shell, something like a side-wheel steamer. The piled-up silicon shells of diatoms, which have collected over millions of years, form the fine crumbly substance known as *diatomaceous earth*, used as an abrasive in silver polish and toothpaste and for filtering and insulating materials.

THE PYRROPHYTA

The Pyrrophyta is also largely composed of single-celled algae, the dinoflagellates ("spinning flagellates"), of which about 1,000 different species are known, almost all marine forms. In the dinoflagellates, the flagella beat within two grooves, one which circles the body like a girdle and a second which is perpendicular to the first. The beating of the flagella in their respective grooves causes the organism to spin like a top as it moves. Dinoflagellates, like the phytoflagellates, are primarily plant-animals.

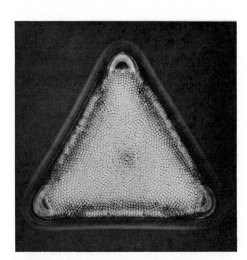

2–21 *Diatoms are microscopic algae which secrete skeletal structures made of silica in a great variety of geometric shapes and patterns. The cell wall consists of two overlapping halves, like a tiny pillbox. They are remarkably abundant, and much of the productivity of the oceans, from the tiniest animals up to the great whales, depends largely on diatoms. (Eric V. Gravé)*

185   *The First Plants: The Thallophytes*

2–22 *The marine dinoflagellate Gonyaulax polyedra. The cell is enclosed in a stiff wall, consisting of polygonal plates of cellulose closely joined together. Many of the marine dinoflagellates, including the armored Gonyaulax, are luminescent, converting chemical energy into flashes of light to produce the "burning" of the sea at night. (Courtesy of Scripps Institute of Oceanography)*

2–23 *Sea squirts (ascidians) on the "leaves" of Fucus, the common rockweed, seen at low tide on the seashore. Brown algae furnish food and hiding places for many marine animals. (Dr. Douglas P. Wilson, F.R.P.S.)*

Most of them are photosynthesizers. Many of them have stiff cellulose outer walls, which often look like strange helmets or ancient coats of armor. These dinoflagellates are often red in color, and the infamous red tides, in which thousands of fish often die, are caused by great blooms of the red dinoflagellates. The poison in these red tides has been traced to one species of armored dinoflagellate, *Gonyaulax catanella*, and has proved to be such an extraordinarily powerful nerve toxin that it is currently under study by the chemical-warfare division of the Army. One gram of it is enough to kill 5 million mice in 15 minutes. Blooms of *Gonyaulax catanella* appear regularly on the Pacific Coast, where they are eaten by the mussels, which concentrate the poison and so become dangerous for consumption by vertebrates, including man. Many dinoflagellates are bioluminescent, converting chemical energy into flashes of light to produce the "burning" of the sea at night.

THE BROWN ALGAE

The most common brown algae are the kelps, the large floating seaweeds. The Sargasso Sea is made up of brown algae torn loose from the shores of Caribbean islands during tropical storms and swept off by ocean currents. The brown algae contain chlorophylls *a* and *c* (like the Chrysophyta) and also a xanthophyll, which gives them their brown color. They differ from most other plants in that they store their food as a sugar or sometimes as oil but never as starch, as do the green algae and the higher plants.

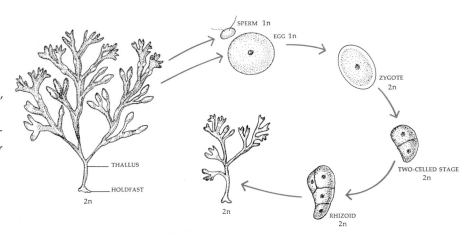

2–24 *Sexual reproduction in Fucus is very similar to that in animals. The diploid plant produces haploid gametes—a sperm and an egg—which fuse to form a diploid zygote. The zygote germinates, giving rise to a new diploid plant. Fucus and its close relatives are the only multicellular plants in which the multicellular haploid stage is completely absent.*

Many of the brown algae have quite complex shapes. *Fucus*, the common rockweed, for example, has a structure known as a *holdfast*, by which it attaches itself to the bottom, a "stem" which is many cells in thickness, and an outer cortex of photosynthetic cells surrounding an inner pith of cells that live on organic materials diffused inward to them. Bladderlike inflated regions, which serve for flotation, are often found in certain species. Also, unlike most other algae but like the higher plants, growth in *Fucus* takes place only at the tip of its branchlike structures and not throughout the entire thallus, as in the simpler forms.

Sexual reproduction in *Fucus* resembles that seen in animal organisms. The plant is always diploid, and only the gametes are haploid. The male gamete is small and motile, while the female gamete, or egg, is large and immotile. This mode of reproduction is very rare in plants. Assuming that each type of alga developed separately from a single-celled phytoflagellate, the wide range of reproductive processes seen in these divisions can be regarded as a series of "experiments" in solving the problems of reproduction encountered by multicelled organisms.

A reproductive cycle similar to that of the higher plants is seen in the brown alga *Laminaria. Laminaria* is characterized by an alternation of generations in which one generation, the sporophyte, is large (in exceptional individuals of some species, it may be as long as 150 feet or more), while the gametophyte may consist of only a few cells and may be visible only under the microscope. The spores produced by the large plant turn into tiny gametophytes, which in turn produce sperm or eggs. These are released into the water and ultimately fuse to produce a new sporophyte.

RHODOPHYTA

The rhodophytes, or red algae, are most commonly found in the warm waters of the globe and comprise the other principal group of large sea-

2–25 *Three species of brown algae exposed at low tide. The lettucelike, curly-edged "leaves" are Laminaria saccharina. The large flat "leaves" at the top, which look like pastry dough rolled very thin, are Laminaria digitata, and the light-colored plant supported on a "stem" in the middle is Laminaria ochroleuca. (Dr. Douglas P. Wilson, F.R.P.S.)*

weeds. The red algae contain chlorophylls *a* and *d* and also certain phycobilins which give them their distinctive colors.

Most of the seaweeds of the world are red algae, of which there are some 4,000 species. Less than 2 percent are freshwater forms. Red algae usually grow attached to rocks and other algae; there are no red algae capable of prolonged life in the floating state, like the brown algae of the Sargasso Sea. As you would expect from their red color, they tend to grow at greater depths than other algae; they have been found attached 600 feet below the ocean surface. They never attain the size of the largest of the brown kelps, but some are several yards in length. They are characterized by a peculiar reproductive pattern in which neither of the gametes is motile, the male being carried to the fixed female reproductive cell by the movement of the water.

Perhaps the most useful direct commercial application of these algae is in the preparation of agar, which is made from a mucilaginous material extracted from the algal cell walls. Agar is used to make the capsules that hold vitamins and other drugs, as a dental-impression material, as a base for cosmetics, and most important, from the point of view of biology, as a culture medium for bacteria and other microorganisms. It has a consistency somewhat like that of gelatin, which is an animal product made from connective tissues, but has the advantage of being firm at higher temperatures.

2–26 *Stalked jellyfish clinging to a red sea-weed. (Dr. Douglas P. Wilson, F.R.P.S.)*

|– 5mm –|

THE FUNGI

Although the structure of the fungi is somewhat similar to that of the algae, their role in the natural world is entirely different. The algae, as we saw, are the great photosynthesizers, the "primary producers" that convert inorganic materials into the organic materials used by other organisms. The fungi are principally decomposers. Most of them live on dead organic matter, returning it to the soil and air, where it can be reused by plants. The fungi, together with the saprophytic bacteria, are responsible for the removal of organic debris. It has been estimated that every tree would eventually be inundated in its own fallen leaves if it were not for the action of these decomposers. The decomposition releases carbon dioxide into the atmosphere, where it can be reused by green plants. It also modifies the soil color and texture and moistens and aerates it. Rich black soils contain *humus* which is actually a mixture of many organic substances and of the soil micro-organisms, both fungi and bacteria, that are in the process of decomposing them.

The Fungi and Man

The decomposing effect of the fungi is not always useful from the human point of view. Especially in the tropics, where warmth and dampness promote **fungal growth, cotton goods, leather, and waxes and materials**

189 *The First Plants: The Thallophytes*

2–27 *Stem rust on the underleaf surfaces of barberry. In the spring, the fungus infection appears on the barberry leaves as small swollen areas. Within these swellings are groups of spores, or cluster cups. As growth proceeds, the cups push through the leaf surface and open, exposing the yellow-orange spores. The mature spores then fall from the cup and are carried away by air currents. If the spores fall on a susceptible host plant— wheat, small grains, or grasses—they will cause the fungal disease known as rust. The stem rust does not damage the barberry but simply uses the plant as a host for the first stage of its two-stage life cycle. One such "Typhoid Mary" can carry enough of the fungus to infect a whole field of grain. (Courtesy of the U.S. Department of Agriculture)*

used in insulating electronic equipment are attacked and often destroyed by mildews and other fungi. Molds of bread and of other foods are among the principal problems of commercial food producers.

A small percentage of the fungi derive their food directly from living organisms. These are the parasitic fungi that cause many common diseases of plants and animals. Fungal diseases of man are usually skin diseases (ringworm, athlete's foot) or diseases of the mucous membrane (thrush), but sometimes inhaled fungal spores infect internal organs; such internal diseases are rare, but when they do occur, they are often very serious. Of greater economic importance are the fungal diseases of plants, such as the rusts, smuts, and powdery mildews of domesticated plants, the Dutch elm disease, and the chestnut blight that has destroyed nearly all these beautiful ornamental trees in North America. The Irish potato famine of 1845 to 1847, caused by the potato blight, was responsible for over a million deaths from starvation and initiated large-scale emigration from Ireland to the United States; within a decade, the population of Ireland fell from 8 million to 4 million. Ergot is a fungal parasite of rye which, although it is seldom sufficiently widespread to cause destruction of the crop, is particularly dangerous because even a small amount of ergot mixed with rye grains is enough to cause severe illness among domestic animals or among the people who eat bread made with the flour. *Ergotism*, as the disease is called, is often accompanied by gangrene, nervous spasms, delirium, and convulsions. The disease occurred frequently during the Middle Ages, when it was known as St. Anthony's fire. As recently as 1951, there was an outbreak in France, causing a number of deaths.

Many of the fungi are of economic importance. Chief among these are the yeasts, a large group of single-celled fungi. Yeast cells break down glucose into carbon dioxide and alcohol, useful to the baker and the brewer. The release of carbon dioxide from fermenting yeast cells (leaven) causes uniform aeration of bread dough, and the transformation of glucose to alcohol turns the juice of fruit and grains into wine and beer.

Fungi give cheeses the flavor, odor, and character so highly prized by the gourmet. One such mold was first found in caves near the French village of Roquefort. Legend has it that a peasant boy left his lunch, a mild fresh piece of goat cheese, in one of these caves and on returning found it marbled, tart, and redolent. Only cheeses from the area around these particular caves are permitted to bear the name of Roquefort.

As early as the seventeenth century, ergot, the fungus of rye, was used to facilitate childbirth. One of its effects is the contraction of the involuntary muscles, particularly of the uterus. In the twentieth century, ergot has once more attracted interest as the source of the chemical from which the hallucinogenic drug LSD is derived. Most of the modern antibiotics are produced by fungi. The first of these was discovered by Alexander Fleming, who noted that a mold of the genus *Penicillium* which had contaminated a culture of staphylococcus growing on a nutrient agar plate had completely halted the growth of the bacteria. Antibiotics, of which many hundreds have now been discovered, are substances produced by a living organism that injure another living organism. It is not known whether antibiotics actually serve a protective function for the organisms that produce them or whether their harmful effects on other cells are accidental by-products.

Biology of the Fungi

The fungi, although they do not have chlorophyll, resemble green plants in that they generally have definite cell walls, are immotile, and reproduce by means of spores. There is little differentiation of structure or specialization of function among the fungal cells.

Except in the yeast and a few other single-celled fungi, the thallus of a fungus is a fine mat made up of interwoven branches. The mat is known as a *mycelium*, and the branches are called *hyphae*. Some mycelia are long, continuous tubes filled with protoplasm. In other groups, there are cross walls (*septa*) with interconnecting pores. In either case, the cytoplasm streams quite freely along the hyphae. The walls of the hyphae are made either of cellulose or of chitin, a tough hard polysaccharide of the type that forms the exoskeletons of insects. Fungi receive their nourishment through these cell walls. Often they release digestive enzymes out onto the medium on which they are feeding, so that digestion takes place outside the fungal body, and then absorb the digested materials into their protoplasm.

Most species of fungi reproduce by the formation of spores. A single cell or an isolated portion of a hypha divides to form a large number of small cells, the spores, each of which can germinate to give rise to a new mycelium. Spores of some species are less than a micron in diameter and so can remain suspended in the air for long periods and be carried for great distances. Often the spore-containing bodies are raised above the mycelium so that the spores will be easily caught up and transported by air currents. The bright colors and powdery texture associated with many types of molds are produced by the spores; often the mycelium grows beneath the surface of the material on which it is feeding.

The spores may form singly, in chains, in clusters, within spore cases (*sporangia*), in sacs (*asci*), or in special club-shaped hyphal cells (*basidia*). These structures may occur alone, or they may be clustered together in a fruiting body. The mushroom is an example of a fungus whose spore-bearing hyphae are grouped together in a fruiting body. Fungi are classified largely on the basis of their spore-bearing structures and fruiting bodies.

191   *The First Plants: The Thallophytes*

Spores are formed either sexually or asexually. In the sexual cycle, one or more egg cells will form inside of a hypha. These cells can be fertilized by conjugation with a special sperm-containing hypha from a mycelium of an opposite mating strain (in a manner similar to conjugation in *Spirogyra*) or by invasion of one of the egg-producing hypha by male gametes released into air or water. Molds are haploid, with the zygote forming the only diploid cell in the life cycle. Sexual and asexual reproduction do not necessarily occur alternately, as they do in many of the algae and in all of the higher plants.

REPRODUCTION IN RHIZOPUS

Asexual and sexual reproduction in the common black bread mold *Rhizopus* are diagrammed in Figure 2–28. This mold first lays down a mycelium on the surface of the bread, fruit, or other material which it has infected. Once the mycelium is firmly established, specialized spore-bearing hyphae,

2–28 *Asexual and sexual reproduction in the common black bread mold Rhizopus. The mold consists of masses of tangled and branched hyphae, from which stalked, globular sporangia grow. At maturity, the fragile wall of the sporangium disintegrates, releasing the asexual spores, which are carried away by air currents. Under suitable conditions of warmth and moisture, the spores germinate, giving rise to new masses of hyphae. In sexual reproduction, when two hyphae from different mycelia come into contact, specialized side branches form, in much the same way that the conjugation tube forms in Spirogyra. When the wall between the two branches breaks down, their contents fuse to become a zygospore. The zygospore enlarges, developing a thick warty outer wall. After a period of dormancy lasting from one to several months, the zygospore germinates to produce a new mycelium.*

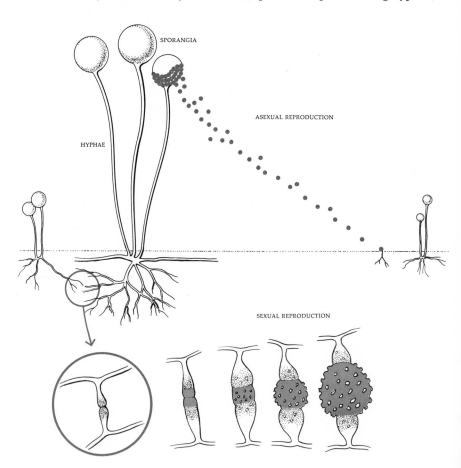

SPORANGIA

ASEXUAL REPRODUCTION

HYPHAE

SEXUAL REPRODUCTION

2–29 *Highly regarded by gourmets for their delicate flavor, morels are ascomycetes, a group of fungi which includes the yeasts and mildews. (Rutherford Platt)*

the sporangia, are pushed up into the air. As these mature, they become black, giving the mold its characteristic color. Simultaneously, other hyphae form rootlike structures known as *rhizoids,* which anchor the aerial hyphae firmly to the substrate. Rhizoids perform the attaching function of true roots and also may, as in the case of *Rhizopus,* absorb water or nutrients, or both, but they are similar to the vegetative hyphae and do not have the specialized conducting tissue of the true roots found in the higher plants. Each spore can germinate to produce a new mycelium.

Sexual reproduction in *Rhizopus* occurs by the fusion of the specialized hyphae of two different mating strains. Cross walls form, separating these tips from the parent hyphae, and the tips then fuse to form a tough, resistant zygote. Meiosis occurs at the time of germination of these zygospores, and the resulting hyphae are again haploid.

Classes of Fungi

The Division Eumycota, the "true fungi," consists of four classes: the Phycomycetes, the Ascomycetes, the Basidiomycetes, and the Fungi Imperfecti.

THE PHYCOMYCETES

The Phycomycetes or water molds, are so called because many are aquatic. Also some species reproduce by means of flagellated gametes or flagellated spores—like certain of the green algae but unlike any other fungi. Most of them have hyphae with numerous nuclei but no cross walls, and none of them produces conspicuous fruiting bodies. One aquatic form, all too well-known to tropical-fish fanciers, is the white fungus that infects the skin of fish. The swimming spores of this fungus spread it rapidly and often fatally through an aquarium. A common terrestrial form is the black mold of bread, the life cycle of which we have just described. If you leave a damp bit of bread in the air for a few hours and then cover it with a dish to prevent its drying out, in a few days you will almost undoubtedly be rewarded by the appearance of black bread mold.

THE ASCOMYCETES

The Ascomycetes comprise the largest class of fungi, including the yeasts and mildews and many of the common black and blue-green molds. They are the cause of many plant diseases and are the source of most of the antibiotics. The red bread mold *Neurospora,* which has played a major role in the history of modern genetics (see Chapter 3–4), is an ascomycete.

In ascomycetes, the hyphae are divided by cross walls. Each compartment generally contains a separate nucleus, but the cross walls have pores

2–30 *The stinkhorn fungus, a basidiomycete, is so called because of its evil smell, which strongly resembles the odor of rotten meat. The mature plant consists of a hollow stalk with a swollen tip, on the surface of which the spores are borne. Flies, beetles, and other carrion-eating insects are attracted to the plant and carry away the spores on their bodies. (L. West)*

in them through which the cytoplasm and even the nuclei can move. Asexual spores, the *conidia*, are formed either singly or in chains at the tip of a specialized hypha. The sexual spores are produced in a saclike structure, the *ascus*, formed from the enlarged end of a hypha, in which meiosis takes place immediately following nuclear fusion. There is usually only one diploid nucleus in the life cycle of an ascomycete. Each ascus usually contains eight spores. In most ascomycetes, the asci are carried on fruiting structures.

BASIDIOMYCETES

The most familiar Basidiomycetes are mushrooms and toadstools. The mushroom is the fruiting body. The mycelium from which the mushrooms are produced spreads underground, forming a diffuse mat which may grow as large as 100 feet in diameter. In an open area, the mycelium will expand evenly in all directions and will fruit at the outer edges, where it grows most actively since this is the area in which there is the most fresh nutritive material. As a consequence, the mushrooms will appear in rings, and as the mycelium grows, the rings become larger and larger in diameter. Such circles of mushrooms, which might appear in a meadow overnight, were known in European folk legends as "fairy rings."

The basidiomycetes have hyphae subdivided by perforated walls, like those found in the ascomycetes. An important difference, however, is that in the basidiomycetes, the spores are borne externally, on a specialized hypha (called a *basidium*, from the Greek word for "base" or "club"), while in the ascomycetes, the cells develop within the closed ascus. The spores of the basidiomycetes, like those of the ascomycetes, are the product of meiosis, which immediately follows nuclear fusion. Many of the larger basidiomycetes seem to have lost the capacity to produce asexual spores.

The best known mushrooms belong to the group known as the gill fungi, which includes *Agaricus campestris*, the common field mushroom. Varieties of this species are the only mushrooms it has been possible to cultivate commercially. The gill fungi also include the mushrooms of the genus *Amanita*, which are the most highly poisonous of all mushrooms. Even one bite of the white *Amanita verna*, the "destroying angel," can be fatal. Other types of mushrooms include puff balls (some of which have a diameter of 3 feet or more), earthstars, stinkhorns, and the bird's-nest fungi. These last look like miniature birds' nests complete with eggs.

Although mushrooms look fleshy in texture, like fruit, if you dissect one and look at it under a magnifying lens, you can see that it is actually composed of a large number of filaments, the hyphae. Because of the extremely rapid appearance of mushrooms, it is believed that most of the actual growth takes place underground and that the protoplasm from the hyphae of the mycelium is poured into the new hyphae of the fruiting body as it forms and balloons up above the ground.

The spores of the gill mushrooms are contained in the furrows, or "gills," under the cap. If you take a ripe mushroom and place it on a piece of white paper, it will release fine spores that will trace out a negative copy of the gill structure. The spores, which come in a variety of colors, are a useful means of identifying various mushrooms.

THE FUNGI IMPERFECTI

This class comprises fungi whose complete reproductive cycles are unknown, either because they have not been sufficiently studied or because some part of the process has been lost in the course of evolution—hence the adjective "imperfect."

Many of the Fungi Imperfecti are parasites which cause diseases of plants, animals, and human beings. Treatment with antibiotics may make infections of these fungi get worse instead of better because the antibiotics destroy not only the pathogenic bacteria but also the harmless and the beneficial ones and so leave conditions more favorable for fungal growth.

Several forms of Fungi Imperfecti have sticky loops or branches specially adapted to capture microscopic animals. A few species actually can trap small worms. They form rings which swell suddenly when stimulated by a passing worm, constricting around the worm like a noose. Other hyphae then invade the body of the animal and digest it.

THE LICHENS

A lichen is not a single plant but is a combination of two plants, a fungus and one or more of the algae. Classification of the lichens is based on their highly characteristic fungi. Lichens grow on rocks, wood, tree trunks, the ground, and many other substrates. The body of the lichen, which may be feltlike, crusty, or branched and bushy, is composed largely of fungal mycelium. Held within this mycelium, which usually has a very complex structure, are numerous algal cells. These cells are often small, single, and globular. The hyphae of some species of fungus clasp an individual spherical algal cell in much the same way your fingers would hold a baseball. From the underside of the lichen, rhizoids often extend down for short distances into the substrate. These secrete acids which can dissolve minerals in rocks. Eventually, in the course of long periods of time, the surface layer of the rock may become soft enough to hold moisture and to provide a foothold for higher plants. Most of the nutrients of the lichen are taken in from the air, however, which is why these plants are particularly vulnerable to air pollution. The abundance and

2–31 *The "British soldier" lichen, Cladonia cristatella. The branched and shrublike lichens of this genus cover great areas of the Arctic tundra. Part alga, part fungus, lichens offer a classic example of symbiosis. (Rutherford Platt)*

|——— 0.5mm ———|

195   *The First Plants: The Thallophytes*

kinds of lichens in any given area are very sensitive indices to the degree of pollution.

The lichens have long intrigued scientists interested in symbiosis because the two organisms together form a closely integrated unit which can grow under conditions where neither the fungus nor the alga alone could survive, although the rate of growth may be very slow—as little as 1/10 inch a year. (On this basis, you could estimate the age of some large lichen plants at 1,000 years or more.)

At one time, it was generally agreed that the secret of the lichen's success was that the fungus provided moisture for the algae and the algae shared the products of photosynthesis with the fungus. Now it is recognized that the fungus does not hold water; in fact, one of the reasons that lichens often grow so slowly is that they dry out so readily. By 10 A.M., when surrounding plants are just beginning the day's work of photosynthesis, the lichen has shut down production because of water loss. More recently, it has become possible to grow the two components separately in pure culture. These studies have shown that both partners need nutrients when they are growing apart that they do not need when they are growing together. Once they are separated, it is very difficult to make them grow together again. In many cases, attempts have led to the death of the algal cells. In nature, the fungi involved have never been found growing without the algae, although the algal cells, or cells very much like them, have been found without the fungi. These findings suggest that the fungi are parasitic upon the algae and that, as a consequence, they have

2–32 *The leaflike (foliose)* Parmelia *lichen growing on rock. Lichens slowly manufacture soil by breaking up the bare rock on which they grow. (Rutherford Platt)*

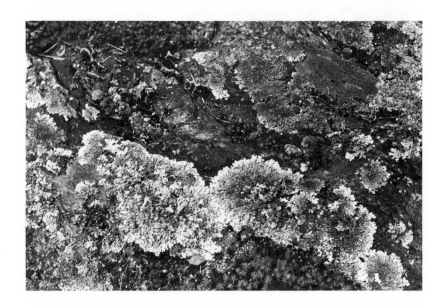

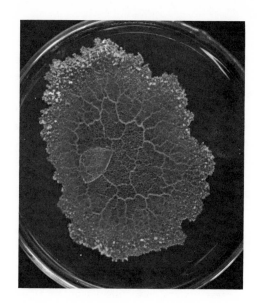

2–33 *The plasmodium of the slime mold Physarum polycephalum growing on nutrient agar in a petri dish. Taxonomists disagree about whether to classify slime molds as animals or plants, since they seem to have the qualities of both. The slime-mold plasmodium is made up of a streaming mass of protoplasm which differentiates and becomes plant-like in the reproductive phase, when spore cases form. A plasmodium can pass through a piece of silk or filter paper and come out the other side unchanged. (Dr. Peter A. Stewart, Primitive Motile Systems in Cell Biology, Academic Press, Inc.)*

been specially modified to live on an algal host. Although the algae may be inhibited in their growth rate by the fungi, they apparently receive certain benefits, probably some minerals and also protection from high-intensity light.

Most reproduction of lichens is vegetative; that is, a portion of the lichen containing both algal and fungal cells breaks off and becomes planted somewhere else. Sometimes the fungi make fruiting bodies which, although they do not contain the algae, are surrounded by them; when the spores are released, minute algal cells may cling to them or be dispersed with them and when they germinate, a new lichen is formed.

THE SLIME MOLDS

The slime molds, or myxomycetes, although nonphotosynthetic are classified with the plants since they reproduce by spores, which is a plantlike characteristic, and since these spores are reported to have walls of cellulose. The spores germinate under favorable conditions, and each spore produces one to four flagellated swarm cells. These swarm cells, which are haploid, either may behave as isogametes, fusing in pairs soon after their formation, or may first lose their flagella and undergo a number of divisions before mating. The zygote, which is diploid, grows by a series of mitotic nuclear divisions, resulting in a large mass of protoplasm known as a *plasmodium*, which contains many nuclei but is composed of one cell mass. A plasmodium may also be formed by the coming together of many zygotes, and it may incorporate any other zygotes and smaller plasmodia that it encounters in its migrations. As the plasmodium moves, it picks up small bits of decayed plant and animal matter, which it phagocytizes. It may grow to weigh as much as several ounces, and since it is spread thin, it may cover an area of several feet. At maturity, the plasmodium thickens and the nuclei undergo meiosis. Each haploid nucleus, with a portion of the cytoplasm, is finally enveloped by a thick wall and develops into a spore. The fruiting bodies are often extremely ornate.

Most slime molds live in cool, shady, moist places in the woods—on decaying logs, dead leaves, or other damp organic matter. One of the common species (*Physarum cinereum*), however, which may form a plasmodium several feet in diameter, is sometimes found creeping across city lawns. The plasmodia come in a variety of colors and can be spectacularly beautiful.

The myxomycetes are of little economic importance, but they are of scientific interest as a model system of cellular streaming, since the streaming in the plasmodium is the most rapid known and is visible under a hand lens. Every minute or so, the streaming movement, which takes place along the conspicuous veins of the plasmodium, may reverse its course, first coming to a momentary stop, and then flowing in the opposite direction. Curiously, individual rivers of protoplasm, as observed with a lens, do not flow in the direction of movement of the plasmodium any more often than they flow in the opposite direction, a finding which does not help to clarify the problem of amoeboid motion.

Another group of slime molds, the cellular slime molds, also begin as amoeba-like organisms but differ from the plasmodial slime molds in that the amoebas, on swarming together, do not lose their cell membranes but retain their identity as individual cells. This group is known as the Acrasiales, and their relationship to the Myxomycetes, the "true" slime molds, is obscure. The life cycle of this interesting group of organisms is described in detail in Chapter 4–1.

SUMMARY

The lower plants, or thallophytes, are without such specialized tissues as roots, stems, and leaves that possess water-conducting tissue, or xylem, and in these plants, the egg cell does not develop in a multicellular ovary. The two principal types of thallophytes are the algae, which are photosynthetic, and the fungi, which are not.

Of the seven divisions of algae, the green algae (the Chlorophyta) are interesting to many scientists because of their relationship to the higher plants. Evidence for this relationship is based primarily on the chemical structure of the chlorophylls, the presence of a cellulose cell wall, and the storage of the energy reserves in the form of starch.

Reproductive cycles in the green algae were discussed with special emphasis on *alternation of generations*, which is a characteristic of many types of algae and of all the higher plants. "Alternation of generations" designates a reproductive cycle in which sexual reproduction and asexual reproduction (by means of spores) occur in alternating generations. In one generation, the plant body, known as the *gametophyte*, produces haploid ($1n$) gametes, which fuse to form the next generation, a diploid ($2n$) *sporophyte*. The sporophyte produces spores by meiotic division. A spore, is a single cell that, unlike a gamete, can develop into a complete plant without combining with another cell. In alternation of generations, the spore, which is haploid, produces the haploid gametophyte.

The other major groups of algae were described briefly in terms of their natural distribution, their special characteristics, and their interest and importance to man.

The fungi are nonphotosynthetic thallophytes. Their principal natural role is the decomposition of organic matter. The fungi, with the saprophytic bacteria, are responsible for the removal of organic debris, for the return of carbon (in the form of carbon dioxide) to the air, where it can be reused by the plants, and for the production of *humus*. The fungi are of importance to man as a cause of decomposition of cotton, leather, and other man-made goods, as a cause of food spoilage, as a cause of disease, particularly the diseases of plants, and as a source of many products of economic value.

The thallus of the fungus is usually a fine mat, or *mycelium*, made up of many interconnecting branches, the *hyphae*. Reproduction is either vegetative or by means of sexual or asexual spores. The spores may appear singly, in clusters, in spore cases (*sporangia*), in sacs (*asci*), or in club-shaped cells (the *basidia*). These structures may be grouped together in *fruiting bodies*. The fungi are classified largely on the basis of their spore-bearing structures.

There are four classes of fungi: the Phycomycetes, which include the water molds and land molds with simple sporangia; the Ascomycetes, in which the spores are formed within asci; the Basidiomycetes, the mushrooms and toadstools, in which the spores are formed in a club-shaped hypha, the basidium, and are borne externally; and the Fungi Imperfecti, whose complete reproductive cycles are unknown.

The lichens, combinations of fungi and algae, are classified with the fungi. Because the fungi and algae in combination can live in environmental situations in which neither can exist alone, the nature of their association has been of particular interest to scientists.

The slime molds are nonphotosynthetic but are plantlike in their reproduction, which involves the formation of spores and fruiting bodies. The "true" slime mold forms a *plasmodium*, which consists of a multinucleated mass of cytoplasm. The slime molds are of special interest to investigators of cytoplasmic movements.

The Transition to Land

The fossil record tells us that at the end of the Paleozoic period, some 230 million years ago, a number of different types of plants first appeared on the land.* The establishment on the land of large complex plants (as distinct from the soil-dwelling algae) required a number of new adaptations.

Water is well suited to plant life. In a watery environment, no individual cell need be more than a cell or two away from a direct source of water and of nutrients. Even when the plants are very large, as are some of the brown algae, no special supporting structures are needed since the weight of the plant body is buoyed by the water.

The invasion of the land by plants was one of the most significant events in biological history. It resulted directly in the evolution of the higher plants and prepared the way for evolution of terrestrial animals.

Most of the kinds of plants that took part in this early invasion are now extinct and are known to us only by their fossil record. The plants which are still represented today are grouped in two divisions, the Bryophyta and the Tracheophyta, in the subkingdom Embryophyta. The embryophytes differ from the thallophytes in showing a strong tendency toward an increasing specialization of tissues, with differentiation of parts of the plant body and the development of special organs. This tendency reaches its fullest expression in the flowering plants, the angiosperms. More specifically, in the embryophytes (as the name implies) the egg cell typically develops in the body of the parent plant in a special multicellular receptacle, the *archegonium*. Alternation of generations is seen in all the embryophytes, although the pattern differs from class to class.

* See Appendix 2 for a listing of the geological eras.

2–34 *Generations of liverworts growing on solid rock have gradually decomposed its surface. The soil resulting from this decomposition has been increased and enriched by the addition of organic material in the form of decaying remains of liverworts. About half an inch of soil is shown being peeled back from the rock surface. (Courtesy of the U.S. Department of Agriculture)*

THE BRYOPHYTA: MOSSES AND LIVERWORTS

One group of plants to adapt to a terrestrial existence was the Bryophyta, which include the mosses and liverworts. These plants, like frogs and toads, are essentially amphibious. They grow largely in moist shady places and in bogs. Some of them, like sphagnum and peat moss, are capable of absorbing and holding large amounts of water, so that they maintain a watery existence even on dry land.

In the damp environments frequented by the Bryophyta, individual cells can, with relative ease, absorb water and nutrients directly from the air or by diffusion from nearby cells. The plants do not have any stiff supporting structures to hold them erect, and in general, they have no conducting cells to transport water up the plant body. As a consequence, many of them are very small, and even the largest can raise their heads, which are supported by soft stalks, little more than a foot above the ground. Free water is necessary for the completion of their sexual cycle, as it is in the animal amphibians. Most bryophytes are tropical plants, but many species occur in temperate regions, and some even reach the Arctic and Antarctic.

Unlike the algae and fungi that grow on land, the bryophytes have special structural adaptations to a terrestrial existence. They have small leaf-like structures in which photosynthesis takes place, and as in the higher plants, the body of the plant is specialized for support and food storage. Thus the bryophytes resemble other land plants far more than they do the algae, although they are not usually classified as "higher plants" and do not seem to have been their ancestors.

The bryophytes do not have true roots; the little individual plants grow up like branches from a network of horizontal filaments known as *protonemata*. A single moss plant, interconnected by protonemata, may grow to a conspicuous size, but most liverworts are so small that they are noticeable only to a keen observer. In both mosses and liverworts, small leaflike structures lack the specialized structures of the leaves of higher plants and are only one or a few cell layers thick; hence they are believed to have evolved separately from "true" leaves.

Sexual Cycles in the Bryophyta

The Bryophyta are members of the subkingdom Embryophyta. This means that they, like the higher plants, have multicelled sexual organs in which the sperm and the egg cells develop. The male organ is known as the *antheridium*, and the female organ is the *archegonium*.

The bryophytes, like all the Embryophyta, also have a definite alternation of generations, although they differ from other plants in their pattern of alternation. In the bryophytes, the haploid gametophyte is the dominant generation—the conspicuous, green, leafy photosynthetic plant—

2–35 *Alternation of generations in moss. The long-stalked sporophyte is seen growing out of the gametophyte. (Rutherford Platt)*

and in all species the sporophyte is small, relatively simple, and attached to the gametophyte and dependent on it for food. (In the thallophytes in which we observed alternation of generations, you will recall that each generation, whether gametophyte or sporophyte, led a nutritionally independent existence, if only as a few cells and for a brief period.) In some species, one gametophyte will produce both eggs and sperm, while in others, one plant will produce only male or only female gametes.

The antheridia and archegonia develop near the apex, or growing tip, of the gametophyte. Each antheridium produces hundreds of sperm cells, while a single egg is formed in each archegonium. When sufficient moisture is present, the sperm, which are flagellated, are released from the antheridium. Meanwhile, in the flask-shaped archegonium, if the egg cell has matured, the cover cells capping the neck dissolve and a chemical that attracts the sperm is secreted. The egg cell is fertilized, and the zygote thus formed develops within the archegonium and remains on the gametophyte. The sporophyte that develops from the zygote soon grows and differentiates a sporangium, a spore-producing organ in which meiosis takes place to produce the haploid spores. In most mosses, the sporangium is raised up into the air on a stalk. The sporophyte remains attached to the gametophyte and sheds its spores. If the spores land in a favorable situation, they develop into a spreading network of threadlike filaments, from which new leafy gametophytes develop. The spores are tough and often able to withstand cold and desiccation—another adaptation to the terrestrial environment.

THE TRACHEOPHYTA: THE VASCULAR PLANTS

As we have seen, the Bryophyta never managed to solve completely the problems of independent existence on dry land. Instead, they generally circumvented these problems. All bryophytes grow in relatively protected moist environments or during the moist cool times of the year. The truly successful land plants are those in which cells became differentiated into a vascular system made up of specialized conducting and supporting tissues. These tissues conduct water, nitrogen salts, and minerals up to the leaves and sugar from the leaves to the other parts of the plant. In addition, they serve as systems for support, allowing the plants that possess them to reach impressive size.

The vascular system consists of two distinct tissues: the phloem, which conducts material down from the leaves to other parts of the plant body, and the xylem, which conducts water and other materials up from the roots. The conducting elements of the phloem are the sieve cells, and the conducting elements of the xylem are the tracheids and vessel elements. In the stems, the strands of xylem and phloem usually appear together, either

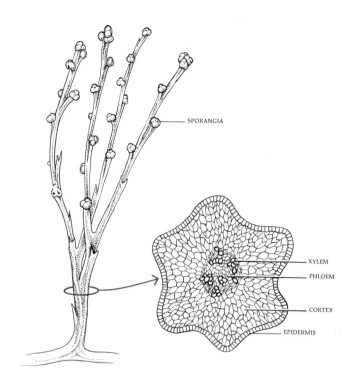

2–36 *One of the few living representatives of the Psilopsida, Psilotum nudum, or whisk fern, closely resembles plants that lived 420 million years ago. It has upright green branches but no leaves and no true roots. Some of the branches bear large sporangia. As you can see in the cross section, a core of conducting tissue runs up the center of the branches and stems. The thick-walled cells of the xylem are indicated by the heavy lines. The Psilopsida are the simplest and most primitive of the living vascular plants. (Photograph by Dr. Virgil Argo)*

in the form of vascular bundles or arranged in a cylinder in which one tissue (typically the phloem) appears on the outside of the other.

Plants with such special conducting and supporting systems are known as *Tracheophyta*, or vascular plants. Four groups of vascular plants have living representatives: the Psilopsida, the Lycopsida (club mosses), the Sphenopsida (horsetails), and the Pteropsida (modern ferns, gymnosperms, and flowering plants). The first three groups seem to represent "false starts" in evolutionary history; the fourth comprises the dominant group of land plants of the present day. Only the Pteropsida have complex leaves and a simple vascular skeleton.

The Psilopsida

There are only two living genera of Psilopsida, and both are tropical. The group is well represented in the fossil record, however, and these fossils show a wide diversity of structure.

Psilopsida have rhizoids but not true roots, and they either have no leaves, as in the whisk fern, or have small ones which lack a vascular

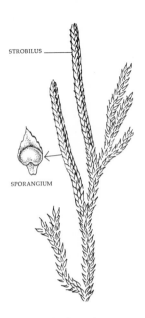

STROBILUS

SPORANGIUM

2–37 *The Lycopsida which are known as club mosses or ground pine are often gathered for Christmas decorations. The branches are densely covered with small leaves packed in spirals.*

skeleton. However, as Figure 2–36 shows, the Psilopsida have simple but definite vascular bundles. The parts of the plant above and below ground have the same vascular pattern of strands, unlike all other vascular plants. The Psilopsida were once thought to be ancestral to the other land plants, and it is possible that they resemble the ancestral forms more closely than the other groups do. New fossil finds, however, indicate that the four groups of vascular plants, and the mosses and liverworts as well, were all contemporaries; the actual connections between them are thus obscure. In any case, the Psilopsida, both modern and fossil, are the least specialized of the vascular land plants.

One species of Psilopsida, of the genus *Psilotum*, ventures as far north as Florida and South Carolina, where it is known as the whisk fern. In the whisk fern, spores are released from the sporangia on the branches. These spores develop into small, inconspicuous, short-lived but independent gametophytes which produce immotile eggs and swimming sperm. Since such sperm can only reach the eggs in water, these plants have never completely escaped their dependence on the existence of free water for the completion of their life cycle.

The Lycopsida

The Lycopsida, or club mosses, have a more highly developed vascular system than the Psilopsida. They have different patterns of vascular organization in the roots and in the stems, and their small leaves have a single, unbranched vein or vascular bundle. The main stem usually runs horizontally along the ground, and from this rhizome, branches protrude upward. On the branches are small dark leaves arranged in a spiral. At the top of each branch is a structure known as a *strobilus*, which is composed of tightly packed spiral leaves, each bearing a sporangium cupped to its base.

Most living species of Lycopsida are grouped in two genera: *Lycopodium* and *Selaginella*. In *Lycopodium*, the sporangia are all of one kind, and the small independent gametophytes produce both motile sperm and eggs. In *Selaginella*, a large genus comprising over 700 species, there are two kinds of sporangia. One produces the relatively large *megaspores*, in which egg-bearing gametophytes grow; the other produces *microspores*, from which sperm-bearing gametophytes grow. As we shall see, this is a foreshadowing of the condition found in the flowering plants.

Although modern club mosses are small, some of their now extinct relatives achieved treelike proportions, reaching to heights of more than 100 feet. Then a widely diverse group, they were among the most common plants of Carboniferous times, coexisting with huge amphibians and dragonflies with wingspans of more than a foot.

2–38 *Horsetails derive some of their rigidity from deposits of silicon in their cell walls. The species shown here is the common scouring rush, so called because it was used by colonial Americans as a pot scourer. The strobilus at the top of the ridged hollow stem is made up of sporangiophores, each containing many spore cases, or sporangia. The spores are equipped with appendages, which coil and uncoil rapidly with changes in the humidity of the air. The movement of these appendages inside the sporangium probably contributes to the expulsion of the spores. In addition, the appendages serve as wings, carrying the spores away from the parent plant.*

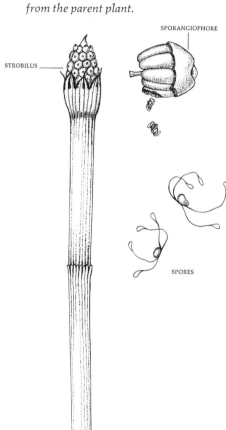

STROBILUS

SPORANGIOPHORE

SPORES

The Sphenopsida

The Sphenopsida, or horsetails, are represented today by a single genus, *Equisetum,* with only fourteen species, found nearly all over the world in moist places. Their stems are lined with distinct knobby siliceous ridges and are conspicuously jointed, the small leaves being arranged in whorls at these "joints." At the tips of some of the stems are conelike structures, the strobili. These are made up of sporangiophores, which attach to the stem like small umbrellas (see Figure 2–38) and, when ripe, airdrop the spores by Paleozoic parachutes. In favorable situations, the spores germinate to produce the small gametophytes, which in turn liberate motile sperm and bear eggs.

The horsetails have deposits of silicon in their epidermis, which made them useful to colonial housewives for scouring their pots and pans but not so agreeable to horses and other ruminants, which can get severe indigestion from grazing on them. Horsetails have leaves, stems, and differentiated roots, and they often grow from rhizomes, which are sometimes several feet underground. Like other plants that grow from buried rhizomes, horsetails are perennials, reappearing each year; they are very difficult to eradicate, since even a small section of a rhizome can generate a new plant.

These strange plants, which even in their modern forms look as if they belonged in some more primitive landscape, were widespread in the Devonian period, when some of them grew to be more than 30 feet tall.

The Pteropsida

FERNS

The ferns differ from the previously described plants in the size and complexity of their leaves, a characteristic they share only with the other members of the Pteropsida. Many ferns are virtually all leaf, and even in the giant tree ferns, the leaf is the dominant organ, the "stem" being composed of a mass of overlapping leaf bases. Ferns also have true roots and stems, although the latter usually take the form of subterranean rhizomes. The leaf may be bladelike, or more typically, it may be finely dissected from edge to midrib into a regular fringe of smaller leaflets.

The leaves of ferns usually originate from tightly coiled structures popularly known as *fiddleheads.* The fiddleheads of our most familiar woodland ferns often develop underground for several years. In their final season, they burgeon rapidly, pushing their coiled tops above ground, and in a few weeks of growth and uncoiling, they become mature fern fronds. Young fiddleheads cooked like asparagus were once considered a great delicacy and served in season in fashionable New England hotels.

The spores of ferns are borne in sporangia on the undersides of the leaves. They are usually clustered; the clusters (*sori*) have a brownish

205　*The Transition to Land*

2–39 *A coiled, immature fern frond, known as a* fiddlehead. *As the fern grows, the cells of the inner side of the leaf elongate more rapidly than those of the outer surface, causing the tip to uncurl slowly.* (Dr. Virgil Argo)

color and are often mistaken for insect eggs or patches of disease. In certain kinds of ferns, such as the cinnamon fern (*Osmunda cinnamomea*), only specialized leaves bear the sporangia; in most ferns, however, they are borne on all mature leaves. The patterns in which the sporangia are arranged are often distinctive. The clusters of sporangia are uncovered in some ferns, while in others, such as the common maidenhair fern, the sporangia appear on the margins of the leaves and the leaf edges curl back to cover them. Many ferns, however, including the familiar Christmas fern (*Polystichum acrostichoides*), have groups of sporangia covered by a special thin scale, the *indusium*.

In most genera, the spores are held together in sporangia by a ring of specialized cells. As the spores mature, the indusium dries and shrivels, exposing the sporangia. Then the cells in the ring begin to dry and shrink until the now tight girdle of cells pops open, catapulting the powderlike spores into the air. The number of spores produced on a single leaflet may be as high as 52 million, but only a few of these germinate into gametophytes, and of these few, fewer still produce gametes which actually mate and give rise to new sporophytes. The sperm swim to the egg, and therefore, free surface water is required for sexual reproduction.

THE SEED

The humid Paleozoic era was the age when our coal deposits were formed from rotting masses of vegetation in great swamps. At the close of this period, in the Permian epoch, were worldwide changes of climate, with the advent of widespread glaciers and drought. Amphibians gave way to the reptiles, which began their climb to Mesozoic prominence, and plants needing free water for fertilization were at a disadvantage. The seed offered a solution to this problem. It was not a new invention; according to the fossil record, some of the club mosses and also some of the fernlike plants had seeds. But it was not until the Permian epoch that the seed, which freed plants from their dependency on free water, became a distinct advantage, and the seed plants took over the world.

To understand the nature of the seed, let us reexamine one of the Lycopsida, *Selaginella*. *Selaginella* has two kinds of sporangia: One produces megaspores, which give rise to egg-producing gametophytes, and the other produces microspores, which give rise to sperm-producing gametophytes. The egg-producing gametophytes are held within the megaspore wall and produce their eggs within this wall, which cracks open as the gametophyte develops.

The seed plants have carried this evolutionary trend one step further. The megaspore with its enclosed gametophyte is held on the parent plant in a specialized structure called the *ovule*. The gametophyte is enclosed within the tissues of the sporophyte and is dependent on it nutritionally.

2–40 *Fern spores are always developed within sporangia, which are usually found in clusters on the underside of the leaf. These clusters, or sori, may be arranged in various ways on the leaf, depending on the species, and they are usually at least partially covered by thin, membranous structures known as* indusia. *In the shield fern (a), the sori are arranged along the margin of the leaf and are protected by circular indusia. The sori of the lady fern (b) are in two rows along the midribs of the leaf sections; the indusia are attached along one side of the sori. The sporangia of the bracken fern (c) cluster in long rows along the margin. In this picture the indusia have dried and shriveled. In the maidenhair fern (d), the edge of the leaf rolls over the sorus, forming a false indusium. (Charles Neidorf)*

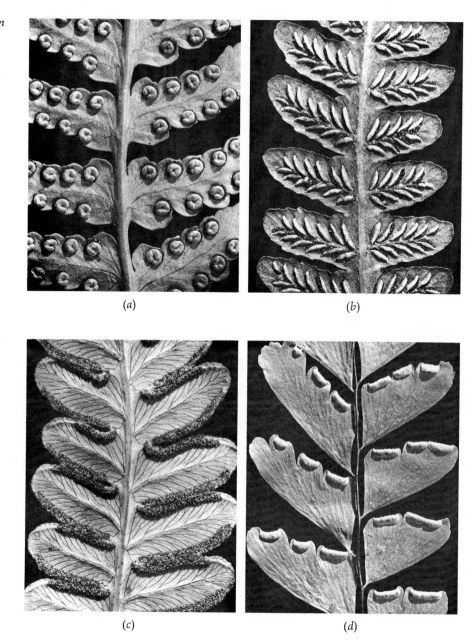

(a)

(b)

(c)

(d)

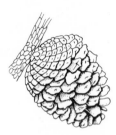

2–41 *The seed-producing female pine cones are larger and higher in the tree than the male cones, which produce the sperm, or pollen. The female cone in the picture is beginning to ripen. As it ripens, it turns downward and its scales loosen, allowing the fertilized seeds within the cone to fall to the ground.*

Fertilization takes place inside this ovule on the parent sporophyte, and a zygote is formed. Still on the parent plant, the zygote begins to divide mitotically and eventually produces a young sporophyte, or embryo. Early in the growth of this embryo, its development is arrested. A seed is formed from the ovule which encloses the embryo in a hard, cold- and drought-resistant protective covering. The seed is shed from the parent plant, the coat splits, and the embryo resumes growth, eventually producing the adult sporophyte of the next generation. Within the seed coat is stored a mass of reserve food, accumulated during the maturation of the seed and available to the young sporophyte for its early period of growth.

Seed ferns were abundant and widespread during the carboniferous period. These were true seed plants despite their fernlike appearance, and they are believed by some botanists to be the direct ancestors of the flowering plants that are the dominant plants of our era.

The modern seed plants are divided into two groups: the *gymnosperms*, or naked-seed plants, and the *angiosperms*, the flowering plants.

2–42 *Jack-pine cones shedding pollen. For fertilization to take place, a grain of pollen must come in contact with an egg cell inside a female cone. Since the only means of pollination among conifers is by the wind, billions and billions of pollen grains must be produced for every few that succeed in reaching the ovule. (from Patterns of Life: The Unseen World of Plants by William M. Harlow, 1966)*

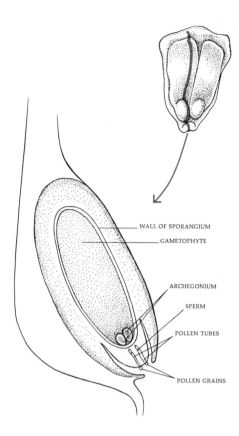

WALL OF SPORANGIUM

GAMETOPHYTE

ARCHEGONIUM

SPERM

POLLEN TUBES

POLLEN GRAINS

2–43 *Each scale of the female pine cone bears two ovules, as shown at the top right. The ovule shown in cross section on the left has developed a mature gametophyte, and the egg cells in the archegonia are ready for fertilization. The pollen grains drawn into the neck of the ovule have become mature male gametophytes, which have, in turn, produced two male gametes, or sperm nuclei. The sperm are traveling toward the egg cells through pollen tubes formed in the tissue of the ovule by the male gametophytes.*

GYMNOSPERMS

The most familiar gymnosperms are the *conifers,* or "cone bearers," which include the pines, spruces, cedars, and firs. The largest and tallest trees in the world—the coast redwoods of California—are gymnosperms. Characteristic of these trees are their two types of cones. The small "male" cones resemble the strobili of the club mosses, while on the larger "female" cones, the scales which bear the ovules are much harder, thicker, tougher, more complex, and more protective. In the male cones, specialized cells in the sporangia undergo meiosis to produce spores, which differentiate into the microscopic wind-borne pollen, or young male gametophytes. Since the wind is an unreliable messenger, the pollen is produced in great excess. The male cones are generally lower on the tree than the female ones. Can you guess why? You may not be able to tell until you read the section on genetics, Section 3.

Fertilization

Within the ovules of the female cones, megaspores are formed as a consequence of meiosis within a sporangium. Of the four spore cells produced by each reduction division, three disintegrate and the remaining one germinates to form a tiny gametophyte. This gametophyte grows within the cone and develops two or more archegonia (female sex organs), in each of which a single egg cell forms. The development from the spore to the gametophyte with its egg cells may take many months—slightly more than a year, for example, in the common pine. The ripening ovule secretes a sticky liquid. When the cones become dusted with pollen, some of it sifts down into the tightly packed cone and comes in contact with the liquid. Pollen grains are caught in the liquid, and as it dries, they are drawn into the neck of the ovule. Here the pollen grain continues its development into a mature male gametophyte, which eventually produces two immotile nuclei which serve the role of male gametes. These travel toward the egg through a structure known as the *pollen tube,* which is produced by the male gametophyte and which grows through the tissue of the ovule. (See Figure 2–43.) During this period, both male and female gametophytes draw their nourishment from the tissues of the ovule-bearing sporophyte.

Since the drought-resistant pollen is blown to the ovules of the female cones directly by the wind and since the sperm nuclei are carried to the egg by the pollen tube, the conifers are not dependent on free water for fertilization. This independence doubtlessly accounts, in part, for their success as land plants.

Following fertilization, the zygote begins to divide. The outer wall of the ovule hardens into a seed coat, enclosing both the embryo and the remains of the female gametophyte, into which food material is transferred from the parent sporophyte. As the cone ripens, it releases its seeds. In

209 *The Transition to Land*

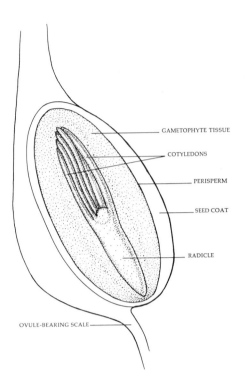

GAMETOPHYTE TISSUE

COTYLEDONS

PERISPERM

SEED COAT

RADICLE

OVULE-BEARING SCALE

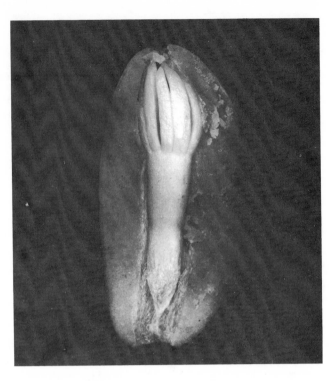

2–44 *Piñon pine seeds in cross section. The ovule has hardened into a seed coat, enclosing the remains of the female gametophyte and the embryo, which now consists of an embryonic root or radicle, and a number of seedling leaves, or cotyledons. When the seed germinates, the radicle will emerge from the seed coat and penetrate the soil. When the root takes in water, the tightly packed cotyledons will elongate and swell with the moisture, rising above ground on the lengthening stem, and forcing off the seed coat. (Photograph by Dr. Virgil Argo)*

most conifers, the seeds are winged and are spread widely by the wind. Some species of pine shed their seeds promptly, while others hold the seeds within the tightly closed cone scales and retain the cones themselves on the branches. Cones can be burst open by heat, as you know if you have ever roasted a ripe pine cone on the fire and extracted the hot nutlike pine seeds from within it. The release of conifer seeds by heat explains why these "closed-cone" pines repopulate a forest so rapidly after a fire.

Figure 2–44 shows cross sections of a pine seed. The seed coat and the wing on which the seed is carried arise from the hardened outer layers of the ovule, derived from the mother sporophyte. The next layer represents the body of the gametophyte; swollen and packed with stored food reserves, it grows and crushes out most of the original sporophyte tissue. The inner core is the embryo with its many *cotyledons*, the embryonic leaves which will appear as the first leaves of the shoot of the new sporophyte when the seed germinates. The lower part of the embryo, the radicle, will form the root. As you can see, a seed really represents three generations under one roof.

The Stem

In the conifer, the xylem tissue is made up of tracheids and the phloem tissue is made up of sieve cells in which the nuclei are retained at maturity. The conducting tissue is not scattered throughout the stem in vascular bundles but is arranged in two concentric circles; this arrangement is also seen in some of the ferns and club mosses, but it is not typical of them. The development of the vascular system in the higher plants will be described in Chapter 2–5.

The Needle

Another feature commonly associated with the conifer is its needlelike leaf. Figure 2–45 shows a cross section of the needles of a pine leaf, which may be 4 or more inches long but only 1/16 inch in diameter. In the center you can see the single vein, the vascular transport system, with its tracheids and sieve tubes. Outside the vein are the parenchymatous cells, in which photosynthesis takes place. The two ducts on facing sides of the needles carry resin; this substance is released if the plant is wounded and serves to close the break. The outside layer of cells is porous but very hard. Although most conifers are "ever-green," they shed their leaves at regular intervals—but not all at once, as the deciduous trees do each fall.

2–45 *Cross section of a pair of pine needles. The vein in the center, consisting of tracheids and sieve tubes, is surrounded by parenchymatous cells, in which photosynthesis takes place. The outside layer of cells comprises a hard but porous covering. The two ducts on the facing sides of each needle carry resin. (Courtesy of Ward's Natural Science Establishment)*

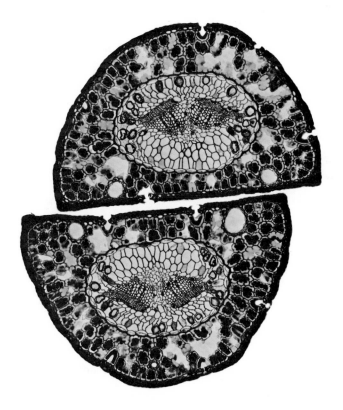

2–46 *The generalized structure of a flower. The sex organs are shown in color. In the center is the female sex organ, the carpel, consisting of the ovary, the style, and the pollen-catching stigma. Each of the two adjacent male organs, the stamens, consists of a supporting filament and a pollen-producing anther. The sex organs are surrounded by petals, and at the base of the flower are the sepals, which once enclosed the entire structure in the bud.*

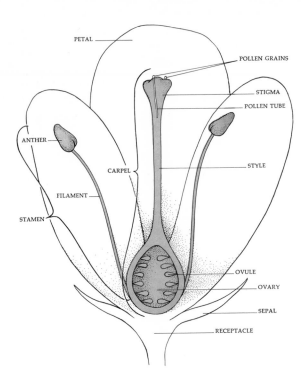

ANGIOSPERMS

Angiosperms, the flowering plants, are one of the great evolutionary puzzles. They became abundant in the fossil record a mere 75 million years ago, in the late Cretaceous period, as the dinosaurs were vanishing and the small rodentlike mammals were making their first appearance. They must have been in existence for a long time before this, because numerous genera appeared suddenly at this time and a majority of these seem to have been very similar to our modern plants. Some evidence, which includes a scattering of fossils of rather doubtful identity, suggests that their origin, like that of the modern conifers, may be found in the Permian epoch—200 million years before they became abundant in the fossil records.

Over 300,000 different species of angiosperms are known. Just listing them, one after another, would require a book twice the size of this one. They include not only the plants with conspicuous flowers but also most of the great trees, the oak, the willow, the elm, the maple, and the birch; all the fruits and vegetables, nuts and herbs; the cactus and the coconut; and all the corn, wheat, rice, and other grains and grasses which are the staples of man's diet and the basis of his agricultural economy all over the world.

The angiosperms have two new, interrelated features that distinguish them from all other plants: the flower and the fruit.

2–47 *As flowers move higher on the evolutionary scale, they tend to have simpler structures, with fewer flower parts. The daisy, one of the most advanced of the dicot flowers, provides a good example of this trend. Although it appears to be one flower, it is actually made up of many very simple flowers united into one blossom. Each outer white ray, often miscalled a petal, is a separate flower with a forked stigma leading to the ovule. The yellow center is composed of hundreds of small flowers or florets. This arrangement makes the collection of little flowers as conspicuous as a large flower for attracting pollinating insects. (S. John Shannon, National Audubon Society)*

2–48 *Can you identify the various parts of these flowers? (Dr. William J. Jahoda)*

The Flower

Figure 2–46 shows the generalized structure of a flower. The outer green leaflike structures, called the *sepals*, are apparently derived from leaves, in an evolutionary sense, and are the structures that enclose the bud before it opens. The petals are usually colored and play an important role in attracting animals to the flower. Inside the petals is a circle of stamens, forming the male sex organs. Each stamen has a slender stalk, the filament, at the top of which is the anther, the pollen-bearing organ, normally containing four sporangia. In the center of the flower are the female sex organs, consisting of one or more fused or free carpels.* Each carpel has three parts: the ovary, which is at the base and in which the ovules are contained; the style, which is a slender stalk; and the stigma, which usually has a sticky surface on which the pollen is deposited.

Carpels may occur singly or in groups, and the groups are sometimes fused together. The pea plant, for example, has a single carpel; the Christmas rose has five separate carpels; and the tulip has three carpels fused together. As a result, the appearance of the female sex organ of the plant varies widely from family to family.

* The female organ of the flower used to be called the *pistil* because certain fused carpels resemble the pestle used in medieval apothecary shops, but this term has now largely been abandoned.

Flowers often have nectaries, sometimes situated so that they can be reached only by a particular type of insect. Nectar is a watery fluid which is about 25 percent sugar. The biological role of nectar is to attract animals to the flower. Some flowers without nectar are attractive because of their pollen alone; pollen is an important source of protein for many insects, such as larval bees. Other flowers have false nectaries which do not contain any food but which nevertheless attract insects, especially flower flies.

Pollination

An important evolutionary innovation among the angiosperms was the development of new and far more efficient methods of pollination. These methods involve not only the wind, as in the gymnosperms, but also bees, butterflies and all manner of insects, birds, and even bats. The visitors travel from one plant to another, lured by nectar and pollen, inadvertently picking up pollen in one and depositing it in the next.

To ensure the continued visits of the pollinators, the flowers "advertise" by a variety of adaptations involving color, scent, and form. Flowers which depend on animal pollinators can be recognized by their bright colors and conspicuous forms. Red is invisible to insects, and so an all-red color is a sure sign that a particular flower is pollinated by birds. Flowers often have scents also—some have the sweet scents that signal nectar, and some have more surprising odors. One species, the African starfish flower, both smells and looks like rotten meat; this attracts female carrion flies, which pollinate the plant and even lay their eggs on it, although, of course, the larvae cannot use the plant for a food source. Some species of tropical trees that are pollinated by bats have flowers that smell like a mouse, are dull in color, and open only at night. One American orchid has a distinct chocolate odor, appealing to a particular species of bee. Several types of flowers look like female insects and so lure the males into attempts at copulation, during which the flowers are pollinated.

Plants and their pollinators have become beautifully adapted to one another by long years of variation and evolution. You can identify the angiosperms that have become insect-pollinated by the fact that these flowers produce relatively little pollen—as compared, for example, with the male cone of a pine tree—which is a reflection of the efficiency of their pollinator systems. Can you see why it is useful for a particular species of flower to appeal to a particular species of pollinator and, if possible, to deny access to others?

The Fruit

When a pollen grain lands on the stigma, it germinates there. In the angiosperms, the cells of the stigma are rich in sugar, which both promotes the growth of the gametophyte and directs the course of the pollen tube down

(a)

2–49 *Three plant-pollinator relationships. Animals are attracted to flowers as a source of food and, in moving from flower to flower, distribute the pollen. For example, the honeybee shown in (a) emerging from a cotton flower is dotted with pollen. As it dips into other cotton flowers, it will cross-pollinate these flowers. Like many flowers, the cotton flower is also self-pollinating. In (b) a sphinx moth drinks nectar through its long sucking mouthpart and in (c) a bat (Leptonycteris sanborni) is taking nectar from the blossom of Agave schotti, the shin dagger cactus. These bats also pollinate the flowers of the saguaro and the organ pipe cactus. (U.S. Department of Agriculture (a); A. D. Webb, Frank W. Lane (b); Bruce Hayward (c))*

(b)

(c)

215   The Transition to Land

A significant difference between angiosperms and gymnosperms involves their modes of pollination—pollen reaches the naked ovules of gymnosperms directly and the enclosed ovules of angiosperms indirectly. Wind pollination is universal in gymnosperms, while insect pollination is characteristic of angiosperms. Some modern angiosperms, including the grasses and some trees, are wind-pollinated. It is clear, however, that primitive angiosperms were insect-pollinated and that the wind-pollinated forms evolved secondarily from the insect-pollinated ones. Angiosperms unquestionably evolved from gymnosperms, and insect pollination was essential to this evolutionary step. The reduced sticky stigmatic surface, typical of most angiosperms, functions well only in a system involving insect pollination. Indeed, wind-pollinated angiosperms are characterized by enlarged, often feathery stigmatic surfaces—a modification of the smaller stigmas of the insect-pollinated angiosperms. The evolutionary development of a restricted stigma in angiosperms is associated with the enclosing of the ovules in an ovary. This enclosing of the ovule may have been an important strategy for preventing the generalized early insect visitors of flowers from coming in direct contact with and, perhaps, devouring the vital ovules—an event that would clearly render pollination of little significance!

the style to the ovary, where the female gametophyte (reduced in the angiosperm usually to eight nuclei) produces an egg. One haploid nucleus of the gametophyte moves down the pollen tube and fertilizes the egg. The other unites with the fused nuclei of two polar bodies. From this fertilized $3n$ cell, the endosperm develops, which will provide the nutrients for the embryo. After fertilization, the embryo begins to form within the ovary, the petals of the flower fall away, and the wall of the ovary develops into the outer fleshy coating of the fruit. In the peach, for instance, the skin, the fleshy edible portion of the fruit, and the stone are the matured ovary wall, and inside is the seed. This is a simple seed formed from a single ovule. In the pea, the mature ovary wall is the pod and the peas themselves are the seeds. The raspberry, for example, is an aggregate of many tiny fruits, each formed from a separate carpel.

Fruits provide additional protection for seeds and new and ingenious ways for their dispersal. In the tumbleweed, for example, the whole plant is blown across the open country, scattering seeds as it goes. In some plants, the fruit itself carries wings, as in many of our common trees; in others, the fruit bursts open, shooting out the seeds. Some species of geranium send forth their seeds by a sort of slingshot. Often, the fruits are edible and brightly colored, tempting birds and animals to eat them. The seeds within the fruit pass unharmed through the digestive tract hours later and often miles away. Burs adhere to fur, feathers, or one's trouser legs, to be carried by unwilling messengers to far-off fields and meadows. Angiosperm seeds travel much farther and faster than the simpler seeds of the gymnosperms.

Monocots and Dicots

The angiosperms are divided into two classes: Monocotyledons and Dicotyledons, familiarly known as *monocots* and *dicots*. Cotyledons, you will recall, are the leaflike structures already visible in the embryo which often form the first leaves of the young plant. Monocots generally have one cotyledon, dicots almost always two.

There are a number of other general differences between the two groups. The monocots do not form any true wood, while the dicots often do. Monocots have scattered vascular bundles; in the dicots, the vascular tissues are

2–50 *The angiosperms, or flowering plants, are divided into two broad groups—dicots, with about 250,000 species, and monocots, with about 50,000 species. Some of the basic differences between the two groups are summarized in this drawing. A typical dicot stem has a central core, in which food is sometimes stored, a series of xylem layers, a ring of cambium, and an outer layer of phloem. The stem diagrammed here shows secondary growth. The monocot stem is often soft, with scattered vascular bundles. In the dicots, tap roots are characteristic, while monocot roots may be very fibrous. The veins of dicot leaves form a herringbone pattern. Monocot leaves tend to be simpler than dicot leaves, with parallel main veins and straight edges.*

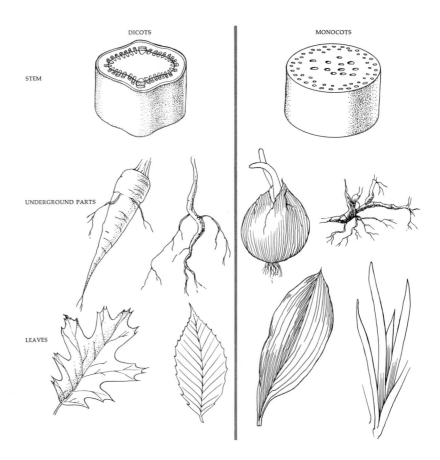

DICOTS   MONOCOTS

STEM

UNDERGROUND PARTS

LEAVES

217 *The Transition to Land*

usually arranged in concentric cylinders. The monocots tend to have fibrous or bulbous roots; the dicots, woody taproots. The monocots, and not the dicots, normally have horizontal underground stems which may be especially modified for the storage of food. The tulip bulb is an example of such a modified stem. You can usually tell a monocot from a dicot by its leaves. Monocot leaves are often shaped like blades of grass, smooth-edged and all in one piece, and they tend to have parallel main veins. Dicots have a greater variety of leaf shapes, and their venation tends to make a feathery or herringbone pattern. There are about 250,000 species of dicots, including most of the flowering trees, shrubs, and herbs, while the monocots have about 50,000 species, including the lilies, palms, grasses, and orchids.

Some of these differences are summarized in Figure 2–50. As a shortcut, think of an oak tree or a geranium as a typical dicot and of grass as a typical monocot.

SUMMARY

All living representatives of those plants which invaded the land some 230 million years ago are Embryophyta. This subkingdom is characterized by an increasing specialization of tissues and by the development of such special organs as the *archegonium,* the organ on the parent plant in which the egg cell forms. The embryophytes are divided into two groups: the *Bryophyta* (mosses and liverworts) and the *Tracheophyta* (vascular plants).

The bryophytes were early land plants, and they have remained essentially amphibious. Most of them are very small, with no supporting structures to hold them erect and, in general, no conducting cells to transport water up the plant body. Free water is necessary for the completion of their sexual cycle.

The tracheophytes are distinguished by their specialized supporting and conducting tissues. There are four classes of tracheophytes: the Psilopsida; the Lycopsida (club mosses); the Sphenopsida (horsetails); and the Pteropsida (modern ferns and seed plants), which are the dominant land plants today.

Of all embryophytes, the seed plants are best adapted to life on land since they do not need free water to complete their reproductive cycle. The *megaspore,* with its enclosed gametophyte, is held on the sporophyte parent plant in a special organ, the ovule, and is dependent upon the parent for food. Fertilization occurs in the ovule; a zygote forms and produces a new sporophyte, which is arrested in development and encapsulated in a seed coat. This seed, with its embryo sporophyte, is then shed from the parent plant and, under suitable conditions, will resume growth to become an adult sporophyte and so renew the cycle.

The *gymnosperms*, or naked-seed plants, include the conifers, which have two types of cones: small "male" cones, which produce male gametophytes in the form of wind-borne pollen, and larger "female" cones containing the ovules in which the seeds develop.

By far the most important land plants are the *angiosperms*, or flowering plants. The 300,000 species of angiosperms include not only all the plants with conspicuous flowers but also most of the large trees and most of the food plants—fruits, vegetables, nuts, grasses, and grains. They are distinguished from all other plants by two interrelated features—the flower and the fruit. Flowers represent a new and far more efficient mode of pollination. Bees, butterflies, insects, birds, and even bats are attracted to the flower as a food source and inadvertently carry pollen from one flower to another. After fertilization, the embryo begins to develop within the enclosed ovary, the flower petals fall away, and the wall of the ovary forms into the outer fleshy coating of the fruit. The seed, enclosed in the fruit, thus gains additional protection and, often, new means of dispersal. The development of flower and fruit enabled the angiosperms to spread farther and faster than the gymnosperms, which are dependent upon the wind both for fertilization and for seed dispersal.

There are two classes of angiosperms—Monocotyledons and Dicotyledons. The dicots, with 250,000 species, include herbs, the flowering trees and shrubs; the monocots, with 50,000 species, include the lilies, palms, grasses, and orchids.

The Life of the Plant

Growth

The higher animals stop growing when they reach maturity, but plants continue to grow during their entire life-span. Growth in the plant substitutes in large part for the mobility which animals have. By growth, a plant modifies its relationship to the environment, moving toward the light and extending its roots toward water. Continued growth in plants is made possible by the presence of meristematic tissue, which is an essentially embryonic type of tissue that persists in the plant at certain key growth centers.

THE ROOT

By the time the embryo has become encased in the hard seed coat, the root meristem is well organized, and when the mature seed germinates, it is in this portion of the embryo that cell division and cell enlargement first begin, with the young root breaking open the seed coat. Figure 2–51 shows a simplified diagram of a growing zone of the root of an angiosperm. At the very tip is the root cap; these cells serve a protective function, being worn away as the root tip is pushed through the soil and being constantly replaced by cells from the overlying meristem. The cells in the meristem designated as *apical initials* are those that initiate the growth process; all the other cells in the root can be traced back to these relatively few cells at the tip of the meristem. The apical initials continually divide. Some of the daughter cells replace the cells in the root cap, some remain in the tip of the meristem, and some differentiate after they divide. The maximum rate of cell division occurs at a point well above the tip of the meristem. Then, soon after cell division ceases, the cells begin to elongate, growing to ten or more times their previous size, often within the span of a few hours. This elongation process is the immediate cause of root growth, although, of course, growth is ultimately dependent on the production of

2–51 *The growing zone of a root. Growth begins in the apical initials, cells within the meristem. As they divide and elongate, the root is pushed downward into the soil. The cells above the meristem undergo a characteristic series of changes as the distance increases between them and the root tip. First, there is maximum cell division, followed by cell elongation, which accounts for most of the lengthening of the root. As the cells elongate, they differentiate into the various specialized tissues of the plant. Some of the cells formed in the apical meristem move downward to form the protective root cap. (from* The Living Plant *by Peter M. Ray, 1963, Holt, Rinehart and Winston, Inc.)*

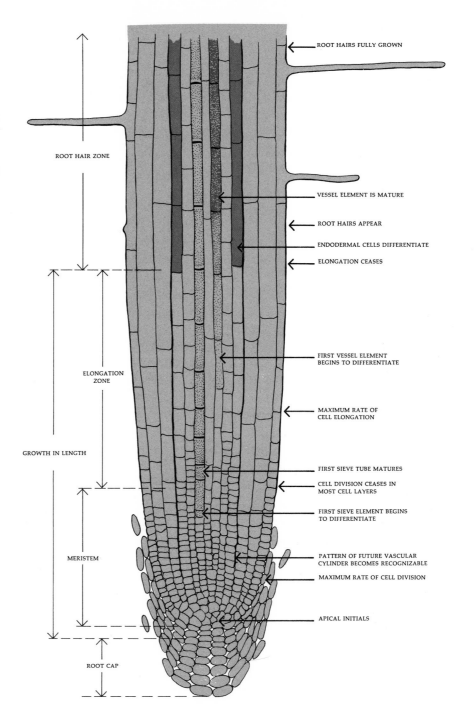

ROOT HAIRS FULLY GROWN

ROOT HAIR ZONE

VESSEL ELEMENT IS MATURE

ROOT HAIRS APPEAR

ENDODERMAL CELLS DIFFERENTIATE

ELONGATION CEASES

ELONGATION ZONE

FIRST VESSEL ELEMENT BEGINS TO DIFFERENTIATE

MAXIMUM RATE OF CELL ELONGATION

GROWTH IN LENGTH

FIRST SIEVE TUBE MATURES

CELL DIVISION CEASES IN MOST CELL LAYERS

FIRST SIEVE ELEMENT BEGINS TO DIFFERENTIATE

PATTERN OF FUTURE VASCULAR CYLINDER BECOMES RECOGNIZABLE

MERISTEM

MAXIMUM RATE OF CELL DIVISION

APICAL INITIALS

ROOT CAP

221   *The Life of the Plant*

the new cells which move into the elongation zone. As the cells divide and elongate, the distance between them and the tip of the meristem, the apical meristem, increases.

At about the time that cell division ceases, various cells begin to show signs of differentiation into sieve cells and vessel elements and, further up the root, into the endodermal (inside skin) cells, which form a cylinder around the vascular tissue of the root, and the epidermal cells, from which the root hairs grow. As you can see, these hairs are simply an extension of a single cell. This same basic pattern is seen in a seedling growing its first roots and in the growing root tips of a tree a hundred feet tall.

THE SHOOT

The growing region of the shoot is the meristematic tissue of the shoot tip. The organization of this growing region is analogous to that seen in the root—a zone of maximum cell division followed by a zone of cell elongation and differentiation. The pattern of development is more complicated, however, than in the root tip since the apical meristem of the shoot is the source of tissues that give rise both to new leaves and to new

2–52 *Longitudinal section of the shoot tip of a lilac* (Syringa vulgaris). *At the tip of the stem is the* apical meristem, *the central zone of cell division. The* leaf primordia, *from which new leaves will form, originate along the sides of the shoot apex. In the picture, the bumps on either side of the meristematic dome are two leaf primordia emerging from the apical meristem. Successively older leaf primordia have formed on both sides. The developing stem below the apical meristem and the young leaves on either side are also regions of active cell division. (from* The Living Plant *by Peter M. Ray, 1963. Holt, Rinehart and Winston, Inc.)*

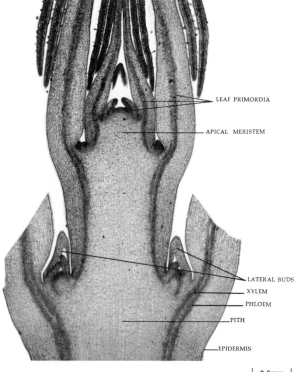

LEAF PRIMORDIA

APICAL MERISTEM

LATERAL BUDS

XYLEM

PHLOEM

PITH

EPIDERMIS

|−0.5mm−|

branches. Figure 2–52 shows the shoot tip of lilac (*Syringa vulgaris*) and shows the apical meristem, which is very small (only a few hundred microns in diameter), and the beginnings, or *primordia*, of the forming leaves and buds. As you can see, leaves are formed in an orderly sequence at the shoot tip. The leaf originates by the division of cells in a localized area along the side of the shoot apex. In some species, leaves arise simultaneously in pairs opposite one another, as in our figure. In other species, the leaves occur in circles or are spirally arranged. The points on the stem at which the leaves arise are called *nodes*. The nodes become separated from one another by the elongation of the shoot, so that the leaf pairs clustered so tightly together around the apex in Figure 2–52 will eventually be spaced out along the stem of the plant. The vascular tissue begins to differentiate in the leaf primordia and eventually becomes part of the general vascular system that connects the plant from root to leaf tip.

In young animals, growth takes place simultaneously (although at different rates) in many areas of the body; in plants, any increase in the height of the plant is the result of growth near the shoot meristem. If you mark the stem of a young plant with crayon and inspect the mark a week or two later, the crayon mark will not have moved, even if the plant has grown to twice its previous height. Similarly, if you carve your initials on a tree trunk, the letters will stay the same distance above ground for the entire life of the tree.

PRIMARY AND SECONDARY GROWTH

Primary growth is the process which leads to the elongation of stems and roots and to the differentiation of the vascular bundles and other specialized tissues of the young stem or root. A few millimeters below the apical meristem, it is possible to recognize three different primary meristematic tissues. Derived directly from the apical meristem, these are the protoderm, the ground meristem, and the procambium. The protoderm, which is the outermost layer of cells, develops into the protective, covering cells of the epidermis. The ground meristem, the most extensive of the three meristematic tissues, develops into the pith, which is in the very center of the stem, and into the cortex, the layer which lies between the epidermis and the vascular tissues. The procambium cells develop into the primary vascular tissues—the primary xylem and the primary phloem— and also, in plants in which there is secondary growth, into the vascular cambium. Primary growth is the only kind of growth found in many herbaceous plants.

Secondary growth is the process by which woody plants increase the thickness of trunks, stems, branches, and roots. The so-called "secondary tissues" are not derived directly from the primary meristematic tissues but are the result of the production of new cells by the vascular cambium and

2–53 *This cross section of the trunk of a young conifer shows the years of growth in the rings which have been added to the girth of the trunk. Surrounding the central core of pith are layers of xylem, the tubes that conduct water up the tree from the roots. The ring of cambium which encloses the xylem is made up of meristematic cells. The cambium cells divide continually during each growing season, forming a new layer of xylem on the inner surface and new phloem on the outer surface. In this way, the trunk increases its diameter as the tree grows. The cambium and the phloem are pushed out farther and farther from the center of the trunk as the xylem enlarges.*

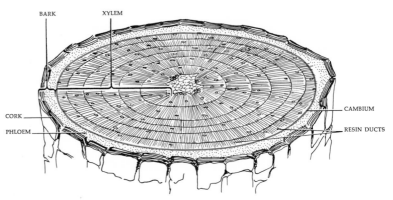

2–54 *You can determine the age of a tree by counting the growth rings in the lower part of its trunk. Do the growth rings shown here tell you anything else about this particular tree? (from Patterns of Life: The Unseen World of Plants by William M. Harlow, 1966)*

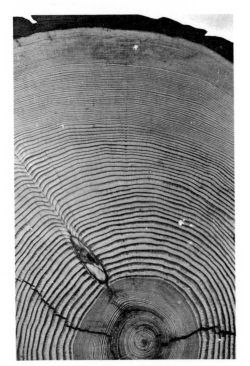

the cork cambium. The vascular cambium forms a cylinder of tissue completely surrounding the xylem and completely surrounded by the phloem. The cambium cells divide continually during the growing season, adding new xylem cells, *secondary xylem*, on the outside of the primary xylem and *secondary phloem* on the inside of the primary phloem. Some daughter cells remain as a cylinder of undifferentiated cambium. As the tree grows older, the xylem in the center of the tree, which becomes known as *heartwood*, ceases to function.

Cork cambium in most plants arises from outer cortical cells. Unlike vascular cambium, which persists for the life of the tree, cork cambium is typically shortlived, with new cork cambium arising each year.

Figure 2–53 shows the cross section of the trunk of a young conifer in which some secondary growth has taken place. In the center of the trunk is a collection of loosely packed parenchymatous cells, the pith. The first cylinder of tissue around the pith is xylem, composed of tracheids which conduct water through the small pits in their lateral walls. The next ring is meristematic tissue, the cambium. Each year, during the growing season, the cambium divides, forming new xylem on its inner surface and new phloem on its outer surface. This continuous formation of layers of xylem and phloem makes it possible for tree trunks to increase their diam-

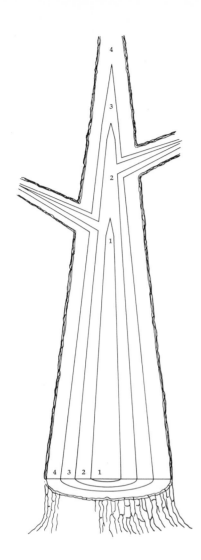

2–55 *A longitudinal section of a 4-year-old tree, showing why a tree trunk will contain a complete record of the tree's growth only in the lower portion of the tree. (After Robbins, Weier, and Stocking, 1964)*

eter as they increase their height. As they grow, season after season, the new xylem forms visible rings, each growth season leaving its trace, so that the age of a tree can be estimated by counting the number of growth rings in a section near its base. (Can you see why only the trunk near the base will contain all the growth rings? If not, look at Figure 2–55.) Since the rate of growth of the tree depends on climatic conditions, it is possible to determine from the width of the annual rings of trees fluctuations in temperature and rainfall that occurred hundreds of years ago. In the humid tropics, where there is no seasonal variation, no rings are formed.

As the xylem enlarges, the cambium is pushed out further and further from the center and the phloem, in turn, is pushed outside of the cambium so that it actually forms a part of the bark. If you strip the bark off a tree, the phloem will come with it, and the roots of the tree and the portion of the tree below the injury will starve—which is why a tree dies if even a narrow but complete girdle of bark is removed. Some three hundred years ago, the Italian scientist Marcello Malpighi observed the fate of a tree when the bark was removed in this way and so was able to conjecture on the relative roles of phloem and xylem. The outer layer of the bark is the cork, composed of dead cells of the type Hooke first saw in his microscope and to which the word "cell" was first applied. In the giant redwoods of California, the bark may be several feet thick.

Conducting Systems

WATER

The successful establishment of large plants on dry land was dependent primarily on the development of a system for conducting water from under the ground to the top of the plant. Since plants have openings to the air for absorption of carbon dioxide, water is readily lost by evaporation and their water supply has to be renewed constantly—and in tremendous quantities. A single corn plant which weighs 1 pound at harvest time will have absorbed, transported, and released into the atmosphere 300 to 400 pounds of water in its lifetime, that is, 40 to 50 gallons. An acre of corn requires 4 to 5 million pounds of water, more than half a million gallons.

Loss of Water

The loss of water from the leaves is known as *transpiration*. To understand transpiration and why the loss of water is so enormous, it will be helpful to look again at the structure of the leaf (Figure 1–32). As you will recall, the epidermis of the leaf is thin and transparent but nearly waterproof and airproof, with a waxy outer surface. Immediately below are the closely packed palisade cells, in which most of the photosynthesis of the plant takes place. Beneath the palisade cells is a loose, spongy layer of paren-

225 *The Life of the Plant*

2–56 *Water's power of cohesion is important in plant transpiration. In every water molecule, the pair of hydrogen atoms (small, colored spheres) is linked to a single oxygen atom (white spheres). Also the hydrogen atoms are held to the oxygen atom of the nearest water molecule by hydrogen bonds, indicated by the arrows. This secondary attraction can produce a tensile strength of as much as 2,000 pounds per square inch in a thin column of purified water. Cohesion thus helps a plant raise water many times higher than any pump is able to.*

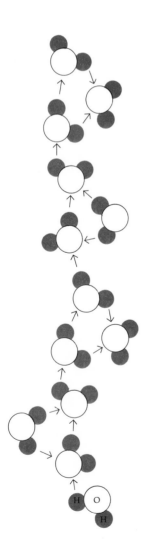

chyma, containing extensive air spaces. The veins, bundles of xylem and phloem, pass through this spongy layer. The lower layer, like the top, is transparent epidermis. In many plants, the stomata are located on the lower surface of the leaf only; in others, they are found on both sides. They may also be found in some plants in the epidermis of young stems.

Photosynthesis takes place in the sunlight and requires carbon dioxide. In the spaces around the loosely packed parenchyma cells, carbon dioxide is exchanged for oxygen by diffusion as each cell carries on its work of photosynthesis. During the process, moisture is lost by evaporation from these intercellular spaces. Closing of the stomata can prevent the escape of water, but it also cuts off the needed carbon dioxide.

Intake of Water

Much of the intake of water in land plants occurs in the root hairs, which are fine extensions of the epidermal cells of the roots. The root hairs poke their way into the small crevices between particles of earth, absorbing the water by osmosis. Osmosis, you will recall, draws water to the point of lowest water concentration. The root hairs pick up and concentrate salts and minerals from the earth, so that there is more pure water in the soil than in the roots. In soils that have too high a concentration of salts, the roots are not able to absorb water, even if water is available.

The pressure in the roots created by osmosis may be sufficient to move the absorbed water some distance up the stem, but then what? How can water reach 60 feet high to the top of an oak tree or travel three stories up the stem of a vine? As students of physics know, it requires a strong pressure to raise water even a few stories off the ground. Nor can suction account for it; even a complete vacuum within the tree could not raise water more than 32 feet, the weight supported by one atmosphere of pressure at ground level. Yet a vine creeping to the top of a tall building has sufficient water for its topmost leaves, as does a redwood tree 300 feet tall. This is a problem which has puzzled and fascinated botanists for centuries. The current theory is that the water is not pushed up the plant but is pulled up. This is known as the *cohesion-tension theory*. Water molecules are held to one another by hydrogen bonds. As molecules move out of the leaf into the atmosphere in the course of transpiration, water moves into the leaf cells to replace them, starting a chain of events by which the water further down in the xylem is pulled up through the narrow tubes of dead cells. Within these narrow passageways, tension is built up, so that considerable force is required to break the chain of climbing molecules. It is believed that the pull on the molecules creates differences in pressure between the roots and the topmost branches, but no method has yet been devised for measuring the pressure directly without interfering with the cohesion of the water molecules.

MINERAL ABSORPTION

In addition to carbon, hydrogen, and oxygen, which can be absorbed from water or from the atmosphere, plants require a number of minerals which must be taken in from the soil. These mineral requirements have been determined by studying the capacity of plants to grow in distilled water to which small amounts of various soil constituents are added. Sometimes, it has been found, a substance—chlorine, for example—is needed in such small amounts that it is almost impossible to set up experimental conditions that exclude it; in such minute concentrations, it is difficult to prove that a substance is required. As a result of these studies, six elements have been identified which the plant requires in relatively large amounts, and some additional ones that are needed in smaller quantities. As you can see in Table 2–2, nitrogen, which is absorbed by higher plants in the form of nitrogen salts, is required in the largest quantities. It is inaccurate, however, to say that nitrogen is "more essential" than the other elements, since the complete deprivation of any material that a plant requires even in minute quantities is fatal.

As the example of chlorine indicates, there need be no correlation between the availability of a substance and its uptake by the plant. Comparisons of the mineral contents of a plant cell with the mineral contents of the water in which it grows show that there can be marked differences in the concentrations of various components. In other words, substances from the soil do not diffuse passively into the root cells but are carried across cell membranes, often against the diffusion gradient, by the energy-requiring processes of active transport. By growing plants in solutions that contain the required minerals in the form of radioactive isotopes, it has been shown that, once absorbed by the root cells, the mineral ions are carried up the plant by the flow of water in the xylem.

Minerals are an important factor in determining what plants grow in certain areas and the rates at which they grow. When we speak of a soil as being rich, we do not mean that it is rich in organic substances, like a piece of cake, but that it is able to provide nitrogen and the other minerals required by the plant. The arid and relatively lifeless soil of the desert can prove remarkably "rich" when supplied with adequate water.

TRANSPORT OF NUTRIENTS

All the food of the plant—its energy source—comes from the products of the photosynthetic reactions that take place in the leaf and so must be transported to the other parts of the plant body. The transport of nutrients is known as *translocation*. Translocation is carried out by the phloem, the conducting cells of which are the sieve cells. Functional sieve cells, unlike tracheids and vessel elements, are living cells, although in the angiosperms, they lose their nuclei as they mature.

227   *The Life of the Plant*

Table 2–2 *A Summary of Minerals Used by Plants**

Element	Form in which absorbed	Quantity utilized**	Functions
MAJOR ELEMENTS			
Nitrogen	NO_3^- (or NH_4^+)	3.5	Amino acids, proteins, nucleotides, and chlorophyll.
Potassium	K^+	3.4	Enzyme, amino acid and protein synthesis. Cell membranes. Ionic balance.
Calcium	Ca^{++}	0.7	Calcium of cell walls. Development of stem and root apices.
Phosphorous	$H_2PO_4^-$ (orthophosphate)	0.4	Formation of "high-energy phosphate" (ATP and ADP). Nucleic acids. Phosphorylation of sugars. Several essential coenzymes.
Magnesium	Mg^{++}	Small quantity	Part of the chlorophyll molecule. Activator of some of the enzymes in phosphate metabolism.
Sulfur	SO_4^{--}	Small quantity	Proteins which contain thiol (–SH) groups. Coenzymes.
MINOR ELEMENTS			
Iron	Fe^{++}	Small quantity	Chlorophyll synthesis. Cytochromes.
Chlorine	Cl^-	0.8	Osmosis and ionic balance; probably essential in photosynthesis in the reactions in which oxygen is produced.
Copper	Cu^{++}	Trace***	Activator group of certain enzyme systems.
Manganese	Mn^{++}	Trace	Activator of some enzymes.
Zinc	Zn^{++}	Trace	Activator of some enzymes.
Molybdenum	Mo^{+++} or Mo^{++++}	Trace	Nitrogen metabolism.
Boron	BO_3^{---} or B_4O^- (borate *or* tetraborate)	Trace	Influences Ca^{++} uptake and utilization. Differentiation and pollen germination.
Cobalt	Co^{++}	Trace	Various roles in symbiotic nitrogen-fixing plants, not essential in others.
Fluorine, nickel	F^-, Ni^{++}	Trace	Not known, but possibly essential in some cases.
NONESSENTIAL ELEMENTS			
Silicon	$H_2SiO_4^{--}$	1.0 (grasses)	Straw formation (calcium silicates). Not essential to most plants.
Sodium	Na^+	Trace	Osmotic and ionic balance, probably not essential to most plants.
Aluminum	Al^{+++}	Trace	Not essential. May cause upset to cell-division system.

* W. M. M. Baron, Organization in Plants, Edward Arnold (Publishers), 1963

**(Approx.) as percentage of dry weight of plant

***Less than 0.0001 percent

2–57 *An aphid feeds on the underside of a linden branch. Inserting its stylet into the bark, the aphid taps a sieve cell (a unit of the sugar-transporting tubes, or phloem, of the tube), thus receiving a continuous flow of dissolved sugar. It releases surplus sugar in the form of a "honeydew" droplet once every half hour. (Dr. Martin H. Zimmerman)*

The solution carried in the phloem system is rich in sugar, mostly in the form of sucrose (some 10 to 25 percent by volume). It also contains amino acids and minerals.

Experiments in which plants are grown in an atmosphere in which some of the carbon dioxide contains radioactive carbon (carbon 14) show that sugar may pass from leaves to roots at rates as high as 40 inches an hour, which is very much faster than it could move through the cytoplasm by simple diffusion. Each sieve cell is refilled from three to ten times per second!

Some plant physiologists have hypothesized that the sugar may move through the phloem system by a pressure-flow mechanism. According to this theory, sugar is actively transported into the sieve cell from the parenchyma cells of the leaves through the selectively permeable membranes of the sieve tube. Then, as a result of osmosis, water moves into the sugar-filled solution, producing turgor pressure. When sugar is removed by a part of the plant that needs it—a growing shoot tip, for example, or a root—pressure is lowered in that part of the system, and so the flow of sugar solution is driven in that direction.

Translocation has been a difficult problem to study because until a decade ago, plant physiologists could not collect solutions from the delicate sieve cells without cutting into the phloem and thereby changing the pressure within the system and also, perhaps, the composition of the sap. An answer to the problem came from an unexpected source—the feeding habits of aphids.

Aphids are small insects that feed on plants, sucking out their juices; you probably have seen them on rose bushes. The aphid drives its sharp mouthpart, or *stylet*, like a hypodermic needle through the epidermis of a plant and then, as electron micrographs reveal, taps the contents of a single sieve cell. If the aphid is anesthetized, it is possible to severe the stylet, leaving it still in place in the cell. The solution will continue to exude through the stylet from the sieve cell for several days, and pure samples can be collected for analysis. Many of the findings reported here were made possible by this simple and ingenious technique.

Regulatory Systems in Plants

In the higher animals, nerve tissue makes possible rapid communication between an organism and its environment and between the different parts of the organism. Plants, which lack nerve tissue, are almost entirely dependent on chemical messengers—*hormones*—for the coordination of their activities. A hormone, by definition, is a substance produced in one part of an organism that has effects on other tissues of the organism. Hormones are typically active in very small quantities. Since the principal way in which a plant responds to environmental stimuli is by alterations in its patterns of growth, the principal action of these regulator substances is on the various growth patterns.

THE AUXINS

The discovery of the plant-growth hormones was the outcome of experiments begun by Charles Darwin. Darwin noticed that if the tip of a young seedling was covered with a lightproof cap, the familiar tendency of the plant to turn toward light was inhibited. Since the bending takes place below the tip, he postulated that a substance is produced in the tip under the influence of light which acts on the tissue below the tip. If the tip is covered by a lightproof cap or is removed, the bending does not occur. If the area below the tip is covered, the bending occurs normally.

Modern experiments in *phototropism*, as this phenomenon is called, were carried out by Frits Went, using grass seedlings. In these monocots, the young leaf is protected in the earliest stages of growth by a hollow cylindrical tube known as the *coleoptile*. Went was able to prove that the bending is caused by a chemical substance produced in the tip. His experiment was a simple one: He cut off the tip of a young coleoptile and placed it on a small cube of agar. After about an hour, he set the cube of agar on the stump of the coleoptile; the coleoptile was once more able to respond to light. A substance produced in the tip had collected in the agar cube. Went called this substance *auxin*. Several auxins have now been identified, the most common of which is indoleacetic acid, commonly known as IAA. As you can see in Figure 2–58, it has a simple chemical structure.

Light causes a differential distribution of auxin in the coleoptile. Apparently it causes the auxin to migrate to the other side of the stem. The result is that the side of the stem opposite the light has a higher concentration of auxin; therefore, the cells on this side of the stem enlarge, and as a consequence of this unequal growth rate, the stem is turned toward the light. Auxin, which is also produced in growing leaves, acts similarly upon the stem, or petiole, of the leaf so that the leaf orients itself toward the sun.

Growth Control

It is now known that auxin is produced in the rapidly dividing tissue at the shoot tip and in the young leaves. It moves downward from the shoot tip and influences the elongation of some of the cells below the shoot tip; the rate of growth in the elongation zone of the stem can be correlated directly with the amount of auxin present. The way in which auxin influences elongation of the cells is not known. Early experiments showed that auxin acts by softening the cell wall and so permitting the cell to enlarge by osmosis. It is now apparent that this effect is the end result of some more complex activity.

INDOLEACETIC ACID (IAA)

2–58 *The chemical structure of IAA (indole-acetic acid), a common auxin.*

2–59 *The role of the growth hormone auxin in the response of a corn sprout to gravity (geotropism) and to light (phototropism). (a) When the coleoptile is perpendicular (on the left), the auxin is distributed evenly and the shoot grows straight up. When the coleoptile is placed on its side, the auxin concentrates on the bottom, and the cells on this side enlarge. The unequal growth rate causes the coleoptile to bend up away from gravity. (b) Darwin's experiment on phototropism. On the left, the coleoptile bends toward the source of light, as shown by the arrows. If an opaque cap is placed on the tip, the coleoptile does not bend, but an opaque tube placed over the base of the coleoptile, not covering the tip, does not prevent bending. Can you explain why? (c) The tip of the coleoptile is cut off and placed on a cube of agar. After several hours, the cube is placed on the stump; the coleoptile bends away from the side on which the agar is placed. This experiment is carried out in the dark or in red or green light which does not affect coleoptile bending.*

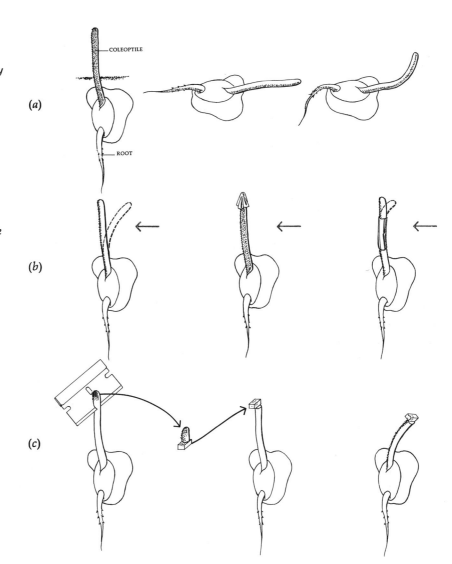

Like most hormones, auxin (1) is potent in very small amounts (its effects on a seedling can be detected even though the pure chemical is diluted a millionfold) and (2) has different effects on different target tissues. The same amount of auxin that produces growth in the stem inhibits the growth of roots. When a seedling is lying horizontal on the ground, the auxin concentration builds up in the lower part of both the stem and the roots. As a consequence, the cells on the upper root surface grow more rapidly, and the root tip curves downward; but those on the *bottom* of the stem grow more rapidly, so the stem bends up. This process is known as *geotropism*, and it is independent of light. We do not know why auxin builds up on the bottom of stems and roots, but the auxin molecules are in solution and thus cannot settle in response to gravity. The isolated roots of many species of plant grow very well in cultures with no added auxin, so either the root does not need auxin or it makes the needed auxin itself. Since it is technically difficult to prove that *no* auxin is present in the root tissue, this question remains unresolved.

Apical Dominance

In many plants, auxin has an inhibiting effect on growth of lateral buds. As we saw previously, these buds are formed in the region of the apical meristem, but they remain inactive while the main shoot continues to grow. What happens if we pinch off this growing tip in a houseplant, such as the familiar coleus? As every home gardener knows, the lateral branches then tend to grow out, making the plant fuller and more compact. If the stump of the shoot is treated with auxin, growth is once more inhibited in the lateral branches.

In the intact plant, the lateral branches begin to grow once the growth of the shoot has sufficiently diminished the concentration of auxin. As the stem elongates, the distance increases between the source of auxin (the rapidly growing tissue) and the lateral buds. The auxin supply is thus diminished, and the lateral branches grow. As the branches grow, their rapidly dividing tissue produces its own auxin supply, which promotes cell elongation and inhibits the growth of lateral buds on these branches.

The control of the growth of the lateral branches by the growing tip of the shoot is known as *apical dominance*.

Antiauxins

These examples of the differential effects of auxin illustrate an important point regarding any hormonal regulatory system: The hormone must be rapidly destroyed. Experiments have proved that auxin loses its activity

2–60 *An experiment with the common house-*
hold plant coleus demonstrates the im-
portance of auxin in plant growth. The
intact plant is shown in (a). In (b), two
leaves have been cut off, depriving the
leaf stalks of their source of auxin. One
leaf stalk is then dabbed with auxin (c),
and this stalk remains firmly attached
to the plant stem while the other stalk,
when its auxin level declines, falls off
(d). (Lee Boltin)

(a)

(b)

(c)

(d)

as it passes through plant tissues; if this were not the case, all the auxin produced at the shoot tip would accumulate in the roots. Several enzymes have been identified that destroy auxin, and other chemicals, antiauxins, have been found that interfere with its activities. Some experiments by Arthur Galston of Yale University indicate that the chief natural regulator of the auxin IAA is the enzyme IAA oxidase. Galston and his co-workers have found also that an increase in the concentration of IAA increases the amount of IAA oxidase produced. Such a relationship is known as a *feedback system*, by analogy with electric systems in which the end product regulates the system that produces it. A simple example of a feedback system is the thermostat that controls a furnace. When the temperature drops, the thermostat turns the furnace on; a rise in temperature,

2–61 *The chrysanthemum on the right was treated at intervals with gibberellic acid. The treatment first heightened the stem moderately, then lengthened the flower stalks, and finally speeded flowering. The plant on the left which received no treatment, stands 12 inches high and shows typical growth. (Courtesy of the U.S. Department of Agriculture)*

the result of the activity of the furnace, "feeds back" to turn off the machinery that produced it. In an analogous fashion, IAA seems to regulate the rate of its own destruction.

THE GIBBERELLINS

The gibberellins are a group of plant-growth hormones discovered as the result of studies on a disease of rice in the Orient known as "foolish-seedling disease." The affected seedlings, which grew abnormally and at a rapid rate, were found to be infected with a fungus known as *Gibberella fujikouri,* which, it was found, produced the hormone. At last report 23 separate gibberellins had been isolated, and more probably remain to be discovered. The effects of these hormones are sometimes even more impressive than those of auxin; a cabbage may grow to the size of 6 feet, and a bushy bean plant can be transformed into a rapidly climbing vine. Some dwarf varieties of plants respond to applications of gibberellins by growing to normal size, which suggests that these varieties may be dwarfs because of a genetic deficiency in their production of the hormone.

Application of gibberellins can also trigger several developmental events that are ordinarily under environmental control, such as flowering and the breaking of dormancy, supporting the concept that the growth hormones are the means by which the plant keeps in touch with its environment.

THE KININS

The kinins, or cytokinins, as they are sometimes called, were first discovered in 1956. Kinetin and other members of this group of plant growth hormones, in the presence of auxin, specifically stimulate cells to divide. (Auxin alone, you will recall, causes them to elongate.) The kinins have been found in a variety of plant tissues, including seedlings, yeast cells, immature fruits, and coconut milk, all of which contain rapidly dividing cells. Unlike auxins, the kinins increase the growth of roots. They are also strong promoters, at least under experimental conditions, of bud growth, thus modifying the apical-dominance phenomenon produced by auxin.

HORMONE INTERACTIONS

The more the plant hormones are studied, the more difficult it becomes to make simple statements about antagonisms between them or "division of labor" among them. All these hormones, and probably others not yet discovered, interact to produce the total growth pattern of the plant.

Apparently, the undifferentiated plant cell has two courses open to it: It can divide or it can enlarge. Enlargement leads to differentiation, while the dividing cell remains essentially undifferentiated or embryonic. In recent studies of tobacco stem tissues, addition of IAA to the tissue culture produced rapid cell expansion so that giant cells were formed. Kinetin alone had little or no effect. IAA plus kinetin resulted in rapid cell division, so that large numbers of relatively tiny cells were formed. In other words, addition of the kinetin (although, you will notice, not kinetin alone) switched the cells to a meristematic course.

In another tissue-culture study, in which artichoke tuber tissue was used, it was shown that a third substance, a calcium ion, can modify the action of the auxin-kinin combination. In this study, IAA plus low concentrations of kinetin was shown to favor cell enlargement, but as Ca^{++} was added to the culture, there was a steady shift in the growth pattern from cell enlargement to cell division. High concentrations of calcium, which is a component of the plant cell wall, probably prevent the plant wall from expanding, and therefore the cell switches course and divides. Thus not only do hormones modify the effects of hormones, but these combined effects are, in turn, modulated by nonhormonal factors.

Growth Cycles and Dormancy

Plants of temperate North America and other, similar areas alternate periods of growth with periods of dormancy. In subtropical regions, periods of dormancy also occur in parts of the year when rainfall is scarce or absent. Dormancy enables plants to survive periods when water is scarce, either because of lack of rainfall or because the available water is locked in the ground in the form of ice, and when delicate growing buds, shoots, new leaves, and root tips would not be able to survive.

There are characteristic differences among plants as to which structures die and which remain alive but dormant. In the annuals, which include many of our weeds, wild flowers, garden flowers, and vegetables, the entire cycle from seed to vegetative plant to flower to seed again takes place within a single growing season, and only the dormant seed bridges the gap between one generation and the next. In biennial plants, two seasons are needed from seed germination to seed formation. The first season of growth ends with the formation of a root, a short stem, and a rosette of leaves near the soil surface. In the second growing season, flowering, fruiting, seed formation, and death occur, completing the life cycle.

Perennials are plants in which vegetative structures as well as seeds or spores survive year after year. Some perennials pass unfavorable seasons as dormant underground roots, rhizomes, bulbs, or tubers. Others, the woody perennials, which include vines, shrubs, and trees, survive above ground but usually stop growing during the unfavorable seasons.

Growth stops in deciduous trees and shrubs as a result of the loss of their leaves, which are a source of food for the plant and also, as you will recall, the main source of water loss. As children, we were taught that the frost was responsible for the changes in the leaves in the fall. It is true that frost may kill a leaf, but characteristically, the changes we observe are initiated within the leaf itself. If a deciduous tree is transplanted south—such as the red maple to Florida—the leaves will change color and fall at about the same time as they would in the northern climate. The fall of the leaf comes about as a result of the formation of an *abscission layer*, a special growth of thick-walled parenchyma cells across the stem, or petiole, that holds the leaf to the branch. The abscission layer first appears as early as midsummer, and as the summer progresses, the cells in this layer become dry and separate from one another until the leaf is held to the stalk only by a few strands. When it finally drops, a scar is left at the point of attachment. Similarly, abscission layers develop in the fruit stem as fruits ripen.

As the water supply to a leaf is cut off, new chlorophyll can no longer be formed and the green color gradually disappears, unmasking the yellows and oranges of the carotenoids. Some leaves also contain red, blue, and purple pigments, the anthocyanins. These same pigments color flowers, the leaves of trees such as the purple beech, the hazel, and some types of maple, and turnips, radishes, purple cabbage, and apples. Unlike chlorophyll and the carotenoids, the anthocyanins are not found in plastids but are in solution in the cytoplasm of the cells. Some anthocyanins show their colors all year round, but some, such as those in the autumn leaves, depend on chemical changes brought about by the combination of cold and bright sunlight characteristic of fall days.

Studies of the formation of the abscission layer show that it is related to the diminishing production of auxin by the aging leaf or ripening fruit. Applications of auxin delay the growth of the abscission layer. Commercial fruit growers often spray their orchards with auxin preparations in order to keep the ripe fruits on the trees until they can be harvested.

BREAKING DORMANCY

One of the most interesting problems with which plant physiologists are concerned is the nature of the environmental cues that cause plants to awaken, or break dormancy. We know plants bud and bloom in the spring—but how do they recognize spring? If warm weather alone were enough, in many years all the plants would bud during Indian Summer, to be destroyed by the winter frost, or would break dormancy during any one of the warm spells that often punctuate the winter season. We can find a suggestion of how dormancy is regulated in our own experience. If branches of flowering trees and shrubs are cut and brought inside in the fall, they do not flower, but the same branches left out until late winter or early spring will bloom in the warmer temperature indoors. Similarly, bulbs such as those of tulips, hyacinths, narcissus, and jonquils can be "forced," that is, made to bloom inside in the winter, but only if they have previously been outside or in a cold place. Deciduous fruit trees, such as the apple, chestnut, and peach, cannot be grown in climates where the winters are not cold.

Scientific investigations carried out under carefully controlled environmental conditions confirm these suggestions that cold is required for the breaking of dormancy in many species. Most varieties of peach for example, must rest for 600 to 900 hours at temperatures below 4.4°C (40°F) before they will respond to the awakening influence of warmer temperatures and longer days. Some plants will respond to a brief exposure to freezing temperatures; if one bud of a greenhouse-cultivated lilac bush is briefly exposed to freezing temperatures, that bud and that alone will break into bloom soon after. Cold is not required to break dormancy in all cases, however. In the potato, for instance, at least two months of dry storage is the chief requirement, with temperature not a factor. In the desert, some seeds do not take their cues from temperature or day length but germinate only when sufficient rain has fallen to leach away inhibitory chemicals in the seed coat, a signal that sufficient moisture is present for the plant to complete its hasty annual cycle from seed to flower to seed again. Requirements as to time and temperature differ even among varieties of the same species, depending on the geographic areas in which they are found.

Studies of dormancy in plants and seeds have shown that the problem of trying to determine the particular factor or factors responsible for initiating, maintaining, or breaking dormancy is complicated by the fact that, in many plants at least, dormancy can be divided into three periods. The plant enters a predormant state, during which dormancy can be induced by conditions, such as a shortening of the hours of daylight, that will not produce dormancy in the plant at another time of year. Following the predormancy period, the bud or seed may enter a period of true dormancy, during which no growth can be induced by any means. Once true dormancy is over and the postdormant period is reached, warm temperatures, long days, treatment with growth hormones, or a combination of procedures, depending on the species, can initiate growth.

There is some evidence that true dormancy may be induced by the presence in the plant tissue of chemical inhibitors, the concentrations of which may be altered by exposure to cold or by passage of time or, if the chemicals are present in the seed coat, by being washed or worn away. So far, however, no natural inhibitor has been isolated from one plant that will induce dormancy in another, which would be a convincing demonstration of this theory. On logical grounds, we might suppose that there is not just one mechanism for dormancy but a large number, since dormancy became an evolutionary advantage only comparatively recently, as the climate became colder. Presumably, dormancy has evolved independently in many separate groups of plants.

Dormancy in vegetative parts of plants usually does not last for more than a season, after which the plant either breaks dormancy or dies, but seeds may survive a long time in the dormant condition, enabling a plant to exist for years, decades, and even centuries under unfavorable conditions. In 1879, seeds of 20 species of common Michigan weeds were stored away for an experiment designed to continue 160 years. At the last sampling, the seeds of three species were still viable. Although this is impressive, it does not approach the record of the lotus seeds found by a Japanese botanist in a peat deposit in Manchuria. Radiocarbon dating showed the seeds to be 1,000 years old, but when the seed coats were filed to permit water to enter, every single one germinated!

HOW PLANTS TELL TIME

The stages of growth, particularly in flowering plants, are timed very precisely to occur at certain seasons, as anyone knows who has been in Washington, D.C., at the time of the cherry blossoms. Such synchrony in timing is extremely important to the plant since it assures maximum chances of cross-pollination. But what brings about this simultaneous, often spectacular burst of bloom? Studies on this subject indicate that it often depends upon the relative length of day and night. Ragweed, for instance, starts making flowers when the day is about 14 1/2 hours long. Similarly, spinach requires 14 hours of light per day for a period of at least two weeks in order to flower. As a result, some strains of ragweed and all the spinach plants in a given area flower at the same time. Also, as a result of these requirements, neither ragweed nor spinach flower in the tropics. Furthermore, although these strains of ragweed could flower in northern Maine, they could not survive there since days as short as 14 1/2 hours do not occur at this latitude until after the first of August. Other strains of ragweed with different photoperiodic requirements do, however, occupy these northern areas.

MECHANISMS OF PHOTOPERIODICITY

The cocklebur, a common weed, proved to be particularly useful for studying *photoperiodism,* as this phenomenon is known. The cocklebur is a fall-flowering, short-day plant. It requires 14 1/2 hours *or less* of light in a 24-hour cycle to flower. One single exposure under laboratory conditions to a short-day cycle will induce flowering a few weeks later, even if the plant is immediately returned to long-day conditions. Furthermore, the cocklebur can withstand a great deal of rough treatment, surviving even if its leaves are removed. If all the leaves are stripped off, no flowering occurs, but if as little as one-eighth of a fully expanded leaf is left on the stem, the single short-day exposure will initiate flowering.

In their experiments with the cocklebur, K. C. Hamner and James Bonner made the critical discovery that led to an understanding of the underlying mechanism of photoperiodism. If the period of darkness is interrupted by as little as a one-minute exposure to a 25-watt bulb, flowering does not occur. Interruption of the light period by a period of darkness has no effect on flowering whatsoever. The cocklebur does not measure light but darkness! Subsequent experiments with other short-day plants showed that they, too, require periods of uninterrupted darkness. Commercial florists now use this trick to hold back blooming in chrysanthemums in order to have flowers to sell in the late fall for football games and other festive occasions.

Long-day plants also measure darkness. A long-day plant that will flower if it is kept in a laboratory in which there is light for 16 hours and dark for 8 hours will also flower on 8 hours of light and 16 hours of dark if the dark is interrupted by even one minute.

2–62 *Photoperiodicity in flowering plants. Short-day plants flower when the day length is below some critical value, and long-day plants flower only when it exceeds some critical value. The short-day plant in the drawing requires a day length of eight hours or less to bloom; if the 16-hour period of darkness is interrupted even very briefly, as shown on the right, the plant will not flower. The long-day plant, on the other hand, will flower only when the day length exceeds eight hours or if the period of darkness is interrupted.*

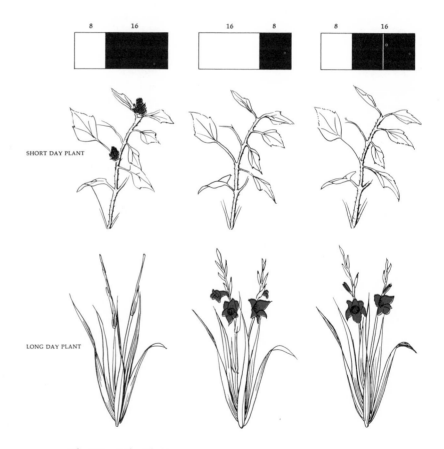

SHORT DAY PLANT

LONG DAY PLANT

The measuring of darkness has been found to depend on a pigment called *phytochrome*. Just as retinine changes in the vertebrate eye, phytochrome changes in the leaf in response to either light or dark. In some plants, such as the cocklebur, one minute of light is enough to turn all the pigment into light-type phytochrome. In the hours of darkness, the light type gradually turns to dark type. When a sufficient amount of this dark type accumulates, it acts as a trigger to stimulate or inhibit enzyme responses associated with flowering. In the short-day plants, the accumulated dark-type phytochrome initiates flowering; in long-day plants, accumulated dark-type phytochrome inhibits flowering.

Phytochrome is now believed to occur widely in the plant world and to be involved with a number of other processes, such as dormancy, leaf formation, and seed germination.

Circadian Rhythms in Plants

Some types of plants spread their leaves during daylight and raise them to the stem at night. In 1729, the French geophysicist Jean-Jacques de Mairan noted that these "sleep movements" in plants may continue at about the same time intervals even when the plants are kept in darkness. Such regular cycles are now known as *circadian rhythms* (from *circa*, meaning "about," and *dies*, meaning "day"). Circadian rhythms have been found to exist almost universally throughout the plant and animal kingdoms.* They are currently being studied by a number of investigators from widely divergent fields, including physiologists, students of animal behavior, clinical psychologists, and space scientists.

One such investigator is J. Woodland Hastings of Harvard University, who has been carrying out a series of studies of circadian rhythms in the single-celled marine alga, *Gonyaulax polyedra*, a dinoflagellate which is a close relative of the poison-producing *Gonyaulax catanella* and grows with it. The dinoflagellate is bioluminescent; the Indians of the Northwest learned to watch for the flashing of the waters at night, which they recognized as a warning that the mussels in the area, a staple of their diet, were poisonous.

No less than three separate functions have been shown to operate with separate circadian rhythms within the single cell of *Gonyaulax polyedra*: (1) luminescence, which reaches a peak of brightness in the middle of the night; (2) photosynthesis, which reaches its peak in the middle of the day; and (3) cell division, which is restricted to the hours just before dawn. If *Gonyaulax* is kept in continuous dim light, these three functions continue

* The only major groups of organisms in which the occurrence of circadian rhythms has not been demonstrated are: the bacteria, the blue-green algae, the viruses, and the bryophytes.

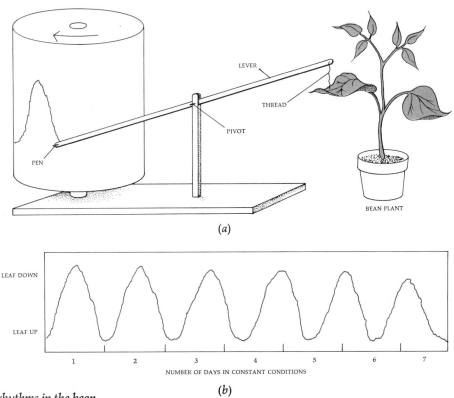

LEVER

THREAD

PIVOT

PEN

BEAN PLANT

(a)

LEAF DOWN

LEAF UP

1   2   3   4   5   6   7

NUMBER OF DAYS IN CONSTANT CONDITIONS

(b)

2–63 *"Sleep movement" rhythms in the bean plant. Many legumes—such as the bean—orient their leaves perpendicular to the rays of the sun during the day and raise them to the sides of the stem at night. These "sleep movements" can be easily transcribed on a rotating chart by a delicately balanced pen-and-lever system attached to the leaf by a fine thread (a). The rhythm will persist for several days in continuous dim illumination. A representative recording is seen in (b).*

to occur with the same rhythm for days and even weeks, long after a number of cell divisions have taken place.

The fact that these rhythms in *Gonyaulax,* as in other organisms studied, tend to be circadian—that is, occurring at intervals slightly longer or shorter than 24 hours—is considered of great theoretical importance. That they do not occur on a regular 24-hour schedule indicates that the cycles are not dependent on any outside environmental factor, associated with the rotation of the earth, but by endogenous factors, that is, factors within the organism itself. These unidentified endogenous factors are often referred to as *biological clocks* since, like man-made clocks but unlike a sun dial, they do not measure "the shining hours" but count off time without reference to the outside world.

Another important feature of these rhythms is that they do not speed up as the temperature rises, as you might expect since enzymatic activities must be involved and enzyme reactions take place more rapidly at high temperatures than at low ones. Therefore, the clock must contain within its workings some type of compensatory mechanism—a feedback system that adjusts it to temperature changes. This idea is supported by Hastings' observation that in *Gonyaulax*, the circadian rhythms seem to slow down as the temperature rises, rather than speed up, suggesting that overcompensation may be taking place.

CHANGING THE RHYTHMS

The rhythms in *Gonyaulax*, like most circadian rhythms, can be altered by modifying the cycles of illumination in the laboratory. For example, if the investigators expose cultures of the cells to alternating light-dark periods of six or seven hours each, the rhythmic functions of the organisms will follow the imposed cycle. There seem to be two ways in which the rhythm of the organism can be synchronized with the environment: entrainment and resetting. By entrainment, the rhythm of an organism is adjusted to the slightly different rhythm of the environment. When the clock of an organism is reset, however, it begins to follow an entirely new rhythm. Exposure to bright light of a culture of *Gonyaulax* that has been raised in continuous dim light will reset its biological clock so that it begins to follow a new circadian rhythm. The ability of an organism to adjust its inner rhythm to that of the outside world is an obvious advantage.

2–64 *Rhythmic luminescence in Gonyaulax: (a) The 24-hour cycles of luminescence persist even when the organisms are placed in constant dim light. (b) Exposing the organisms to a different day-night cycle—in this case, six hours of light, six hours of dark—alters the rhythm. However, the usual circadian pattern returns when the organisms are again placed in constant dim light. (After Hastings, 1965)*

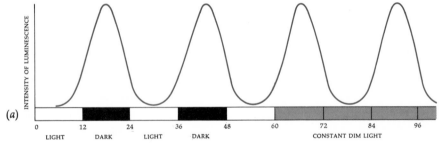

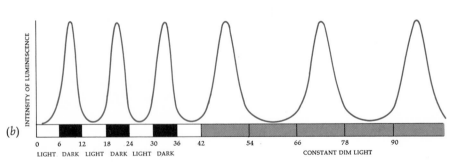

In some cases, the adaptive significance of the biological clock is evident. Some plants, for example, secrete nectar at certain specific times of the day. As a result, bees—which have their own biological clocks—become accustomed to visiting these flowers at these times, thereby ensuring maximum cross-pollination for the flowers. In other cases, the biological significance is not so clear. For instance, there seem to be links between photoperiodism and circadian rhythms, but these links have not been identified.

In many cases, the endogenous rhythm has no apparent significance. It is becoming clear, however, that the total physiological organization of an organism is dependent for its most efficient operation on the integrated control of all its activities. Thus, some of the phenomena that can be observed—such as the midnight bioluminescence of *Gonyaulax*—may not be useful in themselves but may simply be a by-product of this overall integration, a sign that the biological clock is running.

SUMMARY

All growth originates in the meristematic tissue of the plant. *Primary growth*—the growth in length of stems and roots and the differentiation of their specialized tissues—occurs in three different meristematic tissues: the protoderm, the ground meristem, and the procambium. These are derived from the meristem. *Secondary growth*—the thickening of stems, branches, and roots—occurs in vascular cambium and cork cambium.

Unlike animals, plants do not recirculate their water but lose it through the leaves by *transpiration*. Carbon dioxide necessary for photosynthesis enters the plant through intercellular spaces, the *stomata*, usually found on the underside of the leaves. As a result of photosynthesis, oxygen and moisture are given off through the stomata into the atmosphere.

Water enters the plant by osmosis (the movement of water to an area of higher salt concentration) through the root hairs. The *cohesion-tension theory* is the current explanation of how water is moved up the plant. As water molecules move out of the leaf into the air by transpiration, water moves into the leaf cells by osmosis. This sets up a chain reaction, so that water is pulled up through the plant as a result of the coherence of the water molecules because of the hydrogen bonds between them and the tension created by transpiration.

Minerals needed by the plant, such as nitrogen and potassium, enter the root cells from the soil, often against the diffusion gradient, by means of the energy-requiring processes of active transport.

Translocation is the process by which various molecules in the leaves—the food of the plant—are distributed throughout the plant. This is accomplished by the conducting cells of the phloem, known as *sieve cells*.

Alteration in patterns of growth is the chief way in which plants respond to environmental stimuli. Growth patterns are regulated by the activities and interactions of at least three groups of *growth hormones:* the auxins, the gibberellins, and the kinins. The *auxins,* which are produced in the rapidly dividing tissue of the shoot tip and in the young leaves, regulate the response of the plant to light (*phototropism*) and gravity (*geotropism*). Under the influence of auxin, cells elongate, thus creating an unequal growth rate. The auxins of the growing tip also inhibit the growth of lateral buds, a process known as *apical dominance.* The inhibitory effects of auxin are controlled by enzymes which deactivate the auxin as it moves down the plant. The *gibberellins* promote growth, flowering, and the breaking of dormancy, and the *kinins* stimulate cell multiplication of bud growth.

In temperate areas, alternating periods of growth and dormancy (when little or no growth occurs) enable the plant to adjust to periods when water is not available, either because of lack of rain or because it is frozen in the ground. In the *annuals,* the cycle from seed through flower to seed occurs in one growing season; in the *biennials,* it takes two seasons. *Perennials* are plants in which vegetative structures as well as seeds survive year after year. Woody perennials (trees and shrubs) become dormant above ground by shedding their leaves and thus stopping photosynthesis and water loss.

Breaking of dormancy occurs only when certain requirements have been filled. For many plants, the decisive factor is cold—a certain number of days with the temperature below a specific point must pass before growth is renewed.

The stages of plant growth are timed very precisely to occur during certain optimal seasons. Both long- and short-day plants require a period of uninterrupted darkness before they will flower. The pigment *phytochrome* is the means by which the plant detects the difference between light and darkness. This synchronization of growth activities by changes in day length is called *photoperiodism.*

The occurrence of certain activities and movements in regular cycles throughout the day, a phenomenon first observed in plants, is known as *circadian rhythm.* Experiments with the circadian rhythms of the bioluminescent marine alga *Gonyaulax* are discussed.

The Lower Invertebrates

Introduction

The diversity of living things has always been a source of wonder and delight to man, and in the pages that follow we hope to add to this sense of the variety of nature. Our chief emphasis, however, in this introduction to the group of organisms that we classify as animals will be on the sameness of living things rather than their differences, and even though we may be looking at animals as superficially unalike as a jellyfish and a grasshopper, we shall try to keep in mind that all organisms—orchids, starfish, squids, cows, and elm trees—are evolutionary solutions to the same set of problems.

Let us begin by regarding an organism as a cell or group of cells. A primary need of the organism is to supply each cell with the materials it requires (in the case of most heterotrophic cells, these are oxygen, water and salts) and to eliminate wastes, including excess carbon dioxide, nitrogenous wastes from the breakdown of amino acids, and in some cases, excess water. Cells that live individual or colonial lives in a watery environment or that spread themselves thin, as in the thallus of an alga, can solve these problems in relatively simple ways, but as organisms get larger, thicker, and more complex, the problem of servicing each individual cell becomes correspondingly complicated. Insects have solved the oxygen-supply problem in a totally different way than earthworms, for example; sharks have adapted to their salt water environment by a different means than the mackerel. Many terrestrial animals soon die without fresh water, but the seagoing birds drink only seawater—which would be fatal to a man dying of thirst—and the kangaroo rat that lives in the baking desert may never drink a drop of water in its entire life. Each has found in the course of evolutionary history answers that fit it to a particular environment and a particular way of life.

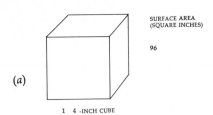

SURFACE AREA
(SQUARE INCHES)

96

(a)

1 4-INCH CUBE

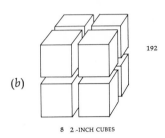

192

(b)

8 2-INCH CUBES

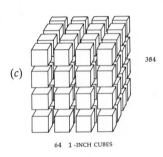

384

(c)

64 1-INCH CUBES

2–65 *The total volume of each of the cubes in (b) and (c) is the same as that of the 4-inch cube at the top, but the total surface area of (b) is twice as great and that of (c) is four times greater.*

Another set of problems that an organism must solve in order to exist arises from the fact that it is more than just a group of cells. It is, in fact, a complex society, in which the needs of each individual cell or cell type are subordinated to the needs of the society. In a population of *Paramecium*, the organisms may have common requirements but each is in competition with the others. In a society of a few thousand cells—a small crustacean, for instance—the individual cells are dependent on the existence of the group and are organized in a system of mutual cooperation. The second group of problems faced by organisms, therefore, relates to the organization or integration of activities. Hormones are one of the chief means of integration in both plants and animals. In the animals, another integrating mechanism has evolved: the nervous system, by which the organism keeps in touch with its environment and coordinates its own activities.

A QUESTION OF SIZE

At this point, one might well ask: Why bother being larger, when it involves so much extra trouble? What selective advantages are there to the larger, more complex animals as compared with the smaller ones? Some answers to these questions are obvious and simple. Larger animals are, in general, more likely to eat than be eaten. Larger organisms, especially those that live under water or on land, are generally able to travel faster and farther than small ones, and this is an advantage. A small ciliate, for instance, might starve only a few centimeters from a food supply.

Perhaps even more important, however, than mobility and edibility is what the famous French physiologist Claude Bernard called *milieu interieur*, the internal environment. A single-celled organism is as cold or as hot and as wet or as dry as its surroundings, whereas a larger animal is more independent and, to some extent, controls the environment in which its cellular society lives. Control of the internal environment is more readily understood if we review some simple geometry: A cube with sides 1 centimeter square has a surface area of 6 square centimeters and a volume of 1 cubic centimeter, a 6:1 ratio of surface area to volume. Now let this cube grow until each dimension is doubled; the area then becomes 24 square centimeters (6×2^2), while the volume becomes 2^3, or 8 cubic centimeters, a 3:1 ratio. Triple the dimension, and the ratio is 2:1. In cells, diffusion takes place across the surface area. This is a principal reason why a cell, which depends for its existence on the exchange of substances with the outside environment, cannot be very large. On the other hand, since it may be advantageous to conserve certain substances, such as water and heat, an organism may be better off, within limits of weight and mobility, if its comparative surface area is reduced. One-celled plants and animals can live successfully only in the water or as parasites in the bodies of other organisms, which amounts to the same thing. The many-celled organisms can live not only in the water but on the land, in the sky, and even, as we are now beginning to discover, in outer space—which is a very logical extension of an old evolutionary trend.

About 1 1/2 million different species of animals have been named and classified into some 20 different phyla. We shall look at a few examples from eight of the major phyla which illustrate both the diversity and the progressive levels of complexity arrived at in the course of evolution.* The chief emphasis in this part of the discussion will be on the invertebrates. Then we shall give a brief account of the evolutionary history of the animals as biologists now reconstruct it, together with some of the evidence for their theories. Finally, in Chapter 2–8, we shall look at some of the common problems with which animals contend—such as respiration, sexual reproduction, and integration of activities—and review some of their solutions.

CLASSIFICATION OF ANIMALS

Classification of animals is based largely on body plan. Body plans are not simply structures; they are also reflections of functions, that is, the ways in which animals do things—how they move, eat, and perform other activities vital to the organism and to the species. In these chapters, therefore, we shall describe not only the structural organizations of various animals but also the functions which are interrelated with these organizations.

The Protozoa

The Protozoa are the one-celled members of the animal kingdom. As we emphasized in Section 1, there is little fundamental difference in basic cell structure and metabolic activities—those activities necessary to sustain life—between the one-celled organisms and other cells. However, unlike most of the cells of multicellular organisms, most protozoans are motile. Classification of the Protozoa into three of their four major groups is based upon their characteristically different methods of locomotion: (1) by flagellar movement (the flagellates), (2) by pseudopodia (the sarcodines), and (3) by ciliary movements (the ciliates). The fourth major group, the Sporozoa, are nonmotile during the major phases of their lives.

THE FLAGELLATES

The flagellates include the flagellated single-celled algae, which are also claimed by the botanists, and the closely related nonphotosynthetic species, such as *Peranema*. There are also some flagellates which are clearly not related to plantlike forms. Most of these are parasitic. The *Trypanosoma gambiense*, a flagellate that causes African sleeping sickness, is a pro-

* A complete listing of the phyla can be found in Appendix 1.

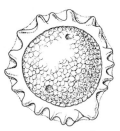

|— 25μ —|

2–66 *Arcella is a sarcodine, a class of protozoans which also includes Amoeba. The jellylike body of the sarcodine is not protected by the stiffening pellicle found in other protozoans, but many surround themselves with hard shells. Arcella secretes a keratinlike substance which forms a characteristic, cup-shaped covering, here seen from above. Its pseudopodia extend from a single, small opening in the underside of the shell.*

2–67 *Actinosphaerium bristles with thin, pointed spicules which function as a trap. When a prey organism touches one of the spicules, it becomes stuck in an adhesive secretion that coats the surface. The secretion also apparently contains enzymes that initiate digestion of the prey, which eventually is enclosed in a food vacuole and drawn into the cell.*

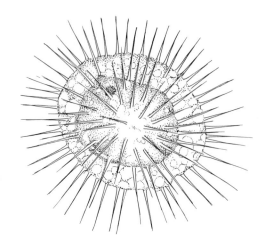

|— 50μ —|

tozoan of this type. It is carried by the tsetse fly. As the fly bites its victim, it deposits the flagellate into the bloodstream. There the parasite multiplies, and usually after some weeks or months, it makes its way into the cerebrospinal fluid, causing torpor and, if the victim is untreated, death. Usually by this time, since the disease is a protracted one, the patient has been bitten by another tsetse fly, which then carries the parasite off to start a new colony.

THE SARCODINES

The Sarcodina are amoebalike organisms which have no stiffening pellicle outside their cell membranes and which generally move and feed by the formation of pseudopodia. They take their name from the word "sarcode," coined in the early nineteenth century to describe the "simple, glutinous, and homogeneous jelly" of which simple cells were supposed to be composed. The concept of a "primitive living jelly" as the essence of all forms of life has long since disappeared, yet in all truth, a naked amoeba does look like what one might imagine an animated drop of primordial ooze to be.

Many of the sarcodines cover their amoebalike characteristics with firm bright shells. Some, like *Arcella*, secrete a hard, keratinlike material, while others, like *Difflugia*, exude a sticky organic substance on which then forms a sort of haphazard mosaic made up of specks of sand and bits of the discarded shells of other minute creatures. Some, the *sun animals*, resemble pincushions, with sharp silica spicules radiating from their soft bodies. *Actinosphaerium*, the protozoan shown in Figure 2–67, may reach as large as a millimeter in diameter and may sometimes be seen as a tiny white speck floating on the surface of a pond. Other sarcodines, the Foraminifera, have snail-like shells and live in the sea. Their shells are made of calcium carbonate, extracted from the seawater. The white cliffs of Dover and similar chalky deposits throughout the world are the result of the long accumulation of these discarded shells. The shells of the Foraminifera have been accumulating on the ocean bottom for millions of years, and in many areas, as a result of geologic changes, thick deposits of their skeletons (the *foraminiferan ooze*) can be found on the surface of the land or under later rock formations. Since the skeletons have evolved over this long period of time, it is possible to date a particular stratum by the type of Foraminifera that it contains, a fact which has proved of immense practical value in locating oil-bearing strata in Texas, Oklahoma, and many other oil-rich areas.

THE CILIATES

The Ciliophora, or ciliates, are the most highly specialized and complicated of the Protozoa. Two of these ciliates, *Paramecium* and *Euplotes*,

|——— 0.2mm ———|

2–68 *The Foraminifera begin life soft and shapeless and then secrete chalky shells around themselves, enlarging the shells with new chambers as they grow. When they die, their shells form an important part of the ooze that covers the ocean floor. Much of the limestone and chalk deposits in the earth are formed from foraminiferal shells. (Eric V. Gravé)*

were described in Chapter 1–2. A larger and more imposing ciliate than either of these is *Stentor*.

Because the shape of *Stentor* extended is like that of a trumpet, this group of ciliates came to be named, imaginatively, after bronze-voiced Stentor of the *Iliad*, "who could cry out in as great a voice as 50 other men." The most familiar type is *Stentor coeruleus*, which in color is a delicate cerulean, or heavenly blue. *Stentor* is crowned with a wreath of membranelles—groups of cilia which adhere to one another to form a paddlelike structure. These beat in rhythm, creating a powerful vortex which draws edible particles up to and into the funnel-like groove leading to the cytostome. *Stentor* is striped with elastic protein threads, the *myonemes*, which permit it to stretch out to its full stentorian length or, alternatively, contract into an almost perfect sphere.

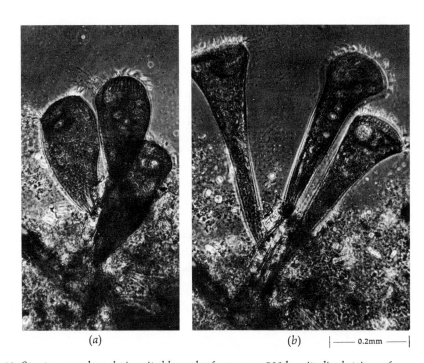

(a)   (b) |——— 0.2mm ———|

2–69 *Stentor coeruleus derives its blue color from some 500 longitudinal stripes of pigment. Underlying the clear stripes are myonemes, contractile protein threads that enable Stentor to contract almost into a sphere (a) or to stretch out into a trumpet shape (b). In the pictures, you can clearly see the "crown" of cilia. What function do these cilia perform? (Eric V. Gravé)*

249   *The Lower Invertebrates*

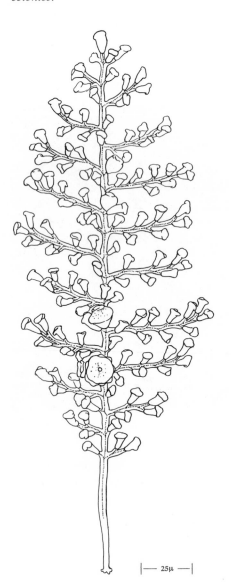

2–70 *The ciliated cells that make up Zoothamnium are interconnected by contractile threads (shown here by the dotted lines) that run through the trunk and branches of the "tree." The cells at the tip of the stalk and the ends of the branches divide to increase the size of the colony. The larger cells (near the main stalk) break loose to found new colonies.*

|— 25μ —|

Some kinds of ciliates as well as flagellates form colonies, some of which are very precise and well ordered. One such ciliate colony is *Zoothamnium*, of which there are several species, both marine and freshwater, all of which have an elegant treelike shape. The cells that make up the colony are interconnected by a thread of protoplasm running through the stalk. If one of the ciliates is touched, even slightly, either the whole branch or the entire colony, depending on the species, will contract right down to the base. As with *Volvox*, only certain cells of the colony are reproductive.

THE SPOROZOA

The fourth group of Protozoa are the Sporozoa, almost all of which are parasitic. The Sporozoa include *Plasmodium*, which causes malaria. As recently as 1937, there were at least a million cases of malaria annually in the United States, and although the disease has now virtually disappeared from North America, there are still some 250 million cases annually throughout the world. *Plasmodium*, like other Sporozoa, has no natural means of locomotion but is passed back and forth between man and the *Anopheles* mosquito. The female mosquito requires blood for the development of her eggs—the male lives on a more sybaritic diet of nectar—and if she draws her blood from a person with malaria, she will pick up *Plasmodium* cells, which multiply within her body, although they do not harm her, and travel to her salivary glands. When she bites her next victim, she will inject a droplet of salivary fluid under his skin, which may serve to anesthetize him against the bite or to keep the blood from clotting so that it will flow freely through her fine proboscis, and ultimately, through an allergic reaction, will raise the familiar welt. This drop of salivary fluid also carries *Plasmodium*, which eventually enter the blood cells and begin to multiply. The *Plasmodium* break out of the blood cells at regular intervals —usually every 48 or 72 hours, depending on the species—which is why malaria is characterized by recurrent bouts of chills and fever.

REPRODUCTION

In general, reproduction in the single-celled organisms is by mitotic division into two separate daughter cells. There are some exceptions, such as the Sporozoa, in which a single cell may divide into as many as 1,000 individuals before they separate. The flagellates form mirror images as they divide. The amoeba pulls apart into two new, equally shapeless amoebas. The ciliates divide transversely, with a new one forming below the old. Some of the Protozoa, such as *Euglena* and the common amoebas, have no sexual cycle, but others have means for combining and exchanging hereditary material, as in *Chlamydomonas* (Chapter 2–4). The ciliates have an unusual form of sexual recombination: Two individuals conjugate, fusing along their ventral surfaces, and exchange genetic material. After conjugation is completed, the animals separate, and then each continues to reproduce by mitotic division.

Sponges

Sponges seem to have had a different origin from other members of the animal kingdom and to have traveled a solitary evolutionary route. For this reason, they are often classified in a subkingdom of their own, the Parazoa ("alongside of animals"). In fact, until the eighteenth century, the sponges were classified as plants since they are all sessile. Sponges are found on ocean floors throughout the world. Most live in shallow water, but some, such as the fragile glass sponges, are found at great depths, where the water is always motionless.

The sponges are made up of a number of different cell types, the most characteristic of which are the choanocytes, or "collar cells." Similar cells, the choanoflagellates, are found as either solitary or colonial Protozoa. Some biologists suggest that the sponges arose directly from colonies of choanoflagellates; others, pointing out that the larval, or immature, cells of sponges bear little resemblance to choanoflagellates, believe that the similarities between choanocytes and choanoflagellates are purely coincidental.

The outer surface of the sponge is covered with epithelial cells. Among these epithelial cells are cells which contain myonemes and are contractile (like *Stentor*); movements of the adult sponge are dependent upon the contraction of these individual cells, which are known as *epitheliomuscular cells* since they combine the functions of epithelium and muscle. The epitheliomuscular cells will respond to touch or to irritating chemicals by contracting, and in so doing, they will close up incoming or outgoing channels. Each cell acts as an individual, however; there is no coordination among them. Between the epithelial cells and the choanocytes is a middle, jellylike layer, and in this layer are found largely undifferentiated cells, known as *archeocytes,* which may develop into a number of other cell types. Some of these cells form *amoebocytes,* amoebalike cells which carry digested food particles from the choanocytes to the epithelial cells. Others secrete stiffening skeletal structures, or spicules, which may be horny and fibrous, as in the bath sponges; calcareous (of calcium carbonate), as in the chalk sponges; or of silica, as in the delicately beautiful glass sponges, fossils of which remain from the Cambrian period. The 5,000 or so different species of sponges are divided into classes on the basis of the type of skeletal material they secrete. Most of us know the sponges only by their skeletons and would probably not recognize even the common bath sponge alive in its native habitat; it looks like a piece of raw beef liver.

The sponges are somewhere between a colony of cells and a true multicellular organism. The cells are not organized into tissues or organs, and

| —— 100mm —— |

2–71 *The skeleton of Euplectella speciosissima, a species of glass sponge picturesquely known as Venus's flower basket. These fragile sponges, with their delicate siliceous skeletons, are usually found at great depths, where the water is motionless. (Courtesy of the American Museum of Natural History)*

251 *The Lower Invertebrates*

2–72 *The body of the sponge is dotted with tiny pores, from which the phylum derives its name (Porifera, or "pore bearers"). Water containing food particles is drawn into the internal cavity of the sponge through these pores and is exhaled out the "mouth." The water is kept in motion by the beating of the flagella within the high collars of the choanocytes. Food particles adhere to the sticky outside of the collar and are drawn down its outer surface to the base, where they are engulfed into the cell body. The digested food is then shared by diffusion with other sponge cells. A sponge must filter a ton of water to gain an ounce of body weight.*

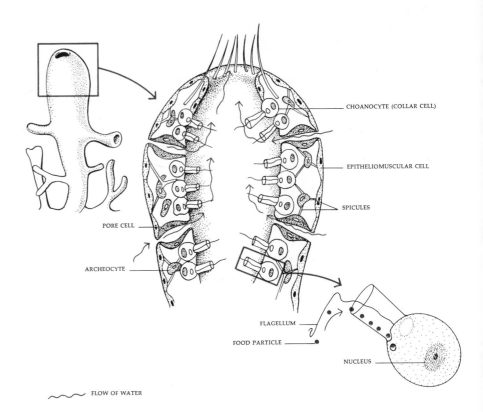

CHOANOCYTE (COLLAR CELL)

EPITHELIOMUSCULAR CELL

SPICULES

PORE CELL

ARCHEOCYTE

FLAGELLUM

FOOD PARTICLE

NUCLEUS

～～～ FLOW OF WATER

although there is some cooperation among them, each lives an independent existence. Because all of its digestive processes are carried out by the individual choanocytes, even a giant sponge—and some stand taller than a man—can eat nothing larger than microscopic food particles.

Sponges may reproduce sexually, with the archeocytes dividing and differentiating to produce eggs or sperm. The sperm cells are released into the interior cavity of the animal and then swept out with the water currents. With luck, they are drawn into the body of a sponge with a ripe egg cell. The sperm fertilizes the egg cell while the latter is still attached to the wall of the parent sponge. The zygote then develops into a free-swimming flagellated form, the larva, which swims around for a while before it settles down, attaches itself, and grows into an adult sponge. Many sessile animals are hermaphroditic—that is, capable of making both male and female gametes—and most of these sessile forms produce free-swimming offspring, the larvae. Can you explain why these two features are adaptive?

Sponges may also reproduce asexually, by forming branches which break away from the parent animal or by producing *gemmules*, aggregations of archeocytes within a hard protective outer layer. In this protective

|— 20mm —|

2–73 *Three different species are seen in this cluster of sponges from a pier pile in Plymouth, England. There are about 5,000 recognized species of sponges. (Dr. Douglas P. Wilson, F.R.P.S.)*

2–74 *All adult coelenterates are radially symmetrical and conform to one of two basic body plans: the vase-shaped polyp (left) or the bowl-shaped medusa (right).*

package, the cells can survive cold or drought, and when favorable conditions recur, they break out, aggregate in a mass, and grow into a new sponge.

The Coelenterates

The coelenterates are a large (at least 10,000 species) and often strikingly beautiful group of aquatic organisms. They constitute the only major phylum of animals that are radially symmetrical throughout their life cycle. As you can see in Figure 2–74, the basic body plan is a simple one: The animal is essentially a hollow container, which may be either vase-shaped, the *polyp*, or bowl-shaped, the *medusa*. The polyp is usually sessile; the medusa, motile. Both consist of two layers of tissue, epidermis and gastrodermis. Between the two layers is a gelatinous filling, the *mesoglea* ("middle jelly"), which is made of a collagenlike material. In the polyp form, the mesoglea is usually very thin, but in the medusa, it often accounts for the major part of the body substance.

The distinctive feature of the animals in this phylum is the *coelenteron*, a digestive cavity from which the group derives its name. Within this cavity, enzymes are released that break down food, partially digesting it extracellularly, as our own food is digested within the stomach and intestinal tract. The food particles are then taken up by the cells lining the cavity, which complete the digestive process and pass on the products to the other cells of the animal. Inedible remains are ejected from the opening. Almost all members of this phylum are carnivorous and are able to eat almost any other animal they can hold onto long enough to encompass in their remarkably expandable coelenterons.

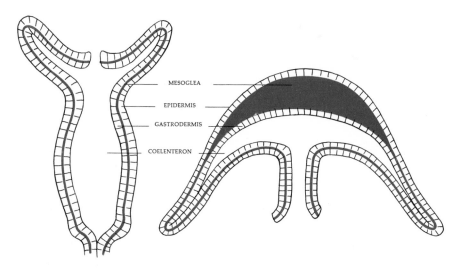

MESOGLEA
EPIDERMIS
GASTRODERMIS
COELENTERON

253   *The Lower Invertebrates*

2–75 *A distinguishing feature of coelenterates are their cnidoblasts, specialized cells located in the tentacles and body wall. The interior of the cnidoblast is filled by a nematocyst, which consists of a capsule containing a coiled tube, as shown on the left. A trigger on the cnidoblast, responding to chemical and/or mechanical stimuli, causes the tube to shoot out, as shown on the right. The discharge mechanism apparently involves a sudden increase in the permeability of the capsule wall, which causes an inrushing of water and a greatly increased pressure. As a result, the capsule is forced open, the tube turns inside out, and the entire nematocyst explodes to the outside. Four of the many different types of nematocysts are shown here. In (a) and (b), the tube is sticky and is used by the animal to fasten its tentacles to solid objects as it moves. The tube in (c) is used to wrap around and entangle prey. Nematocyst (d) is armed with barbs and spines; the tube penetrates the tissues of the prey and injects a paralyzing poison.*

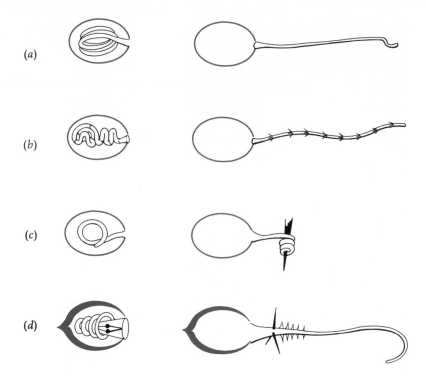

CNIDOBLASTS

Coelenterates capture their prey by means of tentacles which circle the rim of the coelenteron. These tentacles are armed with *cnidoblasts*, special cells that contain nematocysts (thread capsules). Nematocysts are discharged in response to chemical stimulus or touch. The discharged threads, which are often poisonous and may be sticky or barbed, can rope in prey, harpoon it, or paralyze it—or some useful combination of all three. Sticky threads may also be used by the animal to anchor itself. Cnidoblasts, which are always found in the tentacles and sometimes also in the body wall, are another distinctive characteristic of this phylum, whose members, for this reason, are also referred to as *cnidarians*.

Like the epitheliomuscular cells of the sponge, the cnidoblasts are *independent effectors*; that is, they both receive and respond to stimuli independently, although the general condition of the animal can affect the response. For instance, a well-fed coelenterate will not "fire a harpoon" under the same conditions that will trigger the cnidoblasts of a hungry coelenterate.

THE HYDROZOA: Hydra

The most thoroughly studied of the coelenterates is *Hydra*, a small com-

2–76 *The structure of the body wall of Hydra. The outer layer of cells, the epidermis, is primarily for protection, while the inner layer, the gastrodermis, performs the digestive function. What roles do the various types of epidermal and gastrodermal cells play in these activities?*

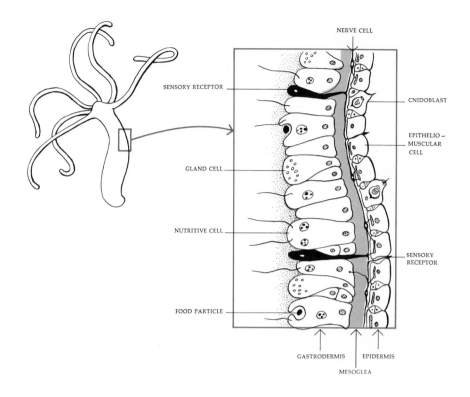

mon freshwater form which is convenient to keep in the laboratory and lively and interesting to observe. Figure 2–76 shows a small section of the body wall of *Hydra*. The gastrodermis is made up of cells concerned with digestion. One type of digestive cell secretes the digestive enzymes that are released into the coelenteron. The other type, the nutritive cell, first uses its flagella to mix the food as it is being processed and then extends pseudopodia to collect the food particles for further digestion.

The epidermis is composed largely of epitheliomuscular cells, which perform a covering, protective function and also serve as muscle tissue. Each cell has contractile fibers, myonemes, at its base and so can contract individually, like the epitheliomuscular cells of the sponge. In *Hydra*, however, as distinct from the sponge, a network of cells underlies the epitheliomuscular cells and coordinates their muscular contractions, making possible a wide variety of activities.

In addition to cnidoblasts and epitheliomuscular cells, which are independent effectors, the hydra also contains *sensory receptor* cells. These cells, which can be found on both the outer surface and the inner, feeding surface, are more sensitive than other epithelial cells to chemical and mechanical stimuli. When stimulated, they transmit their impulses to an adjacent cell or cells. The adjacent cell may be simply an epitheliomuscular

255   *The Lower Invertebrates*

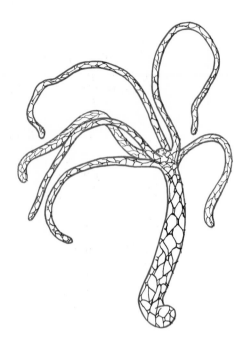

2–77 *The nerve cells in Hydra form a diffuse continuous network, as shown here. Hydra's nerve organization is the simplest example of a nervous system that unites an entire organism into a functional whole.*

2–78 *Gonionemus murbachi, a common jellyfish of shore waters, shown here swimming actively. (Dr. Douglas P. Wilson, F.R.P.S.)*

|—— 3mm ——|

cell, an effector, which then responds. Note that this system is one step more complicated than the epitheliomuscular cell or cnidoblast which acts as both receptor and effector. Alternatively, the sensory cell may feed into a conducting system; the cells of this conducting system make up the third type of specialized nerve cells found in *Hydra*. Unlike the neurons of higher animals described in Chapter 1–5, these nerve cells of *Hydra* appear to lack specialized synaptic connections and so are not polar—that is, impulses can travel through them in either direction. This is the simplest example of a nervous system that links an entire organism into a functional whole.

Hydra represents a large class of coelenterates, the Hydrozoa, which also have simple polypoid structures for all or most of their lives. Many of these hydrozoans live in colonies, such as the graceful *Obelia* or the much-feared Portuguese man-of-war, which is a large colony of coelenterates attached to a gas-filled sac that acts as a float and a sail for the entire colony.

THE SCYPHOZOA: JELLYFISH

A second major class of coelenterates are the Scyphozoa, or "cup animals," in which the medusa form is dominant. The Scyphozoa, more commonly known as *jellyfish,* range in size from less than an inch in diameter up to animals 12 feet across and trailing 30-foot tentacles. In the adult animal, the mesoglea is so firm that a large freshly beached jellyfish can easily support the weight of a human being. The mesoglea of some jellyfish is filled with wandering, amoebalike cells, which serve to transport food from the nutritive cells of the gastrodermis. Unlike *Hydra,* the Scyphozoa have true muscle cells; these underlie the epidermis, contracting rhythmically to propel the medusa through the water.

The life cycle of one of these coelenterates, the common jellyfish *Aurelia,* is shown in Figure 2–79. The ancestral coelenterates, it is believed, went through a similar, polyp-to-medusa life cycle.

NERVOUS SYSTEM OF MEDUSA

In the medusa, the nerve net is condensed into two rings of nerve cells, which encircle the margin of the bell. These nerve rings connect with fibers innervating the tentacles, the musculature, and the sense organs. This grouping of nerve cells into bundles makes possible speedy transmission of nerve impulses around the bell ring.

The bell margin is liberally supplied with sensory receptor cells sensitive to mechanical and chemical stimuli. In addition, the jellyfish has two types of true sense organs: statocysts and light-sensitive ocelli.

Statocysts are specialized receptor organs that provide information by which an animal can orient itself with respect to gravity. The statocyst is

2–79 *The life cycle of Aurelia. Sperm and egg cells are released from adult medusas into the surrounding water. Fertilization takes place, and the resulting zygote develops first into a hollow sphere of cells, the blastula, and then elongates and becomes a ciliated larva called a planula. The planula eventually settles to the bottom, attaches by one end to some object, and develops a mouth and tentacles at the other end, thus transforming into the polyp stage. The body of the polyp grows and, as it grows, begins to form medusas, stacked upside down like saucers, which bud off, one by one, and grow into full-sized jellyfish.*

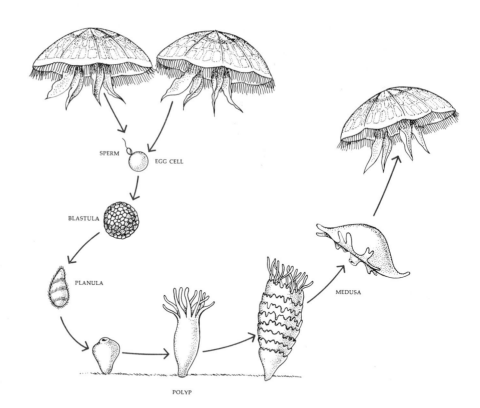

2–80 *In the medusa, the nerve net is condensed into two rings of nerve cells, represented by the two dark rings, which encircle the margin of the bell. What advantage does this kind of nerve grouping offer?*

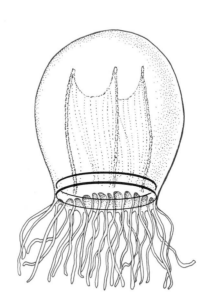

257   *The Lower Invertebrates*

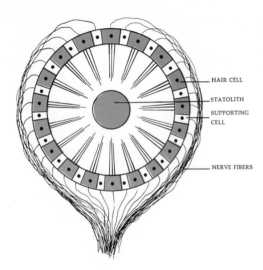

2–81 *The statocyst is a specialized receptor organ which orients the jellyfish with respect to gravity. When the bell tilts, gravity pulls the statolith down against the hair cells. This stimulates the nerve fibers and signals the animal to right itself.*

essentially a hollow sphere. Its walls are made up of sensory cells from which short stiff hairs protrude, projecting into the interior cavity. In contact with these bristles are grains of hardened calcium salts, the *statoliths*. When the bell tilts, the statoliths, responding to the pull of gravity, press down on the underlying hairs and stimulate the cells. The animal is thus signaled to right itself. The statocyst seems to be the first special sensory organ to have appeared in the course of evolution, and it has persisted virtually unchanged to the present day, appearing throughout the animal phyla.

Ocelli are groups of pigment cells and photoreceptor cells. Figure 2–82 diagrams the three types of ocelli found among the jellyfish. You will notice that like the vertebrate eye, the third type is inverted; that is, light must first pass through the axons of the sensory cells before reaching the light-absorbing pigments and the photoreception areas of the sensory cells. The ocelli are typically located on the outer bases of the tentacles.

THE ANTHOZOA

The Anthozoa ("flower animals")—the corals and sea anemones—are members of a class of coelenterates which, like *Hydra*, have lost the medusa stage. They differ from *Hydra* in having a gullet lined with epidermis and a coelenteron divided by vertical partitions. In the corals, which are colonies of Anthozoa, the epidermal cells secrete protective outer walls, usually of calcium carbonate (limestone), into which each delicate polyp can retreat. Although individual polyps of different species of coral are very similar, the shells they secrete are remarkably diverse in shape and color. If you look carefully at a dried, bleached piece of coral, you can see within it the minute chambers formerly occupied by generations of coelenterates.

2–82 *Three types of light receptor organs, or* ocelli, *found in jellyfish.*

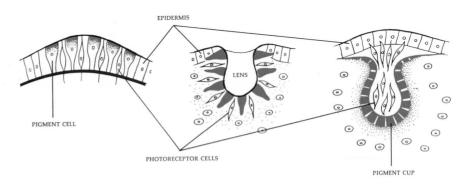

2–83 *Sea anemones of the species Actinia equina in an aquarium tank. The flowerlike appearance is deceptive; anemones are carnivorous animals belonging to a class of coelenterates which, like Hydra, have dropped out the medusa stage. In common with other coelenterates, their tentacles are equipped with stinging nematocysts. (Dr. Douglas P. Wilson, F.R.P.S.)*

| —— 50mm —— |

Flatworms

With the coming of the flatworms (Platyhelminthes), the Animalia made the change, with only an occasional and secondary relapse, to *bilateral symmetry*. The bilaterally symmetrical, worm-shaped animal, elongated from front to back, can move more efficiently than its radially symmetrical predecessors. It also has a top and a bottom or, in more precise terms (applicable even if it is turned upside down), a dorsal and a ventral surface. Like most bilateral organisms, the flatworm also developed a distinct "headness" and "tailness." When one end started to go first, it became advantageous to collect the sensory cells into that end, and with the aggregation of sensory cells, there came a concomitant gathering of nerve cells at the anterior of the animal; this gathering was the forerunner of the brain.

In addition to bilateral symmetry and the beginning of a brain, flatworms have three distinct tissue layers—ectoderm, mesoderm, and endoderm—a characteristic of all animals above the coelenterate level of organization.

THE PLANARIAN

The Platyhelminthes are a large and varied group, and we shall single out just one for special examination, the *freshwater planarian*. The ectoderm of the planarian is made up of cuboid epithelial cells, many of which are ciliated, particularly those on the ventral surface. It has two clearly visible light-sensitive areas, the *ocelli*, and also epithelial cells sensitive to

2–84 *The first bilaterally symmetrical organisms were the flatworms, which have both a nervous system and the beginnings of a brain. The species belonging to this phylum are widely various in shape and general appearance, but nearly all are small, with flattened bodies. They are grouped according to the number of branches in the digestive tract. The planarian (a), for example, has a digestive tract with three main branches, and is known as a triclad. The marine worm Prostheceraeus (b) is known as a polyclad since its digestive tract has many branches. Planarians live in freshwater ponds and streams; you can usually find them on the undersides of docks and dead leaves. Prostheceraeus is found along marine shores, among weeds and under stones. ((a) Dr. James V. McConnell; (b) Dr. Douglas P. Wilson, F.R.P.S.)*

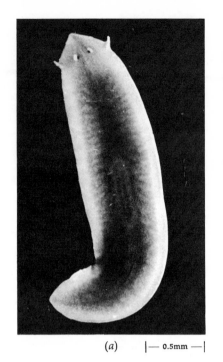 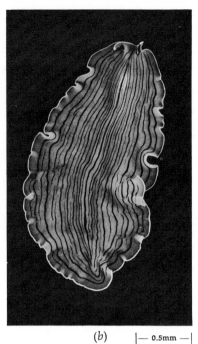

(a) |— 0.5mm —| (b) |— 0.5mm —|

chemicals and to touch. Ventral ectodermal cells secrete mucus, which provides traction for the planarian as it moves by means of its cilia along its own slime trail. The planarian is about the largest animal that can use cilia for locomotion; the cilia in larger species are usually employed for moving water or other substances along the surface of the animal, as in the human respiratory tract, rather than the animal through the water.

The planarian has an endoderm composed largely of amoeboid cells, which, although they are phagocytic, are not wandering cells like the amoebocytes of the jellyfish. Between the ectoderm and the phagocytic endoderm is a *mesoderm,* or middle tissue layer. In the planarian, as in the higher animals, the mesoderm contains the principal organ systems of the animals.

The planarian, like the coelenterates, has a digestive cavity with only one opening, located on the ventral surface. This digestive cavity has three main branches, which is why planarians are placed in the order of flatworms known as *triclads.*

Like other flatworms, the planarian is carnivorous. It is not a hunter, however, and eats either dead meat or slow-moving animals it can fasten itself to or subdue by sitting on, such as smaller planarians. It feeds by means of a muscular tube, the pharynx, which is free at one end. The free end can be stretched out through the mouth opening. Muscular contrac-

The body organization of the freshwater planarian.

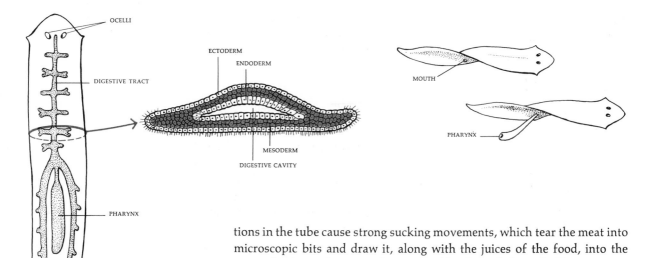

tions in the tube cause strong sucking movements, which tear the meat into microscopic bits and draw it, along with the juices of the food, into the internal cavity, where it is phagocytized by the endodermal cells.

In the planarian, we see our first example of an excretory system, another necessary organ system for animals that have tissues more than a few cells away from a watery environment. The excretory system of the planarian is a network of fine tubules which runs the length of the animal's body. Side branches of the tubules contain flame cells, each of which has a hollow center in which a tuft of cilia beats, flickering like a tongue of flame, moving water along the tubules to the exit pores between the epidermal cells. The flame-cell system appears to function largely to regulate water balance; most of the waste products probably diffuse out through the ectoderm or the endoderm.

The most primitive of the flatworms have only a nerve-net type of conduction system like that of *Hydra,* but in the planarians, some of this nerve net has become condensed into two channels, one on either side of the flat, ribbonlike body.

The nerve cells, or neurons, of the modern planarian are connected by synapses. The synapse is a one-way junction in the conduction system. Although transmission across synaptic junctions slows the speed at which the nerve impulse travels, it makes possible redirections and modifications in the impulse and permits more varied and complicated behavior. As a consequence, a stimulus results in a specific rather than generalized response.

Planarians, which are hermaphroditic, have a complicated reproductive system. The eggs are fertilized internally. At mating, each partner deposits sperm in the copulatory sac of the other partner. These sperm then travel along special tubes, the *oviducts,* to fertilize the eggs as they become ripe.

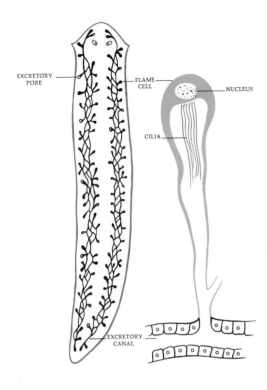

Labels on figure:
EXCRETORY PORE
FLAME CELL
NUCLEUS
CILIA
EXCRETORY CANAL

2–86 *In the flatworms, the beginnings of a tubular excretory system can be seen. The system usually consists of two or more branching tubules running the length of the body. In the planarian and its relatives, the tubules open to the body surface through a number of tiny pores. At the ends of the side branches are small bulblike structures known as flame cells. Within each of these cells, a tuft of cilia in constant motion resembles the flickering of a flame. Water and some waste materials from the tissue fluids are moved by the cilia through the tubules to the excretory pores, where the collected liquid leaves the body.*

Some species of planarian also reproduce asexually by what is known as the *tail drop,* in which the tail, often quite suddenly, seems to develop a "will of its own," gripping the surface as the anterior of the animal moves ahead until finally the tail is left behind. The tail portion subsequently regenerates into a whole planarian.

TAPEWORMS AND FLUKES

Two-thirds of the Platyhelminthes are tapeworms and flukes, parasitic forms which can cause serious and sometimes fatal diseases among the higher animals. Members of both of these parasitic orders have outer protective cuticles that are resistant to digestive fluids and, usually, suckers on their anterior ends by which they fasten to their victims. The flukes (or trematodes) also feed through suckers, but the tapeworms, which have no mouths or digestive cavities, merely hang on and absorb food saprophytically. Tapeworms are found in the intestines of many vertebrates, including man, and may grow as long as 15 to 20 feet. They cause illness not only by encroaching on the food supply but also by the wastes they produce and by their obstruction of the intestinal tract. The most common human tapeworm, the beef tapeworm, infects people who eat the undercooked flesh of cattle that have eaten fodder contaminated by human feces.

All parasites, including parasitic flatworms, are believed to have originated as free-living forms and to have degenerated, that is, lost certain tissues and organs (such as the digestive tract), as a secondary effect of their parasitic existence.

The Annelids

If one were to select one shape which best exemplified the animal kingdom, it would be the worm shape—a long, supple, streamlined tube. "Wormness" finds its culmination in the annelids, of which the earthworm is our most familiar example.

Annelid means "ringed" and refers to the most distinctive feature of this phylum, which is the division of the body into segments, not only by rings on the outside but by partitions on the inside. This segmentation of the body is a characteristic that persists in the body plan of the higher animals, at least in the embryonic stage of their existence.

Another extremely important feature, evolutionarily speaking, which we find in the earthworm is the coelom. In the flatworms, as we saw, the mesoderm is packed solid with tissues, but in the annelids and in all higher animals, there is a fluid-filled cavity in this middle layer known as the *coelom.* (Note that the term "coelom," although it sounds similar to *coelenteron* and comes from the same Greek root, meaning "cavity," refers quite specifically to a cavity *within* the mesoderm, whereas the coelenteron is a digestive cavity lined by endoderm.)

2–87 *African tapeworm found in a female rhinoceros. (Luvenia C. Miller)*

The development of space within the mesoderm, although it may seem less dramatic than other evolutionary innovations, is extremely important. Within such a space, organ systems can bend, twist, and fold back on themselves, increasing their functional surface areas and filling, emptying, and sliding past one another, surrounded by lubricating coelomic fluid. Consider the human lung, constantly expanding and contracting in the chest cavity, or the 20 or so feet of coiled human intestine; neither of these could have evolved until the coelom made room for them.

A third innovation in the annelids is the one-way digestive tract, in which food goes in one end and digestive wastes come out the other. This seemingly simple "invention" revolutionized the digestive process. Once it was no longer necessary for undigested, half digested, and indigestible food particles to be mixed together, each section of the digestive tube could be specialized to perform a particular function, like an assembly line.

THE EARTHWORM

Figure 2–88 shows a portion of the body of an earthworm. Note how the body is compartmentalized into regular segments. Most of these segments, particularly the central and posterior ones, are identical, each exactly like the one before and the one after. Each identical segment contains four pairs of bristles, or *setae*; two *nephridia*, excretory tubules that

2–88 *The body organization of the earthworm. On each segment are four pairs of bristles, which are extended and retracted by special muscles. These are used by the worm to anchor one part of its body while it moves another part forward. Two excretory tubes, or nephridia, are in each segment (except the first three and the last). Each nephridium really occupies two segments since it opens externally by a pore in one segment and internally by a ciliated funnel in the segment immediately in front of it.*

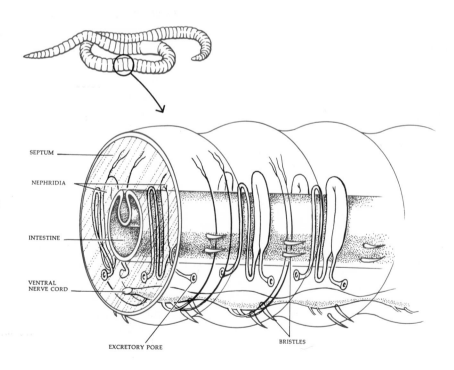

SEPTUM

NEPHRIDIA

INTESTINE

VENTRAL NERVE CORD

EXCRETORY PORE

BRISTLES

263   *The Lower Invertebrates*

2–89 *Cross section of the earthworm, showing the chloragen cells surrounding the intestine.*

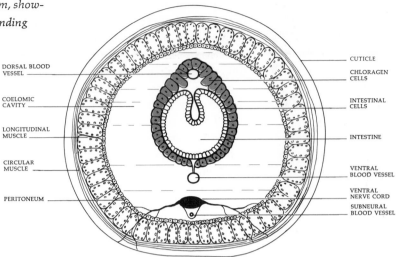

DORSAL BLOOD VESSEL

COELOMIC CAVITY

LONGITUDINAL MUSCLE

CIRCULAR MUSCLE

PERITONEUM

CUTICLE

CHLORAGEN CELLS

INTESTINAL CELLS

INTESTINE

VENTRAL BLOOD VESSEL

VENTRAL NERVE CORD

SUBNEURAL BLOOD VESSEL

pick up waste materials from the body fluids and excrete them through pores on the ventral surface of the worm; four sets of nerves branching off from the central nerve cord running along the ventral surface; and a portion of digestive tract. The chief exceptions to this rule of segment structure are found in the most forward segments. In these, sensory cells, a cluster of nerve cells, and specialized areas of the digestive and circulatory systems are found.

Figure 2–89 shows a cross section of the earthworm. Yellowish-colored cells, the chloragen cells, surround the intestine in the earthworm and synthesize and store glycogen and fat. In the human body, these functions are performed by the liver. The fluid-filled coelomic cavity, which is quite large, as you can see, not only supports and lubricates the various organ systems but also acts as a hydraulic skeleton for the animal—much like a fire hose that is filled out and stiffened by water. Contraction of the circular muscles lengthens the worm, while contraction of the longitudinal muscles draws its body together.

Digestive Tract

In the earthworm, the digestive tract is a long straight tube. The mouth leads into a strong, muscular pharynx, which acts like a suction pump, drawing in decaying leaves and other organic matter, as well as dirt, from which organic materials are extracted. The earthworm makes burrows in the earth by passing such material through its digestive tract and depositing it outside in the form of castings, a ceaseless activity which serves to break up, enrich, and aerate the soil. The narrow section of tube posterior to the pharynx, the *esophagus,* leads to the crop, where food is stored. In the gizzard, which has thick muscular walls lined with protective cuticle, the food is ground up with the help of the ever-present soil particles. The rest of the digestive tract is made up of a long intestine, which has a large fold along its upper surface that increases its surface area. The intestinal epithelium consists of enzyme-secreting cells and ciliated absorptive cells.

Circulation

Another important evolutionary development exemplified by the earthworm is an efficient circulatory system. In an animal in which individual cells have to depend on the random movements of extracellular fluid to bring them food and oxygen, no tissues can develop that are more than two or three cells thick, which imposes a strict limit on the size of a complex animal. This problem was solved by the development of a system for circulating fluids throughout the body.

The circulatory system of the earthworm is composed of longitudinal vessels running the entire length of the worm, one dorsal and several ventral. The largest ventral vessel underlies the intestinal tract for its entire length, collecting nutrients from it and distributing them by means of many small branches to all the tissues of the body and to the three smaller

2–90 *The circulatory and digestive systems of the earthworm.*

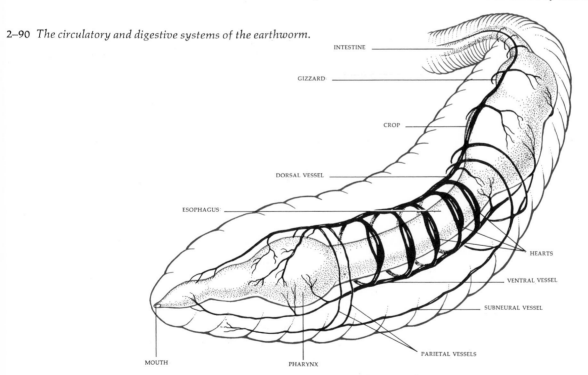

INTESTINE

GIZZARD

CROP

DORSAL VESSEL

ESOPHAGUS

HEARTS

VENTRAL VESSEL

SUBNEURAL VESSEL

PARIETAL VESSELS

MOUTH

PHARYNX

ventral vessels that surround the nerve cord and nourish it. Numerous small capillaries in each segment carry blood from the ventral vessels through the tissues to the dorsal vessel. Also in each segment are larger parietal vessels transporting blood from the subneural vessels to the dorsal vessel. Fluids collected in this way from all over the animal's body are fed into the muscular dorsal vessel, which propels the blood forward.

Connecting the dorsal and ventral vessels (Figure 2–90) are five pairs of hearts—muscular pumping areas in the blood vessels—whose irregular contractions force the blood down to the ventral vessels and also forward to the vessels that supply the more anterior segments. Both the hearts and the dorsal vessel have valves that prevent a backflow.

Excretory System

The excretory system of the earthworm consists of pairs of tubules, the nephridia; one pair for each segment. Each nephridium consists of a long tubule which terminates in a ciliated funnel opening into the coelomic cavity. Coelomic fluid is carried into the funnel by the beating of the cilia and is excreted through an outer pore. As the fluid makes its way through the long tubule, sugar, salts, and other needed material are returned to the coelomic fluid through the walls of the tubule, while other materials are absorbed into the tubule for excretion.

Respiration

The earthworm has no special respiratory organs; respiration takes place by simple diffusion through the body surface. The gases of the atmosphere dissolve in the liquid film on the surface of the earthworm's body, which is kept moist by secreted mucus and excreted water. Oxygen travels inward by diffusion since the surface film, exposed to the oxygen-rich atmosphere, contains more oxygen than the coelomic fluids or the blood in the underlying vessels. Carbon dioxide moves out to the surface film and then into the air by the same principle. All gas exchange in the animal whether the organism is land-dwelling or water-dwelling takes place on a moist membrane.

Nervous System

The earthworm has a variety of sensory cells. These include touch cells, or mechanoreceptors, containing tactile hairs which, when stimulated, trigger a nerve impulse; light-sensitive cells; and special cells concerned with the detection of moisture.

In the nervous system of the earthworm, the two conducting channels of the planarian have come together in a double nerve cord which runs along the ventral surface of the body. The conducting channels are made up of neurons bound together in bundles like cables. These large neurons can transmit signals rapidly. An impulse running down the neurons and branching to individual muscles causes a sudden contraction of the entire body of the worm.

Each segment of the worm is supplied by nerves which receive impulses from sensory cells and nerves which cause muscles to contract. The cell bodies for these nerves are grouped together in clusters known as *ganglia* (singular, *ganglion*). The movements of each segment of the earthworm are directed by a pair of ganglia.

The double nerve cord runs almost the entire length of the animal, extending from the tail to the base of the pharynx, at which point it divides, circles the pharynx, and meets again in the cerebral ganglia. Impulses conducted along the double nerve cord serve to integrate the activities of the animal.

Reproduction

Earthworms are hermaphroditic. They are seldom self-fertilizing, but when two meet, each is able to inseminate the other. Hermaphroditism is frequently found in solitary slow-moving animals, such as flatworms, earthworms, and snails, and it ensures that every mating will result in two sets rather than one set of fertilized eggs.

Each earthworm deposits sperm in the two paired spermathecas of its partner by means of a tube formed from the mucus-producing glands of the clitellum, a special collection of glandular cells. Two or three days after the worms separate, the clitellum forms a second mucous sheath surrounded by an outer protective layer of chitin. This sheath is pushed forward along the animal by muscular movements of its body. As it passes over the female gonopores it picks up a collection of mature eggs, and then, continuing forward, it picks up the sperm deposited in the spermathecas. Once the mucous band is slipped over the head of the worm, its sides pinch together, enclosing the now fertilized eggs into a small capsule from which the infants hatch.

THE POLYCHAETE WORMS

The earthworms belong to an order of annelids known as the *oligochaetes* ("few hairs"). About two-thirds of the annelid phylum is made up of an order of marine and freshwater worms known as the *polychaetes* ("many hairs"), which are believed to be a more primitive order from which the oligochaetes arose. Polychaetes are very common around the seashore, where they crawl beneath the rocks and make themselves burrows in the soft mud and sand. Many of the polychaetes live in tubes which they make of sand grains cemented together by mucus, and all are naturally seclusive. They usually can be found only by diligent searching, although some of them, like the common *Nereis* worm of the New England coast, may grow as long as a foot.

2–91 *The molluscan body plan has been modified in the various groups. The shell is indicated by the heavy black line, and the foot by stippling. (After Buchsbaum, 1965)*

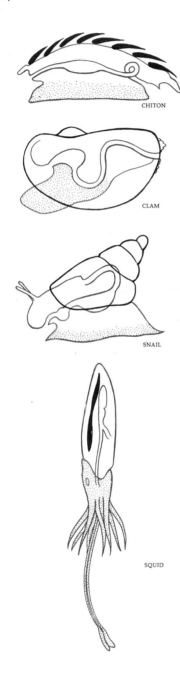

CHITON

CLAM

SNAIL

SQUID

The nereid is distinctly segmented, like the earthworm, and each segment contains a *parapod*, or "side foot," which is a flattened fleshy lobe from which bundles of horny setae protrude. In common with many other polychaetes, the nereid has a complex head structure, including antennae, bristles, fleshy feeler organs (the palps), and protrusible pincerlike jaws.

The Mollusks

Mollusk means "soft-bodied," and throughout this phylum, the bodies of the different groups, although similar in basic plan, have been contorted into a number of surprising and quite dissimilar shapes. Figure 2–91 shows the body structures of representatives of four main classes of mollusk: the chiton, the clam, the snail, and the squid.

CHITONS

The chiton is believed to resemble the ancestral mollusk most closely and so to afford the clearest picture of the original molluscan plan. The chitons of the Atlantic Coast are small, often less than an inch in length, but some Pacific Coast species range up to a foot or more in size. Algae eaters, they are found browsing among the rocks and in the tidal pools along the shore.

All species have a shell that consists of eight separate and overlapping plates, although in some chitons these are so deeply embedded in the underlying flesh that they are not visible externally. The shells are secreted by an underlying blanket of tissue, the *mantle*, that is characteristic of this phylum. As the animal grows larger, the growing zone of the mantle makes additional shell; you have probably seen the ridges, or striations, marking the growth rings of a large clamshell. Between the edge of the blanketlike mantle and the strong muscular fleshy foot (also characteristic of this phylum) is a space known as the *mantle cavity*. The chiton clings so tightly to rocks and other surfaces that its mantle cavity is converted into two enclosed semicircular tubes by the pressing down of its body. Along each of these grooves is a row of leaf-shaped *gills*, 11 to 26 on a side, depending on age and species. The gills are covered with cilia, the beating of which keeps a continuous flow of oxygen-bearing water over the gill surfaces. A thin-walled flat or sometimes feathery extension of the epidermis, the gill is richly endowed with blood vessels and serves the same respiratory function that the earthworm's skin does. However, by providing a much more localized area for respiration, the gills make it possible for the rest of the animal's body to be covered and protected.

The oxygenated blood is collected from the gills by a pair of hollow muscle-lined chambers, the *atria*, which pump the blood into a third, more muscular chamber, the *ventricle*. From the ventricle, the blood is sent to the various other tissues of the body. This three-chambered heart, typical of the mollusks, is the most efficient heart found among the invertebrates since it prevents the mixture of oxygenated and unoxygenated blood. The cephalopods have special additional pumps, gill hearts, for propelling fluid through the small circulatory channels of the gills.

The digestive tract is far more convoluted than that of the annelids. It includes a stomach, where food is held and mixed with enzymes, which are produced by a large digestive gland overlying and opening into the stomach. The food is absorbed by the cells lining the stomach and the anterior intestine, and from them, it is passed into the bloodstream. A convoluted digestive tract provides more working surface than the straight-line tract of the annelid.

A characteristic organ of the mollusk, found only in this phylum, is the *radula*, a rasplike tongue. The chiton uses it for scraping seaweed from the rocks, just as the snail scrapes algae from the walls of an aquarium. Certain snails—whelks, in particular—can file through the tough exoskeletons of lobsters or crabs or even through the shells of oysters to make their way to the soft flesh underneath.

BIVALVES

Clams, oysters, scallops, and other two-shelled mollusks are known as

2–92 *The body structure of the chiton. As you can see, the animal is bilaterally symmetrical, with a mouth at one end and an anus at the other. However, it lacks a distinct head—a structural feature which is probably related to its sluggish, almost sessile, way of life. Chitons creep about on the rocks of shallow waters, rasping off pieces of algae with a horny toothed organ called a radula. Its broad flat foot takes up most of the ventral surface.*

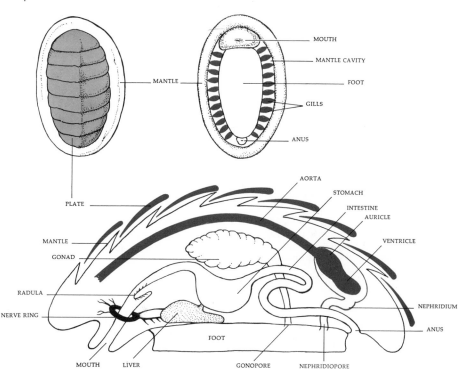

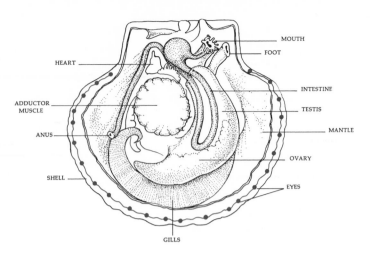

2–93 *The body structure of the scallop is typical of the bivalves. These animals are filter feeders; that is, they strain small particles of food from water. Water enters through tiny pores in the gills, and the microscopic food particles it contains are trapped in streams of mucus that flow along the gills and enter the mouth. The mucus is kept moving by beating cilia. The shells are drawn closed by the cylinder-shaped adductor muscle, the part of the scallop that is most frequently marketed commercially.*

2–94 *A gray sea slug (on the right) feeding on sea anemones. The sea slug has lost the true molluscan gills and breathes through fingerlike projections along the side of its body. (Dr. Douglas P. Wilson, F.R.P.S.)*

|— 20mm —|

Pelecypoda, or "hatchet feet," because of the shape of the muscular feet in some of the animals. Their bodies are flattened, and all "headness" has disappeared. The bivalves are generally sessile forms, and many of them secrete stringy anchor ropes by which they attach themselves to rocks or to the bottom. Some are surprisingly lively. A clam, using its spade foot, can dig itself into a sandy bottom with remarkable speed, and an alarmed scallop can leap a foot or two by clapping its shells together and expelling water through its mantle cavity.

The bivalves close their shells tightly only in response to irritation or to threats of danger. The rest of the time, they keep the shells slightly open, filtering water through the gills, which fill up most of the aperture between the shells. Food is circulated through the sievelike gills by the beating of gill cilia, which also serve to move small organisms and particles of food toward the mouth. After some sorting is done by gills and palps, the food enters the digestive tract. The shells are held together at the hinge by a strong ligament and are drawn closed by a large muscle connecting the two shells near the hinge. These muscles are the part of the scallop with which most of us are familiar; they are the tender white cylinders that commonly appear on menus as "scallops," although they represent only a small portion of the animal. The muscle connecting the bivalve shells is a smooth muscle, and so, although it is not as fast as striated muscle would be, it can remain fixed, locking the shells together, for long periods of time.

SNAILS

The mollusks that have undergone the most radical changes from the ancestral form are the gastropods. First, the digestive tract turned back to form a complete loop, so that in the modern animal, the mouth and anus and also the gills share the same comparatively small cavity, the single opening in the snail shell. Second, the stomach and large digestive

270 ORGANISMS

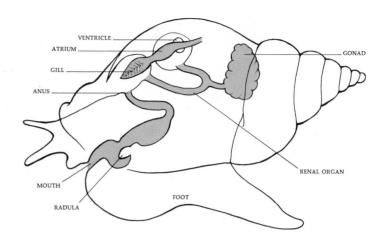

2–95 *The gastropods constitute by far the largest class of mollusks. As you can see in this diagram of the whelk, the gastropod organization is asymmetrical, with the digestive tract looped back, so that the anus opens in the front, above the head. Many gastropods feed like chitons, rasping off fragments of vegetation by means of the radula, but the whelk is a carnivore. It grasps its prey with its large muscular foot and then attacks it with a long extensible proboscis, which has the radula at its tip. Using its proboscis, it can bore holes even through the hard armor of lobsters and crabs.*

gland have become twisted upward in a visceral hump. As a result of this displacement and consequent crowding of the internal organs, the gill and nephridium of the right side have been lost. In some close relatives of the snails, such as the slugs, the digestive tract has become straightened out again by another course of evolutionary events, in which the shell was lost but the missing organs were not regained. (As we learn more about the mechanisms of genetics and of changes, or mutations, it will become clearer why evolutionary losses, in general, can never be recovered.)

Land-dwelling snails do not have gills, which are especially adapted for extracting oxygen from water. The area in their mantle cavities once occupied by gills is extremely rich in blood vessels very near the surface, and the snail's blood is oxygenated in this area. Some snails which were once land dwellers have returned to the water, but they have not regained gills. Instead, they must bob up to the surface at regular intervals to entrap a fresh bubble of air in their mantle cavities.

CEPHALOPODS

In the cephalopods (the "head-foots"), the "foot" has come to be wrapped around the head and divided up into "arms," some 70 or 80 in the nautilus, 10 in the squid, and 8 in the octopus. The nautilus, as the only modern shelled cephalopod, offers an indication of some of the steps by which this order disposed of the shell entirely. The animal occupies only the outermost portion of its elaborate and beautiful shell, which serves primarily as a flotation chamber. In the squid and its relative, the cuttlefish, the shell has become an internal, stiffening support, and in the octopus, it is lacking entirely. This makes the octopus somewhat less efficient as a swimmer but more effective in crawling, exploring, and manipulating objects with its sensitive tentacles.

2–96 *Land snails are gastropods in which an area of the mantle cavity has been modified for air breathing. (Walther Rhodich, Frank W. Lane)*

271   *The Lower Invertebrates*

The common cuttlefish (Sepia officinalis) swimming. The cuttlefish resembles the squid in structure and habits. (Frank W. Lane)

|——— 50mm ———|

The octopus' body seldom reaches more than a foot in diameter (except in the movies), but giant squids sometimes attain true sea-monster proportions. One caught in the Atlantic some hundred years ago was 50 feet long, not counting the tentacles, and was estimated to weigh 2 tons!

Freedom from the shell has given the mantle greater flexibility. One of the most obvious effects of this is the jet propulsion by which cephalopods dart through the water. Water taken into the mantle cavity usually bathes the gills and is expelled slowly through a tube-shaped structure, the *siphon;* but when the cephalopod is hunting or being hunted, it can contract the mantle cavity forcibly and suddenly, thereby squirting out a sudden jet of water. Contraction of the mantle-cavity muscles usually shoots the animal backwards, head last, but the squid and the octopus can turn the siphon in almost any direction they choose. In addition to the siphon, cephalopods have sacs from which they can release a dark fluid to camouflage their retreat and confuse their enemies. These colored fluids were at one time a chief source of commercial inks. *Sepia* is the name of the genus of cuttlefish from which a brown ink used to be obtained.

MOLLUSCAN NERVOUS SYSTEMS

Throughout the molluscan phylum, there is a wide range of development of the nervous system. The bivalves, which are limited in behavior by their sessile mode of existence, have three pairs of ganglia of approximately equal size—cerebral, visceral, and pedal (supplying the foot)—and two long pairs of nerve cords interconnecting them. They have a statocyst, usually located near the pedal ganglia, and sensory cells for discrimination of touch, chemical changes, and light. The scallop has quite complex eyes; a single individual may have a hundred or more eyes located in the tentacles on the fringe of the mantle. The lens of this eye cannot focus on images, however, so it does not appear to serve for more than the detection of light and dark.

Gastropods, which lead a more mobile, active existence, have a ganglionated nervous system with as many as six pairs of ganglia connected by nerve cords. There is a concentration of nerve cells at the anterior end of the animal, where the tentacles, which have chemoreceptors and touch receptors, and the eyes are located. In some of the animals, the eyes are quite highly developed in structure; they appear, however, to function largely in the detection of light, like the eyes of the scallop.

The cephalopods have well-developed brains, composed of many groups of ganglia, in keeping with their highly developed sensory systems and their lively, predatory behavior. These large brains are covered with cartilaginous cases, a feature not to be reencountered until the vertebrates. The rapid responses of the cephalopods are made possible by a bundle of giant nerve fibers which control the muscles of the mantle. Many of the studies on conduction of the nerve impulse are made with the giant axon of the squid, which is large enough to permit the insertion of an electrode.

MOLLUSCAN REPRODUCTION

The sessile mollusks, like many of the invertebrate ocean dwellers, do not copulate but rather release sperm and eggs into the surrounding waters, where some of the former manage to meet some of the latter. The number of gametes produced is very great, some 500,000 in a single spawning in the case of the oyster, to compensate for this inefficiency of the fertilization process.

Land snails practice internal fertilization and, like most animals which do not have a very active social life, are hermaphroditic, so that every encounter is doubly productive. The cephalopods, in which the individuals are either male or female, have more complex courtship and mating behavior. The male octopus removes a packet of sperm from the gonad within his mantle cavity using one of his tentacles, which may have a shape especially adapted to this function, and deposits the packet deep within the mantle cavity of the female where they will fertilize the eggs when they are released. In some species, the male deposits not only the sperm packet but the entire arm as well, after which he swims away to grow another, while the new mother remains to guard the eggs and, depending on the species, the young, when they emerge.

The Echinoderms

The starfish and its relatives are known as *echinoderms,* or "spiny skins." Adult echinoderms are radially symmetrical, like the coelenterates, and for a long time they were believed to be related to the members of that more ancient phylum. Scientists now believe that the radial symmetry of the echinoderms is a secondary development. This opinion is based on the fact that the echinoderm is clearly a coelomate, and the echinoderm larva is clearly bilateral.

STARFISH

The most familiar of the echinoderms is the starfish, which consists of a central disk from which radiate a number of arms. Most starfish have five arms, but some have multiples of five. The animal has no head, and any arm may lead in its sluggish creeping movements along the sea bottom. The central disk contains a mouth on the ventral surface, above which is the stomach. The outer skin is covered by a rough cuticle, from which the phylum derives its name. Underlying the skin layers are a number of separate calcium-containing plates held together by the skin tissues and by muscles to form an endoskeleton. Each arm contains a pair of digestive glands and also a nerve cord, with an eyespot and a tentacle at the end. These latter are the only sensory organs, strictly speaking, of the starfish, but the epidermis contains thousands of neurosensory cells (as many as 70,000 per square millimeter) concerned with touch and chemoreception. Each arm also has its own pair of gonads, which open directly to the exterior through small pores.

The starfish has no circulatory tract, but there is a large coelom through which the fluid circulates, with canals running through the thick layer of ectoderm. Respiration is accomplished by many small fingerlike projections, the skin gills, which are protected by spines. Amoeboid cells circulate in the coelomic fluid, picking up the wastes and then escaping through the thin walls of the skin gills, where they are pinched off and ejected.

The water vascular, or hydraulic, system is a unique feature of the phylum. Each arm contains two or more rows of water-filled tube feet (see Figure 2–98). These tube feet are interconnected by a central ring and radial canals and filled with water taken in through the sieve plate, which is on the dorsal surface. Water filling the soft hollow tubes makes them rigid enough to walk on. Each tube foot connects with a rounded muscular sac, the *ampulla.* When the ampulla contracts, the water is forced under pressure through a valve into the tube foot, this extends the foot; which attaches to the substratum by its sucker. When the muscles contract, water is forced back into the ampulla, and the animal is pulled forward.

If the tube feet are planted on a hard surface, such as a rock or a clam shell, the collection of tubes will exert enough suction to pull the starfish forward or to pull apart a bivalve mollusk, a feat that will be appreciated by anyone who has ever tried to open an oyster or a clam. When attacking bivalves, which are its staple diet, the starfish everts its stomach through its mouth opening and then squeezes the stomach tissue through the minute space between the bivalve shells. It is reported that the stomach tis-

2–98 *The water vascular system of the starfish is its means of locomotion. Water enters through minute openings in the sieve plate and is drawn, by ciliary action, down a tube to the ring canal. Five radial canals, one for each arm, connect the ring canal with many pairs of tube feet, which are hollow, thin-walled cylinders terminating in suckers. Each tube foot connects with a rounded muscular sac, the ampulla. When the ampulla contracts, the water in it, prevented by a valve from flowing back into the radial canal, is forced under pressure into the tube foot. This extends the elastic foot, which attaches to the substratum by its sucker. The longitudinal muscles of the foot then contract, forcing the water back into the ampulla and drawing the animal forward. (In this drawing, the digestive glands on top have been shown diagrammatically to obtain a better view of the radial canals and tube feet underneath.)*

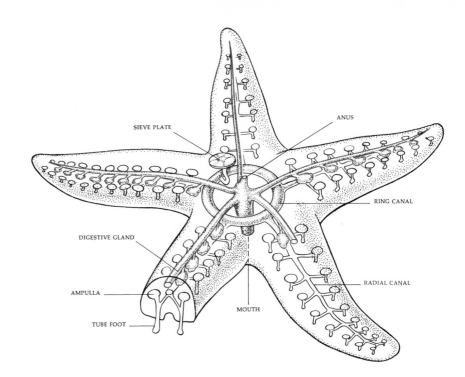

sues can insinuate themselves through a space as little as 0.1 millimeter and begin to digest the soft tissue of the resident.

The tube feet extend from grooves along the ventral surfaces of the arms. A row of movable spines that guard the margins of these grooves can close together to cover them completely.

SEA URCHINS

Sea urchins, which look like large animated burs, are unlike starfish externally but resemble them internally, having five radial chambers, skin gills, tube feet, and a large coelomic cavity. The sea urchin does not have a skeleton made of movable plates, as does the starfish, but instead has a single shell, which underlies its ectoderm. The movable spines and tube feet of the sea urchin extend through small perforations which form regular, radially symmetrical patterns on the calcium shell.

SEA LILIES

A less familiar group of echinoderms are the sea lilies. One of the most ancient of the living types of echinoderms, sea lilies flourished in the early Paleozoic period. The animals are very flowerlike in appearance, often having a long stalk from which emerge feathery branches. The most primitive have five branches, or arms, but some possess as many as 80 or 100. Food is propelled down the branches into the centrally located mouth.

275 *The Lower Invertebrates*

More recent members of this class of echinoderms are the feather stars, which have arms similar to those of the sea lilies but which have lost their stalks and have become more mobile. This group of echinoderms provides additional support for the hypothesis that the echinoderms developed from a bilateral, and so presumably mobile, coelomate ancestor, settled down to a sessile life and radial symmetry, and then began to move about again, although retaining the radial symmetry of sedentary animals.

REPRODUCTION

In most echinoderms, eggs and sperm are shed in large numbers and fertilization takes place externally. Since gametes are easy to obtain from mature animals, the echinoderm—and, in particular, the sea urchin (which has an almost transparent egg cell)—has been a useful study tool for the embryologist.

SUMMARY

We began this chapter by defining some of the basic problems that organisms must solve in order to exist. A primary need is to supply each cell with oxygen, water, and nutrients and to dispose of wastes. In one-celled organisms, these materials are exchanged across the cell membrane, but larger and more complex organisms have developed special systems for circulation, respiration, excretion, and other essential functions. Also, as organisms become more complex, special systems for organizing and integrating the various functions are required. Some of the selective advantages in becoming larger and more complex were reviewed; these include greater mobility, freedom from predation, and most important, the capacity for regulating the internal environment.

The Protozoa, the one-celled animals, are divided into four general classes: the flagellates, the sarcodines, the ciliates, and the Sporozoa. The first three classes may be identified on the basis of their locomotor structures. Members of the latter group, which is composed largely of parasitic forms, are generally immotile.

The sponges are composed of a number of different cell types, including *choanocytes*, or collar cells, which are the feeding cells of the sponge; *epitheliomuscular* cells, which are independent effectors; and *archeocytes*, largely undifferentiated cells from which other cell types, such as eggs and sperm, may arise. In the sponge, there is little coordination among the various cells. The animal, although it may grow very large, is limited nutritionally to very small particles of a size that can be ingested by the choanocytes.

The distinctive features of the *coelenterates* are (1) a two-layered body in which the two layers, the epidermis and the gastrodermis, are divided by a jelly-like substance, the mesoglea; (2) the *coelenteron,* a cavity in which the food can be partially digested extracellularly; and (3) the cnidoblasts, special stinging cells found only rarely outside of this phylum. The coelenterates may take the form of either the *polyp* or the *medusa;* in many species, both forms are seen in the course of each life cycle. The hydra, a common freshwater coelenterate in which only the polyp form is seen, has a variety of sensory cells and also a continuous nerve net that coordinates the movements of the entire animal. *Aurelia,* a jellyfish in which the medusa form predominates, has in addition to special sensory cells, two specialized sense organs, *statocysts* and *ocelli.*

The *flatworms* are bilaterally symmetrical and elongated, with a distinct "headness" and "tailness" and a concomitant clustering of nerve cells in the anterior region. The flatworms have three distinct tissue layers and also an elaborate excretory system that serves largely to maintain water balance.

The *annelid* worms, of which the earthworm is an example, have segmented bodies; *coeloms,* which are cavities within the middle layer, or mesoderm; a one-way digestive tract; and a circulatory system with five pairs of hearts. Excretion is accomplished by special organs, the *nephridia,* which are convoluted tubules. The nephridia collect fluids from the coelom and exchange salts and other substances with the body fluids as the urine passes along the tubules for excretion. The earthworm has a relatively complex nervous system, consisting of a double nerve cord, running ventrally, and encircling the pharynx at the anterior end of the animal, and pairs of ganglia (clusters of nerve cells), one pair to each segment, which receive sensory impulses and trigger motor activities in each segment.

There are four main classes of *mollusks*—represented by the chiton, the clam, the snail, and the squid. In each of these animals, the basic body plan is the same but has been modified in the course of adaptation to a particular environment. The nervous system and behavior also differ characteristically among the four classes. In the mollusks, respiration is carried out by means of a gill; the gill is a thin-walled extension of the epidermis which is richly endowed with blood vessels and serves as the area of gaseous exchange (respiration). The gill, by providing a specialized local area for respiration makes it possible for the rest of the animal's body to be covered and protected.

The echinoderms, which include the starfish, the sea urchin, and the sea lilies, are radially symmetrical in their adult forms; the larvae, however, are all bilaterally symmetrical, and radial symmetry is believed to be a secondary development. An unusual characteristic of this phylum is the water vascular system, which provides an hydraulic skeleton for the animal and also provides suction for the clinging and pulling activities associated with moving and predatory behavior.

The Higher Animals: Arthropods and Chordates

In this chapter, we shall introduce the arthropods, by far the most complex of the invertebrates, and the chordates, the phylum to which we ourselves belong. We shall close the chapter with a brief review of some of the theories and speculations about the evolutionary relationships among the members of the animal kingdom.

Arthropods

The arthropods, the "joint-footed" animals, make up by far the largest of all the animal phyla and the most diverse. Of animal species so far recorded, about 1 million—80 percent—are arthropods, and it has been estimated that the total number, known and unknown, may be as many as 10 million species.

ARTHROPOD CHARACTERISTICS

Segmentation

Arthropods are much the same in body plan throughout the entire phylum. They are all segmented animals, like the annelid worms, although in some of them, outward evidence of segmentation can be found only on the ventral surfaces and appendages. In the primitive arthropod, as evidenced by the fossil trilobites, all the segments tended to be the same and each appendage was identical. In the modern arthropods, however, the first six segments have become fused into the head, which often bears a number of elaborate sensory appendages and mouthparts. In the more highly evolved members of the phylum, not only is each pair of head appendages different but each pair of legs has its own special structure and function, serv-

2–99 *The mouthparts of insects consist of the same basic components, modified for various methods of feeding. Shown here are the three most common types: (1) The grasshopper has biting mouthparts, with large toothed jaws (mandibles). (2) The butterfly has sucking mouthparts; the sucking tube consists of two elongated maxillas, each forming half the tube. (3) The mosquito has piercing mouthparts; the mandibles are thin stylets with teeth at the end, and the maxillas hook together to form a groove through which the food is drawn up.*

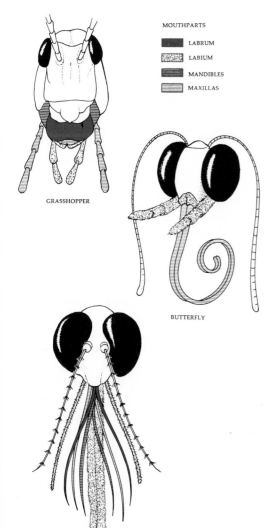

MOUTHPARTS

�	LABRUM
▦	LABIUM
▤	MANDIBLES
▤	MAXILLAS

GRASSHOPPER

BUTTERFLY

MOSQUITO

ing as jaws, gills, poison fangs, tongs, egg depositors, legs, hooks, antennae, paddles, or pincers.

Exoskeleton

The second and most obvious characteristic of the group is the *exoskeleton,* which is secreted by the animal's epidermal cells. The innermost layer of the skeleton is composed of chitin, a tough but pliable polysaccharide, and protein. The second layer is also chitin, but in some heavily shelled animals, like the lobster, it is stiffened with calcium or other minerals. The third layer is protein and lipid, which gives the armor a waxy outer surface that serves to reduce water loss in the terrestrial forms. The exoskeleton serves as a support for the soft tissues of the animal and also provides some protection against predation.

The exoskeleton creates two special problems: movement and growth. Movement is solved by the presence of many separate joints in the skeleton, particularly in the appendages. Each segment has its own muscle system. The animal does not move about within its shell, like a snail, but the muscles are attached to the various segments of the exoskeleton, just as they are attached to the various bones of the endoskeleton in vertebrates, and when the muscles contract, the exoskeleton moves.

The exoskeleton is not composed of living tissue and therefore cannot grow. When an arthropod outgrows its exoskeleton, it must molt. *Molting* is the process by which the old exoskeleton is discarded and a new and larger one formed. At molting time, the epidermis secretes an enzyme that dissolves the inner layer of the exoskeleton, and a new skeleton, not yet hardened, is formed beneath the old one. The animal wriggles out from the old skeleton, which splits open. After emerging, the animal expands rapidly by taking up air and water; during this period the new exoskeleton is first stretched and then hardened. A soft-shell crab is not a special type of crab but only an ordinary hard-shell crab caught soon after a seasonal molt.

Crustaceans, such as crabs and lobsters, continue to molt throughout their adult existence, but most insects do not grow or molt once they reach their adult form. In some insects, the larval stage may last only 10 days, but in others, the immature period lasts for years, as is the case with the "seventeen-year" cicadas. Often the adult forms of insects do not feed but mate soon after reaching maturity, lay their eggs, and die.

Molting is dangerous since the newly molted animal is particularly vulnerable to predators and also subject to water loss, in the case of terrestrial forms. Many arthropods go into hiding until their new cuticle has hardened. Molting is also costly in terms of metabolic expenditures, although a number of insects and some freshwater crustaceans limit their losses by thriftily eating the old exoskeleton.

279 *The Higher Animals: Arthropods and Chordates*

Circulatory System

The circulatory system of the arthropods is an open system, as compared with the closed system of the annelids, for instance, in which the blood circulates entirely within special vessels. In the open, arthropod system, the blood flows from blood vessels into blood sinuses, or cavities, from which it then returns to the vessels. The heart is a dorsal tube with paired openings, the *ostia*, which is suspended within a large blood cavity. Blood flows into the ostia; when the heart contracts, the ostia close and the blood is driven along the aorta into the tissues, bathes the various organs, and then seeps back along open channels into the area around the heart.

Nervous System

The nervous system of the arthropods is a ladder system, with a paired ventral nerve cord and a fused pair of ganglia in each segment, as in the annelids. It is more highly developed, however, with an increased concentration of nerve tissue in the cerebral ganglia. This arrangement is concomitant with the increased number of special head appendages and with the large number and variety of sensory organs, the largest found in any of the phyla.

CRUSTACEANS: THE LOBSTER

Figure 2–100 shows the structure of a lobster, which is a convenient arthropod to examine since it is familiar to most of us. The crayfish, which is more likely to be available in warmer climates, differs morphologically from the lobster only in minor respects, the most obvious of which is the size of the claws.

The lobster has 20 segments, the first 13 of which are united on the dorsal side in a combined head and thorax. The abdomen consists of 6 distinct segments. (To lobster eaters, the abdomen is the "tail," but to biologists, the designation *tail* is usually reserved for areas of the body posterior to the anus.) The various appendages have special functions. The antennae are sensory. The mandibles, or jaws, are for crushing; like all arthropod jaws, they move laterally, opening and closing from side to side like a pair of ice tongs rather than up and down like vertebrate jaws. The maxillas and the maxillipeds serve chiefly to collect food, mince it, and pass it on to the mouth. The claws are unequal in size in the full-grown lobster; the larger claw is used for crushing, and the smaller claw, which has the sharper teeth, seizes and tears the prey. The first two pairs of walking legs have small pincers, which can seize prey. The last pair of walking legs also serves to clean the abdominal appendages. The flattened posterior appendages are used for swimming, like flippers. The claws and abdomen are filled almost entirely with large and edible striated muscles. These muscles are extremely powerful. A lobster can snap his "tail" ventrally with

2–100 *The anatomy of the lobster. Like most highly specialized segmented animals, the lobster has single large organs (or pairs of organs) instead of small local structures in each segment. Of the systems shown here, only the nervous system and the appendages are clearly segmental. In primitive arthropods, the appendages were all alike and were sufficiently generalized in structure to serve several different functions. The appendages of the lobster offer a striking example of the development of specialization; while those on the abdomen are simple swimming flaps very similar to their primitive counterparts, those of the head and thorax have become highly diversified in structure and function.*

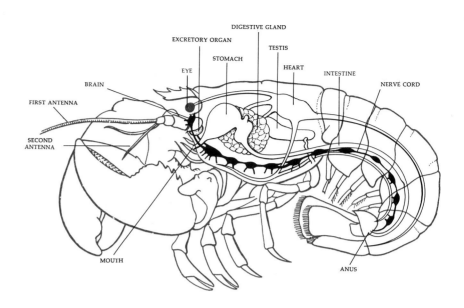

enough force to shoot backward through the water, and a large lobster can shatter the shell of a clam or oyster with its crushing claw. Any one of its appendages can be regenerated at the next molt if lost, and a lobster will often break off a claw or a leg in order to escape from a natural or man-made trap.

The anterior and posterior regions of the digestive tract, the foregut and hindgut, are lined with cuticle. As a consequence, most of the food is absorbed through the midgut and through the cells of the large digestive gland, or "liver." The anterior segment of the stomach is used for storage. The midsection, which has sharp chitinous teeth, functions as a gastric mill, grinding the food by muscular contractions. The third section sorts the food, routing the smallest particles to the digestive glands, the larger ones to the intestinal tract, and the coarsest ones to the gizzards.

Respiration is accomplished by 20 pairs of feathery gills which lie in the thorax between the body wall and the exoskeleton, where water can flow freely over them. The excretory organ, the *nephridium*, is in the head; wastes extracted from the blood are collected into a bladder and excreted from a pore at the base of each of the second antennae. Fertilization is external; the sperm, which are deposited near the female gonopores, fertilize the eggs as they are laid, and the fertilized eggs cling, by a sticky secretion, to the swimmerets of the female until they hatch.

Lobsters are crustaceans, a large class of arthropods that also includes crabs, shrimps, barnacles, water fleas (*Daphnia*), and numerous other small animals. Almost all the crustaceans are aquatic, but some, crabs in particular, are amphibious or land dwellers. Amphibious crabs continue to breathe with gills, carrying around water in their thoracic cavities with which to keep the gills wet and aerating the water through holes in their exoskeletons. The true land crab has lost the gill structures and instead has an area of highly vascularized epithelial tissue through which oxygen is exchanged. The land snail, you will recall, solved the respiratory problems involved in the transition from water to land in an analogous way.

CHELICERATES

The arachnids and the horseshoe crab belong to a subphylum of the arthropods, the Chelicerata. The arachnids include spiders, ticks, mites, scorpions, and daddy longlegs. Spiders and the other arachnids can be distinguished from insects because they have *chelicerae* instead of jaws and antennae. The chelicerae are appendages in front of the mouth which usually take the form of pincers or fangs. In spiders, the chelicerae are sharp and pointed and are used for capturing and then paralyzing the prey by the injection of a poison. Ducts from a pair of poison glands lead through the chelicerae and open near their perforated tips. Also, arachnids usually have four or five pairs of legs, while insects usually have three pairs.

Except for the horseshoe crab, chelicerates live on a completely liquid diet. The prey is masticated by the mouthparts, and then enzymes from the midgut are poured out over the torn tissues to produce a partially digested broth. The liquid is pumped into the stomach by the muscular pharynx, where digestion is completed and the juices absorbed. Spiders

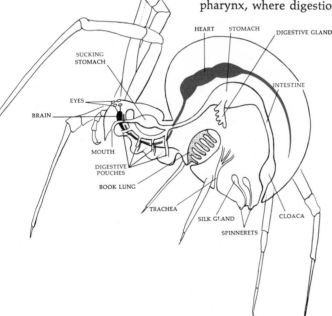

2–101 *The structure of an orb-weaving spider, showing the typical arachnid features. The mouth is too small to swallow solid food; instead, the spider masticates the food with its mouthparts, pours a digestive fluid over its prey, and then sucks up the predigested, liquified tissues by means of its muscular sucking stomach or pharynx. It is capable of taking up very large quantities of food at one time, storing it, and then gradually absorbing it. By comparing this drawing with Figure 2–102, can you determine the principal differences between arachnids and insects?*

and scorpions respire by means of *book lungs*, which are a series of leaf-like plates within a chitin-lined chamber. Air is drawn into the chamber and expelled by muscular action.

Figure 2–101 shows an orb-weaving spider with the typical arachnid features. In addition, on the posterior portion of its abdominal surface is a cluster of *spinnerets*, fingerlike organs from which a fluid protein exudes that hardens into silk as it comes into contact with the air. Silk is used not only for the variety of webs made by the different species but for a number of other purposes as well, such as for a drop line, on which the spider goes sky diving, for a cocoon, for lining a burrow, for the shroud of a victim, or for wrapping an edible offering presented to the female of certain species by the courting male. Most spiders can spin several kinds and thicknesses of silk.

The horseshoe crab (*Limulus*) has sometimes been called a living fossil since it has existed apparently unchanged for the last 200 million years. Viewed dorsally, it is difficult to classify among the arthropods, but if you turn it over, you can see clearly its clawlike chelicerae and its four pairs of walking appendages. Several species of this strange-looking animal survive; all are closely related and are classified in the same family. On the movable bases of its legs, the horseshoe crab has spiny, teethlike projections with which it can rip apart and mince the worms and mollusks on which it feeds.

INSECTS

More than half of the animals in the world are insects, and the described species number some 700,000. There are more than 300,000 different species of beetles and weevils alone. The adaptive success of the insects lies in their extraordinary versatility. They are so diversified that literally hundreds of different types can occupy the same few feet of territory.

Figure 2–102 shows a grasshopper. Here you can see many of the characteristic features of insects: three main divisions—the head, the thorax, and the abdomen—a single pair of antennae, and a set of mouthparts somewhat similar to those of the lobster. The front lip, the *labrum*, is not a paired appendage like the other mouthparts but is a movable flap that helps hold food between the jaws and that funnels masticated food into the mouth. In the more primitive insects, such as the grasshopper, the mouthparts are used for moving food and masticating food, but in the more highly evolved and specialized groups, the mouthparts are often molded into sucking, piercing, slicing, or sponging organs, many of which are exquisitely adapted to the nectaries of special flowers.

Most adult insects have two pairs of wings made up of light strong sheets of chitin; the veins in the wings are chitinous tubules that serve primarily as braces. The wings of the various orders of insects have evolved

*The grasshopper exhibits many typical
insect features. Can you identify them?*

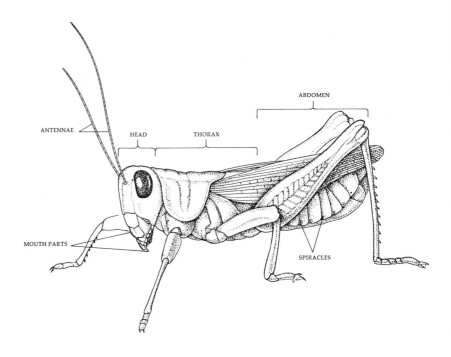

separately from one another. In some, such as the fleas and lice, they have
been partially or totally lost, returning the insect to the condition of its
wingless ancestors.

Digestive System

The foregut and hindgut of the insect digestive tract are lined with chitin.
Salivary gland fluids are carried with food into the crop, where digestion
begins. The stomach, which lies mainly in the abdomen, is the chief organ
of absorption. In the grasshopper, digestive pouches open into the stomach, releasing digestive juices which are especially adapted to the grasshopper's diet of leaves and grasses. Insects have digestive enzymes as specialized as their mouthparts, the structure of the enzymes depending on
whether the insect dines on blood, seeds, other insects, eggs, flour, cereal,
glue, wood, paper, or your winter clothes. Excretion is carried out through
tubules which lie in the body cavity and which lead into the hindgut. In
the grasshopper and many other insects, the nitrogenous and other wastes
are eliminated in the form of nearly dry crystals, an adaptation that promotes water conservation.

Respiratory System

The respiratory system is unlike that seen in any other phylum. It consists
of a network of chitin-lined tubules through which air circulates to the
various tissues of the body, supplying each cell directly. Muscular move-

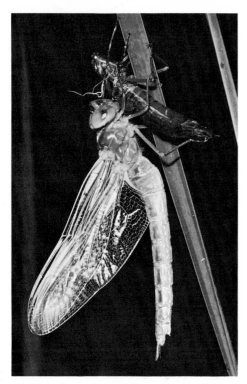

|— 10mm —|

2–103 *The dragonfly undergoes incomplete metamorphosis. The young form, or nymph, lives at the bottom of ponds, lakes, and streams. When it matures, it crawls up out of the water, its skin splits down the head and thorax, and the adult emerges. In this photograph, the adult dragonfly has just emerged. Its soft, limp wings have begun to expand and harden as blood is pumped into them. (L. West)*

ments of the animal's body improve the circulation of air. The amount of incoming air and also the degree of water loss can be regulated by the opening and closing of small openings, or spiracles.

Metamorphosis

Most insects go through definite developmental stages. In some species, the infant, although sexually immature, looks like a small copy of the adult; it grows larger by a series of molts until it reaches full size. In others, like the grasshopper, the newly hatched young is wingless and somewhat different in proportions from the adult, but it is otherwise similar. These immature, nonreproductive forms are known as *nymphs*. Almost 90 percent of the insects, however, undergo a complete metamorphosis, so that the adult is completely different from the immature form. The immature eating and feeding forms may all correctly be referred to as *larvae*, although they are also commonly known as caterpillars, grubs, or maggots, depending on the different species. Following the larval period, the insect undergoing complete metamorphosis enters an outwardly quiescent pupal stage in which extensive remodeling of the organism occurs. The adult insect emerges from the pupa.

The insect that undergoes complete metamorphosis exists in four different forms in the course of its life history. The first form is the egg. The second form is the larva, the animal that hatches from the egg; larvae are concerned almost entirely with eating and growth. In many larvae, such as those of the fly, growth takes place not by an increase in the number of cells, as in most animals, but by an increase in the size of the cells, in somewhat the same way that it takes place in certain plant tissues. During the course of its growth, the larva molts a characteristic number of times— twice in the fruit fly, for example. The stages between molts are known as *instars*. Then, when the larva is full-grown, it molts to form the pupa. During this outwardly lifeless pupal stage, many of the larval cells break down and an entirely new group of cells, set aside in the embryo, begin to proliferate, using the degenerating larval tissue as a culture medium. These groups of cells are known as *imaginal disks* since they form the *imago*, the adult insect which, according to Aristotle, is the perfect form or ideal image which the immature form is "seeking to express." These imaginal disks develop into the complicated structures of the adult.

Hormone Control of Metamorphosis

Almost 30 years ago, Sir Vincent B. Wigglesworth, the great insect physiologist, proved that metamorphosis was controlled by hormones. For his initial studies, Wigglesworth used the South American bloodsucking bug *Rhodnius prolixus*. *Rhodnius* was particularly useful because molting could be triggered by feeding and occurred at a quite specific interval fol-

2–104 *The larva of the spicebush swallowtail butterfly. Its startled expression is permanent; the wide-open "eyes" are not sensory organs but surface markings. They form an important part of the animal's defense against predators (see Chapter 6–3). (L. West)*

2–105 *The South American bloodsucker Rhodnius prolixus requires only a single meal between each growth period and can live for months after being decapitated—two reasons why it played such an important role in early studies of hormone control of metamorphosis. (After Williams, 1950)*

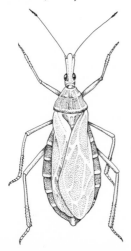

lowing a meal. *Rhodnius* also lends itself well to decapitation, a procedure that was important in the experiments, since it does not need to eat continuously (one blood meal per instar is enough) and also, as you can see in Figure 2–105, it is ideally shaped for decapitation.

Rhodnius undergoes an incomplete metamorphosis, during which it molts five times. Wigglesworth found that if *Rhodnius* is decapitated 7 to 10 days after feeding, it will molt normally, though headless. If, however, it is decapitated 1 to 2 days after feeding, it fails to molt, although it will live for months if it has had its blood meal. But when the blood of an insect decapitated just before it is ready to molt is transfused into an insect decapitated early in the instar, the latter will molt. This evidence suggests that early in the instar, something is transmitted from the head of *Rhodnius* through the bloodstream that causes molting.

It was subsequently shown that the molting process is initiated by a special secretion released from neurons in the brain. This "brain hormone", as it is called, stimulates a gland in the thorax to produce a second hormone, ecdysone, which actually promotes cellular growth, the discarding of the cuticle, and the formation of the new exoskeleton. When *Rhodnius* is decapitated late in the instar, enough brain hormone has accumulated so that the gland in the thorax will continue to secrete ecdysone. A series of small blood meals, even though they total a large one in quantity, will not promote molting; the actual mechanical distension of the body produced by one large meal is needed to release the brain hormone.

During incomplete metamorphosis such as that of *Rhodnius*, the nymph undergoes a series of molts. All its developmental stages resemble one another until the last molt—the fifth, in the case of *Rhodnius*—after which an adult, sexually mature insect appears.

Why is the last molt different from the others? Wigglesworth found the answer to this question in the *corpora allata*, small glands located beneath the brain of *Rhodnius*. Because of the long thin head of this insect, it was possible to remove either the brain or the corpora allata or both. The corpora allata, Wigglesworth found, were the source of still another hormone, which was produced during the first four instars but not during the fifth instar. Only when this hormone was absent could the adult form of the insect emerge. If blood from an insect in an early instar was infused into the nymph or if the corpora allata from a young larva were implanted, *Rhodnius* did not become an adult but simply continued, by a series of molts, to become a larger and larger larva. Wigglesworth named this hormone the *juvenile hormone* because it inhibits the development of adult characteristics.

Work on the hormonal control of metamorphosis, so brilliantly begun in *Rhodnius*, has been continued in a number of other insects, particularly in the North American giant silkworm cecropia. Cecropia undergoes a

2–106 *The cocoon of a cecropia moth, cut open.*
The outlines of the antennae and wings
can be seen in the pupal covering.
(Photograph by Lynwood M. Chace,
National Audubon Society)

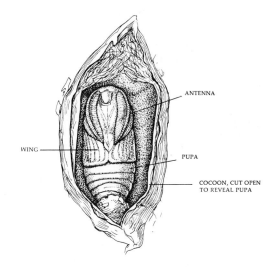

WING

ANTENNA

PUPA

COCOON, CUT OPEN
TO REVEAL PUPA

|— 1cm —|

complete metamorphosis, passing through several caterpillar molts, then
forming a large pupa in which the insect spends the winter, and finally
emerging in the spring as a quite spectacular moth. Carroll Williams of
Harvard, who has been in the forefront of these studies, prepared extracts
of juvenile hormone from cecropia moths and showed that when these
extracts were injected into a pupa, the pupa molted into a second pupa,
rather than forming a moth. Since cecropia pupae are readily available,
relatively large, and easy to inject and since the amount of hormone needed
is very small, they have provided a useful assay system for juvenile-hormone activity. As a result of such essays, it has been shown that a number
of different chemicals, including extracts of vertebrate endocrine glands,
have some juvenile-hormone activity.

Recently, Williams and his associates have reported that the paper on
which several daily newspapers are printed contains a chemical with strong

287 *The Higher Animals: Arthropods and Chordates*

2–107 *The three stages in the complete meta-*
morphosis of a polyphemus moth. It
first passes through several larval molts,
then spends the winter as a large pupa,
and finally emerges in the spring as a
moth. In this picture, the pupa is being
injected with an extract of juvenile hor-
mone. The result of the injection, it has
been shown, is that the pupa will molt
into another pupa instead of becoming
a moth. (Mrs. Carroll Williams)

juvenile-hormone activity in at least one group of insects.* The papers cited were *The New York Times,* the *Wall Street Journal,* and the *Boston Globe.* (Since we do not know what other journals were assayed, it is difficult to evaluate the literary significance of the finding, although the biological implications are clear.) The hormone has been traced to the wood pulp of the balsam fir from which the newsprint for these particular papers, among others, is made. The investigators have suggested that the hormone may be produced by the trees as a defense against insects. A chemical which prevents insects from ever reaching an adult reproductive stage and is absolutely harmless to all other organisms would, of course, be an ideal insecticide, so this discovery has important practical applications.

The Pheromones

The pheromones play an important part in the morphogenesis of the social insects. Pheromones are chemicals secreted by one organism that exert their effects on other organisms. In the beehive, for example, the queen bee produces a pheromone, the *queen substance,* which is passed orally through all the members of the hive and which inhibits the workers, all females, from producing eggs. A more complex set of pheromone-controlled social relationships is found in termite societies, in which sev-

* This discovery was the by-product of a laboratory "accident," not unlike the chance contamination of Fleming's bacterial cultures that led to the discovery of penicillin.

TERMITES

Termite societies are by far the most ancient communities in the world. Man has existed as a social animal for less than 1 million years, ants for about 100 million years, and termites for something like 200 million years. There are 5 different families and almost 2,000 species of termites. All species are social; some termitaries contain as many as 3 million individuals.

Termite societies are organized by a rigid caste system in which differences of occupation are clearly reflected in body size and shape. The largest member of the colony is the queen, which may in some species reach several inches in length, far larger than any members of her court. Huge, grublike, and almost shapeless, she serves as an egg factory, being constantly fed by the workers and laying as many as 10,000 eggs a day. Even if she were able to move, her swollen body could not pass through the narrow chambers of the termite colony, so she spends her entire existence, often 10 or 15 years, sealed in her nuptial chamber. In many species, the king, the sole reproductive male of the colony, is sealed in the chamber with her. The two largest termite castes are the soldiers and the workers. The soldiers, defenders of the community, possess large, strong mandibles and also, in some species, a syringelike beak from which they can eject a thick, irritating liquid. In many species, the headparts of the soldiers have become so massive that they are no longer able to feed themselves and must be taken care of by the workers, who also tend the royal couple, feed the young, and maintain the many-chambered colony.

The eggs laid by the queen develop into nymphs. All nymphs are the same through the first instars. If the colony is short of workers, the nymphs will develop, in their final molt, into workers; if soldiers are needed, a proportion of nymphs will become soldiers. (On the other hand, if there are too many soldiers, the workers will destroy some of them.) If the king or queen should die, a nymph will develop into a reproductive form and assume the burdens of the royal chambers. At specific periods in the year, depending on the species and the climate, termite colonies produce winged, reproductive males and females. These leave the colony on a brief nuptial flight, form pairs, lose their wings, and dig a burrow in which they will close themselves forever from the outside, thereby founding a new colony.

Termites lead most of their lives in hermetically sealed, warm, damp, burrows, and many species perish of dessication if exposed to the drying effects of light and air outside their burrows. This is why, incidentally, they can do so much damage when they infest a building, since they will hollow out entire beams without exposing themselves. The common destructive form prevalent in the United States has one important point of vulnerability: a need to return to the soil, apparently for moisture or nutrients.

289   *The Higher Animals: Arthropods and Chordates*

Consequently, those termites can be destroyed by chemicals injected into the soil. For the trips to the soil, the workers build networks of covered passageways through which they can travel if they need to pass along a concrete surface, for example. These passageways are often the first signs of termite infestation.

2–108 *In the rigidly structured termite society, the different occupations of the several castes are reflected in anatomical specializations. Shown here are three workers and, in the center, a soldier, distinguished by its larger size and massive jaws. (Dr. Ross E. Hutchins)*

|——— 5mm ———|

2–109 *With her enormous abdomen, the largest member of the termite colony is the queen. Her entire adult existence, which may last for 15 years or more, is spent producing eggs. Constantly fed by the workers, she lays as many as 10,000 eggs a day! (Dr. Ross E. Hutchins)*

|——— 5mm ———|

2–110 *Swarming termites: winged males and queens on the nuptial flight. (Dr. Ross E. Hutchins)*

|——— 4mm ———|

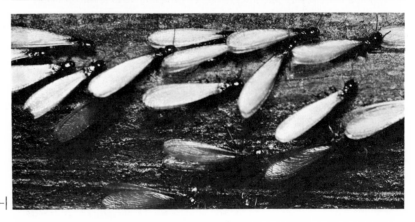

eral different castes exist, including workers, soldiers, king, and queen. Any given nymph can develop into a worker, a soldier, or a member of the royal family, depending on the pheromones exchanged among the members of the termite colony. The queen, for example, produces chemicals that ordinarily inhibit other females from developing into reproductive forms, while the king pheromones similarly inhibit the males. Pheromones affect not only body size and structure but also behavior patterns.

Chordates

In shallow marine waters all over the warmer parts of the world, there lives a small sliver-shaped semitransparent animal, which, although it can swim very efficiently, spends most of its time buried in the sandy bottom with only its mouth protruding above the surface. This animal is the amphioxus ("sharp at both ends"), or lancelet, as it is more commonly known. It has three features that identify it as a member of the chordate phylum. The first is the notochord, a cartilaginous rod which extends the length of the body and serves as a firm but flexible axis. The notochord, from which the phylum derives its name, is not a nerve cord but only a structural support. Because of it, the amphioxus can swim with strong undulatory movements that move it through the water with a speed unattainable by the flatworms or aquatic annelids.

The second chordate characteristic is the nerve cord, a hollow tube that runs along the dorsal surface of the animal above the notochord. (The principal nerve cord in the invertebrates, by contrast, is always on the ventral surface.)

2–111 *Amphioxus, the lancelet, exemplifies three distinctive chordate characteristics: (1) the notochord, the cartilaginous rod which extends the length of the body and gives support to the soft tissues, (2) the dorsal tubular nerve cord, and (3) the pharyngeal gill slits.*

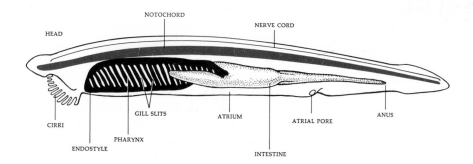

2–112 *X-ray of an elk fetus. The bones have been stained to show them more clearly, so that you can see the extent to which the skeleton is still cartilaginous. Notice the legs, for example. Only the dark areas are bone; these will gradually grow and replace the cartilage as the animal matures.* (Donald H. Fritts)

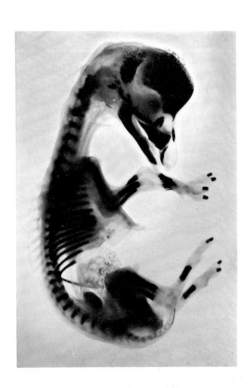

The third characteristic is a pharynx with gill slits. The pharyngeal gill slits become highly developed in fishes, in which they serve a respiratory function, and traces of them even remain in the human embryo. In the amphioxus, they serve primarily for collecting food. The cilia around the mouth and at the opening of the pharynx pull in a steady current of water that passes out through the pharyngeal slits into a chamber, the *atrium*, and out through the atrial pore. Food particles are collected in the sieve-like pharynx, mixed with mucus, and channeled along ciliated grooves, the *endostyles*, to the intestine, where they are digested with the aid of enzymes from the digestive gland. There is no separate heart; the blood is pumped through the body by the contractile ventral vessel. The amphioxus has a tail, an extension of the body and the notochord behind the anus. The tail is found almost exclusively in the chordate phylum. Amphioxus, which belongs to the small subphylum Cephalochordata, is of interest to biologists because it so clearly illustrates the basic chordate body plan.

THE VERTEBRATES

The vertebrates are a large and familiar subphylum of the chordates. All vertebrates have a backbone, or vertebral column, as their structural axis —a flexible bony support which develops around the notochord, supplanting it entirely in most species. Dorsal projections of the vertebrae encircle the nerve cord along the length of the spine. The brain, the culmination of the nerve cord, is similarly enclosed and protected by bony skull plates. Between the vertebrae are cartilaginous disks, which give the vertebral column its flexibility. Associated with the vertebrae are a series of muscle segments, the *myotomes,* by which sections of the vertebral column can be moved separately. This segmented pattern persists in the embryonic forms of the higher vertebrates but is largely lost in the course of development.

One of the great advantages of this bony endoskeleton, as compared with the exoskeletons of the invertebrates, is that it is composed of living tissue that can grow with the animal. In the developing embryo, the skeleton is largely cartilaginous, with bone gradually replacing cartilage in the course of maturation. Figure 2–112 shows the cartilaginous tissue of a vertebrate embryo. In the vertebrates, the growing tips of the bones remain cartilaginous until the animal reaches its full adulthood. In addition to its powers of growth, a broken bone can also repair itself, unlike the lifeless tissue of a clamshell, for example.

The various classes of vertebrates are generally familiar to you: the fish, the amphibians, the reptiles, the birds, and the mammals. In Chapter 2–8, we shall describe some of the special vertebrate structures and functions.

EVOLUTIONARY HISTORY

The history of evolutionary relationships, or *phylogeny,* is built upon two types of evidence: (1) the fossil record and (2) resemblances among present-day organisms. Each of these is uncertain in its own way. As Darwin said of the geologic record, the fossils are a "history . . . imperfectly kept . . . only here and there a short chapter has been preserved; of each page, only here and there a few lines." Whether or not a creature became fossilized depended both on its own structure and on the circumstances of its death. Soft-bodied organisms disappeared without a trace, while the ancient trilobites contributed a well-formed carapace to the fossil history at every molt. More than half of the Cambrian fossils are trilobites. Similarly, ferns and dinosaurs, which lived in swamps and marshes and could be swallowed up in the preserving mud, are far more likely to have left their remains than organisms whose bodies fell on the hard forest floor, prey to decomposers and scavengers. Reading the fossil record, the science of paleontology, is a highly specialized branch of biology and one which will be touched upon only lightly in this account.

Resemblances between present-day organisms provide evidence that must also be handled with caution since no creature now alive can be ancestral to another present-day form. Sometimes this evidence seems quite conclusive, however. For example, one of the reasons that we no longer consider the echinoderms to be related to the coelenterates, despite the apparent radial symmetry of the former, is that the echinoderms have a coelom and the coelenterates do not. Similarly, the fact that human beings share certain blood groups with the great apes is convincing evidence for a quite close affinity. Just recently, new techniques have made possible studies of the biochemistry of organisms—comparison of details of protein structure, for example—that may reveal new evidence of phylogenetic affinities and perhaps alter some of our present ideas.

How Animals May Have Originated

Figure 2–113 depicts the family tree of the Animalia; this is the scheme that appears to be the most widely accepted at the present time, although it is not the only one by any means. As you can see, sponges are shown as a separate branch, and it is the coelenterates, with their simple two-layered body plan, that are indicated as the ancestral stock from which we have all evolved. One of the bases for this hypothesis is the characteristic free-swimming ciliated planula larva. Here we must use our imaginations, for there are no facts and it is not likely that fossil evidence will be found, but a transition is not difficult to imagine between a colonial flagellate and a primitive planulalike animal which might then develop into an animal resembling this ciliated larva. For example, do you remember *Volvox* (Chap-

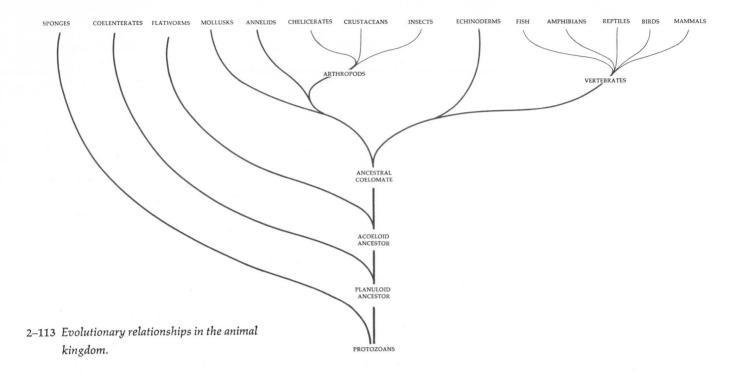

SPONGES COELENTERATES FLATWORMS MOLLUSKS ANNELIDS CHELICERATES CRUSTACEANS INSECTS ECHINODERMS FISH AMPHIBIANS REPTILES BIRDS MAMMALS

ARTHROPODS

VERTEBRATES

ANCESTRAL
COELOMATE

ACOELOID
ANCESTOR

PLANULOID
ANCESTOR

PROTOZOANS

2–113 *Evolutionary relationships in the animal
kingdom.*

2–114 *A hypothetical ancestral flatworm,
representing a combination of various
primitive features displayed by different acoels. (After Barnes, 1963)*

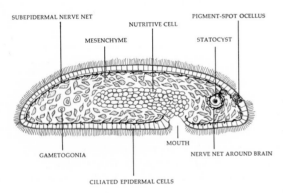

SUBEPIDERMAL NERVE NET
NUTRITIVE CELL
PIGMENT-SPOT OCELLUS
MESENCHYME
STATOCYST
GAMETOGONIA
MOUTH
NERVE NET AROUND BRAIN
CILIATED EPIDERMAL CELLS

ter 2–3)? Imagine the outer cells of *Volvox* dividing and the daughter cells migrating inward until the entire sphere is filled. What you would then have would look very much like the planula. Alternatively, the planula might have arisen from other Protozoa. It might, for instance, have developed from a solid amoeba-flagellate colony; these cells do not have the firm cellulose outer walls characteristic of the volvocine line, and so the transition might be more likely. Some biologists, although these are a distinct minority, believe that a planulalike ancestor may have developed from a ciliate which, as it grew larger, divided itself into individual cells. In any case, despite the unresolved and perhaps unresolvable controversies about the origin of the ciliated planula, there is wide agreement that an organism very much like it is the ancestral form of the coelenterates and the first member of the Kingdom Animalia.

The planula larva supplies a possible clue to the origin of the flatworms, even though these origins, like those of the coelenterates, are not documented in the fossil record. Suppose this larva, instead of swimming around or settling down into a sessile, radially symmetrical polyp, began to crawl along the ocean bottom. What useful adaptations might it then develop in the course of a few million generations of random variation and natural selection? It might develop a head and a tail and an upper and a lower surface—in other words, bilateral symmetry. It might even develop

2–115 *The free-swimming larval form of most annelids and all mollusks is the tro-chophore. Shown here is an annelid trochophore, but all trochophores including the molluscan ones, are very similar. Because of this similarity, we know that an evolutionary relationship exists between the two phyla even though the adult forms are not at all alike. (Dr. Douglas P. Wilson, F.R.P.S.)*

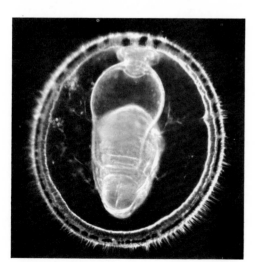

| — 0.2mm — |

a mouthlike opening on its ventral surface, and it might come to look something like the animal depicted in Figure 2–114, which is a hypothetical flatworm, the most primitive member of this phylum. Though this, too, is hypothetical, the logic is compelling, and it is generally agreed that the ciliated planula larva of the coelenterates was the starting point of the flatworms.

PAEDOMORPHOSIS

The development of a new group of animals from an earlier stage of an ancestral form is known as *paedomorphosis* ("taking shape from a child"). Presumably, in the course of this process, larval forms came to be more and more dominant in successive generations until eventually they became sexually mature and able to reproduce themselves. *Hydra,* for example, is believed to represent a stage in the animal which was once juvenile but then became reproductive. The planula larva seems, over a long period of time, to have gone through a similar process and so to have gone off on an extremely consequential evolutionary journey of its own. Paedomorphosis, as we shall see, also played an important role in the evolution of our own phylum.

The Coelomates

At some point after the coming of the flatworm, we reach what some experts consider a distinct fork in the evolutionary pathway. Right at this fork is a hypothetical animal which, if it ever existed, was almost certainly a worm with a digestive tract that was a straight tube from mouth to anus and with a coelom. One group of descendants from this hypothetical coelomate includes the mollusks, the annelids, and the arthropods—probably in that order, historically speaking. The other branch of the family includes the echinoderms and the chordates.

PROTOSTOMES AND DEUTEROSTOMES

One of the chief reasons for separating the mollusks, annelids, and arthropods from the echinoderms and chordates is found in observations of early embryonic development in the two groups. In its earliest stages, every embryo is a sphere of cells; then an opening, the *blastopore,* appears, and in its second major developmental stage, the embryo is a one-hole sac. In most species of mollusks, annelids, and arthropods, this opening develops into the mouth, with a second opening forming for the anus; these animals are therefore known as the Protostomia ("first the mouth"). In the echinoderms and chordates, the blastopore generally forms the anus and the mouth appears second; these are therefore the Deuterostomia ("second the mouth").

295 *The Higher Animals: Arthropods and Chordates*

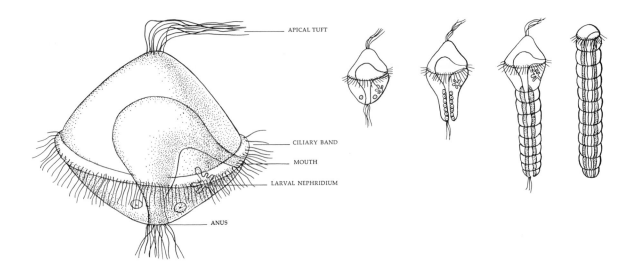

APICAL TUFT

CILIARY BAND

MOUTH

LARVAL NEPHRIDIUM

ANUS

2–116 *How the annelid trochophore develops into a segmented worm. The process begins with the elongation of the lower part of the trochophore. The elongated region then becomes constricted into segments, which soon develop bristles. The apical tuft disappears, and the upper part of the trochophore becomes the head. The worm will continue to grow throughout its lifetime by adding new segments just in front of its rear segment.*

THE TROCHOPHORE

The annelids and the mollusks have little superficial resemblance to one another. Here again, a link is found in the larval stage. Many of the annelids (the oligochaetes excepted) begin their lives as a very distinct larval form known as the *trochophore* because of its *trochos*, or "wheel," of cilia. Figures 2–115 and 2–116 show the trochophore and its development into a segmented worm. All marine mollusks (except the cephalopods) also pass through a trochophore stage in their development. Until fairly recently, the lack of segmentation in the mollusks seemed to argue against the evidence of close affinity provided by the trochophore. In the 1950's, however, 10 living specimens of *Neopilina*, a genus of mollusks previously known only from Cambrian fossils, were dredged from a deep ocean trench off the coast of Costa Rica. *Neopilina*, which is little more than an inch long, resembles a combination of gastropod and chiton, with a single large bilateral shell and five pairs of gills, five pairs of retractor muscles, and six pairs of nephridia, all arranged in a distinctly segmental pattern. It has been argued that this segmental arrangement, since it does not appear elsewhere in the mollusks, may be a secondary development, like radial symmetry in the echinoderms. At present, however, the evidence that the mollusks and the annelids arose from some common ancestor is widely accepted.

The Evolution of the Chordates

Amphioxus was once considered the modern form of the most ancient provertebrate, and certainly, because of its structural simplicity, it is a useful introduction to the chordate phylum. Owing largely to the studies

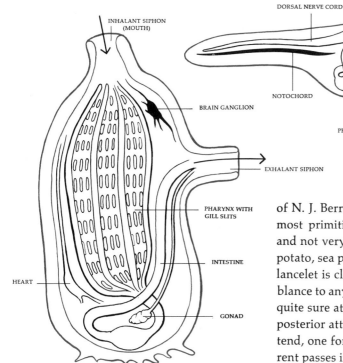

Labels on the diagram:

INHALANT SIPHON (MOUTH)

DORSAL NERVE CORD   MOUTH

NOTOCHORD

HEART

PHARYNX WITH GILL SLITS

BRAIN GANGLION

EXHALANT SIPHON

PHARYNX WITH GILL SLITS

INTESTINE

HEART

GONAD

2–117   *Two stages in the life of an ascidian. At the upper right is the "tadpole" larva; the adult form is shown on the left. After a brief free-swimming existence, the larva settles to the bottom and attaches at the anterior end. Metamorphosis then begins. The larval tail, with the notochord and dorsal nerve cord, disappears, and the animal's entire body is turned 180°. The mouth is carried backward to open at the end opposite that of attachment, and all the other internal organs are also rotated back. The larval and adult forms are clearly very different; which form has features that link it to the vertebrates and what are those features?*

of N. J. Berrill of McGill University, it is now generally accepted that the most primitive surviving chordate is not the amphioxus but a peculiar and not very prepossessing animal known variously as the sea squirt, sea potato, sea peach, and sea pork—or, more technically, as the ascidian. The lancelet is clearly fishlike, but the adult ascidian bears no obvious resemblance to any vertebrate, and indeed, as its names imply, one would not be quite sure at first glance whether it is even an animal. It is sessile, with its posterior attached to the substratum. From its upper end, two siphons extend, one for incoming and one for outgoing currents. The incoming current passes into a pharyngeal basket with gill slits, like the pharynx of the amphioxus, and the water then passes into the atrium and out through the exit siphon, leaving behind the food particles, which pass into the intestine. The exit siphon also serves to carry out undigested products from the anus and the eggs and sperm. The organ systems of the animal are enclosed in an outer covering, or tunic, which is made of a type of cellulose; the ascidians are the only known cellulose-making members of the animal kingdom. The tunic may be opaque like a potato, peach or porklike in color or texture, smooth and marbled, or translucent with the internal organs shining through.

The most interesting feature of the ascidian, from an evolutionary point of view, is its larval form. Externally, the larva looks very much like a tadpole, and it is the larval form that is seen as the link between the ascidians and the vertebrates. As some biologists reconstruct the past, tunicate larvae wriggled up the rivers, where they gave rise, after many generations and millions of years, to the ancestral vertebrates.

THE FISH

The fish are by far the oldest of the vertebrates. The most primitive are the Agnatha, the "jawless." The lamprey and the hagfish are modern representatives of this group. They lack true bones; in fact, the body of the hagfish is so flexible that it can tie itself in a knot. These *cyclostomes*

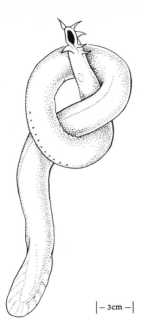

|— 3cm —|

2–118 *The most primitive of all fish are the Agnatha, of which the hagfish, shown here, is a modern representative. Lacking true bones, the hagfish is so flexible that, as you can see, it can tie itself into a knot. (After Jensen, 1966)*

2–119 *The heavily armored placoderm is the ancestor of two major classes of present-day fish—the Chondrichthyes (cartilaginous fish) and the Osteichthyes (bony fish). (Courtesy of the American Museum of Natural History)*

("round mouths"), as they are called, are highly predatory, attaching to other fish by their suckerlike mouths and rasping through the skin into the viscera of their hosts. The juvenile lamprey, however, feeds by sucking up mud containing microorganisms and organic debris—as, most probably, did the primitive Agnatha.

The placoderms were a group of fish that had heavy, bony exterior armor. The placoderms are known only as fossils but are included here for the sake of completing the record since they represent nature's first experiment with the vertebrate jawbone and since they are established as the ancestors of the two major modern classes of fish. One group of placoderms gave rise to the cartilaginous fish (the Chondrichthyes), which, among modern forms, include the shark and the skate. According to fossil evidence, the Chondrichthyes were originally bony fish, and these modern representatives are skeletally immature adult forms. A second group of placoderms evolved into the bony fish (the Osteichthyes), which comprise nearly all the familiar modern freshwater and saltwater forms.

Most experts believe that the fish evolved in fresh water. The Chondrichthyes returned to the sea early in their development, while the bony fish went through most of their evolution in fresh water and spread to the seas at a much later period. Some still recapitulate in each lifetime this difficult physiological transition. The Pacific salmon, for example, returns to fresh water to spawn, while eels leave the fresh waters of the continents to return to the Sargasso Sea at breeding time, from which distant point the young begin the long, difficult journey, often lasting many years, back to the rivers and lakes.

Some primitive osteichthyans had lungs as well as gills, although the lungs were not efficient enough to serve as more than accessory structures. These lungs were a special adaptation to fresh water, which, unlike ocean water, may stagnate and, because of decay or of algal bloom, become depleted of oxygen. A few modern lungfish exist. These can live in water that does not have sufficient oxygen to support other fish life. Lungfish surface and gulp air into their lungs in much the same way that the water-dwelling pulmonate snails bob to the surface to fill their mantle cavities.

Using their supplementary oxygen supply, the primitive osteichthyans could waddle, dragging their bellies on the ground, up the muddy bottom of a drying stream bed to seek deeper water or perhaps even make their way from one water source to another one nearby. Lungfish were the most common fish in the later Devonian seas. In most of them, the lung evolved into an air bladder, which is a closed sac that serves as a flotation chamber. The fish is able to raise or lower itself in the water by adding gases to the air bladder or removing oxygen from it. The oxygen is supplied and removed by the bloodstream. Other lungfish retained the lung and increased its efficiency, making way for the first amphibians.

THE AMPHIBIANS

By the end of the Devonian period, some of the lungfish had begun to develop skeletal supports in their fleshy fins. They looked more like four-legged fish than like the modern amphibians; they were heavy and clumsy, with short sprawling legs, big flattened heads, and stubby tails. Some of them were large, as much as 4 or 5 feet long. Although they could walk on land, they probably spent most of their lives in the water; nor, in fact, have their descendants, the modern amphibians, freed themselves entirely from the water, but at best, as their name implies, they lead two lives (*amphi-bios*).

Amphibian eggs are nearly always laid in the water and develop there into gill-breathing tadpoles. Only later do the tadpoles develop lungs to replace their gills and do their limbs develop and mature. Modern amphibians include the toads and frogs, both of which lose their tails in the course of metamorphosis from the larval aquatic form, and salamanders, which still have tails. Some of the salamanderlike amphibians, such as the mud puppy and the axolotl, never complete their metamorphosis, remaining essentially aquatic, larval forms. In some species, these larvalike forms can be induced to metamorphose into adult forms by hormone injections, indicating that the genetic capacity for this later developmental stage has not yet been lost completely.

THE REPTILES

As you will recall, the vascular plants freed themselves from the water by the development of the seed. Analogously, the vertebrates became truly terrestrial with the evolution in the reptiles of the amniote egg, an egg which can be laid on land. The reptilian egg, which is much like the familiar hen's egg in basic design, contains a large yolk, the food supply for the

2–120 *This "four-legged fish" is a salamander larva. Unlike their fellow amphibians, the toads and frogs, salamanders retain their tails through metamorphosis.* (L. West)

developing embryo. A membrane (usually the amnion) surrounds the developing embryo in a liquid-filled space that substitutes for the ancestral pond. In mammals also, although their eggs typically develop internally, the embryos are enclosed in water within an enveloping membrane.

The reptiles evolved slowly, making their appearance long after the bony fish. They became large in numbers, species, and individual size during the Jurassic and Cretaceous periods, when they were the predominant terrestrial animals. Then, within a relatively short time, the majority of the species became extinct. The reason for their disappearance is not known. It seems most reasonable to attribute it to climatic changes. From the fossil record and from their great size, it is evident that many of the reptiles had to live in marshy lands, where the water and mud would have helped to support their weight. These same marshes would have provided the enormous amounts of lush vegetation required by the grass-eating dinosaurs, which, in turn, fed the carnivores. So one can speculate that when the great marshes declined, the great reptiles also declined, and both disappeared together.

Present-day reptiles are small remnants of this once mighty class. Of these, the lizard best exemplifies reptilian characteristics. The lizard retains the general shape of fish and salamanders, but unlike them, its backbone and tail are not its locomotor apparatus. The vertebral column, which has become stiffer and stronger but less flexible, now acts as a girder, carrying body weight and transmitting it to the legs. Unlike the amphibians, the body of the lizard is fully supported by its legs when it is walking and its belly does not drag on the ground. The snake is not a primitive reptile, as you might think, but a degenerate form, the descendant of a group of burrowing lizards. Other modern reptiles include alligators, crocodiles, turtles, and tortoises.

2–121 *The lizard has retained the general shape of fish and salamanders, but its vertebral column has become stiffer and stronger. Unlike the amphibians, the body of the lizard is fully supported by its legs when it is walking and its belly does not drag on the ground. (Courtesy of the National Publicity Studios, New Zealand)*

|— 6cm —|

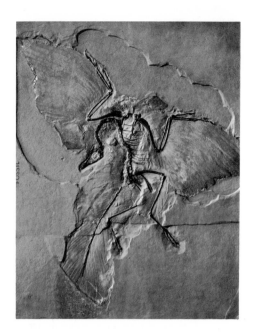

2–122 *The oldest known fossil bird, Archaeop-teryx, dates from the middle Jurassic period, about 150 million years ago. It still had many reptilian characteristics. The teeth and the long jointed tail are not present in modern birds. (Courtesy of the American Museum of Natural History)*

THE BIRDS

Birds are essentially reptiles highly specialized for flight. Their skeletons are very similar to some of the flying reptiles of prehistoric times. They have feathers, however, which is one of the categorical distinctions, and they maintain a high and constant body temperature, which provides the high metabolic rate required for sustained flight. Their bodies are lightened by air sacs and also by the development of hollow bones. The oceanic frigate, a seagoing bird with a 7-foot wingspread, has a skeleton that weighs only 4 ounces. The most massive bone in the bird skeleton is the breastbone, or *sternum*, which provides the keel for the attachment of the huge muscles that operate the wings. Flying birds have jettisoned all extra weight; the female's reproductive system has been trimmed down to a single ovary, and even this becomes large enough to be functional only in the mating season. Most of the common nonflying birds, such as the penguin and the ostrich, are believed to have evolved secondarily from flying types.

THE MAMMALS

The mammals also descended from the reptiles. Some chief points of difference between mammals and reptiles are (1) mammals are hairy rather than scaly, (2) mammals nurse their young, and (3) mammals maintain a constant body temperature. In nearly all mammalian species, the young are born alive, as they are in some fish and reptiles which retain the eggs in their bodies until they hatch. Some very primitive mammals, however, such as the duckbill platypus, lay shelled eggs but nurse their young after hatching. The marsupials, which include the opossum and the kangaroo, also bear their young alive, but they differ from the major group of mammals in that the infants are born at a tiny and immature stage and are kept in a special protective pouch in which they suckle and continue their development. Most of the familiar mammals are *placentals*, so called because they have an efficient nutritive connection, the *placenta*, between the uterus and the embryo. As a result the young can develop to a much more advanced stage before birth. This is a big advantage because it affords protection to the young during their most vulnerable developmental period without seriously interfering with the mobility of the mother. The earliest placentals were small, shy, and probably nocturnal; they undoubtedly lived mostly on insects, grubs, and worms, devoting much of their energies to avoiding the carnivorous dinosaurs. Shrews, which closely resemble these primitive mammals, have retained their shy habits.

In the mammals, the skull bones are reduced in number and enlarged in size, as compared with those of the fish and reptiles, an example of the fact that "simpler" and "more primitive" may have quite opposite meanings. A bony platform or partition has developed that separates nasal and

301   *The Higher Animals: Arthropods and Chordates*

2–123 *Marsupial infants are born at an immature stage and continue their development attached to a nipple in a special protective pouch of the mother. This tiny kangaroo accidentally became dislodged from its mother's pouch. As you can see, it is still attached to the nipple. After the picture was taken, the baby was restored to the pouch, with no apparent ill effects from its premature introduction to the outside world. (Courtesy of the New York Zoological Society)*

food passages far back in the throat, making constant breathing possible. The jawbones have been reduced to one, which is far larger and more powerful than the reptilian jaw, although mammals have lost that useful ability of a reptile to unhinge its jaw—an ability which makes it possible for an anaconda, for example, to swallow an entire pig.

Mammals also have other distinctive features. In all mammals, the interior of the body is divided transversely by a muscular sheet, the *diaphragm*, so that the coelom is compartmented into the pleural (lung) cavity and the peritoneal cavity, which contains the digestive, excretory, and reproductive organs. All mammals have red blood cells that lack nuclei, as distinct from other vertebrates, in which the nuclei are retained. Finally, all mammals, including the mouse, the elephant, the giraffe, the whale, and yourself, have exactly seven vertebrae in the neck, a reminder of the evolutionary relationship.

SUMMARY

In this chapter, we described the two animal phyla which are the most complex and the most recently evolved, the arthropods and the chordates. The second portion of the chapter was concerned with a brief review of some of the evidence on which the present theories regarding the evolutionary relationships of the animals are based.

The arthropods constitute the largest of the animal phyla, in both species and numbers. Characteristically, arthropods are segmented animals with jointed exoskeletons and a variety of highly specialized appendages and sensory organs. The arthropods are also characterized by an open circulatory system and a "ladder" type of nervous system consisting of a series of ganglia, a pair per segment, interconnected by a double ventral nerve cord.

The predominant groups of arthropods are the crustaceans, the chelicerates, and the insects. Examples of each class were given: the lobster (crustacean), the spider (chelicerate), and the grasshopper (insect).

During development, most insects go through a series of stages culminating in an adult form which is very different from any of the immature forms (complete metamorphosis). The four stages in complete metamorphosis are egg, larva, pupa, adult. Development from larva to adult takes place by a series of molts during which the exoskeleton is shed and a new one is formed. The period between molts is known as an *instar*. Molting is controlled by hormone interaction; the hormone that initiates the molting process is produced by cells in the brain. This brain hormone stimulates a gland in the thorax to produce a second hormone, ecdysone, which actually triggers the molting process and the formation of the new exoskeleton. A pair of glands, the corpora allata, located at the base of the brain, are the

2–124 *Mule-deer fetus within the amniotic sack. Placentals develop to a much more advanced stage before birth than do other animals. (Donald H. Fritts)*

source of a chemical substance known as *juvenile hormone* because it inhibits the development of adult characteristics in the insect. Pheromones, chemicals secreted by one organism that affect other organisms, play an important part in the morphogenesis of social insects, affecting body size, structure, reproductive maturation, and also behavior patterns of the individuals.

The three primary characteristics of the chordates are the notochord, a cartilaginous rod which serves as the structural axis of the body (present only in embryonic life in the vertebrates); the nerve cord, which is a hollow tube located on the dorsal surface; and a pharynx with gill slits. Amphioxus clearly illustrates this basic chordate body plan. The vertebrates, the largest subphylum of the chordates, all have a vertebral column, a flexible bony support which develops around and supplants the notochord and encloses the nerve cord. The vertebrates include the fish, the amphibians, the reptiles, the birds, and mammals.

According to the most widely held present theories, the multicelled animals developed from colonial forms and one-celled organisms, possibly of the volvocine line. The planula larva is believed to be the transitional form between the Protozoa and the coelenterates and also between the coelenterates and the flatworms. One group of flatworms is believed to have given rise to a coelomate worm, of which no living representative is known. One line of development leads from this coelomate ancestor to the mollusks, the annelids, and the arthropods. These three major phyla are *protostomes,* animals in which the mouth appears first in the course of embryonic development. The mollusks and annelids are both characterized by the trochophore larva. The annelids and arthropods have a very similar, segmented body plan. The echinoderms and chordates are both *deuterostomes.* The ascidian, or tunicate, is believed to represent the type of chordate from which the vertebrates arose; evidence for this relationship is found in the fishlike ascidian larva. On the basis of fossil evidence as well as present-day resemblances, it is possible to trace a direct line of development from fish to amphibians to reptiles and from reptiles to the birds and to the mammals.

Chapter 2–8

How Animals Live

As we stated in the introduction to Chapter 2–6, all living organisms share a few common problems. In Chapters 2–6 and 2–7, we looked at some selected animals to see how different structures and functions offer different solutions to these common problems. We saw that, in general, the evolutionary trend has been toward greater complexity and that, with increasing complexity, animals have been able to exploit a continually wider range of environments.

In this chapter, instead of looking at selected animals, we are going to focus on the problems that animals face. In this way, we shall have an opportunity to review some of the material presented previously, looking at it from a slightly different viewpoint, and also to introduce new material, most of it dealing with the vertebrates.

In general, animals need oxygen and nutrients; they need to circulate these to all the cells in their bodies, and they need to excrete wastes, to maintain water balance, and to regulate their internal environment. Reproduction is essential if the species is to survive. Finally, they need to coordinate the many different functions involved with these activities and to integrate them with the environment.

Respiration and Breathing

As we saw in Chapter 1–8, oxygen plays a major part in the energy-producing reactions of cells, and carbon dioxide is a by-product of these reactions. Respiration is the exchange of these gases—the movement of oxygen into cells and the movement of carbon dioxide out.* In a protozoan, these gases move in and out of the organism by diffusion. Similarly, in the sponges and coelenterates, each cell is near enough to the outside medium to respire individually; the thick mesoglea that makes up most of the

* This exchange of gases is also sometimes termed *external respiration* to distinguish it from the intracellular respiratory cycle previously described.

bulk of the jellyfish is lifeless and therefore does not require oxygen. In animals that are more than a few cells thick, however, simple diffusion does not suffice and oxygen must be transported to the cells. This is usually a function of the circulating blood. In the annelid worm, for example, oxygen is picked up and carbon dioxide released by blood flowing in capillaries just one cell layer beneath the epidermis. As the blood travels through the interior of the worm, the oxygen diffuses out to the cells; the deoxygenated blood then recirculates to the surface of the animal, where it picks up more oxygen. By the principle of diffusion, oxygen will always move from a region of high oxygen to a region of less oxygen, and the rate of diffusion will be in proportion to this difference in oxygen concentration. Therefore, the less oxygen the blood contains, the more it will pick up and carry to the tissues. The amount of oxygen that can diffuse into the blood is also proportional to the surface area that is exposed. This priniciple is very simply illustrated by the behavior of the tubifex worm. If you have an aquarium at home, you may be familiar with these worms since they are frequently sold as fish food. If these worms are placed in an environment low in oxygen, they will stretch out as much as 10 times their normal length and thus increase the surface area through which oxygen diffusion can occur. The development of gills or lungs is another solution to this same problem of increasing the respiratory surface.

THE GILL

The gills of invertebrates are localized outgrowths of epithelial tissue. The respiratory surface is a one-cell-thick layer of epithelium exposed to the environment on one side and to an internal circulating medium on the other. The layers of gill tissue may be spread out flat, stacked in layers, or convoluted in various ways. The gill of a clam, for instance, has the configurations of a steam-heat radiator, which is also designed to provide a maximum surface-area-to-volume ratio. The vertebrate gill, although it is similar in function to the invertebrate gill, is different in evolutionary origin. Primitive chordates such as amphioxus respire largely through the skin, like the earthworm. The gill slits function primarily in filtering food from the water and play only a minor role in respiration. The water passes through these slits, where gases are exchanged with the water currents. In the fish, which have developed protective outer coverings, these pharyngeal slits have become specialized for respiratory functions by the development of thin, vascularized layers of tissue bordering them. In most fish, the water in which oxygen is dissolved simply pours in the mouth and out across the gills; its rate of entry is regulated by muscles that are related, in an evolutionary sense, to the muscles we use in smiling and frowning.

THE LUNG

Air is a far more efficient source of oxygen than water; about one-fifth of the air is made up of free oxygen, whereas at ordinary temperatures, even when water is saturated with oxygen, only about 1 part in 25 is free oxygen. Also, oxygen diffuses much more rapidly through air than through water and so is much more rapidly replenished as it is used up by the respiring organisms. However, breathing in air creates a special problem: The thin, delicate surfaces through which oxygen enters the body must be moist. The gill is useless as soon as it dries out; moreover it collapses out of water. The chief difference between a lung and a gill is that the lung is designed to maintain its form, with free movement of air, and to preserve this film of moisture.

The lungs of lungfish developed directly from the pharynx as simple damp "pockets" into which air could be gulped. In the other air-breathing vertebrates, the pharynx has become extended into the windpipe, or *trachea*. The trachea then branches into the bronchial tubes, which form increasingly fine and numerous passageways and chambers into which air can be drawn. These internal surfaces can be kept relatively moist, so that respiration, on land as in the water, occurs on a moist membrane.

Amphibians have relatively small lungs and breathe to a large extent through their skin. A frog sitting by the edge of a damp pond is getting about half of the oxygen it needs through its moist skin, and if the animal is submerged in cold water, the skin alone is enough to supply its entire oxygen requirement. The amphibian has openings, the *nares,* leading into its air tracts, so that it can breathe with its mouth closed. It fills its lungs by a swallowing motion; people whose respiratory muscles have been paralyzed can sometimes learn to fill their lungs by "frog breathing."

Reptiles breathe entirely by lungs, although these lungs are not much more highly developed than those of the amphibian. In the reptile lung, however, air is pulled in by movement of the body muscles. For instance, in lizards, contraction of the thoracic muscles expands the size of the chest cavity, and air is drawn in rather than pushed in or gulped, as in the frog and the lungfish.

The lungs of birds are extraordinarily efficient. They are small and are expanded and compressed by movements of the body wall. Also, each lung has several air sacs attached to it which empty and fill like balloons at each breath. The fresh, oxygenated air passes through the main ducts of the lungs into the air sacs and then, at expiration, flows through the smaller lung passages in which the gas exchange actually takes place. In this way, the lung is almost completely flushed with fresh air at every breath. In the human lung, by contrast, only about 10 percent of the air is usually exchanged at every breath, although as much as 80 percent can be exchanged by deliberate deep breathing. The air sacs of birds do not in

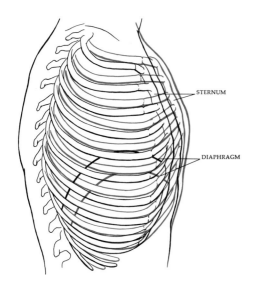

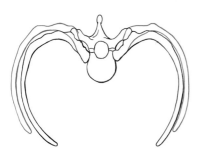

STERNUM

DIAPHRAGM

2–125 *The mechanics of human breathing. We inhale by contracting the muscles between the ribs to pull the rib cage up and out and by contracting the muscular diaphragm to pull it downward. These motions together increase the volume of the thoracic cavity (as shown in color), thereby reducing the pressure in the cavity and pulling air into the lungs. The lungs empty as the muscles relax. (The resting position is shown in black.)*

themselves serve any direct respiratory function, but they do play an important part in breathing and also lighten and cool the body.

Mammalian lungs are relatively complicated structures, with many fine ducts leading into vast numbers of tiny blind air sacs. Lung volume is controlled by the change in the size of the thoracic cavity, which is enlarged by contraction of the muscles between the ribs and of the muscular diaphragm (Figure 2–125). As the chest volume increases, the lungs fill passively, and they empty as the muscles relax. The rate of muscular contractions is controlled by nerves which, in turn, are regulated by a "respiratory center" at the base of the brain. This respiratory center is sensitive to changes in the chemical composition of the blood and is stimulated by an increase in the level of carbon dioxide in the blood. You can, of course, deliberately increase your breathing rate by contracting and relaxing the chest muscles, but breathing is normally under involuntary control. It is impossible to commit suicide by deliberately holding your breath; as soon as you became unconscious, the involuntary controls would take over once more.

In mammals, air is warmed and cleaned in the nasal passages and then passes to the lungs through the trachea. The trachea is strengthened, as it is in birds, by rings of cartilage that prevent it from collapsing during inspiration. The actual exchange of gases occurs in the air sacs, the *alveoli*. Each pair of human lungs has 300 million alveoli, providing a respiratory surface area of some 70 square meters, about 40 times the surface area of the entire human body.

RESPIRATORY PIGMENTS

The ability of the blood to carry oxygen is greatly increased by the presence in the blood of respiratory pigments, of which hemoglobin is the most common. In vertebrates, hemoglobin is packaged in red blood cells. Blood with a normal amount of hemoglobin in the red cells can carry 60 times more oxygen than plasma alone. Persons adapt to low pressures of oxygen, as at very high altitudes, by an increase in the manufacture of red blood cells, a process which, in adult higher vertebrates, takes place in the bone marrow. Some annelids, mollusks, and crustaceans carry hemoglobin in their plasma. Another respiratory pigment is hemocyanin, a copper compound which turns blue in combination with oxygen. Hemocyanin, which is always dissolved in plasma and never packaged in cells, is found in the squid, the octopus, some snails, and some crustaceans. Chlorocruorin, an iron-containing pigment with a rich green color, is found in the plasma of some annelids.

Digestion

Digestion is the means by which nutrients obtained from the environment are processed for use by the organism. In protozoans and sponges, all digestion takes place within the individual cells. In all other animals, as well, each cell carries out processes of intracellular digestion, breaking down larger molecules into smaller ones to obtain energy and to secure the building blocks, such as amino acids, from which to make other complex molecules. In higher animals—that is, animals "higher" than protozoans and sponges—digestion also takes place extracellularly, freeing larger organisms from a reliance on microscopic food particles.

In our survey of the invertebrates, we saw four major evolutionary advances in the process of digestion: (1) the development of extracellular digestion; (2) the evolution of the one-way digestive tract, which makes possible the separation of digested and undigested food; (3) the lengthening of the digestive tract, thereby increasing its absorptive capacities; and (4) the increasing specialization of various areas of the digestive tract. These last two evolutionary trends continue in the vertebrates.

In the vertebrates, digestion begins in the mouth. Most vertebrates have teeth especially adapted either for tearing or for grinding. Some, such as birds and turtles, rely on horny bills. The tongue, also a vertebrate development, serves largely to move and manipulate the food. In some animals, it has other special functions. The tongues of hagfish and lampreys have horny "teeth." Many frogs and toads are able to flip out their tongues (which are attached at the front end but not at the back) to catch insects with the sticky tip. In some reptiles, the tongue acts as an accessory olfactory organ. Mammalian tongues carry the taste buds, and in man, the tongue is used in formulating sounds for communication.

In mammals, enzymatic processes often start in the mouth. The salivary glands secrete amylases, enzymes that break starch down into sugar. In many human cultures, natives make alcoholic beverages from starchy vegetables, usually roots or tubers, by first chewing them long enough to break the starch down into sugar, spitting out the pulp into bowls, and leaving it for the airborne yeast cells to work upon.

The stomach of man and some other vertebrates secretes hydrochloric acid that loosens the tough, fibrous components of tissues and erodes the cementing substances between cells, making the food more susceptible to digestive enzymes. Various cells lining the stomach also produce mucus and digestive enzymes, primarily pepsin, which begin the breakdown of proteins.

The major stages in digestion, however, occur in the small intestine. The digestive enzymes hydrolyze the bonds that hold small units such as amino acids or fatty acids together in large molecules, such as proteins or fats. These smaller molecules are then absorbed into the cells of the intes-

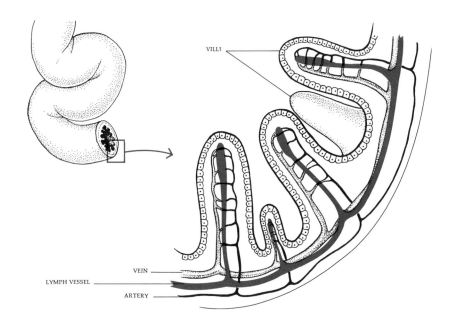

2–126 *A section of the human small intestine, where the major stages of digestion occur and the products of digestion are absorbed. The absorptive area of the small intestine is very large. The entire small intestine of an adult male is about 23 feet long and an inch in diameter. The absorptive area is further increased by numerous small fingerlike projections, called* villi, *which cover the entire internal surface of the intestine.*

VILLI

VEIN

LYMPH VESSEL

ARTERY

tinal tract. The absorptive area of the small intestine is often greatly increased by numerous *villi,* small fingerlike projections that cover its surface.

In the course of digestion, large amounts of water—some two or three quarts—enter the stomach and small intestine from the body fluids and are absorbed back into the tissues with the digested food. This is why such large amounts of water can be lost during severe attacks of vomiting or diarrhea, which interfere with the normal resorption process.

In normal digestion, the additional water from the tissues has been largely resorbed by the time the undigested remains of the food, the feces, have reached the lower intestinal tract. Here any remaining water is absorbed and the feces stored for excretion. The undigested food is eventually passed out through the anus. In the mammal, the anal opening is separate from the other body openings, but in many of the vertebrates, a single chamber, the *cloaca,* serves as the common exit for the urinary, digestive, and reproductive systems.

The pancreas and the liver are specialized digestive organs, developing —both in the embryo and in the course of evolutionary history—from the digestive tract. The pancreas is an important source of digestive enzymes, which are passed into the small intestine. Special cells of the pancreas also synthesize insulin and glucagon, hormones concerned with the regulation of glucose concentration in the blood.

The liver manufactures bile, which is stored in the gall bladder and then released into the intestine. Bile emulsifies fats, helping to break fat globules down into small droplets and so exposing them more thoroughly to the action of fat-hydrolyzing enzymes. The liver also serves as a storage place for sugar, picking up glucose from the bloodstream and converting it to glycogen for storage. The glycogen is released as glucose when the concentration of sugar in the blood is low. The liver has numerous other important functions, including synthesis of urea from nitrogenous wastes and breakdown and detoxification of substances in the bloodstream.

Circulation

In a one-celled organism, oxygen and nutrients are taken in from the surrounding medium and carbon dioxide and any other metabolic by-products pass out through the membrane. Oxygen and carbon dioxide travel by simple diffusion, but salts and other materials often must be pumped in and out of the cell by active transport.

In sponges and coelenterates, each cell is close enough to the outside world and to the cells concerned with nutritive functions so that no special system for circulation of materials is necessary, although in some of the large animals, amoebocytes may aid in the distribution of food.

The need for a special circulatory system is imposed by size and, particularly, by complexity. When areas of the organism have specialized functions, such as respiration and digestion, there must be a way to circulate materials to and from these production or exchange centers.

BLOOD-CIRCULATING SYSTEMS

The first efficient circulatory system is found in the annelid worms, which have a network of closed tubes through which fluid bearing oxygen and nutrients is transported. The fluid is pumped by the muscular contraction of one or more of these tubes serving as hearts. Mollusks have more efficient pumping systems; the blood is first collected in two chambers, the *atria*, which pump it into the ventricle, and from there, it is dispatched to the various tissues of the body.

The arthropods have open circulatory systems. The pumping organ lies in a blood-filled cavity, from which it collects fluid through small openings, or *ostia*. The blood travels through the tissues and seeps back into the cavity, refilling the heart. In the insects, the blood does not carry oxygen, which is brought to the tissues by other routes. Some of the more sedentary mollusks also have an open circulatory system, but this is believed to be a secondary development rather than a molluscan characteristic.

All vertebrates have closed circulatory systems. Blood is pumped from the heart out through the arteries, which have heavy muscular walls. The arteries branch into finer and finer pathways, the *arterioles*, and finally into the capillaries, the smallest of which may be less than 15 microns in diameter. There is a capillary within rapid diffusion distance of every cell in the body—the total length of the capillaries in man, for example, is more than 50,000 miles. Capillaries, not the main blood vessels, supply the tissue. In fact, even the cells in the walls of the veins and arteries depend on this capillary system for their blood supply, and the heart itself, as well as all the other organs of the body, is dependent for its blood supply on this microcirculatory system.

After the blood has passed through the capillaries, it returns to the heart by way of the veins. By this time, it has lost much of its pressure; venous return depends on a combination of factors: (1) Negative pressure in the thoracic cavity, produced by its bellowslike expansion, causes the principal vein returning the blood to the heart (the *vena cava*) to expand, drawing the blood upward toward the heart. (2) There are valves along the veins that prevent the blood from flowing backward. (3) Contraction of muscles lying next to the veins squeezes them, moving the blood toward the heart. Soldiers who faint while standing at parade attention do so because they hold their muscles so still that blood collects in their feet and legs, depriving the brain of oxygen.

THE HEART

The heart has changed in the evolution of the vertebrates. The heart of the fish and the juvenile amphibian is two-chambered. Blood is pumped from it through the microcirculatory system of the gills and then through the tissues. In this way, the tissues always receive freshly oxygenated blood, which is desirable, but circulation is inefficient since the blood loses some of the pressure gained from heart contraction in passing through the gill capillaries.

The frog has a three-chambered heart. Oxygenated blood from the lungs enters the left atrium, and the mixed blood is passed again through the body tissues. By this arrangement, the blood is delivered to the body tissues under full pressure since it no longer has to traverse the gill capillaries first. However, blood with oxygen passes again through the lung, while some blood that is deoxygenated passes again through the tissues.

In the reptiles, the beginnings of a separation of the ventricles to form two chambers (or a four-chambered heart) appear, but the separation of the two ventricles is not complete enough for oxygenated and deoxygenated blood to be completely separated.

Birds and mammals have full separation of both atria and both ventricles. Thus, they essentially have two hearts, one for pumping blood through the lungs and one for pumping freshly oxygenated blood through the body tissues. The blood is pumped through the lungs under relatively low pressure, compared with the force with which it is propelled through

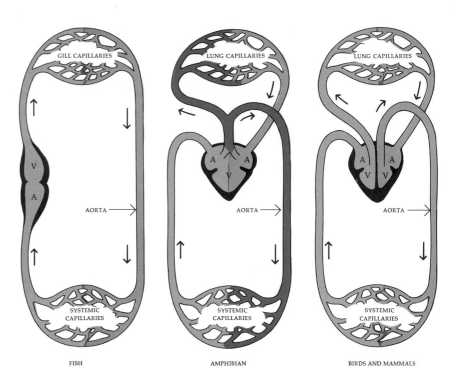

GILL CAPILLARIES   LUNG CAPILLARIES   LUNG CAPILLARIES

AORTA →   AORTA →   AORTA →

SYSTEMIC CAPILLARIES   SYSTEMIC CAPILLARIES   SYSTEMIC CAPILLARIES

FISH   AMPHIBIAN   BIRDS AND MAMMALS

2–127 *Vertebrate circulatory systems. In the fish, the heart has only one atrium (A) and one ventricle (V). Blood aerated in the gill capillaries goes straight to the systemic capillaries without first returning to the heart. In amphibians, the single primitive atrium has been divided into two separate chambers. Oxygenated blood (indicated by color) from the lungs enters the left atrium, where it is mixed with the oxygen-poor blood (gray) in the heart; the mixed blood is then passed through the body tissues. By this arrangement, some oxygenated blood passes again through the lungs, while some deoxygenated blood passes again through the tissues. This problem of mixing oxygenated and deoxygenated blood is solved in the birds and mammals by a division of the ventricle into two separate chambers, so that there are in effect two hearts, one for pumping oxygen-poor blood through the lungs and one for pumping oxygen-rich blood through the body tissues.*

the tissues. When the blood is pumped into the lungs under higher pressure, as occurs in certain diseases, fluid escapes from the capillaries and collects in the lung. This efficient solution of the circulatory problem is closely correlated with the high metabolic rate of both birds and mammals, with their constant body temperature, and with their generally high level of physical and mental activity.

Figure 2–128 shows a diagram of the human heart. The atria are the receiving chambers. Blood returning from the body tissues enters the right atrium, while blood returning from the lungs enters the left atrium; the atria, which are thin-walled compared with the ventricles, expand to receive the blood. The left and right atria contract simultaneously, assisting the flow of blood through the open valves into the ventricles. Then the ventricles contract simultaneously, closing the valves; the right ventricle propels the blood into the lungs, and the left ventricle propels it into the aorta, from which it travels to the other body tissues.

The vertebrate heart will continue to contract even after it is removed from the body if it is kept in a solution in which the tissues can continue to live; in fact, embryonic heart cells isolated in tissue culture will beat. In other words, the heartbeat originates in the heart itself. The beat of the cardiac muscle is synchronized by a special area of the heart known as the *pacemaker*, which is located in the right atrium. The pacemaker is com-

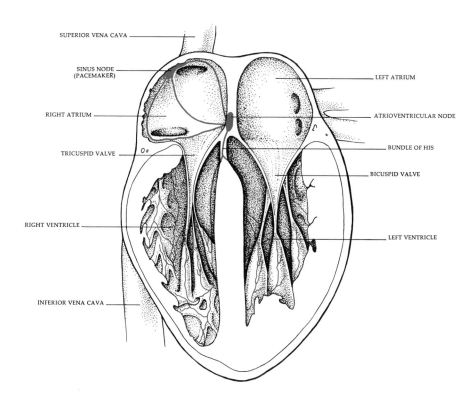

2–128 *The human heart.*

SUPERIOR VENA CAVA

SINUS NODE
(PACEMAKER)

RIGHT ATRIUM

TRICUSPID VALVE

RIGHT VENTRICLE

INFERIOR VENA CAVA

LEFT ATRIUM

ATRIOVENTRICULAR NODE

BUNDLE OF HIS

BICUSPID VALVE

LEFT VENTRICLE

2–129 *An electrocardiogram showing six normal heartbeats. Each beat is denoted by a series of waves that record the electrical activity of the heart during contraction. Analysis of the rate and character of these waves can reveal abnormalities in heart function.*

posed of *nodal tissue*. Nodal tissue is unique in that it can contract like a muscle and also transmit impulses like a nerve. From the pacemaker, the wave of contraction spreads to the left atrium. Impulses from both atria stimulate, in turn, a second area of nodal tissue, the atrioventricular node. From there, stimulation passes to the bundle of His (named after its discoverer), which sets up a contraction of the ventricles.

In some invertebrate hearts, the heartbeat is originated by an outside nerve impulse rather than within the heart itself. Although the nervous system does not initiate the human heartbeat, it does control the rate of

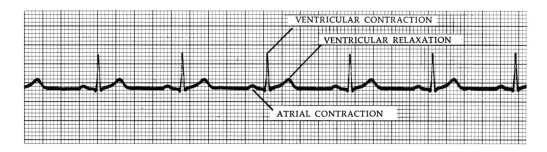

VENTRICULAR CONTRACTION

VENTRICULAR RELAXATION

ATRIAL CONTRACTION

the heartbeat; as you know from your own experience, the heartbeat quickens when you are frightened or excited.

COMPOSITION OF THE BLOOD

In vertebrates, the blood consists of a suspension of red and white blood cells in an almost colorless fluid, the *plasma*. The plasma, which is more than 90 percent water, contains thousands of different types of compounds in solution or, in the case of some of the larger proteins, in colloidal suspension. The chemicals carried by the bloodstream include fibrinogen, the protein from which clots are formed; nutrients, such as glucose, fats, and amino acids; various ions; antibodies, hormones, and enzymes; and waste materials such as urea and uric acid.

LYMPHATIC SYSTEM

In addition to blood, animals have other body fluids which bathe the tissues and occupy and fill the body cavities. These fluids seep out into the tissues from the blood vessels and, in the vertebrates, are collected and returned to the blood by the lymphatic system. In the lymphatic system, the lymph makes its way back into the blood system through progressively larger lymphatic ducts that empty into the veins. Frogs and many other vertebrates have lymph "hearts" which help to keep the fluid in circulation. Mammals rely chiefly on their muscular movements. Mammals also have lymph nodes, which drain the lymph system. These serve as collecting areas for cellular debris, bacteria, and other infectious organisms picked up by the circulating lymph. In addition, the lymph nodes are the primary site for production of the special white blood cells, *lymphocytes*, that produce antibodies.

Excretion, Chemical Regulation, and Water Balance

One of the primary trends in evolution is toward increasing freedom from the effects of changes in the environment. More than any of the other organ systems, the excretory system is the mechanism by which an organism achieves this freedom because it is in large part by the excretory system that an animal creates its own chemical environment.

Regulation of the chemical environment involves three distinct excretory processes. One is the elimination of toxic or excess by-products of metabolism. The two chief by-products are carbon dioxide and the nitrogen compounds, like ammonia, produced by the breakdown of amino acids. Carbon dioxide is eliminated as a gas or is dissolved in water. In simple aquatic organisms, ammonia also diffuses out dissolved in water, but in larger, more complex organisms, it often must be converted to some other form since accumulated ammonia is highly toxic. In most vertebrates, including man, ammonia is converted in the liver into a less toxic, soluble compound, *urea*.* Birds and insects conserve water by eliminating waste nitrogen in the form of uric acid, which can be excreted as crystals. In birds, the uric acid is mixed with the undigested wastes in the cloaca and the combination is dropped as a semisolid paste, familiar to frequenters of public parks and admirers of outdoor statuary. This nitrogen-laden substance forms a rich natural fertilizer; guano, the excreta of sea birds, collects in such quantities on the small islands where these birds gather in great numbers that it is profitable to harvest it commercially.

Chemical regulation also involves maintaining very closely controlled concentrations in the blood and other body fluids of ions such as H^+, Na^+, K^+, Mg^{++}, Ca^{++}, and the important anions (negatively charged ions) Cl^- and HCO_3^-. Such precise regulation demands that the body fluids be analyzed and processed constantly.

A third and closely related problem is that of water content. The concentration of a particular substance depends not only on the absolute amount of the substance but on the amount of water in which it is dissolved. Thus, although the fundamental problem is the same—the chemical regulation of the internal environment—the solution to the problem is strongly influenced by the habitat of the animal, that is, by the availability of water.

The earliest organisms probably had a salt and mineral composition much like that of the environment in which they lived. The early organism and its surroundings were probably also *isosmotic*; that is, each had the same total effective concentration of dissolved substances, so water did not tend to move either in or out of the cell. When organisms moved to fresh water (a *hypoosmotic* environment), they had to develop systems for "bailing themselves out," since fresh water tended to move into their bodies by osmosis; the contractile vacuole of *Paramecium* is an example of such a bailing device. Probably some waste materials are also pumped out by the vacuole, but many biologists think that this is a decidedly secondary function. With the transition to land, the problem became one of conserving water. These questions will be considered in more detail in the discussion that follows.

Regulation of the internal environment is known as *homeostasis*, a word which means "steady state." In physiological terms, homeostasis is a steady state that is always changing—a shift here, a compensation there—but always remains within the limits of what the individual tissues can tolerate. Less specialized animals operate over a much wider range of

*Urea played a crucial role in the history of biology. In 1828, the German chemist Friedrich Wöhler reported that he had been able to synthesize the compound in his laboratory. He thereby dealt a blow to the proponents of vitalism, who claimed that the chemistry of living things could not be duplicated in the laboratory or, indeed, even be fathomed by the mind of man.

internal environmental conditions than do the complex ones, and the evolutionary trend has been toward more and more precise regulatory mechanisms.

In the planarian, as we saw, the excretory system is a diffuse network of tubules that collect fluids directly from the body tissues and propel them out of the body, carrying wastes along with them. In the earthworm, the excretory system operates as a regulatory system as well as to maintain water balance. Each segment of the earthworm contains two paired tubules, the *nephridia*. At the end of each nephridium is a nephrostome ("kidney mouth"). The nephrostome is ciliated, and the cilia propel the fluid from the coelom into the tubule. The tubules are long and convoluted and are surrounded by tiny blood vessels. As the fluids pass along the tubules, materials are exchanged between the tubules and blood vessels. The tubule empties into a storage bladder, from which the fluid is passed to the outside.

The excretory systems of all higher animals work in this same way. The anatomical unit is always a tubule; the tubules may occur in pairs, as in the annelids, or be collected into organs, such as the kidney. All such tubules collect fluids and process them by a combination of secretion and absorption—that is, by passing materials into the tubule through the cells lining the wall and by absorbing fluids from the tubule along its length.

In the flatworm, all materials are collected by the tubules directly from the body fluids; in the earthworm, materials are collected partly from the coelomic fluid and partly from the circulation. In higher vertebrates, the tubules are closely interconnected with the circulatory system and all collection is from the blood. As a result, a diffuse excretory system, such as that seen in the flatworms and annelids, is not necessary. In fact, because of the highly efficient circulatory system of vertebrates, all the excretory tubules can be brought together in a relatively small area; in man, they are all contained in the kidneys, two organs no larger than your fists.

The Nephron

The excretory unit of the vertebrate is known as the *nephron*, which consists of a closed bulb called a *Bowman's capsule* and a long tubule. Each kidney in man contains about a million nephrons. The function of the nephron is intimately connected with the circulation of the blood. The kidney receives a rich blood flow from the renal artery. Associated with each Bowman's capsule is a tight, twisted cluster of capillaries known as the *glomerulus*. Blood pressure in the capillaries of the glomeruli forces fluid out into the capsule; blood cells and blood proteins, both of which are too large to pass through the capillary walls, are left behind. The fluid then begins its long passage through the tubule, which is lined with a layer of epithelial cells especially adapted for active transport. The tubules of the nephrons empty into collecting tubules, which lead to a common duct, the ureter. The ureter transmits the urine to the bladder for storage before excretion through the urethra. Some 180 liters (about 48 gallons) of blood a day are filtered by the human kidneys; many times a day, all the fluids of the body pass through the kidneys, where they are filtered, analyzed, and so carefully adjusted that they can be considered to be completely made over.

Most substances and almost all the water contained in the filtrate that enters the tubule are returned to the blood through the blood capillary system that surrounds the long, convoluted tubule. Some of these substances, and some others from the blood, may be taken back into the tubule from the capillary bed surrounding it. For example, glucose, most amino acids, and most vitamins are returned to the bloodstream by a healthy kidney. By-products of amino acid breakdown, such as urea, are excreted. Sodium and other ions may be excreted or may be retained, depending on the physiological status of the body.

REGULATION OF WATER CONTENT

If fish evolved in fresh water, as is generally believed, the first function of the nephron, phylogenetically speaking, was to pump out water and to retain salt. In freshwater fish, the kidney works primarily as a filter and absorber and the urine is hypoosmotic—that is, it has a lower concentration of solutes than the body fluids. In the nephrons of freshwater fish, a loop of Henle (see page 320) is missing, and these animals cannot concentrate their urine. The urine is made hypoosmotic by the reabsorption of salt without water in the distal tubule.

Saltwater fish have a different problem. Their body fluids are less concentrated than their environment, and so they tend to lose water by osmosis. Their need is to conserve water and thereby keep their body fluids from becoming too salty. Different groups of fish adapted in different ways. In the hagfish, for example, the body fluids are isosmotic with the salt waters of the surrounding ocean. Cartilaginous fish, such as the shark, solved the problem in a unique way. They developed an unusual tolerance for urea, so instead of constantly pumping it out, as do all other fish, they retain a high concentration of it in the blood. This high concentration of urea makes their body fluids isosmotic in relation to the seawater. Hence they do not tend to lose water by osmosis. Cartilaginous fish produce urine which has about the same salt concentration as their body fluids—which is, of course, much lower than that of seawater.

The bony fish spread to the sea at a much later period than the cartilaginous ones, and their body fluids are hypoosmotic in relation to the en-

Animals that inhabit environmental niches in which fresh water is scarce show some unusual adaptations. The camel solves the problem by tolerance and compromise. In the first place, the camel has a wide range of body temperatures. It can let its temperature drop at night to several degrees below that which can be tolerated by man, and it can let its temperature rise in the daytime to some 41°C before it starts sweating, whereas man starts sweating as soon as his temperature begins to rise above 37°C. Therefore, the camel loses much less water from its body surface. Also, it can lose more than 40 percent of its body water without danger, whereas most mammals can tolerate, over a short period of time, only about a 20 percent loss.

Another desert organism, the kangaroo rat, has a different solution. The kangaroo rat may spend its entire life without a sip of water. It lives on seeds and other dry plant materials, and in the laboratory, it can be kept for months on a diet of only barley or rolled oats. Analysis shows that the rat manages because it is highly conservative in its water expenditures. It has no sweat glands, and being nocturnal, it searches for food only when the external temperature is relatively cool. Its feces have a very small water content, and its urine is highly concentrated, far more so than that of other mammals so far studied. Its major water loss is through respiration. By all these economies, it manages to keep its water loss in balance with water gained through oxidation of food. For this reason, the type of food the kangaroo rat eats is extremely important. When 1 gram of glucose is oxidized, 0.6 gram of water is formed. When 1 gram of protein is oxidized, only about 0.3 gram of water is produced. Oxidation of a gram of fat, however, produces 1.1 grams of water because of the high hydrogen concentration in fat. The kangaroo rat, you will not be surprised to hear, prefers a diet of fatty seeds. If it is fed high-protein seeds, such as soybeans—which produce a large amount of nitrogen waste and a relatively small amount of water—it will die of thirst.

Marine mammals solved the problem by developing special mechanisms for the excretion of salt. Whales and seals get their water by eating fish, most of which have a high water content and an osmotic concentration only about one-third that of seawater. A man on a life raft cannot survive by eating fresh fish, however, rumor to the contrary notwithstanding. Man cannot form urine with a salt concentration higher than about 2.2 percent. Although a fish's fluids are less concentrated than this, a fish contains a large amount of protein; so our hypothetical shipwreck survivor is placed in the same position as the kangaroo rat eating soybeans. He would, of course, be much worse off if he drank seawater, since the salt concentration of seawater is about 3.5 percent and he would have to expend some of his precious body water to dispose of the excess salt. (A kangaroo rat, however, which excretes a highly concentrated urine, can maintain water balance by drinking seawater.)

Marine birds, such as sea gulls, have special glands in the head which can secrete salt at a concentration of about twice that of seawater. This gland is not in any way a "second kidney"; it secretes only sodium chloride. Turtles have a similar salt gland, which is located near their eyes. Since ancient times, turtle watchers have reported that these great armored reptiles come ashore to lay their eggs with tears in their eyes, but it is only recently that biologists have come to know that this is caused by neither an excess of pain nor an excess of sentiment but is merely a useful solution to the common problem of excess salt.

vironment, having an osmotic pressure only about one-third that of sea water. Thus, like terrestrial animals, they have the problem of drying out. In physiological terms, *drying out* means losing so much water that the solutes in the body fluids become too concentrated and the cells die. In bony fish, this problem has been solved by the evolution of special gland cells in the gills that excrete excess salt. Hence these fish can take in salt water freely and still remain hypoosmotic.

Since terrestrial animals do not always have automatic access to either fresh or salt water, they must regulate water content in other ways, balancing off gains and expenditures.

Animals gain water by drinking fluids, by eating water-containing foods, and as an end product of the glycolytic cycle, as we saw in Chapter 1–8. Some insects can also absorb it through thin areas of their exoskeletons under conditions of high humidity, but this is a rare capacity. All animals lose water by respiration in dry air; this loss can be minimal, as in the case of insects, or quite sizable, as you know from the droplets of moisture you can see condensed in your exhaled breath on a cold day. Animals also excrete water in the feces, and in animals that perspire, considerable water may also be lost in this form; a man can sweat a gallon an hour. Also, all animals need to use a certain amount of water to excrete their soluble wastes.

As a water-conservation measure, birds and mammals have developed the ability to excrete a hyperosmotic urine, one that is more concentrated than their body fluids. This ability is associated with a hairpin-shaped section of the nephron known as the *loop of Henle* (Figure 2–130). By sampling the fluids in and around the nephron and analyzing the amount of sodium present in each sample, physiologists have been able to figure

319   *How Animals Live*

2–130 *The formation of hyperosmotic urine in the human nephron. As you can see, the nephron consists of a closed bulb, called a* Bowman's capsule, *enclosing a tuft of capillaries, the* glomerulus, *and a long coiled tube. Body fluids filter first through the capillary wall into the Bowman's capsule, then through the proximal convoluted tubule, the long loop of Henle, the distal convoluted tubule, and finally into the collecting tubule. As the urine passes up the ascending branch of the loop of Henle, the cells lining the tubule pump out sodium into the surrounding fluid. The sodium ions diffuse passively into the descending branch and are recirculated to the ascending branch where they are pumped out again. As a consequence of this recirculation of sodium, the loop of Henle and the lower section of the collecting tubule are constantly bathed in a salty fluid. The cells of the ascending loop are apparently impermeable to water, since it does not diffuse out when the sodium is pumped out, but in the lower segment of the collecting tubule the membrane becomes permeable again, the water pours out into the surrounding salty fluid, and a hyperosmotic urine is passed down the tubule to the bladder.*

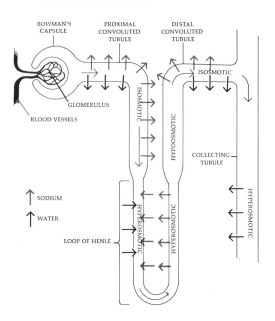

out how this deceptively simple-looking structure makes this function possible.

As shown in the diagram, the fluid entering the renal capsule first enters the proximal tubule, descends the loop of Henle, ascends it, and then passes through the distal tubule into the collecting tubule. (Figure 2–130 is a diagram of the nephron, not a picture; in actuality, the proximal and distal tubules are both highly convoluted and the entire nephron is, of course, surrounded by a network of capillaries.)

The fluid entering the proximal tubule is isosmotic with the blood; that is, it has the same salt concentration. As the urine descends the loop of Henle, it becomes increasingly concentrated. In the ascending branch, it becomes less and less concentrated, and as it enters the distal tubule, it is hypoosmotic. By the end of the distal tubule, it is once more isosmotic, but as the fluid descends to the collecting tubule, it may even be hypoosmotic in relation to the blood. In animals needing to conserve water, the fluid descending the collecting tubule becomes increasingly concentrated, and the urine that is excreted is distinctly hyperosmotic in relation to the circulating blood.

This is how these findings are explained: Water diffuses freely through the cells lining the walls of the nephron, while sodium is actively pumped from the tubules back to the fluid surrounding them. The sodium pumped out of the ascending loop passes back into the descending loop by simple diffusion since the fluids surrounding the descending loop are more concentrated than those within it. Thus the salt recirculates to the ascending loop, where it is pumped out again. This recirculation of the sodium has two consequences: (1) As the urine passes the loop of Henle, much salt but little water is removed; and (2) the lower part of the loop of Henle and also the lower part of the collecting tubule are surrounded constantly by a salt bath. Consequently, as the urine—which has become isosmotic by the time it leaves the distal tubule—descends the collecting tubule, water pours out of the collecting tubule by osmosis, leaving within the tubule a urine that is isosmotic with the surrounding briny fluid but hyperosmotic in relation to the body fluids as a whole. As you can see, this is another circumstance in which structure, the actual physical shape of an organ, is indispensable to function.

When a person drinks a large amount of water, however, the excreted urine is hypoosmotic. How is this possible? Recently, it has been discovered that the permeability of the collecting ducts to water is not constant. Under the control of a pituitary hormone, the antidiuretic hormone, the ducts can become very permeable to water, in which case a hyperosmotic urine is formed. Or they can be very impermeable, and then hypoosmotic urine is formed. The concentration of the urine varies under precise control to meet the needs of the body to conserve or to excrete water.

Reproduction

Reproduction may take place either asexually or sexually. There are many forms of asexual reproduction, which superficially appear to be different. One-celled organisms divide by fission. Sponges form gemmules. Hydras bud, with the mature buds breaking loose and swimming away from the parent animal. Flatworms drop their tails. All these types of asexual reproduction are basically similar, however, since each is the result of mitotic division and the progeny is consequently a replica of the parent.

Sexual reproduction, although this, too, may take place in a variety of ways, always involves the fusion of genetic material derived from two parent organisms and meiotic division, and it results necessarily in the production of offspring different from either parent. Sexual reproduction fosters the slight variations on which natural selection acts, the "raw material" of evolution.

THE GAMETES

In one-celled organisms, such as *Chlamydomonas* and *Paramecium*, there may be several types of gametes, or mating strains. In the many-celled animals, there are two: male and female. Typically, the female gamete, which contains the food supply for the zygote, is the larger of the two and is immotile, while the male gamete, or sperm, is small and motile, contributing little more than its genetic material to the zygote.

Gametes of higher animals are produced by meiotic divisions. In the case of the male gamete, the diploid *spermatocyte* divides twice to produce four haploid cells, which then differentiate into the spermatozoa.

In the *oocyte,* the diploid cell from which the egg is formed, differentiation and meiosis proceed simultaneously, with the egg cell increasing greatly in size as it matures. At meiosis, the oocyte does not divide to form four ova. Instead, a single ovum and several *polar bodies* are formed. When the oocyte is ready to undergo meiosis, the nuclear membrane breaks up and the chromosomes move to the surface of the egg cell. As the nucleus divides, the cytoplasm of the oocyte bulges out. Half of the chromosomal material moves into the bulge, which then pinches off into a small cell, the first polar body. The second meiotic division is carried out in the same way, producing one haploid cell and another polar body. In this way, the accumulated food reserves of the egg are preserved. The first polar body may also divide, although there is no functional reason for it to do so. All the polar bodies eventually die, presumably as a result of their impoverished cytoplasmic contents.

The egg cell may increase greatly in size during maturation. For example, the oocyte of the frog *Rana pipiens* is only 50 microns in diameter, while the diameter of the fully developed egg is 1,500 microns, an increase in volume of 27,000 times!

In many of the lower invertebrates, eggs and sperm are produced by the same individual. A few such hermaphrodites, such as the parasitic worms, are self-fertilizing. Most hermaphrodites, however, like the earthworm and the snail, practice cross-fertilization. Sexual reproduction among the vertebrates always involves cross-fertilization.

THE GONADS

In the simplest of the animals, such as the sponge, gametes develop directly from generalized, undifferentiated cells, but in the flatworms and all other animals higher on the evolutionary scale, the gametes are formed in special organs, the *gonads*. The eggs, or ova, are formed in the ovaries, and the sperm in the testes. In the vertebrates, the sperm-producing areas of the testes are long tubules, the *seminiferous tubules*. The sperm duct leads from the testes through sacs in which the sperm are stored and then through the prostate gland, which adds fluid to the suspension of sperm cells. Sperm and fluid together form the seminal fluid, which in mammals is released through the urethra. The ovary is typically an oval mass of cells. In its outer layer are the large germ cells, which are surrounded by vascular tissue, connective tissue, and follicle cells. The follicle cells supply sustenance to the developing egg. In the female vertebrate, as in many other coelomates, the eggs are released into the coelom and then drift into the oviducts (called the Fallopian tubes in the human female) as a result of the beating of cilia around the funnel-shaped opening.

MATING

The most primitive form of sexual reproduction, phylogenetically speaking, is external fertilization, in which gametes are released from the parent animals and the egg cell is fertilized externally. This is feasible only in aquatic animals since the sperm cells must have fluid in which to swim and the egg cells must be protected against desiccation. This method results in great wastage of gametes and therefore requires a tremendous excess of sperm and eggs.

In fully terrestrial animals, the zygote develops either internally or within a waterproof shell. Consequently, internal fertilization of the female is necessary. In some animals, this is facilitated by a penis, an organ that is especially adapted for the introduction of sperm. A penis is not essential, however; birds and reptiles mate by juxtaposition of their cloacae. Depending on the kind of animal, the sperm may be deposited in the *vagina*, which is connected to the oviduct, or in a special receptacle, the *spermatheca*, in which they can be stored until needed, as in the earthworm. The queen bee, for example, receives all the sperm she will require for a lifetime—as long as seven or eight years—in one nuptial flight and releases them gradually from the spermatheca into the oviduct, where they fertilize the eggs as they are laid.

In the bedbug, some flatworms, and a few other organisms, the male reproductive duct ends in a sharp spine, which is driven into the female, injecting the sperm directly into her body cavity.

In a variety of organisms, the sperm are not injected directly into the female from the male reproductive tract but are enclosed in a special packet, the spermatophore. In the salamander, the males of some species deposit spermatophores on leaves and sticks in freshwater pools for the females to find. In this case, the parents do not even meet. In other salamander species, the male, after a brief courtship, deposits the spermatophore on the ground and the female, moving over it, takes it into her cloaca. The male pseudoscorpion maneuvers the female over the spermatophore in the climax of the courtship dance.

In some animals, such as the leech, the spermatophore is cemented onto the skin of the female, where, forming an ulcer, it eats its way into the coelomic cavity. Attempts at artificial fertilization of the eggs of these animals have failed. Apparently, the passage through the body of the female somehow prepares the spermatozoa for fertilization.

REPRODUCTIVE SYNCHRONIZATION

In most animals, breeding is only seasonal and the production and release of the male and female gametes must be synchronized for fertilization to take place. Often the sexes are brought into reproductive synchrony by some outside, environmental trigger. Many environmental cues may serve to trigger reproduction: changes in day lengths, seasonal rainfall, temperature changes, and even moon cycles! In some organisms, the same trigger must initiate a series of behavioral responses that bring the organisms together in space as well as in time. Examples are the annual migrations

2–131 *Scorpions performing a mating dance.* (*Dr. Ross E. Hutchins*)

|——— 4cm ———|

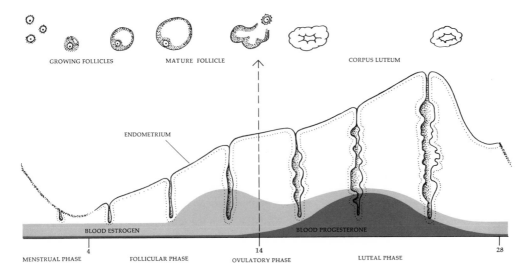

GROWING FOLLICLES   MATURE FOLLICLE   CORPUS LUTEUM

ENDOMETRIUM

BLOOD ESTROGEN   BLOOD PROGESTERONE

4   14   28

MENSTRUAL PHASE   FOLLICULAR PHASE   OVULATORY PHASE   LUTEAL PHASE

2–132 *Diagram of the menstrual cycle. The cycle begins with the follicular phase, immediately following menstruation, which occurred at the end of the preceding cycle. During the follicular phase an increase in the follicle-stimulating hormone (FSH) promotes the growth of the follicles, which, in turn, begin to secrete estrogen. The estrogen stimulates the lining of the uterus to thicken. At the end of the follicular phase, one follicle has gained ascendancy; the other follicles then stop growing. The ascendant follicle now ovulates under the influence of luteinizing hormone (LH). In the luteal phase, still under the influence of luteinizing hormone, the old follicle is converted into a yellowish mass of cells known as the* corpus luteum, *which begins to secrete progesterone. This hormone functions to prepare the uterus for the embryo. If no fertilization occurs during a normal cycle, the corpus luteum stops secreting progesterone, the thickened lining (endometrium) of the uterus begins to slough off, and the cycle begins again.*

of birds, turtles, eels, and salmon and many other fish, and the coming together of sea birds, seals, penguins, and other usually solitary animals to a common breeding ground. Males often call to the females, as in the chorusing of frogs, the singing of crickets and locusts, and the flashing of fireflies. These behavioral aspects of fertilization will be examined in more detail in Chapter 5–5.

The final stages in synchronization are usually dependent on some form of courtship behavior. Usually the male takes the initiative in courtship, and the female, playing the passive role, reserves the right of choice. Some biologists believe that this is adaptive; far more spermatozoa are produced than eggs and the selection process by the female tends to increase the probability of fitness in the next generation. Sometimes the signals exchanged between the species are of only a few seconds' duration. The oyster, for example, releases a chemical into the water that stimulates the release of egg cells by another oyster. The release of the egg cells stimulates, in turn, the release of the spermatozoa. In birds, by contrast, elaborate courtship ceremonies may last for days or weeks.

Ovulation in most mammals is controlled by internal mechanisms and occurs at specific intervals, about every 28 days in the human female, for example. Except for humans, the periods of receptivity in the female coincide with periods during which the egg is mature. These periods are known as heat, or *estrus.** Cats, for instance, come into heat every two or three months, dogs twice a year, and rats every third or fourth day.

*Menstruation in the human female is not the same as estrus, although estrus does produce slight bleeding in some mammals. Menstruation occurs not during ovulation (which is the period of estrus) but at the end of the ovulatory cycle and is the result of the shedding of some of the material lining the uterus that was being prepared to receive the zygote.

324 ORGANISMS

The periods of estrus may last from only a few hours to three or four weeks. In animals, such as dogs, that produce eggs continually during this period of estrus, the eggs may be fertilized at different times and by different males, which explains in part why a mixed-breed litter can contain such an astonishing variety of siblings and also why there may be a great size variation even among purebred pups, many of which are actually different ages at birth. In some mammals, such as cats, rabbits, and minks, although the egg is mature and the female receptive during estrus, ovulation does not occur without copulation, thereby assuring maximum efficiency in the utilization of the gametes.

PRENATAL CARE

The eggs of some animals are laid immediately after fertilization, while others are retained for various lengths of time. In birds and reptiles, fertilization takes place high in the oviduct (as it does in man), and the yolk, albumen, and shell are added as the egg travels down the long tube. (See Figure 2–133.)

Some reptiles retain the eggs inside their bodies until they hatch. Birds, however, which tend to jettison all unnecessary weight as a part of their special adaptations to flight, always lay their eggs promptly.

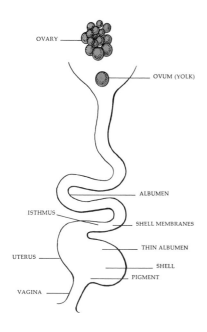

2–133 *Diagram of the reproductive organs of the female bird (top) and an egg in cross section (bottom). The ovum progresses from the ovary through the oviduct, a long winding tube in which it acquires layers of albumen, shell membrane, shell, and pigment. The total time the egg takes to pass through the oviduct varies according to the species; it is about 24 hours in the domestic hen and about 41 hours in the pigeon.*

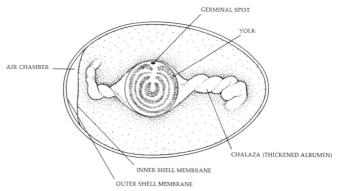

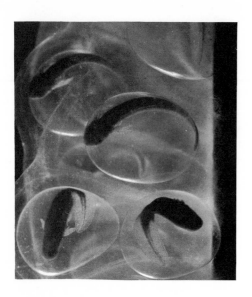

2–134 *Larvae of the tiger salamander, each contained in a capsule of jelly. (L. West)*

2–135 *A baby being born. At birth, the calves are half the length of the mother. Because porpoises breathe air, the young would drown if they were not born tail first, as shown here. (Courtesy of the Miami Seaquarium)*

Internal fertilization is practiced by some species of fish, and some fish (guppies, for instance) retain the eggs in their bodies until they hatch, thereby protecting the young. Sometimes, the roles of the parents are reversed. The female sea horse, for example, deposits the eggs within the pouch of the male, at his invitation, and they are fertilized there and develop there until the live young are released.

In all animals except mammals, the egg receives no nourishment directly from the mother after it is fertilized. In the placental mammals, the egg attaches itself to the wall of the uterus, where it develops as a parasite within the mother until it is released at the moment of birth.

REGULATORY SYSTEMS

In the following pages, we shall describe the structures and functions of the endocrine and nervous systems. We shall close with an account of biological clocks, a type of regulatory system about which we know comparatively little but in which there is much current interest.

Endocrine System: The Hormones

In 1849, A. A. Berthold, a physician and professor in Gottingen, carried out the first scientific experiment in endocrinology. Using six young cockerels, he set up three experimental groups: (1) Two birds were castrated; these became "typical capons" in which the combs, wattles, plumage, aggressiveness, crow, and sexual urge characteristic of the mature cock failed to develop. (2) Two additional birds were castrated, and the removed testis was reimplanted in the same animal but at a new site, distant from ducts, nerves, or any possible previous connections except with the circulatory system. These birds developed into normal cocks. (3) Two birds were subjected to "sham" surgery and served as controls to demonstrate that the results obtained in the first four animals were really related to removal and reimplantation of the testis and not to surgical procedures alone.

With this experiment, there began a wholly new concept of controlling mechanisms: that substances produced by particular tissues of the body could be carried by the bloodstream and could exert specific effects on distant tissues. Such substances came to be known as *hormones*, from the Greek word meaning "excite," although it is known that many of the hormones—the juvenile hormone of insects, for example—act as inhibitors rather than exciters. The hormones are better described as *chemical messengers*, establishing communications between the various parts of the body. Some of the communications are concerned with homeostatic regulation, the perpetual adjustment of the internal environment. Others are involved with change—the changes with sexual maturation or in response to

TEMPERATURE REGULATION

Aquatic animals, except mammals, have about the same temperature as their environment. This is generally low, in mammalian terms, and it is remarkably constant. A widely fluctuating temperature would probably be disadvantageous because, as we know, enzymes and other complex molecules are very temperature-sensitive, with different configurations being stable only at particular temperatures. Furthermore, the rate of biochemical reactions is also temperature-dependent.

On land, temperature swings in the external environment are much wider and many terrestrial animals regulate temperature by a combination of physiological and behavioral activities. Studies of insects and reptiles, which do not have internal heat-regulating mechanisms, have shown that they orient themselves very carefully in relation to the sun to achieve the maximum benefits of its warming effects, seeking shade when a certain maximum temperature is reached. By alternately seeking sun and shade and varying their activities, lizards are able to keep their body temperature from rising or falling more than a few degrees some 75 or 80 percent of the time. They can also control their temperature to some extent by the contraction or expansion of pigment-containing cells. When a reptile is kept in the cold, however, it becomes more and more torpid and sluggish since the biochemical processes on which its activities depend run more and more slowly as the temperature drops. Insect metabolism also runs down in cold weather. You have probably noticed a butterfly on a cool morning flapping its wings to "rev up its motors" so that it can create enough heat for the rapid motions required for flight. When temperatures get cooler, solitary insects either die or go into a state of suspended animation until spring.

Most birds and mammals maintain an almost constant body temperature. Birds require it for their special activities, including sustained flight. In the mammals, high constant temperature is undoubtedly associated with activity and alertness and, as a consequence, the evolution of intelligence. Maintaining constant temperature adds significantly to an animal's energy requirements, however. Flying birds have a particularly difficult problem since they must keep their weight down and therefore cannot store much food for energy; thus they need to refuel constantly to keep warm and to keep flying. A bird eating high-protein foods, such as seeds and insects, commonly consumes as much as 30 percent of its body weight per day. Fall migrations are necessary not so much because of the colder weather, since a well-fed bird can maintain its temperature, but rather because of the reduced food supply and the shortened day, which gives the diurnal bird less time to feed. Similarly, birds

2–136 *Lizards, which do not have internal heat-regulating mechanisms, control their body temperature by alternately seeking sun and shade. (Willis Peterson)*

return to the temperate zones to breed partly because the longer days give
them more time to seek food to meet the high-energy demands of their young.

It is more difficult, in terms of energy expenditure, for a small animal to
maintain a high body temperature than a large one since the surface-area-to-
volume ratio of small animals makes them such efficient radiators. Mice nest,
making a communal heat. Hamsters hibernate, permitting their body
temperatures to drop very low and their metabolic processes to slow down. Bats
maintain a high body temperature when they are flying but allow it to drop
immediately every time they rest, thereby conserving energy. The hummingbird
pays for its ceaseless activity, small size, and high body temperature with
a very short life.

Temperature loss in both birds and mammals is retarded by feathers, fur, or
clothing. Seagoing mammals, like the whales and seals, use their outer skin
layer as a sort of clothing. These first several inches of skin and fat, which are
normally several degrees colder than the inner areas of the body, act as a
kind of wet suit to reduce heat loss from the interior.

Mammals have a temperature-regulating center at the base of the brain.
When external temperatures go down, the small blood vessels, particularly
those in the skin, constrict, allowing the skin to cool and conserving the heat
within the body, as with the seal's wet suit. A further decrease in temperature
brings on shivering, which serves to increase heat production as a result of
muscular activity. If external temperatures rise, another set of activities is set
in motion. The small blood vessels near the skin relax and dilate, and blood
passing through them radiates heat out into the atmosphere. Many mammals
sweat; some of them from all over the body surface, like men and horses, and
some from such localized areas as the pads of the foot. Dogs and other animals
pant, so that air passes rapidly over the moist tongue and mouth surfaces.
Cats achieve somewhat the same effect by licking themselves all over.
Evaporation of the moisture cools the body surface.

---

emergencies or, in amphibians and reptiles, changes in skin color in response to changes in the surroundings.

Most of the investigations of animal hormones have been carried out with arthropods or vertebrates; it now seems clear, however, that most, if not all, groups of invertebrates also produce hormones. In this discussion, we shall limit ourselves to some of the hormones produced by the vertebrates and, in particular, by the mammals. A list of the principal hormones is given in Table 2–3.

Table 2–3 *Principal Endocrine Glands of Vertebrates and Their Hormones*

Gland	Hormone	Principal action	Mechanism controlling secretion
Pituitary, anterior lobe	Thyrotropic hormone (TSH)	Stimulates thyroid	Thyroid hormone in blood; hypothalamus
	Follicle-stimulating hormone (FSH)	Stimulates follicle of ovary	Estrogen in blood; hypothalamus
	Luteinizing hormone (LH)	Stimulates testes in male, corpus luteum in female	Testosterone or progesterone in blood; hypothalamus
	Adrenocorticotropic hormone (ACTH)	Stimulates adrenal glands	Adrenal cortical hormone in blood; hypothalamus
	Growth hormone	Stimulates bone and muscle growth	
	Prolactin	Stimulates milk secretion, parental behavior (such as nest building in birds)	Hypothalamus
Pituitary, midlobe	Melanophore-stimulating hormone	Regulates skin color in amphibians and reptiles	Nervous system
Pituitary, posterior lobe	Oxytocin	Stimulates uterine contractions, milk ejection	Nervous system
	Vasopressin	Controls water excretion	Nervous system
Thyroid	Thyroxine	Controls metabolism, some aspects of development	TSH
Parathyroid	Parathyroid hormone	Controls calcium metabolism	Concentration of calcium in blood (not fully known)
Ovary, follicle	Estrogens	Develops and maintains sex characteristics	FSH
Ovary, corpus luteum	Progesterone	Promotes growth of uterine tissue	LH
Testes	Testosterone	Develops and maintains sex characteristics	FSH
Adrenal cortex	Cortisone, cortisonelike hormones, aldosterone	Controls carbohydrate metabolism, salt and water balance	ACTH
Adrenal medulla	Adrenaline	Increases blood sugar, dilates blood vessels, increases heartbeat	Nervous system
Pancreas	Insulin	Lowers blood sugar, increases storage of glycogen	Concentration of sugar in blood
	Glucagon	Stimulates release of glycogen from liver	Concentration of sugar in blood

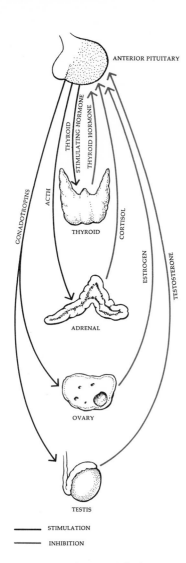

ANTERIOR PITUITARY

THYROID STIMULATING HORMONE

THYROID HORMONE

GONADOTROPINS

ACTH

THYROID

CORTISOL

ESTROGEN

TESTOSTERONE

ADRENAL

OVARY

TESTIS

——— STIMULATION

——— INHIBITION

2–137 *The interactions of some of the hormone-producing glands of the human body. Under the influence of the hypothalamus, the anterior lobe of the pituitary produces tropic hormones that regulate the secretions of the thyroid, the adrenal cortex, and the sex glands. These target glands produce hormones that not only have specific effects on various body tissues but also serve to regulate the output of the tropic hormones by the pituitary.*

The existence of the hormones and their effects were discovered in large part as a result of medical studies on persons in whom the effects of hormone deficiencies or excesses were seen. It is a commentary on the smooth normal functioning of the endocrine system that its existence should be discovered only from those rare instances in which it is not operating normally. The special organs in which the hormones are produced are known as the *ductless glands*, stressing the fact that the chemicals they synthesize are not carried to their target tissues by ducts—as the digestive enzymes are carried to the small intestine by the pancreatic duct or as the bile from the liver is carried by the bile duct—but are released directly into the body fluids. Thus the effects of hormones depend not only on their distribution to a particular area but on the responsiveness of certain tissues to the hormone.

Figure 2–137 shows the location of some of the major hormone-producing glands in the human body. As the diagram indicates, these form an interrelated system of chemical influences. The master gland—the "conductor of this chemical symphony," as it has been called—is the pituitary. The pituitary, which is about the size and shape of a kidney bean, is situated right at the base of the brain in the geometric center of the skull, the most heavily protected area in the entire human body. It secretes nine known hormones, of which four are shown in this diagram. These four, all of which are produced by the anterior lobe of the pituitary, are the *tropic hormones*, hormones that act upon other glands to regulate their secretions. The tropic hormones, like all the other hormones produced in the anterior pituitary, are protein molecules.

The glands upon which the tropic hormones act are the thyroid, the sex glands, and the adrenals. The thyroid, under the influence of the thyroid-stimulating hormone, produces thyroxine, which, in chemical structure, is an amino acid combined with four atoms of iodine. Thyroxine controls metabolism in man and certain other mammals; the rate of oxygen consumption (metabolic rate) is used as an index of how much thyroid hormone the tissues are receiving. Deficiency of thyroid hormone in infancy retards physical development and leads to a syndrome known as *cretinism*, characterized by serious mental deficiency. Identification of the causes of cretinism, with the consequent administration of thyroid hormone, is one of modern medicine's many valuable contributions to human welfare.

The sex glands, the ovaries in the female and the testes in the male, are the source of the sex hormones, testosterone and estrogen, which promote growth of the reproductive structures and of the secondary sexual characteristics, such as breasts, hair distribution, and body-fat distribution. Testosterone, the male sex hormone, also generally promotes the growth of muscle and of red blood cells. Progesterone, produced by the corpus luteum of the ovary, stimulates growth of the uterine mucosa and

2–138 *The chemical structure of thyroxine, the hormone secreted by the thyroid gland. Note the four iodine (I) atoms; iodine present in the bloodstream is taken up selectively by the thyroid gland to produce this hormone. When an adequate amount of thyroxine is present, the pituitary stops production of thyroid stimulating hormone (TSH). In the absence of iodine, thyroxine cannot be produced and constant TSH stimulation may cause a goiter.*

promotes development of mammary glands during pregnancy. All these chemical regulators are *steroid hormones,* which are characteristically extremely potent in very small amounts. A normal female, for example, produces less than a teaspoonful of estrogen in an entire lifetime.

The adrenal glands are situated above the kidneys. The outer layer, or *cortex,* is the source of a large number of steroids with hormonal activity. Some 50 different steroids, all very similar in structure, have so far been isolated from the adrenal cortex of various mammals. Some of these undoubtedly represent steps in the synthesis of various compounds rather than different hormones. We are still far from knowing all the products of these glands; nor do we know which ones are active in the body or the full range of their activities. One general group is concerned primarily with the formation of glucose from protein and fat. The most familiar of these hormones is cortisone, although it is less important in the body than several others. The principal one of these hormones is cortisol. It is this group that is responsive to the effects of the tropic hormone ACTH. A second group, of which aldosterone is the primary example, is concerned with the regulation of the salt and water balance. Aldosterone stimulates the cells lining the distal convoluted tubule of the nephron to increase their reabsorption of sodium. The reabsorption of sodium leads to reabsorption of water, producing a rise in blood volume and so in blood pressure. Unlike the sex hormones, the hormones of the adrenal cortex are essential for maintaining life.

The adrenal cortex is also a source of male sex hormones, which is why an adrenal tumor, which may lead to increased production of these hormones, may produce facial hair and other masculine characteristics in a woman. In addition to their actions on the various tissues of the body, thyroxine and the steroid hormones all have a second action: They inhibit secretion by the pituitary of the tropic hormone that stimulated their production. This is another example of a feedback system. When a sufficient quantity of a particular hormone is produced, the system shuts itself off; when hormone concentrations decrease, the pituitary produces more of the appropriate tropic hormone, and synthesis is resumed.

GROWTH HORMONE

Growth hormone is another important protein hormone produced by the anterior pituitary. Growth hormone, sometimes called *somatotropin,* promotes the growth of bone and muscle. As is the case with most of the hormones, somatotropin is best known, both to scientists and laymen, by the effects when too much or too little is produced. If there is a deficit in somatotropin production in childhood, a midget results, the so-called "pituitary dwarf." An excess of somatotropin results in a giant; most circus giants are the result of an excess of growth hormone. Excessive growth

2–139 *The chemical structures of some important steroid hormones, which are secreted by the adrenal cortex and the sex glands.*

TESTOSTERONE

ESTROGEN

PROGESTERONE

CORTISOL

CORTICOSTERONE

ALDOSTERONE

hormone in the adult does not lead to giantism, since not all adult tissues respond to growth hormone, but to acromegaly, an increase in the size of the jaw and the hands and feet, adult tissues that are still sensitive to growth-hormone effects.

Interactions of the Endocrine and Nervous Systems

There is an intimate connection between the workings of the nervous and endocrine systems. The pituitary gland is at the base of the brain, underlying an area known as the *hypothalamus*. The hormones of the anterior lobe of the pituitary are released under the control of special chemical substances formed in the hypothalamus. The posterior lobe of the pituitary contains the terminations of cell fibers, the cell bodies of which are located in the hypothalamus. The two hormones secreted by the posterior lobe are synthesized in the neurons of the hypothalamus and pass down their axons into the pituitary, where they are stored.

The hormone adrenaline, from the adrenal medulla, is released as a result of nervous stimulation of the adrenal tissue. Nervous stimulation also causes the pituitary gland to increase its output of ACTH and so increase the supply of cortisonelike hormones. Both adrenaline and the cortical steroids have immediate effects on the concentration of sugar in the blood, making quick energy available to the organism. Patients with adrenocortical deficiency (Addison's disease) are in particular danger during periods of stress and require administration of additional cortisone at times of physical or emotional crisis.

Although the general effects on the organism of many of the important hormones are now fairly well known, the way in which hormones act at the cellular level still remains to be discovered. We do not know, for example, how they can act in such small amounts and also why they act on some tissues and not on others. Some hormones appear to affect the entry of substances into cells. For example, in diabetes, which is caused by a deficiency of insulin, there is a high concentration of sugar in the blood, so high that sugar appears in the urine. At the same time, the individual cells of the body are starving for lack of glucose. When insulin is administered, sugar enters the cells and leaves the bloodstream. Other hormones, some investigators hypothesize, may act directly on enzyme systems, either by stimulating synthesis of the enzymes or by promoting their activity. Because of the potency of the hormones and their wide variety of effects, this is a subject of great interest to biochemists and physiologists—and also, of course, to scientists concerned directly with medical research.

The Nervous System

The nervous system, like the endocrine system, is a means of communication between the different parts of the organism and between the organism

Simple nervous pathways. The epitheliomuscular cell shown in (a) *is an independent effector, a cell which both receives a stimulus and responds to it. The pathway shown in* (b) *is slightly more complex: The receptor cell receives the stimulus and transmits the nervous impulse to an effector. The third drawing* (c) *shows the most common type of pathway: The impulse is transmitted from the receptor cell to an association neuron, from which it goes to an effector. This last arrangement makes possible alternate pathways of nervous transmission.*

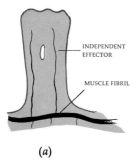

INDEPENDENT EFFECTOR

MUSCLE FIBRIL

(a)

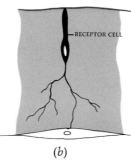

RECEPTOR CELL

(b)

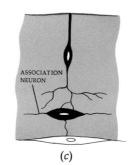

ASSOCIATION NEURON

(c)

and the outside world. Functionally, it differs from the endocrine system chiefly in its capacity for rapid response—a nerve impulse can travel through the body in a matter of milliseconds, while it may take seconds or even minutes for the stimulation of hormone production, the synthesis of the needed hormone, and the initiation of its effects on the target tissue, and weeks or even months before its full effects are felt. In this discussion, we are going to focus largely on the role of the nervous system in maintaining the internal stability of the body; other aspects of nervous-system function, including some of the special sense organs, will be discussed in Section 5 as they relate to animal behavior.

First, let us review some of the simpler components of nervous-system function: The simplest sort of nervelike cell is the independent effector— the epitheliomuscular cell of the sponge or the cnidoblast of the coelenterate—a cell that receives information from the environment and acts upon it. At slightly higher levels of complexity, the functions of receiving information, transmitting it, and acting upon it may be divided among several more specialized cells: receptors, conductors, and effectors. As these pathways become more complex, they come to involve other nerve cells, known as *association neurons*, that can switch impulses from one circuit to another. As an example, if you touch a hot surface, you will not only "automatically" jerk your hand away, you may also say "Ouch!"

THE NEURONS

The reception area of the neuron is known as the *dendritic zone*. As we saw in Chapter 1–5, the dendrites may consist of fibers that receive impulses from other cells and conduct them toward the cell body; a single neuron may have many dendrites or dendritic zones. An axon is an elongated cytoplasmic extension of the neuron that conducts impulses away from the cell body and stimulates other cells; a neuron usually has only one axon, although the axon may be branched. Vertebrate axons are often enveloped in a myelin sheath formed by Schwann cells. The sheath speeds up the transmission of impulses along the axon. An axon may be many feet in length in a large animal. A nerve usually consists of a bundle of separate nerve fibers, each wrapped in a separate sheath and each capable of transmitting separate messages, like the wires in a telephone cable.

THE SYNAPSE

The nerve impulse is produced by a change in electric potential running along the cell membrane of the axon. The impulse can travel in either direction; thus any stimulus transmitted to the nerve net of *Hydra* travels through it in all directions. The synapse, however, is a one-way junction in the conduction system. Furthermore, the nerve impulse, although it follows an "all-or-nothing" course along any single fiber, can be interrupted, redirected, and cross-circuited in a number of ways at synaptic junctions. The terminals of a single axon may impinge on a number of different cells, and dendrites may receive stimuli from a number of separate sources. As a result, *facilitation* or *inhibition* of the nerve impulse may occur. Facilitation results when a repeated impulse across one synapse, or many impulses across a number of synapses, produces excitation in a neuron that does not respond to the stimulus of any single impulse. Inhibition is the result of the excitation in one neuron blocking synaptic transmission to another.

Transmission across the synaptic junction in mammals, according to current theories, is by chemical means. Each synaptic knob contains numerous small vesicles, visible in the electron microscope (Figure 1–49). The nerve impulses apparently cause these vesicles to discharge their contents, and the discharged chemical rather than an electric impulse stimulates the adjacent neuron. Transmission across a synaptic junction is slower than transmission along a nerve fiber; the more synapses involved, the slower the information travels. One of the chief transmitter chemicals in both invertebrates and vertebrates is a substance known as acetylcholine. Once acetylcholine is released and has stimulated the adjacent neuron, it is rapidly destroyed by an enzyme called cholinesterase. The action of cholinesterase is indispensable for the smooth functioning of the nervous system.*

As you can see, although it is convenient to think of the endocrine communication system as a chemical one and the nervous system as electrical, the distinction is not nearly so clear-cut.

*Many insecticides act by destroying the cholinesterases of the insect. The animal's nervous system then runs wild, causing spasms and eventually death.

|—— 5mm ——|

2–141 *Each body segment of the millipede has two pairs of legs which are under the control of a separate pair of ganglia.* (L. West)

CENTRALIZATION OF THE NERVOUS SYSTEM

In the flatworm, we saw the beginnings of two evolutionary trends that reach their culmination in the higher vertebrates: the condensation of the nervous system, which leads to more rapid conduction of an impulse (as in the squid, for example, in which a single giant axon conducts an impulse the entire length of the animal's body), and the accumulation of neurons in the anterior portion of the body. This latter development is associated with bilateral symmetry and the concomitant evolution of "headness" and "tailness." The echinoderms, for example, have no comparable aggregation of neurons.

Clusters of cell bodies are known as *ganglia*. (The vertebrate brain is somewhat like a large ganglion.) In the segmented animals, such as the annelids and arthropods, each segment is under the control of a separate pair of ganglia, which are relatively autonomous. The isolated thorax of an insect, for example, can accept an object handed to it or can walk across the floor. The larger ganglia at the anterior of the animal, however, can direct the activities of the entire animal; a flash of light can trigger an impulse that travels down the animal's entire body, causing it, for instance, as in the case of the earthworm, to snap back into its burrow.

In vertebrates, many of the so-called "reflex" actions are under the jurisdiction of groups of nerve cells located in the spinal cord, but there is an increasing tendency for sensory nerve impulses to be transmitted to the

335 *How Animals Live*

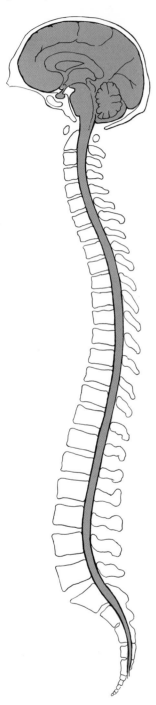

2–142 *The spinal column and skull form a bony outer covering for the central nervous system of the vertebrate.*

brain and there integrated with other sensory information, on the basis of which the most useful response is decided upon. Also in the vertebrates, there is an evolutionary tendency for more and more of the central nervous system to be composed of association neurons, as compared with the proportion of receptors and afferent and efferent neurons.

As you know, the central nervous system of the vertebrates is encased in bony supporting and protecting structures, the vertebral column and the skull. The vertebrate spinal column, the "trademark" of this subphylum, is much the same from fish to man. Figure 2–143 shows a segment of the human spinal cord, with pairs of spinal nerves entering and emerging from the cord through spaces between the vertebrae. Each of these pairs innervates the skeletal muscles of a different and distinct area of the body. In mammals, there are 31 such pairs. The cell bodies of all these nerves are in the spinal cord—as contrasted, for example, with the insects, in which the neuron cell body is in the epidermis.

The neurons carrying impulses outward to the muscles are the *efferent* nerves, also often called the motor neurons. The motor neurons transmit impulses to the effectors, which are muscles, glands, or other tissues. The nerves receiving impulses from the sensory cells are called *afferent* neurons. The efferent and afferent neurons constitute the peripheral nervous system.

Reflex Arc

Figure 2–144 diagrams the *reflex arc*. In the simple reflex action—again, your finger touching a hot surface is a convenient example—the stimulus is received by a receptor cell (a pain-sensitive cell, in this case) and is transmitted to the spinal cord, where this afferent neuron synapses with association neurons, which, in turn, relay the impulse to the appropriate efferent (motor) neuron. The efferent neuron causes the appropriate muscle to contract, which moves your arm. Afferent nerve impulses feed into the spinal column on the dorsal side and ascend toward the brain. Neurons descending from the brain make synapses with efferent neurons, which emerge from the spinal column on the ventral side.

The Autonomic Nervous System

The motor, sensory, and association neurons of the vertebrate make up the somatic, or *voluntary*, nervous system. In vertebrates, there is also an important subdivision of the nervous system known as the *autonomic*, or visceral, nervous system. It comprises the nerves that control cardiac muscle, glands, and smooth muscle, the type of muscle found in the walls of blood vessels and in the digestive, respiratory, and reproductive tracts. The autonomic nervous system is thus generally categorized as the *involuntary* system.

143 *A segment of the spinal cord.*
Spinal nerves enter and emerge
through spaces between the vertebrae,
afferent nerves on the dorsal side
and efferent nerves on the ventral side.
Each pair of spinal nerves innervates
a separate area of the body.

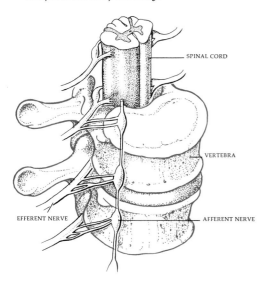

SPINAL CORD

VERTEBRA

EFFERENT NERVE

AFFERENT NERVE

You will readily recognize that the distinction between voluntary and involuntary is not clear-cut. Skeletal muscles often move involuntarily, as in a reflex action, and it is reported that some persons, particularly practitioners of yoga, can control their rate of heartbeat and the contractions of some smooth muscle. Anatomically, the efferent neurons of the somatic system are distinct and entirely separate from the efferent neurons of the autonomic nervous system, although both types of neurons may be carried in the same nerve bundle. Also, the cell bodies of the efferent neurons of the somatic system are located in the central nervous system, with long nerve fibers running uninterruptedly all the way to the skeletal muscle. The efferent fibers of the autonomic nervous system also originate in cell bodies inside the central system; however, they generally do not travel all the way to their target organ, or effector, but instead form a synapse with a second neuron, which carries the impulse on to the muscle or gland. These *postganglionic* neurons or fibers, as they are called, are characteristic of the autonomic system.

The autonomic nervous system has two divisions, the sympathetic and the parasympathetic, which are anatomically and functionally distinct. The parasympathetic system consists of nerves from the brain and from

144 *Diagram of the reflex arc. Impulses from*
a receptor cell travel along the sensory
neuron to the spinal cord. The cell
body of the sensory neuron is located
in a dorsal-root ganglion lying just out-
side the spinal cord. The sensory axon
enters the cord and synapses with a
motor neuron in the gray matter of the
cord. The motor neuron carries impulses
to the effector muscle.

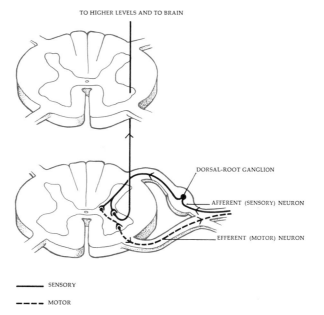

TO HIGHER LEVELS AND TO BRAIN

DORSAL-ROOT GANGLION

AFFERENT (SENSORY) NEURON

EFFERENT (MOTOR) NEURON

——— SENSORY

- - - - MOTOR

337   *How Animals Live*

2–145 *The autonomic nervous system, consisting of the sympathetic and the parasympathetic systems. The presynaptic neurons of the parasympathetic system exit from the medulla region of the brain and from the sacral region of the spinal cord. The sympathetic system originates in the thoracic and lumbar regions. Most, but not all, internal organs are innervated by both systems, which function in opposition to each other. In general, the sympathetic system produces the effect of exciting an organ and the parasympathetic system produces an opposite effect. Thus while the one system stimulates activity, the other system inhibits it. Our normal state, somewhere in between absolute excitement and absolute calm, is the result of a constant interplay of these two systems.*

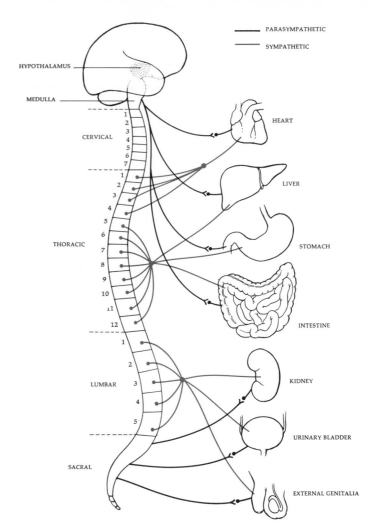

the lower region of the spinal cord. The sympathetic nervous system originates in the thoracic and lumbar areas of the spinal cord. In the parasympathetic system, the point of synapse is near or in the target organ, while in the sympathetic system, the synapses are in a regular chain of ganglia running parallel to the spinal cord. Most postganglionic sympathetic nerve endings release adrenaline or related compounds (the same compounds released by the adrenal medulla) and an adrenalinelike chemical (noradrenaline), while all parasympathetic endings release acetylcholine.

As you can see in the Figure 2–145, most of the major visceral organs of the body are innervated by fibers from both the sympathetic and the parasympathetic systems. The effects of the sympathetic system are often antagonistic to those of the parasympathetic system, and vice versa. As a consequence, whereas the somatic nervous system can only excite or not excite a particular effector, the autonomic nervous system can have both an excitory and an inhibitory effect.

For example, do you recall what it feels like to be in an absolute rage? The physical characteristics of a rage result from a simultaneous discharge of many of the sympathetic fibers. The blood vessels in the skin and intestinal tract contract; this increases the return of blood to the heart, raising the blood pressure and sending more blood to the muscles. The heart beats both faster and stronger, and the respiratory rate increases. The pupils dilate. The muscles underlying the hair follicles in the skin contract; this is probably a legacy from our furry forebears, which looked larger and more ferocious with their hair standing on end. The sphincters, the muscles that close the intestines and the bladder, contract; this tends to close down digestive operations, but sympathetic nervous activity may also have the decidedly unuseful result of involuntary defecation or urination. Sugar is released in large quantities from the liver into the bloodstream to supply the muscles. The adrenal gland is stimulated to release adrenaline. The body is prepared for fight or flight.

The parasympathetic system, on the other hand, is more concerned with the restorative activities of the body—rest and rumination. Parasympathetic stimulation slows down the heartbeat and increases the muscular movements of the intestine and the secretions of the salivary gland. Most large organs, such as the heart, are under the control of both sympathetic and parasympathetic nerves, and these work in close cooperation for the ultimate regulation of these important structures. Some tissues, such as the hair muscles, the small blood vessels, and the sweat glands, are under sympathetic control alone.

In general, of course, we are usually neither in a rage nor in a complete state of vegetation but somewhere in between—a state resulting from a constant interplay of forces, a dialogue between the sympathetic and parasympathetic systems.

BIOLOGICAL CLOCKS

Circadian rhythms, first discovered in plants almost 250 years ago, now have been shown to exist widely throughout the animal world. They are considered by many scientists to be an important internal regulatory mechanism.

Hamsters, rats, cockroaches, and a number of other nocturnal animals show regular periods of "nocturnal" activity even when they are not receiving any environmental clues as to day and night. Studies in mammals have shown that the pituitary secretes more ACTH at certain times of the day and that, furthermore, the adrenal is more responsive to ACTH at these times than at other times. Even the isolated cells of the rat heart growing in tissue culture have been reported to show daily fluctuations

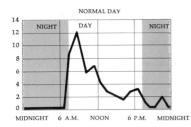

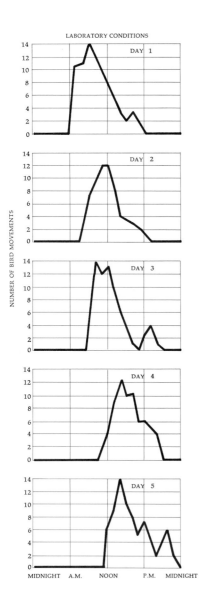

2–146 *Results of a study of activity rhythms in birds. The spontaneous locomotor activity of a caged robin was automatically recorded in a natural day-night situation and for five consecutive days in the laboratory in conditions of continuous illumination of a constant intensity and constant temperature. The curve shown at the top is representative for robins in their natural habitat: Activity is restricted to daylight hours, with a major surge of activity just after sunrise and a secondary increase in the cool evening before nightfall. Under laboratory conditions, the activity pattern remains approximately the same, but each day the active phase of the rhythm starts and ends a little later than the previous day; the period of the rhythm has become slightly longer than 25 hours.*

in rate of contraction, and circadian variations in electrical activity have been demonstrated in isolated neurons.

Presumably because of these daily fluctuations in metabolic activities, time affects the susceptibility of animals to various kinds of stress. A dose of insecticide that kills 10 percent of beetles at dawn kills almost 90 percent three hours later. Rats are much more severely harmed by radiation exposure at night than in the daytime. A poison that will kill 85 percent of mice at their subjective noon kills less than 5 percent at their subjective midnight.

Physicians and clinical psychologists are becoming increasingly interested in the application of these findings. Man is similarly tied to his own endogenous rhythm. It has long been known that he is more likely to be born between 3 and 4 A.M. and also to die in these same early morning hours. Body temperature fluctuates as much as 2°F during the course of the day, usually reaching a high about 4 P.M. and a low about 4 A.M. Hormone secretion, heart rate, blood pressure, urinary excretion of potassium, sodium, and calcium—all vary according to a circadian rhythm.

Some physicians have suggested that serious surgical procedures should perhaps not be scheduled for the early morning, as they frequently are now, but should be gauged to coincide with the optimum stage of the rhythm of the particular patient. A related question concerns the effects of travel in the jet age on temporal organization. A recent study by the Federal Aviation Agency shows that pilots flying from one time zone to another—from New York to Europe or from San Francisco to the Orient—show "jet lag," a general decrease in mental adroitness and the ability to concentrate and an increase in decision time and physiological reaction time. Comparable changes are not seen in pilots on north-south flights, such as the South American run, even though these flights are of equal length. The normal daily changes in body temperature take as long as four days to shift to the new schedule, and other physiological functions take even longer to adjust, leaving the body "out of synch" for as much as a week. The question of being able to function efficiently after an abrupt time shift is of concern, of course, not only to jet pilots but to many others who travel—to diplomats, for example, at international meetings and to troops being flown into combat.

SUMMARY

In this chapter, we reviewed the major problems of the animals and discussed and compared some of the solutions to them.

Respiration is the exchange of oxygen for carbon dioxide. In a protozoan or a small multicellular organism, all the cells of the body can be supplied by diffusion of the gases across the individual cell membranes. In larger and more complex organisms, specialized structures, the gills and the lungs, have evolved. Gills and lungs provide a greatly increased, localized surface area for gaseous exchange; in the lung, this surface area must be protected against drying out since diffusion into the body fluids must take place across a moist membrane. Both gills and lungs function in conjunction with a circulating fluid (the blood) that transports the oxygen to and removes the carbon dioxide from the various cells of the body.

Digestion takes place both intracellularly and extracellularly. In the invertebrates we saw the evolution of extracellular digestion followed by the development of a one-way digestive tract with increasingly specialized areas for the processing of food. In the vertebrates, the major stages in extracellular digestion take place in the small intestine, where digestive enzymes hydrolyze the bonds that unite small molecules into proteins and fats. The pancreas and the liver are specialized digestive organs; the pancreas secretes digestive enzymes and the liver produces bile, both of which are released into the intestine. Both organs also are involved in the regulation of blood sugar.

The *circulatory system* provides the means for transporting oxygen, nutrients, wastes, and other materials from specialized tissues, such as the lungs and digestive tract, to other parts of the organism. All vertebrates have closed circulatory systems in which the blood is pumped out from the heart into the arteries to the arterioles and finally to the capillaries, from which, by way of the veins, it returns to the heart. The fish has a two-chambered heart; the returning blood is collected in one chamber (the *atrium*) and pumped from the other chamber (the *ventricle*) into the gills, from which it passes to the tissues. The frog has a three-chambered heart; freshly oxygenated blood from the lungs returns to one atrium, and blood from the tissues goes to the other atrium, but both are mixed in the ventricle before being circulated through the tissues. Birds and mammals have a four-chambered heart, which makes possible separate circulatory systems for the lungs and tissues. The vertebrate heartbeat originates within the heart itself and is synchronized by a special area of *nodal tissue*, the pacemaker.

The *excretory system* is concerned with the regulation of the internal environment. Regulation is accomplished by (1) elimination of the toxic by-products of metabolism, in particular, nitrogenous waste; (2) control of the ionic content of the body fluids; and (3) maintenance of water balance. The excretory unit of the vertebrate is known as the *nephron*; each nephron consists of a long tubule and a closed bulb (*Bowman's capsule*). Bowman's capsule is associated with a twisted cluster of capillaries, the *glomerulus*, from which fluids are forced into the nephron. The human kidney contains about a million nephrons through which the circulating fluids of the body pass many times each day. By a combination of filtration, reabsorption, and secretion, the fluids are processed during their passage along the tubules.

Problems of water balance are different for animals living in saltwater (hyperosmotic), freshwater (hypoosmotic), and terrestrial environments. Terrestrial animals generally need to conserve water. An important means of water conservation is the capacity for excreting a urine that is hyperosmotic in relation to the blood. The structure and function of the *loop of Henle*, the portion of the mammalian nephron that makes possible the production of a hyperosmotic urine, were described.

Reproduction may take place asexually or sexually; asexual reproduction always involves mitotic division and produces offspring which are copies of the parental type. Sexual reproduction, which takes place by the fusion of gametes, involves meiotic division and produces offspring that differ from the parents. Special adaptations for bringing together the male and female gametes, both in time and in space, were described. Trends in vertebrate evolution have included the synchronization of mating activities by endocrine secretions and by courtship behavior; the development of the amniote egg, which freed the vertebrates from the terrestrial environment; and increasing prenatal and postnatal care of the young.

Regulatory systems are concerned with the organization of activities of complex organisms and their integration with the environment. One of the principal regulatory systems in animals is the *endocrine system*. The endocrine system produces hormones, extremely potent chemicals that are synthesized in particular tissues of the body (the endocrine or ductless glands) and carried by the bloodstream to other tissues, where they exert specific effects. Interactions involving the pituitary, thyroid, sex, and adrenal glands were described as examples of endocrine regulation.

The nervous system provides for rapid communication in animal organisms. In the invertebrates, we traced two important evolutionary trends

—the condensation of the nervous system and the accumulation of neurons in the anterior portion of the animal. Nerve impulses are transmitted by changes in electric potential along the membranes of nerve cells, the *neurons*, and from nerve cell to nerve cell across *synaptic junctions*. Facilitation and inhibition of the nerve impulse occurs at synaptic junctions.

The central nervous system, which is enclosed by the vertebrae and the skull in vertebrates, consists of the spinal cord and the brain. The neurons receiving impulses from sensory cells and transmitting them to the central nervous system are called *afferent* neurons. Neurons transmitting impulses from the spinal cord to the muscles are *efferent* neurons, also called motor neurons. The afferent and efferent neurons make up the somatic, or *voluntary*, nervous system.

A second important subdivision of the nervous system is the *autonomic nervous system*, which comprises the nerves that control the heart, the glands, and smooth muscle, all of which are generally under involuntary control. The autonomic nervous system has two divisions: the *sympathetic* and the *parasympathetic* systems, which are anatomically as well as functionally distinct. In general, the effects of the sympathetic system are antagonistic to those of the parasympathetic system, the former being chiefly concerned with promoting "fight or flight" reactions and the latter with digestive and other restorative functions.

A third regulatory system of great current interest is the *biological clock*. Some of the current research on biological clocks and its implications were discussed.

SUGGESTIONS FOR FURTHER READING

ALEXOPOULOS, CONSTANTINE JOHN: *Introductory Mycology*, 2nd ed., John Wiley & Sons, Inc., New York, 1962.

A brief, crisply written, up-to-date review, for students who want to know more about the fungi.

BARNES, ROBERT D.: *Invertebrate Zoology*, W. B. Saunders Company, Philadelphia, 1963.

A thorough, phylum-by-phylum description of the invertebrates.

BUCHSBAUM, RALPH: *Animals without Backbones*, rev. ed., The University of Chicago Press, Chicago, 1948.

A delightful introduction to the invertebrates, for the general student.

BURNETT, A. L., AND THOMAS EISNER: *Animal Adaptation*, Holt, Rinehart and Winston, Inc., New York, 1964.*

The authors use the mosquito as the basis for a discussion of adaptation in organisms as a whole and, in the process, provide an insight to the kind of reasoning that motivates biologists today.

DAWSON, E. YALE: *Marine Botany: An Introduction*, Holt, Rinehart and Winston, Inc., New York, 1966.

A short, lively, up-to-date text that covers marine bacteria, fungi, phytoplankton, and sea grasses as well as algae.

HOAR, WILLIAM S.: *General and Comparative Physiology*, Prentice-Hall, Inc., Englewood Cliffs, N.J., 1966.

This text, although designed particularly for the advanced undergraduate and the graduate student, can be read easily by the student who has understood and enjoyed chapters 2–5 through 2–8.

JAHN, THEODORE L., AND FRANCES F. JAHN (ED.): *How to Know the Protozoa*, William C. Brown Co., Publishers, Dubuque, Iowa, 1949.*

An identification manual recommended to anyone who would like to see some of the "marvelous animals" at first hand.

RAY, PETER M.: *The Living Plant*, Holt, Rinehart and Winston, Inc., New York, 1963.*

A short introduction to the plant world, with emphasis on the biological activities of living plants.

SMITH, ALEXANDER H.: *The Mushroom Hunter's Field Guide*, 2nd ed., The University of Michigan Press, Ann Arbor, Mich., 1966.

A clear, concise, well-illustrated guide to edible mushrooms, enlivened with good advice and pertinent anecdotes.

SMITH, HOMER W.: *From Fish to Philosopher*, Doubleday & Company, Inc., Garden City, N.Y., 1959.*

Dr. Smith is an eminent specialist in the physiology of the kidney. Writing for the general public, he tells the role of this remarkable organ in the story of evolution.

STANIER, ROGER Y., et al.: *The Microbial World*, Prentice-Hall, Inc., Englewood Cliffs, N.J., 1963.

An introduction to the biology of microorganisms, with special emphasis on the properties of bacteria.

TORREY, JOHN G.: *Development in Flowering Plants*, The Macmillan Company, New York, 1967.*

How flowering plants develop from single cells to adults.

WELTY, JOEL: *Life of Birds*, Alfred A. Knopf, Inc., New York, 1963.

A comprehensive and enjoyable discussion for the general reader of all aspects of the life of birds—their physiology, behavior, habitats, and evolution.

*Available in paperback.

GENETICS

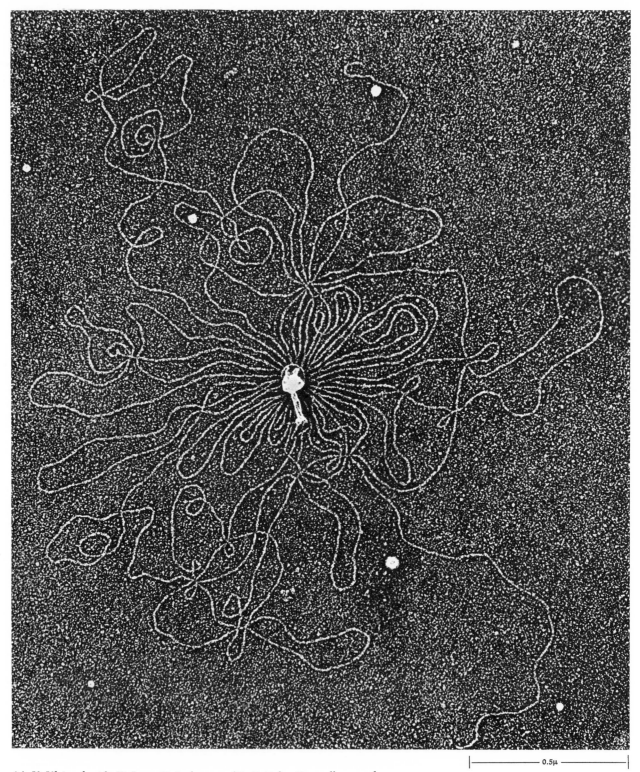

0.5μ

(*A. K. Kleinschmidt, D. Lang, D. Jacherts und R. K. Zahn, Darstellung und Längemessungen des gesamten Desoxyribonucleinsäure-inhaltes von T₂-bakterio-phagen, Biochim. et Biophys. Acta, 61 (1962) 857–864, fig. 1.*)

PART I. CLASSICAL GENETICS

Chapter 3–1

Concepts of Heredity

Among all the symbols in biology, perhaps the most widely used and most ancient are the handmirror of Venus (♀) and the shield and spear of Mars (♂), the biologists' shorthand for female and male. Ideas about the nature of biological inheritance—the role of male and female—are even older than these famous symbols. Very early, men must have noticed that certain characteristics—hair color, for example, a large nose, or a small chin —were passed from parent to offspring. And throughout history, the concept of biological inheritance has been an important factor in the social organizations of men, determining the distribution of wealth, power, land, and royal privileges.

Sometimes the trait that is passed on is so distinctive that it can be traced through many generations. A famous example of such a characteristic is the Hapsburg lip (Figure 3–1), which has appeared in Hapsburg after Hapsburg, over and over again since at least the thirteenth century. Cases such as this have made it easy for men to accept the importance of inheritance in the formation of the individual, but it is only comparatively recently that we have begun to understand how this process works. In fact, the study of heredity as a science did not really begin until the second half of the nineteenth century. Yet the problems posed in this study are among the most fundamental in biology since self-replication, the essence of the hereditary process, is the cornerstone of the definition of life.

We shall, in this section, trace the development of the science of genetics from man's early ideas about heredity to the complex investigations of today, and we shall describe what we know now in historical terms, by presenting the facts more or less in the order in which they were discovered.

The history of this particular branch of biology tells us a great deal about how biologists—and, in fact, all scientists—think and work. In the course of this review, we shall also discuss some of the ideas which, as it

347 *Concepts of Heredity*

3–1 *The Hapsburg lip is a famous example of an inherited trait. These portraits of members of the Hapsburg family encompass a period of almost 350 years, and yet each shows the same peculiar formation of the lower lip. Upper left and right are Rudolph I (1218–1291), King of Germany, and Maximilian I (1460–1519), Holy Roman Emperor; on the bottom, left and right, Charles V (1500–1558), Holy Roman Emperor; and Ferdinand I (1503–1564), Holy Roman Emperor. Do you see any other special physical trait that these men have in common? (The Bettmann Archive)*

3–2 *A "sea horse" from a sixteenth century Italian book on marine animals. (The Bettmann Archive)*

turned out, were mistaken. It is easy for us to feel somehow superior to people who did not know the things that today we take for granted. We can wonder, for example, how our ancestors could possibly have thought that the vast universe wheeled around our insignificant little planet. Yet most of us would be hard put to prove on our own that the earth revolves around the sun, much less to measure the distance between ourselves and a star. The mistaken ideas of earlier generations are presented to help formulate certain crucial questions of biology. The answers, after all, are not particularly interesting unless one is reminded of what the questions were. Perhaps also, these accounts will serve as a reminder that even "logical" hypotheses can turn out to be false.

Early Ideas about Heredity

Far back in human history, men learned to improve domestic animals and crops by inbreeding and crossbreeding. In the case of date palms, male and female flowers are found on different trees and artificial fertilization of the palm was well known to the ancient Babylonians and Egyptians. The nature of the difference between the two flowers was understood by Theophrastus (380–287 B.C.). "The males should be brought to the females," he wrote, "for the male makes them ripen and persist." The mule, a man-made hybrid (a cross between a male donkey and a mare), was well known in the days of Homer. Noah's animals, according to early Biblical history, went aboard the ark two by two and so provided for the continuity of the species. Both Plutarch and Lucretius noted in their writings that some children resemble their mothers, some resemble their fathers, and some even skip back a generation to resemble a grandparent; this fact, so easy to observe, continued to puzzle people for a very long time.

Since no genetic laws were known, bizarre crossbreeds were the subject of many legends. The wife of Minos, according to Greek mythology, mated with a bull and produced the Minotaur. Folk heroes of Russia and Scandinavia were traditionally the sons of women who had been captured by bears, from which these men derived their great strength and so enriched the national stock. The camel and the leopard also crossbred from time to time, according to the early naturalists, who were otherwise unable —and it is hard to blame them—to explain an animal as improbable as the giraffe. Thus folklore reflected early and imperfect glimpses of the nature of hereditary relationships.

The first scientist known to have pondered the nature of heredity was Aristotle. He postulated that the male semen was made up of a number of imperfectly blended ingredients and that, at fertilization, it mixed with the "female semen," the menstrual fluid, giving form and power (*dynamis*) to this amorphous substance. No one had a better idea—or indeed many ideas at all—for two thousand years. Seventeenth century medical texts show various stages in the coagulation of the embryo from the mixture of maternal and paternal semens. Indeed, many scientists as well as laymen did not believe that such mixtures were even always necessary; they held that life, at least the "simpler" forms of life, could arise by spontaneous generation. Worms, flies, and various crawling things, it was commonly believed, took shape from putrid substances, ooze, and mud, and a lady's hair dropped in a rain barrel could turn into a snake. Jean-Baptiste van Helmont, a noted seventeenth century physician and scientist, published his personal recipe for the production of mice: One need only place a dirty shirt in an open pot containing a few grains of wheat, and in 21 days mice would appear! He had performed the experiment himself, he said. The mice would be adults, both male and female, he added, and would be able to produce more mice by mating.

The First Experiments

In 1677, the Dutch lens maker Anthony van Leeuwenhoek discovered living sperm—*animalcules*, he called them—in the seminal fluid of various

3–3 *It took men a very long time to realize that living things come only from other living things of the same species and never from another species or from lifeless matter. This picture from an old Turkish history of India shows a wak-wak tree, which bears human fruit. According to the account, the tree is to be found on an island in the South Pacific. (The Bettmann Archive)*

349 *Concepts of Heredity*

SPONTANEOUS GENERATION

Most of the early biologists, including Aristotle, believed that simple things such as worms, beetles, frogs, and salamanders could originate spontaneously in dust or mud and that rodents formed from moist grain and plant lice condensed from a dewdrop. In the seventeenth century, Francesco Redi performed a famous experiment in which he put out decaying meat in a group of wide-mouthed jars —some with lids, some covered by a fine veil, and some open—and proved that maggots arose only where flies were able to lay their eggs.

By the nineteenth century, no scientist continued to believe that complex organisms arose spontaneously. With the advent of microscopy, however, belief in spontaneous generation was vigorously revived. It was necessary only to put decomposing substances for a short time in a warm place and tiny "live beasts" appeared under the lens, before one's very eyes. In 1860, little more than a hundred years ago, the controversy had become so spirited that the Paris Academy of Sciences offered a prize for experiments which would throw new light on the question. The prize was claimed in 1864 by Louis Pasteur. Using swan-neck flasks, Pasteur showed that microorganisms appeared in infusions only if contaminants from the air were permitted to enter. If the liquid in the flask was boiled and if the flask was then sealed, or if the air entering it was filtered through the long slender neck of the flask, the cultures would remain sterile—some of his original flasks, still sterile, remain on display—but if the neck of the flask was broken off, microscopic growth soon appeared. "Life is a germ, and a germ is Life," Pasteur proclaimed at a brilliant "scientific evening" at the Sorbonne before the social elite of Paris. "Never will the doctrine of spontaneous generation recover from the mortal blow of this simple experiment!"

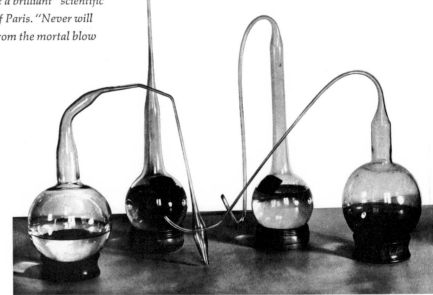

Pasteur's swan-neck flasks, which he used to counter the argument that spontaneous generation failed to occur in sealed vessels because air was excluded. These flasks permitted the entrance of oxygen, known to be essential for life, but their long curving necks trapped spores of microorganisms and thereby protected the liquid in the flask from contamination. (Courtesy of Pasteur Institute and Rockefeller University Press)

animals, including man. Enthusiastic followers peered through Leeuwenhoek's "magic looking glass" (his homemade microscope) and believed they saw within each human sperm a tiny creature—the *homunculus*, or "little man." This little man was the future human being in miniature. Once implanted in the female womb, the future human being was nurtured there, but that was the only contribution that the mother made. Any resemblance a child might have to its mother, these theorists held, was because of "prenatal influences." In the very same decade that Leeuwenhoek first saw human sperm cells, another Dutchman, Régnier de Graaf, described for the first time the ovarian follicle, the structure on the surface of the ovary in which the human egg cell forms. Although the actual human egg was not seen for another 150 years, the idea that there was such a thing as a human egg was rapidly accepted. In fact, de Graaf developed a school of followers, the ovists, who were as convinced of their opinions as the animalculists, or spermists, were of theirs and who soon contended openly with them. It was the female egg, the ovists said, which contained the future human being in miniature; the animalcules in the male seminal fluid merely stimulated the egg to grow. Ovists and animalculists alike carried the argument one logical step further. Each homunculus had within it another perfectly formed homunculus, and in that was still another one,

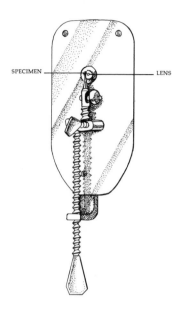

3–4 *One of the many microscopes made by Anthony van Leeuwenhoek, through which he saw living sperm cells. "Little animalcules," he called them, "Very prettily a-moving." The lens is a glass bead (ground, not fused) set in a hole in a copper plate. The specimen was mounted on a movable pin, which was then adjusted to the lens. The whole apparatus was held up very close to the eye. During his lifetime, Leeuwenhoek made many hundreds of microscopes.*

3–5 *What the animalculists, or spermists, of the seventeenth and eighteenth centuries believed they saw when they looked through a microscope at sperm cells. This is a homunculus ("little man"), a future human being in miniature, in a sperm cell. Except for "prenatal influences," the only contribution that the mother made to the forming of the child was to carry it in her womb.*

and so on—children, grandchildren, and great-grandchildren, all stored away for future use. Some ovists even went so far as to say that Eve had contained within her body all the unborn generations yet to come, each egg fitting closely inside another like a child's hollow blocks. Each female generation since Eve has contained one less, they explained, and after 200 million generations, all the eggs will be spent and human life will come to an end.

The Cell Theory

By the middle of the nineteenth century, careful observations coupled with more sober thinking began to prevail. Artificial crossing of ornamental plants showed that, in general, regardless of which plant supplied the pollen and which the ova, both contributed equally to the characteristics of the new variety. The cell theory, first formulated about 1840, became more widely accepted, and it came to be recognized that both the ova and the spermatozoa, the "little animalcules" of Leeuwenhoek, are also cells. These special cells were called *gametes,* from the Greek word *gamos,* meaning "marriage." Each parent contributed one tiny cell to each future offspring. But how did all the hundreds of characteristics of each parent get packed into a single gamete?

Blending inheritance was the most widely held theory of the nineteenth century. According to this theory, the mixing of hereditary material resulted in a blend, analogous to a blend of fluids, which then could not be separated back to the original parts. For example, the offspring of a black animal and a white animal would be gray, and *their* offspring would also be gray because the black and white hereditary material, once blended, could never be separated again.

To Charles Darwin, the theory of blending inheritance presented difficulties that he was never able to resolve. For example, with blending inheritance, Darwin was unable, as he recognized, to explain *reversion,* that is, resemblances that might skip a generation or even several generations and then suddenly reappear. More important, blending inheritance did not fit comfortably with Darwin's theory of evolution, since with blending inheritance, sexual reproduction would tend rapidly to produce uniformity. In order for a *variation,* to use Darwin's term, not to be blended out, like a drop of ink in a gallon of water, one had to preserve a very high rate of change (many drops of ink all of the same color). This led Darwin to seek for ways in which variations could be collected and passed on. As a consequence, in his later years, Darwin came to accept, at least to some degree, the ideas of Jean Baptiste Lamarck as offering part of the explanation, and the later editions of *The Origin of Species* show Lamarck's influence.

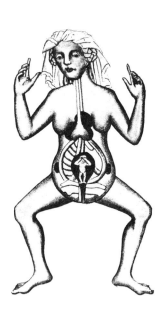

3–6 *Fifteenth century miniature showing the internal organs of the female sex. (The Bettmann Archive)*

3–7 *The sexual organs of the pea blossom are completely enclosed by its petals. Since the flower does not open until after fertilization has taken place, the plant normally self-pollinates. Why was this characteristic so important to Mendel in his crossbreeding experiments?*

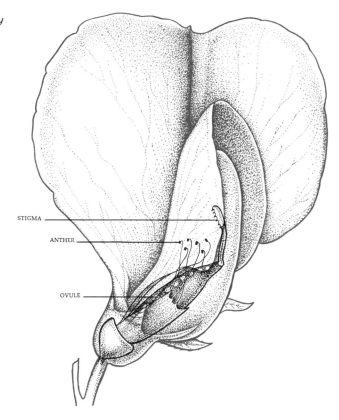

STIGMA

ANTHER

OVULE

Mendel's Experiments

Perhaps you have read about the famous experiments in the crossbreeding of garden peas carried out by Abbot Gregor Mendel in Brünn, Austria. The picture some of us have of Mendel is that of a gentle old ecclesiastic who took up gardening as a hobby. Actually, he was a highly intelligent and sophisticated thinker. With a background in physics and mathematics, he approached the question of inheritance in a thoroughly scientific way by clearly defining the problem, reducing it to its essentials, and attacking it with a series of carefully designed experiments. He was one of the first to apply mathematics to the study of biology. Even though his mathematics was simple, the idea that exact rules could be applied to living organisms was startlingly new.

Also new was Mendel's use of well-defined contrasting traits (smooth vs. wrinkled seeds, red vs. white flowers) within the same species of organism. Most of his predecessors had concentrated on crosses between species. By tracing clear-cut differences through the first, second, and succeeding generations of a species, Mendel was able to demonstrate that inheritance is not a blending of characteristics, as had been thought, but that inherited characters are carried as discrete units, which are parceled out in different ways, or *reassorted*, in each generation. This concept of discrete rather than continuous inheritance is the essence of Mendel's results and is his great contribution to the development of the science of genetics.

Mendel's choice of pea plants for his experiments was a very deliberate one. The plants were commercially available and easy to cultivate. Different varieties had clearly different characteristics which "bred true," reappearing in crop after crop, and although the plants could be crossbred experimentally, accidental crossbreeding could never occur to confuse the experimental results. In Mendel's own words, quoted from his original paper, "The value and utility of any experiment are determined by the fitness of the material to the purpose for which it is used."

PRINCIPLE OF SEGREGATION

Mendel began with 32 different types of pea plants, which he studied for two years to see which characteristics were clearly defined. As he said later in his report on this work, he did not want to experiment with traits in which the difference could be "of a 'more or less' nature, which is often difficult to define." As a result of these observations, he selected for study seven traits which appeared as conspicuously different characteristics in different types of plants. One variety of plant, for example, always produced yellow peas, or seeds, while another always produced green ones.

Table 3–1 *Mendel's Pea-plant Experiment*

Trait	Dominant	Recessive	F_2 generation Dominant	Recessive	Total
Seed form	Smooth	Wrinkled	5,474	1,850	7,324
Seed color	Yellow	Green	6,022	2,001	8,023
Flower position	Axial	Terminal	651	207	858
Flower color	Red	White	705	224	929
Pod form	Inflated	Constricted	882	299	1,181
Pod color	Green	Yellow	428	152	580
Stem length	Tall	Dwarf	787	277	1,064

In one variety, the seeds, when dried, had a wrinkled appearance; while in another variety, they were smooth. The complete list of alternate traits is given in Table 3–1.

When Mendel performed the experimental crosses, he found that in every case in the first generation (now known as F_1 in biological shorthand), one of the alternate traits disappeared completely without a sign. All the progeny of the cross between yellow-seeded plants and green-seeded plants were as yellow-seeded as the yellow-seeded parent. This trait and the other such traits of the F_1 generation Mendel called *dominant*; the traits that disappeared in the first generation he called *recessive*.

The interesting question was: What had happened to the recessive trait —the wrinkledness of the seed or the greenness of its color—which had been passed on so faithfully for generations by the parent stock? Mendel let the pea plant itself carry out the next stage of the experiment by permitting the F_1 to self-pollinate. The recessive traits reappeared in the second (F_2) generation! In Table 3–1 are the results of Mendel's actual counts. Before you read any further, look at these figures and see if you can detect any relationships between them. Some interpreters of Mendel's work believe that he first formulated his theory and then performed the experiments to test it. Others believe that he examined the data first and then worked out an hypothesis to explain them. In either case, it was on the basis of these numbers—and with no more information than you have at this moment—that Mendel formulated the "laws" of classical genetics.

One additional point that might be made here, in relation to this first application of statistical principles to biology, is the importance of collecting a large enough sample. The relationships that Mendel discovered between the numbers of dominants and of recessives would not have held true if Mendel had studied only a few plants. If you toss a coin, it might turn up heads five times in a row, at which point it would be very easy to conclude that a tossed coin always turns up heads. If you keep on tossing it, however, the tendency of heads and tails to show up equally will increase as the sample gets larger.

Perhaps by now you have noticed that the dominant and recessive traits appear in the second, or F_2, generation in ratios of 3 to 1. How do the recessives disappear so completely and then appear again, and always in such constant proportions? It was in answering this question that Mendel made his greatest contribution. He saw that it was necessary to assume that hereditary characters were always determined by discrete factors* which appeared in pairs, one inherited from each parent. This hypothesis is known as *Mendel's first law*, or the *principle of segregation*.

* Mendel called these factors *Elemente*. Today they are known as *genes*, and hereafter we shall refer to them as genes.

3–8 *A cross between a pea plant with two dominant genes for red flowers (WW) and one with two recessive genes for white flowers (ww). The phenotype of the offspring in the F₁ generation is red, but note that the genotype is Ww. The F₂ generation is shown by a Punnett square. The W allele, being dominant, determines the phenotype. Only when the offspring receives a w allele from each parent and the genotype is ww, does the recessive trait (white) appear. The ratio of dominant to recessive phenotypes is thus always expected to be 3 to 1.*

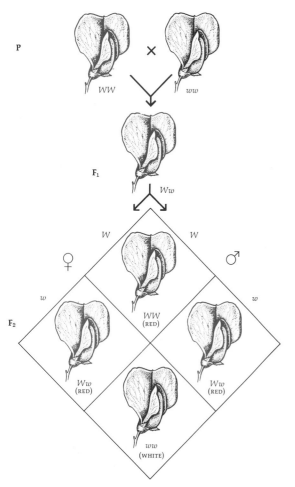

The two genes in a pair might be the same, in which case the plants or other organisms would breed true. Or the two genes might be different; such different, or alternative, forms came to be known as *alleles* (short for *allelomorph*, which means "alternative form"). Yellow-seededness and green-seededness, for instance, are alleles, different forms of the gene for seed color. When the genes of a gene pair are the same, the organism is said to be *homozygous* for that particular trait; when the genes of a gene pair are different, the organism is *heterozygous* for that trait.

When gametes are formed, genes are passed on to them; but each gamete contains only one of two possible alleles. When two gametes combine, the genes occur in matched pairs again. One allele may be dominant over another allele; in this case, the organism will appear as if it had only this gene. This appearance is known as its *phenotype*. However, in its genetic makeup, or *genotype*, each allele still exists independently and as a discrete unit even though it is not visible in the phenotype, and the recessive allele will separate from its dominant partner when gametes are formed. Only if two recessive alleles come together—one from the female gamete and one from the male—will the phenotype then show the recessive.* When pea plants having red flowers are crossed with pea plants having white flowers, only pea plants with red flowers are produced, although each plant in the *F₁* generation will carry a gene for red and a gene for white. Figure 3–8 shows what happens in the *F₂* generation.† Notice that the result will be the same if the individuals are cross-fertilized with others, which is the way these experiments are performed with plants that are not self-pollinating and with animals.

* Many tragic congenital diseases can be seen in the light of Mendel's work to be the result of the accidental coming together of parents who are each the unknown carriers of the same destructive recessive gene, which may have been carried intact but unsuspected for generations.

† The checkerboard diagram shown in Figure 3–8 was first used for the analysis of genetic distributions by the English geneticist L. C. Punnett. It is called a *Punnett square*. Note also in the figure that the symbols *W* (for red) and *w* (for white) designate the dominant gene with an uppercase letter and the recessive gene with a lowercase letter. This convention, started by Mendel, is generally observed in genetic notation.

On the basis of the information so far, Figure 3–8 diagrams not a fact but an hypothesis. Mendel tested this hypothesis by two additional experiments. He crossed white-flowering plants with white-flowering plants and found that he got only white-flowering plants. Next he crossed one of his hybrids, the result of an F_1 cross between red- and white-flowering plants, with a white-flowering plant. To the outside observer, it would appear as if Mendel were simply repeating his first experiment, crossing plants having red flowers with plants having white flowers. But he knew that if his hypothesis was correct, his results would be different from those of his first experiment. In fact, he actually predicted the results of such a cross before he made it. Can you? The easiest way is to diagram it, as in Figure 3–9. This experiment, which reveals the genotypes, is known as a *testcross* or *backcross*.

INDEPENDENT ASSORTMENT

In a second series of experiments, Mendel studied crosses between pea plants that differed simultaneously in two characteristics; for example, one parent plant had peas that were smooth and yellow, and the other had peas that were wrinkled and green. The smooth and yellow traits, you will recall, are both dominant, and the wrinkled and green are recessive. As you would expect, all the seeds of the F_1 generation were smooth and yellow. When the F_1 seeds were planted and the flowers allowed to self-pollinate, 556 seeds were produced. Of these, 315 showed the two dominant characteristics, smooth and yellow, but only 32 combined the recessive traits, green and wrinkled. All the rest of the seeds were unlike either parent; 101 were wrinkled and yellow, and 108 were smooth and green. Totally new combinations of characteristics had appeared. This experiment did not contradict Mendel's previous results. Smooth and wrinkled still appeared in the same 3:1 proportion, and so did yellow and green. But the smooth and the yellow traits and the wrinkled and the green ones, which had originally combined in one plant, behaved as if they were entirely independent of one another. From this, Mendel formulated his second law, the *principle of independent assortment*.

3–9 *A testcross between a hybrid and a white flowering plant. The hybrid is one of the F_1 generation shown in Figure 3–8. Do you see how the expected results of this cross confirm the hypothesis of Figure 3–8 with respect to the genotypes shown in that figure?*

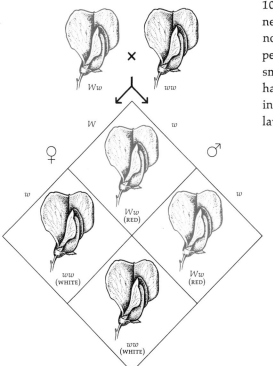

357   *Concepts of Heredity*

3–10 *One of the experiments from which Mendel derived his principle of independent assortment. A plant having round, smooth (RR) and yellow (YY) peas is crossed with a plant having wrinkled (rr) and green (yy) peas. The F_1 generation are all smooth and yellow, but notice how the traits will, on the average, appear in the F_2 generation. Of the 16 offspring, 9 should show the two dominant traits (RY), 3 should show one combination of dominant and recessive (Ry), 3 should show the alternate combination (rY) and 1 should show the two recessives (ry). This 9:3:3:1 distribution is always the expected result from a cross involving two pairs of independent recessive alleles.*

Figure 3–10 diagrams the explanation of these results and shows why, in a cross involving two pairs of allelomorphs, each pair with one dominant and one recessive allele, the ratio of distribution will be 9:3:3:1, with 9 representing the proportion of F_2 progeny which will show the two dominant traits, 1 the proportion that will show the two recessive traits, and 3 and 3 the proportions of the two alternative combinations of dominants and recessives. This is true whether one parent carries both recessive traits and the other both dominant ones, as in the experiment just described, or each parent carries one recessive and one dominant trait. You can demonstrate this by drawing a Punnett square.

INFLUENCE OF MENDEL

During the time that Mendel was working in the monastery garden at Brünn, Darwin was doing very similar experiments on his country estate in England—looking for the answers that, unknown to him, Mendel had found.

Ironically, Mendel's experiments, although included today among the great triumphs of biological thinking, had almost no immediate effect on the course of scientific history. They were first reported in 1865 before a small group of people in the local village—the Brünn Natural History Society—none of whom, apparently, understood what Mendel was talking about. But his paper was published the following year in the *Proceedings* of the Society, a journal which was circulated to libraries all over Europe. In addition, realizing the importance of his findings, Mendel himself continued for a number of years to send copies of his paper to other biologists—apparently not to Darwin, although he was aware of Darwin's work. We wonder today whether or not Darwin would have grasped the significance of Mendel's discoveries. If so, Darwin would have had the answers to some of the problems that never ceased to trouble him throughout his entire career.

P   RRYY   rryy

F_1 RrYy

RY   RY
Ry   Ry
rY   rY
ry   ry

♀   ♂

F_2

ROUND YELLOW
ROUND GREEN
WRINKLED YELLOW
WRINKLED GREEN

By 1900, biology was finally prepared to accept Mendel's findings. Within a single year, his paper was rediscovered simultaneously and independently by three scientists working in three different European countries. Each of them had done similar experiments and was searching the scientific literature to seek confirmation of his results. And so, Mendel's brilliant analysis, written 35 years too soon, was rediscovered, but only after his death.

SUMMARY

In this chapter, we started with man's earliest ideas about inheritance and traced the gradual development of these ideas into a science. The first question with which this new science was concerned was the mechanics of inheritance. How are hereditary characteristics passed from one generation to another?

By the middle of the nineteenth century, it was recognized that ova and spermatozoa were cells and that the egg and sperm both contributed to the hereditary characteristics of the new individual. But how were these special cells, called *gametes*, able to pass on the many hundreds of characteristics involved in inheritance? One answer to this question was the theory of *blending inheritance*, which held that the traits of the parents blended in the offspring, like a mixture of two fluids.

The great contribution of Gregor Mendel was to replace the blend theory with a *unit* theory. According to Mendel's *principle of segregation*, hereditary characters are always determined by discrete factors (now called *genes*), which appear in pairs, one of each pair inherited from each parent.

The genetic makeup of an organism is known as its *genotype*. Its appearance, or outward characteristics, is its *phenotype*. Both genes in a pair may be alike (a *homozygous* condition), or they may be different (*heterozygous*). Two genes forming a heterozygous pair are called *alleles*. Although both alleles are present in the genotype, only one may be detected in the phenotype. The gene that is expressed in the phenotype is the *dominant* gene; the one that is concealed in the phenotype is the *recessive* gene. When two organisms that are homozygous for different alleles of the same gene are crossed, the ratio of dominant to recessive in the phenotype is 3 to 1.

Mendel's other great principle, the *principle of independent assortment*, applies to the behavior of two or more genes. This law states that the members of each pair of genes segregate independently. In crosses involving two independent pairs of alleles, the expected phenotypic ratio is 9:3:3:1.

The Physical Basis of Heredity

Between the completion of Mendel's experiments in 1865 and their rediscovery in 1900, some very important observations were made. As you will
recall, by Mendel's time microscopists had seen both human spermatozoa
and human ova and had recognized them to be cells and to be the carriers
of the hereditary links between parents and offspring. But no one had actually seen fertilization occur. In 1875, the German zoologist Oscar Hertwig witnessed this event in the egg of a sea urchin. In sea urchins, as in
many other aquatic animals, the eggs are fertilized after they have been
laid by the female. For this reason, it was relatively simple for Hertwig to
observe a sperm cell entering the ovum and to follow the subsequent development of the embryo.

The Discovery of Chromosomes

Once the role of the gametes was thus definitely confirmed, biologists set
out to analyze the problem still more carefully. What structures in the
gametes were responsible for transmitting the hereditary material? This
question was brought into sharper focus by the fact that in almost all
plants and animals, eggs and sperm are very unequal in size. The only
structures that seemed analogous in both of them were the nuclei, and
since egg and sperm appeared to contribute equally to the offspring, it was
logical to guess that whatever each contributed had something to do with
their equal-sized nuclei.

On the other hand, cytologists had observed that the nuclei appeared
to dissolve at the time of cell division and to form anew once division
was completed. If this were true, it would be hard to argue that the nuclei
were the guardians of genetic constancy.

3–11 *A sea urchin crawling on the ocean floor. It was in the sea urchin that the fertilization process was first closely observed. Like many other aquatic animals, male sea urchins fertilize the eggs after they have been laid by the female. For this reason, it was relatively simple for investigators to observe the sea urchin sperm cell entering the ovum.* (H. Pederson)

Speculation might have stopped here had not work in cytology been tremendously stimulated by a rapid series of improvements, beginning in the 1870s, in the instruments and methods of microscopy. Among the most important of these was the development of staining techniques, which made visible some previously undescribed structures in the cell. Particularly interesting to cytologists was a collection of little rodlike objects which could be found from time to time within the nucleus of suitably stained cells. These rods were given the name *chromosomes,* which means simply "colored bodies," although the term took on far wider implications. The chromosomes were a subject of controversy for several years. They could not always be found, and the appearance of those that *were* seen changed from specimen to specimen. Some cytologists doubted whether these elusive structures really existed at all, suggesting that they might be merely by-products of the staining.

The Mechanism of Heredity

MITOSIS AND REDUCTION DIVISION

In 1882, order was brought out of chaos by the painstaking work of the German cytologist Walther Flemming. By studying hundreds of specimens, Flemming pieced together the separate steps in *mitosis,* the process in which the cell divides into two copies of itself. These steps were described in Chapter 1–4, and it might be useful for you to review that material before proceeding with the discussion.

Once the existence of chromosomes was confirmed, more and more cytologists began to observe them and to count the numbers of them present in different types of dividing cells. From their accumulated data, some facts emerged which, although they are already familiar to you, we shall review in their historical context:

1 The number of chromosomes in the somatic cells of any one species is nearly always constant.
2 In the course of cell division, the chromosomes of the parent cell are always evenly distributed between the two daughter cells.
3 The sperm and egg cells of any given species each have half the number of chromosomes of the somatic cells of that species. When the two gametes fuse to form the zygote, the diploid number is resolved.

By 1901, when Mendel's paper was being read and reread in biological circles, the way in which the chromosomes were reduced to the haploid number to form the gametes had been observed, although the meaning of the process was not yet understood.

361 *The Physical Basis of Heredity*

The ability of living things to reproduce themselves is the principal way that we distinguish them from nonliving things. Simple cell division, or replication, is the basic heredity mechanism which ensures the continuing of life. This process, known as mitosis, *is the means by which somatic cells multiply. All life begins with a single cell, which divides into two, then into four, and so on, and during this growth, an organism gradually takes shape.*

The important thing to remember about the mitotic process is that the chromosomes remain the same through successive cell divisions. The cell first doubles its chromosome complement and then divides the chromosomes equally between the two daughter cells. The result is that the chromosome makeup of a cell is the same as that of the cell from which it derived.

But in almost all higher forms of life (above the one-cell organisms), reproduction usually takes place not by simple cell division but by a joining of gametes. These gametes are produced by meiosis, *which results in the production of cells with new combinations and therefore the passing on of differences from one generation to another. Thus there is an important distinction between mitotic cell division, the end product of which is continuity and stability of the genetic material, and meiotic cell division, which results in variation and change.*

Bi-parental reproduction is not particularly efficient as a purely reproductive mechanism. What do you suppose its evolutionary advantages are? In other words, from a biological point of view, what is the purpose of having two sexes?

Cytology and Genetics Meet: Sutton's Hypothesis

Nineteenth century biologists interested in heredity had been concerned with the effects of inbreeding and crossbreeding in plants and animals. Cytologists during that fruitful century had devoted themselves to descriptions of cells and their structures. In 1902, cytology and genetics met, and it was a fateful encounter. Since that time neither has been the same. Walter S. Sutton, a graduate student at Columbia University, was studying the formation of gametes in the male grasshopper. In the grasshopper, as in other males, the gametes are formed from a special group of cells in the testes, the *spermatagonia*. These cells, it is important to remember, like all the cells of the body, arise originally from a single cell, the *zygote*, and are the result of repeated mitotic divisions of this original cell. At the time the gametes are formed, the spermatagonia undergo two more cell divisions, the meiotic divisions, and then differentiate into sperm.

Observing the process of meiosis, Sutton was struck by the fact that the chromosomes that paired with one another at the beginning of the reduction divisions had physical resemblances to one another. In diploid cells, chromosomes apparently came in pairs. These pairs—or *homologues,* as they came to be called—were only obvious at meiosis, but the discerning eye could find the homologues in the unpaired chromosomes when they became visible at the time of mitosis. They can be separated by the movements of the spindle during the first meiotic division. When gametes—the newly formed sperm and egg—come together at fertilization of the egg, each chromosome from the sperm cell has a new homologue, the corresponding chromosome in the egg. (The one exception is in the case of the sex chromosomes, which will be discussed in the next chapter.)

Sutton postulated that the homologues that he could observe undergoing separation in the formation of the sperm cells of the grasshopper were replicas of the homologous chromosomes that had come together to make the zygote, the fertilized egg, at the first moment in that particular grasshopper's biography. In other words, if one homologue of a chromosome pair came from the grasshopper's mother, the other homologue must have come from the father. The two had been copied faithfully in cell division after cell division through the grasshopper's several stages of development until the time of meiosis, when they were once again separated.

Suddenly the facts fell into place. Suppose chromosomes carried genes, the *Elemente* described by Mendel! This idea does not seem very startling to us now, but remember that the gene was just an abstract idea or mathematical unit to the geneticist and that the chromosome was just an unidentified colored body to the cytologist. Suppose, Sutton reasoned, alleles occurred on homologous chromosomes. Then the alleles could always remain independent and so could separate at meiosis, with new pairs of alleles forming when the gametes came together in the zygote. Mendel's law of the segregation of inherited traits could be explained by the segregation of the homologous chromosomes at reduction division.

Now, suppose that two of the chromosomes of the male grasshopper—let us call them chromosome A and chromosome C—were inherited from the mother and chromosome B and chromosome D, were inherited from the father. At the time of meiosis, A and C need not stay together. The gamete that received chromosome A could not receive B, the homologue of A, but it could receive either C or D. So maternal traits could readily be separated from one another, and paternal also. Or in terms of the garden pea, cross-fertilization of a plant having smooth and yellow seeds with a plant having green and wrinkled seeds could produce, in the F_2 generation, plants with smooth and green seeds and plants with yellow and wrinkled seeds, although neither parent plant had had this phenotype.

Mendel's law of independent assortment could be explained on the basis of the probability that chromosomes that were originally maternal would become separated from one another at the time of reduction division and the equal probability that paternal chromosomes would also be separated.

Sutton's arguments in support of the hypothesis that Mendel's factors, or genes, are carried on chromosomes can be summarized as follows:

1 All hereditary characters are carried in the sperm and egg cells since these cells are the only bridge from one generation to another.
2 Since sperm cells lose almost all their cytoplasm as they mature, the hereditary factors must be carried in the nucleus.
3 The only visible parts of the nucleus which are accurately divided during cell division are the chromosomes. This suggests that the factors, or genes, must be carried on the chromosomes.
4 Chromosomes obey Mendel's laws.
   a Chromosomes occur in pairs; so do Mendelian factors.
   b Chromosomes segregate at meiosis; Mendelian factors segregate at the formation of the gamete.
   c The members of a chromosome pair appear to segregate independently of other chromosome pairs; Mendelian factors segregate independently.

As occurs often in the history of science, two other biologists recognized the correlation between the behavior of Mendel's *Elemente* and the observed movements of the chromosomes, but young Sutton's paper appeared first, and his presentation was by far the most convincing.

DISTRIBUTION OF THE GENETIC MATERIAL

With the publication of Sutton's tightly argued hypothesis, it became possible to visualize the distribution of the genetic material at meiosis in very concrete terms, comparable to dealing out a pack of cards.

As an analogy, imagine that you have before you that pack of cards. The cards have been sorted into two piles, red and black. The red cards represent the chromosomes inherited from the maternal side, and the black cards the paternal chromosomes. The two piles are arranged in the following order: ace to deuce of hearts and ace to deuce of diamonds in one pile; ace to deuce of spades and ace to deuce of clubs in the other pile. This is equivalent to the pairing that takes place before the first meiotic division. The ace of hearts and the ace of spades are homologues, as are the king of hearts and the king of spades, and so on right through the pack.

Now deal out these two piles into two new ones. You must always place a red card in one pile and a black card in the other, so each pile gets only one homologue. But the red king can go just as easily with the black ace

3–12 *The eight ways in which you can sort three red and three black cards, providing that no two cards of the same value are placed in any one pile. (The sequence of the cards in a pile does not matter.) This is analogous to the distribution of genetic materials at meiosis. The red cards represent chromosomes inherited from the maternal side, and the black cards those from the paternal side. Cards of the same value (i.e., red ace and black ace) represent homologous chromosomes before the first meiotic division. The eight sets of two piles each show all the possible combinations of these chromosomes. If you started out with 12 cards rather than 6, how many possible combinations could you obtain?*

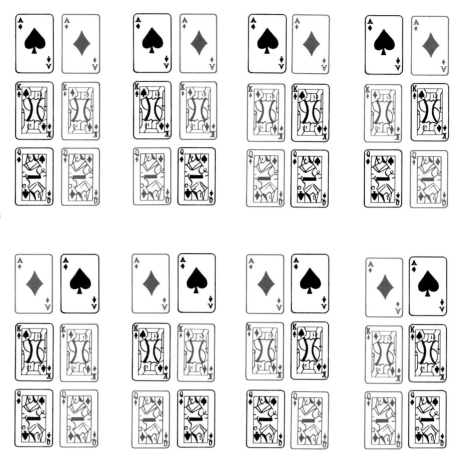

as with the red ace. And where you put each red ace and where you put each homologous king has no influence at all on where you put each of the homologous queens. The number of cards in the deck is 52; this corresponds, following our analogy, to $2n$, the diploid number. Can you figure out how many different ways you can sort this number into two piles, following the rule of homologues?

If you have only two cards, there is only one possible distribution—one card in each pile. If you have four cards, you can arrange these four cards in four ways. If you have six cards, you can arrange them in eight ways, or if you have eight, in sixteen ways. (See Figure 3–12.) By now you may be able to see that the number of possible arrangements of 52 cards is 2^{26}, and the general formula for such arrangements is 2^n, with n representing the haploid number.

365 *The Physical Basis of Heredity*

FORMATION OF SPERM CELLS

Man has 46 chromosomes and so is capable of producing 2^{23} different kinds of sperm cells—in other words, 8,388,608 different combinations of chromosomes, as many as there are different individuals in New York City. Only two different combinations are formed from each meiotic division, but since a single ejaculation of male semen contains about 240 million sperm, each of these combinations can be realized. These sperm are constantly being produced in the testes by meiotic division of spermatocytes. (See Figure 3–13.)

FORMATION OF EGG CELLS

The human female usually produces only one egg at a time, and the other products of meiotic division, which in the male make up three separate additional gametes, are discarded from the cell in what are known as *polar bodies*. Unlike the male, who is constantly producing more gametes, the female is born with a fixed number of potential gametes already present in the ovaries; in fact, the ova have begun their first meiotic division before the infant girl is born. In some cases, two eggs are produced simultaneously, and if both are fertilized, two infants will be born at the same time. Such infants, known as fraternal twins, actually bear no closer

3–13 *The series of changes which result in the formation of sperm cells begins with the growth of spermatogonia into larger cells known as primary spermatocytes. These divide (first meiotic division) into two equal-sized cells, the secondary spermatocytes. In the second meiotic division, four equal-sized spermatids are formed. By a complicated process of growth and change, the spermatids become functional sperm.*

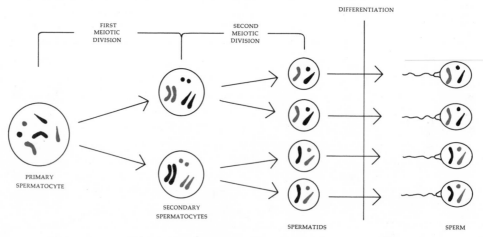

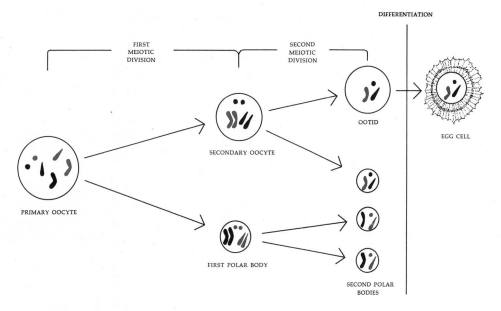

3–14 *Egg cells develop in the ovary from primary oocytes, which are formed from oogonia. The first meiotic division results in one large cell, the secondary oocyte, and one small cell, the first polar body. (In order to show them more clearly, the polar bodies are pictured here much larger than they actually are in relation to the oocytes and egg cell. The polar body is so called because it appears as a small speck at the animal pole of the egg.) In the second meiotic division, the secondary oocyte divides into the ootid and a second polar body. The first polar body may also divide. The ootid then becomes an egg cell, or ovum, and the three small polar bodies disintegrate. In human females, the formation of primary oocytes from oogonia begins about the third month of fetal development, and by the time of birth, the two ovaries contain some 400,000 primary oocytes which have reached prophase of the first meiotic division. These primary oocytes remain in prophase until the female matures sexually. Then, under the influence of hormones, the first meiotic division resumes and is completed at about the time of ovulation. This may be some 45 years after meiosis began!*

genetic resemblance to one another than do any brothers and sisters. Sometimes, however, the fertilized egg, or zygote, may undergo a mitotic division before development of the embryo begins. In this case, two infants will result which will have identical sets of chromosomes. Such identical twins are the only individuals in the world with the same genetic makeup.

367   *The Physical Basis of Heredity*

Exceptions to Mendel's Principles

During the decade following the discovery of Mendel's paper—the first decade of the twentieth century—many studies were carried out which confirmed his work in a large number of different kinds of plants and animals. At the same time, some important exceptions to Mendel's principles were found. Dominant and recessive traits are not always so clear-cut as in the pea plant. Some traits do appear to blend. Figure 3–15, for instance, diagrams the cross between a red and a white snapdragon. The first generation is pink. But when this generation is allowed to self-pollinate, the traits sort themselves out once again. More important exceptions were found in the study of characteristics, such as coat color, in animals. In nearly all cases, these were discovered to be governed not by one but by several genes. Most of the inherited characteristics in man, such as skin color, are similarly controlled by a number of separate genes.

MUTATIONS

A particularly interesting exception to the Mendelian laws was noted by one of Mendel's three rediscoverers, a Dutch botanist named Hugo De Vries. De Vries was working with the evening primrose—which is just another example of the biological axiom that studies of lions or elephants do not necessarily yield the most portentous results or inspire the boldest conclusions. Heredity in the primrose was generally orderly and predictable, as in the garden pea, but occasionally a characteristic appeared that was not present in either parent or indeed anywhere in the lineage of that particular plant. De Vries hypothesized that this characteristic came about as a result of a change in a gene and that the trait embodied in the changed gene was then passed along like any other hereditary trait. De Vries spoke of this hereditary change as a *mutation* and of the organism that carried it as a *mutant*.*

De Vries reported this work in 1903, the same year that Sutton published his classic paper. This, then, completed the data which Darwin had needed. To explain Darwinian evolution required (1) a means for continuity of hereditary expression and (2) a mechanism for small constant variations, minute changes upon which natural selection could operate. Independent assortment, as provided for by the random segregation of the chromosomes at meiosis, and mutation are the necessary means of variations.

* It is one of the ironies of history that only about 2 of some 2,000 changes in the evening primrose observed by De Vries were actually mutations. The rest were due to new combinations of chromosomes rather than actual changes in any particular gene. However, De Vries's definition of a mutant and his recognition of the importance of the concept of mutation are still valid, although his examples are not.

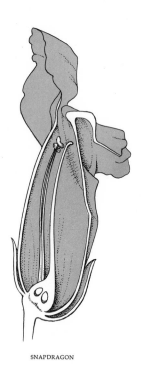

SNAPDRAGON

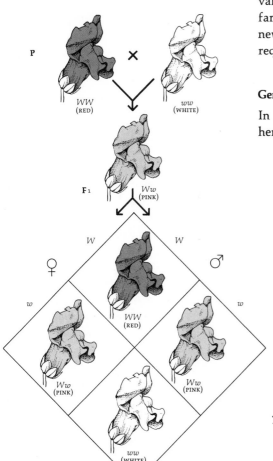

3–15 *A cross between a red and a white snapdragon. This looks very much like the cross between a red- and a white-flowering pea plant shown in Figure 3–8, but there is a significant difference. The hybrid (Ww), instead of showing the dominant red, is pink. Does this seem to support the theory of blending inheritance? But genes must be involved—since the traits sort themselves out again in the F_2 generation and do so in accordance with Mendel's 1:2:1 ratio; the traits are not actually blending. The explanation is that this is a case in which neither allele is dominant.*

Some years later, in 1927, H. J. Muller found that treatment of gametes by x-rays greatly increased the rate of appearance of mutations. It was soon discovered that other radiations such as ultraviolet light, and some chemicals as well, could also act as *mutagens*, the agents that produce mutations. The ability to produce mutations was essential as a technique for genetic studies on a variety of organisms. Since the time of Muller's experiments, the great majority of the mutations deliberately produced by radiations and chemicals and subjected to laboratory study have been detrimental to the organism, and many of them have been lethal. This is not surprising. If one takes a finely tuned piece of machinery or a Shakespearean sonnet and makes a random change in it, it is extremely unlikely that the change will be an improvement. Consider what would happen if you changed a wire at random in a TV set!

The ability of x-rays to produce mutations and so threaten future generations is a major cause of concern to many scientists in assessing the dangers of fallout from the testing of nuclear bombs. Very low doses of x-ray and other radiations have been shown to produce genetic changes, and it is not known whether there is any detectable dose so low that it can never produce changes in the genetic makeup. It is generally agreed that the value of medical uses of x-rays, such as for chest or dental examinations, far outweighs any possible risk to the patient, but new instruments and new techniques are constantly under development to decrease the dose required and to make exposures even briefer and safer.

Genes in Populations: The Hardy-Weinberg Law

In the days when most biologists believed in some sort of blending inheritance, it was difficult to understand why rare characteristics did not simply become so diluted that, for all intents and purposes, they disappeared. After the rediscovery of Mendel's work in the early 1900s, this question reappeared in a somewhat different form: If one trait is dominant and one is recessive, why doesn't the dominant trait drive out the recessive? For instance, early in the history of genetics, a family had been described in which certain members had short stubby fingers, a condition called *brachydactylism* (Figure 3–16). A study of the family records showed that brachydactylism was inherited as a simple Mendelian dominant. If the individuals with stubby fingers continued to intermarry with the rest of the people in the world, would all the people in the world someday have short fingers? Why not?

If this question seems puzzling at first, you may find consolation in the fact that it puzzled many of the best biologists of the early 1900s. Some of them even went so far as to say that the stubborn persistence of recessive traits disproved Mendel's principles. In fact, as you will see in a minute, just the opposite is true; according to Mendel's formulations, the recessives cannot be eliminated.

For example, let us take a hypothetical population; this may be a population of human beings, which is the meaning we generally give to the word "population," but it need not necessarily be. In biological terms, a population is simply any group of interbreeding individuals. One-half of the population is homozygous (i.e., in the zygote, both genes of a pair are alike) for the dominant gene *A*, and the other half is homozygous for the recessive gene *a*. Assume that the population interbreeds *at random* (with respect to genes *A* and *a*), which means that an *AA* (or *aa*) individual is no more likely to meet with another *AA* (or *aa*) individual than would be determined by chance, given the frequency in the population of *A* (or *a*).

In the second generation, as the Punnett square (Figure 3–17) reminds us, 75 percent of the population will resemble the *AA* parents and 25 percent will resemble the *aa* parents. At this point, you may well believe that the dominants are taking over, but wait a moment. Assuming that *AA*, *Aa*, and *aa* are equally viable, that is, equally likely to have offspring, and unless other factors intervene, the third generation will have just the same proportion of *AA*'s, *Aa*'s, and *aa*'s, and so will the fourth and the fifth.

This fact was pointed out simultaneously in 1908 by G. H. Hardy, an English mathematician, and G. Weinberg, a German physician, and is known as the *Hardy-Weinberg law*. The law is a deduction from the Mendelian principles of heredity and the assumption of random mating. It states that *in the absence of forces that change gene populations, the relative frequencies of each gene allele (as established in the second generation) tend to remain constant from generation to generation.*

To see why this is true, we shall return to our example. The proportions of *AA*, *Aa*, and *aa* in the original population were 1:0:1. They are now, in

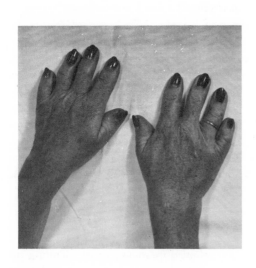

3–16 *A dominant gene is responsible for the trait known as* brachydactyly (*short fingers*). *In the brachydactylous hands shown here, the first bones of the fingers are of normal length but the second and third bones are abnormally short.* (*Dr. Victor A. McKusick*)

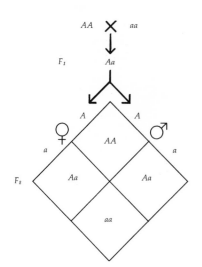

3–17 *Punnett square, showing the 3:1 phenotype and 1:2:1 genotype ratios of the F$_2$ generation.*

the F$_2$ generation, 1:2:1—in other words, 1/4 of the population is now *AA*, 1/2 *Aa*, and 1/4 *aa*. This means, for example, that in the third generation, 1/4 × 1/4, or 1/16, of the total number of crosses will be *AA* with *AA* (*random* mating, remember), 1/8 (1/4 × 1/2) will be *AA* with *Aa*, 1/8 (1/2 × 1/4) will be *Aa* with *AA*, and 1/4 (1/2 × 1/2) will be *Aa* with *Aa*. From these figures and the Punnett squares shown in Figure 3–18, we can determine what proportion of the third generation will be *AA*. Since all the progeny of *AA* × *AA* will be *AA* and since *AA* × *AA* represents 1/16 of the total number of crosses, *AA* × *AA* will contribute *AA*'s in the amount of 1/16 (1 × 1/16) of the total F$_3$ population. Only 1/2 of the progeny of *AA* × *Aa* will be *AA*; therefore, this cross will also contribute *AA*'s in the amount of 1/16 (1/8 × 1/2) of the total F$_3$ population. By the same reasoning, *Aa* × *AA* and *Aa* × *Aa* will each contribute 1/16. The proportion of *AA*'s in the F^3 generation is therefore 1/16 + 1/16 + 1/16 + 1/16 = 1/4. Note that this proportion is the same as it was in the F$_2$ generation.

Try working out the proportions for *Aa* and *aa*. Are they the same for both F$_2$ and F$_3$? Can you see why the gene distribution in F$_3$ will be the same in all succeeding generations?

NOTE: It must be remembered that the model we have used is essentially an artificial one since our results are accurate *only* when (1) the population is large enough so that accidents of sampling can be ignored, (2) mates are chosen at random, (3) mutations from *A* to *a* or from *a* to *A* are ignored because they are so infrequent, and (4) the carriers of *AA*, *Aa*, and *aa* are equally fit—that is, they leave an equal number of offspring.

3–18 *From an original cross of AA and aa, the four possible F$_2$ crosses that will produce AA in F$_3$.*

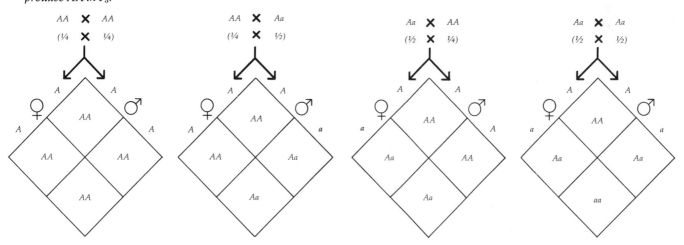

The Hardy-Weinberg law can be expressed algebraically by the equation $p^2 + 2pq + q^2 = 1$. In this equation, p stands for the frequency of the dominant gene in the population. The gene frequency is the proportion of the particular gene in relation to all the genes in the population. In a population of higher organisms, the number of genes will equal twice the number of individuals. Gene frequency can be expressed either as a fraction or as a percentage. Similarly, q stands for the frequency of the recessive gene in the population, and $2pq$ is the frequency of the heterozygote. To

3–19 *The Hardy-Weinberg equilibrium. The checkerboard diagram illustrates the random mating of individuals homozygous and heterozygous for genes A and a. Since the sum of the gene frequencies of the three types of individuals (AA, Aa, and aa) of both sexes equals 1.00, the overall area of the square is 1.00. The frequency* p *of gene A is the frequency of the AA individuals plus one-half the frequency of the heterozygotes (Aa's); the frequency* q *of gene a is the frequency of aa individuals plus one-half the frequency of the Aa's. (Thus* p + q = 1.) *Therefore, the frequencies of AA, Aa, and aa individuals produced after random mating are* p², 2pq, *and* q², *respectively, and* p² + 2pq + q² = 1.00. *Since* p² + 1/2 (2pq) = p(p + q) = p(1) = p,*the gene frequencies of p and q must remain constant and the frequencies of AA, Aa, and aa are therefore also constant.*

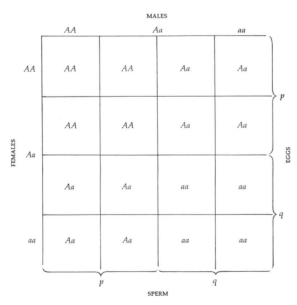

assume random matings is equivalent to combining at random the pooled genes from all the individuals in the population. Under this circumstance, the frequency with which gene A will pair with gene A will be equal to $p \times p$, or p^2. The frequency with which a will pair with a will be equal to $q \times q$, or q^2. The frequency with which a sperm with gene A will pair with an egg with gene a will equal $p \times q$, or pq, while the frequency with which a sperm with gene a will pair with an egg with gene A will equal $q \times p$, which is conveniently expressed also as pq. The total adds up to the total population—100 percent if the frequencies have been expressed in percentages, or simply 1 if they have been expressed in fractions or decimals, as is most usual. This shows that counting genes at random gives just the same results as considering the consequences of combining individuals at random and adding up the types of offspring they produce, as we did above.

Let us see how this equation works, returning to the now familiar example of yellow and green peas. We have a hypothetical population of male and female flowers (in peas, this can be the same flower, of course, but this does not alter the principle) from which 100 pollen cells and 100 ova will recombine at random. Seventy of the pollen cells carry the dominant allele Y, thirty carry the recessive allele y; in other words, the gene frequencies are 0.70 and 0.30. Similarly, among the ova the gene frequency for Y is 0.70 and for y is 0.30.

♀ ♂	Product	Frequency
Yellow × yellow	0.70 × 0.70	0.49
Yellow × green	0.70 × 0.30	0.21
Green × yellow	0.30 × 0.70	0.21
Green × green	0.30 × 0.30	0.09
		1.00

Notice that only 9 percent of the progeny will be phenotypically green but that 42 percent will carry the recessive gene heterozygously. Since $p + q$ will always equal 1 (or 100 percent), you can readily determine the proportions of both recessive and dominant genes in a population simply by counting the number of recessives that appear phenotypically, dividing that number by the total population, and taking the square root of the result to obtain q.

The Hardy-Weinberg method is used by medical geneticists in calculating the probabilities, for example, of a man who has inherited one allele for a particular gene encountering a woman who harbors the same allele of that particular gene. This can be of great importance if the homozygous recessive for that gene will be seriously handicapping. It is also useful for population geneticists and students of evolution who want to trace trends in large populations.

Of greater importance to the general biology student is the underlying principle of the Hardy-Weinberg law. Genes, even if they are recessive, tend to persist in stable proportions in a biological population—but only provided that they confer no selective advantage or disadvantage. Remember that *if the Hardy-Weinberg law were universal in application, evolution could never have taken place.* Here again, we have the two interacting themes of genetics: constancy, as expressed by the unchanging ratios of the Hardy-Weinberg equation, and variability, provided in this case by the forces of mutation and recombination.

Mendelian Inheritance in Man

A number of man's many inherited characteristics have been traced to single genes. One such characteristic, which was mentioned previously, is *brachydactylism,* and there are other characteristics involving fingers and toes, including possession of extra ones, which seem to involve simple dominants. Another simple dominant trait is tongue rolling (Figure 3–20). Can you roll your tongue? Can your parents? What is your genotype for tongue rolling? If you cannot roll your tongue, does this mean that neither of your parents can? This may seem to be a very trivial sort of characteristic, one that neither natural selection nor society would favor, but oddly enough, very small differences such as this may have considerable importance over an evolutionary time span.

RETINOBLASTOMA

The development of a rare form of cancer of the eye, retinoblastoma, is also under the influence of a dominant gene. At one time, most of the persons with this gene died in childhood, yet the disease did not seem to decrease in frequency, as one would expect in the case of a dominant gene with a lethal effect. This indicates to geneticists that new mutations must constantly occur which keep the gene in the population. Within the last generation, cancer specialists have begun to save the lives of children with retinoblastoma, although in nearly all cases, it is necessary to sacrifice the sight of one or both eyes. As a consequence, these genes are being retained in the gene pool. If the mutation rate remains constant, there may well be

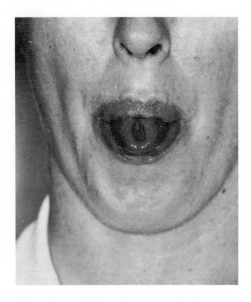

3–20 *The tongue-rolling ability is transmitted by a dominant gene. Seven out of ten people have this ability; do you? You can perform a simple experiment in genetics by checking to see if your parents and your brothers and sisters can do it.*

an increase in the incidence of this tragic hereditary disease, though the increase is likely to occur very slowly.

If a woman with a gene for retinoblastoma were to marry a man genetically free of the disease, what percentage of their children would be likely to develop retinoblastoma? If you were a doctor, what would you tell such a couple? As a voter, would you support legislation restricting such people from having children?

SICKLE-CELL ANEMIA

Another example of a human disease caused by a single gene is sickle-cell anemia, common in the tropics. In this disease, a large proportion of the red blood cells "sickle"—that is, form a sickle shape—and are eliminated from the bloodstream. This produces a serious and often fatal anemia in persons homozygous for the sickling gene. Persons heterozygous for the gene have both normal red cells and "sickle" cells. The heterozygotes usually have enough normal hemoglobin to function normally, and in such persons the presence of the recessive gene can usually be detected only by special laboratory tests.

Very few of the homozygous recessives ever have children, so one might expect the disease to decrease slowly. But in fact, there has been no decrease in the disease. Nor can we explain the persistence of the disease on the basis of new mutations, as is the case with retinoblastoma; the mutation rate would be far too high.

Further study has shown that persons heterozygous for the sickle-cell gene have a relatively high resistance to malaria, a disease caused by a protozoan parasite which grows in red blood cells. As a consequence, in areas where malaria is prevalent, the heterozygote is "selected" over both homozygotes—or, to put it more simply, a person who is well has a chance to raise more children than a person who is either dying of sickle-cell anemia or chronically ill with malaria. So the reproductive advantage of the heterozygote outweighs the disadvantage of the homozygote—evolutionarily speaking—and retains the gene in the population.

In this case and in the case of retinoblastoma, it might seem that the Hardy-Weinberg law is being broken. Not so. This law, as formulated, applies only to dominants and recessives now existing in the population, deliberately excluding both natural selection and mutation.

BLOOD GROUPS

Probably the most familiar characteristic in human beings that is determined by a single group of alleles is the ABO blood type. The existence of blood groups was discovered in 1900 by Karl Landsteiner. Mixing samples of blood taken from members of his laboratory staff, Landsteiner found that sometimes the red blood cells would clump together, or *agglu-*

3–21 *The round shapes of the normal red blood cells shown in this photomicrograph are interspersed with the characteristic half-moon shapes of sickle cells. Sickle cells tend to rupture as they circulate in the bloodstream, leaving the individual with fewer and fewer red cells. The result is a steadily progressing anemic condition, almost always fatal. (Roland G. Hiss, M.D.)*

|—25u—|

3-22 *Blood-group reactions to transfusions can be demonstrated equally well in test tubes, as shown here. The blood which is shown agglutinating has natural antibodies against the donor blood. You can see why persons with type O blood are called* universal donors *and those with type AB blood are* universal recipients.

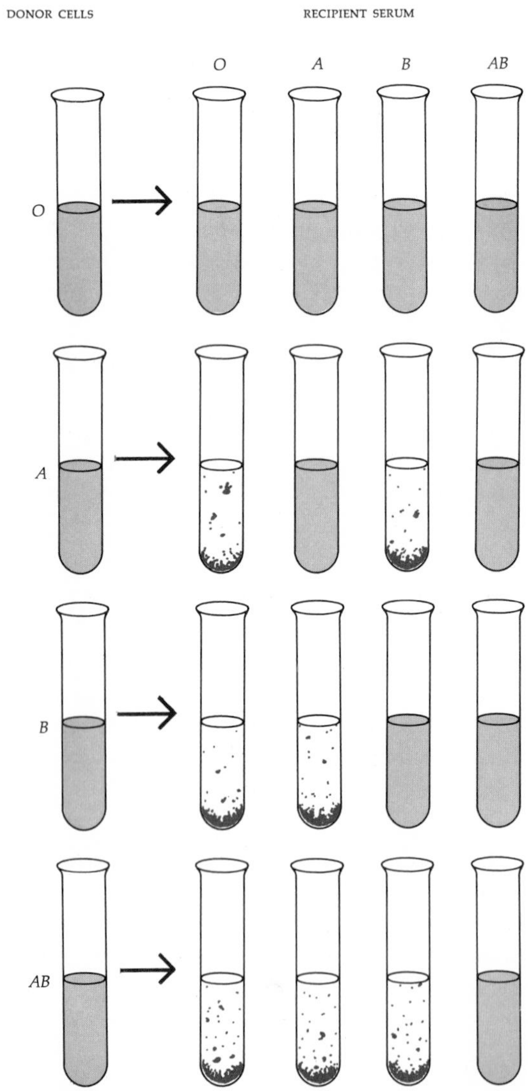

DONOR CELLS   RECIPIENT SERUM

O   *A*   *B*   *AB*

O

A

B

AB

tinate, and sometimes they would not. From these experiments, he developed the theory that there were different categories of blood—mixing blood of different categories would result in agglutination, while mixtures of blood of the same category would not agglutinate. He worked out four major blood groups: A, B, AB, and O. Before long, it was established that these blood types were inherited according to normal Mendelian laws.

Antibodies

The agglutination reaction seen in persons with incompatible blood types is caused by globular proteins known as *antibodies.* Antibodies are produced by special white cells called *lymphocytes* and by the *plasma cells* in lymphoid tissue in reaction to the presence of a foreign substance. The antibodies combine with the foreign substance in much the same way that an enzyme combines with its substrate. When an antibody combines with a foreign substance, that substance becomes more vulnerable to destruction by the phagocytes, the amoeboid white blood cells. Antibodies are our chief defense against viruses, bacteria, and other disease-causing organisms.

The first time the antibody-evoking reaction occurs, it is relatively slow. If, however, the same foreign substance invades the bloodstream a second time, the response is much swifter, which is why a single attack of many diseases, such as measles, mumps, and chicken pox, confers a lasting immunity.

Immunity does not always work to mankind's advantage, however. If your blood type is A, this means that on the surface of your red blood cells is a specific sugar (polysaccharide), A, that is not found on the surface of blood cells of persons of other blood types. Persons with type B have polysaccharide B on their red blood cells; persons with type AB have the two types of polysaccharides; and persons with type O have neither A nor B polysaccharides. People of blood type A have in their blood antibodies to B. Similarly, type B have antibodies to A. Type O have antibodies to both A and B, while type AB have neither. The antibodies that cause blood to agglutinate are known as "naturally occurring antibodies" since it is not necessary to have had a previous transfusion of incompatible blood for the reaction to occur. These "naturally occurring antibodies" are probably formed early in life against bacterial cells that are carried in the body and that have A and B polysaccharides on their surfaces. As a consequence, if you—still hypothetically blood type A—are given a transfusion of blood type B or blood type AB, your body's antibodies against the B or AB cells will agglutinate the donor B-type cells in your bloodstream. This reaction can be so violent that it is sometimes fatal. You can receive O cells safely, however, since they contain no polysaccharide that your body will recognize as foreign. For this reason, persons with O-type blood are known as *universal donors*. If you have AB-type blood, you are a *universal recipient*, since neither A nor B polysaccharides will be foreign to you. (See Figure 3–22 and Table 3–2.)

Blood-type Inheritance

Blood types are directly inherited, and the manner of inheritance can be determined from Table 3–2. If you have AB blood, it means that one of your parents is A or AB and the other is B or AB. If you have A blood, it means that you inherited an A gene from one parent and either an A gene or an O gene from the other. If you have O-type blood, you must have had parents who each carried one O gene, although they may have been, phenotypically, either A or B.

In the famous Charlie Chaplin paternity case in the 1940s, the baby's blood was B, the mother's A, and Chaplin's O. If you had been the judge, how would you have decided the case?* As you can see in Table 3–3, it can never be proved that someone is the father of a particular child, but it *can* be proved that someone could not be the father.

The blood groups are examples of multiple alleles (A, B, and O), and they remind us that there is no reason for the existence of only two alternative genes, although only two alleles can be present in a diploid cell at one time.

Rh Factor

The Rh factor is named after the rhesus monkey, which is used as a test animal for it. If a woman is Rh negative, meaning that she lacks the Rh factor, and her husband is homozygous for the Rh factor, any child that is conceived will be Rh positive. The mother may form antibodies against the

* As a matter of fact, Chaplin was judged guilty. Blood-group data are not admitted as evidence by some states in cases of disputed parentage.

Table 3–2 *Blood Groups*

| Group | Genotype | Reaction with antibodies | | Antibodies in blood plasma |
		Antibody-A	Antibody-B	
O	O/O	—	—	Antibody-A, Antibody-B
A	A/A, O/A	+	—	Antibody-B
B	B/B, O/B	—	+	Antibody-A
AB	A/B	+	+	None

377   *The Physical Basis of Heredity*

Table 3–3 *Blood-type Inheritance*

Parents		Children possible	Children not possible
A	A	A, O	AB, B
A	B	A, B, AB, O	
A	AB	A, B, AB	O
A	O	A, O	AB, B
B	B	B, O	A, AB
B	AB	A, B, AB	O
B	O	B, O	A, AB
AB	AB	A, B, AB	O
AB	O	A, B	O, AB
O	O	O	A, B, AB

Rh substance on the red blood cells, and if these antibodies enter the infant's circulation across the placental barrier, an agglutination reaction may occur, endangering the infant's life. Transfusion of the baby's blood at the time of birth—or even before, by new techniques—can flush the mother's antibodies out of the baby's system and greatly increase its chances of survival. Discovery of the ABO blood groups, which made such transfusions safe and practicable, and of the Rh system rank among the great medical advances of the twentieth century.

Immunological Reactions

Since the fetus, too, is a foreign substance, why doesn't the mother's body immediately react against it? Apparently, the fetus is protected from such reactions by a number of special mechanisms. The most important of these protective mechanisms probably have to do with the membranes in which the fetus is wrapped, and with the placenta, which serves as a filter for substances passing from the mother's body to that of the embryo. Some investigators have suggested that the process of birth may be related to the breakdown of these protective mechanisms and may be initiated by an immunological reaction.

One of the most important current problems involving genetics and immunological reactions is that of tissue transplantation. The surgical procedures involved in the transplantation of most organs of the body can now be carried out with reasonable safety, but the serious limiting factor to supplying "spare parts" for ailing bodies is the development by the patients of immune responses to the foreign organs. Such immune responses cause the destruction of the skin, kidney, or other transplanted tissue. In some cases, the use of drugs that suppress the formation of antibodies by white blood cells (lymphocytes) appears to have made the patient more tolerant of the foreign tissues. In other cases, the use of tissues from a donor closely related to the patient seems to have resulted in a lower rate of rejection of the grafted tissues. The only tissue transplants that can be carried out with any assurance of success at the present time, however, are those between identical twins since only such individuals have tissues that are genetically identical, that is, that carry no substance that will be recognized as foreign.

An interesting sidelight to this problem is the fact that the ability to recognize a substance as foreign does not develop until late in embryonic life. If tissues from another organism are transplanted into the embryo before this time, not only are they not recognized as foreign and no immunological reaction develops against them, but they actually come to be recognized as "self." If other tissues from the same donor are implanted in the same organism in adult life, they, too, will evoke no immune reaction.

SUMMARY

In the 1870s, rapid advances in the tools and methods of microscopy led to the discovery of chromosomes and, subsequently, to the analysis of the processes of mitosis and meiosis.

These discoveries were subsequently correlated with the theories of Mendel by Sutton, who proposed that the factors (genes) described by Mendel are carried on chromosomes. Chromosomes appeared to come in pairs, and Sutton postulated that alleles occur on these *homologous chromosomes*. The chromosome pairs separate at meiosis, and new pairs form again when the egg is fertilized.

Some important exceptions to Mendel's principles were found in the early 1900s. The most significant of these findings was the discovery by Hugo De Vries of the sudden appearance, in generations of evening primroses, of unpredictable hereditary changes. De Vries called these *mutations*. Some years later, in 1927, it was demonstrated that x-rays increased the rate of occurrence of mutations.

Mutations, together with the reassortment of the genetic material at meiosis, provide the mechanism for the small constant variations needed for evolution. An explanation for the way in which dominant and recessive genes may persist in stable proportions in populations was supplied by the *Hardy-Weinberg law,* which is actually an extension of Mendel's principles. The Hardy-Weinberg law states that, in the absence of forces that change gene populations, the relative frequencies of each gene allele tend to remain constant from generation to generation. The algebraic statement of the law is $p^2 + 2pq + q^2 = 1$, where the total population is expressed as 1 and p and q are the frequencies in the population of the dominant genes and recessive genes, respectively.

A number of man's inherited characteristics have been traced to a single gene. Among these are anatomical characteristics such as brachydactylism, certain muscular abilities (tongue rolling), and various diseases (retinoblastoma and sickle-cell anemia). Blood type is perhaps the most familiar example of inheritance from a single group of alleles. The four major blood groups are A, B, AB, and O. When different blood types are mixed, an *agglutination reaction* occurs; this is caused by *antibodies,* which are proteins produced by white blood cells (lymphocytes) and plasma cells in lymphoid tissue in reaction to the presence of a foreign substance in the body. The formation of antibodies is known as an *immunological reaction.*

Chapter 3–3

Chromosome Maps

Sutton showed that there was a relationship between the behavior of the chromosomes and the Mendelian laws, but he did not actually prove that the genes, which were still abstract concepts, were really carried by the chromosomes. His closely argued thesis demonstrated only that whatever cellular organelles did carry the genes would have to behave like chromosomes. Proof of the physical location of the gene was to depend on another series of studies, and these studies are the subject of this chapter.

Sex Chromosomes

In the 1890s, microscopists noticed that male and female animals showed chromosomal differences, and they began to suspect that these differences were related to sex determination. One pair of chromosomes differs between the sexes, and these are known as the *sex chromosomes*; all the other chromosomes, which are the same whether the animal is male or female, are known as *autosomes*. In many animals, the two sex chromosomes are identical in the female but are dissimilar in the male, with one male sex chromosome usually smaller and of a different shape. The chromosome found in both cells is called the X chromosome, and the unlike chromosome characteristic of male cells is called the Y chromosome. Thus we can characterize the two sexes as XX (female) and XY (male).

In some insects, however, including the grasshopper which Sutton had studied, the Y chromosome is missing entirely. In this case, we usually speak of XX females and XO males. In birds, moths, and butterflies (and in occasional species in other groups), the chromosomes are reversed; the male has the two X chromosomes, and the female only one. The Y chromosome may or may not be present.

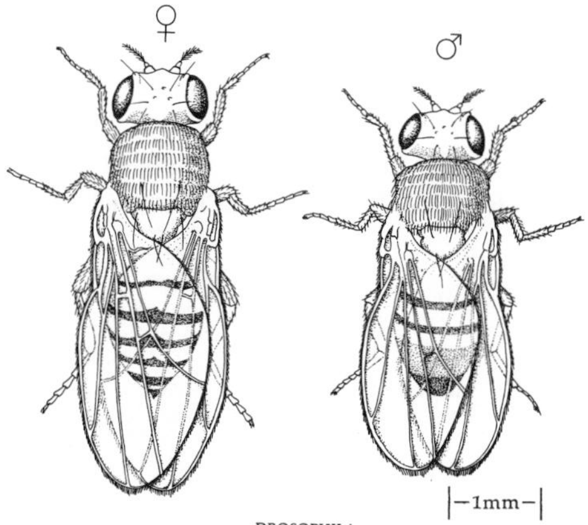

DROSOPHILA

|−1mm−|

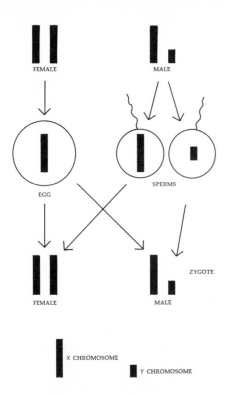

3–23 *How the sperm cell determines the sex of human offspring. During meiosis, the egg receives an X chromosome and the spermatocyte divides into four sperm cells, two receiving X chromosomes and two receiving Y chromosomes. (For simplicity, only two cells are shown in the drawing.) Whether the zygote becomes XX (female) or XY (male) depends on which of the sex chromosomes is carried in the sperm.*

Human beings have 22 pairs of autosomes, which are structurally the same in both sexes. Women have a twenty-third matching pair, *XX*. Men, as their twenty-third pair, have one *X* and one *Y*. During meiosis, as each diploid spermatocyte undergoes reduction division into four haploid sperm cells, two of the sperm cells receive *X* chromosomes and two receive *Y* chromosomes. The ovum always contains an *X* chromosome, since the human female does not generally possess the *Y* in any of her cells. Thus the zygote will become *XX* or *XY*, depending on which of the sex chromosomes is carried in the sperm that fertilizes the egg. (See Figure 3–23.) It is in this way that the sperm cell determines the sex of the future offspring, and it is the process of meiosis that governs the almost equal production of male and female babies.*

The Famous Fruit Fly

Early in the 1900s, Thomas Hunt Morgan began a study of genetics at Columbia University, founding what was to be the most important laboratory in the field for several decades. By a remarkable stroke of good fortune, he selected as his experimental material the tiny fruit fly *Drosophila.*†

Drosophila means "lover of dew," but actually this useful little fly is not attracted by dew but feeds on the fermenting yeast which it finds in rotting fruit. You yourself have probably seen clusters of *Drosophila* hovering around a bowl of overripe grapes or peaches. Mashed bananas are particularly favored by the flies, and Morgan maintained his large colony on this diet for decades. Next time, before you wave the little flies away, you may want to capture a few to look at under a magnifying lens.

Drosophila was a likely choice for a geneticist since it is easy to breed and maintain. A new generation of flies can be produced every two weeks, and each female lays hundreds of eggs at a time. Also, *Drosophila* has only four pairs of chromosomes, a feature that turned out to be particularly useful, although Morgan could not have foreseen that. Three pairs of these are autosomes, and the fourth is an *XX* pair in the female and an *XY* pair in the male (Figure 3–24).

* In actual fact, the ratio of human male to human female births is about 106 to 100. The reason for this is not known, but it has been suggested that the male-determining sperm, because of its slightly lighter chromosome burden, may have an advantage in getting to the egg.

† Notice how often geneticists use for their experiments "insignificant" little plants and animals—organisms that seem to occupy very unimportant and out-of-the-way places in the natural order. These organisms are usually selected for their biological convenience—because they are "fit materials"—not because of any particular interest in the organisms themselves. Underlying this approach is the geneticist's assumption that genetic principles are universal, applying equally to all living things.

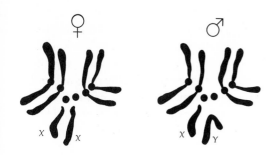

3–24 *Drosophila has only four pairs of chromosomes, a fact that simplified Morgan's experiments.*

3–25 *Offspring of a cross between a white-eyed (w) female and a red-eyed (W) male, illustrating what happens when a recessive gene is carried on an X chromosome. The F₁ female, having two X chromosomes, is heterozygous for the recessive and so will be red-eyed. But the F₁ male, with one X chromosome carrying the recessive (w) trait, will be white-eyed because the Y chromosome carries no gene for eye color.*

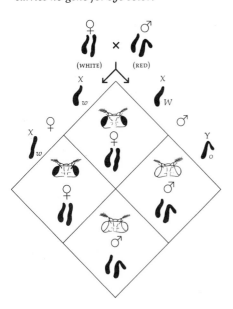

Sex-linked Characteristics

DROSOPHILA

Morgan was looking for genetic differences between individual drosophilas which he could study by interbreeding experiments. Shortly after he established his colony, such a difference appeared. One of the prominent and readily visible characteristics of the wild-type *Drosophila* is its brilliant red eyes. ("Wild-type" is a term frequently used by geneticists to describe an organism as it normally occurs in nature.) One day, a white-eyed fly, a mutant, appeared in the colony. The mutant, a male, was bred to a red-eyed female. All members of the first generation were red-eyed, indicating that the mutation was recessive. Then the members of the F_1 generation were interbred, following Mendel's now familiar course of action. Of the 4,252 fruit flies in this second generation, 2,459 were red-eyed females, 1,011 were red-eyed males, and 782 were white-eyed males—there was not one single white-eyed female. Morgan was aware of Sutton's work, and it occurred to him that perhaps the reason for only males being white-eyed was that the gene for white-eyedness was carried on a chromosome possessed only by males, in other words, the Y chromosome.

To test this idea, the original white-eyed male was crossed with one of his red-eyed daughters. Presumably the results should have been the same as those seen in the F_2 generation. But they were not. From this union were produced 129 red-eyed females, 88 white-eyed females, 132 red-eyed males, and 86 white-eyed males. The gene for white eyes could not be on the Y chromosome; females could also show the effects of this gene. Then still another cross was made. A white-eyed female was bred with a wild-type red-eyed male. All the females derived from this cross were red-eyed, and all the males had white eyes.

Can you figure out what was happening? Morgan finally did. As he had guessed first, the secret was in the sex chromosomes, but in the X chromosome rather than in the Y. Draw a Punnett square showing what will happen if a recessive gene is carried on an X chromosome. It should turn out to look something like Figure 3–25.

Notice that in Figure 3–25, X and Y do not stand for genes or traits but rather for the chromosomes on which these traits are carried. W and w stand for red-eyed and white-eyed, respectively. A female carrying the w trait on one chromosome only will be heterozygous for the recessive and so will be red-eyed. A male carrying the w trait on his X chromosome will be white-eyed since no dominant allele for red is present, as the 0 indicates. As it turned out, the Y chromosome of *Drosophila* carries relatively little genetic information.

COLOR BLINDNESS

The following year, in 1911, E. B. Wilson, the great cytologist, pointed out that the gene for color blindness in the human being is probably transmitted in the same way as the white-eyed *Drosophila* gene—as a recessive carried on the X chromosome. Can you explain why color blindness occurs in about 8 percent of men and only about 0.5 percent of women? Bearing in mind Morgan's experiments with red-eyed vs. white-eyed drosophilas, you should, by examining Figure 3–26, be able to see why the defect usually is carried by the mother but found in the sons.

3–26 *Color blindness in humans is carried by a recessive gene on the X chromosome. In the chart, the mother has inherited one normal and one defective gene. The normal gene will be dominant, and she will have normal color vision. However, half her eggs (on the average) will carry the defective gene, and half the normal gene—and it is a matter of chance as to which kind is fertilized. Since her husband's Y chromosome, the one that creates a son rather than a daughter, carries no gene for color discrimination, the single gene the wife contributes (even though it is a recessive gene) will determine whether or not the son is color-blind. Therefore, half her sons (on the average) will be color-blind.*

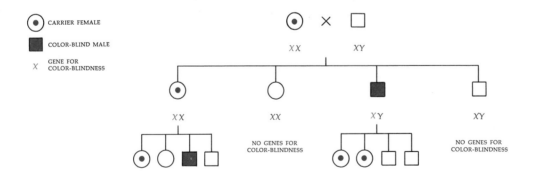

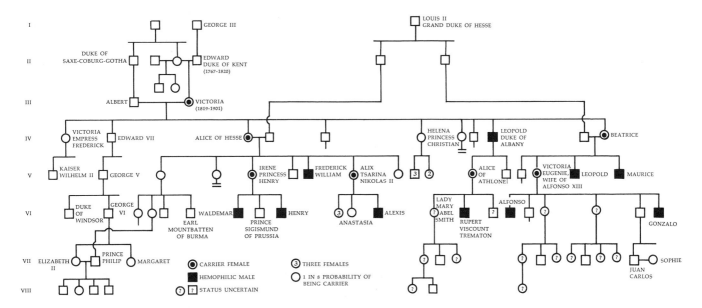

3–27 *As this chart shows, Queen Victoria was the original carrier of the hemophilia that has afflicted male members of the royal families of Europe since the nineteenth century. This is another case of a recessive inheritance transmitted on the X chromosome.* (Chart courtesy of Dr. Victor A. McKusick; photograph from The Bettmann Archive)

HEMOPHILIA

A classic example of a recessive inheritance transmitted on the X chromosome is the hemophilia which has afflicted the royal families of Europe since the nineteenth century. Hemophilia is a disease in which the blood does not clot normally, so that even minor injuries carry the risk of the patient's bleeding to death. Queen Victoria was probably the original carrier in the family. Since none of her forebears or collateral relatives was affected, the mutation may have occurred on an X chromosome in one of her parents or in her own early embryonic stage. One of her sons, Leopold, Duke of Albany, died of hemophilia at the age of 31. Prince Albert, Victoria's consort, could not have been responsible; male-to-male inheritance of the disease is impossible. At least two of Victoria's daughters were carriers since a number of *their* descendants were hemophiliacs. And so, through various intermarriages, the disease spread from throne to throne across Europe. In the Czarevitch, son of the last Czar of Russia, and in the princes of Spain, the gene for hemophilia inherited from Victoria had considerable political consequences.

385   *Chromosome Maps*

Morgan's discovery of the way in which white-eyedness is transmitted in *Drosophila* was useful in explaining the puzzling hereditary patterns of conditions such as color blindness and hemophilia. That such diseases are sex-linked could probably only have been proved to everyone's satisfaction in species in which backcrosses and other interbreeding experiments are practicable. The primary importance of this finding, however, in terms of the progress of genetics as a whole, was that it provided overwhelming evidence that at least one gene was a physical part of one particular chromosome. From this time onward, there was little argument about Sutton's hypothesis.

Linkage and Crossing-over

Perhaps by now you have noticed that geneticists are going to encounter difficulties if they try to assign each gene to a different chromosome, since the number of genes greatly exceeds any possible number of chromosomes. In fact, at the time he proposed the chromosome hypothesis, Sutton predicted that some genes would be found linked together on the same chromosome. On the other hand, genes like those for smoothness and yellowness in the garden pea could only follow the rules for independent assortment if they were on different chromosomes. If the two genes were on the same chromosome, wouldn't any pea that was smooth also have to be yellow? It was found that some of the genes assorted independently in breeding experiments, like smoothness and yellowness in the garden pea, while others tended to remain together. Genes that tended to travel together were said to be in the same *linkage groups*.

As increasing numbers of mutants were found in Columbia University's *Drosophila* population, the mutations began to fall into four linkage groups, in accord with the four pairs of chromosomes visible in the cells. Indeed, in all organisms which have been studied in sufficient genetic detail, the number of linkage groups and the number of pairs of chromosomes have been the same.

The idea that genes were carried on chromosomes and that many genes could be carried on a single chromosome was accepted rapidly. And almost as rapidly, difficulties arose. Most drosophilas, for example, have gray bodies and long wings. In Morgan's large colony, two mutant types arose that had black bodies and short wings; both of these mutations were recessive. If a cross was made between a wild-type fly and a fly carrying both mutations, the F_1 offspring would all be gray with long wings. Then if the F_1 were interbred, one of two outcomes seemed theoretically possible:

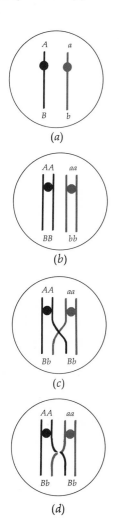

3–28 *The probable mechanism of crossing-over. At the start of meiosis, the homologous chromosomes form pairs, with their long axes parallel (a). Each chromosome duplicates to form two chromosomes (b). The chromatids bend across one another (c). Due possibly to tension resulting from this coiling, the two chromatids break at the point of contact, and each chromatid fuses with a portion of the other (d).*

1   The two recessives would be assorted independently and would appear in the 9:3:3:1 ratio, indicating that they were on different chromosomes.

2   The two recessives would be linked. In this case, 75 percent of the flies would be gray with long wings and 25 percent, homozygous for both recessives, would be black with vestigial wings.

In the case of these particular traits, the results most closely resembled outcome 2, but they did not conform exactly. In a few of the offspring, the traits seemed to assort independently, not together; that is, some few flies appeared that were gray with vestigial wings and some that were black with long wings. How could this be? Somehow the genes had moved out of their linkage groups.

To find out what was happening, Morgan tried a testcross, the same sort of testcross originally designed by Mendel and diagrammed in Figure 3–10. If black and gray, long and vestigial assorted independently—that is, if they were on different chromosomes—25 percent of the offspring of this cross should be black with long wings, 25 percent gray with long wings, 25 percent black with vestigial wings, and 25 percent gray with vestigial wings. On the other hand, if the two traits (color and wing size) were on the same chromosome and so moved together, half of the offspring of the testcross should be gray with long wings and half should be black with vestigial wings. But actually, as it turned out, over and over, in counts of hundreds of fruit flies resulting from such crosses, 41.5 percent were gray with long wings, 41.5 percent were black with vestigial wings, 8.5 percent were gray with vestigial wings, and another 8.5 percent were black with long wings.

Morgan was convinced by this time that genes were located on chromosomes. It now seemed clear that the two traits were located on the same chromosome since they did not show up in the 25:25:25:25 percentage ratios of separately assorted genes. The only way in which the observed figures could be explained was if one assumed (1) that the two genes were on one chromosome and their two alleles on the homologous chromosome, and (2) that sometimes genes could be exchanged between homologous chromosomes. It was therefore necessary to explain how alleles could change chromosomes.

Recall that at meiosis, the chromosomes pair, or undergo synapsis, before they divide. Consequently, four homologous chromosomes are lined up alongside each other before the first meiotic division. In 1909, the Belgian cytologist F. A. Janssens had observed breaks—*chiasmata*, he called them—in the adjoining homologues and had suggested that an exchange of chromosomal material might take place. (See Figure 3–28.) This exchange is difficult to see and interpret in the living cell, so that the suggestion was not so obvious as it now may seem. Furthermore, there is still no explanation of how homologous chromosomes manage to break in exactly corresponding sites and so exchange equal amounts of chromosomal material following each break. Vast accumulations of data have now confirmed that such exchanges, or *crossovers*, as they are called, do take place, and at virtually every meiosis.

Mapping the Chromosome

With the discovery of crossing-over, it began to seem clear not only that the genes were carried on the chromosomes, as Sutton had hypothesized, but that they must be arranged in a definite, fixed linear array along the length of the chromosome. Furthermore, all the genes must be at corresponding sites on particular chromosomes. If this were not true, exchange of sections of chromosomes could not possibly result in an exact exchange of alleles. (This is shown in Figure 3–29.) In other words, the genes were arrayed along the chromosome like beads along a string; this simile was widely used in genetics for several decades.

STURTEVANT'S HYPOTHESIS

As other traits were studied, it became clear that the percentage of separations, or crossovers, between any two genes, such as gray body and long wing, was different from the percentage of crossovers between two other genes, such as gray body and long leg. In addition, these percentages were very fixed and predictable. It occurred to A. H. Sturtevant, one of the many brilliant young geneticists attracted to Morgan's laboratory during these golden days of *Drosophila* genetics, that the percentage of crossovers probably had something to do with the distances between the genes, or in other words, with the order in which they were arranged along the chromosome. (You can see in Figure 3–29, for example, that in a crossover, the chances of *BC* and *bc* recombining to give *Bc* and *bC* are much less than the chances of *BF* and *bf* becoming *Bf* and *bF*.) This was the beginning of *chromosome mapping*.

Sturtevant postulated that genes must be arranged in a linear series on the chromosome. In 1913, he set out to test his hypothesis by crossover studies of the chromosomes of fruit flies. Such studies, if his hypothesis was true, would show him both the order in which the genes were arranged and the relative distances between them. As his standard unit of measure, he arbitrarily took the distance that would give (on the average) one crossover per 100 fertilized eggs. Thus genes with 10 percent crossover would be 10 units apart; those with 8 percent crossover would be 8 units apart.

3–29 *On the homologous chromosomes in (a), alleles are shown schematically in linear array. These two chromosomes exchange their parts during a single crossover (b). A double crossover is shown in (c).*

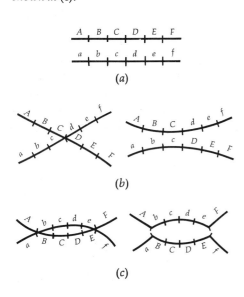

As fixed locations were assigned on a chromosome to each gene and the maps began to develop, geneticists could begin to predict the amount of crossing-over that should occur and what traits the offspring of any cross should exhibit. These predictions could then be tested by making the indicated crosses, and the whole procedure was confirmed if the offspring turned up with the predicted traits in the predicted proportions.

AN EXAMPLE

Suppose that you discover that two traits—called *A* and *B* for simplicity —in the prolific fruit fly occur together in 92 percent of the offspring and recombine with their recessive counterparts *a* and *b* in 8 percent (Figure 3–30*a*). Suppose that you then conduct breeding experiments to deter-

3–30 *How to "map" a chromosome. As shown at (a) and (b), genes A and B recombine with a and b in 8 percent of the offspring and genes A and C in 25 percent of the offspring. Using as a unit of measure the distance that will give (on the average) one crossover per 100 fertilized eggs, A is spaced 25 units from C and 8 units from B. To determine whether B is to the right or to the left of A, you must establish the percentage of recombination for B and C. If it is 33 percent, B is to the left of A; if it is 17 percent, B is to the right of A. What could you conclude if the B–C recombination percentage turned out to be a different figure (neither 17 nor 33)?*

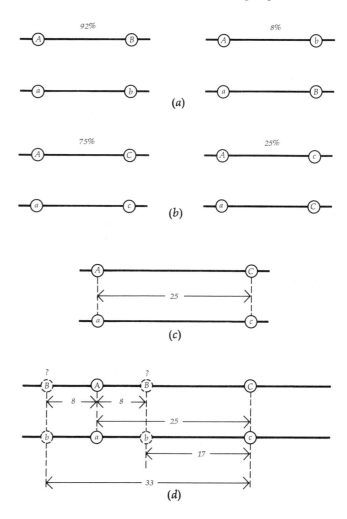

mine the percentage of recombinants between A, a and another pair of genes, C, c. These experiments show that AC and ac remain together in 75 percent of the offspring but recombine in 25 percent (Figure 3–30b). Now draw a hypothetical pair of chromosomes—simply as straight lines. Using Sturtevant's arbitrary units, the number 25 can represent the distance between A and C, a and c (Figure 3–30c). Now B and b can be located, with 8 representing the distance between A and B, a and b. Indicate where B should go on the hypothetical chromosome. If you don't know how to do this, you're right. From the information available so far, there is no way to know whether B is 8 units to the left of A or 8 units to the right of A, but it is not difficult to design an experiment to prove which is correct. One need only crossbreed a drosophila which shows the traits B and C with one having traits b and c. If recombination occurs in 33 percent of the cases, B is to the left of A ($8 + 25 = 33$); if it occurs in 17 percent of the cases, B can be placed 8 units to the right of A and 17 units to the left of C ($8 + 17 = 25$). (This is shown in Figure 3–30d.) Then, by similar experiments, any other trait linked to any of those already located can be placed on the line in relation to the others.

CONCLUSIONS

The figures used in the example are, of course, "ideal." In a case of actual mapping, the recombination "fractions" for a long-distance A–C would be smaller than those for A–B plus B–C. This is because more than one chiasma, or break, may occur along the length of the chromosome and so A–C may become separated by one break and then recombined by a second, and perhaps even separated again for a third. Since this happens frequently enough to distort the percentages for genes that are far apart from one another, the "units" are considered valid only for short distances. It is also true, as Sturtevant realized from the beginning, that the recombination fractions do not necessarily always reflect distance but may equally well reflect something about the structure of the chromosome in particular areas that may make it more or less likely to break at certain points.

By chromosome mapping, involving literally thousands and thousands of crossbreeding experiments, more than 500 different genes have been located in relationship to one another on the four chromosome pairs of *Drosophila melanogaster*, the most commonly studied species.

Perhaps the most important conclusion of all from the mapping studies of *Drosophila* was the incontestable proof this work provided that the genes occurred along the chromosome in an ordered linear array. Chromosome mapping has now been carried out in a variety of other organisms—viruses, bacteria, molds, plants, and animals—and this basic tenet has been found to hold true for them all.

3–31 *A portion of the genetic map of Drosophila melanogaster showing some of the genes on chromosome 2 and the distances between them, as calculated on the basis of frequency of crossovers. As you can see, more than one gene may affect a single characteristic, such as eye color. (After Watson, 1965)*

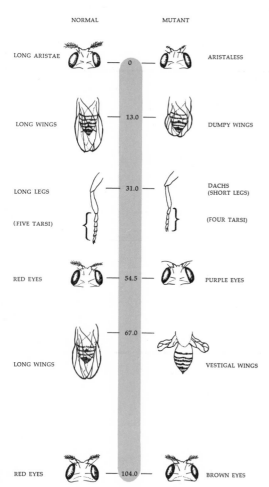

NORMAL   MUTANT

LONG ARISTAE — 0 — ARISTALESS

LONG WINGS — 13.0 — DUMPY WINGS

LONG LEGS — 31.0 — DACHS (SHORT LEGS)

(FIVE TARSI) (FOUR TARSI)

RED EYES — 54.5 — PURPLE EYES

— 67.0 —

LONG WINGS VESTIGAL WINGS

RED EYES — 104.0 — BROWN EYES

3–32 *Chromosomes in the salivary gland of a drosophila larva. These chromosomes are 100 times larger than the chromosomes in ordinary body cells, and their details are therefore much easier to see. (This is a photomicrograph taken with a light microscope, not an electron microscope.) Experiments showed that given traits were controlled from specific sites on these chromosomes, and the light and dark bandings were found to correspond almost exactly with previously plotted genetic maps, showing the correspondence between "genetic" and "physical" distances along the chromosome. (Dr. Berwind P. Kaufmann)*

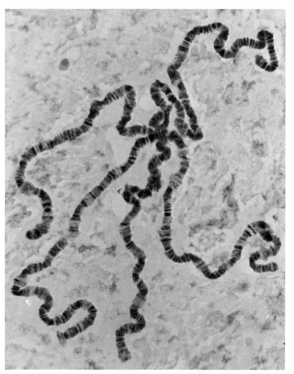

|——20µ——|

Giant Chromosomes

In 1933, 20 years after Sturtevant published his first experiments on mapping, the maps became somewhat less theoretical. It was found that in *Drosophila*, as in many other insects, there are certain cells that do not divide after the larval stage of the insect. In such cells, however, the nuclear material continues to replicate, over and over again. The chromosomes do not separate but become larger and larger. Such chromosomes were found in the salivary glands of the larvae of *Drosophila*. As you can see in Figure 3–32, these giant chromosomes are marked by very distinctive dark and light bands. Changes in these banding patterns were found to correlate with observed genetic changes in the flies. In addition, crossovers and breaks could actually be *seen*. Thus it was possible to confirm at a different level findings that had been based solely on breeding experiments.*

* What is, perhaps, most interesting is that the banding of salivary chromosomes in flies had been observed and recorded by cytologists before the 1900s—and Morgan and his group were not aware of this! While the geneticists were laboriously performing thousands of testcrosses, a simple means of confirming their hypotheses lay buried and forgotten. That they were able to develop such an accurate "map" of the chromosome without ever having seen the banding was an extraordinary intellectual achievement.

3-33 *A chromosomal inversion occurs when a middle segment of the chromosome breaks off, is turned 180°, and rejoins by the "wrong" ends. As you can see, an inversion results in a reversal of the sequence of genes, as shown in the righthand chromosome below. The drawing on the right shows how pairing takes place between two chromosomes one of which carries a large inverted segment.*

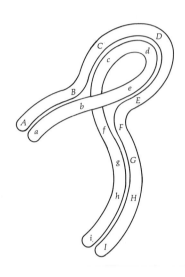

3-34 *Inversion was hypothesized on the basis of mapping studies. The hypothesis was substantiated by direct observation of pairing in giant chromosomes, such as the ones shown here. What would be the appearance of a chromosome pair in which each chromosome had an identical inversion?*

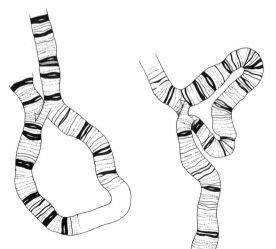

The giant chromosomes proved to be particularly useful in regard to the phenomenon known as *inversion*. Morgan and his group had guessed from some irregularities observed in the mapping experiments that, in some cases, portions of the chromosome might form loops at the time of breaking and crossing-over and that these segments might then reattach themselves by the wrong ends, as shown in Figure 3–33. Studies of the giant chromosomes showed that such inversions—previously only a brilliant hypothesis—actually did occur (Figure 3–34), and so it became possible to locate the genes involved in terms of particular chromosomes and, by extension, to guess the position of other genes.

Sex Determination

DROSOPHILA

For a number of years, maleness, at least in *Drosophila*, was assumed to be a function of some activity of the Y chromosome since that was universally present in males and absent in females. An unusual system for testing this assumption was found by Calvin Bridges, who, like Sturtevant, was a student in Morgan's laboratory.

3–35 *An example of nondisjunction. In this case, the X chromosomes have not sorted naturally. The result is that* both *X chromosomes go into one daughter cell, leaving the other daughter cell with no X chromosome at all.*

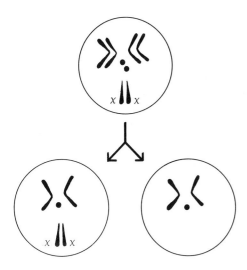

Sometimes in the course of meiosis, pairs in the tetrad fail to separate, and by a process known as *nondisjunction* (Figure 3–35), a gamete may be produced which has an extra chromosome. Searching for such gametes, Bridges found a female drosophila which had been produced from a gamete that had received two complete sets of all four chromosomes. The fertilization of this gamete had resulted in the addition of yet another set of chromosomes, so that rather than being 1*n* (haploid) or 2*n* (diploid), this particular female was 3*n* (triploid).

By mating the 3*n* female with normal males and also with males which themselves had an unusual additional chromosome or two, Bridges was able to get offspring with wide variations in chromosome numbers. Analysis of the results of the offspring of this remarkable female showed that sex in *Drosophila* is not a matter of the presence or absence of single chromosomes but is a question of balance.

When one pair of *X* chromosomes is balanced with three pairs (one set) of autosomes (Figure 3–36*a*), a female is produced. This is true even if a "male," or *Y*, chromosome is present. It is also true when the balance is reached by having a triploid set of *X* chromosomes and a triploid set of autosomes (Figure 3–36*b*). If the balance is tipped by the addition of extra sex chromosomes (Figure 3–36*c*), the fly is female in appearance but is sterile. If the balance is tipped by the subtraction of *X*'s or the addition of *Y*'s (Figure 3–36*d*), femaleness is lost and maleness begins to appear. One

3–36 *Combinations of sex chromosomes and autosomes in Drosophila showing that sex in the fruitfly is determined not by the presence or absence of specific sex chromosomes but by a balance between the X chromosomes and the autosomes (of which there are six in the species shown). Normally a female is produced by a ratio of 2X chromosomes to 6 autosomes and a male by 1X chromosome to 6 autosomes (see Figure 3–24). As you can see by the examples given here, as long as the ratio is 2:6 or greater the individual will have the characteristics of a female; if it is 1:6 or less, the individual will be male. What is the chromosome ratio in the intersex (far right) in which the individual has both male and female characteristics?*

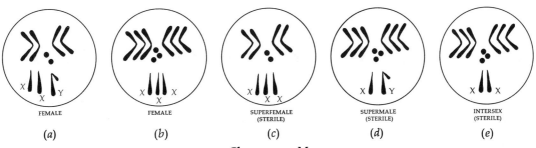

FEMALE	FEMALE	SUPERFEMALE (STERILE)	SUPERMALE (STERILE)	INTERSEX (STERILE)
(a)	(b)	(c)	(d)	(e)

393 *Chromosome Maps*

X chromosome in combination with one set of autosomes, the usual situation in the male fly, produces a male. Proportions in between the 2:6 balance of the normal female and the 1:6 balance of the normal male produce intersexes with the characteristics of both (Figure 3–36e). Maleness in the fruit fly is an expression not of some function of the Y chromosome but apparently of some gene or, more probably, genes on one or more of the autosomes, which can be overridden by the X chromosomes.

BEES

An even more striking example of the question of modulation and balance in determining sex can be found in the bee. The queen bee is inseminated only once in her lifetime, and the supply of sperm that she receives at that time is stored in her body and can be used to fertilize each egg as she produces it. Each fertilized egg develops into a female; the workers, all of

3–37 *The normal diploid chromosome number of a human being is 46, 22 pairs of autosomes and the two sex chromosomes. In this picture, the chromosomes of a white blood cell of a human male are arranged to show the karyotype. The chromosomes are in metaphase of mitosis, the stage at which each chromosome consists of two identical chromatids. These will separate in later phases. By convention morphologically similar chromosomes are grouped together, as shown. (Courtesy of Paediatric Research Unit, Guy's Hospital Medical School, London)*

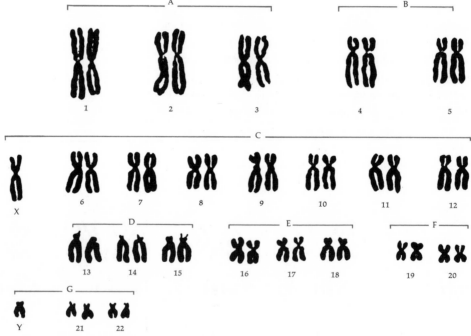

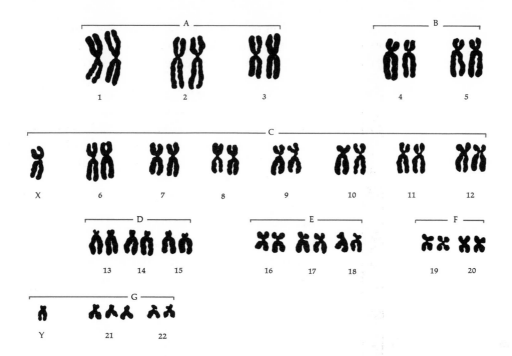

3–38 *The karyotype of a patient with Down's syndrome. Note that chromosome 21 is represented three times. (Courtesy of Paedriatic Research Unit, Guy's Hospital Medical School, London)*

which are sterile females, are required in large numbers for the economy of the hive. From time to time, however, males are needed to fertilize new queens, either because the hive has become too big and is dividing or because the old queen is nearing the end of her life. At these times, the queen bee produces eggs without releasing sperm, so that some bees develop parthenogenetically, that is, from unfertilized eggs. These are males. Female bees have 32 chromosomes, the diploid number, but the males have only 16, the haploid number.

HUMAN CHROMOSOMES

The *Drosophila* studies showing the nonimportance of the Y chromosome in sex determination, together with the fact that the grasshopper and other animals have no Y chromosome, led many geneticists to conclude that it is generally true throughout the animal kingdom that the Y chromosome is not the sex determiner. However, studies in Japan on the silk moth showed the opposite result; the Y chromosome is the important factor in sex determination. *XXY* and *XY* are both females (remember that moths have *XY* females and *XX* males).

395 *Chromosome Maps*

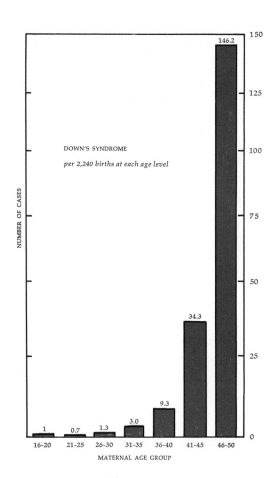

3-39 *The frequencies of mongoloid births in relation to the age of the mothers. As you can see, the risk of having a mongoloid child increases steadily with age; in any five-year period, the risk is about three times greater than that of the preceding five-year period. About 0.1 percent of all births are mongoloids, and about 40 percent of these mongoloid children are born to women over forty. (After Penrose, 1939)*

And in the human being, the relatively tiny Y chromosome is always associated with maleness and is essential for it. Nondisjunction may occur in the human gamete as well as in *Drosophila,* and men and women have been studied who, instead of the normal chromosome complement, or *karyotype* (Figure 3–37), have abnormalities in chromosome number. An *XY* combination in the twenty-third pair, as you know, is associated with maleness, but so is *XXY* and *XXXY* and even *XXXXY,* even though all these males are sexually undeveloped and sterile. *XXX* combinations sometimes produce normal females, but many of the *XXX* women and all *XO* women are sterile.

Human Autosomal Abnormalities

In both men and women, the presence of additional chromosomes tends to result in mental deficiency. In fact, most abnormalities in human chromosome number have been found in studies of the karyotypes of patients in mental hospitals. For example, compare the normal karyotype shown in Figure 3–37 with the karyotype of a mentally deficient patient, Figure 3–38. Apparently, genetic imbalance has a more drastic effect on the working mechanism of the brain than it has on other organs, reminding us that the abnormal chromosome number is usually found not only in the gametes but in every cell in the body. It is not surprising that these patients often have abnormalities of the heart and other organs as well.

You are probably familiar with the form of mental deficiency known as *mongolism.* This name derives from a peculiar and typical appearance of the eyefold in these patients which makes them look "foreign," or mongoloid, to us. Mongolism is not actually a single disease but a *syndrome,* a group of disorders which occur together, and nowadays it is usually called *Down's syndrome,* after the physician who first described it. The syndrome includes, in most cases, not only mental deficiency but a short, stocky body type with a thick neck and, often, abnormalities of other organs, especially the heart. Patients with Down's syndrome also have a peculiar pattern of palm prints (Figures 3–40 and 3–41), and these patterns occur with greater frequency among mothers and brothers and sisters of the patient than they do among the general population.

Down's syndrome and a number of other defects involving gross abnormalities of chromosomes are more likely to occur among infants born to older women. The reasons for this are not known, but as you may recall, the formation of the egg cells is well under way in the human female before she is born, so the increasing incidence of abnormalities is believed to be correlated in some way with the aging of the pre-egg cells.

Parents who have had one abnormal child are faced with the terrible decision of whether or not to risk having another infant. Now there are

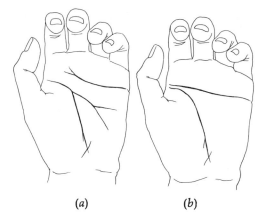

(a)   (b)

3–40 *Certain physical traits present in most patients with Down's syndrome are also present in a greater-than-normal frequency in the patient's parents, particularly the mothers. The picture shows such a trait. On the left is a normal palm, and on the right is the hand of a mongoloid individual. Note the simian, or four-finger, fold in (b).*

3–41 *The relative positions of several points on the palms of two normal parents and their mongoloid children. An angle of greater than 57° is found in over 80 percent of all mongoloids but in only 7 to 9 percent of the general population. In mothers of mongoloids, the frequency of this abnormal configuration is 15 to 16 percent. (After Penrose, 1954)*

special clinics throughout the country which can help them in this decision. In these clinics, skin cells from stillborn or abnormal infants are cultivated in the test tube for examination at the time of mitosis, when the chromosomes become visible. If an infant is found to have an abnormal karyotype, the skin cells of his parents can be similarly tested. If the parents show an abnormality, they are warned that they are likely to transmit it to the infant through their gametes. The abnormality involved is called *translocation.* When cases of translocation mongolism are studied, it is usually found that one parent, although phenotypically normal, has only 45 separate chromosomes—one chromosome 15, one chromosome 21, and an extra, translocation chromosome composed of most of chromosomes 15 and 21 joined together. The offspring of this parent can be expected to have one of the following

1   Normal chromosomes 15 and 21 (normal infant)
2   Chromosome 15 alone (probably lethal)
3   Translocation chromosome 15–21 and normal 21 (Down's syndrome),
4   One 21 (like the parent)

Not a very cheerful prognosis!

If, however, the karyotypes of both parents are normal, the parents are advised that the abnormalities in the child were probably "accidental" —a mistake that took place during meiosis—and that they do not run a greater-than-normal risk of having another congenitally ill child. The defect in this case is the result of nondisjunction, an accidental failure of

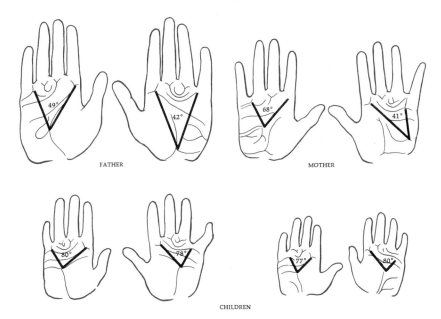

chromosomes to separate either in the ovum during meiosis or in the early cleavage stages of the zygote. This causes an extra chromosome—a third chromosome 21 (Figure 3–38)—in the cells of the defective child.

Thus studies that began with the white-eyed *Drosophila* have greatly increased our understanding of ourselves. As the young science of genetics progresses, it will undoubtedly lead to further progress in the elimination of hereditary diseases.

SUMMARY

The developments which led to a final proof of Sutton's hypothesis that the gene is located on the chromosome began, in the late nineteenth century, with studies of chromosomes in animals. It was found that in all animals, one pair of chromosomes (the *sex chromosomes*) differs between the male and the female. All the other chromosomes (the *autosomes*) are the same in both sexes. Both sex chromosomes of females of most species are X; most males have one X and one Y. Men and women, for example, have 22 pairs of autosomes; women have, in addition, an XX pair, and men have an XY pair.

In the early 1900s, experiments with mutations in the fruit fly *Drosophila* showed that certain characteristics are *sex-linked*, that is, carried on the sex chromosomes. Female *Drosophila* are XX, and males are XY. The sex-linked characteristics, it was found, are carried on the X chromosome; the Y chromosome contains almost no genetic information. Therefore, while a female heterozygous for a sex-linked characteristic will show the dominant trait, a single recessive gene in the male, if carried on the X chromosome, will result in a recessive phenotype since no dominant allele is present. Recessive genes transmitted on the X chromosome will thus appear in the phenotype far more often in males than in females; examples of this are color blindness and hemophilia.

Further studies of *Drosophila* demonstrated that genes are sometimes exchanged between homologous chromosomes at meiosis. Such *crossovers* could only take place if (1) the genes were arranged in a fixed linear array along the length of the chromosome and (2) the genes were at corresponding sites on homologous chromosomes. These assumptions were proved when *chromosome maps*, showing the relative locations of gene sites along the *Drosophila* chromosomes, were developed from crossover data provided by breeding experiments with *Drosophila*. Physical confirmation of these findings was subsequently supplied by the chromosomes in the salivary glands of *Drosophila*. In these giant chromosomes, gene sites, crossovers, and breaks could actually be seen.

Sex is determined in humans by the presence or absence of the Y chromosome, which is essential for. maleness. In *Drosophila*, maleness and femaleness depend on a balance between the X chromosomes and the autosomes. One pair of X chromosomes and one set of autosomes (three pairs) produces a female; one X chromosome and three pairs of autosomes produces a male. Variations in these proportions result in gradations between normal femaleness and normal maleness.

The studies described in this chapter have greatly increased our understanding of the hereditary diseases in man (particularly mental deficiencies such as Down's syndrome) which are caused by chromosomal abnormalities.

A BRIEF REVIEW OF CLASSICAL GENETICS

Organisms arise from other organisms which are similar to them. Their basic common features, or similarities, are passed from organism to organism by means of *genes*. Genes control the hereditary traits; they may occur in alternative forms, or *alleles*, which produce alternative traits. Although one allele may be dominant over another and the recessive allele may not be detectable in the phenotype, the recessive allele continues to persist as an independent unit in the genotype. In sexual reproduction, genes are transmitted by the *gametes*, the ovum and the sperm, which come together to form the fertilized egg, or *zygote*.

Genes are carried on chromosomes in a linear array. Chromosomes are passed from cell to cell throughout the life of an organism by *mitosis*, a process which ensures the equal assortment of the chromosomes at cell division. In most somatic cells, or body cells, chromosomes come in homologous pairs; such cells are termed *diploid*. Alleles occupy corresponding sites on homologous chromosomes.

Gametes, which are *haploid* cells, contain only one of each homologous chromosome and therefore only one of each allele. The process by which the chromosomes are reduced to the haploid number is called *meiosis*. At meiosis, the homologues are assorted randomly in the gametes; the number of possible assortments of chromosomes is 2^n, with n equaling the haploid number. During meiosis, alleles may move from one homologue to another by chromosome breakage and crossing-over.

Mutations may occur in genes either "spontaneously"—which means for reasons that are not understood—or under the influence of agents such as x-rays. The great majority of mutations are harmful, but some few are beneficial in their effects.

The reassortment of the genetic material at meiosis and the slow accumulation of beneficial mutations ensure a constant pattern of small variations in living things. Evolution is caused by the action of natural selection upon these variations.

PART II. MOLECULAR GENETICS

Chapter 3—4

Molds and Microbes

By the early 1940s, the existence of the gene and the fact that it occupied a position on the chromosome were no longer in doubt. But what were genes? What did they really do? What does biological inheritance mean? When we say "She has her mother's eyes," we obviously mean something quite different than if we say "She has her mother's pocketbook." "He inherited his father's intelligence" is not at all the same as "He was left his uncle's yacht." The microscopic fertilized egg contains neither eyes nor intelligence. All that can be inherited, biologically speaking, is a potentiality, an ability to develop in certain ways. The turning point between classical genetics and molecular genetics came when biologists ceased to ask how the genes were transmitted and began to ask how they functioned—and this is still one of the crucial biological questions of our time.

Gene-Enzyme Relationships

"INBORN ERRORS OF METABOLISM"

In 1908, an English physician, Sir Archibald Garrod, presented a series of lectures in which he set forth a new concept of human diseases, which he termed "inborn errors of metabolism." With a leap of the imagination that covered almost half a century, Garrod postulated that certain diseases which were caused by the lack of a specific enzyme were hereditary in nature. In other words, a change in the genetic material caused a change in an enzyme. This was the first suggestion of a direct link between genes and enzymes.

One of the most familiar examples of such a disease is phenylketonuria, or PKU, as it is commonly known. (See Figure 3–42.) PKU is caused by lack of the enzyme that breaks down the amino acid phenylalanine. When this enzyme is deficient, phenylalanine accumulates. Such an accumulation is particularly harmful to the cells of the brain and may result in mental retardation. About 1 in every 15,000 infants is homozygous for this recessive gene. Detection of PKU is relatively easy, involving only a simple urine or blood test, and tests for PKU in newborn infants are now required in many states. Phenylalanine is an "essential" amino acid, which means not that it is more essential than any other amino acid but that it cannot be synthesized in the body and must be taken in the diet. Therefore, infants with PKU are fed a special diet low in phenylalanine in an attempt to prevent the harmful accumulation of this substance.

Garrod's work foreshadows the beginning of modern biochemical genetics. In postulating the existence of a relationship between genes and body chemistry, he anticipated by almost 30 years the coming together of genetics and chemistry. An essential feature of modern biology is that it attempts to explain genetic mechanisms in terms of the laws of physics and chemistry. It was not until the mid-1930s, however, that further research made it possible to begin to develop the role of genes in controlling enzyme production.

BIOCHEMICAL MUTANTS IN NEUROSPORA CRASSA

The problem was to devise a way to test the hypothesis that genes act by influencing enzyme-controlled chemical reactions. Characteristics such as

3–42 *A pedigree showing the occurrence of the disease phenylketonuria, or PKU, in a family. PKU is an inherited metabolic disease in man that may result in feeble-mindedness. It is caused by a deficiency of the enzyme which breaks down the amino acid phenylalanine. Such a disease is an example of what Sir Archibald Garrod called an "inborn error of metabolism." What is there about the family relationships shown in this diagram that would tend to support the hypothesis that PKU is caused by a recessive gene?*

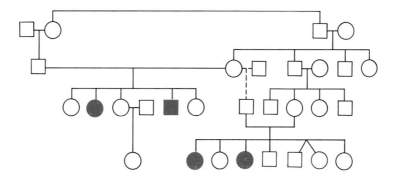

3–43 *The life cycle of* Neurospora crassa. *The mold comes in two mating types, shown in the figure as* **type a** *on the left and* **type A** *on the right. The plant normally reproduces asexually, but fertilization can occur when a spore from one mating type lands on a specialized hypha of the other type. The two nuclei then fuse to form a double nucleus with two sets of chromosomes (2n). A saclike structure called an ascus forms around the cell. The cell undergoes meiotic division, resulting in four nuclei, each containing only one of each pair of chromosomes (1n). Next, each nucleus reproduces by mitosis, and cell walls form around each of the eight resulting sexual spores.*

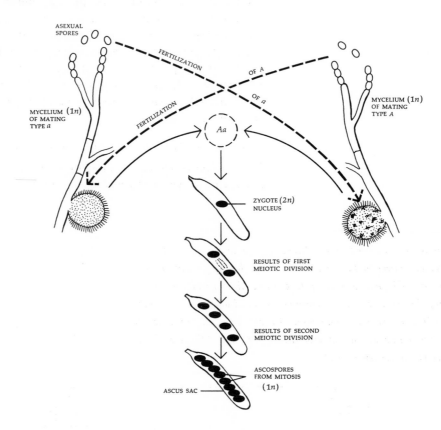

ASEXUAL SPORES

FERTILIZATION

OF A

OF a

FERTILIZATION

MYCELIUM (1*n*) OF MATING TYPE *a*

MYCELIUM (1*n*) OF MATING TYPE *A*

Aa

ZYGOTE (2*n*) NUCLEUS

RESULTS OF FIRST MEIOTIC DIVISION

RESULTS OF SECOND MEIOTIC DIVISION

ASCOSPORES FROM MITOSIS (1*n*)

ASCUS SAC

size and wing shape in *Drosophila*—or indeed the visible features of any organism—are the end product of a vast number of chemical reactions, most of which are still unknown. In 1941, George Beadle and Edward L. Tatum decided to turn the problem around, and in so doing, they changed the course of genetics and won a Nobel prize. Instead of picking a genetic characteristic and working out its chemistry, they decided to begin with known chemical reactions—controlled by enzymes—and see how genetic changes affected these reactions. Their experiments are worth examining in some detail because of their influence on both the theories and the techniques of genetics in the next quarter century.

First, like Morgan and Mendel before them, they chose a suitable organism. For their purposes, it was the pink bread mold *Neurospora crassa*, which has since become almost as famous a research tool in genetics as the fruit fly. This organism has several obvious advantages for genetic research: (1) its life cycle is brief; (2) it can be grown in vast quantities in the laboratory; and (3) unlike most higher organisms, it is haploid; that is, it has only one set of chromosomes (seven in number) rather than two. As a consequence, when a mutation occurs, its effects make themselves known immediately since they cannot be masked or dominated by the presence of an allele.

But the most important feature of *Neurospora* from the point of view of the investigators was the fact that they could grow it on a very simple medium, containing any one of several sugars as a carbon source, a vitamin (biotin), and a few inorganic salts. All the amino acids, other vitamins, polysaccharides, and other essential substances for growth and functioning this undemanding mold can make for itself. On the other hand, if a substance—a particular amino acid, for example—is provided in the medium, *Neurospora* will use it "as is" rather than synthesize its own. The synthesis of an amino acid or a vitamin requires, as we know, a series of reactions which are each mediated by a particular enzyme. If, as a result of mutation, *Neurospora* were to lose one of these enzymes, it could no longer grow in the simple minimal medium, but it could survive on a supplemented one. Thus it suddenly became possible for geneticists to study not just the distant effects of gene activity, such as white eyes and short fingers, but the most immediate products of gene function. (Mutations which cause a loss of functions that would be fatal under certain conditions but not under others—such as growth in a supplemented medium— became known as *conditional lethal mutations*. You should be sure to understand the principle of how such mutations are studied because genetic procedures involving conditional lethals have become increasingly important in modern genetics; as one geneticist put it, "It's a way of having your cake and eating it too.")

The life cycle of *Neurospora* is diagrammed in Figure 3–43. Typically, it spreads out in a flat network, the mycelium, made up of filamentous branches, the hyphae. It generally reproduces asexually, either by continued spreading growth or by means of very small, powdery salmon-colored spores. Tufts of spores, the fruiting bodies, are raised up above the mycelium on stalks. In nature, these spores are carried through the air to form a new colony. They may act as seeds, or if they encounter another

3–44 *Meiosis of a Neurospora zygote resulting from crossbreeding an albino mutant and a wild type. The diagram shows the only two possible distributions of mutant and wild-type spores in the ascus. These ascospores can be tested directly for their genetic properties, making it possible for the investigator to observe segregation in a single ascus. How does this research procedure differ from segregation analysis with most plants and animals? What advantage does this seem to offer the geneticist?*

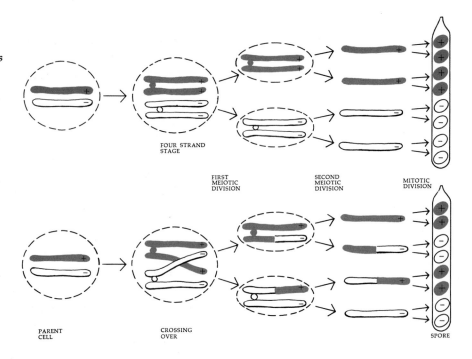

FOUR STRAND
STAGE

FIRST
MEIOTIC
DIVISION

SECOND
MEIOTIC
DIVISION

MITOTIC
DIVISION

PARENT
CELL

CROSSING
OVER

SPORE

NORMAL PARENT
(+ indicates location of normal genes)

ALBINO PARENT
(− indicates location of albino genes)

strain of *Neurospora crassa*, they may fertilize it. Fertilization takes place when a spore from one strain lands on a specialized hypha from another strain. The nuclei then fuse to form a zygote, and from this zygote, sexual spores, or ascospores, are produced. Each group of eight ascospores is packaged in a sac, or ascus. The entire fruiting body contains several hundred of these tough, weather-resistant asci.

Beadle and Tatum x-rayed the spores of *Neurospora* to increase the mutation rate. They then permitted the spores to develop in a supplemented medium. Those that grew were crossed with wild-type *Neurospora*. The ascospores were collected from the asci and allowed to grow out in the supplemented medium, and then portions of the mycelium were tested for growth in the minimal medium. The loss of ability to grow in the minimal medium suggested that an enzyme or enzymes had been lost. By patient trial and error, Beadle and Tatum were able to pinpoint the loss. For example, a strain that had lost the ability to make the amino acid tryptophan could grow in the minimal medium plus only tryptophan but not, under any circumstances, without tryptophan; one that could not make lysine could grow in the minimal medium plus lysine; and so forth. Many such strains were produced that had lost specific biosynthetic abilities as the result of mutations.

3–45 *The chain of chemical reactions postulated by Beadle and Tatum to account for Neurospora's biosynthesis of the amino acid arginine. As shown, each step is directed by an enzyme, and each enzyme, in turn, is controlled by a gene. Thus, a strain of Neurospora with a mutation in gene 2 could not produce citrulline or arginine, while one with a mutation in gene 3 could produce citrulline, but not arginine.*

How was it possible to tell that just one gene was involved? Here *Neurospora* has special characteristics which were again important. Following mating in *Neurospora*, a diploid zygote is formed (Figure 3–43). The zygote then undergoes meiosis and returns to the haploid state. This is, of course, the opposite of what happens with the gametes of most animals, in which meiosis usually precedes fertilization instead of following it. Also unlike the gametes of most animals, only a tiny fraction of which will ever develop into mature organisms even under the most favorable conditions, every single one of the meiotic products of *Neurospora* can survive and be tested. Results can be based on actual counts, not statistics involving hundreds and thousands of chance events.

Meiotic division takes place within the forming ascus, and because of the narrow, tubelike shape of the ascus, the cells cannot slip past one another as they are formed. Figure 3–44 shows the consequence of this unusual restriction. If only one mutation is involved, half of the spores will be mutants and half will be wild types, and only two distributions of mutants and wild types will be possible. In this way, the investigators could be sure that they were dealing not with a product of some gross genetic damage but with a single change in a single gene.

It soon became possible to identify the exact enzyme involved. For instance, three different mutants were found which could not synthesize the amino acid arginine. It was possible by crossbreeding experiments to demonstrate that these mutations involved different genes. Beadle and Tatum hypothesized that these three different mutations each involved a different one of a series of enzymes required to make the amino acid. (See Figure 3–45.) This could be proved in two ways:

1. If an arginine-requiring strain regained the ability to make arginine when citrulline was added to the medium, it was clear that the missing enzyme was enzyme 2. On the other hand, if the strain could make arginine when ornithine was added, it was clear that enzymes 2 and 3 were present but enzyme 1 or some prior enzyme was absent.
2. The mutant molds could be broken up and analyzed chemically. In this way, cellular extracts from the mutants could be shown to be lacking in the activity associated with the particular enzyme—and present in the wild-type hyphae.

At the time this experiment was first performed, enzymatic assembly lines had been worked out for very few organisms. Since that time, however, it has been found that a great variety of cells, including bacteria, yeast, and even the cells that make up the tissues of the human body, are very similar in their enzyme systems and in their stepwise synthesis of the various basic cellular nutrients.

One Gene, One Protein

The Beadle-Tatum hypothesis that each gene was responsible for a particular enzyme was quick to gain acceptance. That all enzymes are proteins had first been demonstrated in the 1930s. At that time, proteins were shown to consist of up to 20 different amino acids hooked end to end in a linear fashion. (See Chapter 1–7 for a review of protein structure.) Not all proteins are enzymes, however; some, for instance, are hormones, like insulin. Others may be involved in particular structures, like collagen. These proteins, too, are under genetic control.

This expansion of the original concept did not modify it in principle: "One gene, one enzyme," as the theory was first abbreviated, was simply amended to the less memorable but more precise "one gene, one polypeptide chain." In other words, proteins are the direct products of the gene and from proteins all other substances are built.

Speculative thinkers in the field of biology were quick to see that the amino acids, the number of which was so provocatively close to the number of letters in our own alphabet, could be arranged in a variety of different ways and that these different arrangements might account for both the great diversity and the great specificity of biochemical reactions within the cell. The proteins were seen as making up a sort of language—"the language of life"—which spelled out the directions for all the many activities of the cell. (As we shall see, this hypothesis turned out to be wrong, and another type of molecule is considered today to contain "the language of life.")

THE STRUCTURE OF HEMOGLOBIN

Linus Pauling was one of the first to see some of the implications of these new ideas. Hemoglobin, for instance, is also made up of chains of amino

3–46 *Paper electrophoresis of normal hemoglobin* (AA), *of the hemoglobin of a person with sickle-cell anemia* (SS) *and of the hemoglobin of a heterozygote for the sickle-cell trait* (AS). *Because of slight differences in electric charge, the normal and sickle cell hemoglobins move differently in an electric field. The hemoglobin taken from the heterozygote separates into hemoglobin* A *and hemoglobin S.*

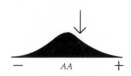

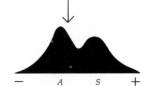

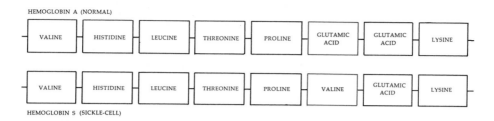

HEMOGLOBIN A (NORMAL)

| VALINE | HISTIDINE | LEUCINE | THREONINE | PROLINE | GLUTAMIC ACID | GLUTAMIC ACID | LYSINE |

| VALINE | HISTIDINE | LEUCINE | THREONINE | PROLINE | VALINE | GLUTAMIC ACID | LYSINE |

HEMOGLOBIN S (SICKLE-CELL)

3–47 *An example of the remarkable precision of the "language" of proteins. Portions of the beta chains of the hemoglobin A (normal) molecule and of the hemoglobin S (sickle-cell) molecule are shown. The hemoglobin molecule is composed of two identical alpha chains and two identical beta chains, each chain consisting of about 150 amino acids, or a total of 600 amino acids in the molecule. The entire structural difference between the normal molecule and the sickle-cell molecule (literally, a life-and-death difference) consists of* one *change in the sequence of each beta chain—one glutamic acid is replaced by one valine!*

acids. Perhaps, Pauling reasoned, human diseases involving hemoglobin can be traced to a slight variation from normal in the protein structure of the hemoglobin molecule—a typographical error in one important sentence in the hypothetical language of the cells. He took samples of hemoglobin from normal persons, from persons with sickle-cell anemia, and from persons heterozygous for the disease. To study the differences in these proteins, he used a process known as *electrophoresis*, in which organic molecules are dissolved in a solution and exposed to a weak electric current. Very small differences, even in very large molecules, are reflected in the electric charges of the molecules, and the molecules will move differently in the electric field. Figure 3–46 shows the results of Pauling's experiment. The normal person makes one sort of hemoglobin, the person with sickle-cell anemia makes a different sort, and the person who carries one copy of the recessive gene for sickling makes a hemoglobin that is somewhere in between. Actually, as you can see in the figure, the heterozygote makes both kinds of hemoglobin molecule, but he has enough "good" molecules to prevent anemia and enough "bad" ones to discourage the malaria parasite. (Notice that the terms "dominant" and "recessive" are beginning to take on a different meaning.)

A few years later, it was found that the actual difference between the normal and the sickle hemoglobin molecules is 1 amino acid in 300. The hemoglobin molecule is composed of four polypeptide chains—two identical alpha chains and two identical beta chains. Each chain consists of about 150 amino acids. In a precise location in each beta chain, one glutamic acid is replaced by one valine. (See Figure 3–47.) The language of proteins is fantastically precise, and the consequences of even a small error or small variation may be great.

The Chemistry of the Gene: DNA vs. Protein

During the 1930s and 1940s, scientists became more and more concerned with the question "Exactly what is a gene?" The attempt to identify the chemical nature of the gene gave rise to two opposing schools of thought, and the controversy lasted for a number of years—until, as we shall see, it was conclusively resolved in 1953.

On the one hand, many prominent investigators, particularly those who had been studying proteins, believed that the genes themselves were proteins, that the chromosomes contained master models of all the proteins that would be required by the cell, and that enzymes and other proteins active in cellular life were copied from these master models. This was a logical hypothesis, but as it turned out, it was wrong.

THE TRANSFORMING FACTOR

To trace the beginning of the other hypothesis—the one that proved right —it will be necessary to go back to 1928 and pick up an important thread in modern biological history. In that year, an experiment was performed which seemed at that time very remote from either biochemistry or genetics. Frederick Griffith, a public health bacteriologist, was studying the

3–48 *How dead bacterial cells impose their genetic character on live cells of a different strain. The virulent S (smooth) cells are encapsulated, while the harmless R (rough) cells are not. Small fragments from the chromosomes of the heat-killed S cells enter the chromosomes of the live R cells. When the R cells divide, the S chromosome fragments become part of the hereditary character of the daughter cells. If an S fragment carries the gene which controls the formation of the capsule, the resulting R cell is transformed into an encapsulated S-type cell. (After Watson, 1965)*

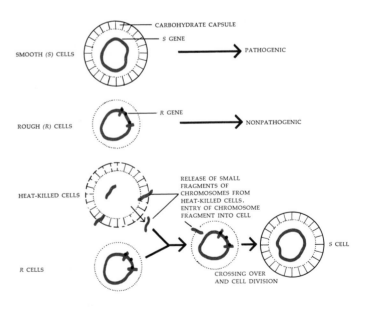

SMOOTH (S) CELLS — CARBOHYDRATE CAPSULE — S GENE → PATHOGENIC

ROUGH (R) CELLS — R GENE → NONPATHOGENIC

HEAT-KILLED CELLS

R CELLS

RELEASE OF SMALL FRAGMENTS OF CHROMOSOMES FROM HEAT-KILLED CELLS. ENTRY OF CHROMOSOME FRAGMENT INTO CELL

CROSSING OVER AND CELL DIVISION

S CELL

bacterial cells, pneumococci, that cause one kind of pneumonia. In those days, before the development of modern antibiotics, bacterial pneumonia was a serious disease, the grim "captain of the men of death." Pneumococci, as Griffith knew, come in either virulent (disease-causing) forms or avirulent (harmless) forms. Griffith was interested in finding out whether injections of heat-killed virulent pneumococci, which do not cause disease, could be used to vaccinate against pneumonia. In the course of various experiments, he performed one that gave him very puzzling results. He injected mice simultaneously with heat-killed virulent bacteria having capsules (gelatinous coats) and with living but nonvirulent bacteria having no capsules. Both of these strains were harmless, but all the mice died! When Griffith performed autopsies on them, he found their bodies filled with living bacteria with capsules.

The results of a second experiment were even more puzzling. Live type II pneumococci with no capsules were injected into mice simultaneously with type III pneumococci which were encapsulated but heat-killed. Again, the mice died, and live virulent pneumococci were isolated—but these were type III, not type II. Moreover, these bacteria as they divided transmitted to their progeny, generation after generation, the type III characteristics. Thus something had been passed from the dead virulent type III cells to the living type II cells which endowed the type IIs with the virulent type III character.

Within the next few years it was shown that the same phenomenon could be reproduced in the test tube. Extracts from the killed encapsulated bacteria, when added to the living harmless bacteria, could transmit to them—and through them to their progeny—their virulent character and their ability to make capsules. In other words, the cells somehow—it was a biological heresy—acquired an hereditary characteristic.

One of the laboratories that worked on the nature of this *transforming factor*, as it came to be called, was that of O. T. Avery. After almost a decade of patient chemical isolation and analysis, Avery and his co-workers were convinced that the chemical substance in the cellular extracts of killed bacteria that transmitted the new genetic quality was the compound known as *deoxyribonucleic acid*. (See Figure 3–49.) Subsequent experiments showed that a variety of genetic traits could be passed from one colony of bacterial cells to members of another, similar colony by means of isolated deoxyribonucleic acid, which soon took on the now familiar abbreviation of DNA.

The Nature of DNA

At this point, we shall examine DNA a little more closely and try to put its discovery into historical perspective—in order to understand why Avery's

3–49 *Chemical method for isolating the transforming factor. It took almost 10 years of careful chemical analysis to determine which type of molecule was responsible for genetically transforming pneumonia bacteria. The result was published in 1944, at a time when many scientists still believed that genes were proteins. (After Watson, 1965)*

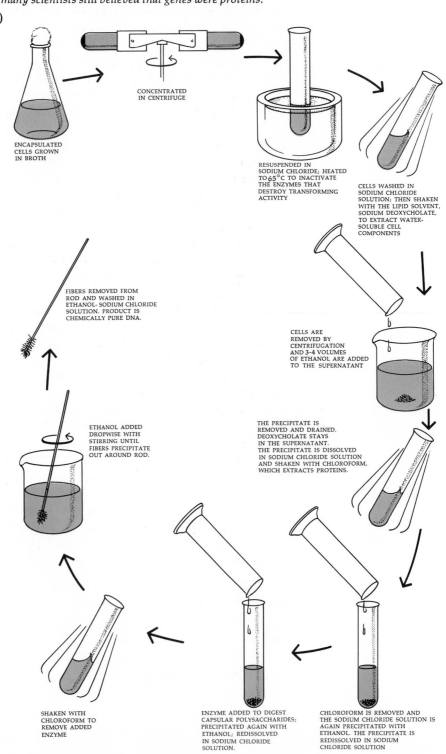

ENCAPSULATED CELLS GROWN IN BROTH

CONCENTRATED IN CENTRIFUGE

RESUSPENDED IN SODIUM CHLORIDE; HEATED TO 65°C TO INACTIVATE THE ENZYMES THAT DESTROY TRANSFORMING ACTIVITY

CELLS WASHED IN SODIUM CHLORIDE SOLUTION; THEN SHAKEN WITH THE LIPID SOLVENT, SODIUM DEOXYCHOLATE, TO EXTRACT WATER-SOLUBLE CELL COMPONENTS

CELLS ARE REMOVED BY CENTRIFUGATION AND 3-4 VOLUMES OF ETHANOL ARE ADDED TO THE SUPERNATANT

THE PRECIPITATE IS REMOVED AND DRAINED. DEOXYCHOLATE STAYS IN THE SUPERNATANT. THE PRECIPITATE IS DISSOLVED IN SODIUM CHLORIDE SOLUTION AND SHAKEN WITH CHLOROFORM, WHICH EXTRACTS PROTEINS.

CHLOROFORM IS REMOVED AND THE SODIUM CHLORIDE SOLUTION IS AGAIN PRECIPITATED WITH ETHANOL. THE PRECIPITATE IS REDISSOLVED IN SODIUM CHLORIDE SOLUTION

ENZYME ADDED TO DIGEST CAPSULAR POLYSACCHARIDES; PRECIPITATED AGAIN WITH ETHANOL; REDISSOLVED IN SODIUM CHLORIDE SOLUTION.

SHAKEN WITH CHLOROFORM TO REMOVE ADDED ENZYME

ETHANOL ADDED DROPWISE WITH STIRRING UNTIL FIBERS PRECIPITATE OUT AROUND ROD.

FIBERS REMOVED FROM ROD AND WASHED IN ETHANOL- SODIUM CHLORIDE SOLUTION. PRODUCT IS CHEMICALLY PURE DNA.

experiment, although beautifully designed and executed, did not receive full recognition for almost a decade.

DNA was first discovered in that same remarkable decade in which Darwin published *The Origin of Species* and Mendel presented his results to an audience of forty at the Natural History Society in Brünn. In 1869, a German chemist, Friedrich Miescher, had extracted a substance from the nuclei of cells which was white, sugary, slightly acid, and contained phosphorus. He called it nucleic acid, which was later amended to deoxyribonucleic acid to distinguish it from a closely related chemical, ribonucleic acid, which subsequently was also isolated from the cell.

In 1914, another German, Robert Feulgen, discovered that DNA had a remarkable attraction for fuchsin dye, but he considered this finding so unimportant that he did not trouble to report it for a decade. *Feulgen staining*, as it was called when it finally made its way into use, revealed that DNA was present in all cells and was characteristically located in the chromosomes.

There was no particular interest in DNA for several decades since no role had been postulated for it in the cellular metabolism. Most of the work on its chemistry was carried out by the great biochemist P. A. Levene, who showed that DNA could be broken down into the four nitrogenous bases—adenine and guanine (the purines) and thymine and cytosine (the pyrimidines)—a five-carbon sugar, and a phosphate group. From the proportions of these components, he made two deductions:

1 Each nitrogenous base is attached to a molecule of sugar and to one of phosphate to form a single molecule, a *nucleotide*. This hypothesis was right.
2 Since in all the samples he measured, the proportions of the nitrogenous bases were approximately equal, all four nitrogenous bases must be present in nucleic acid in equal quantity. Furthermore, these molecules must be grouped in clusters of four, a *tetranucleotide* he called it, which repeated over and over again along the length of the molecule. This hypothesis, which was wrong, dominated scientific thinking about the nature of DNA for more than a decade.

Because of Levene's tetranucleotide theory, given great weight by his renown as a biochemist, biologists as a whole were slow to recognize the importance of Avery's experiment. How could a chemical whose structure was "known" to be so simple and uniform be associated with something as complicated and various as heredity? For almost a decade, most influential biochemists continued to believe that proteins were the genetic material. In the next chapter, we shall review some of the evidence that made them change their minds.

411 *Molds and Microbes*

SUMMARY

Classical genetics had been concerned with the mechanics of inheritance —how the units of hereditary material were passed from one generation to the next and how changes in the hereditary material were expressed in individual organisms. In the late 1930s, new questions arose and geneticists began to explore the nature of the gene—its structure, composition, and properties and its role in the internal chemistry of living organisms.

In their now famous experiments, in 1941, with the bread mold *Neurospora crassa*, Beadle and Tatum established the "one-gene–one-enzyme" principle. They were able to trace biochemical mutations in *Neurospora* to specific enzymes and to relate each of these enzymes to a specific gene.

It was soon discovered that other proteins, such as hormones and collagen, are also under genetic control, and the one-gene–one-enzyme principle was expanded to "one gene, one polypeptide chain." Proteins, it was found, are the direct gene products from which all other substances are built.

The amino acids that make up the protein molecule can be arranged in a variety of ways, and even a very slight difference in structure between two amino acid chains can result in differences in function. Using electrophoresis, Linus Pauling demonstrated that the hemoglobin of a normal person was slightly different from the hemoglobin of a person with sickle-cell anemia. Subsequently, it was shown that the actual difference lay in just two amino acid changes among the 600 amino acids making up the polypeptide chains in the molecule.

During the 1940s, many investigators believed that genes were proteins, but others were convinced that the hereditary material was deoxyribonucleic acid (DNA). DNA was first discovered in 1869, but its role in genetics was not widely accepted and understood until the 1950s. In the next chapter, we shall discuss the development of the DNA theory.

Chapter 3–5

Deoxyribonucleic Acid

In the decade following Avery's discovery that the transforming factor is DNA, additional evidence accumulated from several sources that finally led to general acceptance of DNA as the chemical basis of heredity. This evidence involved two new materials for genetic study, materials which proved in the course of events to be as important as the garden pea, the fruit fly, and the pink bread mold. One of these was a type of bacterium known as *Escherichia coli*, a usually harmless inhabitant of the human intestinal tract. The other was a group of tadpole-shaped viruses, the T-even bacteriophages. Both of these will be introduced in this chapter and then examined in detail in the chapters that follow.

The Role of DNA in Viral Infection

THE BACTERIOPHAGES

At about the same time that Beadle and Tatum began their studies with *Neurospora*, another pair of scientists, Max Delbrück and Salvadore Luria, were investigating the potentialities of another "fit material." Delbrück and Luria were both physicists by training, but since they were enemy aliens, they were barred from work in "sensitive" fields. Both were ininterested in the problem of how living things reproduce, and both were casting about for a new and useful area of research.

Many years before, during World War I, a French physician, Felix d'Hérelle, had discovered a group of viruses which attacked bacterial cells and which he therefore named *bacteriophages*, or "bacteria eaters." D'Hérelle became convinced that these "bacteria eaters" could cure all bacterial diseases, and he spent the rest of his life attempting, by various experiments, to prove this. His work attracted interest for a time, but when it was finally established that the bacterial viruses had no apparent practical value, the work was abandoned.

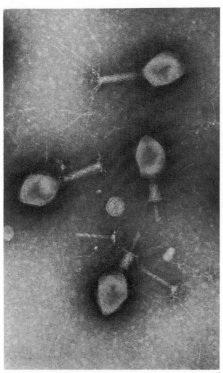

|— 0.1μ —|

3–50 *Electron micrograph of T4 bacterio-*
phages. Notice the highly distinctive,
"tadpole" shape; each bacteriophage
consists of a head, which looks hexag-
onal in electron micrographs, and a
complex tail. Like all viruses, they are
extremely small—smaller even than bac-
teria. Before the development of the
electron microscope, no one had ever
seen a virus. Visible light merely "flows"
around particles this small, but the elec-
tron beam in the electron microscope is
stopped by viruses. (E. Boy de la Tour)

Delbrück and Luria decided to look at the bacterial viruses in a new light, "taking sides neither with the viruses, nor with the bacteria," as Delbrück put it. Bacteriophages were inexpensive, readily available, and demanded little space or equipment—essential factors for any program not part of the war effort. Furthermore, they were phenomenal at reproducing themselves. As d'Hérelle had shown, only 20 minutes after the infection of one bacterial cell by one virus particle, the cell would burst open and 200 or more new viruses would be released.

Every known type of bacterial cell is preyed upon by its own type of bacterial virus, and many cells are host to a dozen different kinds of virus. Delbrück, Luria, and the group that joined them in these studies agreed to concentrate on a series of seven related viruses that attacked *E. coli.* These were numbered T1 through T7, with the T standing simply for "type." As it turned out, most of the work was done on T2 and T4, which came to be known, collectively, as the *T-even bacteriophages.*

At the time that these studies were undertaken, bacteriophages had never been visualized. Viruses are so small relative to the wavelengths of visible light that they cannot be seen in a light microscope. The smallpox virus, the largest of all viruses, is only just on the margin of visibility with the light microscope. What first made viruses "visible" was the electron microscope, developed in 1937. The bacteriophages were identified in 1944.

In the early days of electron microscopy, most viruses, cellular organelles, and accidental by-products of the methods used to fix cells for study all looked very much alike. On the other hand, as you can see in Figure 3–50, bacteriophages have highly distinctive shapes. This fact facilitated studies of their presence and activities, making them even more a "fit material" for genetic investigation.

VIRAL INFECTION OF *E. coli*

According to electron-microscope studies of infected *E. coli* cells (broken open at regular intervals after infection), the bacteriophages totally disappeared the moment after infection, and for half of the total infectious cycle, not a single particle could be found within the bacterial cell. Then, depending on when the cell was opened during the course of the infection, increasing numbers of completed phage* particles could be found and, mixed with them, odds and ends that resembled bits of incomplete phage. The phages increased at a regular rate during this period, not geometrically—2, 4, 8, 16, 32, 64, like bacteria—but linearly, one after another, as if they were coming off an assembly line.

Occasional mutants were noticed in the bacteriophage population. One strain of T2, for example, would turn up that could not infect a strain of

---

* Biologists find it convenient to shorten "bacteriophage" to "phage."

3–51 *The experiment which demonstrated that only the DNA component of the T2 bacteriophage contains the genetic information. The results of this experiment offered further evidence that the genetic material is DNA and not protein. (After Watson, 1965)*

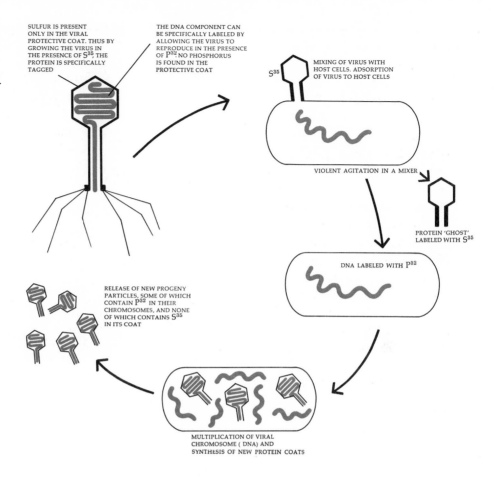

SULFUR IS PRESENT ONLY IN THE VIRAL PROTECTIVE COAT. THUS BY GROWING THE VIRUS IN THE PRESENCE OF S^{35}, THE PROTEIN IS SPECIFICALLY TAGGED

THE DNA COMPONENT CAN BE SPECIFICALLY LABELED BY ALLOWING THE VIRUS TO REPRODUCE IN THE PRESENCE OF P^{32}. NO PHOSPHORUS IS FOUND IN THE PROTECTIVE COAT

S^{35}

MIXING OF VIRUS WITH HOST CELLS. ADSORPTION OF VIRUS TO HOST CELLS

VIOLENT AGITATION IN A MIXER

PROTEIN 'GHOST' LABELED WITH S^{35}

DNA LABELED WITH P^{32}

RELEASE OF NEW PROGENY PARTICLES, SOME OF WHICH CONTAIN P^{32} IN THEIR CHROMOSOMES, AND NONE OF WHICH CONTAINS S^{35} IN ITS COAT

MULTIPLICATION OF VIRAL CHROMOSOME (DNA) AND SYNTHESIS OF NEW PROTEIN COATS

E. coli which could be infected by the wild-type strain. Another strain would appear that lysed (disintegrated) the cell more rapidly or more slowly than the parent strain. Soon it was observed that if a bacterial cell was infected simultaneously with two different types of phages, recombinants would appear that were crosses between the parent strains. Mating occurred even in viruses! This raised the possibility, of course, of performing genetic analysis and mapping studies, although at this time the extent of the studies that would eventually become possible could not be foreseen.

PHAGE DNA

Chemical analysis of the bacteriophages revealed that they consisted quite simply of DNA and of protein, the two contenders for the leading genetic-material role. The question of which one carried the viral genes—the hereditary information by which new viral particles are made—was an-

415 *Deoxyribonucleic Acid*

3–52 *Electron micrograph of two conjugating cells. The bacterium on the left is being infected by particles of T4 bacteriophage. The bacterium on the right belongs to a strain of E. coli that is resistant to this bacteriophage. As you can see, the T4 particles attach themselves to the bacterium by their tails. The head of the bacteriophage consists of a protein coat and a core of DNA. The phage DNA passes into the cell, while the protein coat remains outside. The empty protein shells are called ghosts. Inside the cell, the phage DNA dictates a reorganization of the cell machinery to manufacture 200 or so copies of the T4 virus, complete with protein coats. These then burst through the cell wall, ready to begin the cycle again. The whole process takes about 20 minutes. (Dr. Thomas F. Anderson)*

|————————1μ————————|

swered in 1952 by a simple and ingenious experiment. Alfred D. Hershey and Martha Chase grew *E. coli* on a medium which contained radioactive phosphorus and radioactive sulfur and then infected the bacterial cells with T2. After a cycle of multiplication, the newly formed viruses all contained radioactive sulfur and radioactive phosphorus in place of the common isotopes of sulfur and phosphorus. Since proteins contain sulfur but no phosphorus, all the radioactive sulfur was confined to the protein. Conversely, since only the DNA contained phosphorus, only DNA was labeled with radioactive phosphorus. The labeled viruses were used to infect fresh *E. coli* cells growing in a normal medium. Once infection was begun, the cells were washed free of extra virus, broken apart, and their contents analyzed. Almost all the radioactive phosphorus was found inside of the cells and almost none of the radioactive sulfur, showing that the DNA of the phage entered the cell while the protein "coat" stayed outside attached to the bacterial surface.

Electron micrographs (Figure 3–52, for example) have now confirmed that the phage attaches to the bacterial cell wall by its tail and injects its DNA into the cell, leaving the empty protein coat on the outside. In short, the protein is just a container for the bacteriophage DNA. It is the DNA of the bacteriophages that enters the cell and that carries all the hereditary message of the virus particles, directing the formation of new viral DNA and new viral protein.

Further Evidence for DNA

The role of DNA in transformation and viral infection formed very convincing evidence for believing that DNA was the chemical basis of the gene. Two other lines of work also helped to lend weight to the argument. Alfred Mirsky, in a long series of careful studies, showed that all the tissue cells of any given species contain an equal amount of DNA. The only exceptions are the gametes, which regularly contain just half as much DNA as the other cells of the same species.

A second important series of contributions was made by Erwin Chargaff. Chargaff analyzed the purine and pyrimidine content of the DNA of many different kinds of living things and found that the nitrogen bases do not occur in exact proportions. The DNA molecule, he found, can have a great deal of variety in its composition. Furthermore, the proportion of nitrogen bases is the same in all cells of a given species but varies from one species to another. Therefore, these variations could very well provide a "language" in which the instructions controlling cell growth could be written. Some of Chargaff's results are reproduced in Table 3–4. Can you, by examining these figures, notice anything interesting about the proportions of purines and pyrimidines?

Table 3–4 *Composition of DNA in Several Species**

Source	Moles per 100 gram atoms (%)			
	Adenine	Guanine	Cytosine	Thymine
Man	30.4	19.6	19.9	30.1
Ox	29.0	21.2	21.2	28.7
Salmon sperm	29.7	20.8	20.4	29.1
Wheat germ	28.1	21.8	22.7	27.4
E. coli	26.0	24.9	25.2	23.9
Sheep liver	29.3	20.7	20.8	29.2

* After Erwin Chargaff, *Essays on Nucleic Acids*, 1963.

The first step is a chemical analysis. The kinds of atoms present, and their proportions, are determined. Then the various molecular subgroups are identified. In an amino acid, for example, the amino group (NH_2) has certain chemical properties, and so does the hydroxyl group (OH).

A relatively recent analysis technique is based on the fact that different substances absorb different wavelengths of visible, infrared, or ultraviolet light. The characteristic absorption patterns are measured with spectrophotometers, and these measurements help determine a substance's chemical composition.

The physical structure of the molecule, that is, the spatial arrangements of the atoms within it, is investigated next. One widely used tool for answering such questions as "How far apart are the atoms?" and "What are the angles and lengths of the chemical bonds that hold the atoms together?" is x-ray diffraction. An x-ray beam is projected through a crystal at various angles. The x-rays are deflected by the atoms in the crystal, and the deflection pattern is registered on a photographic plate (Figure 3–53). From this pattern, the way in which the atoms are arranged in the molecule is inferred by mathematical procedures. It was by this technique that investigators determined the structure of such simple crystals as those of ice and salt.

The methods of x-ray diffraction have been extended to the complex organic molecules of proteins and nucleic acids. But these giant molecules offer considerable difficulty since they contain a great many subgroupings and therefore so many planes for the x-rays to deflect from that it is sometimes impossible to interpret the photographic record. For this reason, when dealing with these complex molecules, scientists employ the technique of model building. (Linus Pauling worked out the structure of the protein molecule in this way, and there is the famous DNA model built of scrap tin by Watson and Crick.) Once a model is constructed that is consistent with available information on interatomic distances, bond angles, x-ray diffraction patterns, and so on, additional x-ray diffraction patterns can be predicted. If these predictions are then confirmed, the evidence for the correctness of the structure is greatly strengthened.

The Hypothesis is Confirmed

The final explanation of the way that the genetic information is contained in DNA was found in the structure of the DNA molecule. We have seen that the genetic material must meet at least four requirements:

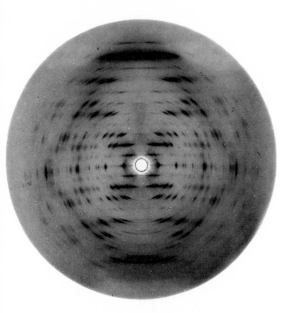

3–53 *A diffraction pattern produced by x-rays deflected from the atoms in a DNA crystal. The helical structure of DNA is suggested by the crossways pattern of x-ray deflections. (Dr. Robert Langridge)*

1 It must carry genetic information from cell to cell and from generation to generation. Further, it must carry a great deal of information. Consider how many instructions must be contained in the set of genes that directs, for example, the development of an elephant—or a tree, or even a paramecium.

2 It must copy itself, for the chromosome does this with every cell division. Moreover, it must do this with great precision; from mutation-rate data, we know that a human gene must on the average be copied for millions of years without a mistake.

3 On the other hand, it must sometimes mutate. When a gene changes, that is, when "a mistake is made," the "mistake" must be copied rather than what was originally there. This is a most important property, perhaps the unique attribute of living things, for without the capacity to replicate "errors," there could be no evolution by natural selection.

4 There must be some mechanism for decoding the stored information and translating it into action in the living individual.

It was when the DNA molecule was found to have the size, the configuration, and the complexity required to code the tremendous store of information needed by living things and to make exact copies of this code that DNA became widely accepted as the genetic material.

The scientists primarily responsible for working out the structure of the DNA molecule were James Watson and Francis Crick, and their feat is one of the milestones in the history of science. It will be discussed in some detail in the following paragraphs.

The Watson-Crick Model

In the early 1950s, a young American scientist, James D. Watson, went to Cambridge, England, on a research fellowship to study problems of molecular structure. There, at the Cavendish Laboratory, he met physicist Francis Crick. Both were interested in DNA, and they soon began to work together to solve the problem of its molecular structure. They did not do experiments in the usual sense but rather undertook to examine all the data about DNA and attempt to unify them into a meaningful whole.

THE KNOWN DATA

By the time Watson and Crick began their studies, quite a lot of information on the subject had already accumulated:

1 It was known that the DNA molecule was very large and also that it was long and thin.

2 There were the original data of Levene and his postulates on how the nucleotides were assembled.

3   The laboratories of Maurice Wilkins at King's College, London, were
     an important source of information. Wilkins had been studying DNA
     by x-ray diffraction techniques. X-ray diffraction studies depend on
     the properties of crystals. When substances crystallize, their atoms
     line up in a latticework of regularly repeating units. These units will
     deflect x-rays in a regular pattern, and by studying these patterns, one
     can sometimes determine the distances between various atoms in the
     latticework. Although no one had yet successfully interpreted the dif-
     fraction patterns of DNA, the x-ray plates showed markings that al-
     most certainly reflected the turns of a giant spiral, or *helix*.

4   Linus Pauling, in 1950, had shown that a protein's component chains
     of amino acids are often arranged in the shape of a helix and are held
     in that form by hydrogen bonds between successive turns in the
     helix. Pauling had suggested that the structure of DNA might be simi-
     lar.

5   Also crucial (as you will see in the following paragraphs) were the data
     of Chargaff indicating, as you perhaps noticed, that the ratio of nu-
     cleotides containing adenine to those containing thymine is 1 to 1 and
     so is the ratio of nucleotides containing guanine to those containing
     cytosine.

BUILDING THE MODEL

From these data, some of them contradictory, Watson and Crick attempted
to construct a model of DNA that would fit the known facts. They were
very conscious of the biological role of DNA. In order to carry such a vast
amount of information, the molecules should be heterogeneous and varied.
Also, there must be some way for them to replicate readily and with great
precision in order that faithful copies could be passed from cell to cell and
from parent to offspring, generation after generation.

On the other hand, they could not be sure that the chemical structure of
DNA actually would reflect its biological function. After all, this idea had
never really been tested rigorously. Perhaps DNA was merely some sort
of biological clay on which some outside "vital force" operated. "In pes-
simistic moods," Watson recalled in a review of these investigations, "we
often worried that the correct structure might be dull—that is, that it
would suggest absolutely nothing."

It turned out, in fact, to be unbelievably "interesting." By piecing together the various data, they were able to deduce that DNA did not have a
single-stranded helix structure, as do proteins, but was a huge entwined
double helix—a structure that meets all the requirements for a self-repro-
ducing molecule.

The banister of a spiral staircase forms a single helix. If you take a
ladder and twist it into the shape of a helix, keeping the rungs perpendicu-

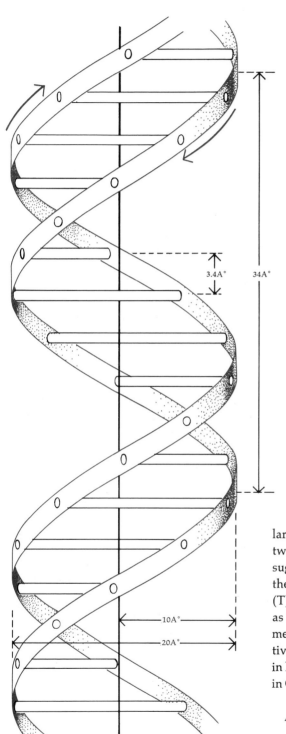

3.4A° 34A°

10A°

20A°

3–54 *The double-stranded helix structure of DNA was first postulated in 1953 by Watson and Crick. The two major strands (the "railings") of the helix are composed of sugar-phosphate units, alternating. The rungs are formed by the four nitrogenous bases—the purines, adenine and guanine, and the pyrimidines, thymine and cytosine—attached to each strand at precise intervals. Each rung consists of two bases joined in the center by hydrogen bonds. Knowledge of the distances between the atoms, determined from the x-ray diffraction pictures, was crucial in establishing the structure of the molecule.*

lar, this would form a crude model of the molecule. (See Figure 3–54.) The two railings, one of which runs up and the other down, are made up of sugar and phosphate molecules, alternating. The perpendicular rungs of the ladder are formed by the nitrogenous bases—adenine (A), thymine (T), guanine (G), and cytosine (C)—one base for each sugar-phosphate, as Levene had shown, and two bases forming each rung. The paired bases meet across the helix and are joined together by hydrogen bonds, the relatively weak, omnipresent chemical bonds that Pauling had demonstrated in his studies of the structures of proteins. (Hydrogen bonds are described in Chapter 1–6.)

421   *Deoxyribonucleic Acid*

3–55 *The chemical structure of part of one chain of the double-helix DNA molecule. The sugar-phosphate molecules form the outer strand, to which are attached the nitrogenous bases. The sugar of each nucleotide is linked by a phosphate group to the sugars of the adjacent nucleotides. Each nucleotide consists of a sugar, a phosphate group, and a purine or pyrimidine base. The sequence of nucleotides is very irregular and varies from one molecule to another. In the figure, the order of nucleotides is TTCAG.*

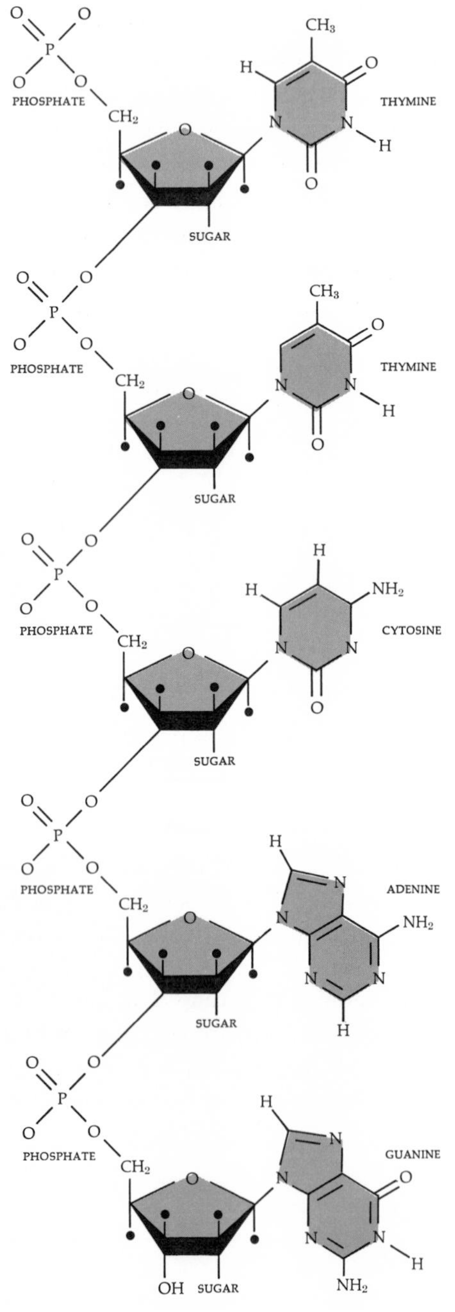

The distance between the two sides, or railings, according to Wilkins' measurements, is 20 angstroms (an angstrom is equal to 1/250,000,000 inch). Two purines in combination would take up more than 20 angstroms, and two pyrimidines would not reach all the way across. But if a purine paired in each case with a pyrimidine, there would be a perfect fit. The paired bases—the "rungs" of the ladder—would therefore always be purine-pyrimidine combinations.

As Watson and Crick worked their way through these data, they assembled actual tin and wire models of the molecule, seeing where each piece would fit into the three-dimensional puzzle. First, they noticed, the nucleotides along any one chain of the double helix could be assembled in any order: ATGCGTACATTGCCA, and so on. (See Figure 3–55.) Since a DNA molecule may be several hundred nucleotides long, there is a possibility for great variety. The meaning of this variety, the molecular heterogeneity of DNA, will be explored more thoroughly in the next chapter.

The most exciting discovery came, however, when they set out to construct the matching strand. They encountered an interesting and important restriction. Not only could purines not pair with purines and pyrimidines not pair with pyrimidines, but because of the configurations of the molecules, adenine could pair only with thymine and guanine only with cytosine. Look at Chargaff's table (Table 3–4) again and see how well these physicochemical requirements confirm his data.

DNA AS A CARRIER OF INFORMATION

You will recall that a necessary property of the genetic material is the ability to carry genetic information. The Watson-Crick model shows clearly how the DNA molecule is able to do this. The information is carried in the sequence of the bases, and *any* sequence of the four pairs (AT, TA, CG, and GC) is possible. Since the number of paired bases ranges from about 5,000 for the simplest known virus up to an estimated 5 billion in the 46 chromosomes of man, the possible variations are astronomical! The DNA from a single human cell—which if extended in a single thread

3–56 *The chemical structure of a portion of the double-helix DNA molecule. Do you see why a paired combination of two purines or two pyrimidines would be impossible in this configuration? And why compound A can join chemically only with T, and G only with C?*

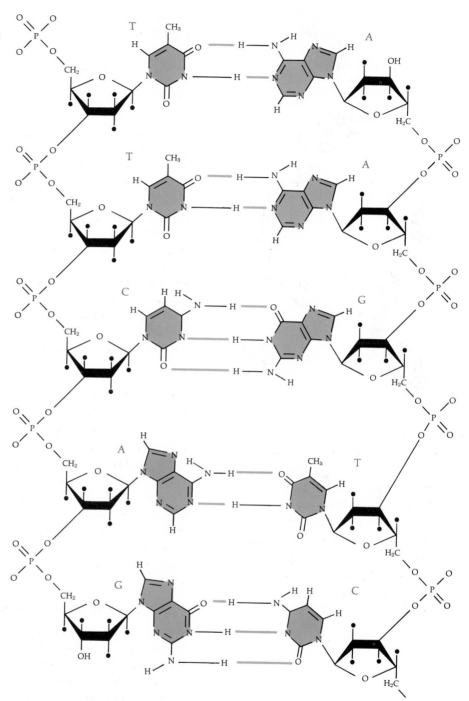

423   *Deoxyribonucleic Acid*

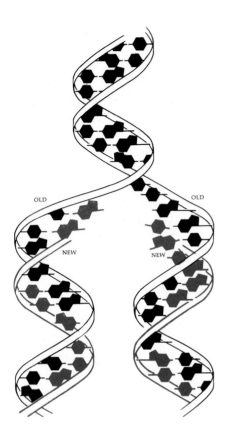

3–57 *The DNA molecule shown here is in the process of reproduction, separating down the middle as its base units break apart at the hydrogen bonds. (For clarity, the bases are shown out of plane.) Two exact replicas of the original molecule then form on the two separated strands as new complementary base-and-strand units are assembled from surrounding matter in the cell.*

would be about 5 feet long—contains information equivalent to some 600,000 printed pages averaging 500 words each, or a library of about a thousand books. Obviously, the DNA structure can well explain the endless diversity among living things.

DNA REPLICATION

Another necessary property of the genetic material is the ability to make exact copies of itself. Does the Watson-Crick model satisfy this requirement? In their published account, Watson and Crick wrote, "It has not escaped our notice that the specific pairing we have postulated immediately suggests a possible copying mechanism for the genetic material." Implicit in the double and complementary nature of the DNA helix is the method by which it reproduces itself. The molecule simply "unzips" down the middle, the bases breaking apart at the hydrogen bonds. The two strands separate, and new strands form along each old one, using the raw materials in the cell. If a T is present on the old strand, only an A can fit into place with the new strand, a G will pair only with a C, and so on. In this way, each strand forms a copy of the original partner strand, and two exact replicas of the molecule are produced. The age-old question of how hereditary information is duplicated and passed on, duplicated and passed on, for generation after generation had in principle been answered.

Support for the Watson-Crick Structure

TEST-TUBE SYNTHESIS OF DNA

Confirmation of the Watson-Crick hypothesis came swiftly. In 1957, Arthur Kornberg isolated an enzyme system that would form new molecules of DNA when placed in a test tube with a DNA sample, or primer, and a sufficient supply of nucleotides and energy sources. The composition of the molecules synthesized by the enzyme was the same as that of the primer DNA. Furthermore, the copies then made copies of *themselves*. Although there is still doubt about whether Kornberg's enzyme is the enzyme that actually replicates the DNA in the living cell, his work confirmed the important hypothesis that the DNA does replicate by the formation of complementary strands.

SEMICONSERVATIVE REPLICATION

A quite different sort of confirmation came from researchers at the California Institute of Technology. They found direct chemical evidence for the pattern of reproduction postulated by Watson and Crick by using an *analytical ultracentrifuge*. In this technique, a solution of cesium chloride containing molecules of varying densities is spun at extremely high speed. The molecules suspend themselves at different levels in the liquid, and the

3–58 *E. coli cultured in a medium containing heavy nitrogen (N^{15}) accumulated a "heavy" DNA, as shown in the parent molecule. Reproduction of the daughter molecules (both F_1 and F_2) took place in "light" nitrogen (N^{14}). If Watson and Crick were right, the first generation DNA molecules should contain one heavy and one light strand, as shown here, and the second generation should be composed of half mixed and half light molecules. By extracting the DNA and comparing the weights of the DNA molecules in the three generations, the investigators confirmed the hypothesis diagrammed here, providing strong support for the Watson-Crick theory.*

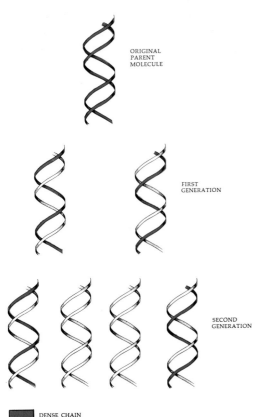

ORIGINAL PARENT MOLECULE

FIRST GENERATION

SECOND GENERATION

■ DENSE CHAIN

□ LESS DENSE CHAIN

position of any given band indicates the density of the molecules that compose it.

They grew *E. coli* for several generations in heavy nitrogen (N^{15}) until virtually all the nitrogen in the cells was N^{15}, replacing the normally occurring isotope (N^{14}). This procedure increases the density of the DNA in the bacteria by about 1 percent over those containing only N^{14}. DNA from the N^{14} and N^{15} culture mediums will therefore "band" in an ultracentrifuge at two different levels.

They then placed the cells in a medium of the "light" nitrogen (N^{14}) long enough for the cells to divide once (as determined by a doubling of the number of cells). The purpose of their experiment was to find out if Watson and Crick were right about how DNA replicates. (Perhaps you have noticed by now that the best experiments are those in which a single question is put very simply and very clearly.) If the Watson-Crick hypothesis was correct, this first generation should have one dense and one less dense chain in each DNA molecule, as shown in Figure 3–58. Can you explain why? As it turned out, that is exactly what happened; this generation of DNA molecules formed a band in the ultracentrifuge halfway between the N^{14} and N^{15} molecules.

A second generation was then grown in the N^{14} medium. This time, according to the theory, half the DNA molecules should be composed of one dense chain (containing the N^{15}) and one less dense chain (containing the N^{14}), while the other half should have N^{14} in both chains. Half the DNA molecules should therefore band in the ultracentrifuge at the intermediate position (halfway between the N^{14} and N^{15} positions), and half should band at the N^{14} position. Which is also what happened.

The important point that was confirmed by this experiment is that DNA replication is *semiconservative*; that is, half of each parent molecule (one chain) is conserved in each daughter molecule, so that the daughter molecule consists of one old chain (from the parent) and one new chain formed from the surrounding medium.

SUMMARY

During the 1940s, additional evidence accumulated to confirm the role of DNA as the genetic material. An important series of experiments involved the use of a new material for study, the T-even bacteriophages. Tracing the cycle of infection of *E. coli* bacteria by T2 bacteriophages demonstrated that the bacteriophages recombine, that is, that they exchange genetic information. In 1952, the use of radioactive isotopes proved that the genetic material in these viruses is DNA.

Further support for the genetic role of DNA came from two more findings: (1) All tissue cells of any given species contain equal amounts of

DNA. (2) The DNA molecule varies greatly in its composition, and while the nucleotide proportions are the same in all cells of a given species, they are different in different species.

The hypothesis that the genetic information is contained in DNA was confirmed in 1953 by Watson and Crick. The DNA molecule, they found, is a double-stranded helix, shaped somewhat like a twisted ladder. The sides of the ladder are two strands composed of repeating groups of a phosphate and a five-carbon sugar. To these are attached the "rungs," made up of paired bases, one purine base pairing with one pyrimidine base. There are four bases—adenine (A), guanine (G), thymine (T), and cytosine (C)—and A can only pair with T, and G with C. The four bases are the four "letters" used to spell out the genetic message. The paired bases are joined by hydrogen bonds.

The DNA molecule is self-replicating. The two strands come apart down the middle, breaking at the hydrogen bonds, and each strand forms a new partner strand by finding complementary bases in the surrounding material. Confirmation of this came soon after from two sources: (1) DNA was synthesized in the laboratory; and (2) by means of an ultracentrifuge, it was proved that DNA is semiconservative—that is, half of the parent (one strand) is conserved in each daughter molecule.

The discovery of the structure of DNA and of the process by which it duplicates itself is one of the great imaginative achievements of the twentieth century. In the next chapter, we shall see how this discovery was used to develop a whole new genetic theory.

Chapter 3–6

The Making of Proteins

In 1953, Watson and Crick described their findings in a short but now classic account in *Nature*, "A Structure for Deoxyribose Nucleic Acid." From that time on, there was no longer any real dissent about the genetic role of DNA. Most objections had been answered. Like many other significant discoveries, however, this new development raised a host of new questions, questions that became increasingly the major focus of modern biological research.

The Genetic Code

As Beadle and Tatum had shown, genes control the synthesis of proteins. When it had been thought that genes *were* proteins, scientists had hypothesized that the "gene proteins" formed the models or the molds for the cellular proteins, the basic structural matter of life. During this period, scientists began talking about *templates*. Templates are patterns or guides, and the word "template" is usually associated with the metalwork patterns used in industry. By extension, the word came to be applied to a biological molecule which, by its shape, directs or molds the structure of another molecule. Each old strand of DNA serves as a template for the formation of its new partner strand during replication of the DNA molecule. For a time after the structure of DNA was elucidated, scientists struggled with the problem of how DNA could also be a template for the formation of protein molecules. Several ingenious schemes were proposed, but it was simply not possible to get a satisfactory physicochemical "fit." The relationship between DNA and protein was a more complicated one. If the proteins, with their 20 amino acids, were the "language of life," to extend the metaphor of the 1940s, the DNA molecule, with its four nitrogenous bases, could be envisioned as a sort of *code* for this language. So the term "genetic code" came into being.

As it turned out, the idea of a "code of life" was useful not only as a dramatic metaphor but also as a working analogy. Scientists seeking to understand how the DNA so artfully stored in the nucleus could order the quite dissimilar structure of the protein molecule approached the problem by the methods used by cryptographers. There are 20 biologically important amino acids, and there are four different nucleotides. If each nucleotide "coded" one amino acid, only four could be provided for. If two nucleotides specified one amino acid, there could be a maximum number, using all possible arrangements, of 4^2, or 16—still not quite enough. Therefore, at least three nucleotides must specify each amino acid, following the code analogy. This provides for 4^3, or 64, possible combinations. This postulate, the *triplet code*, was almost immediately adopted as a working hypothesis, although, as you will see, it was not actually *proved* for another decade.

Perhaps it has occurred to you that 64 different code "words" are too many for the efficient specification of 20 amino acids. At one time, it was thought that the cell might employ fewer than the 64 possible triplets. But all available evidence has now confirmed that most (if not all) of the 64 triplets, called *codons*, are used. Each amino acid except one (tryptophan) is specified by at least two different codons, and a few amino acids are specified by as many as six different codons. Of the 64 codons, 61 have been shown to specify one or another of the 20 amino acids. The remaining three seem to act to signal the beginning or the end of a genetic message. Thus the genetic messages are conveyed in "sentences," complete with "punctuation."

Sometimes, however, analogies get out of hand. The term "language," in its primary meaning, applies to a form of intelligent communication between living things. Nucleic acids do not speak a language that proteins understand, and although we may talk from time to time about grammar, syntax, and punctuation, the activities of the cell are in truth governed not by the formal properties of language but by the laws of biochemistry. From this point of view, the two most important factors in understanding the biosynthesis of proteins are (1) the idea of a template and (2) the role of weak bonds such as hydrogen bonding. Bonds stronger than those formed by the hydrogen atoms would require too much energy to break apart, while those weaker would not provide enough stability in template formation.

The RNAs

During the decade following the publication of the Watson and Crick findings, a number of investigators here and in France and England concentrated on elucidating the biochemical steps between the codons of the

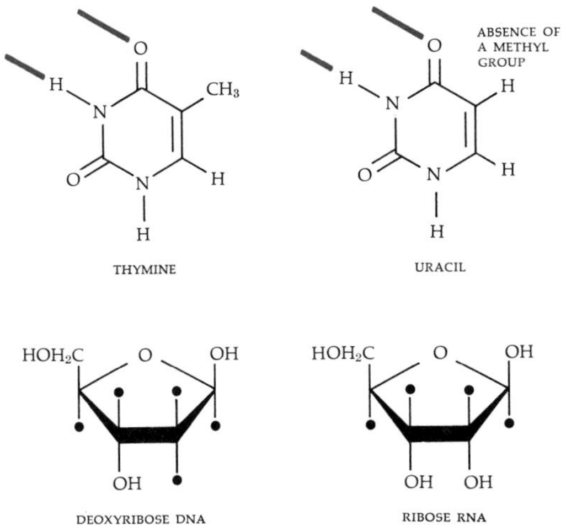

THYMINE

URACIL

ABSENCE OF A METHYL GROUP

DEOXYRIBOSE DNA

RIBOSE RNA

3–59 *Chemically, RNA is very similar to DNA, but there are two differences in its chemical groups. One difference is a minor modification of the sugar component; instead of deoxyribose, RNA contains ribose, which has an additional OH (hydroxyl) group. The other difference is that instead of thymine, RNA contains the closely related pyrimidine uracil (U). (A third, and very important, difference between the two is that most RNA does not possess a regular helical structure and contains many single-stranded sections.)*

chromosome and the sequence of amino acids in the protein molecule. It was soon discovered that DNA does not form proteins directly but works in a complex way through another cellular chemical closely related to DNA. This chemical is ribonucleic acid (RNA).

RNA differs from DNA in a few significant respects. The sugar, or ribose, component of the molecule contains one more atom of oxygen (*deoxy* simply means "minus one oxygen"), and in place of thymine, RNA has another pyrimidine, uracil (U). (See Figure 3–59.) Perhaps more significant, since this part of the story has to do with the function of RNA, the RNA molecule is only rarely found in a fully double-stranded form, which means that its properties and activities are quite different from those of its sister molecule, DNA.

There are three kinds of RNA, all produced directly from DNA by the same process by which DNA copies itself:

1 *Ribosomal RNA*. This form of RNA was the first to be discovered. Its function is not yet known, but it is found with proteins in the ribosomes in the cell. New proteins are manufactured only in the presence of ribosomes.

2 *Transfer RNA (tRNA)*. Discovered in the mid-1950s, this is a smaller molecular form of RNA, with each molecule averaging about 80 nucleotides in length. There are many different types of tRNA molecules, and their function is to carry specific amino acids to the sites of protein production.

3 *Messenger RNA (mRNA)*. A large molecule, varying in size from a few hundred nucleotides to 10,000, mRNA has the function of transcribing a strip of the master code from DNA and transporting it to the ribosomes.

We shall now review some of the developments which brought a clearer picture of the intricate roles of these RNAs in the building of proteins.

RIBOSOMAL RNA

It had long been suspected that RNA was associated with protein biosynthesis since cells that were making large amounts of protein invariably contained large amounts of RNA. The great bulk of this RNA was found in the *ribosomes*, a collection of small spherical bodies within the cell. Studies using amino acids marked with radioactive atoms showed that new strands of protein formed on the ribosomes.

Many investigators adopted the idea, as a working hypothesis, that the ribosomes contained the information stored in the DNA molecule. (As we shall see, this hypothesis turned out to be wrong, but it was useful.) It was not difficult to see how a strand of DNA could serve as a template for ribosomal RNA, in much the same way that DNA could serve as a tem-

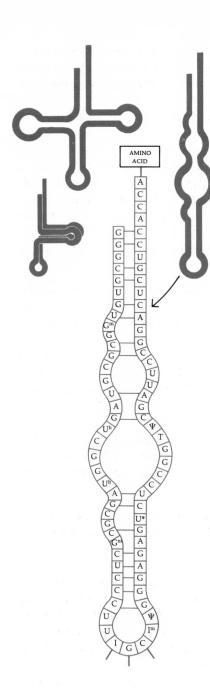

3–60 *The tRNA molecule can assume any of the three shapes shown at the top, although the shape in the upper left is the form presently thought to be the most likely one. The sequence of nucleotides for this particular tRNA molecule is known; 77 nucleotides are linked together in a single chain. As shown at the top, one end of the chain terminates in a CCA sequence and the other end terminates with a guanine nucleotide. The amino acid is linked to the tRNA at the CCA end. Most of the bases are hydrogen-bonded to one another, using the DNA-type base-pairing (A with U, G with C). The number of adenines approximately equals the number of uracils, and the number of guanines is almost the same as the number of cytosines. The correspondences are not exact, however, so that there are some nucleotides left over; these unpaired bases are thus available to "plug in" the molecule to a messenger RNA codon. Notice the relatively high content (9 out of 77) of unusual bases, that is, bases other than A, G, C, and U. (After Robert Holley, 1966)*

plate for a new DNA strand. So this question of the particular step from DNA to RNA was set aside for the moment, and attention turned to the more vexing problem of how nucleic acid—either DNA or RNA—could direct the formation of proteins.

TRANSFER RNA

Paul Zamecnik and his associates at Harvard suspected that this situation was too complex to study in whole cells, and so they made up a protein-synthesizing cellular extract which was to play a very important part in a number of crucial experiments. To make this extract, they broke up *E. coli* cells and separated their material into different layers, or fractions, by spinning them in an ultracentrifuge. Then they added radioactive amino acids to the different fractions and to different combinations of the fractions and examined each one for traces of amino acids knit together into polypeptide chains. It turned out that two fractions were necessary before any peptide synthesis occurred. One of these, as might have been suspected, contained the ribosomes. The other, the fraction known as the *supernatant* because it was the light soluble material floating on the top, contained an entirely new type of RNA molecule. Zamecnik and his group showed that this RNA was essential for the formation of peptides.

This form of RNA came to be known as *transfer RNA* (tRNA)* because it transfers free amino acids to the ribosomes, where they are made into proteins. The molecule consists of a series of about 80 nucleotides forming a long single strand which folds back on itself. A number of nucleotides, however, occur in tRNA which are not the typical A, G, U,

---

* Some scientists prefer the name *soluble RNA* (sRNA).

and C. There are at least 20 different varieties of tRNA molecules, one or more for each amino acid, as it was subsequently discovered. Similarly, some 20 different enzymes were found. Each one of these enzymes attaches one kind of amino acid to one kind of tRNA; the tRNA and the amino acid are linked together by a high-energy bond forged from the energy of an ATP molecule.

In 1964, the nucleotide sequence of a tRNA molecule was first worked out down to the exact position of its more than 2,500 atoms. The molecule, it was found, contains 77 nucleotides. Nine of the 77 bases are not the typical A, G, U, and C but are closely related structures, such as inosine and methyl guanosine. (See Figure 3–60.) The significance of these atypical bases is not yet known. It is believed that the bases are probably altered after the molecule is made (tRNA, like all known cellular RNA, is formed in the DNA template) and that they may give the molecule additional specificity.

MESSENGER RNA

Figure 3–61 shows an electron micrograph of a virus known as the tobacco mosaic virus (TMV). Like all viruses, TMV consists of a nucleic acid, either RNA or DNA, and protein. In the early 1930s, Wendell Stanley had taken aback the scientific world by demonstrating that TMV can be extracted as a pure crystalline substance and that these crystals, when put back into solution, will once again become active, infective, self-replicating viruses. To a world that had ceased to believe that snakes arise from a lady's hair dropped in a rain barrel, this experiment seemed to blur the established boundaries between the live and the inanimate.

In 1956, an experiment was performed which proved that the genetic component of TMV is RNA. When the RNA was extracted from the tobacco mosaic virus and rubbed into a tobacco plant, new viruses were produced, complete with the typical viral protein coat. The conclusion was that the genetic code could sometimes be carried by RNA instead of DNA. This has subsequently been proved to be true for a number of other viruses, including the polio and influenza viruses, in which RNA constitutes the viral chromosome. More important for this chapter of our history, it showed that RNA, as well as DNA, could direct the formation of proteins. In this way, molecular geneticists became prepared to accept the evidence that RNA was the "missing link" between DNA and protein.

In that same year (1956), investigators at Oak Ridge noticed that immediately after infection of an *E. coli* cell by a T2 bacteriophage, a new kind of RNA was synthesized very rapidly within the cell. This RNA resembled the bacteriophage DNA in its composition; that is, its proportions of C, G, U, and A were similar to the proportions of C, G, T and A in the viral DNA—in contrast to ribosomal RNA and tRNA, which usually

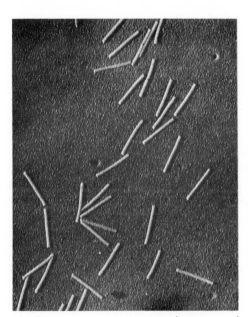

|——0.5μ——|

3–61 *An electron micrograph of tobacco mosaic virus (TMV) particles. This rod-shaped virus is commonly used in virus studies; it is easy to grow and not infectious to humans. (Courtesy of U.S. Department of Agriculture)*

431 *The Making of Proteins*

3–62 *The beginning of the process of protein biosynthesis is the formation of messenger RNA on the DNA template. In the cell's nucleus, a strand of DNA which codes one sequence of amino acids for a protein forms a complementary strand of mRNA (instead of a partner DNA strand). The strand of mRNA is now a "negative print"—an exact reverse replica of the triplet sequence of nucleotides in the DNA.*

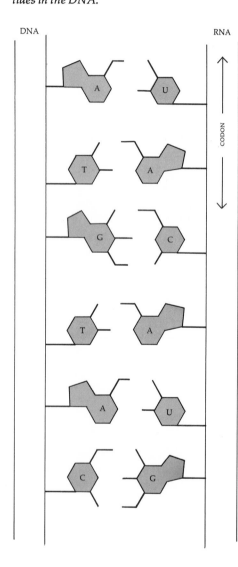

DNA

RNA

CODON

have very different CG:UA ratios from those of the DNA. They were unable to suggest a role for it in bacteriophage replication, however, and for some time their results were ignored or discounted.

Then in 1961, François Jacob and Jacques Monod, engaged in studying the genetics of bacteria (which we shall discuss in more detail in Chapter 3–7), found evidence suggesting the existence of this third type of RNA. Physicochemical studies by a number of investigators confirmed the existence of a long single-stranded molecule like the RNA of the tobacco mosaic virus, which could direct the formation of proteins and which was formed on the DNA template (as shown in Figure 3–62). Jacob and Monod called it *messenger RNA* and suggested that the RNA observed at Oak Ridge was this messenger RNA. Finally, all the pieces of the puzzle had fallen into place.

The RNAs in Protein Biosynthesis: A Summary

From this assemblage of data, a picture of protein biosynthesis emerged, involving all three types of RNA—messenger, transfer, and ribosomal, each playing its individual role. The process is diagrammed in Figure 3–63.

First, a messenger RNA molecule forms against one strand of the DNA template. The same base-pairing rules apply as in the replication of DNA, except that in RNA uracil substitutes for thymine. Once formed, this long single-stranded molecule attaches by one end to the ribosome; the same end must always attach first, otherwise the molecule would be "read" backwards.

At the point at which the mRNA molecule touches the ribosome, the molecule of tRNA, with its captive amino acid, zeros into position. Presumably, the tRNA molecule finds its proper position by means of a nucleotide triplet—sometimes called an *anticodon*—which pairs with the codon on the mRNA molecule.

As the ribosome moves along the mRNA strand, the next tRNA molecule moves into place with its amino acid in tow. At this point, the first tRNA molecule detaches itself from the mRNA molecule. The energy in the bond that holds the tRNA molecule to the amino acid is now utilized to forge the peptide link between the two amino acids, and the tRNA, released, becomes available once more. These molecules apparently can be used over and over again.

Messenger RNA appears to have a much briefer life, at least in *E. coli*. It is usually "read" by several ribosomes simultaneously, thereby producing several polypeptide chains in a matter of seconds. Then it may be read by another group of ribosomes once or twice more, and after that it is destroyed. The average lifetime of an mRNA molecule in *E. coli* is two min-

3–63 *How a protein is made. The process begins, as shown in Figure 3–62, with DNA imprinting a portion of its code on a strip of mRNA. The strip then attaches to a ribosome, which proceeds to "read off" the message, codon by codon. At each codon in the mRNA strip, a tRNA molecule plugs in momentarily. The tRNA molecule carries a specific amino acid at one end and at the other end an anti-codon which fits only the codon for that particular amino acid. Thus, one by one, following the exact order laid down by the DNA code, the proper amino acids are brought into line and formed into a strand of protein, which may be any-where from fifty to hundreds of amino acids long. As the ribosome moves along the strip of mRNA, other ribosomes attach to the disengaged end and start down the strip, making their own strands of protein. (Whether the ribosome moves along the mRNA or the mRNA moves through the ribosome is not at present known.)*

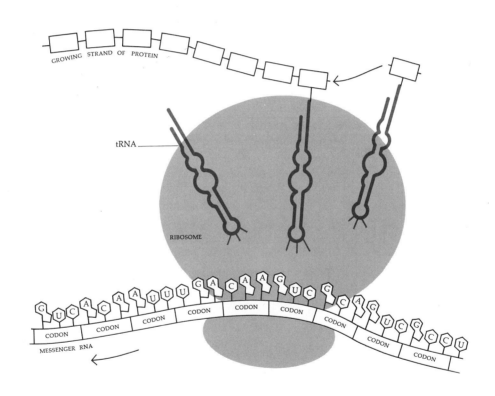

433   *The Making of Proteins*

utes, although its lifetime in other types of cells may be considerably longer. This means that in *E. coli,* continuous production of a protein demands continuous production of the appropriate mRNA molecules. In this way, the bacterial chromosome maintains a very rigid control over the cellular activities. In some other types of cells—some of the Protozoa, for instance—many cellular activities can go on for hours and sometimes even for a day or more after the entire nucleus has been removed; so one is led to suppose that mRNA molecules in these cells have a longer life.

Although the great bulk of cellular RNA is to be found in the ribosomes, the role of ribosomal RNA in protein synthesis is not fully understood. Like mRNA and tRNA, ribosomal RNA is made on DNA templates; and like tRNA but unlike mRNA, it is long-lived. The ribosome, a compact mass of RNA and protein, consists of two approximately spherical particles, the larger of which contains a special groove or notch into which the tRNA molecule fits. The way in which one tRNA molecule is ejected from this binding site to make way for the next and the way in which the ribosome moves along the mRNA molecule are not known.

"Breaking the Code"
NIRENBERG'S EXPERIMENTS

Soon after Jacob and Monod postulated the existence of mRNA, Marshall Nirenberg of the United States Public Health Service set out to test the messenger-RNA hypothesis. He added several crude extracts of RNA from a variety of cell sources and found that they all stimulated protein synthesis in the cell-free *E. coli* extract. In other words, the *E. coli* material would start producing protein molecules even when the RNA "orders" it received were from a "complete stranger." Even the tobacco mosaic virus, which naturally multiplies only in tobacco-plant cells, could be "read" as a messenger RNA by the ribosomes and tRNA molecules of the bacterial cell. The "code" seemed to be a universal language.

Leaving others to ponder the evolutionary implications of his finding,* Nirenberg and Heinrich Matthaei raced ahead to give it practical application. Perhaps if *E. coli* could read a foreign message and translate it into protein, it could read a totally synthetic message, one dictated by the scientists themselves. Synthetic RNA was available; a method had already been developed for linking together ribonucleotides into a long strand of RNA. The trouble with the method, from Nirenberg's point of view, was that there was no way to control the order in which an assortment of ribonucleotides would be assembled. For Nirenberg's purposes, the order

---

* The genetic code may have been functional 3 billion years ago; almost certainly, it is more than 600 million years old! Some scientists have suggested that the code became frozen by the time organisms as complex as bacteria had evolved.

was of the utmost importance. He wanted to know the exact contents of any message that he dictated.

A simple solution for this seemingly perplexing problem suddenly presented itself. Severo Ochoa of New York University synthesized an RNA molecule which consisted of only one ribonucleotide repeated over and over again, the ribonucleotide uracil. Nirenberg and Matthaei prepared 20 different test tubes, each of which contained cellular extracts of E. coli with ribosomes, transfer RNA, ATP, the necessary enzymes, and amino acids. In each test tube, one of the amino acids, and only one, carried a radioactive label. Ochoa's *synthetic poly-U*, as it was called, was added to each test tube. In 19 of the test tubes, nothing detectable occurred, but in the twentieth one, to which radioactive phenylalanine had been added, the investigators were able to detect newly formed, radioactive polypeptide chains. When the polypeptide was analyzed, it was found to consist only of phenylalanines, one after another. Nirenberg and Matthaei had dictated the message "uracil . . . uracil . . . uracil . . . ," and a clear answer had come back, "phenylalanine . . . phenylalanine . . . phenylalanine. . . ."

Within the year following Nirenberg's discovery, which was first reported in 1961, tentative codes were worked out by Nirenberg and Ochoa and their many co-workers for all the amino acids, using synthetic messenger RNA. A synthetic polynucleotide made up entirely of adenine (poly-A), for instance, makes a peptide chain composed entirely of lysine. If two parts of guanine are combined with one part of uracil, the peptide that is dictated will be composed largely of valine, so it was presumed that the code for valine is GUU or UUG or UGU. As you can see, in the synthetic messengers made of more than one type of ribonucleotide, there was no way to tell which order the bases were aligned in.

By Nirenberg's method, it was possible to identify the composition of the codon that dictated a particular amino acid—that is, to determine which bases it contained. However, his method did not reveal what order the bases occurred in. With UUU there is no problem, of course, but adenine, guanine, and cytosine, for example, can be arranged in nine different ways in a triplet code.

The problem could, of course, be solved easily if one could determine the complete amino acid sequence of a protein and the base sequence of the piece of DNA or RNA that codes it. One could then simply compare the two. The amino acid sequence can be laboriously worked out, as we have seen, but for technical reasons, determining the nucleotide sequence of a long nucleic acid molecule is still impossible.

This problem, too, Nirenberg solved in an ingenious way. He found that, by adding nucleotides one at a time, it is possible to synthesize triplets in which the bases appear in known, predetermined order. This single triplet, although useless for the biochemical functions of the cell, will

RNA BASE SEQUENCE	READ AS	AMINO ACID SEQUENCE EXPECTED
$(XY)_n$	...X Y X Y X Y X Y X Y X Y...	$\alpha\beta\alpha\beta$
$(XYZ)_n$	..X Y Z X Y Z X Y Z...	$\alpha\alpha\alpha$
	..Y Z X Y Z X Y Z X...	$\beta\beta\beta$
	..Z X Y Z X Y Z X Y...	$\gamma\gamma\gamma$
$(XXYZ)_n$	...X X Y Z X X Y Z X X Y Z...	$\alpha\beta\gamma\sigma\alpha\beta\gamma\sigma$
$(XYXZ)_n$	...X Y X Z X Y X Z X Y X Z...	$\alpha\beta\gamma\sigma\alpha\beta\gamma\sigma$

serve to bind the appropriate transfer RNA, with its amino acid, to a ribosome. Unbound transfer RNA will slip right through a cellulose filter, but transfer RNA attached to a ribosome will be caught in the filter. Nirenberg prepared combinations of synthetic triplets, amino acids, transfer RNA with a radioactive label (to facilitate its detection), and cell-free ribosome preparations. These combinations, after a brief period of exposure to one another, were passed through the cellulose filter. Then any radioactive material present in the filter was removed and analyzed. Knowing the triplet codon that he had put in the test tube, Nirenberg had only to identify the ribosome-tRNA-bound amino acid for an exact translation of his code word.

ANOTHER METHOD

An alternative approach to the study of the genetic code was developed in the laboratories of H. G. Khorana at the University of Wisconsin. Khorana and his co-workers devised a method for the synthesis of chains of DNA or RNA in which two or three nucleotides could be repeated over and over again in a known sequence. Thus he could make deoxyribose strands of TCTCTCTCTC, which would form a double helix with strands of AGAGAGAGAG, and strands of TGTGTGTGTG, which would form a double helix with ACACACACAC. Then, using RNA polymerase (the enzyme that makes messenger RNA on a DNA template), he could obtain messenger strands of AGAGAGAGAG, UCUCUCUCUC, ACACACACAC, and UGUGUGUGUG.

Each of these RNA chains, when used as a messenger in the cell-free system, produced polypeptide chains of alternating amino acids. Poly-AG produced arginine and glutamic acid; poly-UC, serine and leucine; poly-AC, threonine and histidine; and poly-UG, cysteine and valine. This is, of course, what you would expect from a triplet code, since the messenger would be read AGA . . . GAG . . . AGA. . . . This was the first proof that the messenger RNA is read sequentially (that is, one nucleotide after another); it was also the first proof that the codon consists of an uneven number of nucleotides.

More recently, Khorana has synthesized nucleotide chains consisting of known sequences of three nucleotides. What would you expect the results to be in terms of polypeptide chains produced? (Check your answer with Figure 3–64.)

CONCLUSIONS

All but three trinucleotides have now been identified—61 of the 64 possible combinations. (See Figure 3–65.) These three may be "nonsense," meaning that they do not have any biological significance, or what is

3–65 *The genetic code, consisting of 64 triplet combinations and their corresponding amino acids. Only three combinations—UAA, UAG, and UGA—have not been identified. ("Amber" and "ochre" referred originally to certain mutant strains of bacteria now identified as carrying the indicated codons.) These three codons are probably the "punctuation marks" (i.e., stop signals) of the code. Since 61 triplets code 20 amino acids, there are "synonyms." Most of the synonyms have a common characteristic; can you see what it is? What do you think might be the significance of this characteristic? ("The Genetic Code: III," F. H. C. Crick. Copyright © October 1966 by Scientific American, Inc. All rights reserved.)*

SECOND LETTER

FIRST LETTER		U	C	A	G	THIRD LETTER
U		UUU } PHE UUC UUA } LEU UUG	UCU UCC } SER UCA UCG	UAU } TYR UAC UAA OCHRE UAG AMBER	UGU } CYS UGC UGA ? UGG TRYP	U C A G
C		CUU CUC } LEU CUA CUG	CCU CCC } PRO CCA CCG	CAU } HIS CAC CAA } GLUN CAG	CGU CGC } ARG CGA CGG	U C A G
A		AUU } ILEU AUC AUA AUG MET	ACU ACC } THR ACA ACG	AAU } ASPN AAC AAA } LYS AAG	AGU } SER AGC AGA } ARG AGG	U C A G
G		GUU GUC } VAL GUA GUG	GCU GCC } ALA GCA GCG	GAU } ASP GAC GAA } GLU GAG	GGU GGC } GLY GGA GGG	U C A G

more likely, they may be punctuation marks, signifying the beginning or end of a particular message.

Since 61 combinations code for 20 amino acids, you can see that there are a number of "synonyms" among the codons. Characteristically, these synonyms almost always differ only in the third nucleotide, leading to the speculation that the first two may be sufficient to hold the transfer RNA in most instances.

Some of the biological implications of these findings are strikingly clear. Let us take another look at sickle-cell anemia, for example, in the light of Figure 3–65. Normal hemoglobin contains glutamic acid; sickle-cell hemoglobin contains valine. UGU specifies glutamic acid; AGU specifies valine. So the difference between the two is merely the replacement of one uracil by one adenine in a molecule that, since it dictates a protein which contains more than 300 amino acids, must contain more than 900 bases. In other words, the tremendous functional difference—literally a matter of life and death—between the two hemoglobins can be traced to a single "misprint" in over 900 nucleotides.

SUMMARY

The DNA-to-RNA-to-protein process which we described in the first part of this chapter is the fundamental thesis of modern genetics. Underlying this theory is the one-gene–one-protein concept, first proposed by Beadle and Tatum in 1941. Genetic information is coded in the molecules of DNA, and these, in turn, determine the sequence of amino acid units in molecules of protein. One gene contains the information needed to specify the complete sequence of one polypeptide chain.

To review this process briefly, the way in which the gene directs the production of a protein, according to current theory, is as follows: Each series of three nucleotides along a DNA strand is the *codon* for a particular amino acid. The information in the codon is transferred from the DNA by means of a long single strand of RNA, known as *messenger RNA* (mRNA). The mRNA forms along one of the strands of DNA, following the principles of base pairing first suggested by Watson and Crick, and therefore is complementary to it.

The mRNA strand attaches to a ribosome, one of a group of small cellular organelles composed of RNA and protein. At the point at which the strand of mRNA is in contact with the protein, small molecules of RNA, known as *transfer RNA* (tRNA), which serve as adapters between the nucleic acid and the proteins, are bound temporarily to the mRNA strand. This bonding is believed to take place by the same base-pairing principle that holds together the two strands of the double helix of DNA or that attracts the forming mRNA to the strand of DNA. Each tRNA molecule carries the specific amino acid called for by the mRNA codon into which the tRNA plugs. Thus, following the sequence dictated by the DNA, the amino acid units are brought into line one by one and are formed into a polypeptide chain.

Final proof of the hypothesis came when the DNA/RNA code was "broken," that is, when investigators were able to predict what protein would be formed from a given series of nucleotides. In 1961, Nirenberg was able to determine what bases a codon must contain to form a particular amino acid, but it was not until the latter part of 1964 that he worked out the *order* of bases in the codon required to specify that amino acid. Using an alternative approach, Khorana confirmed these findings and proved that (1) mRNA is read sequentially and (2) the codon consists of three nucleotides.

Today, 61 of the 64 possible triplet combinations of the four-letter DNA code have each been identified with one of the 20 amino acids that make up protein molecules.

Mapping Molecules

In Chapter 3–3, we described how the mapping studies of *Drosophila* helped to establish the physical nature of the gene and revealed its fixed location on the chromosome. In the last decade, there has been a new series of mapping studies; these investigations, performed mainly on bacteria and viruses, have helped to confirm and elucidate the biochemical nature of the gene.

Maps of *E. coli*

At this point, let us retrace our steps to examine some investigations made in the 1950s on the now familiar *E. coli*, the generally harmless bacterial inhabitant of the human intestinal tract.

E. coli, like *Neurospora*, can be grown readily on a simply defined culture medium; even a very small laboratory can accommodate vast numbers of cultures. A bacterial cell can divide as often as every 20 minutes. Theoretically, a single bacterium reproducing at this rate can give rise in 22 hours to a population of more than 10 billion individuals, three times the human population of the earth. Such a population, whose members are all the descendants of one individual cell, is known as a *clone*. Biochemical mutants that occur spontaneously in the large bacterial populations can be identified and analyzed by growing members of the mutant clone on various media, as was done with *Neurospora*.

In fact, in the early 1940s, bacteria seemed to many biologists to be an almost ideal subject for genetic studies, except for one important defect: bacterial cells were not known to undergo any sexual cycle. And if bacteria did not have genes that separated and recombined, genetic analysis of the type that had been carried out on other organisms would not be possible.

Despite this apparent shortcoming, Joshua Lederberg and Edward L. Tatum decided to see if the work accomplished in *Neurospora* could be carried out in *E. coli*. By successive radiation treatments (the same procedure as was used for *Neurospora*), they produced two strains of *E. coli* which were both triple mutants. One was unable to synthesize threonine, leucine, and thiamine; and the other could not produce biotin, phenylalanine, and cysteine. When each of the triple mutants was grown alone, occasional "back mutations" were found which produced strains that required only two of the original three substances, but no strains were produced which did not require any of the supplements.

When the two strains were grown in a mixed culture, however—in a medium supplemented with all four amino acids and the two vitamins—a much larger variety of types was found. Most of the cells still required all three nutrients, but many more were found in the mixed cultures than in the isolated cultures that only required two nutrients; some needed only one, and about one bacterial cell in every million was found to be apparently identical to wild-type *E. coli*, that is, able to make for itself all six nutrients. New genetic functions, such as the ability to make threonine, leucine, and thiamine, had been acquired by certain cells. These new genetic functions, it was found, were incorporated into the hereditary makeup of the cell and were passed on to the daughter cells and their descendants. Scientists could now assume that bacteria do, indeed, undergo some kind of "mating."

The "mating" of bacteria has been observed in electron micrographs (Figure 3–52), although there is some disagreement about whether the attachment between the mating cells is performed by a specially formed cytoplasmic tunnel or by the bacterial *pili*, small hairlike filaments that cover the surface of the cell. In any case, as it was discovered not long afterward, the material that passes from one bacterial cell to another is deoxyribonucleic acid with very little, if any, associated protein. This finding provided another confirmation of the role of DNA as the carrier of the gene.

RECOMBINATION IN *E. coli*

The discovery of mating in *E. coli* opened the possibility that the chromosome of the bacterial cell, like *Drosophila*, might be analyzed by studying its recombinants. François Jacob and Elie Wollman went one step further and demonstrated that the mating process itself could be made to reveal the order of genes on the chromosome.

The French scientists worked with two strains of *E. coli* which had a number of measurably different traits, such as the ability or inability to use a particular type of sugar or to synthesize a particular amino acid. They first noticed that some marker traits showed up in the recipient cells far more often than others. It takes about an hour for conjugation to take place, but cells often separate before conjugation is completed, and they can be separated easily in the laboratory by shaking the culture in an electric blender. The shorter the period of conjugation, the fewer the number of new traits passed to the recipient cell, as might have been expected. On the basis of this evidence, Jacob and Wollman hypothesized that the marker genes always entered the cell in the same order. If the bacterial cells were permitted to conjugate for 8 minutes, they could all receive marker gene A; after 11 minutes, they would all have received A and B; after 15 minutes, A, B, and C; and so on. In other words, the bacterial chromosome enters the conjugation tube one gene at a time, like a freight train entering a tunnel. The marker genes are arranged in an orderly array along this chromosome, and if the temperature and other factors are kept constant, it is possible to construct a very accurate map of the bacterial chromosome by keeping track of the time of entry of each marker. This is accomplished by shaking conjugating cells apart in an electric blender at various intervals after conjugation begins.

THE F FACTOR

In the course of these studies, it was found that mating in bacteria depends on a genetic trait. This trait was called simply F, for "fertility factor." Donor (male) cells have this factor, and recipient (female) cells do not. When the F factor is passed from a male (F^+) cell to a female (F^-) cell, the "female" cell then suddenly becomes "male."

Sometimes, the investigators noticed, only the F factor was transferred during conjugation. In fact, recombination (conjugation involving the transfer of chromosomal material) at first took place only as a very rare phenomenon, but eventually strains were found in which as many as 1 in 10 cells would serve as donors when exposed to suitable partners. These were called Hfr, for "high frequency of recombination."

Two curious differences were noticed in conjugations involving recombination as compared with those involving only the transfer of the F factor. First, the F factor was transferred only very rarely during recombination. Secondly, although the markers in all strains seemed to be aligned along the chromosome in the same order, the same marker did not always appear first. In other words, some strains transferred gene A first, B next, and then C; some started with C, and then D, E, F, and so on, followed right down to the last trait that had been mapped on the chromosome, which we shall call trait Z. And then in these new strains, Z could be followed by A, then B, and so on, until all the markers were passed through the conjugating tube. It was found that in all strains, if the con-

441 *Mapping Molecules*

jugation process were permitted to complete itself, the last trait to be conferred was the F factor.

Jacob and Wollman thought of an ingenious explanation for these perplexing phenomena. (See Figure 3–66.) First of all, and most remarkable, they proposed that the chromosome is circular. This does not mean, of course, that it forms a perfect circle but simply that it has no end to it. This hypothesis has subsequently been confirmed by electron-micrograph studies.

Secondly, in the majority of F$^+$ cells, the F factor exists as a separate genetic unit in the cytoplasm. Only when the F factor attaches to the chromosome can the chromosome move into the female cell. In the Hfr strains, the F factor is always a part of the chromosome. At the onset of a conjugation involving recombination, the chromosome breaks at the point of attachment of the F factor and enters the cell sequentially, F factor last. The location of the F-factor point of attachment therefore determines the order in which the genes enter the F$^-$ cell.

Fragments of genetic material, such as the F factor, which may exist independently in the cytoplasm or which may become integrated with the

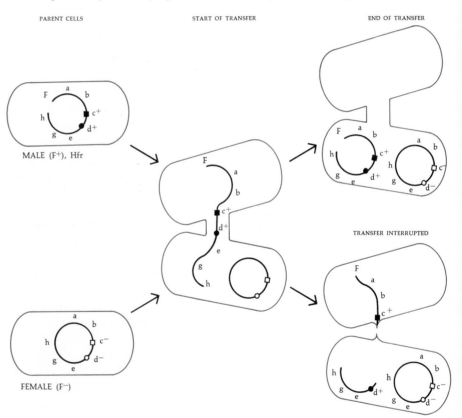

3–66 *Genetic recombination in E. coli. The male (F$^+$) chromosome breaks at the point of attachment of the F factor. The male and female (F$^-$) bacterial cells join together by a narrow cytoplasmic bridge and the male chromosome enters the female cell, F factor last. (E. coli typically contain more than one chromosome; for the sake of simplicity only one per cell is diagrammed here.) The female cell is a mutant, as indicated by the minus signs following marker genes c and d. At 37° C, the transfer of a complete chromosome requires about 90 minutes. By separating conjugating cells at different time intervals and testing the recipient cells for the presence of new genetic traits, it is possible to determine the order of the genes on the bacterial chromosome.*

PARENT CELLS   START OF TRANSFER   END OF TRANSFER

MALE (F$^+$), Hfr

TRANSFER INTERRUPTED

FEMALE (F$^-$)

chromosomes have been given the name of *episomes*. Some viruses and some genetic factors conferring drug resistance also have been found to exist in the bacterial cell in the form of episomes.

TRANSDUCTION

Not long after the discovery of conjugation in bacterial cells, another unexpected means of genetic exchange among bacterial cells was discovered. This phenomenon depends on a type of bacterial virus which, unlike the T viruses of *E. coli*, does not necessarily set up an immediate infective cycle but may lie dormant within the bacterial cell. Such viruses are said to be *lysogenic* since bacterial cells which harbor them will from time to time release virus particles that will infect other cells in the culture and destroy them.

The role of lysogenic viruses in genetic exchanges was discovered in 1952 by Norton Zinder, then a graduate student working with Lederberg at the University of Wisconsin. Zinder, attempting to duplicate Lederberg's studies on conjugation in bacteria, was studying another type of bacteria (*Salmonella*) and was obtaining very puzzling results. He found that genetic characteristics were indeed transferred from time to time but usually only one at a time and usually only the same one, never in a whole series, as in the previous studies on bacterial mating. Was mating actually taking place? Zinder repeated his experiments, but this time he put up a barrier, a fine-pored membrane, between the mutant strains. He found that the exchange of genetic material took place even when any contact was prevented between donor and recipient cells! Following this clue, he was able to demonstrate that the genetic material was being transferred by lysogenic bacteriophages acting as messengers between the two strains of *Salmonella*. The lysogenic bacteriophage, like the F factor, is an episome; that is, it may exist independent of the chromosome (this is its infectious form), or it may be a part of the chromosome and so lie latent within the cell. When the bacteriophage escapes from the chromosome, it may take a small amount of the host's genetic material with it. This material then becomes replicated in the infectious cycle and protein-packaged, and so makes its way into other bacterial cells. If the lysogenic phage sets up another infectious cycle, the genetic material of the previous host cannot be detected, but if the phage establishes lysogeny in its new host, the host will become the recipient of the stolen gene. Since some types of lysogenic bacteriophages have their own place on the bacterial chromosome, they always transfer the same gene or genes.

At one time, viruses were thought to be examples of what the first forms of life may have been like. Now, in the light of what is known about the relationships between viruses and cells, it seems equally reasonable to speculate that viruses may represent portions of DNA or RNA that have

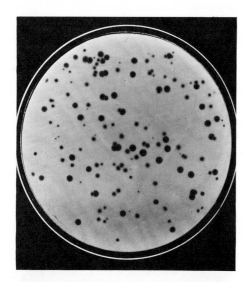

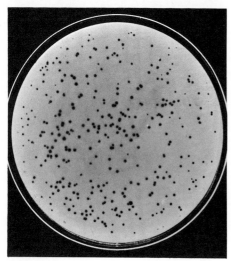

3–67 *A mixed bacteriophage population of wild-type T4 and rII mutants is grown in a medium of E. coli. In strain* B, *on the top, rII mutants produce the large plaques and the wild-type phage produce the small plaques. If the same mixed population is grown in strain* K, *as shown on the bottom, only the small plaques are produced. (Dr. E. Kellenberger)*

broken away from a mother cell and gained the power to synthesize their own protein coats. Luria has described them aptly as "bits of heredity looking for a chromosome." There is no proof for either of these theories, however, nor do either of them answer the question of whether viruses should be considered as "just molecules" or as living creatures. Perhaps it is safest to say that molecular biology has made such questions obsolete.

The Structure of the Gene

RECOMBINATION WITHIN THE GENE

In the mapping studies of *Drosophila,* it had been generally assumed that crossing-over occurred between genes and not within the genes themselves. But if the genetic material was simply a long molecule of DNA, why couldn't crossovers occur just as readily within the gene? If such crossovers did occur, the gene itself could be mapped.

How can crossovers within a single gene be detected? To answer this question, let us examine the findings of Seymour Benzer at Purdue University, who has done the most extensive work on this problem. Benzer chose for study a mutation known as "*r*II" in the T4 bacteriophage. The *r* mutations were among those employed in the early mapping studies in the 1940s. They are particularly useful for laboratory work since they cause a visible change in the type of plaques (round holes where the infected cells have burst their walls) formed on the bacterial "lawn" by the infecting phages (see Figure 3–67). In addition, their mutations affect the ability of the phage to grow on certain strains of bacteria. *r*II will grow in one strain of *E. coli,* strain *B,* in which it produces a distinctive plaque, but it will not grow at all in strain *K.* Wild-type T4, on the other hand, will grow in either of the strains. In other words, *r*II is a conditional lethal mutation, depending on whether strain *B* is used as the "medium" or strain *K.* This can be summarized as follows:

T4 virus	Bacterial strain	
	E. coli B	*E. coli K*
Wild type	Small plaque	Small plaque
*r*II mutant	Large plaque	No growth

Nevertheless, if the *r*II mutant is grown on strain *K* along with a wild-type phage, both can grow normally, although only the small (wild-type) plaques are produced. This is most easily understood if we think of the wild-type chromosome and the mutant chromosome as homologues.

Then, so long as the viral chromosomes exist free (unenclosed by a protective coat) in the bacterial cell, they can complement one another—as in the individual heterozygous for the sickling gene—and the mutant becomes a recessive, to return to Mendelian terms. Or, from the point of view of biochemical genetics, the wild-type, or "normal," chromosome produces enough of what is needed, presumably an enzyme, to provide for not only its own progeny but those of the mutant.

Suppose, however, that two viruses with mutations in the same gene are grown in strain B and then transferred to strain K. Presumably, the two mutants could not "help" each other as the *r*II and wild-type had done, because neither mutant could produce the required enzyme. And if recombination occurs only *between* genes, the progeny would all have the mutated gene. Thus, no plaques would appear in strain K.

But, in fact, the result of this experiment was that plaques *did* appear in strain K. When the mutants recombined, some of the progeny ended up with a normal, or wild-type, gene, giving them the ability to grow in strain K and demonstrating that recombination had occurred within the gene. (See Figure 3–69.)

3–68 *When a bacterium is infected with several genetically different phage particles, genetic recombination can result.*

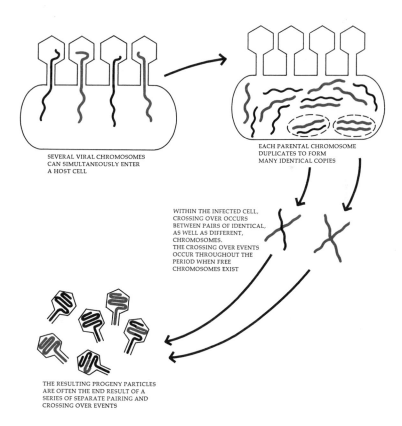

SEVERAL VIRAL CHROMOSOMES
CAN SIMULTANEOUSLY ENTER
A HOST CELL

EACH PARENTAL CHROMOSOME
DUPLICATES TO FORM
MANY IDENTICAL COPIES

WITHIN THE INFECTED CELL,
CROSSING OVER OCCURS
BETWEEN PAIRS OF IDENTICAL,
AS WELL AS DIFFERENT,
CHROMOSOMES.
THE CROSSING OVER EVENTS
OCCUR THROUGHOUT THE
PERIOD WHEN FREE
CHROMOSOMES EXIST

THE RESULTING PROGENY PARTICLES
ARE OFTEN THE END RESULT OF A
SERIES OF SEPARATE PAIRING AND
CROSSING OVER EVENTS

445   *Mapping Molecules*

3–69 *Sequence of recombination of two dif-*
ferent phage mutants. When mutants
obtained from two different cultures
are introduced into a broth of strain-B
E. coli, the two types may infect a single
bacillus. (Mutation sites on the chromo-
somes are indicated by dark circles.)
Recombinations may produce a double
mutant (two circles) and a wild type
(no circles). When the progeny are
plated on strain-B (bottom left), all
grow successfully. When they are
plated on strain K, only the wild-type
recombinants are able to grow (bottom
right). A single standard (wild-type)
recombinant can be detected among as
many as 100 million progeny.

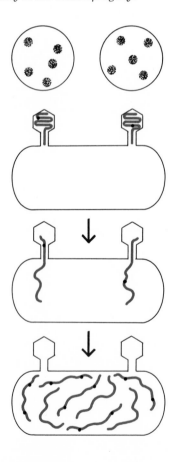

As you will recall, the frequency of recombination depends on how far apart the crossover sites are on the chromosome, so the recombinants Benzer was seeking—recombinants right within the same gene—would be very rare indeed. The extraordinary advantage of working with the bacteriophages, however, is that the results of crosses between millions of individuals can be cataloged; a generation only takes minutes. Further, one wild-type recombinant in a billion mutants can be detected simply by growing the progeny on a culture containing strain *K*, where only the wild-type recombinants will be able to form plaques. Such recombinants were found in surprisingly high proportions. The hypothesis that recombination occurs within the gene was right.

MAPPING THE GENE

Mutants arise spontaneously in the course of multiplication of T4, just as they arise in the multiplication of bacteria. If T4 is permitted to grow on strain *B*, new *r*II mutants appear which can be identified readily by their abnormal plaques. Although the visible effect, the phenotype, of these mutations is always the same, the mutations themselves may be extremely varied. Some may involve very short segments (i.e., one nucleotide pair) of the chromosome, while some may cover practically the whole extent of the *r*II "region." Mutations which involve only short segments are known as *point mutations*. Mutations which affect an extended region of the chromosome are called *deletions*.

By testing literally thousands of mutants—Benzer has now isolated over 5,000 different mutants—and by studying which can recombine and which cannot, Benzer has been able to map the location of many point mutations within the gene.

The first step in this mapping procedure was to determine lengths of the deletions in the *r*II region of a number of different mutants. For this, Benzer used *nonreverting r*II mutants, that is, mutants which did not revert to standard type when they reproduced. (Nonreverting mutants generally have large alterations or deletions, while *r*II mutants that revert spontaneously behave as if their alterations were localized at single points.) A recombination study of hundreds of nonreverting mutants showed that they all could be represented as containing deletions in a single linear structure. Overlapping deletions produce no wild-type recombinants.

Benzer's next step was to locate the point mutations, those occurring in reverting *r*II mutants, with reference to the deletions previously obtained, as shown in Figure 3–70. Another way of mapping point mutations would have been to test thousands of mutants against one another for recombination in all possible pairs, but this would have involved millions of crosses. The use of reference deletions presented a shortcut.

3–70 *Benzer's method of "deletion mapping" to determine the internal structure of the gene. An unknown mutant, X, is crossed with a selected group of reference mutants whose DNA molecules contain deletions of known length in the rII region. When mutant X is crossed with test mutants A and B no standard recombinants are formed indicating that the mutation on X falls within the deletions of test mutants A and B. When X is crossed with C and D, however, standard recombinants can be formed, indicating that X is located outside the area of these deletions. The location of X can be further narrowed by using other mutants with appropriate deletions. The X mutation can then be specifically located by crossing it with other point mutants having mutations within the same deletion segment. The proportion of recombinants obtained gives a quantitative measure of the position of the mutant X in relation to the known point mutant. (After Benzer, 1962)*

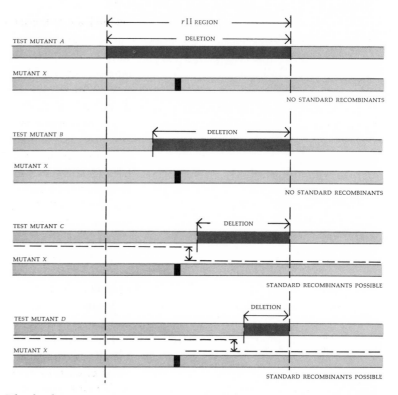

The final step was to test against one another only those mutants having mutations within each deletion. Those that showed recombinations were assigned different sites, and the sequence of sites within the deletion was determined in the usual way, on the basis of recombination frequencies (see Chapter 3–3).

From Benzer's *r*II genetic maps, two important conclusions could be drawn:

1 A large number of different sites of mutation occur within the gene. For the *r*II region, this number is on the order of 1,000 to 1,500.
2 The *r*II genetic maps are unambiguously linear, proving that the gene itself has a linear construction and establishing a correspondence between the genetic sites and the linear sequence of nucleotides in the DNA molecule.

THE CIS-TRANS TEST

At this point in his investigations, Benzer posed the following problem: The *r*II region—the hereditary structure needed by the T4 phage to multiply in strain *K*—had been shown to consist of many parts. Is this region one gene or is it hundreds of genes? Mutation at any one of the sites in the region leads to the same observed defect (inability to multiply in strain K), but that does not necessarily mean that the entire structure is a single functional unit. It might mean, for example, that growth in strain K requires a series of biochemical reactions, each controlled by a different portion of the rII region, and that mutation of any step along the way could block the final result.

To see whether or not the rII region could be subdivided into parts that function independently, Benzer performed an experiment known as the *cis-trans comparison*. Suppose that two mutational sites, X and Y, have been identified in the rII region and that the problem is to determine if they lie within the same functional unit. A *cis* test (from the Latin, meaning "on this side") is first performed. Cells of strain K are infected with a double mutant, containing both X and Y mutations, and with a standard phage. This results in normal replication and provides a control to measure the activity observed in the *trans* test. The *trans* test consists of infecting cells of K strain with two different mutants, one containing X and the other containing Y. If the phage fails to function, the conclusion is that X and Y fall within the same functional unit; if the phage develops actively, the X and Y sites must lie in different functional units.

The result of the *cis-trans* test as applied to rII mutants showed that the rII region is divided into two functional units, which were given the name of *cistrons*, after the cis-trans test by which they were identified. As shown in Figure 3–71, normal phage multiplication in strain K is possible

3–71 *The rII region consists of two distinct functional units (cistrons). Normal growth in a cell of K strain is obtained only when the two mutants infecting the cell are complementary. If both phage particles contain mutations in the A cistron, no active form of the rII–A product is available and it will be impossible for the virus to multiply. This is also true if both mutations lie in the B cistron. (After Watson, 1965)*

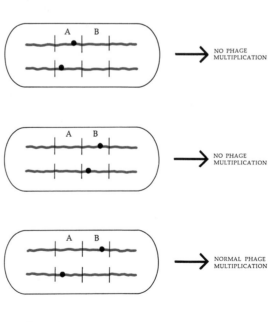

THE MOLECULAR BASIS OF RECOMBINATION

Geneticists in the 1930s, on the basis of cytological observations, hypothesized that crossing-over occurred during meiosis as a result of physical breaks in adjoining chromatids. When these broken ends mended, they united with the corresponding segment of the adjoining chromatid. According to this hypothesis, all recombination took place after replication of the genetic material was completed. As we mentioned previously, there was no explanation for why the chromatids should break and recombine at precisely corresponding points.

Following the demonstration by Benzer and others that crossing-over occurred within the gene, it became necessary to postulate that the breakage points occurred not just between genes, as had been previously assumed, but actually between corresponding nucleotide pairs. Otherwise, one product of the crossover would be different in length from the other and neither would correspond to the parental models. This seemed so exacting a requirement that an alternate hypothesis for the mechanism of crossing-over was developed. According to this second hypothesis, recombination occurs during replication. The new DNA strand being formed along one chromosome switches over to another chromosome and then proceeds to copy that. In a developing germ cell, this would mean that at meiosis, when the homologues (one originally maternal and one originally paternal, you will recall) are paired and replication takes place, the DNA strand forming along one strand of a maternal homologue will switch over to the paternal homologue, or vice versa. In terms of viruses or E. coli, which are haploid, the newly forming strand would switch from one chromosome to another (Figure 3–72). In this way, for instance, the genetic material of a recipient, or female, bacterial cell and the male genetic material received in the course of conjugation could be combined into a single chromosome.

One way in which this question can be answered is to determine whether or not crossing-over can occur without any synthesis of new DNA. This has been accomplished in the E. coli-bacteriophage system. If E. coli is infected with large numbers of two types of bacteriophages, all of which are marked with heavy nitrogen, some of the bacteriophage progeny, although surrounded by freshly synthesized protein coats, contain only heavy DNA. In other words, no replication of these viral chromosomes has taken place. However, when these heavy viruses are separated from the other viral progeny on a cesium chloride gradient and tested for their biological properties, it can be shown that recombination between the two strains has taken place.

On the basis of this and other evidence, most molecular biologists are now convinced that breaking and rejoining of the replicated genetic material is the principal way in which crossing-over occurs. Synthesis of new DNA may also occur; this would serve to mend the "tears" at the point of chromosome breakage. The physicochemical basis for the pairing of the double DNA strands and the reason that they break and rejoin at such exactly corresponding points are still not known, however, and these remain fundamental questions to be solved.

3–72 *Two hypotheses of the way in which crossovers may occur. Shown in (a) is the classical picture of crossing-over, developed in the 1930's. During meiosis, the paired, coiled chromosomes break at the chromatid level, and the broken ends cross over, each end joining with the opposite end of the other chromatid. The result is two reciprocally recombinant chromatids and two parent chromatids. According to an alternative hypothesis (b), which is called* copy choice, *recombination occurs during replication. The new DNA strand being formed along one chromosome switches to the other chromosome and thereafter copies that. If, at the same time, the DNA strand of the second chromosome switches to the first chromosome, two reciprocally recombinant strands will be formed.*

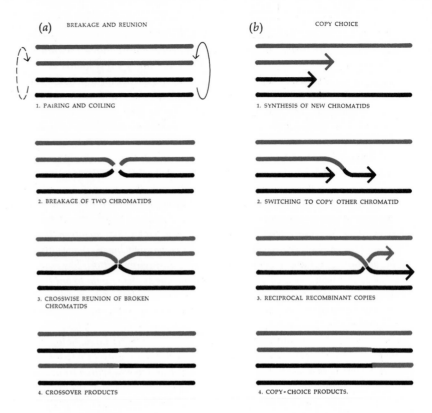

(a) BREAKAGE AND REUNION

1. PAIRING AND COILING

2. BREAKAGE OF TWO CHROMATIDS

3. CROSSWISE REUNION OF BROKEN CHROMATIDS

4. CROSSOVER PRODUCTS

(b) COPY CHOICE

1. SYNTHESIS OF NEW CHROMATIDS

2. SWITCHING TO COPY OTHER CHROMATID

3. RECIPROCAL RECOMBINANT COPIES

4. COPY-CHOICE PRODUCTS.

only when the two mutants infecting the cell contain *complementary* cistrons—a normal (active) *A* cistron in one mutant and a normal *B* cistron in the other. Each mutant chromosome is then able to produce the gene product that its partner is unable to make. Thus two chromosomes can complement one another when the mutations are present in distinct genes, or cistrons, and the product of this complementation is the normal phenotype. (Recombination, on the other hand, involves an actual crossing-over of genetic material from one chromosome to its homologue. The difference between complementation and recombination is an important one for you to understand.)

As a consequence of Benzer's work, a new word and a new concept, the *cistron*, has been introduced into the field of genetics. A cistron is a segment of DNA that makes the molecule of messenger RNA that codes for one polypeptide chain. (A protein, you will remember, is made up of one or more polypeptide chains.) A single gene, in the classical sense of the word, may consist of one or more cistrons from the biochemist's point of view. And so "one gene, one enzyme," with which the story of molecular biology began, became the more ponderous but more explicit "one cistron, one polypeptide chain."

3–73 *The genetic map of the T4 bacteriophage shows the relative positions of the more than 75 genes so far identified (on the basis of mutations). The solid black segments of the circle indicate the locations of genes which are concerned with the development of normal organic forms. The boxed diagrams show which viral components are found in cells infected by mutants defective in the indicated genes. For example, a defect in gene 11 or 12 produces a complete but fragile particle. A defect in gene 57 produces a particle apparently without tail fibers. ("Building a Bacterial Virus," William B. Wood & R. S. Edgar. Copyright © July 1967 by Scientific American, Inc. All rights reserved.)*

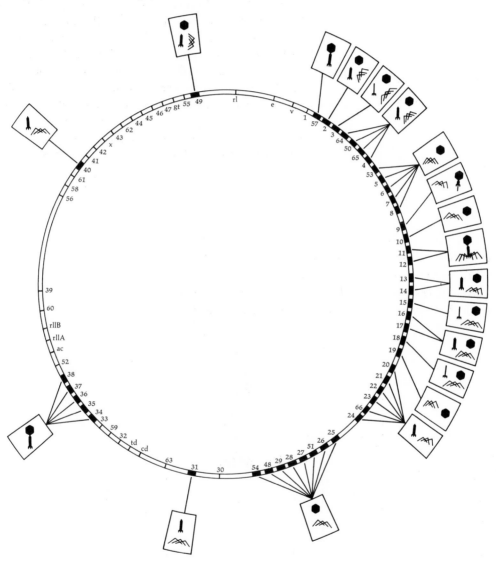

T4 Bacteriophage

At present, the most thoroughly plotted genetic map is that of the T4 bacteriophage (Figure 3–73). This map has been constructed by Robert S. Edgar of the California Institute of Technology and others on the basis of work using conditional lethal mutants. The map, as you can see, forms a circle. The numbers indicated on it represent the more than 75 genes located to date. Before we look at what these genes do, however—or rather, at what does not happen if they do not function—let us take another look at the bacteriophage itself, about which much more has been learned since the early experiments of Delbrück, Luria, and Hershey.

Figure 3–74 shows a diagram of T4, which is a remarkably complicated structure when you consider that some 1 billion of them could be contained inside the space of a letter "o" printed on this page. The protein coat contains at least six different types of protein molecules (many viruses only contain one type). The head consists of about 1,000 copies of the same molecule packed into a polygon. The tail consists of a hollow core surrounded by a sheath; the sheath is an assembly of submolecules which appear to be arranged in a helix. At the tip of the tail and perpendicular to it is the base plate, which looks like a six-pointed star. From the six points

3–74 *The T4 bacteriophage is an assembly of protein components. The head is a protein membrane filled with DNA. It is attached to a tail consisting of a hollow core surrounded by a contractile sheath and based on a spiked plate to which six tail fibers are attached. The spikes and tail fibers fix the virus to a bacterial cell wall. The sheath then contracts, driving the core through the wall, and the viral DNA enters the cell.*

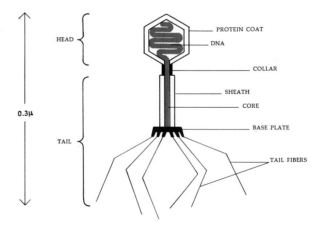

radiate six long fibers, which, when at rest, apparently fold back along the sheath.

When the bacteriophage encounters an *E. coli* cell, the tail fibers of the phage attach to the receptor site of the cell and then draw the base plate to the surface of the cell and fix it there. Next, the sheath contracts, forcing the hollow tail core through the cell wall and through the cell membrane, like a microsyringe. The DNA of the virus is then released into the bacterial cell. The figure at the beginning of this section shows the DNA molecule from a single virus of T4. As you will recall from the Hershey-Chase experiment, only the DNA enters the cell, all of the protein coat being left outside. Furthermore, one single viral DNA molecule is sufficient to set up a cycle of infection by which, within less than an hour, thousands of new T4 viruses will be produced.

As soon as the viral DNA enters the cell, messenger RNA molecules begin to form. From these, a series of proteins are run off. The mapping studies show us what these proteins do in the brief, but amazingly efficient, life cycle of the viruses. As you can see, a number of them are enzymes involved in the synthesis of viral DNA. Mutations in the genes producing these enzymes will result in the production of protein-coat molecules with no DNA inside them. When these genes are functional, viral DNA begins to collect in the bacterial cell within eight minutes after infection. Each of these new units is an identical copy of the DNA molecule that entered the cell at the moment of infection. These long molecules collect in pools within the cell; it is during this period that crossing-over takes place in the strands of DNA.

Coat proteins start to appear at about the same time as DNA molecules, and by the time enough DNA has formed to supply 30 to 40 phages, complete particles begin to appear. The DNA supply always stays a little ahead of the demand, with 30 or 40 chromosomes always available, recombining in the pool.

The mapping experiments show that about half the genes that have been mapped are involved in making coat proteins. As you can see in Figure 3–73, mutations in some of these genes produce particles without tails; in others, particles without heads. Mutations in genes 34 to 38 produce particles that look all right in the electron microscope but are not infective. These may lack tail fibers and so cannot attach to the bacterial cell. All the proteins are not produced simultaneously, but the different kinds are produced at regular periods—and in precise amounts—during the life cycle.

A number of genes seem to be involved with assembly. For instance, one gene makes the head protein, but mutation in seven other genes can also produce headless viruses. These viral assembly genes are of particular interest to molecular biologists because it is believed that some of the cell organelles may be assembled in much the same way. In the case of the viral particles, assembly is remarkably efficient; some 90 percent of viral DNA ends up protein-packaged.

Eventually, after 20 or 30 minutes, an enzyme known as *lysozyme*—also produced by the virus—eats its way through the bacterial cell wall, and the cell lyses. When the cell bursts, two or three hundred viral particles spill out, each one of them containing a circle of DNA which contains all the instructions for carrying out the same sequence of events, all over again.

As you can see, these studies indicate that biology is now approaching the point at which it may become possible to explain the entire life process of a very simple organism in terms of the chemical structure of its DNA molecule.

Turning the Genes on and Off

An important question and one that is dramatically illustrated in the life story of the T4 bacteriophage is how the genetic message is modulated. Each component of the T4 virus is produced in just the required amounts. For each unit of DNA, 1,000 molecules of head protein are turned out, but only some 30 molecules, for instance, of tail-fiber protein. All is produced as needed, and nothing seems to be made in gross excess.

These regulatory abilities are even more striking in a more complex organism. *E. coli* is a good example because this problem of turning the genes on and off has been most intensively studied in this biological system. The chromosome of *E. coli* is long enough to make between 2,000 and 4,000 different polypeptide chains, yet its production of any particular polypeptide seems to be carefully regulated by its needs. For example, *E. coli* that is growing on lactose needs the enzyme B-galactosidase, and when lactose is present, approximately 3,000 molecules of B-galactosidase are present in every normal *E. coli* cell. This represents about 3 percent of the total protein. In the absence of lactose, however, it is rare that one detects a single molecule per cell.

An enzyme which appears only when it is needed—apparently in response to the presence of a particular substrate—is known as an *inducible enzyme*. Inducible enzymes are not stored in inactive forms in the cell but are produced from amino acids as needed, following the production of new messenger RNA.

Obviously, it is of great advantage to a cell to produce a particular enzyme only when it is needed, and in the required amounts. Mutants of *E. coli* have been found which can synthesize almost 15 percent of their protein as B-galactosidase, but these are at a selective disadvantage since they are using their energies uneconomically, and they tend to be replaced by the wild-type strains.

Jacob and Monod, in the work for which they received the Nobel Prize, were able to show by mapping and mutation studies that three different genes affect the production of enzymes (Figure 3–75).

1 *The Structural Gene.* This gene codes for the messenger RNA that dictates the structure of the enzyme. A mutation in this gene leads to an altered enzyme or to no enzyme at all.

2 *The Regulator Gene.* In *E. coli*, if there is a mutation in the regulator gene, the enzyme B-galactosidase is poured out constantly, not just when lactose is present. This fact led to the conclusion that the regulator gene produces something that represses the action of the structural gene. In a bacterial cell with two chromosomes, a functioning regulator gene on one chromosome can affect the structural gene on a second chromosome, indicating that the regulator can act on the structural gene over a distance. A single regulator gene can control the production of a number of structural genes.

3 *The Operator Gene.* Mutations in the operator gene will prevent the structural genes from being repressed even if the regulator is functioning normally. An operator gene always is adjacent to the genes that it controls; it does not act over a distance, as does the regulator gene. Characteristically, an operator controls a series of enzymes that work together. Since these enzymes operate in much the same way as workmen on an assembly line, there is an obvious adaptive value in being able to turn them off and on together as a group—like blowing the factory whistle. The operator and the group of structural genes it controls are known as the *operon,* a particular segment of the assembly line.

Other enzymes, such as those involved in synthesizing arginine or tryptophan, are *repressible* rather than inducible. These enzyme systems continue in operation until a certain amount of the desired end product is produced, at which time they are turned off. It is believed that the repressor substance, the product of the regulator gene, cannot act upon the operon until it is combined with some substance produced by the function of the operon. This combination then acts upon the operon to repress its activities.

The presence of regulators and operons has been demonstrated now in higher organisms, such as corn plants and the evening primrose. In these plants, mutations have been detected that result in the unrestrained production of groups of enzymes similar to the unrestrained production of B-galactosidase in *E. coli.* The regulator-operator-operon principle, or one

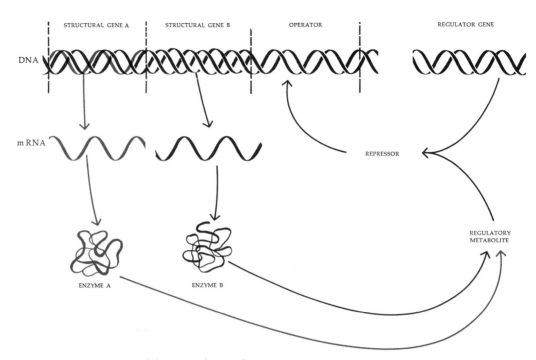

DNA

mRNA

REPRESSOR

REGULATORY
METABOLITE

ENZYME A   ENZYME B

3–75 *The process by which genes are activated and deactivated, according to current hypothesis. The basic theory is that the genes which direct the formation of specific enzymes or other proteins are themselves controlled by regulator genes (shown on the right end of the DNA strand). As a result of the chemical reactions in the cell mediated by the specific enzymes produced by the structural genes, a regulatory metabolite is produced. This regulatory metabolite combines with a substance produced by the regulator gene to form a* repressor *that acts upon the operator gene. When the operator gene is inhibited by the repressor (probably by preventing mRNA synthesis along the adjacent section of DNA), protein production by the structural genes ceases.*

like it, may hold true for genetic systems in general. Mapping studies in bacteria indicate that a single regulator can affect a number of operons and that the number of regulator genes in the cell may be comparable to the number of structural genes. Through these studies, we are beginning to glimpse the way in which the many and varied biochemical activities of the cell can be modulated and brought into a harmonious whole.

Colinearity

Some of the most recent and valuable findings produced by genetic mapping techniques have been those of Charles Yanofsky of Stanford University. Yanofsky's work has solved an interesting and perplexing problem. Implicit in the Watson-Crick hypothesis was the notion that the linear arrangement of the nucleotides in DNA corresponds to the linear sequence of amino acid units in polypeptide chains. Since the nucleotide sequence could not be analyzed, however, this *colinearity*, as it was called, was difficult to prove. In fact, colinearity was not demonstrated to everyone's satisfaction until Yanofsky's elegant experiments were reported in 1966–1967.

Yanofsky selected as his model system the enzyme tryptophan synthetase as produced by various mutants of *E. coli*. Tryptophan synthetase, which catalyzes the last step in the production of tryptophan, was first isolated by Beadle and Tatum in their studies on *Neurospora*. Yanofsky chose to work with bacterial cells rather than *Neurospora* because these lend themselves more readily to mutation and mapping studies. Furthermore, in *E. coli*, it is possible to induce the cells to produce large amounts of the enzyme, up to 2 percent of the total protein of the cell, by using appropriate mutants in which the regulation of the synthesis of the enzyme is impaired.

Tryptophan synthetase, like hemoglobin, is made up of four polypeptide chains, two *A* chains and two *B* chains. The chain studied by Yanofsky and his co-workers was the *A* chain, consisting of 267 amino acids, the identity and sequence of which have now been determined. The study proceeded along two parallel lines. First, a large number of different A-protein mutants, some of which were produced by chemical treatments, were isolated. Using these mutants, Yanofsky constructed a map of the fine structure of the cistron controlling the *A* protein, analogous to the map produced by Benzer for the *A* and *B* cistrons of the T4 bacteriophage. Second, the altered *A* proteins produced by these mutants were collected and analyzed. Map distances on the cistron were plotted for all eight mutations, and the numerical positions of the altered amino acids were also determined. For all the mutations studied, a neat correspondence between the two sequences was found; the question of colinearity has now been laid to rest.

These studies yielded an unexpected dividend. As many as seven different amino acids, they found, may occupy the same position along the polypeptide chain in various mutant types. In almost every known case, the change from one to another amino acid has resulted from the change of a single nucleotide pair. For example, glycine (GGA) may be replaced in one mutant by glutamic acid (GAA) and in another mutant by arginine (AGA). The glutamic acid (GAA) mutant may back-mutate to glycine, or it may change in turn to valine (GUA) or alanine (GCA). Similarly, the arginine mutant (AGA) changes to serine (AGU). So it is possible to con-

3–76 *Genetic mutations can result from the alteration of a single base in a DNA codon. In each of the four mutant DNA sequences shown at the top, a pair of bases is different from that in the normal sequence. The sequence and approximate spacing of the four mutations can be mapped, as shown. The amino acids produced by the normal and mutant DNA sequences are shown on the bottom. (After Yanofsky, 1967)*

NORMAL DNA	G A G	G T T	C C T	A A A	C C T	T A A	A G C	C G G
	C T C	C A A	G G A	T T T	G G A	A T T	T C G	G C C
MUTANT 1 DNA	G C G	G T T	C C T	A A A	C C T	T A A	A G C	C G G
	C G C	C A A	G G A	T T T	G G A	A T T	T C G	G C C
MUTANT 2 DNA	G A G	G T T	C T T	A A A	C C T	T A A	A G C	C G G
	C T C	C A A	G A A	T T T	G G A	A T T	T C G	G C C
MUTANT 3 DNA	G A G	G T T	C C T	A A A	C A T	T A A	A G C	C G G
	C T C	C A A	G G A	T T T	G T A	A T T	T C G	G C C
MUTANT 4 DNA	G A G	G T T	C C T	A A A	C C T	T A A	A C C	C G G
	C T C	C A A	G G A	T T T	G G A	A T T	T G G	G C C

GENETIC MAP   1   2   3   4

NORMAL PROTEIN   LEU — GLN — GLY — PHE — GLY — ILE — SER — ALA

MUTANT 1 PROTEIN   ARG — GLN — GLY — PHE — GLY — ILE — SER — ALA

MUTANT 2 PROTEIN   LEU — GLN — GLU — PHE — GLY — ILE — SER — ALA

MUTANT 3 PROTEIN   LEU — GLN — GLY — PHE — VAL — ILE — SER — ALA

MUTANT 4 PROTEIN   LEU — GLN — GLY — PHE — GLY — ILE — TRP — ALA

struct pedigrees showing the origins of the various mutants. (See Figure 3–76.)

In some cases, tracing these pedigrees has helped to resolve the ambiguities concerning the third letter of the triplet in a particular sequence. For example, of the four possible codons for glycine, only one—GGA—can yield, by a single base change, either arginine (AGA) or glutamic acid (GAA); thus it is possible even to select the correct synonym. As a result of these studies, it is becoming possible for the first time to spell out the particular nucleotide sequence, down to the last "letter," of a particular biologically active segment of DNA.

SUMMARY

In the last decade, the biochemical structure of the gene has been the object of intensive research by geneticists. Mapping studies performed on bacteria and viruses have been of great importance in confirming and elucidating this structure.

Studies of *E. coli* first confirmed that bacteria, like higher organisms, recombine genetic traits in a kind of "mating." It was found that the material which passes from one bacterial cell to another during this "mating" (known as *conjugation*) is DNA, with very little, if any, protein. Because the marker genes always enter the recipient cell in the same order and in the same amount of time, it is possible to construct a very accurate map of the bacterial chromosome by keeping track of the time of entry of each marker.

Another means of genetic exchange among bacterial cells is *transduction*, in which bacterial genes are carried from one bacterium to another by phage particles. This happens when a viral particle is formed that contains a very small portion of its host cell's chromosome. When the viral particle is released from the cell, it attaches to another cell, and the fragment of bacterial chromosome is injected into this new host. The fragment is then inserted into the new host chromosome by crossing-over.

From his studies of recombinants in bacteriophage, Benzer established the concept of the *cistron* as the functional hereditary unit. His maps showing the location of mutations within the *r*II region of the T4 bacteriophage demonstrated (1) that a large number of mutation sites occur within the gene, and (2) that the gene has a linear construction. He thus established a correspondence between the genetic sites and the linear sequence of DNA nucleotides. Subsequently, Yanofsky demonstrated the *colinearity* of the DNA molecule and the protein molecule which it codes.

The way in which genes are switched on and off so that proteins are produced when they are needed by the organism, but only in the right amounts, is not fully understood today. It is believed that the genes which control the structural formation of specific proteins are, in turn, controlled by *regulator genes*, which exercise this control through special repressor substances.

WORK IN PROGRESS

These last chapters have tried to complete the long history of thought and work in the field of heredity by bringing to you some of the most recent findings that have been reported. However, in the light of the swiftly moving events of the last decade, it seems clear that new advances will be made in molecular biology by the time you read these words. If you are interested in following the story further, get copies of the *Scientific American* or of *Science*. If you have understood this section, you should be able to follow almost everything the *Scientific American* prints about molecular biology, a field which it covers very thoroughly. *Science* is more difficult, but you will find many of their articles very rewarding. And in this way, you can bring this section up to date yourself.

SUGGESTIONS FOR FURTHER READING

BEADLE, GEORGE W., AND MURIEL BEADLE: *The Language of Life*, Doubleday and Company, Inc., Garden City, N.Y., 1966.*

A popular account, highly readable, by a very eminent scientist and his wife.

CROW, JAMES F.: *Genetic Notes*, Burgess Publishing Company, Minneapolis, Minn., 1966.

An excellent and succinct summary of genetics for the student.

PETERS, JAMES A. (ED.): *Classic Papers in Genetics*, Prentice-Hall, Inc., Englewood Cliffs, N.J.*

Includes papers by most of the scientists responsible for the important developments in genetics—Mendel, Sutton, Morgan, Beadle and Tatum, Watson and Crick, Benzer, etc. You should find this book very interesting; the authors are surprisingly readable, and the papers give a feeling of immediacy that no other account can achieve.

SINNOTT, EDMUND W., L. C. DUNN, AND THEODOSIUS DOBZHANSKY: *Principles of Genetics*, 5th ed., McGraw-Hill Book Company, New York, 1958.

A standard text, very thorough, particularly in the areas of classical genetics.

STURTEVANT, ALFRED H.: *A History of Genetics*, Harper & Row, Publishers Inc., New York, 1965.

For the "informed layman." You should read this for his account of classical genetics, in which, as you know, he was particularly involved.

WATSON, JAMES D.: *Molecular Biology of the Gene*, W. A. Benjamin, Inc., New York, 1965.*

For the student who wants to go more deeply into questions of molecular biology, this is a detailed and authoritative account.

* Available in paperback.

DEVELOPMENT

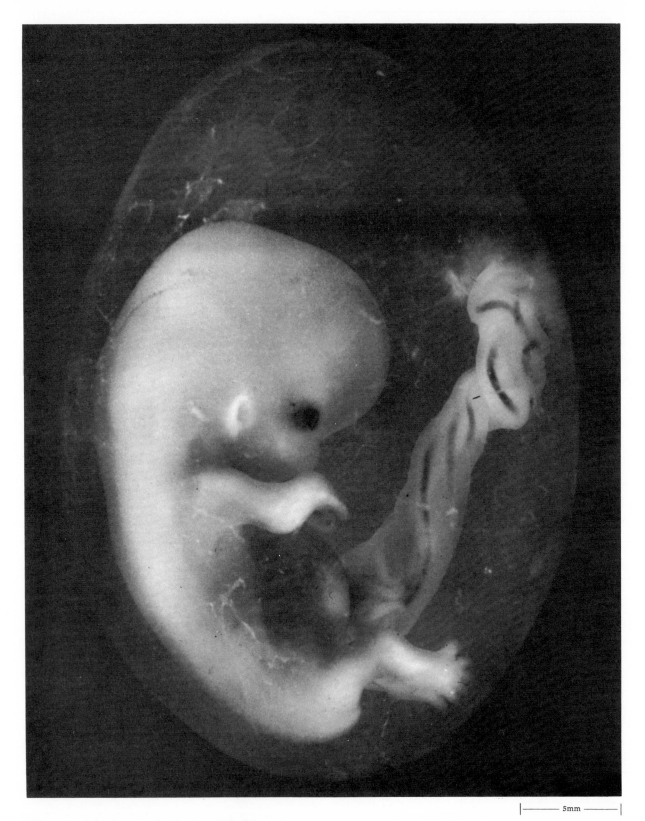

|——— 5mm ———|

(Courtesy of the Carnegie Institution of Washington)

Chapter 4–1

Simple Components of Development

Introduction

In Figure 4–1, you can see a living human egg. Hovering outside its envelope are male sperm cells. When a sperm fuses with the egg cell, forming a zygote, there will be in this single cell—a speck barely visible to the unaided eye—all the potential for a new human being. A gallon jar would easily hold enough human ova to account for the entire population of the world.

In the preceding section, we discussed how the large amount of information necessary to specify a garden pea, a fruit fly, or a human being is stored in a very condensed form in the DNA molecule and so packaged within a single cell. In this section, we shall explore some of what is known —and suggest some of what remains to be discovered—about how the information stored in a single cell can be translated in the course of development into a many-celled, multifunctional individual. We shall begin by looking at the different components of development in some of the simpler organisms. Then we shall analyze the early events of development in a single organism, the sea urchin. In Chapter 4–3, we shall examine some of the components of development as they can be seen in a single tissue, the vertebrate skin. Finally, we shall put together what we have learned and try to use it to examine the process of development in a very complex organism, the mammal.

One-celled Organisms: Growth and Replication

Let us look first at a procaryotic cell, the now familiar *Escherichia coli*. Under the light microscope, we see only very small, dark, rod-shaped particles, but with the electron microscope, it is possible to make out the details of each cell—the special bacterial cell wall, the cell membrane, and a generally unstructured cytoplasm, within which can be seen a number of

4–1 *A living human egg at the moment of fertilization. At the top, a number of spermatozoa are in the process of penetrating the layer of follicle cells surrounding the egg, and several, having passed through this layer, are now outside the egg membrane. (Dr. L. B. Shettles)*

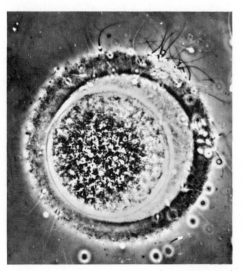

|——— 100μ ———|

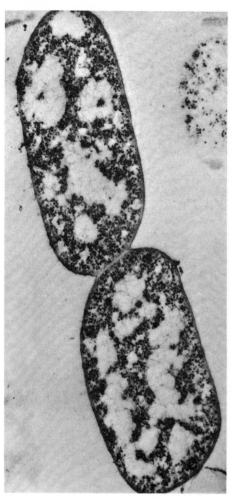

|— 0.5μ —|

4–2 *Electron micrograph of Escherichia coli dividing. Note the transverse wall that has formed between the daughter cells.* (Dr. S. F. Conti)

ribosomes and irregularly shaped patches of fibrillar material. This fibrillar material is almost pure DNA.

On a rich medium containing glucose, a nitrogen source, and some inorganic materials, such as potassium and sulfur, *E. coli* will divide in two almost every 20 minutes. The DNA replicates somewhat faster than the cells, so that most cells in such a culture will contain two, three, or even four patches of DNA. Cell division is always preceded by a period of growth in which the rod-shaped cell gets longer and more cell wall, cell membrane, and cytoplasm are produced. Then a transverse wall begins to form across the midline of the cell. Finally, the wall material becomes continuous, and the original cell splits into two, each new cell containing at least one nucleus and a share of the cytoplasmic material. The new cell begins to grow, and soon it also splits in two. This form of reproduction is known as *fission*. Since each cell becomes two every 20 minutes, where there was one *E. coli*, there will be 8 one hour later, 64 two hours later, 512 three hours later, and so on. This is called *exponential growth*, as distinct from *linear growth*, which proceeds 1, 2, 3, 4, like objects coming off an assembly line. By the end of 24 hours, it has been calculated, providing this growth rate were maintained, there would be 2^{72} cells—some 8 million pounds of *E. coli*. And each of these cells, given no mutations, would be essentially like all the others.

Where does all this *E. coli* come from? Each circular molecule of DNA produces another molecule. This DNA provides the thread of continuity, ensuring that each new cell resembles the parent cell. It provides the information for the tremendous job of synthesis that is required to produce all the structural elements of the cell and also to produce the enzymes and other complex chemical machinery involved with cell metabolism. In other words, *E. coli* takes from the medium some relatively simple materials— sugar, a nitrogen source, and some ions—and imposes on them a particular kind of order, the order known as *E. coli*.

This is the entire life cycle of *E. coli*: replication of genetic information followed by a complicated translation of this information into the substance of the bacterial cell. This transformation of genetic information into substance in *E. coli* appears as the growth phase and in this simple organism is synonymous with development. Growth is the major component of development in complex organisms as well, but we shall see that it is accompanied by other processes.

DEVELOPMENT IN *Amoeba*

Most of the Protozoa also divide by fission, increasing in numbers exponentially, although not at the same rate as a flourishing colony of *E. coli*. The common amoeba, *Amoeba proteus*, prepares for division by withdrawing its larger pseudopodia and assuming a shape resembling a chestnut bur, in which it is studded with very short pseudopodia. The nucleus, or-dinarily visible, disappears, but if the cell is stained, chromosomes become visible at this time. These chromosomes, which are very small, arrange themselves on the spindle and separate. As nuclear division takes place, the cell elongates, a constriction appears in the middle of it, and then the two daughter cells begin to tug apart, each crawling in opposite directions on their own pseudopodia.

Here again is a life cycle composed of replication of the genetic informa-tion and translation of the information during growth. In *Amoeba proteus*, the allocation of the information to the daughter cells takes place by mi-tosis, as in the cells of higher organisms. Each time a somatic cell divides, its genetic material is replicated and divided, just as it is in the amoeba, and as in the amoeba and *E. coli*, replication is followed by a period in which the genetic information is translated into the many and varied processes that constitute growth.

Cellular Slime Molds: Multicellularity

The slime mold *Dictyostelium discoideum*, like the other cellular slime molds, begins life as a group of individual amoebas, smaller than *Amoeba proteus* but not strikingly different in appearance. These individuals un-

4–3   *The life history of a slime mold, showing the several components of its development.*
Can you describe what is happening at each stage? (After Grobstein, 1965)

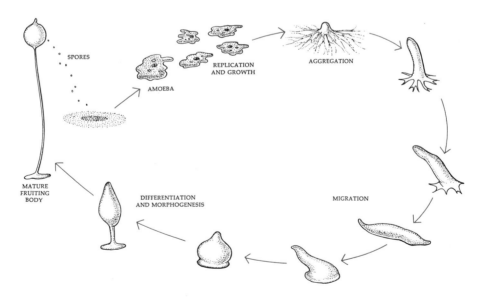

DIFFERENTIATION AND MORPHOGENESIS

Differentiation, as the word indicates, is the development of differences—differences between cells (which is given the special name of cytodifferentiation) and differences between various parts of the same organism. Differentiation implies specialization; when cells or parts of organisms become differentiated, they take on special functions. It does not necessarily mean that a cell becomes more complicated, however. A mature red blood cell is a highly differentiated cell—that is, it is very different from an egg cell or from any other somatic cell—but in terms of structure and functions, it is also a highly simplified cell.

Morphogenesis is the development of a new form or shape. In living things, changes in shape are often accompanied by and made possible by growth. For example, in your own growth, you changed from childlike proportions to those of the adult because parts of your body, such as your legs, grew at a different rate than other parts, such as your head. This is analogous to a sculptor building up certain parts of the form he is shaping by adding more clay to them. Alternatively, the sculptor may take a simple ball of clay and, without adding to it, mold it into a new shape. This second process is comparable to what occurs in the slime mold and also in the early development of most animals. Whether or not growth takes place, the organism changes shape as a result of movements of its "clay." Such movements are known as morphogenetic movements.

4–4 *These amoebalike organisms have hatched from the spores of the slime mold Dictyostelium discoideum. The light gray area in the center of each cell is the nucleus, and the white areas are contractile vacuoles. Note the variations in shape and the irregular pseudopodia. At this stage of slime mold development, the cells are moving at random. (Dr. K. B. Raper)*

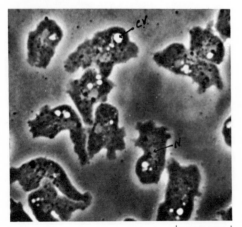

|—— 30μ ——|

dergo fission and grow, thereby increasing the population size. Then, quite suddenly, they stop growing, swarm together, and adhere to form a many-celled sluglike mobile mass. After a period of movement, the cells in this mass begin to differentiate, forming spores, stalk, and base, and the creature quite abruptly toadstools up in a fruiting body on the pinnacle of which is a single shimmering droplet containing hundreds or, in some instances, thousands of tiny spores. These spores are dispersed, and if they fall on warm damp ground, they germinate. Each releases one small, quite ordinary-looking amoeba, and the entire cycle begins again.

Here we have a life cycle in which there are five major components: replication, growth, the transition to a multicellular form, the differentiation of parts, and morphogenesis. Now, with the overall picture in mind, let us look at each of the separate stages.

The amoebas that hatch from the slime-mold spores are small and irregular in shape, with active, blunt pseudopodia. They feed, grow, and replicate by mitotic divisions, following an overall pattern which appears indistinguishable from that of *Amoeba proteus*. This stage of the life cycle is variable in length; it ends when the cells, which feed largely on bacteria,

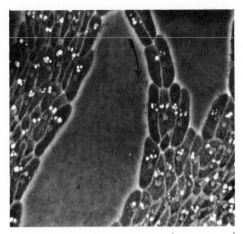

4–5 *Slime mold amoebas aggregating. The direction in which the stream is moving is indicated by the arrow. Notice that the cells have become almost uniformly elongated. (Dr. K. B. Raper)*

4–6 *These flowerlike forms are actually developing pseudoplasmodia. The dark spot in the center of each group is a mass of slime mold amoeboid cells, and the "rays" are streams of aggregating amoebas flowing in toward the center from all directions. The rising, cone-shaped center will grow steadily larger. Soon, it will drop over on its side and begin to move away from the site of its formation. At this point, it has become a migrating pseudoplasmodium. (Dr. K. B. Raper)*

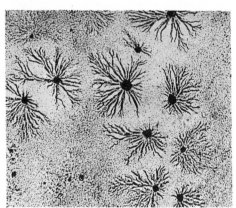

have exhausted their food supply. When the food is gone, a change comes over the colony. The cells alter in both shape and behavior. They become elongated and rectangular in form, and they begin to migrate toward the center of the group.

At first they move as independent cells, but soon they begin flowing in streams, each amoeba sticking to the one ahead of it and the one behind it, bumper to bumper. The streams move toward centrally located cells that "call" the others toward them. These cells emit a still unidentified chemical that has been named *acrasin* after Acrasia, the cruel witch in Spenser's *Faerie Queene* who attracted men and turned them into beasts. As the cells are bathed in this chemical, they become sticky and, in turn, begin to exude acrasin, thus attracting outlying cells. Presumably, there is a higher concentration of acrasin in the center of the mass than at the periphery, for the amoebas continue to move toward the middle with increasing velocity. If the center of one of these aggregating groups is scooped up and moved to the edge of the colony, the streams of traffic turn around, as if they had back and front ends, and flow toward the new center. This "headness and tailness" is known as *polarity*, by analogy with a magnet or other electrically charged system, which has opposite (+ and —) poles. Polarity is one of the fundamental properties of living systems and is found in all the many-celled animals, both in organisms as a whole and in the organs of more complex animals.

Does the acrasin bring about these changes in the shape and behavior of the cells? It appeared at one time that this was the case, but recent studies have shown that the concentration of acrasin is higher during the time the amoebas are feeding and dividing than at the moment they begin to swarm. So it is more logical, on the basis of present evidence, to hypothesize that changes take place in the cells when the food is exhausted that make them responsive to the already present acrasin.

Are the attractive cells any different from the cells they attract? Experiments show that they are not. If the attractive cells are removed, other cells will begin to act as attractive centers, presumably by increasing their production of acrasin. It seems to be the location of the cells, rather than any inherent differences among the cells, that determines their special role.

THE PSEUDOPLASMODIUM

The swarming amoebas pile up in a heap, each new arrival adhering to the mass. At first, they form a cylinder-shaped pile. As the pile grows larger, it drops over on its side, and soon it begins to move. As you can see in Figure 4–7, the "beast" that is formed by these adhering amoebas resembles a common garden slug. With a small pointed "head," or apex, and a broader base, it moves along in sluglike fashion, leaving behind it a track of slime. This mass is technically referred to as a *pseudoplasmodium*. A

467 *Simple Components of Development*

4–7 *Migrating pseudoplasmodia moving on an agar surface. Each advancing "slug" deposits a thin slime sheath, which, like a collapsed sausage casing, lies flat on the surface in its wake. The individual cells of the colony crawl along this slime tract which they continuously secrete and leave behind, moving the entire colony forward. (Dr. K. B. Raper)*

4–8 *At the end of migration, the tip of the slime mold cell mass stops moving while the rear portion continues to gather in, pushing under the main mass and thus causing the pseudoplasmodium to begin to rise vertically. (Dr. K. B. Raper)*

"true" plasmodium (see Chapter 2–4) is a multinucleate mass, not divided by cell membranes. The pseudoplasmodium, on the other hand, is composed of separate cells, and each of these cells retains its individuality; if separated from the group, each cell is quite capable of an independent existence.

However, the cells in the pseudoplasmodium take on new characteristics in the multicellular state. First, as we mentioned, they change their shape at the beginning of aggregation. Their surfaces also apparently change, becoming sticky, since the amoebas in the pseudoplasmodium adhere together, not only back to front, as at the beginning of aggregation, but along all their surfaces. It is possible, by exerting gentle pressure, to dissociate amoebas from this mass; if permitted to remain in close proximity to each other, these dissociated amoebas will promptly reaggregate to reconstitute the slug.

The migrating amoebas actively secrete slime, a mucopolysaccharide, which forms a thin sheath around the pseudoplasmodium. They crawl through this sheath, leaving it behind them. The traction for the colony is not between slug and ground but between individual amoeboid cells and the inside of the sheath. Even the amoebas in the center of the sausage-shaped mass vigorously move their pseudopodia in a coordinated manner.

The pseudoplasmodium as a whole has properties that cannot be demonstrated in the individual amoebas. One of the most striking of these is orientation toward light. Migrating pseudoplasmodia will move toward very faint light sources, such as luminescent bacteria and phosphorescent paint. The individual amoebas, however, show no tendency to move toward light of any intensity; small pseudoplasmodia also lack this capacity. Light orientation is a property found only in a large cell mass.

So we see that not only do the individual cells gain new properties in the multicellular state but also the mass of cells has properties—capacity for slime production, for coordinated movement, and for response to light—that the individual cells do not possess.

The migration of the masses of amoebas may last five hours to two weeks. The end of migration is brought about by external factors, the most important of which is a drop in humidity. When migration stops, a complete change occurs. The front end of the mass stops moving forward, and the rear guard cells bunch themselves underneath the whole. A column rises out of the mass, eventually forming a thin filament with a delicate sphere at the tip.

DIFFERENTIATION

Cellular differentiation and the end of migration begin simultaneously. Three different cell types are formed: spore, stalk, and base. The cells—all of which, you will remember, were identical amoebas until very recently—

468 DEVELOPMENT

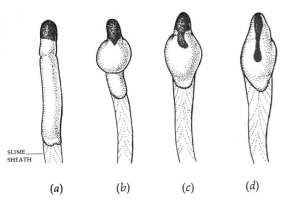

SLIME
SHEATH

(a)   (b)   (c)   (d)

4–9 *How the slime mold stalk is formed.*
(a) The pseudoplasmodium stops its mi-
gration. (The colored cells on the tip
were grafted on to a decapitated slime
mold in order to follow the cell move-
ments during differentiation.) (b) The
rear-guard cells push under the cell
mass. The cells at the tip, which are the
first to differentiate, become swollen
and vacuolated and begin to manufac-
ture cellulose. (c) The cellulose-making
cells push through the cell mass down
toward the base. Once they contribute
cellulose to the forming stalk, they die.
(d) The stalk cells have now reached the
substratum and the stalk is beginning
to grow taller as additional cells are
pushed to the top of the stalk where
they add their cellulose deposit to the
lengthening sheath. (After Bonner,
1967)

become different from one another not only in appearance but also in their synthesis of special materials.

The cells at the apex form stalk cells. They become swollen and vacuolated and begin to manufacture a celluloselike product. This tip of swollen, cellulose-making cells turns inward and pushes down toward the base through the rest of the cell mass. The celluloselike material is deposited outside the cells and forms a stiff cylinder. This cylinder grows in height as additional cells crawl up it, each contributing more cellulose to the tip of the elongating stalk.

At the same time, a small group of cells that were at the rear of the moving pseudoplasmodium are also becoming swollen and vacuolated. These form the circular base of the mature fruiting body, similar in shape and proportions to the foot of a tall-stemmed glass.

With the continued construction of the stalk, the cells that will form the spores are carried upward on the stalk like a minute ball impaled upon a pin. As they move up into the air, they, too, differentiate. Each cell becomes smaller, dry, and rounded and secretes for itself a covering of slime and a hard protective outer coat of cellulose. Above the little sphere of spores-to-

4–10 (a) *The culmination stage in the life cycle of the slime mold Dictyostelium discoideum. The photographs were taken at intervals of about 1½ hours. (b) Mature fruiting bodies of D. discoideum. (Dr. J. T. Bonner)*

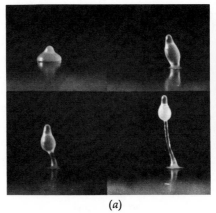 

(a)   (b)

be, the remaining stalk cells climb or are pushed to the top of the cylinder, make their cellulose contribution to it, and drop inside, where they dry out and die. When the last stalk cell has made this ascent, the spore cells are at the very pinnacle of the stalk. Some 85 percent of the original cells have become spores, and only about 15 percent have been sacrificed in the process of raising the spores to where they can be dispersed through the new territory found by the migrating slime mold.

DETERMINANTS IN DIFFERENTIATION

In the completed slime mold, three types of cells are present: stalk, base, and spore. Why does one cell differentiate in one direction while another, identical cell develops in another direction? Are the cells genetically different? This possibility can be quickly ruled out. By simple experiments, it can be demonstrated that pseudoplasmodia form equally well from the members of a clone produced by the multiple divisions of a single amoeba (a clone is a group of cells all of which have a single common ancestor), from a random group of amoebas all liberated from a single fruiting body, or from a mixture of amoebas from a number of different fruiting bodies. In other words, all the free-living amoebas have the potentialities, no more and no less, of all the other cells and can transmit these potentialities indefinitely to generations of daughter cells, just as the free-living *Amoeba proteus* can transmit its particular potentialities from generation to generation.

Does their position in the moving pseudoplasmodium determine the fate of the individual cells? As we have seen, the position of the various cells at the time migration ceases does decide which cells form stalk, base, and spore. But suppose we cut one of these moving sausages into two or three or even more pieces? Each one of these separated parts develops into a small but perfect fruiting body!

The fact that a perfect fruiting body can form from a portion of pseudoplasmodium tells us two important facts. First, it confirms that the information necessary for the whole is contained in all of the parts; the anterior of the slime mold contains the information for making the base, and the posterior contains information for spore formation, even though in the normal course of development—that is, if the slime mold is not cut into pieces—all of this information is never used by any one part. Second, it demonstrates that there is some form of communication among the various cells. If a single segment that would have formed only stalk cells can, when amputated from the rest of the slime mold, form stalk and spores and base, the cells must have some way of "knowing" that the posterior cells have been removed and of redirecting their activities accordingly. How do cells communicate with one another in a developmental system? This is a question to which we shall return frequently in the chapters that follow.

The question of differentiation raises another new problem, not seen with *E. coli* and other single-celled organisms. What happens to genetic information that is not used when the cell differentiates? Is it discarded or destroyed? Apparently not, at least in the case of spore cells, for when these divide, they pass on to their daughter cells the full information for making stalk and base as well as spore. Whatever is communicated intercellularly in the cellular slime molds would appear to be involved either directly or indirectly in this process of activating and repressing the genetic material or its products.

Some ingenious experiments have shown that various stages in development do clearly involve the activation of particular segments of DNA. By use of ultraviolet irradiation, Maurice Sussman and his co-workers have produced an array of mutant slime-mold colonies. In the type of mutant most commonly observed—"Aggregateless"—the amoebas feed, grow, and divide normally, but then everything stops; they do not aggregate. In another type of mutant—"Fruitless"—the amoebas feed, grow, divide, and respond to the call of acrasin and aggregate, but then the cycle stops; once a mound of cells is formed, nothing more happens. In other mutants— "Bushy"—the cells aggregate but form a large number of small pseudoplasmodia that produce irregularly shaped fruiting bodies. In "Dwarf," the fruiting bodies are perfectly formed but are of very small size, consisting of only a few cells.

In short, it appears that in the course of development, at least of the cellular slime molds, the information of different genes is expressed sequentially. The mutants are able to function normally through the early part of the life cycle as long as there is no requirement for the particular piece of information that is deleted or altered by the mutation. Here we might use the analogy of an instruction manual on how to assemble some very complicated piece of machinery. In the mutant slime molds, an important part of the instructions is either wrong or missing, so, although the guide can be followed to a certain point, there is no way just to skip a few pages and proceed, since each step depends on the successful accomplishment of the previous ones.

Using these various mutants, Sussman has shown that if different populations of mutants are mixed together, it may be possible to get normal fruiting bodies. For example, if Fruitless-1, which normally forms loose aggregates but never fruiting bodies, is mixed with Aggregateless-53, which never aggregates, the two together can produce normal mature fruiting bodies.

Such studies remind us of Benzer's work on mutations in bacteriophages. Benzer showed, as you will recall, that two mutants were able to help one another when each could produce what the other could not. From Sussman's work, we conclude that when two types of mutants are

4–11 *Reaggregation of cells dissociated from the sponge Microciona. (a) The sponge has been pressed through a fine sieve to dissociate the cells, which are shown dispersed on a culture dish. (b) 180 minutes later, as the cells migrate over the culture dish and encounter one another, they clump together. (c) 240 minutes after the sponge was first dissociated into separate cells, you can see the further formation of multicellular aggregates. These aggregates will grow into complete new sponges, each with exactly the same architecture as the sponge which was dissociated.*
(Dr. A. A. Moscona)

combined, each can supply something missing in the other. Sussman hypothesizes that it is a chemical passed from one cell to another across the cell membranes. So far, all attempts to demonstrate the passage of such a product—for instance, by putting a thin film of agar between the cells—have failed.

Sponges

The sponges, although the most primitive of the multicelled animals, are more complex both in the specialization of their individual cells and in their multicellular structures than the slime molds. Although sponges in nature do not arise by the aggregation of previously autonomous cells, as do the slime molds, they can be made to behave similarly by a simple experimental procedure.

If a piece of sponge is pressed through a fine cloth, the cells and clumps of cells will reaggregate to form a sponge (Figure 4–11). By placing a sponge in seawater that contains no calcium or magnesium before pressing it through the cloth, it is possible to carry the process further and dissociate

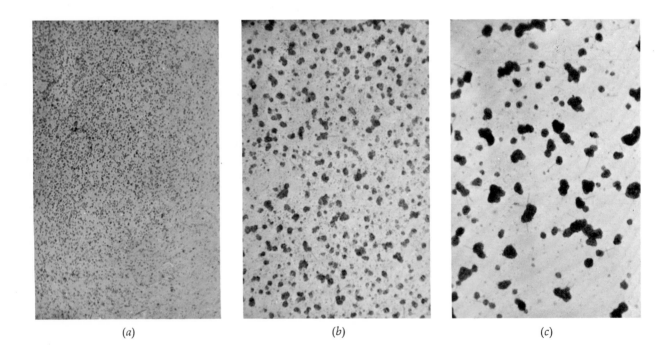

(a)　　　　　　　　　(b)　　　　　　　　　(c)

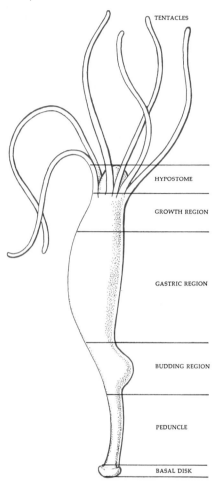

TENTACLES

HYPOSTOME

GROWTH REGION

GASTRIC REGION

BUDDING REGION

PEDUNCLE

BASAL DISK

each individual cell from every other one, leaving no tissue masses. If these separated cells are then put back in normal seawater, they will reaggregate. When the reaggregating clump reaches a sufficient size—a process that takes about six hours under optimal conditions—flagellated chambers begin to appear and canals begin to traverse the mass; in short, a pattern typical of a particular species of sponge emerges.

As we noted in Section 2, the sponges have an unusual alternate form of reproduction, which involves the formation of *gemmules,* collections of amoeboid sponge cells surrounded by a protective outer shell that makes them resistant to cold and drying out. When the shell of the gemmule breaks open, the amoeboid cells climb out, multiply, aggregate around the shell, and eventually begin to grow, differentiate, and take the shape of a new sponge. This reproduction by means of gemmules may be related to the capability of sponge tissue that has been pushed through a piece of fine cloth to clump together again to form a sponge.

It has recently been reported that the reaggregation of sponge cells depends upon materials on the surfaces of the cells which cause them to adhere. The material does not, like acrasin, call the cells together; it binds them when they happen to touch.

With the sponges, some questions arise that did not occur with the slime molds. Separated sponge cells are of a number of kinds, not identical like the slime-mold amoebas. Does each sponge cell find its place in the aggregate, fitting in like a missing piece in a jigsaw puzzle? Or do the cells change in character, depending on their relationship with other cells? What imposes the typical sponge pattern on the forming aggregate? We shall see that these questions reoccur as we investigate development in higher organisms.

Hydras: Constancy and Change

Hydra, the common freshwater coelenterate, is a more complex organism than the slime molds or the sponges. It is composed of a number of different types of cells, many of which are organized into tissues, such as the lining of the coelenteron, and it is capable of much more highly organized and integrated behavior.

If you look at a living hydra under a low-power lens, you will see a delicately formed, almost transparent small organism with a slim cylindrical body crowned with a wreath of contractile tentacles that can stretch out almost as long as the body itself and ending in a base by which the animal attaches itself for feeding. Enclosed by the cylinder is the coelenteron, to which the tentacles deliver the captured prey. The opening to the coelenteron is known as the *hypostome,* and the stalk of the cylinder is the *peduncle.* (See Figure 4–12.)

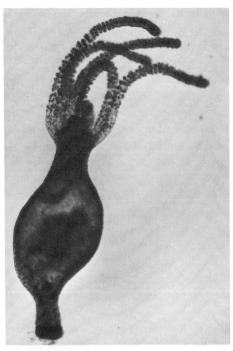

4–13 *Photomicrograph of a living hydra. This animal has recently eaten, as you can see from its expanded coelenteron. (Eric V. Gravé)*

If you take a small slice of tissue from a hydra, cutting across the cylinder, mount it on a slide, and look at it under a high-power lens, you can see that the wall of the cylinder consists of two layers of tissue arranged back to back with a thin layer of mesoglea (the "jelly" of the jellyfish) in between (see Figure 2–76). The gastrodermis of *Hydra* is made up chiefly of the gland cells that secrete enzymes for digestion of the material in the coelenteron and the digestive cells that ingest the food particles. The epidermis is composed chiefly of epitheliomuscular cells—epithelial cells with contractile threads (myonemes) within them—and cnidoblasts, the special stinging cells typical of the coelenterate phylum. Among these specialized cells can be found a scattering of relatively unspecialized, undifferentiated cells known as *interstitial cells*. These cells, in dividing, give rise to the various other cell types.

This description of *Hydra*'s structure is somewhat misleading, however, because it implies that everything is standing still. Actually, if you could keep your lens focused on one segment of a living hydra for a sufficiently long time, all the cells would flow slowly past like a stream. This flow can be demonstrated by a simple experiment, as the Belgian zoologist P. Brien has shown. If you stain bands of cells around the circumference of a hydra, you can watch these stained cells move slowly down the columnar body of the animal and disappear at the base. By staining bands of cells at different levels on the hydra column, Brien was able to show that this cellular movement originates in the tissue just beneath the hypostome. A secondary movement of cells from the area below the hypostome into the tentacles can also be demonstrated.

What causes this flow of cells? Apparently the area just below the hypostome is a region of rapid cell division, analogous to the meristematic region of a plant. The rapid cell division causes a flow of adjacent cells toward tentacles and base. When the cells reach the base, they are sloughed off or perhaps destroyed by enzyme action; studies have shown that the base is rich in lytic enzymes of the sort that are found within lysosomes.

A TURNOVER SYSTEM

A tissue in which all the component cells are constantly being replaced but in which the tissue still remains is referred to as a *turnover system*. Continuous change by cell death and cell replacement is one of the common properties of living systems. We shall look at other examples of turnover systems in Chapters 4–3 and 4–4. Among turnover systems, however, the hydra's is unusual in that all the cells of the entire organism are constantly being renewed and discarded. It is estimated from the motion of the band of stained cells that every cell in *Hydra* is replaced every 45 days. Yet the hydra is still there!

4–14 *While the overall length of Hydra remains approximately the same, it grows*
continuously at the hypostomal end and degenerates continuously at the basal
end. Rapid cell division in the growth region supplies the new cells for growth
and causes a constant flow of cells in two directions: from the growth region
up toward the tentacles and from the growth region down the body column
toward the basal disk, where the old cells are either sloughed off or destroyed.
This cell movement can be demonstrated by the simple experiment shown here.
If you stain a group of cells (indicated by the colored dot) just below the
growth region, you will see them move slowly down the animal's body until
they disappear at the basal end. The hydra, in the meantime, will have grown
at its anterior (hypostomal) end and degenerated at its basal end by approxi-
mately the amount indicated by the dotted lines.

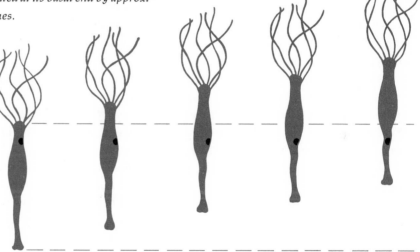

DIFFERENTIATION

As the cells move away from the area beneath the hypostome, they differentiate into a variety of cell types. Those in the epidermis become either
epitheliomuscular cells or cnidoblasts. Epitheliomuscular cells form intracellular myonemes, the contraction of which shortens the body column.
As these cells enter the region of the base, they begin to produce a mucus
that enables the hydra to attach itself.

Cells in the gastrodermis also differentiate as they move away from the
hypostome, forming a variety of glandular cells and the phagocytic digestive cells. Digestive cells, like epidermal cells, develop myonemes, but contraction of these gastrodermal cells causes the animal to lengthen. (If, however, the gastrodermis is separated from the epidermis, the outer cells of
the gastrodermis differentiate into epitheliomuscular cells with myonemes
that act to shorten the body column.) When the cells of the gastrodermis
reach the base, they, too, begin to secrete the adhesive mucus.

475 *Simple Components of Development*

POLARITY AND DIFFERENTIATION IN *Hydra*: AN HYPOTHESIS

Recently a theory has been proposed by A. L. Burnett of Western Reserve by which many of the phenomena observed in Hydra may be explained. According to this hypothesis, two chemical influences are at work in Hydra, one an inducer and the other an inhibitor.

The inducer, according to Burnett's theory, controls polarity and cell differentiation. It becomes bound to the cells with which it comes in contact, and it is produced in the hypostome and is present in concentrations which gradually decrease from head to base. Differences in concentration control the differentiation of the interstitial cells. Thus, under the influence of the maximum concentration of inducer, interstitial cells differentiate into nerve cells, which are concentrated in the hypostome; under the next-highest concentration, they divide to form additional interstitial cells, leading to more cell division. The third-highest concentration produces cnidoblasts, the next sperm cells, and the lowest, eggs.

Recently, a material with properties closely resembling those of the postulated inducer has been isolated and concentrated. It appears to be a small peptide, apparently produced by nerve cells in the hypostomal region. If this preparation is injected into the animal in varying concentrations, Burnett has reported, it is possible to control the direction of cell differentiation. Epithelial cells adjacent to the base, which would ordinarily be sloughed off within a few days, begin cell division characteristic of the growth region when they are treated with inducer and form a head at the level of the base.

The inhibitor, according to Burnett's theory, is produced not by the hypostome but by rapidly dividing cells beneath the hypostome. It diffuses downward, becoming increasingly more diluted. Unlike the inducer, the inhibitor diffuses freely among the cells and even leaks out into the medium. Its activity becomes quite low about midway between head and foot; in this region, inducer is still present, and so a second growth region occurs, the region in which the buds are produced. The dividing cells in the bud, in turn, produce inhibitor, which diffuses down into the peduncle, suppressing divisions in that region. Inhibitor activity becomes low again near the base, but no second growth region results since there is no inducer at this level.

When a portion of a hydra is excised, as in the regeneration experiments, the concentration of bound inducer is greater at the distal surface than at the proximal one and the inhibitor diffuses out from the cut surfaces. Nerve cells forming at the distal end, where the concentration of inducer is greatest, produce more inducer, and cells in the growth area produce more inhibitor; thus polarity and the characteristic pattern of differentiation become established.

So the growth and differentiation phenomena seen in Hydra can be explained in terms of an interplay involving gradients of these two regulatory agents. Burnett's hypothesis, although not confirmed, is an important one because it indicates how a group of seemingly mysterious and apparently unrelated phenomena can be explained in relatively simple and not at all mysterious terms.

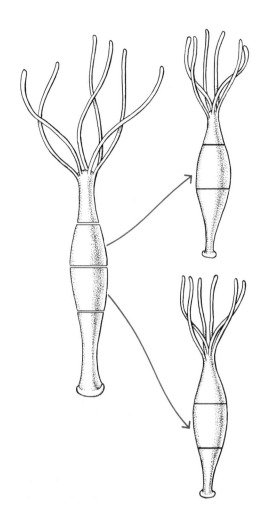

4–15 *If you cut a hydra in pieces, a new hydra will form from each piece. As shown here, the pieces will retain their original polarity as they grow; that is, the head will form from the end that was closest to the head, and the base from the end that was closest to the base.*

What controls the differentiation of these cells? Is it their position in the animal? Position obviously plays a part but does not appear to be the only controlling factor. Cnidoblasts, for example, which are formed in the body of the animal, travel between the other epidermal cells of the hydra into the tentacles to replace discharged cnidoblasts, finding appropriate places in the tentacles. As a result of this migration, the tentacles can be supplied with a complete new arsenal of stinging cells every 24 hours. So, although it is true that the position of a cell in the body of the hydra appears to determine its course of differentiation, it is also true that cells, once differentiated, find their appropriate positions.

REGENERATION

The earliest experiments on *Hydra* were conducted more than 200 years ago by Abraham Trembley, who performed a variety of operations on hydras held in a drop of water in the palm of his hand. Trembley was the first to report on *Hydra*'s remarkable powers of regeneration. If a hydra is cut in two, as you can discover for yourself, two new hydras will form; the top half will grow a base, and the bottom half will grow a hypostome and tentacles. Even if it is cut into a number of segments, each segment will grow a hypostome and tentacles at one end and a base at the other, and in each case, the "head" will form at the *distal* end (that is, the end that originally had been farther from the base) and the base at the *proximal* end (the end nearer the point of attachment). Thus cutting up a hydra is much like cutting up a magnet; each piece rigorously retains its polarity. Even very small sections of the body—accounting for as little as 1/200 of the original animal—can regenerate a complete whole.

Experiments with tiny fragments of hydras show clearly that regeneration in *Hydra* is primarily a process of remodeling. The segment does not simply grow into a new full-sized hydra but instead reorganizes itself into a perfect miniature hydra, which can later grow to full size.

CONTROL CENTER: THE HYPOSTOME

If a small area of hypostome is grafted onto the body of another hydra, the graft will develop into a new head. If other hydra tissues are grafted onto a second animal, however, they are merely absorbed into the moving column of cells. On the basis of such experiments, investigators have long suspected that the hypostome plays a major role in regulating the growth of the entire organism. The question of the control center is a crucial point in understanding development. As we shall see in later chapters, control systems for complex processes frequently involve a controlling or organizing center from which influences emanate. The more complex the organism, the more control centers are probably in operation.

477   *Simple Components of Development*

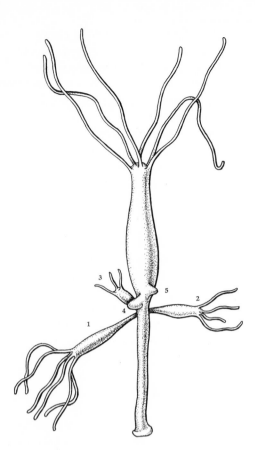

4–16 *Budding in Hydra always occurs in the same localized growth zone. The buds appear successively at approximately 120° from each other, in an ascending spiral up the body column. The numbers in the diagram indicate the order of succession of five buds. (After Brien and Reniers-Decoen, 1949)*

BUDDING

Budding is one means of reproduction in *Hydra;* almost any healthy, well-fed animal will show one or two buds, and some may have as many as five or six. Buds begin as local areas of intensive growth. A small bulge first forms on the side of the column, and this bulge then pushes out from the body of the hydra, carrying elements of both epidermis and gastrodermis with it, and soon becomes cylinder-shaped. As the bud grows, it develops tentacles and a coelenteron and begins feeding while still attached to its parent. Its pattern of growth is very similar to that seen in regeneration. Eventually, the cells at its base become thinner and more vacuolated, and soon afterward, it breaks loose to take up an independent existence.

Buds always form in the lower half of the hydra. Because they appear only at a regular distance from the hypostome, investigators have long suspected that something in the area of the parent hypostome prevents the formation of another hypostome in its vicinity. Recently, some ingenious experiments have been performed to demonstrate this inhibition. For example, it has been shown that if a hydra is cut in half just above the area of a beginning bud, a new hypostome will not grow immediately at that site. But when the bud has elongated, moving its developing hypostome away from the growth area, the new hypostome grows. Similarly, if a hypostome is grafted into a budding area just before budding is initiated, the budding will be inhibited until the moving column of cells has separated the hypostome and the bud area. If the hypostome of the bud has already begun to grow, however, it is not inhibited by the presence of the grafted hypostome.

SEXUAL REPRODUCTION

Hydra can also reproduce sexually. Sexual reproduction involves far greater risks than budding; many egg cells and the great majority of spermatozoa are wasted. It consumes a great deal more time and energy for the production of an individual that is, to all appearances, just like the individual produced by a bud. But, in fact, the two individuals are not exactly the same. The hydra produced by a bud is genetically identical to the parent. In the hydra produced from a fertilized egg—even if both gametes are from the same individual which is not usually the case—new genetic combinations appear.

In some species, both ova and spermatozoa are produced in the same individual, while in other species, some individuals are male and others female. *Hydra* does not have any special reproductive organs such as are found in the higher animals; the gametes are produced directly within the epidermis arising from the interstitial cells.

The spermatozoa form in hollow areas, or cysts, known as *testicular follicles.* Within these follicles, the interstitial cells differentiate into spermatogonia (prespermatozoan cells), which form spermatocytes, undergo meiosis, and finally differentiate into small flagellated spermatozoa, which are released from the follicles. All three types of cells can be found within each follicle, with the spermatogonia at the base and spermatozoa at the apex.

The egg cell is produced by two meiotic divisions in which polar bodies are formed. When the egg is ripe, it bursts through the epidermis, which draws back, forming a shallow cup in which the egg rests. The egg must be fertilized within about a day or it will perish. Sperm cells are attracted to the egg by a chemical substance released by it, and the egg is fertilized while it is still attached to the body of the mother hydra.

DEVELOPMENT OF THE EGG

When the egg is fertilized, it divides into a number of cells of approximately equal size, which come to form a hollow, fluid-filled sphere, the *blastula*. Cells from one hemisphere (the area that is still attached to the mother) then migrate, filling the interior cavity, and the outer cell layer expands to cover the entire surface. By this stage, there is a definite, visible distinction between epidermis and the interior, gastrodermal cells.

The epidermal cells secrete a sticky substance that forms an outer coating, or shell. This eventually hardens around the planula larva, which then drops from the mother hydra. The planula may remain within the shell for 3 to 10 weeks before it hatches and escapes. By the time of hatching, the hypostome, gastric region, and peduncle have begun to differentiate and the gastric cavity has begun to form. Immediately after hatching, the larva settles down, develops tentacles and coelenteron, and completes its metamorphosis into a fully developed small hydra.

SUMMARY

In this chapter, we looked at some of the components of development as seen in comparatively simple organisms: *E. coli*, the common amoeba, the cellular slime mold, the sponge, and *Hydra*.

In the single-celled organisms, the life cycle is an alternation of the replication of the genetic information and the translation of the information into growth. In these simple systems, growth and development are the same.

In the cellular slime molds, growth and cell division are one phase of a more complex life cycle, which involves multicellularity. Multicellularity is seen to lead to the acquisition of new properties by the individual cells and also to the emergence, in the pseudoplasmodium, of properties not present in the cells of which the plasmodium is composed. Experiments have indicated that the total information for the entire organism is contained in each cell and that expression of this information depends on some form of intercellular communication.

The sponge is a more complex organism, composed of a number of different cell types. If the individual cells are dissociated experimentally, they will reaggregate, forming the pattern characteristic of that sponge species. Recent experiments indicate that the adherence of the sponge cells to one another is due to the presence of a yet unidentified material on the cell surface.

Hydra, a more complex organism, exhibits some additional components of development. The entire animal is found to be a turnover system, in which all the cells are regularly replaced. It also offers a remarkable example of regenerative powers, since new animals can form even from very small fragments of the parent organism. Normal reproduction can take place either by budding or by the formation and fusion of gametes. The various phenomena involved in the pattern of continuous growth, in regeneration, in budding, and in sexual reproduction can be interpreted in terms of the existence in the animals of control centers which are sources of growth-promoting and growth-inhibiting influences.

Chapter 4–2

Interactions in Development

Nearly all many-celled organisms return, at some point in their life cycles, to the single cell—the fertilized egg. The continuing existence of every species of higher organism depends on its ability to translate the properties of a single cell into the properties of a multicellular organism. This chapter will be concerned with some of the elements involved in this process of translation.

For many years, biologists have pondered the relationship of the egg cell to the adult individual. In the seventeenth century, when discussions of this sort were flourishing, two main ideas were prevalent. One was the theory of *preformation*, which received new impetus following the development of the microscope as a consequence of what early microscopists thought they could see through this new window on the world. The preformationists maintained that the complete adult organism is already present in the germ cell, somewhat as a flower is already present in the bud, needing only to unfold. The more extreme members of this group claimed actually to see within the spermatozoon the perfectly formed adult, or *homunculus*. Thus development, according to this theory, is only a matter of the growth of each perfect miniaturized part.

The second, opposing theory was that of *epigenesis*. Epigeneticists believed that the egg contained only simple, essentially structureless materials—the bricks, so to speak, from which the organism might be constructed. Early epigeneticists (and the theory can be traced back to Aristotle) believed that the form of the adult was imposed in the course of development by the working of some "creative principle" or "vital force."

Modern embryologists combine the two views. Within the egg cell in the form of DNA is all the information for development—"preformed" and passed along from generation to generation. But in the course of development, new properties arise "epigenetically"—properties that were not

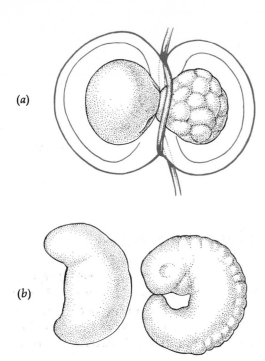

4–17 *Experiment with an amphibian's egg. (a) Before the first cell division, the egg is constricted across the middle with the nucleus in the right half. At the stage shown here, the right half has begun to divide normally. One of the nuclei from this half is then allowed to escape through the "bottleneck" into the undeveloped left half, which presently begins to divide. (b) The twin embryos developed from the two halves. As you can see, development of the embryo on the left (from the left half of the egg) has been delayed, but the embryo is nevertheless normal. What does this experiment prove? (After H. Spemann, 1938)*

present as such in the egg cell. In this chapter, our primary concern will be to show the interplay of these two factors in the control of development.

Nuclear Determinants

August Weismann, the nineteenth century German biologist, was one of the first to offer a coherent theory of how development is controlled genetically. He proposed (1) that the germ cells are set aside very early in development and that only these cells contain all the hereditary information, and (2) that in the early stages of development, as the rest of the cells of the embryo divide, the hereditary material is parceled out in the dividing nuclei to the various daughter cells. This was referred to as the *segregation of determinants*. Thus, according to Weismann's theory, each daughter cell does not receive the same hereditary information as every other daughter cell but rather gets something qualitatively different. The fate of each daughter cell depends on the nuclear material—the hereditary determinants—that it receives. To put Weismann's theory in modern terms, the nuclei and the DNA are different in different types of cells.

This was a good hypothesis because it could be tested. (As far as science is concerned, a hypothesis that cannot be tested, no matter how plausible and imaginative, is virtually worthless.) One of the first to test it was Wilhelm Roux in 1888. Roux waited until the zygote of a frog had undergone the first cleavage division and then destroyed one of the two daughter cells (*blastomeres*) with a hot needle, predicting that he had killed half the embryo. The other half continued to develop for a while, producing what looked like half an embryo and so apparently supporting Weismann's theory of the segregation of determinants.

Not long after, Hans Driesch tried the same experiment with sea urchins, the blastomeres of which could be completely separated more easily. Rather than killing one of the blastomeres, he separated them. In 30 out of 50 cases, Driesch reported, the two isolated blastomeres continued development, forming complete but half-sized embryos. Later, the experiment was repeated with a frog. When the two cells were separated, two complete embryos sometimes formed, one from each half. Nature has performed this same experiment with the human egg; if an ovum divides in two, identical twins will result. No segregation of determinants takes place, at least not at the first cleavage division. The two nuclei do not contain different determinants, as Weismann had proposed, but rather they are equivalent.

How do we explain the results of Roux' initial experiment with the frog's egg? To rephrase it in anthropomorphic terms—and actually no others are any more specific—it is as if the living blastomere "knew" the other one was still there but did not "know" that it was not developing. If the debris of the destroyed blastomere is removed, the living cell can reg-

4–18 *The formation of the gray crescent in a frog's egg. (a) Before fertilization, the upper two-thirds of the egg is covered by a heavily pigmented layer, the greater part of the yolk is massed at the lower, vegetal end and the female nucleus is near the animal pole. (b) The egg has been fertilized; the sperm has entered in the upper right and is moving toward the center of the egg. The trail it leaves behind it is caused by the disruption of pigment granules clustered near the egg surface. The whole pigmented cap has rotated toward the point of sperm penetration. The cytoplasmic region on the other side of the egg, from which the pigment coat has moved away, becomes the gray crescent. (After Waddington, 1966)*

(a)

GRAY CRESCENT

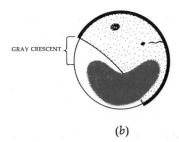

(b)

ulate into a whole embryo, just as a portion of the migrating slug of a slime mold can regulate into a complete fruiting body or a segment of the stalk of a hydra into a complete hydra.

Further proof of nuclear equivalence in early stages was provided by an elegantly simple experiment performed by Hans Spemann in 1914. Spemann constricted the egg cell of a newt before its first division, using a baby's hair, the finest ligature he could find. The half of the egg that contained the nucleus began to divide normally. In the course of these early cell divisions, the nuclei condense and get somewhat smaller (although their DNA content remains the same). For this reason, Spemann was able to slip a single nucleus past the constriction into the undeveloped half of the egg. (See Figure 4–17.) He then tightened the baby-hair noose until the undeveloped half of the egg was completely separated from the part that had been dividing. In many cases, the previously undeveloped half then began to divide and subsequently developed into a separate, whole embryo.

In the 1950s, R. Briggs and T. J. King developed a technique of nuclear transplantation that permitted them to test the capacities of nuclei from later embryonic stages to support the development of the egg. First, they removed the nucleus from a frog's egg. Then, sucking a nucleus out of one of the 16,000 or so cells of a later embryo with a glass pipette, they injected it into the enucleated egg. Many of these eggs were able to develop normally even though the nuclei were taken from cells that had begun to differentiate. It is generally true that the older the embryo from which the nucleus is taken, the less likely it is that the egg will develop successfully. The reason for this is not known. Since *some* of the later nuclei (even from the tadpole stage) are able to support development, it seems more reasonable to assume that these later nuclei are simply more susceptible to damage by the transplantation procedure than that they have lost any particular genetic capabilities. No one has yet devised a test, however, that will distinguish between these two possibilities.

Cytoplasmic Determinants

Let us return to Spemann's early experiments with the frog's egg. Like almost all eggs, the frog's egg contains yolky material for the nourishment of the embryo. The half of the egg in which this yolky material collects is known as the *vegetal hemisphere*, at the apex of which is the *vegetal pole*. The other half of the egg, which is lighter and so floats uppermost, is known as the *animal hemisphere*, and at its center, opposite the vegetal pole, is the *animal pole*. Between the animal and vegetal poles, just below the equator of the egg, is an area known as the *gray crescent*, which appears when the egg is fertilized (Figure 4–18).

483 *Interactions in Development*

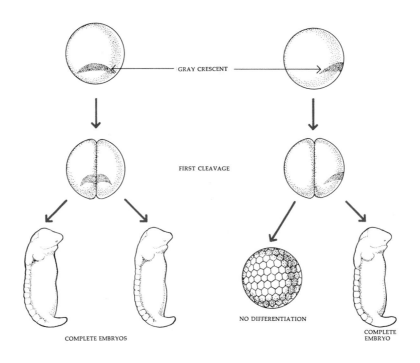

GRAY CRESCENT

FIRST CLEAVAGE

NO DIFFERENTIATION

COMPLETE EMBRYOS

COMPLETE
EMBRYO

4–19 *The importance of the gray crescent in development is demonstrated by sepa-*
rating the two cells formed by the first division of the egg. When the egg on the
left divided, half of the gray crescent passed into each of the two new cells. When
these cells were separated from each other, each formed a complete embryo. The
first division of the egg on the right resulted in all the gray crescent going to
one cell and none to the other. When these cells were separated, the one without
the crescent did not develop.

As we mentioned previously, some, but not all, of the amphibian cells that are separated after the first cell division form normal embryos. Spemann noticed in the course of his experiments that a cell could develop into a normal embryo only if it contained a share of the gray crescent. If only one cell contained the gray crescent, only that cell developed into a normal embryo; if the gray crescent was divided between the two cells, both might develop normally.

In short, in the early stages of development, the nuclei are equivalent and differences in the cytoplasm, rather than in the nuclei determine the course of development. Additional evidence has been found to support this conclusion.

484 DEVELOPMENT

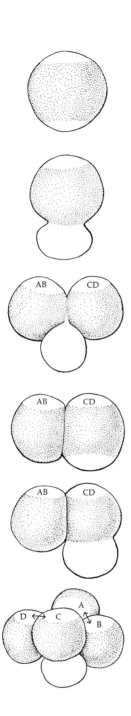

4–20 *The importance of cytoplasmic materials in development is indicated by studies of the mollusk* Dentalium. *When the fertilized egg of* Dentalium *divides, the clear cap of cytoplasmic material at the upper, animal pole is divided equally between the two cells but the clear material at the vegetal pole bulges into a polar lobe. This protudes on one side of the cleavage plane and then passes to only one of the two cells (cell CD). Therefore, as shown here, cells AB and CD are not equivalent in their cytoplasmic content. At the second division, a polar lobe again forms at the vegetal pole, and again it passes to only one cleavage product (in this case, cell C). If the blastomeres are separated at either of these stages, only the one with the polar lobe will develop into a complete trochophore larva. (After Wilson, 1904)*

DENTALIUM

For example, in the egg of the mollusk *Dentalium*, three layers of cytoplasm can be distinguished: a clear layer at the animal pole, a broad, granular layer at the midzone, and a second clear layer at the vegetal pole. When the egg begins to cleave, the cytoplasm at the vegetal pole is pushed out in a protrusion or lobe, which remains connected to the embryo by a narrow cytoplasmic stalk. At the end of the first cleavage, the lobe is attached to one of the two blastomeres; at the end of the second cleavage, it is attached to only one of the four. If the blastomeres are separated at either of these stages, only the blastomere with the lobe attached will develop into a complete (though smaller) trochophore larva. In the other larvae, the rudiments of the mesodermal tissues will be missing. Moreover, if the lobe is removed from the whole embryo, the embryo as a whole will lack the mesoderm. In other words, the influence that causes a cell to become mesoderm is segregated in a particular area of the cytoplasm.

THE ASCIDIAN EGG

In the ascidian, or sea squirt *Cynthia partita*, the determinative role of the cytoplasm is even more striking. Fertilization of the egg is followed by the very active streaming of cytoplasmic substances, which can be distinguished because of their color differences. These cytoplasmic granules establish themselves in highly characteristic positions within the egg, and as the egg divides, these different areas of the cytoplasm become segregated by the formation of cell membranes.

485 *Interactions in Development*

4–21 *In the egg of the ascidian Cynthia partita, four different cytoplasmic substances can be distinguished because of differences in their colors. These undergo an elaborate series of movements at fertilization. (a) Just before fertilization, the whole egg is covered by a peripheral layer of yellow cytoplasm. (b) Immediately after fertilization, the yellow cytoplasm begins to stream down toward the vegetal pole. (c) Shortly after this, a thin gray layer forms just above the yellow. (d) The gray and yellow regions then move up on one side to form two crescents. (After Conklin, 1905)*

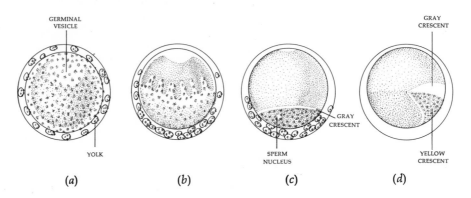

(a) *(b)* *(c)* *(d)*

When the streaming process is completed, the animal hemisphere contains clear, transparent cytoplasm. The vegetal part is taken up by slate-gray cytoplasm, rich in yolk. On one side of the cell, at the equator, are two crescents. One crescent is light gray, and one is yellow. (See Figure 4–21.) In normal development, cells containing the clear cytoplasm give rise to ectoderm, cells containing yellow cytoplasm form the mesoderm, cells containing slate-gray cytoplasm produce endoderm, and cells containing light gray cytoplasm become neural system and notochord.

We could cite many more examples of this sort, but these should suffice to make the point that the differences between the different areas of the cytoplasm are real and that these differences affect the course of development.

Biography of a Sea Urchin

We have now identified two factors in the development of a complex organism from a single egg cell: (1) The genetic material, the instructions that each cell carries. These instructions are apparently equivalent, at least in early developmental stages, but are expressed differently in different cells. (2) Cytoplasmic differences, based on the unequal distribution of ingredients in the egg, are established in the egg cell in the course of its maturation. To test the importance of these factors and the way they interact, let us look at the development of another multicellular organism in somewhat greater detail.

The sea urchin has long been a favorite of embryologists because (1) the eggs, which are produced in large numbers, are fertilized and develop externally, making it possible to study their development under relatively simple laboratory conditions; (2) both egg and developing embryo are almost transparent, so that it is possible to visualize many of the early events without disrupting them; and (3) the process is rapid, early development being completed in about 48 hours.

The series of pictures in Figure 4–22 gives us a rapid overview of sea-urchin development; later, we shall go back and look at some of the specific stages in more detail. Following fertilization, the egg undergoes a process known as *cleavage,* which is common to all eggs. Cleavage involves a number of rapid cell divisions, during which there is little change in the volume of the egg. As a result, by the end of cleavage, the relatively huge egg cell, with its very large ratios of cytoplasm to nucleus and of volume to surface, has been divided into a number of much smaller cells (from 1,000 to 2,000 in the sea urchin). The embryo during this stage of development is known as a *blastula.* The mature blastula is typically a sphere of cells, hollow in the center. Once blastulation is completed, the cells of the embryo embark on a series of morphogenetic movements during which some of the cells turn inward, or *invaginate,* to produce the two-layered organism typical of the mature *gastrula.* As you can see, the gastrula of the sea urchin has the shape that a soft rubber ball would assume if you were to poke one side in until it touched the other side. Cleavage, blastulation, and gastrulation are common to all higher animals, although the details differ somewhat, depending on the type of egg.

In the sea urchin, a larva known as a *pluteus* forms from the gastrula. The pluteus has an alimentary canal of three parts: a mouth and foregut, a dilated stomach, and an intestine with an anus. Its tent-shaped body is supported by a complicated, calcium-containing inner skeleton. It swims by means of cilia, which also serve to waft the minute plankton on which it feeds into its stomach. The pluteus is very small, little larger (though vastly different) than the egg from which it arose. As you can see, the pluteus bears no resemblance whatsoever to the adult urchin, and when it was originally discovered (in 1845), it was not known even to be related to the echinoderms. The adult sea urchin forms from two small sacs of cells within the pluteus larva, in much the same way that the adult fly forms from imaginal disks. As the mature form develops, the pluteus dissolves, serving as nutrient for the second creature growing inside it.

Now let us review the sequence of events from fertilization to the formation of the pluteus in more detail.

4–22 *The early development of the sea urchin. Notice that as the egg divides, the cells become progressively smaller, so that in the blastula stage, at the time of hatching from the egg membrane, they are barely distinguishable, although the magnification has not changed. (Dr. Tryggve Gustafson)*

|— 0.1mm —|

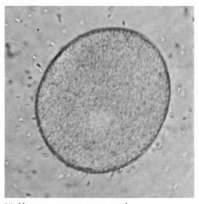

(1) *Numerous spermatozoa can be seen surrounding an unfertilized egg.*

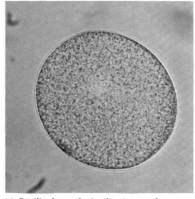

(2) *Fertilized egg; the fertilization membrane has just begun to form. The light area slightly to right of center is the diploid nucleus.*

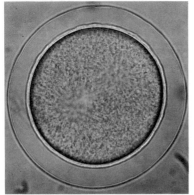

(3) *The fertilization membrane is fully formed. The egg has begun to divide; if you look closely, you can see that there are two nuclei.*

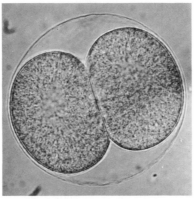

(4) *The first division.*

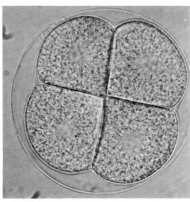

(5) *Four-celled stage.*

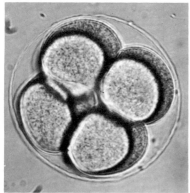

(6) *Eight-celled stage; the upper four blastomeres are smaller than the lower four.*

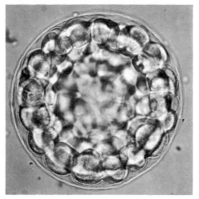

(7) *The blastocoel forms.*

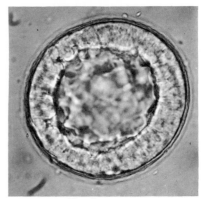

(8) *The mature blastula.*

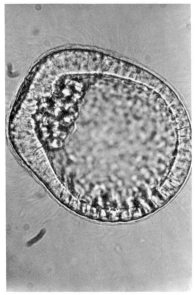

(9) *The beginning of gastrulation; cells at the vegetal pole start to migrate into the blastocoel.*

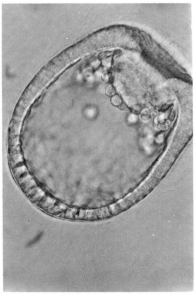

(10) *The vegetal-cell layer folds inward, forming the archenteron.*

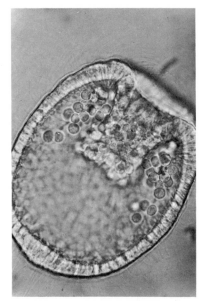

(11) *This cell layer is pulled across the blastocoel toward the animal pole.*

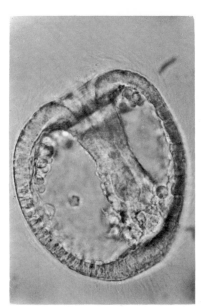

(12) *The mature gastrula.*

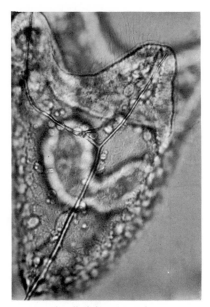

(13) *Gastrula cells differentiate and organize to form the pluteus larva.*

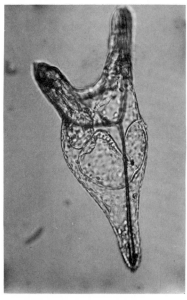

(14) *Within 48 hours after fertilization, the egg has developed into this multicellular organism, the pluteus.*

489   *Interactions in Development*

4–23 *A sea-urchin spermatozoon fusing with an egg cell. As you can see, the membrane of the sperm cell has been stripped away. Just behind the nucleus is a large mitochondrion. To the right, you can see the remnants of a flagellum. (John Runnström)*

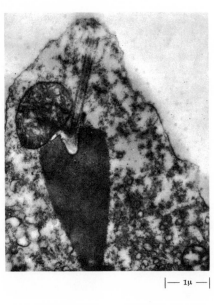

|— 1μ —|

4–24 *The formation of the fertilization membrane in the sea-urchin egg. (a) The surface of the unfertilized egg. (b) When the gametes fuse, the cortical granules explode, releasing their dark bodies and lifting the vitelline membrane. The plasma membrane becomes continuous with the membrane bounding the cortical granules. (c) The dark bodies attach to the vitelline membrane. The formation of the hyaline layer begins with the hemispheric globules building up a layer over the new egg surface. (d) The dark bodies have fused with the vitelline membrane, forming the fertilization membrane. (After Endo, 1961)*

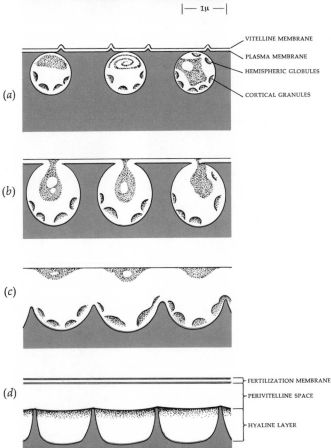

VITELLINE MEMBRANE
PLASMA MEMBRANE
HEMISPHERIC GLOBULES
CORTICAL GRANULES

FERTILIZATION MEMBRANE
PERIVITELLINE SPACE
HYALINE LAYER

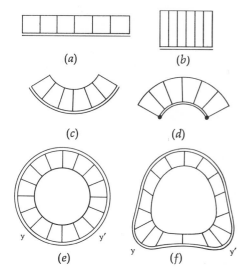

(a) *(b)*

(c) *(d)*

y   y'

(e)

y   y'

(f)

4–25 *The effects of changes in contact between cells and a supporting membrane. (a) Moderate contact between cells and supporting membrane. (b) An increase in contact between cells and a reduction in contact with the supporting membrane results in columnar cells. (c) If contact with the supporting membrane is not reduced when contact between cells is increased, the cells form an arc. (d) If there is a reduction in contact between the cells but if the ends of the cell sheet are fixed, the cell sheet will curve in the opposite direction. (e and f) An increase in contact between the cells at y and y' changes the shape of the blastula. (After Gustafson and Wolpert, 1963)*

FERTILIZATION

Figure 4–23 shows the nucleus of a sea-urchin spermatozoon entering the egg cell. The egg has a diameter of 72 microns. The overall length of the spermatozoon is about 45 microns, most of which is tail. The head, which consists almost entirely of condensed nuclear material, is only about 3 microns long. When a spermatozoon enters the egg, a little bleb or blister forms on the egg surface. This bleb, the so-called "fertilization cone," is caused by the fusion of the cell membrane of the egg with that of the entering spermatozoon, which leaves its outer membrane behind on the egg surface.

Fertilization has three consequences: (1) The genetic material of the male is introduced into the egg. The two haploid nuclei—one paternal and one maternal—fuse to produce a diploid nucleus, which then begins to divide by mitosis. (2) The so-called "fertilization membrane" appears. This is not a new membrane, as it once appeared to be to the light microscopists. As electron microscopy now has shown, the unfertilized egg is surrounded by two membranes—the plasma membrane and the outer, *vitelline membrane.* Just beneath the plasma membrane can be seen a group of dark bodies, the *cortical granules.* When the sperm cell passes through the vitelline membrane, the cortical granules explode, releasing their contents into the space between the two membranes and lifting the vitelline membrane. The space between the two membranes becomes filled with a clear sticky gel, the *hyaline layer,* to which the dividing cells of the embryo adhere. The fertilization membrane, which is actually the elevated vitelline membrane and the underlying hyaline layer, acts to prevent the entry into the egg of additional sperm nuclei. (3) The egg becomes activated, setting in motion the entire chain of events that will lead to the formation of a new individual.

BLASTULATION

After fertilization and formation of the fertilization membrane and the hyaline layer, the egg divides about 10 times at hourly intervals. These are mitotic divisions, like those in *Amoeba proteus,* in which the chromosomes are doubled and exact copies are passed to each daughter cell. As the cells divide, a fluid-filled cavity forms in the center, the *blastocoel.* The cells stick to the hyaline layer and to one another; if you look at the diagrams in Figure 4–25, you can see how contacts among cells and between the cells and the supporting membrane might account for the hollowness of the blastula and for its particular shape. In the sea urchin, the geometry of division can be followed with the help of a band of red pigment granules, which maintain the same position relative to the animal and vegetal poles throughout cleavage and can be traced right into the pluteus. These reveal that this process is highly ordered, and that the fate of the individual cells

491 *Interactions in Development*

is determined by their positions in the developing embryo. After blastulation, little additional cell division takes place until after the formation of the pluteus.

GASTRULATION

When blastulation is completed, the embryo becomes somewhat flattened on the lower surface of the vegetal hemisphere. On the inner surface of the blastocoel, in the region of the vegetal pole, the cells begin to bubble and pulsate. Eventually, some pull loose from the tightly ordered cellular layer and migrate inward. These cells, known as the *primary mesenchyme cells*, orient themselves in a definite pattern, a double ring with two arms extending toward the animal pole. Fibrous pseudopodia of these cells join together in a sort of cable arrangement, fastening the cells into a ring, like beads on a cord. These cords also extend pseudopodia that move at random, seemingly exploring the interior surface of the blastocoel, breaking and forming contacts and rearranging themselves, and finally setting up permanent attachments.

Soon afterward, the remaining vegetal cells and the cells containing the pigment fold inward, forming the *archenteron* (so called because it will become the *enteron,* or digestive tract). The free surfaces of these cells extend pseudopodia that "explore" the inner surface of the blastocoel, attach themselves to the far side, and appear to pull the tip of the archenteron across the blastocoel. The movement of the pseudopodia appears to be random, but the final attachment seems to depend on the randomly exploring pseudopodium making the "right" contact. The archenteron pushes in at first directly toward the animal pole and then, apparently as a result of pseudopodial activity, is turned obliquely away from it toward one side of the blastocoel, which then becomes, by definition, the ventral surface of the organism. At this point, a second axis of development is established, the *dorsoventral* ("back-front") axis between the animal and vegetal poles.

FORMATION OF THE PLUTEUS

Once gastrulation is completed, overt evidence of cell differentiation can be seen. Cells in the mesoderm begin to secrete small calcium-containing granules that develop into tiny three-armed spicules, which finally are enlarged into the supporting skeleton for the pluteus. At the point where the archenteron touches the inner surface of the blastocoel, the ectodermal cells curve inward to form the mouth of the larva; the mouth always forms at this point of contact. The archenteron subdivides into mouth, stomach, intestine, and anus, and a ring of long cilia forms around the mouth region.

By the end of 48 hours, the sea urchin has developed from one single cell, the egg, to a multicellular organism made up of a number of special-

4–26 *An experiment to demonstrate the existence of regional differences in the egg. A sea urchin egg is cut in half across the equator by means of a glass needle. Both halves are fertilized. The animal half develops into a blastula but fails to form endoderm. It grows long cilia, swims about for a number of days, and then dies. The vegetal half forms a partial larva, in which endoderm exceeds ectoderm, but can develop no further. (b) When the egg is cut longitudinally, the two halves develop into normal embryos of half size. (After Barth, 1949)*

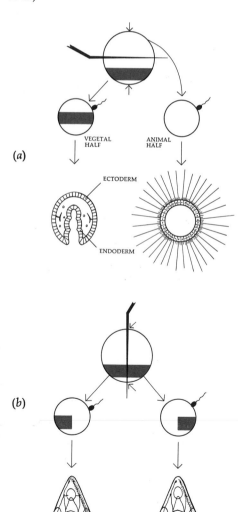

ized, differentiated cells. This differentiation is marked by the fact that the cells have acquired specific functions, such as digestion, have produced new organelles, such as the cilia, and have secreted new products, such as the calcareous skeleton.

ANALYSIS OF DEVELOPMENT

We hypothesized that the nucleus and the cytoplasm each play a role in early development. To test this hypothesis, let us see what happens when we interfere experimentally with the developmental pattern.

Suppose, for instance, we separate the early cleavage cells from one another. The first two cell divisions in the sea urchin take the form of vertical cleavages, running from animal to vegetal pole and perpendicular to one another—just the way you would quarter an apple. Any one of these four daughter cells can develop into a normal embryo. If, however, the embryo is divided in half along the third cleavage line—that is, across the equator (Figure 4–26)—the two halves develop abnormally. The top half is "animalized"; no gut develops, but the tufts of cilia are abnormally large. The bottom half is "vegetalized"; it is almost all gut, with no mouth, no arms, no cilia, and only a few, if any, irregular spicules of skeleton. Later in embryonic development, it is possible to divide the blastula even further below the equator. In these cases, the vegetal half develops a gut so disproportionately large that it grows outside of the embryo rather than inside, owing to interference with the normal process of gastrulation. An embryo with an inside-out gut of this sort is known as an *exogastrula*. In the exogastrula, the mesenchyme cells migrate into the interior, but they usually produce no skeletal spicules or only very small ones. This indicates that in sea-urchin development, the different cytoplasmic determinants balance out or antagonize one another; the vegetal half does not merely lack cilia, it has a great excess of gut, far more than it would have in normal development.

If, at the 16- or 32-cell stage (which is the earliest stage practical for this experiment), the embryo is sliced in three—an animal half, a small vegetal-pole fragment, and a middle piece—and if the animal half and the vegetal-pole fragment are then grafted together, two normal embryos may develop, one from the products of this graft and the second from the middle piece alone. Note that the midpiece will develop normally only if the area near the vegetal pole is removed. Again, we see indications that for normal development, the cytoplasmic materials are needed in the right proportions and that a balance of components is necessary.

Here is further clear-cut evidence of the importance of the cytoplasm in determining the fate of cells. But there is more to this—there apparently is a third component in early development, namely the interrelationships between the cells after cleavage occurs.

493 *Interactions in Development*

We can demonstrate the importance of such intercellular relationships by a simple experiment. If we put the early sea-urchin blastula in calcium-free seawater and agitate the water, the cells will fall apart. The cells still all look the same, and as we shall see, neither their DNA nor their cytoplasm has been altered in any crucial way. But they simply stop dividing, and very shortly they deteriorate and die. Returning the individual cells to normal seawater does not alter their fate. Suppose, however, we put them back into normal seawater and, by gentle stirring, bring them into contact with one another. The cells will then reaggregate, arrange themselves in their former pattern, and once more start to divide! Clearly, multicellularity itself—a new property that has emerged in the course of development—has an effect on cells that is quite distinct from the instructions coded in their genes or the distribution of materials in their cytoplasm.

To complete the argument, let us look once more at what happens in the course of early normal development. From the completion of the blastula right through the development of the pluteus, there is no further cell division. Consequently, at this period, the cytoplasmic-nuclear relationships stay the same; the only demonstrable changes are in the positions of cells relative to one another. This question of the importance of cellular position and the kinds of interactions it makes possible will be explored in greater detail in the chapters to come.

In short, development depends on the product of a number of different influences: One of these is the genetic information of the cell. Others are determinants in the cytoplasm and the interrelationships of cells with one another. It is possible that these latter two exert their effects, directly or indirectly, by activating or repressing elements in the genetic instructions.

SUMMARY

At the beginning of this chapter, we posed the question of how the properties of the egg can be translated into those of the multicelled organism. We looked first at the genetic material of the egg cell; the information for the structures and functions of both egg and organism as well as for the development from one to the other is contained in the molecular properties of the DNA. These molecular properties, however, as embryologists were able to conclude long before DNA had been discovered, can be expressed only as the result of continuing interactions between the nucleus and the cytoplasm of the cell. Finally, we saw that the development of the organism depended on the emergence of a new property not present in the egg —the property of multicellularity. To illustrate this point, we examined the early development of the sea urchin in terms of nuclear-cytoplasmic relationships and of changing relationships among its component cells.

Chapter 4—3

Continuous Development—The Skin

"Skin is a remarkable organ—the largest and by far the most versatile of the body. It is an effective shield against many forms of physical and chemical attack. It holds in the body's fluids and maintains its integrity by keeping out foreign substances and microorganisms. It acts to ward off the harsh ultraviolet rays of the sun. It incorporates mechanisms that cool the body when it is warm and retard the loss of heat when it is cold. It plays a major role in regulating blood pressure and directing the flow of blood. It embodies the sense of touch. It is the principal organ of sexual attraction. It identifies each individual by shaping the facial and bodily contours as well as by distinctive marking such as fingerprints."

These words, which were written by William Montagna of the University of Oregon, are indicative of the degree of enthusiasm the skin inspires in those who become experts in the structures and functions of this remarkable organ. Another biologist specializing in the skin confesses that he has to restrain himself from calling it "miracle wrap," and as you can see by the fact that we can quote him, he was not able to suppress this impulse entirely.

The skin is a particularly useful object of study for developmental biologists. It is readily available and relatively easy to manipulate—compared with one of the internal organs, for example. More important, it is in continuous development even in the adult, and it exhibits, in a somewhat simplified form, most of the phenomena and many of the problems associated with the earlier development of very complicated organisms, such as man.

The Skin Surface

Although we commonly refer to the skin as if it were a single tissue, it actually varies widely from place to place over the surface of the body, a

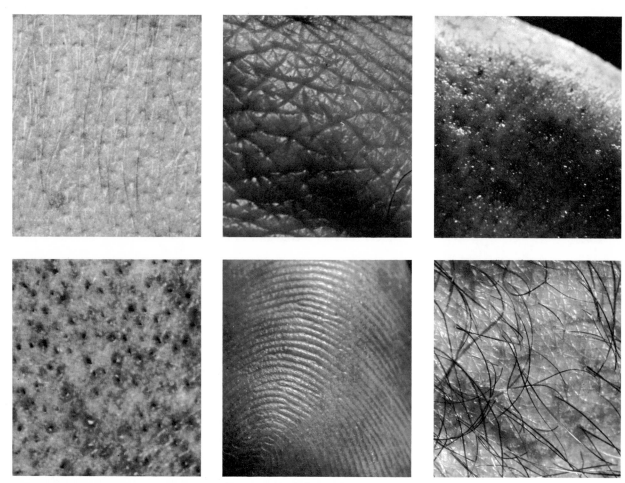

(Dr. R. K. Winkelmann, Dermatopathology by Hamilton Montgomery, M.D., Hoeber Medical Division, Harper & Row Publishers, Inc., 1967)

fact with which we are so familiar that we no longer notice it. The cornea, which is modified skin, is almost perfectly transparent. Much of the skin surface is translucent; if you have a fair complexion, you can probably see the blood vessels beneath the skin surface on the inside of your forearm. In other parts of the body, however, which are more exposed to the sunlight, the skin is thicker and more opaque. In some areas, the skin is loosely attached to the fat or muscular tissues beneath it. Again, the forearm is a convenient example; as you rotate your hand at the wrist, you can see the muscles roll freely beneath the skin. If you pull the skin of the forearm, you will see that it is highly elastic. You know this already from the fact that the skin over the abdomen may stretch to double its size during pregnancy and very quickly spring back to its original dimensions.

496 DEVELOPMENT

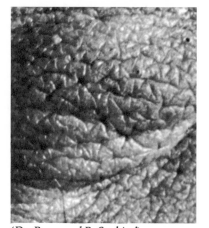

(Dr. Raymond R. Suskind)

4–27 *Variations of human skin. The areas of skin shown here are from a finger, an elbow, a male cheek, a female cheek, the back of a hand, a knuckle, and a nose. Can you tell which is which?*

By contrast, look at the skin on the inner surface of your hands. Here it is stretched taut. The surface is covered with fine furrows and ridges and tends to be slightly moist, all of which improves its gripping properties. The skin on the back of the hands is smooth and dry. It has extra folds over the knuckles to permit the fingers to bend; similar folds of tissue are found at the elbows and knees. The fingertips contain many sensory nerve endings and are able to detect even very slight differences in textures. There are far fewer nerve endings in other parts of the body, however; if you touch someone on the back with your fingertips, he will be unable to tell you whether you are touching him with one finger or two unless your fingers are more than half an inch apart. This is because he will receive a signal from only a single nerve ending since these are widely spaced over this part of the body.

All of these are inherited properties of the skin. Some of the characteristics of the skin are acquired in response to the stresses and strains of time. A baby is born with flexure lines in the hand, for example, but other flexure lines, such as the "crow's feet" around the outer corners of the eyes, are produced by repeated crinkling of the skin in particular areas. Such lines, which are said to produce "character" in a face, have made fortunes for the cosmetic industry. Wherever the skin is subjected to habitual pressure or friction, thickened areas or calluses appear. The pencil-pusher typically has a callus on the inner surface of the second finger. The busy executive who carries home a briefcase every evening will have a light row of calluses on the fleshy pads of his palms, while the guitarist will get them on his fingertips. Some sports enthusiasts, and other men and women who do heavy work with their hands, often develop thick calluses in highly distinctive patterns on their palms and fingers, and it is not unusual for a person who goes barefoot to develop calloused areas more than half an inch thick on the weight-bearing surfaces of the foot.

One of the most useful and remarkable adaptive abilities of the skin is its capacity to repair itself, another property so familiar that we take it completely for granted. When we consider the number of nicks and scratches our skin suffers in the course of even a few months, we can see that, if it did not have this ability for repair, it would be an extremely worn and shabby garment—virtually useless, in fact—by the time any child reached adulthood, if indeed he survived that long. It is by this careful balance and modulation of properties—thickness versus thinness, firmness versus pliability, toughness versus sensitivity—that the skin is able to serve its complex double function, that is, to form a protective barrier between us and our surroundings and, at the same time, serve as the means of communication with the outside world. All these special adaptations of the skin involve continuing developmental processes: growth, differentiation, and also the morphogenesis of special structures such as hair and nails.

The Skin in Cross Section

Figure 4–28 shows a section through the skin, revealing three main layers, or zones. The innermost layer, lying below the skin, is made up largely of fatty tissue, which serves as a cushion and an insulator. If you pinch yourself on the inner part of your upper arm, most of the tissue you hold between your thumb and forefinger is composed of this fatty layer. Above the fatty layer is the lowest layer of the skin itself, the *dermis*. The dermis is a feltwork of fibrocytes surrounded by collagen, other proteins, and mucopolysaccharides. Smooth-muscle fibers underlie the dermis; it is when these muscles contract that your hair stands on end. Small blood vessels twist through the dermis, bringing oxygen and chemical energy to the cells. The tiny nerve endings in the skin register sensations of touch, pain, heat or cold—different receptors for each sensation.

The surface of the dermis forms hills and valleys, *papillae*, into which the overlying layer of skin, the *epidermis*, fits very exactly. The epidermis can be separated from the dermis by special treatments that disrupt or dissolve the thin layer of cementing substance holding them together. When the two tissues are separated, each retains the same papillary pattern, one an exact complement, or negative mold, of the other. It is the papillary pattern that determines the texture of the skin.

4–28 *A section of human skin, showing the epidermis and the dermis, which together make up the skin and the underlying subcutaneous tissue. Intermingled with the cells of the dermis are fine blood vessels, tactile and other nerves, the smooth muscles that raise the hair when contracted, and a variety of specialized glands. Above the dermis are the two layers of epidermis: a lower layer of living cells and a horny layer of dead cells filled with the fibrous protein keratin. At the base of the epidermis are melanocytes, the pigment organs that produce the granules responsible for skin colors.* (After Montagna, 1965)

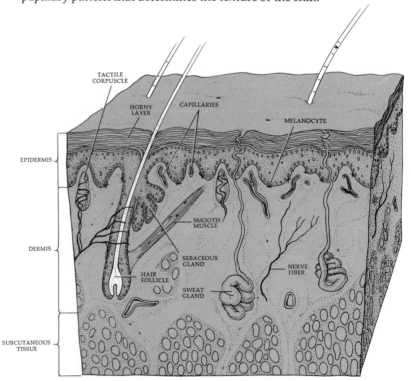

The epidermis, which has no blood supply, depends upon the underlying dermis for food and oxygen. Directly above the dermis is a layer of living epidermal cells which divide constantly to replace cells lost from the skin surface. Among these cells are the *melanocytes*, the pigment-producing cells. The outer layer of epidermis is the *stratum corneum*, or "horny layer," of dead tissue that provides the waterproof outer wrapping on which our survival as terrestrial animals depends. The principal component of the stratum corneum is keratin, the substance from which nails, scales, feathers, claws, horns, hooves, antlers—all epidermal derivatives —are formed.

Morphogenesis: The Formation of Hair

Vertebrate skin serves not only as a covering but as the source of a number of highly specialized structures, including the sweat glands, the oil-producing sebaceous glands, teeth, tusks and other structures formed of keratin, all of which provide examples of morphogenesis. Of these, we shall select hair for a closer examination.

Hair, like the feathers of the bird, appears to have had its phylogenetic origin in the scales of reptiles, but no history remains of how the transition from scale to hair took place. Some experts in comparative anatomy believe that hairs may have originated to serve not a covering function, as scales do, but a sensory one, as they continue to do in the whiskers (*vibrissae*) of cats and other animals. In any case, hair as such is an exclusively mammalian character; in fact, it has been suggested that the Mammalia could just as well be known as the Pilifera, since hairiness is found throughout the entire class. Incidentally, mammary glands apparently evolved from sweat glands, so in either case, our distinctive features appear to be only skin deep.

Hair follicles are the first derivatives of the skin to form in the course of embryonic development. In the human fetus, the beginnings, or *primordia*, of hair follicles (the sheaths in which the hairs are formed) can first be detected at the end of the second month, and as the skin grows to envelop the rapidly enlarging embryo, new hair follicles appear, regularly spaced among those that are already there.

Follicles originate in the epidermis. As the cells of the growing follicle push their way down through the dermis, a little cap of dermal fibroblasts forms at the tip of the follicle-to-be and is pushed along ahead of it. The end of the follicle rounds out into an onion-shaped bulb as it completes its growth. This bulb is not solid but is pushed inward at its lower surface. Enclosed in this inverted area at the base of the bulb is the group of cells carried down from the dermal layers. This group of cells is known as the *dermal papilla*. The dermal papilla is connected with other fibrous tissue that

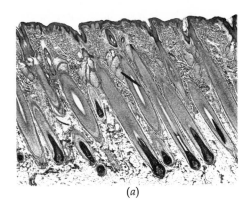

(a)

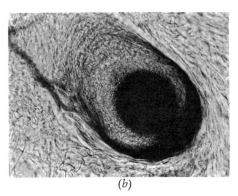

(b)

4–29 (a) *Hair follicles in the human scalp.*
(b) *The dermal papilla of a hair follicle.*
(*Dr. R. K. Winklelmann, Dermato-*
pathology, Hamilton Montgomery,
M.D., Hoeber Medical Division, Harper
& Row Publishers, Inc., 1967)

surrounds the follicle, extending up into the dermal layer of cells. Growth and function of the follicle will not take place in the absence of dermal cells, an example of the importance of tissue interaction, a recurring theme in this story of development.

Once the cylinder has stretched out full length, growth ceases in most of the follicle except for the cells at the tip of the bulb. These cells then begin to flow back up toward the surface, pushing their way through the solid cylinder of epidermal cells. Just as the cells of the slime mold differentiate to form stalk and spore, these cells differentiate to form the inner sheath and the hair shaft. The follicle now consists of three distinct zones: (1) the outer sheath, (2) the inner sheath, and (3) the hair itself. The inner sheath has three layers, forming three concentric circles, each usually only a cell wide. It is attached to the hair and grows along with it to the surface of the skin. The hair shaft is composed of two concentric cylinders. The outer cylinder is made up of cuticle cells which overlap one another like shingles. The central cylinder, the *cortex*, is composed of dead elongated cells, which contain keratin and other fibrous proteins.

The only dividing cells in the mature follicle are found in the tip of the bulb in the area surrounding the dermal papilla. Division here is very rapid; a hair grows an average of 0.35 millimeter a day, a tremendous metabolic feat for this small group of cells to achieve. The cells at the tip of the bulb are indistinguishable from one another, but as they move upward, they begin to differentiate, that is, to become different from one another. As the cells move from the bulb into the much narrower area above it, they become compressed, elongated, and packed together. The outer layers differentiate first. By the time the stream of dividing cells is halfway up the follicle, five distinct types can be distinguished: the cells that make up the three layers of the inner sheath and the cells comprising the two layers of the hair shaft. Each of these five cell types has a distinctive form, and each synthesizes a slightly different group of proteins.

Within these narrowing concentric circles, the cells of the cortex, or central cylinder of the hair shaft, are the last to differentiate. These are the only cells in human hair that contain pigment and so are responsible for hair color, which, as you know, is a genetic characteristic. The pigment comes from melanocytes from the epidermis; the melanocytes are carried down with the dermal papilla by the follicle as it first forms. These cells acquire long branches, or *dendrites*, which extend from the papilla into the upper part of the bulb. The dendrites creep in among the cells of the upper bulb—they cannot get in among the cells of the sheath or hair cuticle because these are already tightly packed in the upper bulb—and inject pigment into them. Also determined genetically is the shape of the hair; the degree of curl in a hair depends on the secondary structure assumed by the protein molecules in the hair shaft.

When the hair cells are mature, they are a completely lifeless combination of keratin and a glassy, fibrous substance.

HORMONAL CONTROL OF HAIR GROWTH

The formation of hair by the epidermis depends, as we have seen, on interactions with the dermis and on genetic properties. Hair formation is also regulated by influences that affect the organism as a whole. The effects of sex hormones, for example, on the growth of human hair are so well known that you need only to be reminded of them. For example, the patterns of hair growth change at puberty with the development of hair in the armpits and pubic region. At this time also, pronounced sexual differences in hair growth appear. Facial hair begins to develop, the hairline at the forehead changes shape, and there is often a growth of hair on the chest, shoulders, and back. Under the influence of male sex hormones, women begin to show male patterns of hair distribution, while eunuchs never develop coarse facial hair or body hair. Nor do eunuchs grow bald. Baldness, as you probably know, "runs in families," and so is probably the result of genetic factors that affect either the follicles themselves or the individual's hormone production. Actually, in the bald man, the hair follicles do not cease to function altogether but begin to produce the fine, soft, colorless hair typical of the skin on the inner arm, for example, instead of the coarser hair produced on the more fortunate scalp.

Man is not alone in exhibiting sexual influences on the skin and its products, as witness the mane of the lion, the beard of the male goat, the plumage of the peacock, and the antlers of the deer.

The Epidermis: A Turnover System

The epidermis, like *Hydra,* is a turnover system. Its chief function, in terms of the entire organism, is to produce the stratum corneum; in the skin, it is only after its death that each epidermal cell serves the function for which evolution produced it. All cell division takes place in the *basal layer,* the single layer of cells directly overlying the dermis; it is possible to show by radioactive-tracer studies that cells above the basal layer do not synthesize DNA, a step which must precede any mitotic division. For every cell division in the basal layer of the adult skin, except during callus formation, a cell moves up from the basal layer and another cell is lost from the surface of the skin. Statistically speaking, each time a cell divides, one of the daughter cells remains a basal cell and one moves out of the basal layer and differentiates. In actuality, both daughter cells become basal cells and may remain so for an indefinite period of time, but on the average, every time a cell divides, a cell somewhere in the vicinity begins its migration to the surface. In other words, cell division and differentiation are two separate developmental events in this system, as they were in the previous systems studied, from the slime mold to the sea urchin.

Once it is free of the basal layer, the cell begins to differentiate. As it moves toward the surface, it changes progressively from a columnar or cuboidal basal cell to a flattened, tile-shaped squamous cell. Also, in the course of this migration, it takes on new synthetic functions, producing keratin, which is a mixture of proteins. The production of keratin continues until the death of the cell, and the keratin deposited in dead cells makes up about half of the total substance of the dead epidermal layer.

The cells of the basal layer are only loosely attached to one another, but once they move out and begin their migrations, they form stable connections with the cells on either side of them. Thickenings of the membrane, called *desmosomes,* can be seen at points where the cells come in contact. Thus the epidermal cells migrate to the surface bonded together into a continuous sheet.

The stratum corneum also forms a continuous sheet. In tissue sections prepared for the microscope, it usually looks like a loosely packed pile of dead cells, but it has been shown recently that this appearance is misleading. By appropriate treatments, the stratum corneum can be removed intact; it is a waterproof, pliable, semitransparent film, thin and tough, like plastic wrap. This horny dead layer of cells is shed in fragments from the human skin, but in animals such as lizards, it peels off every few days almost intact.

Cell Differentiation: Tissue Interactions

As we have seen, the thin layer of epidermal cells that covers the outer surface of our bodies varies widely in texture and pattern—thick, thin, smooth, rough, damp, dry, hard, or hairy—and these overall patterns are determined by the factors governing the differentiation of each new cell as it begins its migration through the epidermis. What decides the different fates of these apparently similar cells? This, as you now know, is a recurrent question in development.

STUDIES IN TISSUE CULTURE

The possibilities for studying the relationships between tissues have been greatly expanded by improvements in techniques for growing somatic cells in tissue culture, that is, apart from the organism. At the present time, many types of embryonic cells can be cultured in a nutrient medium consisting entirely of known ingredients. Most of the studies of the skin carried out in tissue culture have been done with tissues from the chick embryo. Skin from the chick embryo is particularly useful as a model system because it differentiates rapidly and, more important, the variations in differentiation are very marked, as you will see.

Let us look at some of the findings. If chick-embryo skin—dermis plus epidermis—is removed from an embryo less than 5¹/₂ days old and placed in a nutrient medium in tissue culture, it will not differentiate into skin, although it will remain alive. But skin taken from an embryo more than six days old will differentiate in almost every case. Something happens to the skin between the fifth and the sixth day of embryonic life, and whatever happens depends upon the skin's close relationship with the rest of the tissues of the embryo.

What happens is not a single event, however, as we can show by citing one more experiment. If a fragment of skin from a 4¹/₂-day-old embryo is implanted into the flank of a 3-day-old embryo, the implanted skin will begin to make feathers before the host skin does. In other words, something happened to the transplanted skin before 4¹/₂ days, before it was removed, that set it running on its own timetable and gave it a headstart on its host—although without the continuing presence of the host skin, the process of differentiation which had begun could not have been completed.

The action of one tissue causing another to differentiate is known as *induction*. Induction is believed to play a role in most if not all instances of differentiation.

DERMAL-EPIDERMAL INTERACTIONS

Chick skin over six days old will differentiate in tissue culture. The epidermis of 11-day-old skin, whether growing in the chick or the test tube, closely resembles the human epidermis we described previously. The basal layer of cells, which are columnar, undergo mitotic divisions, migrate upward toward the surface, become keratinized, and eventually are discarded.

Suppose, however, that the epidermis is separated from the underlying dermal layer. As N. K. Wessels of Stanford University has shown, the epidermis reacts promptly. Within 8 to 10 hours, the columnar cells flatten out and DNA synthesis and cell proliferation stop. If the dermis or other tissue of mesodermal origin is replaced within 18 hours, proliferation and germination begin again. If it is not replaced, however, the epidermis eventually loses its capacity to respond, and it no longer resembles or acts like normal epidermal tissue. Unlike the interaction between skin and the other tissues of the embryo, which seems to be completed quite early in embryonic life—by the sixth day—a continued interaction between epidermis and dermis is necessary for the characteristic turnover pattern to continue.

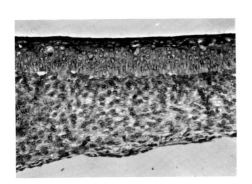

4–30 *A section of the skin of an 11-day chick embryo. As in the human skin, the epidermal layer at the surface is composed of dead, keratinized cells. Directly below this, you can see the epidermal basal layer, consisting of living columnar cells, and then the thick dermal zone.* (Dr. N. K. Wessels)

503 *Continuous Development—The Skin*

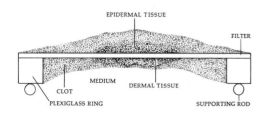

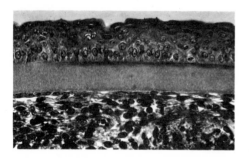

4–31 *The differentiation and proliferation of epidermal cells depend on a continued interaction between epidermis and dermis. However, the two tissues do not have to be in direct contact for the necessary interactions to occur. This has been demonstrated by experiments using the filter apparatus shown here. Epidermis and dermis were grown in culture separated by a thin porous membrane that permitted the passage of molecules but not cells. The epidermal cells directly opposite the dermis continued to divide and differentiate. (After Grobstein, 1964)*

4–32 *Epidermis of an 11-day chick embryo separated by filter from the dermis. As you can see, the epidermal cells are continuing to differentiate. (Dr. N. K. Wessels)*

CELL-FREE INDUCTIVE FACTORS

The epidermis does not need to be in direct contact with the underlying dermis for differentiation and proliferation to occur. In experiments in which the two types of tissue were separated by a narrow strip of filter, the epidermal tissue directly opposite the dermis showed signs of mitotic division and differentiation. Whatever is exchanged between the tissues is probably in the form of large molecules, since it will not pass through a fine cellophane filter. It also cannot travel very far; distances measured in microns seem to be about the limit. Apparently, it is inactivated very rapidly. If this were not the case, it would not be possible, of course, to keep tissue interactions so precisely localized.

Finding that actual cell contact was not required for induction, Wessels made an extract of chick embryo and added this embryo juice to epidermis growing in a nutritive medium. He found that the juice alone could stimulate proliferation and differentiation in the isolated tissue, but only if the tissue had a suitable substrate to attach itself to. For example, if the epidermis was grown on a filter such as the one used in the previous experiment, the cells over the hole in the filter did not shown signs of mitotic activity but the cells over the solid portion of the filter did. Apparently, the cells had to be "on solid ground" in order to assume their normal relationships to one another; this is also necessary for cell division to take place.

TRANSPLANTATION EXPERIMENT

Chick epidermis may take part in the formation of feathers, scales, or beak tissue. It is the underlying dermis that determines the course of differentiation in the epidermis. If epidermis of a suitable age from the back region of a chick, for example, is grafted to dermis of the leg region, this epidermis will develop scales rather than feathers. If it is grafted to dermis of the beak region, the same tissue will keratinize completely and form beak. All these relationships have been worked out in a brilliant series of experiments by Mary E. Rawles of the University of Virginia.

She has found dermis from different areas varies widely in inductive capacity at different ages. Dermis from the foot region does not become strongly inductive until the embryo is about 13 days old, while dermis from the spur region, the back, or the beak, is inductive by 5 days. Epidermis from the back, even if it is 8 days old (before feather development), gives rise to typical down feathers rather than scales when it is grafted to dermis of the foot region that is less than 9 to 11 days of age, although the presence of the dermis is necessary for this development. But epidermis from $5^{1}/_{2}$ to $7^{1}/_{2}$ days old when combined with foot dermis 13 to 15 days old produces scales.

  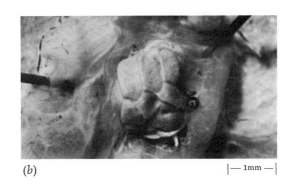

(a) |–1mm–| |— 1mm —| (b) |— 1mm —|

4–33 *Some results of transplantation experiments with chick skin. (a) Down feathers produced from 6-day back epidermis, which would normally give rise only to feathers, in contact with 10½-day foot dermis, which would normally produce scales. (On the right, the feather sheaths have been removed and the feathers allowed to dry.) At 10½ days, the underlying dermis has apparently not developed an inductive capacity intense enough to cause a scale-producing response in the transplanted epidermis. (b) A transplant of 6-day back epidermis responds to specific inductive stimuli from the foot dermis of 12-day embryos. As shown here, the result of such a graft is both scales and feathers. Back dermis, on the other hand, is strongly inductive at a very early stage. Grafts of scale-producing foot epidermis on 5-day back dermis result in normal feathers, such as those shown in (a), instead of scales. (Dr. Mary E. Rawles, Journal of Embryology and Experimental Morphology, Vol. II (Part 4), 1963)*

Even after differentiation has begun, the commitments are not necessarily irreversible. For instance, if 8½-day epidermis from the back region (which will already have feather germs) is transplanted to the beak region, it will remodel itself into beak. This *plasticity*, or ability to change form, is one of the characteristics of epidermal tissue.

THE NATURE OF CELLULAR INTERACTIONS

Studies like these of skin and other tissues confirm that interactions between different types of cells and tissues play an important role in many if not all instances of cellular differentiation. The interactions have been shown to depend, according to filter experiments which have now been carried out with many types of tissue, on the production of chemical substances by the inducing tissues (and perhaps by the induced tissue as well). These substances change the immediate surroundings—the microenvironment of the cells—and bring about changes in either or both of the interacting tissues. In the case of the dermal-epidermal interactions in the skin, induction appears to continue for the life of the tissue.

Dedifferentiation and New Growth

So far in our descriptions of developmental processes in the skin, we have emphasized the continuing orderly relationships of dermis and epidermis and the effects of these relationships on differentiation and morphogenesis. What happens when we disrupt these relationships? This is a simple experiment; we perform it every time we nick a finger. Any injury to the skin's surface sets in motion a whole series of events. First, as a result of exposure to air and to substances released from the wounded tissue, a tough fibrous clot forms from the blood plasma. This is an emergency measure that restores the skin as rapidly as possible to its vital function as a waterproof container and barrier against outside invaders. The small blood vessels in the area of the wound dilate; this is why skin near a wound looks red and feels hot, although it is no hotter than the inside of the body, merely hotter than the rest of the skin. This dilation facilitates the release of white blood cells—phagocytes—into the area. The white cells destroy microorganisms and mop up debris.

More pertinent from the developmental point of view, all the cells in the immediate vicinity of the wound begin to migrate toward the injured area. This migration can involve cells which had already begun to differentiate to form hair follicles, for instance, or sebaceous glands. Cells beyond the margin of the wound begin to proliferate, contributing to the migration. The cells do not move in over the surface of the clot but plunge beneath it, moving down until they make contact with the dermis. As a result of this influx of cells, the epidermis near the site of the wound thickens.

The underlying dermis repairs itself by the production of new fibrocytes, the growth of new blood-vessel tissue where former tissue was destroyed, and the laying down of new collagen. When the dermis has restored its continuity, the excess epidermal cells at the wound site are pinched off or reabsorbed, and the normal equilibrium is restored.

4–34 *How a skin wound heals.* (a) *A fibrous clot, formed from the blood plasma, closes the hole in the skin. The cells of the epidermal basal layer move downward to the dermal connective tissue.* (b) *The wound epidermis thickens due to the continued migration and proliferation of cells in the immediate vicinity.* (c) *The underlying dermis repairs itself by producing new collagen fibers. Isolated epithelial cells then break off and are reabsorbed, so that the contour of the basal layer regains its normal appearance. (After Dunphy, 1960)*

(a)
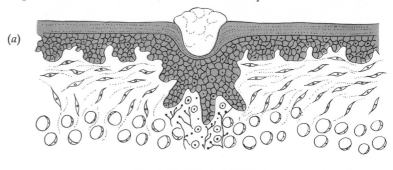

(b)
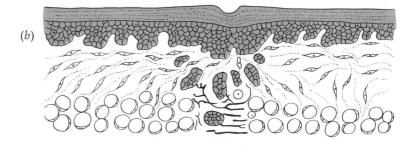

(c)
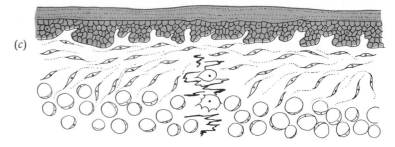

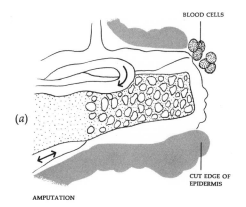

(a)

BLOOD CELLS

CUT EDGE OF EPIDERMIS

AMPUTATION

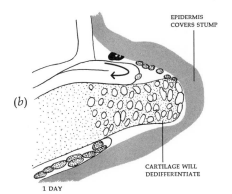

(b)

EPIDERMIS COVERS STUMP

CARTILAGE WILL DEDIFFERENTIATE

1 DAY

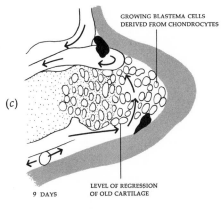

(c)

GROWING BLASTEMA CELLS DERIVED FROM CHONDROCYTES

LEVEL OF REGRESSION OF OLD CARTILAGE

9 DAYS

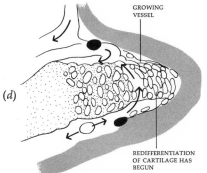

(d)

GROWING VESSEL

REDIFFERENTIATION OF CARTILAGE HAS BEGUN

14 DAYS

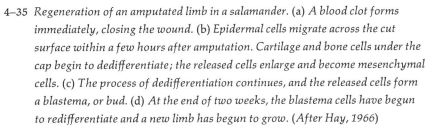

4–35 *Regeneration of an amputated limb in a salamander.* (a) *A blood clot forms immediately, closing the wound.* (b) *Epidermal cells migrate across the cut surface within a few hours after amputation. Cartilage and bone cells under the cap begin to dedifferentiate; the released cells enlarge and become mesenchymal cells.* (c) *The process of dedifferentiation continues, and the released cells form a blastema, or bud.* (d) *At the end of two weeks, the blastema cells have begun to redifferentiate and a new limb has begun to grow.* (*After Hay, 1966*)

REGENERATION

Suppose instead of just nicking our finger, we cut the tip of it right off. Exactly the same train of events would follow, but our fingertip would not be restored. Of course not, you may say; it is a surprise to be reminded that this sort of regeneration can occur very readily not only in animals such as the hydra and the planarian but also in an animal much more like yourself, the salamander. The tissues involved in this regeneration extend considerably beyond skin, but the skin plays an important role.

Following amputation of a limb in a salamander, the very same processes can be seen at work that we have just described. The blood clot forms, closing the wound. Cells migrate in from adjacent areas until a thickened cap of epidermis covers the amputation site. Cell proliferation occurs at the margins of the wound, and the integrity of the skin covering is restored. But then a new sequence of events begins. The cartilage and bone lying just under the cap of epidermis begin to *dedifferentiate*, releasing mesenchymal cells, loose mesodermal cells, which begin to proliferate. This process of dedifferentiation continues from the tip inward until a sizable number of cells are released and a *blastema*, or bud, has formed, not unlike the bud of a hydra, made up of these undifferentiated cells. Finally, three to four weeks after amputation in the adult salamander (the process is quicker in the larva), a new limb begins to form. The limb that grows back out is a perfect replica of the former one.

Does the new limb really grow from the dedifferentiated cells? This was a point of contention for a number of years because many embryologists found it difficult to accept the idea that differentiation could be a reversible process; how do we know, they asked, that the new bone is not simply an outgrowth of the old? This question was answered by a convincing experiment performed by Paul Weiss, now at Rockefeller University (Figure 4–36). Weiss removed the upper arm bone (humerus) from a salamander limb. Then, when the wound healed, he amputated the limb just above the elbow. When the limb regenerated, all of the newly formed limb

507 *Continuous Development—The Skin*

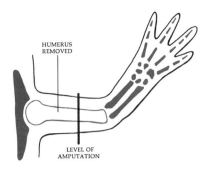

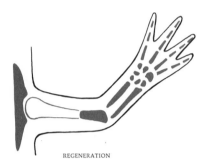

REGENERATION

4–36 *An experiment with regeneration in the salamander. The upper bone (humerus) was removed from the salamander's limb, and when that wound healed, the limb was amputated at the point shown. Although there was no bone or cartilage at the level of amputation, the limb proceeded to regenerate normally. As you can see, the regenerated limb is complete, including the portion of humerus that would have been amputated with the limb if it had not been removed previously. What conclusion would you draw from the results of this experiment? (After Weiss, 1925)*

contained perfectly formed skeleton, even though the upper part of the humerus did not. We do not know, however, from what cell, or even from what general cell type, the new tissue forms.

What is necessary for limbs to reform? One of the components clearly required is nerve tissue. If nerves are not permitted to grow back into the regenerating limb, dedifferentiation will take place but not new limb formation. Apparently, stimulation by the nerve is not the necessary component; implanted sensory nerves will act as well as the motor nerves normally supplying the limb, for example. The nerve seems to act more as a growth promotor or an inductor.

Another necessary component is the cap of epidermal cells that forms over the wound. The dedifferentiation of the mesodermal cells always begins in the vicinity of this epidermal cap. Moreover, the newly forming limb always grows toward the cap. If the position of the cap is changed, the limb will grow in this new direction.

What is the chief difference between the modest amount of wound healing that we mammals are capable of and the process of complete regeneration seen in the limb of the salamander? The difference would appear to be, at least to some extent, a difference in the degree to which a disruption in normal, stabilizing tissue relationships can affect the tissues involved, causing them to start a new cycle of growth, often in a new direction.

CANCER

One of the most remarkable facts about the processes of growth and regeneration is that they stop. In our examination of the skin as a turnover system, we saw that the rate and amount of proliferation are controlled by the relationship between the basal layer of epidermal skin cells and the tissue on which these cells rest; once the cells move out of the basal layer, cell division ceases. When the relationships between epidermal cells and the underlying tissues are destroyed, as in the case of a wound, there is a great increase in cell proliferation; but when the normal pattern is restored, the rate of cell multiplication drops. Cancer is a disease in which cells proliferate abnormally, and for this reason, an understanding of the factors that regulate normal growth is regarded as important to an understanding of the cancer problem.

Let us look, for example, at a basal-cell cancer, a cancer formed from the basal cells of the epidermis. In normal tissues, these basal cells will multiply, as we saw in the tissue-culture experiments, only if they are in contact with underlying tissues. When the cells break loose from the basal layer and begin to keratinize, they form stable connections with the cells on either side of them. Recent studies of basal-cell cancer have indicated that the primary defect in these cells may involve a defect in their ability to produce keratin. Unable to synthesize keratin, they do not enter into combinations with nearby cells that would carry them away from the underlying dermis. Remaining close to it, they continue to proliferate, forming the typical basal-cell cancer. In such cases, cancer may be due to a loss or a repression of a particular genetic ability, that is, keratin production. In some other types of cancer, there are indications that the cancer cell, rather than losing its ability to synthesize a particular product such as keratin, may, by a process of dedifferentiation (such as occurs in wound healing and regeneration), acquire the capacity to synthesize substances that its neighboring cells cannot. Take, for example, a skin cancer composed of squamous cells—epidermal cells that have left the basal layer, have begun to produce keratin, and have assumed a flattened, tilelike shape. There is evidence that these cells can synthesize products that normal squamous cells cannot. Suppose, by a process of dedifferentiation or by a release from some repressor, these cells should begin to synthesize the very inductive factors that they require for growth and that normal epidermal cells must get from the dermis. As a result of such new synthetic capabilities, the cells might be able to free themselves from the normal regulatory controls imposed by cellular interactions. So cancer, which most experts regard not as one disease but as a collection of diseases, may have as one common factor a disruption of normal inductive relationships between tissues.

SUMMARY

In this chapter, we have shown how a single organ system, the skin, demonstrates all the developmental processes previously observed in simple organisms. The morphogenesis of hair was given as an example of the capacity of a tissue to produce highly developed and highly specialized modifications. Hair formation was seen to depend on dermal and epidermal interactions and on general regulatory factors, such as hormonal influences, as well.

The continuing differentiation of epidermal cells depends on an interaction between the epidermis and the dermal layers of the skin. This interaction is an example of *induction*, which results from the passage of chemicals from the cells of one tissue to those of another. Inductive processes are an important part of most, if not all, tissue differentiations.

Finally, we considered the effects of the disruption of tissue relationships by examining the processes of wound healing and of limb regeneration in amphibians. Some implications of these findings for the cancer problem were discussed.

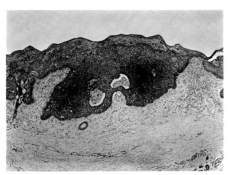

|— 0.5mm —|

4–37 *Basal-cell cancer from the skin of a fifty-year-old woman. Note that the cancer (the dark area in the center) orginates in the epidermis and grows downward. (Hamilton Montgomery, M.D., Dermatopathology by Hamilton Montgomery, M.D., Hoeber Medical Division, Harper & Row Publishers, Inc., 1967)*

Development in Vertebrates: Focus on the Mouse

In this chapter, we are going to examine the highlights in the development of a very complex organism, the mouse. Our purpose is not to give a detailed account but to see how some of the different components of development that we isolated previously in simpler systems operate and interact in this more complicated case. This is analogous to studying a symphony by first isolating some of the recurrent melodies and themes and then seeing how they have been interwoven to produce different effects in the several movements.

The mouse was chosen as an example because it is probably the most useful material for the study of mammalian embryology, which, of course, includes the embryology of man and of most domestic animals. Mice are relatively easy to maintain in the laboratory, have many purebred strains, the genetics of the mouse has been extensively studied and its anatomy is thoroughly understood. Moreover, the embryo develops rapidly, with a complete gestation period of only 20 days.

Gametogenesis

In Chapter 4–1, we saw how the thread of hereditary continuity is passed from cell to cell, generation after generation, in *E. coli*, each daughter cell receiving the same genetic information and, in turn, translating this information in its own cycle of growth and development. Similarly in the higher animals, such as mice and men, each new individual becomes the repository of the genetic material accumulated and selected in the course of thousands of previous generations. In one-celled organisms, the information stored in the nucleus is passed on directly; in higher organisms, it is set aside in specialized cells, the sperm and the egg. Production of specialized cells is called *cytodifferentiation*—the beginning of each new mouse generation begins with the cytodifferentiation of gametes in the preceding generation.

FORMATION OF SPERM CELLS

Sperm production occurs in a continuous cell-turnover system, quite analogous to that of the skin. The testes contain long coiled seminiferous ("seed-bearing") tubules. In a cross section of any one of these tubules, the various stages of spermatogenesis can be seen. Cells in the earliest stages, the spermatogonia, lie at the periphery of the tubule; the next generation, the spermatocytes, form a second layer; while the differentiating spermatozoa are found near the center of the tubule, from which they will be released when they are fully mature. As the spermatogonia divide, some of them remain at the periphery, ready to give rise to a new generation, while others, moving and doubling in volume, go on to become spermatocytes. Each spermatocyte undergoes reduction division, giving rise to four haploid cells, the spermatids, which then differentiate. Each spermatid then goes through a series of remarkable and complicated morphological changes by which it becomes highly specialized to fulfill its sole function: the delivery of its genetic material to the egg. Cells in each stage of development can be seen in Figure 4–38.

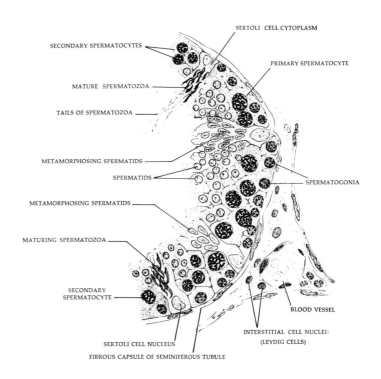

4–38 *Cross section of a seminiferous tubule in a mouse showing spermatozoa in various stages of differentiation. In addition to the germ cells, the tubule contains Sertoli cells, large cells which support and provide nourishment for the developing gametes. The interstitial cells, which are found in the connective tissue surrounding the tubule, are the source of the male hormone testosterone. (Dr. Roberts Rugh, The Mouse, Its Reproduction and Development, Burgess Publishing Co., 1967)*

SECONDARY SPERMATOCYTES

SERTOLI CELL CYTOPLASM

MATURE SPERMATOZOA

PRIMARY SPERMATOCYTE

TAILS OF SPERMATOZOA

METAMORPHOSING SPERMATIDS

SPERMATIDS

SPERMATOGONIA

METAMORPHOSING SPERMATIDS

MATURING SPERMATOZOA

SECONDARY SPERMATOCYTE

BLOOD VESSEL

INTERSTITIAL CELL NUCLEI: (LEYDIG CELLS)

SERTOLI CELL NUCLEUS

FIBROUS CAPSULE OF SEMINIFEROUS TUBULE

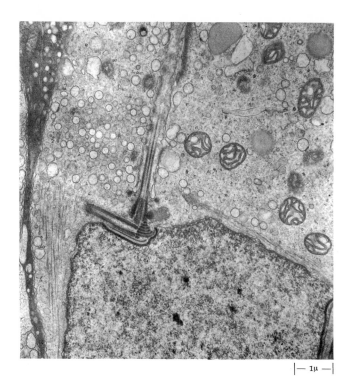

4–39 *A mammalian spermatid in the process of differentiation. The dark area in the lower half of the electron micrograph is the nucleus. The two centrioles have moved to a position just behind the nucleus and the tail has begun to form from one of them. To the right are several mitochondria.*
(Dr. David M. Phillips)

|— 1µ —|

Some of the changes that take place during the differentiation of the spermatid involve the development of a special structure, the *acrosome*. The acrosome contains materials which are believed to be involved in the penetration of the sperm cell into the egg. It is formed in the Golgi complex from a number of small vesicles, each containing a small, dense granule. These vesicles enlarge and coalesce into a single vacuole, which, with the dense material within it, moves to the tip of the elongating sperm nucleus, settles there, and collapses, leaving the acrosome in place.

Another special organelle formed in the spermatid is the tail, or flagellum. During the early stages of acrosome formation, the two centrioles move to the outer cell membrane, and from one of them a fine thread grows out. One centriole eventually lodges in a notch formed at the posterior end of the nucleus, while the other, the one associated with the tail, lies at right angles to the first, as shown in Figure 4–39.

As the tail grows, it shows the characteristic "nine-plus-two" structure found in cilia and flagella generally. Mitochondria aggregate about its basal end forming a continuous spiral, presumably to provide a ready energy source for the flagellar movement.

A third type of change seen in the developing spermatozoon involves streamlining and the elimination of "excess baggage." The nuclear material condenses, squeezing out water. Most of the RNA also is eliminated from the nucleus. Once the tail has formed, the cell undergoes a rapid and pronounced elongation. The cytoplasm flows backward, and the bulk of the cytoplasm, together with the Golgi complex, is sloughed away.

In its final form, the spermatozoon consists of the acrosome, the tightly condensed nucleus, a pair of centrioles, one of which is now serving as the basal body for the tail, and the long, powerful tail itself, which is now, by far, the predominant structure of the cell. In the fully differentiated spermatozoon, all other functions have been subordinated to effective motility.

Sperm production is entirely hormone-dependent, beginning at puberty, which is the time when there is a marked increase in secretion of gonadotropic hormones. Production ceases almost immediately if the pituitary gland is removed and resumes promptly if pituitary gonadotropin is administered.

OOGENESIS

The egg cell develops in the female reproductive gland, the ovary. Unlike the spermatocytes, which are produced continuously, all the oocytes are present when the infant female is born. Oogenesis halts in the first meiotic prophase and does not continue until the egg is almost ready to be released. The wait can be as long as two or three years in the mouse, 45 to 50 years in the human female. Once egg production begins at puberty, as a result of the action of the follicle-stimulating hormone, it follows a regular rhythmic pattern, controlled by the cyclic production of hormones.

The chief visible sign of differentiation in the egg cell is enlargement, representing the storage of nutrient materials for the future embryo. As

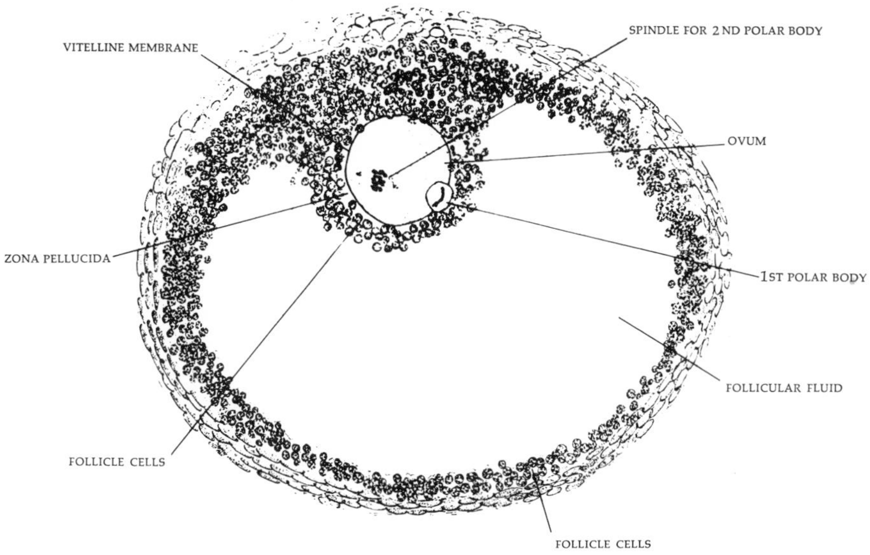

4–40 *A maturing mouse ovum in the enlarging follicle. The egg is enclosed in the vitelline membrane and surrounded by a layer of mucoprotein, called the* zona pellucida, *which is produced by the follicle cells. Outside of the zona pellucida is a layer of follicle cells which are torn loose with the egg as it leaves the ovary.* (Dr. Roberts Rugh, The Mouse, Its Reproduction and Development, Burgess Publishing Co., 1967)

VITELLINE MEMBRANE

SPINDLE FOR 2ND POLAR BODY

OVUM

ZONA PELLUCIDA

1ST POLAR BODY

FOLLICULAR FLUID

FOLLICLE CELLS

FOLLICLE CELLS

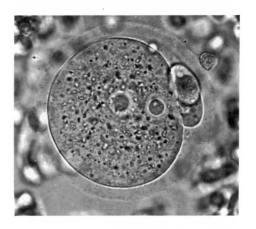

4–41 *A mouse egg shortly after fertilization. The egg has shrunk slightly, and a space has formed under the vitelline membrane. Within this space (on the right), the polar bodies appear. The nucleus of the egg is at the center, and to the right of it, the nucleus of the sperm; the nuclei will migrate towards the center of the cell and fuse. (Biology of the Laboratory Mouse, The Jackson Laboratory, E. L. Green, editor. Copyright 1966 by McGraw-Hill Book Co.)*

4–42 *Fertilized mouse ova after 2½ days of gestation. (Eric V. Gravé)*

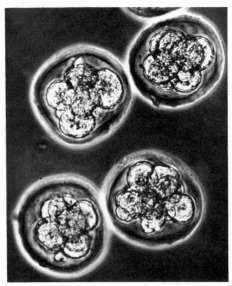

|—— 50µ ——|

the oocyte grows larger, a cavity forms among the surrounding follicle cells. At this point, the follicle and its contents become sensitive to a second pituitary hormone, the luteinizing hormone. This hormone stimulates the oocyte to resume meiosis and initiates the changes in the follicle that lead to ovulation. Under the influence of the luteinizing hormone, the follicle fills with fluid, moves toward the surface of the ovary, and erupts, releasing the oocyte.

As the egg leaves the ovary, some of the follicle cells are torn loose with it. Between the follicle cells and the egg is a layer of mucoprotein, the *zona pellucida*, which is produced by the follicle cells. The egg cell is about 20 microns in diameter, just barely visible to the eye.

Meiotic division in the mammalian oocyte is completed only if the cell is fertilized. Only one gamete is produced; the other three nuclei are discarded in the form of polar bodies. In this way, the egg cell preserves its long-accumulated supply of nutrients and other cytoplasmic materials on which the development of the embryo is to depend.

Fertilization

Fertilization is the means by which the genetic information packaged in the sperm cell is combined with the genetic information of the egg to provide the complete store of instructions for the construction and operations of the future individual. It is the way in which the male parent gains genetic representation in the future generation. Fertilization also activates the egg, initiating its development. However, a variety of artificial stimuli, including the prick of a needle—none of which contributes new material or new information to the egg cell—have been shown to activate eggs. In many species, including sea urchins, frogs, turkeys, and even rabbits, normal development can be completed in these fatherless organisms. In other words, as these experiments show, the egg alone contains everything necessary

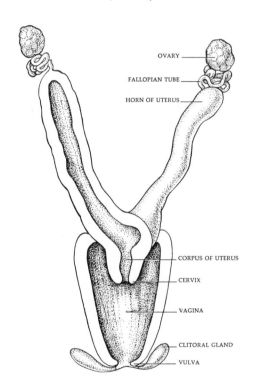

4–43 *The reproductive system of the female mouse showing the ovaries and the two uterine horns in which the embryos develop. (After Rugh, 1964)*

OVARY

FALLOPIAN TUBE

HORN OF UTERUS

CORPUS OF UTERUS

CERVIX

VAGINA

CLITORAL GLAND

VULVA

for development. Fertilization is not necessary for individual development but is important to the species. It is the means by which the genetic information is rearranged and new combinations introduced, providing the possibilities for the variation which is required if evolution is to occur.

Ovulation occurs about every four to five days in the mouse, and it is only during this period, known as *estrus*, that the female is receptive to mating. Fertilization takes place while the eggs are still at the upper end of the oviduct. Although millions of sperm are released at each ejaculation, only about a hundred reach the eggs.

When the sperm touches the egg, its cell membrane fuses with that of the egg, and only the inner contents of the sperm cell enter—nucleus, centrioles, and mitochondria. The nuclei of egg and sperm, each bearing their load of 20 chromosomes (in the mouse, $2n = 40$), both move toward the center of the cell. (See Figure 4–41.) It is tempting to speculate that they attract one another, but it has been shown that if either one of them is removed or destroyed, the movement of the other is in no way affected. The two haploid nuclei fuse at about the center of the egg cell to form the zygote nucleus with its full store of chromosomal material.

Implantation

The first cell division takes place about 12 hours after fertilization, and cell division continues as the embryo makes its way down the oviduct (see Figure 4–42), although the embryo does not grow in size during this period. The journey down the oviduct lasts about four days, and during this time the embryo is nourished by uterine "milk," an unidentified substance in the uterine fluid.

As you can see in Figure 4–43, the uterus of the mouse is divided into two parts, known as the *uterine horns*, which unite just above their junction with the vagina. The outer wall of the uterus is composed of muscle tissue, and the inner surface is lined with epithelium. Between the epithelium and the layer of muscle is the *mucosa*, the tissue that forms the bulk of the uterine wall. The epithelium is indented by numerous small crypts. Each embryo finds its way into a uterine crypt on the ventral, or lower, surface of the uterine horn, coming into close contact with the epithelium. Within a few hours, as a result of interactions between the tissues of the embryo and of the mother, the epithelium near the embryo begins to degenerate and active growth commences in the mucosa, which proliferates until it completely surrounds the embryo.

The embryo was roughly spherical in shape until it made its way into a uterine crypt. By about $7^{1}/_{2}$ days after fertilization, it has elongated into a capsule, enclosed on all sides by a layer of cells. Suppose that, at this stage, we removed the uterus from the mouse and took a thin, lengthwise slice of one of these little embryos for examination under the microscope.

515 *Development in Vertebrates: Focus on the Mouse*

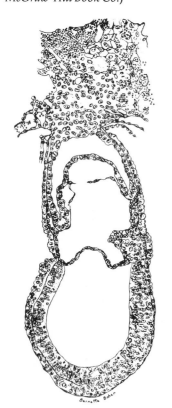

4–44 *A mouse embryo at 7 days 6 hours. The drawing shown here was made from a sagittal section. A sagittal section is a central slice cut lengthwise from front to back. (Biology of the Laboratory Mouse, The Jackson Laboratory, E. L. Green, editor. Copyright 1966 by McGraw-Hill Book Co.)*

In Figure 4–44, you can see what such a cross section would look like. Since it first began to divide on its travel down the oviduct, the embryo has developed into a relatively complicated structure. It is unlikely that you can identify any of the tissues shown here or even the general stage of development. In fact, it is only recently that trained embryologists have been able to do so. The structure shown here, it is now known, is the end result of a series of adaptations that have come about in the long history of evolution. As a consequence, it could not be really understood until a good deal was known about development in other species. So let us follow a similar course, and before we try to decipher Figure 4–44, let us review briefly something of what is known about other embryos and their evolutionary relationships to one another.

Embryology and Evolution

Not long after the establishment of evolutionary theory, the great German biologist E. H. Haeckel, on the basis of his studies of the embryos of a number of organisms, proposed that each organism as it grows from the one-celled egg to the multicelled individual passes through all the evolutionary stages that preceded it—that is, "ontogeny (development) recapitulates phylogeny," or, to put it more simply, "each animal climbs up its family tree." According to this theory, the mouse embryo might first resemble a one-celled amoeba, then a one-layered *Volvox*, then a two-layered coelenterate, and so on, right through fish and amphibian. This intriguing idea gained widespread popularity since much evidence, such as the gill slits of mammals, seemed to provide strong support. Modern biologists realize that Haeckel was only partly right. An early embryo does not resemble any previous, ancestral adult form. It does, however, bear some important resemblances to the *embryos* of its evolutionary predecessors, and it is to these predecessors of the mouse that we shall now turn for clues. We shall begin with the amphioxus, where chordate history traditionally commences.

AMPHIOXUS

The amphioxus is particularly significant because its embryo follows a pattern of early development much like that of the sea urchin. This development, however, does not lead to the tentlike structure of the pluteus larva but leads instead to the elongated axis of the vertebrate organization.

In the amphioxus, as in the sea urchin, the blastula consists of a single layer of cells enclosing a fluid-filled cavity. Gastrulation, again as in the sea urchin, consists of a series of movements which bring the tissues of the blastula into new relationships with one another. First, the layer of cells at the vegetal pole bends inward, and continued inturning leads to a double-

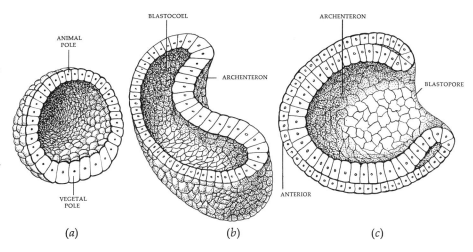

4–45 *Gastrulation in the amphioxus. The blastula (a), like that of the sea urchin, consists of a single layer of cells enclosing a fluid-filled cavity. The layer of cells at the vegetal pole flattens and pushes inward, forming the beginnings of the archenteron, or primitive gut. Continued inturning results in the double-walled cup shape of the gastrula (c). (After Huettner, 1949)*

(a)   *(b)*   *(c)*

walled cup, the opening of which is called the *blastopore*. The double-walled cup elongates as the blastopore constricts. (See Figure 4–45.)

Next, the dorsal region of the elongated gastrula flattens and the cells in this region thicken. The center of this flat ectodermal surface becomes slightly depressed; this is the *neural plate*, from which the entire nervous system will develop. On each side of the neural plate, beginning at its posterior end, a longitudinal ridge appears. The two ridges grow upward and curve toward each other, while the center region of the neural plate becomes depressed and forms a groove; finally, the outer ridges join to form a tube, the *neural tube*. (See Figure 4–46.)

The folding of the neural tube is associated with the origin of mesoderm and the body cavity. The dorsal-lateral regions of the gastrular lining give rise to three longitudinal structures. The central one is the notochord, and the ones on either side are the mesodermal somites, which take the form of segmented blocks. In the amphioxus, as in other chordates, the number of somites increases as the embryo elongates, providing a clear index of the developmental stage.

By the time gastrulation is completed, three distinct layers of tissue are present in the embryo. These layers, sometimes known as the *germ layers*, are the outer ectoderm, the middle mesoderm, and the inner endoderm. The relationships among the three tissue layers and between them and the blastopore are important to note, for these relationships are fundamentally similar in all chordates. The mesoderm first appears between ectoderm and endoderm just dorsal and anterior to the blastopore. In this vicinity, the ectoderm and endoderm are continuous through the blastopore. The notochord extends forward from the blastopore between the segmented mesoderm, or somites. A split in the mesoderm produces the main body cavity, or coelom. As you can see in Figure 4–46, the mesoderm is in close contact

517   *Development in Vertebrates: Focus on the Mouse*

4–46 *Amphioxus development, showing the steps in the formation of the notochord, the neural tube, the somites and the gut. The relationships of the three distinct layers of tissue—ectoderm, mesoderm, and endoderm—are fundamentally the same in all chordates. (After Huettner, 1949)*

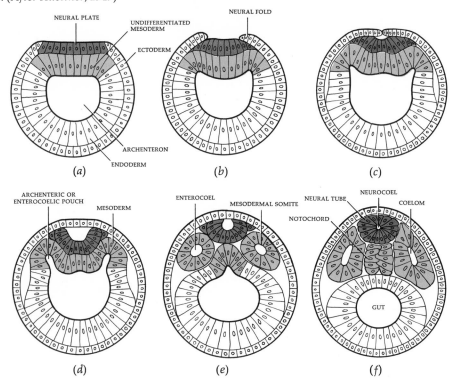

with the ectoderm on one side of the coelom and with the endoderm on the other. The mesoderm-endoderm layer is known as the *splanchnopleure* (from *splanchno*, meaning "viscera," and *pleura*, meaning "side"), and the ectodermal-mesodermal combination is the *somatopleure*. These are words we shall need to use again.

In the amphioxus, the notochord persists as the structural axis of the adult animal, but in the vertebrates, it is replaced by bony tissue which grows from the mesoderm around the neural tube, forming the vertebral column.

FROG

In the frog, the egg looks entirely different from that of the amphioxus but turns out to be fundamentally similar. One main point of difference is that the frog's egg contains more yolky materials, providing more nutrients for the developing embryo. The yolk collects in the vegetal hemisphere, and

The genetic material in a fertilized egg acts as a set of instructions for the construction, maintenance, and operation of an organism adapted to a particular way of life and a particular environment. The sequential development of parts of the organisms reflects the sequential expression of different portions of these instructions. The effects of mutation in a particular gene are seen only when that gene is expressed. As a consequence, different mutations have their effects at different times in development.

Now suppose that a particularly beneficial mutation acting in a particular organ is expressed only after specific steps in the early development of that organ have taken place. Natural selection will select for all the genes required for the expression of that beneficial mutation, and these include, of course, all the genes involved in the early developmental events that preceded and led to the appearance of the new phenotype. Eventually, our hypothetical mutation may lead, as a consequence of the accumulation of further mutations that complement and supplement it, to a whole new function for the affected organ. But bringing these mutations to the point at which their effects are seen will continue to require the retention of the early steps in the organ's development. Consequently, "primitive" developmental sequences, which once led to the development of ancestral structures, will be preserved.

In short, heredity relates to the genetic instructions. Development involves the translation of these instructions into the substance of living organisms. Evolution acts to perpetuate those developmental sequences which produce adaptive structures—and, of course, functions. As a result of the interaction of heredity, development, and evolution, changes appearing at random in the genetic instructions may be adopted by the organism, leading to changes in the corresponding developmental sequences, which are eventually expressed as traits. As a consequence, development often proceeds along bewilderingly indirect pathways. These pathways may serve, however, as guideposts, marking the route that the evolution of the species has taken.

---

as a consequence, the divisions of the cells during cleavage are unequal, with the vegetal cells conspicuously larger. Also, unlike the blastulas of the amphioxus and the sea urchin but like the blastulas of higher vertebrates, the cells making up the blastula of the frog form a layer that is considerably more than one cell in thickness.

In the frog, as in many other embryos, it is possible to follow the fates of individual cells; indeed, such studies are facilitated in the frog by the fact that embryos can be readily stained with vital dyes, making it possible to mark certain cells in order to follow their movements at gastrulation.

519   *Development in Vertebrates: Focus on the Mouse*

Figure 4–47 shows the frog blastula just before gastrulation is about to take place. As you can see, there is a dimpling of the cells just below the equator in the vegetal hemisphere. This is the beginning of inturning to form the blastopore. The first area of inturning becomes the dorsal lip of the fully formed blastopore.

Let us follow the behavior of tissue at the dorsal lip. As the crescent-shaped blastopore forms, the cells begin to move inward. Since they move as continuous sheets, the cells of the outer layer are drawn toward the region of invagination. The cells just above the dorsal lip of the blastopore move around the lip first, reversing direction as they pass over the dorsal lip as though they were being hauled over a pulley. The invaginating layer

4–47 *Development of the frog gastrula. Can you explain what is happening at each stage? (After Huettner, 1949)*

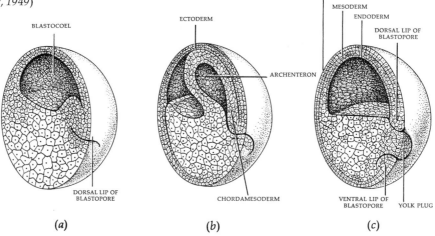

(a)   (b)   (c)

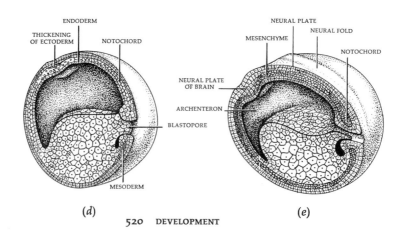

(d)   (e)

—48 *The formation of the neural tube from the neural plate. The thickened elevations of ectoderm on the right and left sides of the neural plate curve inward, form- ing the neural groove. The ridges bordering the neural groove then meet and fuse. Finally, the resulting neural tube pinches off from the rest of the ecto- dermal tissue. (After Huettner, 1949)*

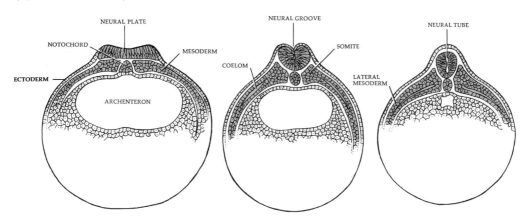

—49 *A salamander embryo, showing the neural folds and neural groove. (Dr. John A. Moore)*

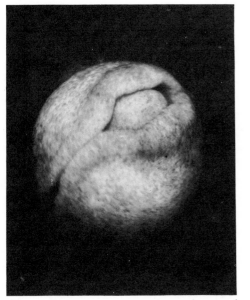

|— 1mm —|

moves along the inner surface of the animal hemisphere in the direction of the future main axis of the animal. The cells at the midline, which were previously at the dorsal lip, are the mesodermal cells that form the noto- chord (and are consequently known as *chordamesoderm*).

As the prospective chordamesoderm moves around the blastopore, the bulky cells from the vegetal hemisphere, although moving more slowly, also invaginate, accumulating in the lower part of the blastocoel. (See Fig- ure 4–47b.) In the vegetal hemisphere, a layer of prospective mesoderm moves in over the lateral and ventral lips and comes to lie between endo- derm and ectoderm. (See Figure 4–47c.) Endodermal tissue moves upward on the inside of the embryo to cover the inner surface of the animal hemi- sphere and complete the primitive gut. Gastrulation concluded, the embryo now consists of three layers of tissue, one within the other: endoderm, mesoderm, and ectoderm. Note that the relationships of these three layers to each other and to the blastopore are fundamentally the same as in the amphioxus.

After this, the first outward signs of tissue differentiation appear: The ectoderm above the chordamesoderm begins to thicken, forming the neural plate. The ridges of the neural plate meet and fuse to form the neural tube, which pinches off from the rest of the ectodermal tissue. The mesoderm underlying the neural tube becomes the notochord. (See Figure 4–48.)

521 *Development in Vertebrates: Focus on the Mouse*

The mesodermal tissue on either side of the notochord breaks up into two longitudinal masses, which segment, forming somites. In the underlying mesoderm, the coelomic cavity, splanchnopleure, and somatopleure are formed. In the amphibian, the yolky endodermal tissue continues to make up the bulk of the body cavity, displacing the gut upward, until the stored nutrients are finally absorbed by the tadpole.

As you can see, the sequences of events in the amphioxus and the amphibian are remarkably similar, and except for the presence of the yolky endoderm in the amphibian, the two embryos closely resemble each other at every stage. What the frog and its close amphibian relatives, the salamanders, have taught us is that the dorsal lip of the blastopore is not only an important structural landmark but also a critical area for controlling development, as we shall see in the next paragraph.

THE ORGANIZER

The tissue that lies at the dorsal lip of the blastopore of the amphibian is one of the most thoroughly investigated in all of embryology. Hans Spemann, in a continuation of the studies described in Chapter 4–2, discovered that he could divide the developing blastula in two and sometimes obtain two normal embryos. Once blastulation was completed and gastrulation had begun, however, he found that he could obtain only one normal embryo from the operation. The embryo that was normal always developed from the half that contained the dorsal lip of the blastopore. (This was actually an extension of his previous experiment of separating cells in the first cleavage stage. The dorsal lip forms in the blastula at the position once occupied in the egg by the gray crescent.)

In 1924, Hilde Mangold, a pupil of Spemann, excised the dorsal lip from one species of salamander and grafted it into the belly region of an embryo of another species. When the embryo which had received the graft developed, it was found that a second embryo had formed within its tissues, a sort of Siamese twin to the first. Because the two different species of salamanders differed in color, it was possible to distinguish the tissues of the host embryo from those of the transplant. The transplanted dorsal lip had developed into notochord, as it would have had it not been removed in the first place. This in itself was noteworthy because previous experiments had shown that other portions of an embryo of similar age, if transplanted, would develop strictly according to the site to which they were transplanted. Even more remarkable, however, was the fact that the rest of the secondary embryo was made up of tissues of the host. As countless repetitions of this experiment have shown, the transplanted dorsal lip has the effect of organizing the tissues of the host into a second embryo. (See Figure 4–50.) This is how the dorsal lip of the blastopore (the prospective chordamesoderm) came to be called the *organizer*.

4–50 *Experiment showing the activity of the organizer. The dorsal lip of the blastopore from one embryo is grafted onto another embryo* (a). *At gastrulation the grafted tissue moves into the interior of the embryo* (b *and* c) *through the blastopore of the host. Two neural plates are formed* (d), *and a double embryo develops* (e). *In* (f) *you see the structure of the secondary embryo under the yolk of the host embryo. The dark cells are derived from the graft, and the light cells are host material that has been induced to undergo these differentiations.* (*After Waddington, 1966*)

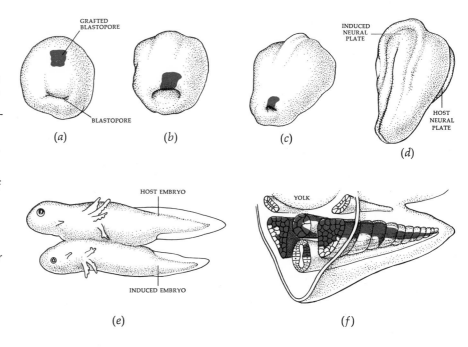

We still do not understand how the dorsal-lip effect is exerted. We do know that the effect of the organizer is not either simple or unique but is rather the first of a series of tissue interactions, such as those described in Chapter 4–3 between dermis and epidermis. As we incompletely understand it, the organizer does not actually *organize*, in the strict sense of the term, but, in effect, sets off a chain of events already prepared in the overlying tissues, just as dermis can interact with epidermis to cause the latter to grow feathers only if the capacity for growing feathers is already present in the epidermis. Yet the chordamesoderm is still frequently referred to as the *primary organizer* since it does begin the sequence of changes that leads to the differentiation of the various embryonic tissues.

In chordate embryos of every species, from the amphioxus to the higher vertebrates, the chordamesoderm serves this same role of primary organizer, inducing differentiation of the overlying ectoderm and also establishing the central axis of development of the embryo.

THE CHICK

We have been progressing by slow stages toward an understanding of the mouse embryo. The next embryo we shall look at, that of the chick, will bring us very close to our objective.

As you will recall, animals finally freed themselves from the water when the reptiles developed the amniote egg. This is a hard-shelled egg in which the embryo floats in a membranous sac that holds its own water supply

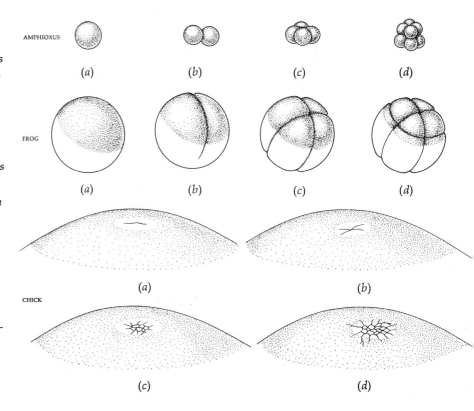

4–51 *Comparative cleavage stages of three types of eggs; the letters from (a) to (d) indicate identical stages. The differences among these early cleavage patterns are determined primarily by the distribution of the yolk in the egg. In the amphioxus, the egg contains a small amount of yolk almost evenly distributed within the cell and the cleavages result in daughter cells that are always about the same size. Eggs which contain a large amount of yolk concentrated in one hemisphere, such as those of the frog, cleave unequally. The first two cleavages split the frog's egg longitudinally to produce four cells shaped like the segments of an orange. The third cleavage (d) separates the yolkier (vegetal) part from the less yolky (animal) part. As you can see, the four animal blastomeres are much smaller than the four vegetal ones. Subsequently, the yolkier cells cleave much more slowly than the less yolky cells, with the result that in the blastula, the dorsal part contains many small cells while the ventral part contains fewer but larger ones. In fish and birds, the cytoplasm and the nucleus of the egg are located on top of a huge ball of yolk. The yolky area does not cleave at all, and only the small cap on top divides into cells. (After Huettner, 1949)*

for the developing organism. The hard-shelled egg of the reptile is the evolutionary predecessor of both the chick egg and the mammalian egg, and we shall look at the chick for the most direct clues to an understanding of the still enigmatic embryo of the mouse.

As we noted previously, the amniote egg represents a radical innovation, but its new features involve not so much the embryo itself as extraembryonic structures. These extraembryonic structures, however—in particular, the large, dense yolk—have some radical effects on development.

The yolk of the amniote egg is very large and dense, so large and dense, in fact, that cleavage never involves the yolk. The only part of the egg that cleaves is a thin layer on top. (See Figure 4–51.) These cleaving cells sit like a cap on the top of the yolk mass, with a slitlike cavity, the *segmentation cavity*, between them and the solid mass of yolk. A blastula of this type is known as a *blastodisk*. Both mouse and man (and all other mammals as well) develop from a blastodisk.

The chick egg is fertilized high in the oviduct. Cleavage takes place as the egg travels down the oviduct, and during this time, the egg is covered with additional layers and membranes contributed by the oviduct. As we saw in Chapter 2–8, these include the albumen, or white, the inner shell membranes, and the hard, calcium-containing outer shell. In this account, we shall be concerned not so much with these structures as with the membranes produced by the embryo itself in the course of its development.

If you break open the fertilized egg when it is first laid, you can see a white disk of cells about 2 millimeters in diameter on top of the yolk. Microscopic examination will show that this disk is made up of a large number of cells (close to 100,000) and that the cells are of two types, with the second type forming a layer below the first. It is debated whether these cells break away from the ones above or move in from around the edges.

If the egg is left intact and incubated, development continues, and within a short period of time, a visible line, the *primitive streak*, appears on the surface of the blastodisk, running from the center of the almost circular disk out to a point on its circumference, as shown in Figure 4–52. The primitive streak is the blastopore of the chick. This is now clear from several lines of evidence: First, studies in which cells of the embryo have been marked with carbon show that cells in the surface of the embryo move toward the area of the streak as it forms. Second, tissue sections taken in the area of the streak show that the streak is the source of invaginating cells, which spread out between the two tissue layers already present to form the mesoderm. Third, by using radioactive labels, investigators have been able to trace cells from the outer surface of the blastodisk through the primitive streak into the mesodermal layer.

If the primitive streak is the blastopore, the notochord should appear just ahead of it. This indeed occurs at a slightly later stage (Figure 4–53), and as the notochord elongates, somites appear on either side. Still later, the head fold and associated neural tube are formed anterior to the primitive streak. As the embryo continues to extend, the primitive streak becomes more and more posterior and less and less conspicuous.

4–52 *Cross-section of a chick embryo at the primitive streak stage.* (*After Huettner, 1949*)

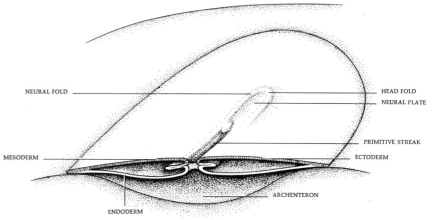

NEURAL FOLD

HEAD FOLD

NEURAL PLATE

PRIMITIVE STREAK

MESODERM

ECTODERM

ARCHENTERON

ENDODERM

525 *Development in Vertebrates: Focus on the Mouse*

4–53 *Dorsal views of a chick embryo, showing development from 14 to 30 hours.*
(Dr. Roberts Rugh, Vertebrate Embryology, Harcourt Brace & Co., 1964)

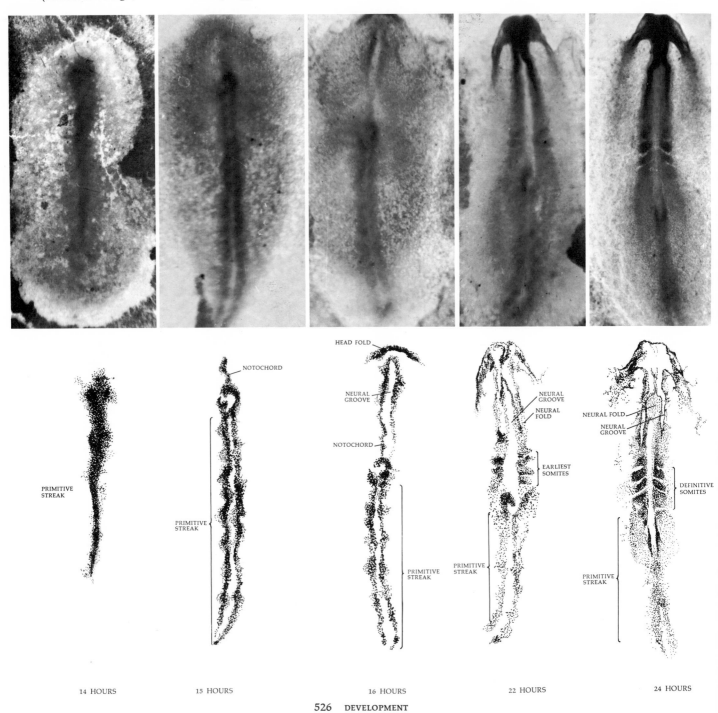

14 HOURS   15 HOURS   16 HOURS   22 HOURS   24 HOURS

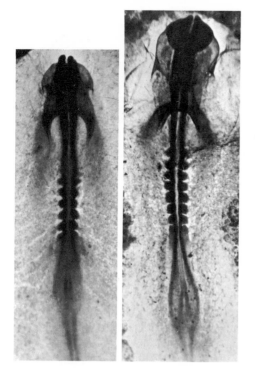

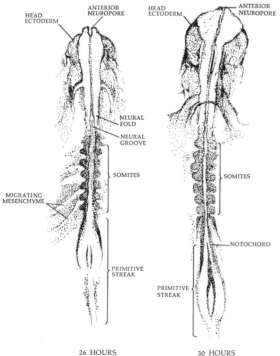

HEAD
ECTODERM

ANTERIOR
NEUROPORE

NEURAL
FOLD

NEURAL
GROOVE

SOMITES

MIGRATING
MESENCHYME

PRIMITIVE
STREAK

26 HOURS

HEAD
ECTODERM

ANTERIOR
NEUROPORE

SOMITES

NOTOCHORD

PRIMITIVE
STREAK

30 HOURS

Extraembryonic Membranes

Apart from recognizing the primitive streak as the equivalent of the blastopore, our interest in the chick centers on the manner in which it forms its extraembryonic membranes. In the formation of these membranes, a crucial role is played by the mesoderm, which has spread out from the primitive streak to all areas of the blastodisk. Along the notochord, the mesoderm is segmentally arranged as somites. From each somite, muscle and part of the skeleton of the embryo will form, and the somatopleure and the splanchnopleure, forming alongside the somites, will line the coelomic cavity. The somatopleure, you will recall, consists of ectoderm and mesoderm, and the splanchnopleure of mesoderm and endoderm. This is the basic body plan of all chordates. In the amniote embryo, however, the somatopleure and the splanchnopleure extend outside of the embryo, spreading beyond its borders to form the extraembryonic membranes.

The yolk sac is formed by splanchnopleure; as you can see in Figure 4–54, the endoderm is on the inner, yolk side of the membrane and the mesoderm is on the outside. An extensive system of blood vessels develops in the mesoderm; through these, the embryo absorbs nutrients from the yolk. Mesoderm and ectoderm grow out together from the periphery of the blastodisk and become elevated over the embryo by a folding process. The folds gradually converge to form two somatopleure membranes. The inner one, the *amnion,* which is ectoderm on the inside and mesoderm on the outside, encloses the embryo in the amniotic cavity. The amnion becomes filled with fluid; this serves to cushion the developing embryo, acting as a shock absorber. The outer, somatopleure membrane, which is mesoderm on the inside and ectoderm on the outside, forms the *chorion,* which surrounds the entire embryo and amniotic cavity. The mesoderm-lined space between the chorion and the amnion is an extension of the coelom and is known as the *extraembryonic coelom.*

The fourth membrane, the *allantois,* is a splanchnopleure membrane which arises as an outgrowth from the rear of the gut and finally extends until it almost fills the extraembryonic coelom. The mesoderm on the outside of the allantoic membrane eventually fuses with the mesoderm on the inside of the chorion to form the three-layered chorioallantoic membrane. This membrane surrounds the albumen and comes to lie just under the porous surface of the egg shell. The primary function of the allantois in the chick is as a receptacle for excretory waste, but the chorioallantoic membrane also serves as the respiratory organ for the embryo through which oxygen diffuses in and carbon dioxide out. (The shell of the chick egg is waterproof but porous enough to permit respiratory exchange.)

As the gut of the chick closes, the embryo becomes more and more cut off from the yolk sac and other membranes, until finally the only connec-

527 *Development in Vertebrates: Focus on the Mouse*

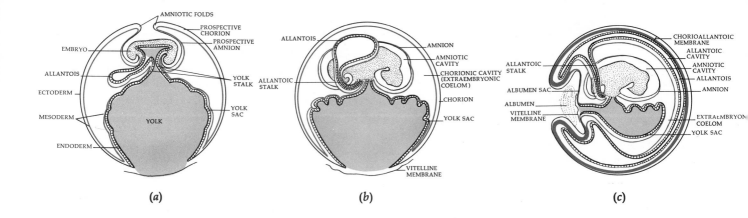

Labels in figure (a):
AMNIOTIC FOLDS
PROSPECTIVE CHORION
PROSPECTIVE AMNION
EMBRYO
ALLANTOIS
ECTODERM
MESODERM
ENDODERM
YOLK
YOLK STALK
ALLANTOIC STALK
YOLK SAC

Labels in figure (b):
ALLANTOIS
AMNION
AMNIOTIC CAVITY
CHORIONIC CAVITY (EXTRAEMBRYONIC COELOM)
CHORION
YOLK SAC
ALLANTOIC STALK
VITELLINE MEMBRANE

Labels in figure (c):
CHORIOALLANTOIC MEMBRANE
ALLANTOIC CAVITY
AMNIOTIC CAVITY
ALLANTOIS
AMNION
ALLANTOIC STALK
ALBUMEN SAC
ALBUMEN
VITELLINE MEMBRANE
EXTRAEMBRYONIC COELOM
YOLK SAC

(a)   (b)   (c)

4–54 *Development of the extraembryonic membranes of the chick. As the embryo develops
from the blastodisk stage, the body folds of
the embryo begin to separate the chick from
the underlying yolk. Extraembryonic splanchnopleure (endoderm plus mesoderm) grows
around and almost completely encloses the
yolk. A second splanchnopleure membrane,
the allantois, arises as an outgrowth of the
rear of the gut. The extraembryonic somatopleure (mesoderm plus ectoderm) is elevated
over the embryo by a folding process during
which the membrane is doubled. When the
folds fuse, two somatopleure membranes are
formed. The inner one is the amnion and the
outer one is the chorion. The mesoderm of
the chorion eventually fuses with that of the
allantois to form the chorioallantoic membrane
which, in the later stages of development, encloses all the other structures. (After Torrey,
1962)*

tion between them consists of two narrow stalks, one leading to the allantois and the other to the yolk sac (see Figure 4–54c). Nutrients and oxygen
are brought into the embryo and waste products and carbon dioxide carried off through the stalk.

While the membranes are forming, the development of the embryo itself
continues. By about 26 hours of incubation, some of the major structures
have begun to take shape. Three bulges have formed at the forward end
of the neural tube. These will become the forebrain, midbrain, and hindbrain. Seven somites can be discerned, the forward part of the gut has become enclosed, major blood vessels have appeared, and the heart has begun to form, beginning as an elongated double tube of mesoderm and
later becoming convoluted to form the complex heart chambers. Even as it
forms, the heart begins to beat. If you open the developing chick egg at
this stage, you can see the earliest contractions of the heart muscle. Posterior to the somites are still the traces of the primitive streak; these will
become obliterated as the embryo continues to develop, extending posteriorly somite by somite.

Interpretation of the Mouse Embryo

Now, with this evolutionary history behind us, let us return to the 7$^{1}/_{2}$-day
mouse embryo and see what we can make of it. First, we shall watch it
through the next 24 hours of development. By the eighth day of gastrulation, one end of the capsule looks like an opaque blister. If we cut through
the blister and take a longitudinal section of it, we find the structure shown
in Figure 4–55d. On the basis of our previous experience, we can immediately recognize the somites. Ahead of them are the heavy neural folds of
the early head region. Extending into the head fold is the foregut, and just
ahead of it are the heart rudiments. Behind the somites is a region of

4–55 *Four stages in the development of a mouse embryo. (a) Early egg-cylinder stage. The inner cell mass has become divided into the rudiment of the embryo proper and the extra-embryonic ectoderm. (b) 5 days 12 hours after fertilization, the amniotic cavity has be-gun to form in both the embryo rudiment and the extraembryonic ectoderm. The latter has produced the ectoplacental cone, which is invading the maternal tissues. (c) The primitive-streak stage, 7 days 6 hours. The cavity inside the egg cylinder is now sub-divided into the amniotic cavity, the extra-embryonic coelom, and the cavity of the ectoplacental cone. (d) Embryo at 7 days 18 hours. The embryo is curved around the amniotic cavity and is concave dorsally. The allantois is growing from the posterior end of the embryo into the extraembryonic cavity. (Biology of the Laboratory Mouse, The Jackson Laboratory, E. L. Green, editor. Copyright 1966 by McGraw-Hill Book Co.)*

unsegmented mesoderm and the base of the notochord. From its position and its relation to the main germ layers, this clearly is the primitive-streak region. What we have discovered is the equivalent of a chick embryo pushed downward into a cup, with the cup, in turn, projecting into a yolk sac. Note that the endoderm-lined yolk sac is continuous anteriorly with the foregut and posteriorly with a small hindgut. Note, further, that the embryo lies in a cavity which is membrane-bound, the inner layer being ectoderm continuous with that of the embryo. By analogy, it is clear that the cavity is the amniotic cavity.

Above the amnion, we find another membrane, the chorion, with meso-derm inside, ectoderm out. The cavity between the two, lined by meso-derm, is the extraembryonic coelom. Extending into the extraembryonic coelom in the hindgut region, as in the chick, is the allantois. In the mouse, the allantois has become entirely mesodermal and is adapted to a new function. It joins with the chorion to produce the embryonic portion of the placenta, the organ through which exchange of nutrients and wastes with the maternal circulation occurs. A special storage organ for wastes is no longer needed since they can be processed through the maternal tissues.

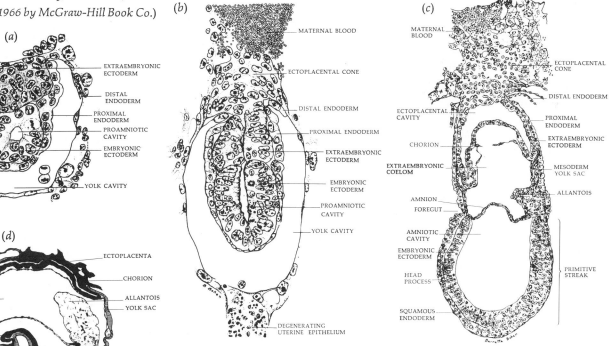

529 *Development in Vertebrates: Focus on the Mouse*

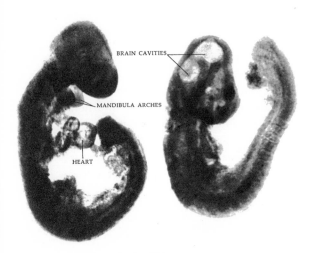

4–56 *Three views of the 9½-day mouse embryo. (Dr. Roberts Rugh, The Mouse, Its Reproduction and Development, Burgess Publishing Co., 1967)*

Having identified the major structures in this embryo, let's try the earlier, 7½-day stage again (Figure 4–55c). Note that the cup-shaped embryonic disk is in the lower half of the cylinder, with about half of its wall in the plane of section composed of primitive streak. Can you see that by pushing the bottom of the cup upward until its inner surface almost touched the amniotic membrane, you could produce a structure that would closely resemble the primitive-streak stage of the chick?

Above the amnion is a mesoderm-lined extraembryonic coelom. The uppermost (and outermost) layer is chorionic ectoderm enclosing the small *ectoplacental cavity.* The largest cavity, within which the whole embryo is contained, is the yolk sac. If you look back to the still earlier stages shown in Figures 4–55a and b, you will see how the yolk sac first forms in the mouse and how much of the early "embryo" is extraembryonic rather than embryonic.

To summarize, the major structures identified in the early somite stage of the chick can be found in the comparable stage of the mouse, although in the mouse the functions, particularly of the extraembryonic structures, are modified. What has happened is actually very simple, though the result looks complicated. Faced with the need to develop in a uterine environment, the mouse—like all mammals—developed its extraembryonic appendages very early to interact with this special environment. The mouse egg, like the eggs of other placental mammals, has no yolk, having no requirement for large amounts of ready reserve, but a yolk sac is still present in the egg. The embryo develops as a small blastodisk on top of the large cavity where the yolk "used to be." Embryo and cavity are surrounded by a single-cell layer, the *trophoblast.* Early in development, the embryo is positioned as though it had suddenly collapsed into the empty cavity, assuming the unusual U shape that is a characteristic only of the mouse and a few other rodents. The mouse embryo develops within the yolk cavity, probably receiving maternal nutrients directly through the chorionic trophoblast. At the time of gastrulation, the spreading mesodermal tissues participate in the formation of additional extraembryonic membranes. These are the same membranes that form in the chick, but all are converted to new functions. The development of the mouse shows its ancestral origins in primitive amniotes but is marvelously adapted to its newer way of life in the uterus.

Quite suddenly, at about the seven-somite stage of development, the embryo begins to rotate. The rotation begins simultaneously at both ends. Looked at from on top, the dorsal surface, the head rotates clockwise while the tail end rotates counterclockwise, each turning a full 180°. As the embryo turns, the neural groove closes. One side of the sheet of endoderm which formed the bottom layer of the embryo flops over on the other sheet as the embryo turns, and the two edges begin to fuse, moving inward from

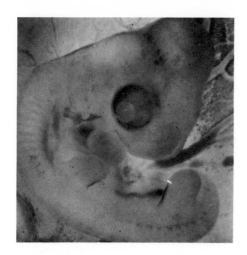

4–57 *A four-day-old chick embryo. By this stage, the chick has most of the major organs. The head, with its bulging brain lobes, makes up almost half the bulk of the embryo. The developing heart can be seen within the curve of the body on the ventral surface. On the dorsal surface, somites are clearly visible. (Dr. John W. Saunders, Jr., Developmental Biology, 5: 147–178, Academic Press, Inc.)*

4–58 *The principal channels of vertebrate development. (After Sussman, 1964)*

both ends, to form the enclosed tubular gut. Similarly, the ectoderm wraps itself around the turning embryo, in much the same way that a blanket folds around a sleeping person turning in his bed. The folding process takes about one day. By the time it is completed, the embryo of the mouse closely resembles other mammalian embryos, including that of man.

Organogenesis

It is convenient to divide embryonic development into three stages: The first stage is *cleavage,* which produces the single-layered blastula. The second stage is *gastrulation,* by which the three-layered embryo is produced. We have now traced these processes in a number of organisms, from sea urchin to mouse. The third major developmental stage is *organogenesis,* the process of more detailed formation of the various organ systems themselves. Organogenesis, as we now understand it, involves interactions of tissues that are brought into contact with one another as a result of the morphogenetic movements that occur at gastrulation. As a result of these tissue interactions, choices between two or more possibilities are made for one or both of the interacting tissues—as in the case of the chick skin, which may produce either feathers, scales, or beak, depending on the influence of the underlying mesoderm. Each choice, once made, may make it possible for the tissue to interact with another tissue, and so on, in a developmental chain reaction, as indicated in Figure 4–58.

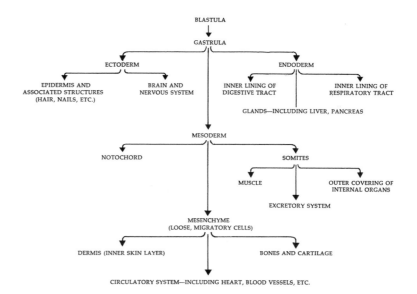

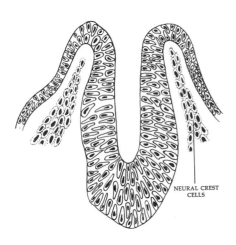

4–59 *During the formation of the neural tube (see Figure 4–48), some of the ectodermal cells at the crests of the neural folds migrate out as the folds come together. Some of these neural-crest cells migrate down toward the spinal cord and aggregate into ganglia. The cells become sensory neurons that send dendrites up to connect with the dorsal part of the spinal cord and axons into the surrounding tissues.*

Organogenesis begins with the interaction of the chordamesoderm and the overlying ectoderm, leading to the formation of the neural tube. This process occurs in the amphioxus, the amphibian, the chick, the mouse, man, and indeed every vertebrate embryo that has ever been studied. If the chordamesoderm is removed, the neural plate will not develop. If the chordamesoderm is suitably transplanted in the early embryo, ectodermal tissue overlying the presumptive notochord will become neural plate.

With this simple example in mind, let us trace the main channels of organ development in vertebrates generally.

ECTODERM

The Central Nervous System

The neural tube stretches out along the dorsal surface, growing and becoming longer and thinner as the embryo increases in size. The cells in the neural tube at first appear to be all alike, but some of them, the future motor neurons, begin to spin out long fibers that extend beyond the neural tube and invade the peripheral organs and tissues. When the neural tube formed, some of the ectodermal cells at the crests of the neural folds were pinched off into the surrounding tissue (see Figure 4–59). Some of these cells from the "neural crest" now migrate into positions around the neural tube and send dendrites to connect with the dorsal part of the tube and axons into the surrounding tissue. (Other neural-crest cells migrate into the epidermis, where they differentiate into the melanocytes.) Schwann cells, which also arise from the neural crest, wrap themselves around the nerve fibers. Meanwhile, mesodermal cells have begun to migrate toward the neural tube and underlying notochord and aggregate around them, differentiating into cartilage and giving rise to the hollow vertebral column. If a portion of neural tube is transplanted to another region of the mesoderm, mesodermal cells will aggregate similarly around it as a result of tissue interaction.

Brain and Eye

The brain begins as three bulges in the foremost part of the neural tube (see Figure 4–60). Almost immediately, two saclike protrusions, the optic vesicles, appear on both sides of the forming brain. These spherical vesicles enlarge and come into contact with the ectoderm, still remaining connected to the neural tube by the narrowing optic stalk. Within this stalk, the optic nerve will develop.

Each step in the development of the eye depends upon interactions of the tissues involved. For instance, suppose that in the early neural-plate stage, we operate on the embryo and remove the mesoderm underlying the area where the optic cup is going to form. Then the optic cup will not develop.

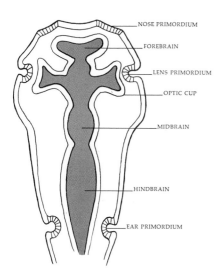

NOSE PRIMORDIUM

FOREBRAIN

LENS PRIMORDIUM

OPTIC CUP

MIDBRAIN

HINDBRAIN

EAR PRIMORDIUM

4–60 *The development of the brain and associated sense organs. At the front end of
the neural tube, local swellings produce
three distinct bulges—the forebrain, the
midbrain, and the hindbrain. The forebrain then bulges laterally, and two
optic vessels appear and develop a cup-
like shape. At the same time, the surface
ectoderm* (the epidermis) *folds inward
to meet the optic cups. These folds are
pinched off and ultimately develop into
eye lenses. The ears and nostrils also
appear at first as epidermal infoldings.
(After Sussman, 1964)*

Or suppose we operate on the embryo at the late neural-plate stage, removing the area of neural plate from which the optic cup would normally
form and transplanting it to another part of the embryo. Then it will develop more or less normally—but only if mesenchyme is present. Thus,
without the presence of the underlying chordamesoderm, development
of the optic cup will not begin. Once it begins, it will continue—but only
under the continued influence of mesenchyme cells.

If the optic cup is cut in half and if one half is transplanted into another
area of mesenchymal tissue while the other half is left in place, each half
develops into a complete small eye! In other words, during its early stages
of development, each part contains the information for the whole, and as
we found by cutting the slime mold, there is some form of communication
among the cells.

When the optic vesicle comes into contact with the inner surface of the
ectoderm, the external surface of the vesicle flattens out and pushes inward. The vesicle thus becomes a double-walled cup. The two walls combine to form the retina, the inner wall forming sensory cells and the
outer wall forming the underlying pigment coat. The rim of the cup becomes the edge of the pupil, and the cavity of the cup is the future posterior
chamber of the eye, which will be filled by the vitreous body. The opening
of the cup is large at first, but the rims bend inward and converge, so that
the opening to the pupil becomes smaller. The rim of the optic cup surrounding the pupil becomes the iris.

At the point where the optic vesicle touches the epidermis, the epidermis
folds in to produce a pocket, which forms a vesicle lying in the opening of
the iris over the pupil, circled by the rim of the optic cup. This epidermis
then differentiates into lens tissue. Other embryonic ectodermal cells are
also able to react to the induction of the optic vesicle, and ectodermal cells
will not normally differentiate into lens without this interaction with the
optic vesicle.

MESODERM

The great bulk of the body tissue of the adult organism is composed of
mesoderm. In the mouse embryo, the two masses of mesodermal tissue lying on either side of the notochord develop into some 65 somites in all. The
inner dorsal portion of the somite, the part lying adjacent to the spinal
cord, is the *myotome,* or muscle segment, from which the voluntary muscles of the body develop. The cells of the myotome elongate longitudinally
and subsequently become differentiated into striated-muscle fibers. In the
amphioxus, the segmented myotome pattern persists in the adult organism,
being well suited to the side-to-side whipping motion by which the amphioxus propels itself through the water. Four-legged locomotion requires
a completely different type of muscular organization, however, and in the

533 *Development in Vertebrates: Focus on the Mouse*

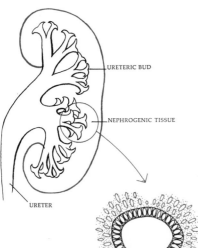

URETERIC BUD

NEPHROGENIC TISSUE

URETER

4–61 *Kidney tubules originate from two different rudimentary tissues, starting at about the eleventh day of embryonic life: These are the nephrogenic tissue, a loose collection of mesodermal cells, and the ureteric bud, a compact tubular tissue also derived from mesoderm. Secretory tubules develop from the nephrogenic tissue, and collecting tubules from the ureteric bud. This development depends on the intimate association of the two tissues; removal of either from the embryo stops the development of the other. (After Arey, 1964)*

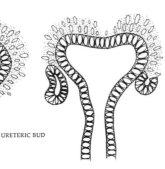

URETERIC BUD

SECRETORY TUBULE

COLLECTING TUBULE

4–62 *The development of a mouse kidney under culture conditions. (a) The ureteric bud and associated kidney-forming cells have been separated from a mouse embryo and placed in a blood clot overlain with a nutrient solution. (b) Two days later, the secretory tubules have begun to form and the ureteric bud has begun to branch into collecting tubes. (c) Four days later. (d) Six days later. If the kidney were still in the mouse, the network of collecting tubes would serve to transport material collected by coiled secretory tubules into the ureter to be voided as urine. (Dr. Clifford Grobstein)*

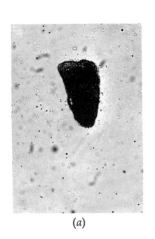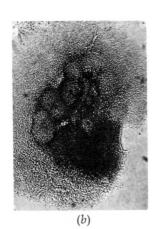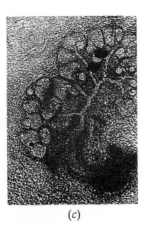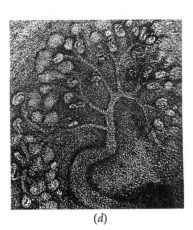

(a) (b) (c) (d)

mouse, as in other terrestrial vertebrates, the myotome pattern is virtually obliterated by the time early development is completed.

Lateral to the somite, which is a solid block of tissue, an opening, the *coelom*, develops in the mesoderm. As we have seen, this divides the lower mesoderm into two sheets of tissue which become the mesodermal components of somatopleure and splanchnopleure. On the periphery, dermis (mesoderm) and epidermis (ectoderm) enter into the tissue interactions described in Chapter 4–3. The splanchnopleure forms the outer layer of the gut, and here mesoderm interacts with endoderm to form the internal organs.

Kidney

The tubules of the vertebrate kidney form from intermediate mesoderm between somite and coelom. The major collecting duct arises very early in the anterior part of the embryo and grows back to the cloaca. A branch of this becomes the ureter, the main excretory duct, which collects the urine from the adult mouse kidney. The branch first appears as a bud which extends posteriorly into the mesenchyme. In this mesenchyme, the filtration units and secretory tubules arise which eventually link up with the ureteric bud to form the functional unit of the kidney. (See Figure 4–61.) If either the ureteric bud or the group of kidney-forming cells is moved, the kidney fails to develop. If either is cultivated in isolation in a nutrient medium, no development occurs, but if the two are cultivated together, tubes and tubules develop as they do in a normal embryo, suggesting an essential interaction. (See Figure 4–62.) This is borne out by experiments with one mutant strain of mice in which the ureter tends to remain short and does not always reach the kidney-forming cells. In these cases, the kidney does not develop. If the ureter just barely makes contact with the mesenchyme, a small kidney develops. Presumably only those cells in close contact with the budding ureter become induced to form kidney tissue.

ENDODERM

The endoderm differentiates into tissues of the respiratory and digestive tracts and a number of other related organs. Early in development, endodermal pouches develop at the anterior end of the endodermal tube and enlarge to touch the ectoderm, which folds inward to meet the pouches, producing a series of grooves on the surface of the embryo. (See Figure 4–63.) Each groove corresponds to an endodermal pouch. In the fish, endoderm and ectoderm fuse and a perforation forms around which gill filaments develop. In the mouse and other terrestrial vertebrates, derivatives of the gill pouches develop into Eustachian tube, tonsils, parathyroid gland, and thymus. Just posterior to the gill pouches, the lungs develop as

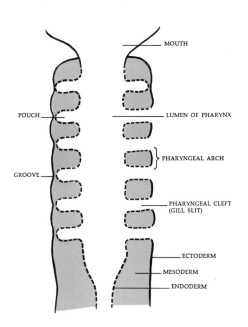

4–63 *Schematic diagram of tissue interactions involving the endoderm. In embryonic stages of all vertebrates, pouches of endoderm which form at the upper end of the endodermal tube, grow toward and meet the ectoderm of the body wall. In the fish, perforations develop, as shown on the right, around which the gills form. In mammals, the pouches develop into thyroid glands, tonsils and other tissues. (After Torrey, 1962)*

MOUTH

POUCH

LUMEN OF PHARYNX

} PHARYNGEAL ARCH

GROOVE

PHARYNGEAL CLEFT (GILL SLIT)

ECTODERM

MESODERM

ENDODERM

similar pouches which form branches as they grow. Further down the endodermal tube, other pouches form which develop into the liver, gall bladder, and pancreas.

By the end of gestation, as a result of this continuing, highly coordinated pattern of tissue interactions—one unfolding after another—the entire organ system of the infant mouse or man is nearly complete. Each event in development is prepared for—exists "preformed"—in the genetic material of the embryo. Each event takes place, however, only if it is evoked by an appropriate stimulus arising in the cytoplasm, in adjacent tissue, or in extracellular chemical substances produced by particular cellular combinations.

4–64 *An advanced-stage human embryo in the uterus.* (*After Torrey, 1962*)

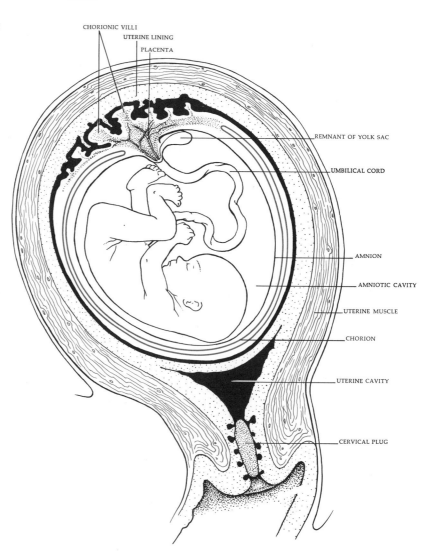

CHORIONIC VILLI
UTERINE LINING
PLACENTA

REMNANT OF YOLK SAC

UMBILICAL CORD

AMNION

AMNIOTIC CAVITY

UTERINE MUSCLE

CHORION

UTERINE CAVITY

CERVICAL PLUG

SUMMARY

In this chapter, we have traced the development of a complex organism, the mouse, which was chosen as an example of a mammalian embryo. *Gametogenesis* is an example of a turnover system, hormone-dependent in both the male and the female. In the male, it operates continuously during adult life, and in the female, it follows the rhythmic cycle dictated by the hormones. In both, the result is the production of highly differentiated cells, the sperm and the egg. At *fertilization*, the genetic material of the sperm is deposited in the egg and development is initiated.

After fertilization, the mouse embryo travels down the oviduct and becomes implanted in the uterus. The uterine tissue, stimulated by the presence of the embryo, swells, increases its blood supply, and encloses the embryo. At $7^1/_2$ days after fertilization, the embryo has developed a number of embryonic and extraembryonic structures. In order to understand these structures, we traced the evolutionary history of several chordate embryos, beginning with the embryo of the amphioxus, progressing to the embryo of the amphibian, and finally arriving at an example of the amniote embryo, the chick. An important factor in embryonic development in amphibians is the dorsal lip of the blastopore, called the *organizer*. In all chordates, the chordamesoderm serves as the primary organizer.

The development of the extraembryonic membranes in the chick is a clue to the organization of amniote embryos in general, including that of the mouse. The mouse embryo is most easily interpreted as a chick embryo which, having "lost" its yolk, develops in the cavity formerly occupied by the yolk.

Embryonic development can be divided into three stages: *Cleavage*, which partitions the egg cells into a large number of undifferentiated cells, is followed by *gastrulation*, in which morphogenetic movements bring tissues into new relationships with one another. As a consequence of these new relationships, a series of tissue interactions begin, the result of which is *organogenesis*, the sequential development of the major organ systems of the animal.

Chapter 4—5

Heredity and Its Modification

As August Weismann formulated the problem quite correctly, there are two principal questions in the field of development: (1) How do all the various cells and tissues and organs of the body become different from one another? They all arise from a single cell—the fertilized egg—yet as the cells divide and assemble, they differentiate into the complex organization of billions of different cells that make up the mature individual. (2) How from this complex adult organism can we once again derive a single line of cells, the germ cells, which will contain the instructions for other complete individuals?

In the preceding chapters, we looked at some aspects of the first question. We examined the interactions of nucleus and cytoplasm and of the various cells and tissues of the body to see how these interactions lead to the emergence of the complex organism. In the light of this discussion, we reexamined Weismann's original proposal that the information in the nucleus was sorted out to the different cells in the course of development. We found that this ingenious and useful hypothesis has not stood the test of time.

In this chapter, we shall look at Weismann's other major hypothesis: that cells containing the hereditary information, or *germ plasm*, as he referred to it, are set aside early in the course of development and that in this way, the long-accumulated store of information is safeguarded for the next generation. We know now that, theoretically speaking, this second hypothesis is no longer necessary. Molecular genetics has shown us that it is possible for somatic cells to carry faithful copies of the entire store of encoded information and pass it on, unaltered and intact, to generations of other cells. Although it has not been proved that this does, in fact, occur,

4–65 *Surface view of an early chick embryo showing the original position of the germ cells which lie in the crescent well beyond the embryo itself. If this germinal crescent is destroyed, no sex cells will be found in the gonads of the chick, although its development will be otherwise normal. (After Swift, 1914)*

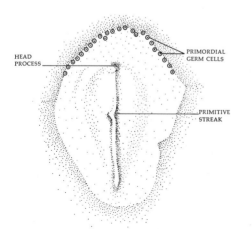

HEAD
PROCESS

PRIMORDIAL
GERM CELLS

PRIMITIVE
STREAK

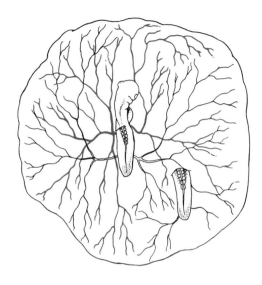

4–66 *An experiment to show that the primordial germ cells of the chick migrate to the gonads by way of the circulatory system. The posterior region of a chick embryo (on the right) was grafted into the extra-embryonic region of another chick embryo. Neither embryo had germ cells in the region of the gonads at the time of the operation. Later the gonads of both embryos became populated with germ cells. If connections are not established between the blood supplies of the host and the graft, germ cells will be found only in the gonads of the host. (After Simon, 1960)*

the evidence points in this direction. For instance, we know (see Chapter 3–4) that, generally speaking, the number of chromosomes and the amount of DNA in the somatic cells of an organism are the same as in any other somatic cell of that organism or of any other member of the species and that the number of chromosomes and the amount of the DNA in the gametes are half of what is in the somatic cells. Apparently, most somatic cells contain all the information necessary for making a whole new organism.

Under these circumstances, it is remarkable to find that Weismann, although wrong in his theory of the segregation of determinants, has proved to be quite right in his proposal that the germ cells, at least in certain organisms, are set aside very early in the course of embryonic development.

Tracking the Germ Cells

Nineteenth century embryologists were in general agreement that the ovaries and testes of the vertebrate animal derive from two elongated ridges, arising in the mesoderm and situated on the roof of the coelom. These are known as the *germinal ridges*. By sectioning and examining embryos of different ages, it is possible to follow the course of development in these tissues. In the frog embryo, in which most of the early work was done, no trace of the germ cells—that is, the cells from which the eggs and sperm are formed—was found in the gonad region until the free-swimming larval stage. When they did appear, these primordial germ cells looked quite different from the somatic elements of the gonad; they were much larger and had different staining qualities. In some specimens, cells of this appearance were also found outside the gonads. So the idea arose that perhaps the germ cells originated elsewhere in the embryo. By examining earlier and earlier specimens, it became possible to track the germ cells back further and further until they could be at least tentatively identified in embryos in the late cleavage stages and in certain areas of the endoderm of slightly older embryos.

Similar findings were made in other species. In the chick, the germ cells were tentatively tracked to endodermal tissue that, at the primitive-streak stage of the chick embryo, lay completely in the extraembryonic tissues which otherwise form the lining of the yolk sac. If this portion of the embryo is excised, development of the embryo continues normally but no germ cells show up in the gonads. Germ cells that do not reach the gonads deteriorate and disappear; moreover, if the germinal ridges are not supplied with germ cells, they cannot complete their normal differentiation and never mature. It has been possible to show that the germ cells of the chick make their long migration to the gonads by way of the circulatory system (see Figure 4–66), although the way in which they recognize their destination once they have arrived is not known.

539 *Heredity and Its Modification*

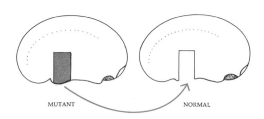

MUTANT   NORMAL

4–67 *A germ-cell transfer operation between a mutant, one-nucleolus embryo of the South African clawed toad Xenopus and a normal embryo of the same species. The tissue (indicated by color) of the mutant embryo that contains the primordial germ cells, is being transplanted into the corresponding position in the normal embryo on the right. This embryo developed into an adult with normal, two-nucleolus somatic cells but with one-nucleolus germ cells. What conclusion can be drawn from this result? (After Blackler and Fischberg, 1961)*

Proving Weismann's Hypothesis: The Independent Origin of the Gametes

The number of original germ cells is very small—only about two dozen at the first stage at which they can be identified in the frog. Yet, at maturity, the female frog lays 2,000 to 3,000 eggs at each mating, and the male produces literally millions of spermatozoa each season. How can we prove that this little cluster of migratory cells that find their way into the gonads are actually the ancestors of all these thousands of gametes? Are all gametes formed from these few primitive germ cells?

This problem has now been solved, first, as a result of a fortuitous finding by workers at Oxford University, and second, and more important, through the design of experiments to exploit the potential value of the observation. The investigators at Oxford were studying methods of producing polyploids—animals with extra sets of chromosomes—in *Xenopus*, the South African clawed toad, and so were taking cell samples from a number of animals for the purpose of chromosome counts. They were using a convenient shortcut. In each haploid set of chromosomes, there is a chromosome which contains a region known as the *nucleolus organizer*. This region, as its name implies, is concerned with the formation of the nucleolus. (As you may recall, the nucleoli disappear at the beginning of mitosis and reform at telophase.) Therefore, in *Xenopus*, for every diploid ($2n$) set of chromosomes, two nucleoli will be present, and there will be three in a triploid cell, four in a tetraploid, and so on. For this reason, the investigators were able to obtain chromosome counts simply by counting the nucleoli in each cell sample.

In the course of these routine studies, one of the laboratory workers found that the somatic cells from one tadpole each contained only one nucleolus! Although the chromosome count showed two sets of chromosomes, only one nucleolus per cell was found in all the cell samples tested. The tadpole, which proved to be a female, was raised to maturity and mated. When the cells of her progeny were analyzed, it could be seen immediately that her one-nucleolus condition was an hereditary trait, a mutation in the nucleolus organizer on one of the two chromosomes that carried it.

In this female, two types of egg cells were formed in the course of reduction division, one with and one without the nucleolus organizers. When she was mated with a normal male, what types of zygotes were formed, in terms of the nucleolus organizer? Check your answer against the results shown in Table 4–1.

Suppose the mutant female had been bred to a one-nucleolus individual like herself, what would be the distribution of the mutations among the progeny?

By this time, largely as a result of the work of this group of investigators, the portion of the endoderm in which the germ cells developed had

Table 4–1 *Gametes and Offspring from a Cross between a Female with One Nucleolus and a Male with Two Nucleoli (N = Nucleolus)*

		♂	
		1N	1N
	1N	2N	2N
♀			
	0N	1N	1N

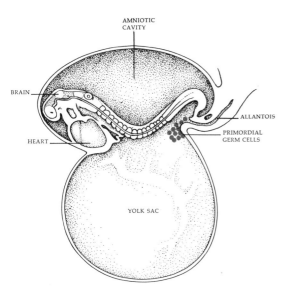

4–68 *An early human embryo (about four weeks), showing the original position of the primordial germ cells. (After Witschi, 1948)*

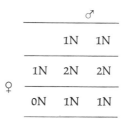

been quite precisely identified. This area of presumptive germ cells was removed from a mutant one-nucleolus embryo and transplanted to the corresponding region of a normal embryo. This embryo matured to produce an adult that had somatic cells with two nucleoli but, as breeding tests showed, germ cells with only one nucleolus. Here, finally, was clear proof of the totally independent origin of the germ-cell line.

Examination of human embryos has revealed a similar small group of cells which can be found, as in the chick, in the extraembryonic endoderm. Experiments with human embryos are not possible, but studies of man's useful embryological stand-in, the mouse, have revealed cells of similar appearance that can be found in a similar location. In the mouse, if all of these germ cells are destroyed, no gametes are ever produced.

Why are the germ cells set in reserve so early in the life of the organism? We no longer believe Weismann's original hypothesis that nuclear determinants are lost from other cells in the course of development (though no one has definitely proved this to be wrong). Alternatively, we may speculate that perhaps many "errors" occur in the copying process which accompanies the mitotic division of somatic cells. Such errors might be inconsequential in a somatic cell but crucial in a germ cell, which needs to supply information for the entire organism. Perhaps the genetic material becomes altered by the influences of certain cytoplasms. Or it may be that this setting-aside process is merely a reflection of history, like the yolk sac or gill slits of the mammalian embryo. As we noticed when we were tracing the early evolutionary development of the volvocines (Chapter 2–3), the first function taken over by specialized cells (or, to put the same thing differently, the first function taken away from the other somatic cells) appears to be that of reproduction. In any case, both evolutionary history and the history of development of the vertebrate embryo lead one to speculate that perhaps the organism's first concern is with its ability to pass its genetic endowment on intact to the next generation.

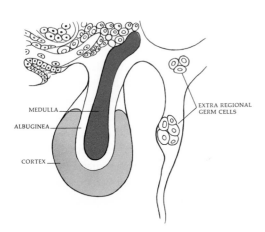

MEDULLA

ALBUGINEA

CORTEX

EXTRA REGIONAL
GERM CELLS

4–69 *In frogs and the higher vertebrates (in-cluding man), the sex glands are neither male nor female during the early stages of development of the embryo. Shown here is the composition of the early, indifferent sex gland. It is composed of two main types of tissue: the cortex and the medulla. In between them lies a thin layer of mesenchyme, the* albuginea. *Germ cells that do not find their way to cortex or medulla remain sexually undifferentiated.* (*After Witschi, 1956*)

How Genetic Information Becomes Effective: Sex Determination

This biological emphasis on the importance to the organism of preserving the hereditary information brings us again to the question of exactly what is inherited. We explored this question previously from the point of view of the molecular biologist and found that we do not inherit blue or brown eyes as such, or a prominent jaw or a weak one, or a tendency to be tall or short; we inherit only a very specific sequence of nucleotides. Under particular circumstances, this sequence of nucleotides can become translated to messenger RNA and from messenger RNA to a particular sequence of amino acids, forming a protein. Depending on the sequence of amino acids (the primary structure of the protein), the conditions of pH and temperature, and the presence of other molecules, the protein will then spontaneously (that is, without any further genetic instructions) assume other configurations and enter into combinations with other molecules. Any "inherited trait" is the end product of many such reactions, perhaps thousands.

Now let us look at this question from the viewpoint of the embryologist, from the outside in, so to speak, taking what might seem to be a simple characteristic: sex. It has long been common knowledge among dairymen that if twin calves of opposite sexes are born, the female calf is often sterile. Such calves are commonly called *freemartins*. In the early twentieth century, a series of scientific investigations was made of this phenomenon, "one of nature's experiments," as it was termed in one of the reports. These investigations disclosed that the females become sterile only when the blood vessels of the extraembryonic tissues of the twin embryos fuse together. Apparently, some substance from the male calf reaches the female through the bloodstream and acts as an antagonist to normal ovarian development.

The discovery that hormonelike substances in an embryo may affect the course of sex differentiation stimulated studies in amphibians, animals more convenient to handle in the laboratory. Here it was found that nature had undertaken some even livelier "experiments." In the amphibian, as in other vertebrates, sex is determined by the genetic constitution of the animal; in frogs of the genus *Rana*, the male is XY, the female XX, while the reverse is true in toads of the genus *Xenopus*. A male, according to the common working definition, has male sex organs, produces sperm, and has male secondary characteristics, including, in the frog, a particular kind of mating call, a characteristic behavior pattern, and a fleshy thumb pad with which it grasps the female during oviposition.

At the tadpole stage of amphibian development, however, none of the phenotypic characteristics associated with maleness (nor any of those associated with femaleness, either) can be detected. The sex glands themselves are indifferent, that is, neither male nor female, up to an advanced

4–70 *The early, indifferent sex gland may*
develop into (a) *a testis or* (b) *an ovary.*
In the testis, the germ cells migrate to
the medullary tissue and the cordlike
tissue of the medulla (shown in color)
predominates in development. In the
ovary, the sex cells lodge in the cortex
which becomes the dominant tissue. If
neither tissue becomes clearly domi-
nant (c), *the animal is an hermaphro-*
dite. (After Witschi, 1956)

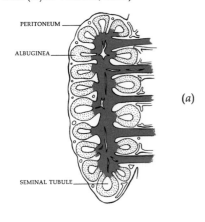

PERITONEUM

ALBUGINEA

(a)

SEMINAL TUBULE

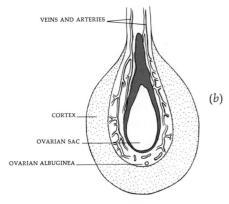

VEINS AND ARTERIES

(b)

CORTEX

OVARIAN SAC

OVARIAN ALBUGINEA

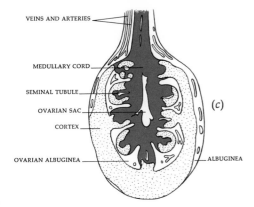

VEINS AND ARTERIES

MEDULLARY CORD

SEMINAL TUBULE

OVARIAN SAC

(c)

CORTEX

OVARIAN ALBUGINEA   ALBUGINEA

larval stage. Emil Witschi, who has been the leading figure in these investigations, has shown that the *indifferent gland* is composed of two main
types of tissue, both of mesodermal origin: the cortex (the outer part of the
gland) and the medulla (the central tissue). Between the cortex and medulla are loose mesenchyme cells, within which, in the course of development, form the blood vessels that supply the gonad. The third major component of the gonad, the germ cells, migrate into the indifferent gland and
lodge in the cortex. (See Figure 4–69.)

During larval development, the process of sex determination begins.
(See Figure 4–70.) In the future female, the cortex predominates, thickening by the rapid multiplication of the germ cells. As they multiply, the
germ cells differentiate into oogonia and oocytes. Fluid-filled cavities develop in the medulla. These are the ovarian sacs, which inflate and push
the blood vessels of the gonad cavity toward the cortex, close to the area
where the eggs will ripen. In the future male, the medulla takes the dominant role in development. The medulla, which is composed of cordlike
strands of tissue, starts massive growth. The germ cells, originally lodged
in the cortical tissue, are attracted by the thickening medullary cords and
begin to migrate across the gonad cavity into the medulla. As the medulla
grows larger, the cortex becomes reduced to a thin membrane, which
forms the cover of the gland. The blood vessels of the former gonad cavity
end up directly beneath this membrane. As the cords of the medulla develop into seminiferous tubules, the germ cells become spermatogonia.
Collecting and efferent ductules extending from the medulla toward the
kidney establish a connection with the duct leading to the cloaca. This duct
system will be completed by the time the male reaches maturity. The rudiments of the oviducts, which are present in newly metamorphosed frogs
of both sexes, develop further only in the females.

In frogs, hermaphrodites occur relatively frequently by the development of both cortex and medulla, with the development of the cortex beginning first. In a few cases, it has been possible, by artificial insemination,
to fertilize the eggs with the sperm of the same individual. The young produced by such self-fertilization are perfectly normal.

The hermaphroditic frogs are genetically female. We know this from
two lines of evidence: (1) The somatic cells are *XX*, which as you recall, is
the chromosome-distribution characteristic of females in the *Rana* species. (2) Offspring produced by crossing hermaphrodites are always female. (Can you explain why? What would be the results of crossing normal
male and normal female frogs with a hermaphrodite?) Remarkably, these
hermaphrodites, although genetic females, are capable of producing not
only eggs but also normal, functional sperm cells!

What then exactly is a female? Witschi has shown that if you take a
genetically male embryo before the tadpole stage and inhibit development

in or destroy the medulla of the gonad, the cortex will develop and the genetic male will become a functional female. Conversely, if the cortex of the genetic female is eliminated, the medullary tissue will develop and typical testes will form. In other words, sex differentiation is the result of the dominance of one system over another. The dominant system, either cortex or medulla, influences the undifferentiated germ cells, stimulating their development as egg cells or spermatozoa, and concomitantly suppresses the development of the other tissue. If salamander embryos are joined together by their vascular systems—like the twin calves described previously—the female will become masculinized if the embryos are approximately the same size, but a larger female can feminize a male embryo under these same conditions.

In frogs, administration of small amounts of testosterone to genetic females can also produce sex reversal; as little as 0.01 microgram in a quart of aquarium water will masculinize all the female frogs. In the toad *Xenopus*, in which the male is XX and the female XY, the genetic male can be induced to develop as a female by the addition of estrogens to the water of the aquarium. In *Bufo*, another genus of toads, removal of the testes of the adult male, it has been shown, results in growth of rudimentary cortical lobes, which then become functional ovaries.

According to Witschi's interpretation, certain somatic cells of the cortex and others of the medulla produce inductive substances which stimulate the germ cells to develop either as eggs or as sperm. These substances, or others produced by the cortex and medulla, antagonize one another. If the genetically dominant tissue is removed or suppressed by hormonal or physical means, the other tissue will then grow. Once the dominant tissue, either of cortex or of medulla, has begun to mature, specialized cells begin to produce the appropriate sex hormone, which further suppresses the other tissue and which stimulates the development of the secondary sex characteristics.

Could such experiments be carried out in human beings? The answer is, theoretically, yes. In the human embryo, the structures that will form the future sex glands remain indifferent—that is, undifferentiated as to sex—until up to the age of about two months. Partial suppression of normal sexual development has now been seen in a number of mammalian species besides the calf in which it was first observed, although complete sex reversal, as in amphibians, has not been achieved.

The chief interest of these studies from the point of view of the developmental biologist is that they serve to emphasize the fact that the genetic information becomes effective only at a certain stage in the course of development and is itself not unalterable. What is transmitted from generation to generation is not sex type but a *bias* as to sex. Not only is this of theoretical interest, but it may be of future practical importance in the control of some hereditary diseases. Take even the most clear-cut example of an inherited defect—sickle-cell anemia, for example. In this disease, as we have seen, the inherited defect can be traced directly to a "typographical error" in the genetic code. But this "error" does not affect the viability of the germ cell; it is not, in fact, expressed until relatively late in development, when the red blood cells begin to differentiate and to produce hemoglobin. The first symptoms do not begin to appear until well after birth, and often the organism and its environment—that is, the child, the family, and the community—do not feel the full effects for a number of years. Furthermore, whether or not the gene for sickle-cell hemoglobin is "bad" or "good," in terms of the survival of the organism, depends entirely on another factor—the presence or absence of the same mutation on the homologous chromosome. So, from this point of view, inheritance is not an event but a continuing process, dependent on the translation of the hereditary instructions and on the environment in which they appear. This leads to the quite realistic hope that it will eventually be possible to interfere in constructive ways with the expression of at least some harmful genetic misfunctions and so eliminate some instances of inherited disease.

SUMMARY

In this chapter, we examined two questions: (1) the derivation of the germ cells, the carriers of the genetic information, and (2) the process by which the genetic information becomes effective in the expression of one genetic characteristic, sex. Experiments have demonstrated quite conclusively that the germ cells derive from a small group of cells which are set aside very early in embryonic development and which later migrate into the developing gonads and there differentiate into eggs or sperm.

Studies in amphibians show that sex is determined by the differentiation of the gonads, which are initially "indifferent," or undetermined, in the course of maturation of the animal. During this maturation process, it is possible to interfere in the normal course of development and to produce sex inversions, resulting in animals that, although genetically of one sex, are anatomically and functionally of the opposite sex. These studies serve to emphasize that the genetic information is in itself not final but becomes effective only in the course of development. This concept is considered important because it implies that it may be possible to control in an analogous way some genetically caused diseases.

SUGGESTIONS FOR FURTHER READING

BALINSKY, B. I.: *An Introduction to Embryology*, 2d ed., W. B. Saunders Company, Philadelphia, 1965.

An excellent general text.

BARTH, L. J.: *Development: Selected Topics*, Addison-Wesley Publishing Company, Inc., Reading, Mass., 1964.*

A lively, thought-provoking introduction to classical questions on the relationship between genetics and evolution.

BONNER, J. T.: *Morphogenesis: An Essay on Development*, Atheneum Publishers, New York, 1963.*

An engagingly written introduction to the overall concepts of development— patterns of growth, morphogenetic movements, polarity, and symmetry—as illustrated primarily in invertebrates.

EBERT, JAMES D.: *Interacting Systems in Development*, Holt, Rinehart and Winston, Inc., New York, 1965.*

A short text with special emphasis on new developments in the field.

HAY, ELIZABETH D.: *Regeneration*, Holt, Rinehart and Winston, Inc., New York, 1966.

A short, up-to-date review of regeneration in animals from protozoans to mammals. Intended for the advanced student, but accessible to the interested newcomer.

MOORE, JOHN A.: *Heredity and Development*, Oxford University Press, London, 1963.*

A highly readable presentation of both classical and molecular genetics, with a detailed description of development in the frog.

SPEMANN, HANS: *Embryonic Development and Induction*, Hafner Publishing Co., New York, 1938.

Spemann was unquestionably the most brilliant experimenter in the history of embryology; this is a first-hand account of his work.

SUSSMAN, MAURICE: *Animal Growth and Development*, 2nd ed., Prentice-Hall, Inc., Englewood Cliffs, N.J., 1964.*

A short general text, broad in scope, designed particularly for the beginning student.

* Available in paperback.

BEHAVIOR

(Courtesy of Wisconsin Regional Primate Research Center)

SECTION 5

BEHAVIOR

Introduction

The study of animal behavior, which is now flourishing in this country and in Europe, has its historical origins in two different and quite widely separated sources. What is generally referred to as the *American School* began about 1888, when Jacques Loeb set out on a series of studies in which he attempted to describe all behavior in physical and chemical terms. Loeb worked on the assumption that all motions of an animal were, in his words, "determined by internal or external forces." Figure 5–1 shows the movement of a wood louse (also known as the pill bug), which is positively phototactic, meaning that it turns toward the light. Loeb explained such movements in the following way:

> Normally the processes inducing locomotion are equal in both halves of the central nervous system, and the tension of the symmetrical muscles being equal, the animal moves as in a straight line. If, however, the velocity of chemical reactions in one side of the body, e.g., in one eye of the insect, is increased, the physiological symmetry of both sides of the brain and, as a consequence, the equality of tension of the symmetrical muscles no longer exist. The animal will thus be compelled to change the direction of its motion. . . . The conduct of animals consists of forced movements.

The modern leader of the American behaviorist school is B. F. Skinner, an experimental psychologist at Harvard University, who has trained hundreds of individual animals, largely rats and pigeons, to carry out a variety of unfamiliar tasks. Skinner, like Loeb, has been interested in studying *principles* of behavior rather than the animal's behavior in nature, and he has been particularly concerned with learning. His work may be considered analogous to that of Mendel, who used the garden pea, or of Morgan, who worked exclusively with *Drosophila* in order to develop general principles of genetics. On the basis of his studies, Skinner has worked out theories of learning which are now widely applied in teaching, particularly in programmed teaching; the chief principle involved is that of immediate reward, or *reinforcement*.

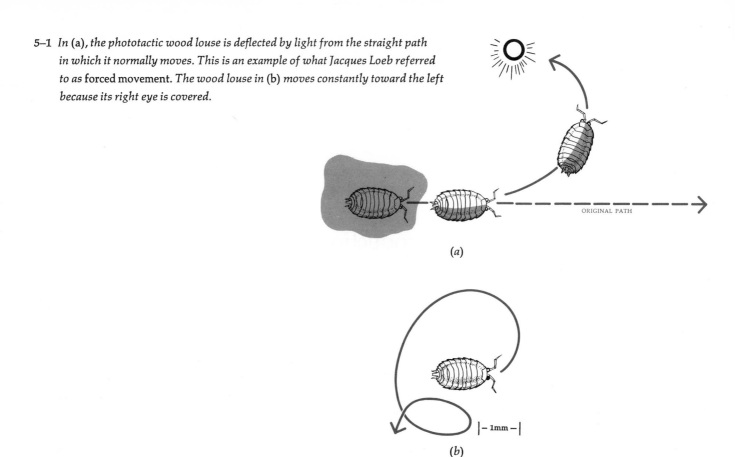

5–1 *In* (a), *the phototactic wood louse is deflected by light from the straight path in which it normally moves. This is an example of what Jacques Loeb referred to as* forced *movement. The wood louse in* (b) *moves constantly toward the left because its right eye is covered.*

ORIGINAL PATH

(a)

|– 1mm –|

(b)

The other school of behavioral studies, the so-called *European School,* is best represented by the Austrian zoologist Konrad Lorenz and his former student, Niko Tinbergen. Lorenz, Tinbergen, and their followers call themselves *ethologists*—from the Greek word *ethos,* meaning "character" or "custom"—and ethology has come to mean the science of behavioral characteristics of species. (Ethology receives more attention in the chapters that follow than the work of the American psychologists because ethology is more directly related to biology.)

The ethologists are interested in analyzing patterns of instinctive behavior in particular groups of organisms and in tracing such patterns among related species, examining the "morphology" of behavior in much the same way a comparative anatomist examines the morphology of a physical structure. They are concerned not so much with modifications of behavior produced by learning as with modifications produced by evolution.

A large part of the work of the ethologists has been performed with fish and birds since these animals have complex patterns of genetically determined behavior which lend themselves well to this type of study. While the work of the psychologists of the American School is of necessity carried out largely in the laboratory, where experimental variables can be controlled, the ethologists seek to watch animal behavior in its natural environment. For this reason, the observations of the ethologists have tended to be descriptive and difficult to confirm, as compared with the precise "learning curves" and other mathematical techniques of the psychologists—although in recent years the ethologists have begun to work out many ingenious new experimental methods for testing some of their theories.

A chief source of disagreement between the ethologists and the psychologists has been the relative importance of "instinct" and "learning" and the difficulties that are involved in defining these two concepts. The conflict was made all the harder to resolve by the fact that the two groups were studying different types of organisms and using different methods. Actually, in the light of more recent knowledge, it can be seen that many of their observations are complementary.

A third group which is making important contributions to the study of animal behavior are the neurophysiologists. Although the oversimplified concepts of "forced motions" have long since been abandoned, the neurophysiologists seek, like Loeb, to find physicochemical bases for behavior.

At the present stage of knowledge, neurophysiology cannot "explain" behavior any more than Loeb's concept of forced movements could account for more than a small fraction of the observable activities of an animal. On the other hand, as the science of behavior advances, it is clear that a greater understanding of underlying physical and chemical forces is going to do more and more to illuminate the meaning of such presently ill-defined terms as "instinct" and "learning." For this reason, the first three chapters of this section describe briefly what is known about the neurophysiological equipment of some selected animals along with examples of their behavior.

Beginnings of Behavior; The Lower Invertebrates

The Basic Responses of Living Creatures

Four important components of the behavior of all living creatures are irritability, habituation, avoidance, and learning. Since these properties are exhibited in their most basic forms in the responses of the one-celled animals, let us look first at behavior in some Protozoa.

IRRITABILITY AND HABITUATION: AMOEBA

When something edible, an algal cell or a fellow protozoan, is in the vicinity of an amoeba, the amoeba can sense it at some distance, at least the length of its own body away. Then it sends out a pseudopodium that is shaped quite specifically for its intended victim. A fine pincerlike projection will be formed for a small, quiet morsel; much stronger and more massive pseudopodia will reach for a large ciliate or vigorously moving object. The stimulation of the amoeba may be caused by chemical changes produced in the water by the prey or by motion disturbing the water currents, or both. If the intended victim moves away, the amoeba will remain in pursuit so long as it is close enough to the prey to receive stimuli from it. As you can see in Figure 5–2, this may involve behavior patterns which look quite complex. The capacity to respond to stimulus is known as *irritability*. Irritability is one of the important components of behavior and is a general property of all living systems.

Amoebas also react to light. If you shine a bright pinpoint of light on the advancing pseudopodium of an amoeba, the pseudopodium withdraws. If the entire body of the amoeba is exposed to bright light, it contracts suddenly and will even extrude any half-eaten food. As you know, the amoeba has no special sensory organelles, and this behavior is most easily ex-

5–2 *An amoeba pursues its prey. The initial stimulus produced by the "prey"— a fragment of hydra tentacle—induces pseudopodia from the amoeba and causes the amoeba to move toward the hydra fragment. As the piece of tentacle is moved away, the amoeba moves after it and will remain in pursuit so long as the prey is close enough to continue the stimulus. Why is this an example of irritability? (Dr. K. W. Jeon)*

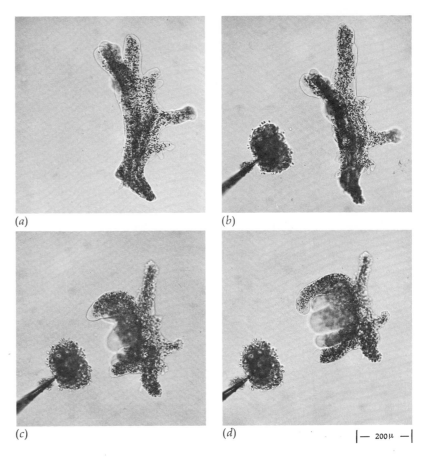

(a)

(b)

(c)

(d)

|— 200μ —|

plained as a direct chemical response to light. Yet, if a light from which it cannot escape is shone from above, the amoeba, after a few moments' hesitation, will resume its normal activities. This latter response, by which the stimulus comes to be ignored and a previous behavior pattern restored, is known as *habituation*. Habituation is a property not shared by nonliving systems. Can you see why it is important as a factor in animal behavior and how the concept of habituation helps to guide us toward a distinction between the behavior of molecules and the behavior of living creatures?

AVOIDANCE: PARAMECIUM

Paramecia show behavior that appears more complex than that of amoebas but is just as simple in principle. They are responsive to a variety of stimuli, including very subtle changes in temperature and chemistry that can be detected by man only by finely calibrated instruments. But the paramecia respond to this variety of stimuli by fixed, or stereotyped movements of avoidance.

553   *Beginnings of Behavior; The Lower Invertebrates*

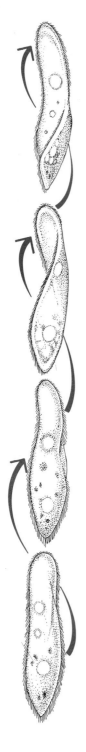

5–3 *Because of the oblique beat of its body cilia, the paramecium rotates as it swims forward.*

As shown in Figure 5–3, the paramecium rotates as it swims forward because of the oblique beat of its body cilia, and it does not swim quite in a straight line because the cilia around the "mouth," or cytostome, beat more strongly than do the body cilia. As a result, the paramecium swerves back and forth like a rowboat in which the oarsman pulls strongly first on one oar and then on the other; and since the animal rotates, the cytostome is alternately on one side and then on the other. The strongly beating cilia around the cytostome create currents which constantly bring to the oral zone, which seems to be the testing area, a sample of the water. In this way, the paramecium is continuously exploring the environment that lies ahead, shifting and sampling. This can be demonstrated by the following experiment: Put a very small drop of India ink, which separates into tiny black particles, on a slide with paramecia. As an animal approaches the drop, a thin stream of particles will begin moving toward it, collecting around the cytostome. (See Figure 5–4.)

In general, *Paramecium* responds to changes in its environment by avoidance reactions. If it receives a negative stimulus, it turns away. If it turns, it always turns in the same direction, to its left, which is the side away from the cytostome; this occurs because of the relaxation of the beat of the body cilia. It does not matter which side the stimulus comes from. If the microscopist takes a blunt needle and jabs a paramecium on the aboral side, it still turns toward that side; and once it has turned, it will continue in this new direction indefinitely.

If the stimulus is a weak one, such as a slight and unfavorable temperature drop in the water ahead, a paramecium, on receiving a sample of the cool water, will turn slightly in its path. As shown in Figure 5–5, if the negative stimulus is powerful, such as a poisonous chemical, the paramecium will stop short, reverse its ciliary beat and back up, turn toward the aboral side about 30°, and then start forward again, testing. If necessary, it will repeat this performance. Under a strong negative stimulus, it will turn a full 360° and will continue to turn until an avenue of escape is found. Paramecia find their way around solid objects in the same way.

The end result of this, of course, is about the same as if the animal were "attracted" to a favorable situation. For example, paramecia are extremely temperature-sensitive. If you place the animals in a culture dish that can be made warmer at one end than another, you will find, by trying different combinations of temperatures, that they will tend to congregate in water that is about 80°F (27°C). If you place the animals on a slide with water that is below 27°C and then warm one little portion of it gently (you can do this by placing a hot needle on the cover slip), the animals will all gather in this warm spot. They reach it by chance as they move about through the water. But once they get into it, they literally cannot get out again, since as soon as they reach the edge of it, they receive a

5–4 *A paramecium samples a drop of India ink. Currents created by the strongly beating cilia draw particles of the ink toward the animal's cytostome.*

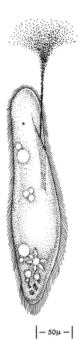

|— 50µ —|

sample of cooler water, which will turn them right back again. Similarly, on a slide that contains water that is too hot, paramecia will trap themselves in an area that has been cooled slightly, even by only a few degrees.

They have also been shown to congregate in the same way in a spot that is slightly acid, by avoiding the neutral or alkaline areas. Bacteria, which are a primary food of paramecia, create a slightly acid environment by their metabolism, and indeed, the paramecium itself creates a slightly acid environment by giving off carbon dioxide; so their avoidance of neutral or alkaline areas enhances the tendency of the animals to group together and also to gather where there is food. This tendency is strengthened further by the fact that paramecia are more likely to cling to some other object—such as the leaf or stalk of a plant, a pile of debris, or even a shred of filter paper—if they are in a slightly acid medium.

As described here, the behavior of a paramecium, helpless to escape from a drop of warm water or forced to cling by the presence of carbon dioxide, seems very unlifelike. Yet, as one watches the animal negotiating the changes in its environment, its actions seem purposeful. Both of these impressions are true. The individual paramecium has no choice as to its behavior, but the behavior of paramecia in general is a result of millions of years of choice, the choice by natural selection. Animal behavior is adaptive. It promotes survival—if not of the individual, at least of the population as a whole. The question "Why does the animal behave as it does?" is a useful one for a behavioral scientist to ask, but answers to such questions must be carefully framed to avoid attributing to animals emotions and intentions for which there is no evidence.

5–5 *Avoidance behavior in the paramecium is exemplified by its actions in relation to a drop of poisonous chemical. When it senses the negative stimulus, it stops short and backs up, turns 30°, and starts forward again in a new direction.*

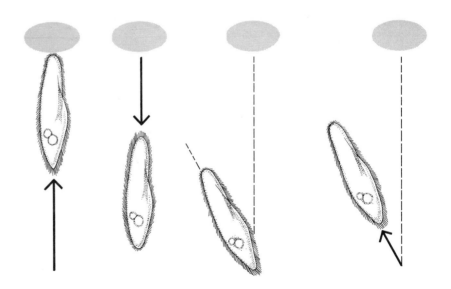

If you poke a stentor with a needle, it will give a standard avoidance response of the sort described in *Paramecium*—bending, always toward the aboral side, regardless of where the poke comes from. If the stentor is poked repeatedly, it will contract its body down to the tailpole and then extend again. If the poking continues, the stentor will probably contract again, perhaps several times, but then either it will ignore the jabbings and continue feeding, which it cannot do in the contracted position, or it will detach itself and swim away. Whether or not it leaves appears to depend at least to some extent on the richness of the food supply.

Similarly, if a stentor is annoyed—by a cloud of ink particles, for instance—it will at first bend, perhaps repeatedly, to the aboral side. (See Figure 5–6.) If the offensive stimulus continues, the stentor will reverse its cilia and start blowing the particles away. If bending and blowing are not successful, it contracts and waits a minute before it stretches forth again. Once it has contracted, it does not bend or blow again, but it may draw back several times and reach out again to sample the water before it withdraws. Again, the length of time that it tolerates the noxious stimulus depends on whether or not its site of attachment had previously proved to be a good feeding area. In short, these reactions of *Stentor* are based at least to some degree on previous experience and so represent a simple form of *learning*. Learning can be defined as the process by which experience produces adaptive change in *individual* behavior. It will be discussed in more detail in Chapter 5–4.

5–6 *A stentor reacts to a cloud of ink particles. It first avoids the particles by bending away from them. If the stimulus continues, it reverses its cilia and tries to blow the particles away. If this is not successful, it contracts, waits a minute, and then expands again after which it may swim away. Stentor has a maximum memory span of one-half minute, and if the experiment is redone within that time, the stentor will not repeat the whole procedure but will simply swim away. Why does this behavior pattern exemplify a form of* learning?

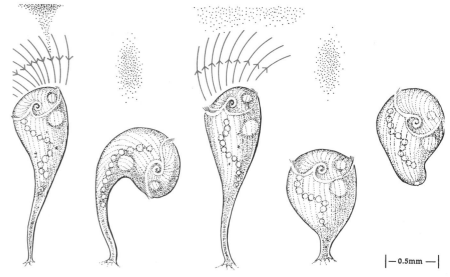

| — 0.5mm — |

Some interesting recent experiments have been performed on learning in paramecia. If a clean platinum wire is lowered repeatedly into the center of a culture of Paramecium aurelia, the paramecia typically avoid the wire. If the wire is lightly baited with bacteria before it is dipped into the culture, the paramecia tend to approach the wire and cling to it. If after 15 such "training trials," a clean wire is lowered into the same culture (even as long as 10 to 12 hours afterwards), the paramecia will approach and cling to the bare wire. In general, the more training trials the culture is given—that is, the more times it is exposed to the baited wire—the greater the number of paramecia that will be found clinging to the bare wire.

On the basis of what you know about the behavior of paramecia, can you criticize this experiment? Remember that the baited wire and the clean wire were placed in the middle of the culture. What effects would this have on the pH of the water in this area? How do such changes in the pH affect the behavior of paramecia? How would you redesign such an experiment?

The Development of the Nerve System

SPECIALIZED NERVE CELLS: HYDRAS

The simplest type of specialized nerve cell is the *independent effector*. An example is the epitheliomuscular cell, found in the lower invertebrates. Like *Stentor*, such a cell contains small muscle fibrils and myonemes and is sensitive to touch; when it is stimulated, it contracts. In sponges, epitheliomuscular cells can be found scattered over the surface of the animal. Contraction of these cells in response to stimuli constitutes the range of behavior of the sponge, which is thus simpler in this respect than many of the Protozoa. This level of activity is well suited to the sponge, however, which, as we have noted previously, is sessile and a filter feeder.

The coelenterates are more complex, as you know. *Hydra,* for example, has three types of nerve cells and a nervous system that unites the entire organism into a functional whole. Hydras are concomitantly active and varied in behavior. For feeding purposes, the hydra attaches itself by its base; usually, in nature, it is found on the leaf of an aquatic plant. It changes location 10 times a day, more or less frequently depending upon the food supply. As shown in Figure 5–7, the hydra travels by a somersaulting motion, with its base and its tentacles alternately in touch with the ground surface. Once in place, it stretches and contracts at regular intervals of a minute or two, and as it stretches, it extends and waves its ten-

5–7 *Hydra may swim, glide on its base, or, as shown here, it may travel by a somersaulting motion. (After Buchsbaum, 1965)*

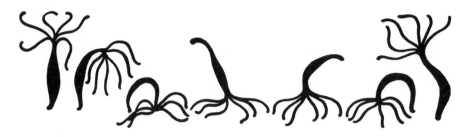

5–8 *When hydra's tentacles contact a prey, the nematocysts are discharged and the victim is paralyzed. The tentacles then contract, helping to convey the prey to the mouth. (After Buchsbaum, 1965)*

tacles. When these come in contact with prey, as shown in Figure 5–8, the nematocysts are discharged, paralyzing the victim, and the tentacles contract. Often the tentacles cooperate in conveying the food to the mouth, which then opens to receive it. The rim of the mouth glides over the prey, encompassing it little by little and finally enclosing it completely, as in a sack. The meal is then forced down into the cavity by circular contractions of the body.

BILATERAL SYMMETRY: PLANARIANS

The evolution of bilateral symmetry brought with it marked changes in the organization of the nervous system as well as of other systems. The most primitive of the flatworms have only a nerve-net type of conduction system, but in the planarians, some of this nerve net has become condensed into two channels, one on each side of the flat, ribbonlike body, which conduct impulses to and from the aggregation of nerve fibers in the anterior end of the body. (See Figure 5–9.) The ocelli of the planarian are usually of the inverted-pigment-cup type. Since they have no lenses, they cannot form an image. A planarian can probably see about as well as you can see with your eyes closed; that is, it can distinguish light

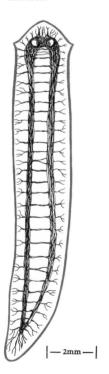

5–9 *The nervous system of the planarian. Two new developments are seen in this system: (1) Some of the nerve net is condensed into two nerve cords, one on each side of the body; and (2) an aggregation of nerve fibers is present in the anterior end—the beginning of "headness, and "tailness."*

|— 2mm —|

from dark. Planarians are photonegative; if you shine a light on a dish of planarians from the side, all will move quickly and steadily away from the source of light.

The head region is rich in *chemoreceptors.* If you place a small piece of fresh liver in the culture water so that its juices diffuse through the medium, the planarians will raise their heads off the bottom and, if they have not been fed recently, will lope directly and rapidly (on a planarian scale) toward the meat, to which they then attach themselves for feeding purposes. The animal locates the food source by repeatedly turning toward the side on which it receives the stimulus more strongly until the stimulus is equal on both sides. If the chemoreceptor cells are removed from one side of the head, the animal will turn constantly toward the intact side.

When a flatworm is cut in two, both anterior and posterior are able to survive. The posterior, however, is very quiet compared with the anterior or with the intact animal, since it is not receiving much in the way of stimulating information about the world around it.

The nervous system of the planarian is not a continuous network, like that of the hydra, but is composed of neurons connected by synaptic junctions. According to some theories, learning occurs as a result of changing connections between neurons at synaptic junctions, like the rewiring of an electronic circuit. On the basis of this theory, James V. McConnell, who is now at the University of Michigan, initiated a series of studies on planarian behavior. He reasoned that the planarian should be the lowest organism in which it would be possible to demonstrate true learning. These studies, which have led to some unexpected and still controversial results, will be described in Chapter 5–4.

The Coming of the Brain

The earthworm lives under the soil in burrows which it constructs by forcing its anterior end through crevices and swallowing the soil. The egested material plus mucus from the gut of the worm is plastered against the burrow wall, where it forms a lining. Some of the egested material may also be deposited on the surface as castings, which you have probably seen. At night when the ground is still wet with dew or after a rainstorm, the earthworm emerges from its burrow, at least partially, to feed on bits of leaf and other vegetable debris.

The earthworm has a variety of sensory cells. It has touch cells, or *mechanoreceptors.* These contain tactile hairs which, when stimulated, trigger a nerve impulse. Patches of these hair cells are found on each segment of the earthworm. The hairs probably also respond to vibrations in the ground, to which the earthworm is also sensitive. The earthworm does not have ocelli—as one might expect, since it lives most of its life in complete darkness—but it does have light-sensitive cells. These cells, which are not visibly different from the other epidermal cells of the worm, are more abundant in its anterior and posterior segments, the parts of its body most likely to be outside of the burrow. These cells are not responsive to light in the red spectrum, a fact exploited by anglers who search for worms in the dark using red-lensed flashlights.

Among the earthworm's most sensitive cells are those concerned with detection of moisture. The cells are located on its first few segments. If the earthworm emerging from its burrow encounters a dry spot, it swings from side to side until it either finds dampness or, failing that, retreats. However, when the anterior segments are anesthetized, the earthworm will crawl over dry ground. The animal also appears to have taste cells. In the laboratory, worms can be shown to select, for example, celery in preference to cabbage leaves and cabbage leaves in preference to carrots.

In the nervous system of the earthworm, you will recall, the two conducting channels come together in a double nerve cord, which runs along the ventral surface of the body. The conducting channels are made up of nerve fibers bound together in bundles like cables. These large fibers can transmit signals rapidly. An impulse running down the fibers causes the sudden contraction of the entire body of the worm—usually resulting, as many fishermen know, in its total disappearance into the safety of its burrow.

5–10 *The reflex arc of the earthworm. A stimulus received by a sense organ is transmitted by a sensory nerve to a ganglion. By means of an association neuron (intercalary cell), the impulse is transmitted to a motor nerve, which, in turn, acts on a muscle.*

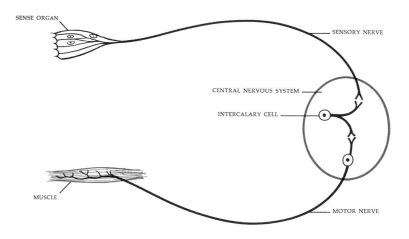

SENSE ORGAN

SENSORY NERVE

CENTRAL NERVOUS SYSTEM

INTERCALARY CELL

MUSCLE

MOTOR NERVE

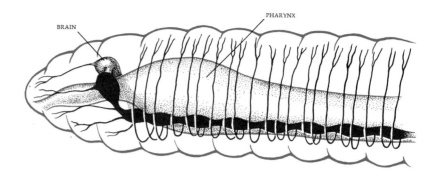

The double nerve cord, with its bulging ganglia, runs almost the entire length of the animal, extending from the tail to the base of the pharynx, the location of the large *subpharyngeal* ("under the pharynx") ganglion. It then forks to encircle the pharynx. This encirclement of the upper digestive tract by the central nervous system is typical of invertebrates which have a ventral nerve cord, including not only the worms but also the mollusks and the arthropods. As shown in Figure 5–11, the two forks of the nerve cord meet again in the cerebral ganglia, which together form a mass sufficiently larger than other ganglia and pairs of ganglia, to be referred to as the *brain*. The subpharyngeal ganglia coordinate the movements of the worm; if these are removed, the worm no longer eats or burrows. Without the cerebral ganglia, or brain, eating and burrowing are normal, although the integration of activities with sensory information is, of course, curtailed.

The Simpler Mollusks

BIVALVES

There is a wide range of complexity in the nervous systems of the mollusks, and this can be generally correlated with their feeding habits and other natural activities. At the extreme end of simplicity are the bivalves—clams, oysters, and scallops—which sift the bottom currents of the ocean bed for small particles of food and spend most of their lives well within the protective enclosure of their shells. Opening and closing these shells constitute a major part of their entire repertory of behavior, although some of them, the scallop in particular, may do this with such force as to jet-propel themselves through the water (Figure 5–12).

The nervous system is also simple, with three pairs of ganglia—cerebral, visceral, and pedal—and two long pairs of nerve cords interconnecting

5–12 *A queen scallop escaping from a starfish.*
The scallop jet-propels itself through
the water by snapping its shell closed,
expelling water out of its mantle cavity.
It can turn by contracting the margin of
its mantle to direct the jet in particular
directions. (Dr. Douglas P. Wilson,
F.R.P.S.)

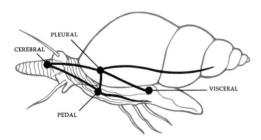

5–13 *The ganglionated nervous system of a*
gastropod. Each circle represents a pair
of ganglia.

them. Every bivalve has a statocyst, usually located near the pedal ganglia, and sensory cells for discrimination of touch, chemical changes, and light. In the scallop, the photoreceptors take the form of quite complex eyes, and a single scallop may have a hundred or more located in the tentacles on the fringe of the mantle. The lenses of these eyes cannot be focused, however, so they do not appear to serve for more than the detection of light and dark. The scallop will not show any startle response if a cardboard model of a starfish is presented to it, but it claps its shells and retreats with vigor if starfish juice is introduced into its environment.

GASTROPODS

Gastropods, which include the snail, the whelk, and the slug, also have ganglionated nervous systems, with as many as six pairs of ganglia connected by nerve cords. (See Figure 5–13.) These animals, while not noted for liveliness of disposition, are much more active than the bivalves. In general, they move with their anterior end first, and there is a concentration of ganglia at this end of the animal. The tentacles, which have chemoreceptors and touch receptors, and the eyes are also located at the anterior end. In some of the animals, the eyes are quite highly developed in structure; they appear, however, to function largely in the simple discrimination between light and dark, as do the eyes of the scallop.

The Octopus

The cephalopods, which are active, predatory animals, are the most specialized in sensory apparatus and the most diversified in behavior of the mollusks and indeed of all invertebrates, with the possible exception of certain of the insects. The best studied of the cephalopods is the octopus, a sea dweller that creeps about actively on its "arms" or swims rapidly through the water by strong rhythmic muscular contractions which expel water from the mantle cavity. The octopus, like the other cephalopods, is carnivorous, living on smaller sea animals such as crabs. It can spring on a victim from a distance of 2 or 3 feet, scooping the prey up in its web and bundling it home to eat it. When it is not actively in pursuit of food, the octopus, lacking any protective shell, lives in small caves behind rocks or in reefs or wreckage. Confronted by a potential enemy—an animal larger than it is—the octopus changes color; *Octopus vulgaris*, the common octopus, turns almost white except for a dark area around the eyes and a trim of violet around the edges of its web. This *display*, as it is known, makes the octopus look larger than it actually is. If the would-be predator is not deterred, the octopus expels a cloud of ink, jet-propels itself away, and darkens, all almost simultaneously, in an escape maneuver which must be baffling to any pursuer. This ink cloud not only blinds the attacker but also, as has been found recently, has a temporary anesthetic effect on the attacker's smell receptors.

5–14 *The common octopus (Octopus vulgaris) literally pales when confronted by an object larger than itself. It flattens and turns almost white except for a dark area around the eyes and a violet trim along the edges of its web. This makes the octopus seem larger than it is and probably serves to deter a would-be predator. The same response can be obtained in the octopus by stimulating its brain with electric currents. (Dr. M. J. Wells and Heinemann Educational Books Ltd.)*

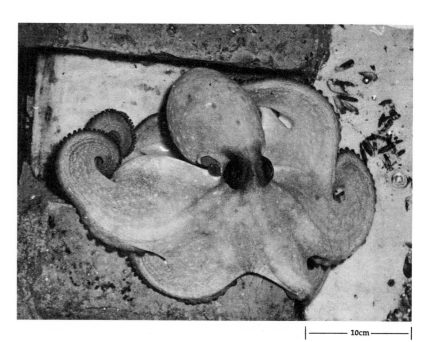

|—————— 10cm ——————|

Some geometric shapes used to test the ability of the octopus to distinguish objects by sight. The proportion of errors made over 60 training trials is shown on the right. As you can see from these figures, the octopus is able to distinguish shapes most easily when they differ in orientation and when this difference can be defined in terms of horizontal and vertical. Since it makes errors half the time when presented with the oblique, mirror-image shapes shown at the bottom, it obviously cannot detect this kind of difference. Apparently, it does not distinguish between shapes because they differ in area or length of outline or because they have more or fewer corners. Its classification of shapes must in some way be related to their distribution about the horizontal and vertical axes. (After Sutherland, 1957)

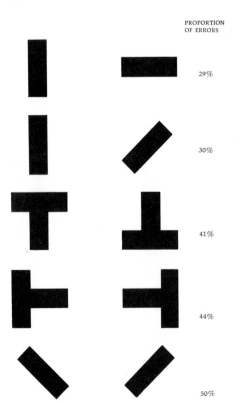

PROPORTION OF ERRORS

29%

30%

41%

44%

50%

Curious, perpetually hungry, and with a high degree of manipulative ability, the octopus makes an extremely apt experimental subject. In a sea-water tank, it will gather together bricks, shells, and any movable debris into a crude sort of house, and there it sits and watches, often bobbing its head up and down. It does not have stereoscopic vision, and apparently this head bobbing is the way it estimates distance, fixing on an object from two points, just as surveyors triangulate a distant landmark. As soon as it becomes accustomed to its new habitat, it will pounce immediately on any object that is placed in the tank. Martin Wells of Churchill College, Cambridge, who has done many of the studies here described, reports that the average life of a floating thermometer in an octopus tank is something less than 20 minutes. If given the opportunity, the octopus will reach an inquiring tentacle out of its tank to take something from the hand of a sometimes startled passerby.

VISION

Behavior in the octopus is dominated by the eye, which is very large in relation to the animal's body size. Its eye is comparable in complexity of structure to the human eye and appears to be capable of an equal degree of resolution.

The sight of a crab can so incite an octopus that its arms weave about and changes appear in its skin color. Unlike the display changes, in which the animal becomes lighter, the octopus darkens on seeing a crab, breaking out in patches of bright blue, pink, black, or purple, depending on the species. These skin changes are brought about by the contraction of muscles which draw out small sacks of pigment, the *chromatophores*, to form a flat plate.

If an octopus sees a crab behind a glass partition, it will rush directly toward it, flushed with excitement, and when it reaches the glass, will press itself against the pane, writhing its tentacles. One of the tentacles may chance over the top of the glass and reach the crab. In this case, the tentacle will close about the crab. The octopus, however, will continue to respond to the visual stimulation of the crab and press excitedly against the glass as if it were still in pursuit of the prey. Apparently the impulses received from the tactile stimulation of the arm are not integrated with those received from the eye, nor is the movement of the arm detectably influenced by the fact that the octopus can see its arm and the prey.

By using a system of rewards (crabs, for example) and punishments (mild electric shock), the investigator can readily teach the octopus to seize certain objects and not to seize others. Such experiments approximate what an octopus must learn in nature—that some objects are edible, some are not, and some may bite or sting. A fiddler crab, for instance, is a meal, but accompanied by its usual commensal, the sea anemone, it had better

564 BEHAVIOR

be left alone. Because of the comparative ease with which such tests can be performed, it has been possible to learn a great deal about what the octopus perceives.

Figure 5–15 shows some of the shapes the octopus can tell apart and some it cannot. The vertical and horizontal rectangles are readily distinguished from one another; in other words, it is easy for the octopus to learn which one is accompanied by a reward and which one by a punishment. On the other hand, it cannot tell the difference between the two oblique rectangles, equally distinct to our eyes. (Curiously, three-to-four-year-old children also find this discrimination difficult.) Yet the eye of the octopus is very similar to our own and equally acute. As you can see in Figure 5–16, it is a so-called "camera" eye, containing, among other features, a lens which focuses an image on a light-sensitive retina. The picture on the octopus retina is the same as that on our own; the difference lies in what goes on in the brain. As you know, what a neuron transmits is an electric signal, and such signals are all qualitatively similar. The brain does not receive a picture in any sense, but only a series of impulses—bits

5–16 *Cross section of the octopus eye. Like man, the octopus possesses camera eyes, but this similarity does not indicate any special relationship between man and the octopus. Each organ evolved independently, and although the information the octopus collects on its retina may be the same as that collected on the human retina, there is a vast difference in the use it makes of this information.*

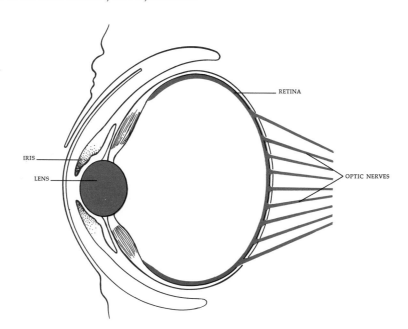

5–17 *A simplified view of the brain and nervous system of the octopus. Note how large the optic lobes are in proportion to the rest of the system.*

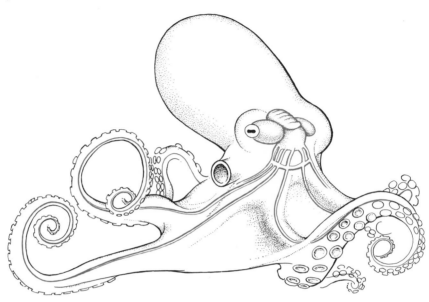

of information analogous to the bits, or units of data, which might be sent through a computer. These bits then are reassembled and analyzed.

Studies of the brain of the octopus suggest some correlations between brain structure and behavior. Figure 5–17 shows a view of the brain. As you can see, it is dominated by the relatively huge optic lobes. Microscopic studies of tissues from these optic lobes have indicated that there may be some correlation between the arrangement of the fibers and the discriminative powers of the animal. In the vertebrates, the fibers in the brain are usually crisscrossed in a random pattern, but in the optic lobes of the octopus, they are largely arranged in horizontal and vertical rows—like a piece of graph paper—which may account for the octopus's tendency to respond to objects in terms of their horizontal and vertical axes.

TOUCH RECEPTORS

More recently, Wells has made studies of the touch receptors of the octopus, which are located on the suckers of its arms. The octopus's suckers are softer and more flexible than our fingertips and so can make discriminations between textures that we would find very difficult. Furthermore, the suckers also contain chemoreceptors which can detect sugars, salts, and other chemicals in dilutions well below the range of discrimination of the human tongue. The octopus can be trained to accept or reject objects on the basis of texture or taste as readily as on the basis of vision. These highly developed sensory capacities are undoubtedly related to the fact that the octopus must often find its prey by reaching a tentacle into a crevice into which it cannot see.

In view of its unusual capacities, it is surprising to find out what the octopus cannot tell by touch. It can distinguish between two quite similar cylinders, such as *A* and *C* in Figure 5–18, but it cannot tell the difference between *A* and *B*. (The percentage figure under each cylinder in Figure 5–18 indicates the amount that cylinder is cut away.) According to Wells's interpretation, the octopus makes its tactile discriminations on the basis of smoothness or roughness, that is, by the amount of surface that does or does not make contact with the suckers. Thus the two cylinders that are cut away an equal amount seem the same to the octopus. It has no discrimination as to the pattern as a whole. Each sucker receives information as an individual unit, and the octopus has no means of integrating the information from the various touch receptors. In other words, it does not know where the parts of its body are. We find it easy, without thinking, to touch our right hand to our left knee, for instance; the equivalent gesture would be impossible for an octopus.

5–18 *The octopus uses its suckers to distinguish between objects on the basis of texture. These discriminations are apparently based on the amount of surface the suckers contact (that is, the smoothness or roughness of the surface) and not on the surface pattern. Therefore, the octopus cannot tell the difference between cylinders A and B, which have very different patterns but have both been cut away 30 percent, but it can distinguish these from cylinder C, which has been cut away only 20 percent.*

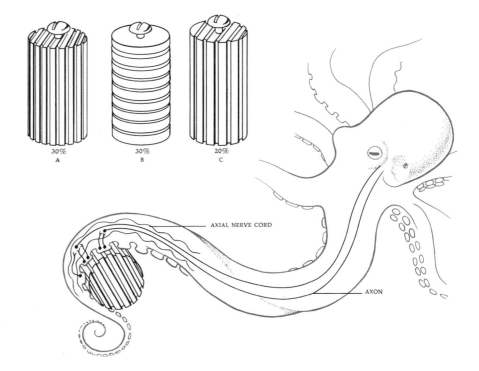

5–19 *Octopus vulgaris crawling over rocks. It might seem that having eight arms would make an organism more efficient than having, say, two. This picture shows quite clearly that, in fact, having eight arms is not necessarily an advantage for most activities. Can you explain why? (Dr. Douglas P. Wilson, F.R.P.S.)*

For similar reasons, the octopus is unable to discriminate between objects on the basis of their weight. The observer can tell which of two objects is the heavier by watching the strain in the animal's muscles, but the octopus lifting the objects cannot. Sensory receptors which provide information about the position of the various components of the body and the stresses and strains upon them are known as *proprioceptors*. The proprioceptors of the octopus obviously function in reflex movements, such as reaching for a crab, but the information from the proprioceptors apparently cannot be analyzed by the brain. In fact, as Wells has pointed out, the problems of handling data received from eight extensible arms, each of which has several hundred suckers and can move separately and in any direction, would probably be insuperable. As we shall see in the following chapter, the severe limitations of movement provided by an articulated skeleton prove to be a great advantage for many types of specialized activities.

SUMMARY

We began our study of animal behavior in this chapter by examining the activities of some of the one-celled animals. In the responses of these organisms, four primary components of behavior are observed: (1) When an amoeba responds to the presence of a nearby prey, it exhibits *irritability*. (2) In its reaction to light, the amoeba displays the property known as *habituation*. (3) Much of the behavior of the paramecium is attributable to its *avoidance* of negative stimuli. (4) A very simple form of *learning* is found in the reactions of a stentor to a negative stimulus.

The behavior of the coelenterates is more active and varied, and their physical organizations are correspondingly more complex. The hydra, for example, has three types of specialized nerve cells and a nerve network by which its activities are integrated and coordinated. Its patterns of feeding and locomotion reflect this greater complexity.

In the *bilateral symmetry* of the planarian begins the first "headness" and "tailness" in animals. The planarian's head region is rich in chemoreceptors, and the animal moves in response to stimuli received through these cells. In the earthworm, the aggregation of nerve cells in the head region has increased still further. A double nerve cord runs the entire length of the body, terminating in the *cerebral ganglia* (groups of nerve cells in the head).

We concluded with a discussion of the behavior of the mollusks, relating this behavior to the neurophysiological equipment which underlies it. The lower mollusks, such as the clams and scallops, have relatively simple nervous systems and exhibit concomitantly simple behavior. The octopus, however, which has highly developed sensory organs and a much larger brain, exhibits complex patterns of behavior and a high degree of learning ability.

Organization of Arthropod Behavior

Arthropod Nervous Systems

The nervous system of the arthropods is constructed along the same general plan as that of the annelids. The two dorsal cerebral ganglia—collectively called the brain—are the chief receptors of sensory information. The brain connects with the subesophageal ganglia by nerve fibers encircling the esophagus. These subesophageal ganglia are the first in a chain of ganglia which form way stations in the bundle of nerve fibers running along the ventral surface of the animal. In most arthropods, each segment is supplied by its own ganglia, but in some families, a number of ganglia have fused together. In the housefly, for example, all abdominal and thoracic ganglia have come together into a single giant ganglion in the thorax.

Despite this similarity of physical organization, the behavior of the typical arthropods is far more complex than that of the worms. Three evolutionary developments in the organ systems of the arthropods have made such behavior both possible and necessary.

1 There was an elaboration of sense organs, including the compound eye, highly sensitive chemoreceptors, and very complex mechanoreceptors such as special organs for hearing and exquisitely tuned proprioceptors.

2 The chitin exoskeleton, by the limitations it imposed on the movements of the arthropod, made possible the evolution of jointed appendages and their subsequent modification into legs and mouthparts of great intricacy. As a consequence, many of the arthropods have a fine manipulative ability. The honeybee, for instance, has six pairs of delicately controlled appendages, each of which is different and has a separate function.

3 A central nervous system evolved which was capable of organizing the wealth of sensory impulses received and coordinating the motions of the many appendages.

As is the case with all animals having a "ladder" type of nervous system, many of the activities of the arthropods are handled at the local level, and a number of species can move, eat, and carry on other functions normally after the brain is removed. In fact, in the arthropods generally, the brain appears to act not so much as a stimulator of the action of the animal but as an inhibitor. The grasshopper, for example, after removal of the brain can walk, jump, or fly; in fact, the brainless grasshopper responds to the slightest stimulus by jumping or flying. The extreme consequences of this releasing of inhibition can be seen in the praying mantis. Mantises are carnivorous and cannibalistic, and the female, being larger than the male, frequently captures her approaching mate and grasping him in her forearms begins to eat him, head first. This decapitation results in the release of strong motor activities by which the headless male struggles loose from the grasp of the female, mounts her, and mates with her. The headless male is more likely to copulate than the intact male; investigators seeking to breed mantises have found that males of special strains that do not mate readily

5–20 *Arthropod nervous systems: a bee, a crayfish, and an ant. The brain is a pair of ganglia at the end of a chain of ganglia which are interconnected by the bundle of nerve fibers running along the ventral surface. Because of the arthropod's "ladder" type of nervous system, many arthropod activities are controlled at a local level, and a number of species can carry on a few of their normal functions after the brain has been removed.*

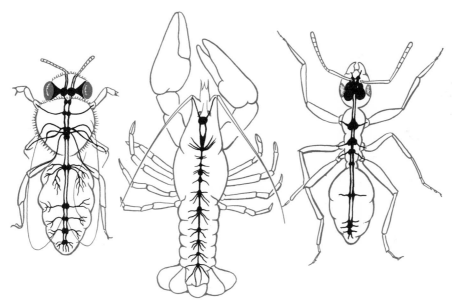

571 *Organization of Arthropod Behavior*

5–21 *After mating, a female mantis sits sunning on a goldenrod, while her late husband dangles headless below. As with other arthropods, loss of the brain seems to act in the male mantis as a (temporary) stimulus to activity. The headless male mantis is more likely to copulate with the female than the intact male. (John C. Pitkin, Frank W. Lane)*

5–22 *The arthropod compound eye, as seen in a long-horned beetle. (Dr. Ross E. Hutchins)*

|— 1mm —|

in captivity will do so after they lose their heads. This heroic adaptation on the part of the male ensures that his own genes will be perpetuated and that the species will not be destroyed.

Arthropod Vision

THE COMPOUND EYE

The most conspicuous sensory organ of the arthropods is the compound eye (Figure 5–23), which is an evolutionary development characteristic of this one phylum. The basic structural unit of this eye is a cone called the *ommatidium*. A dragonfly has some 30,000 ommatidia. Each ommatidium is covered by a cornea, usually with a square or hexagonal surface; these are visible under low-power magnification as individual facets of the eye. Underlying the cornea is a crystalline cone that conducts the light to the photoreceptor cells, which are arranged radially around a translucent central core formed by the receptor cells. This cone, the *rhabdom*, conducts light energy to the far ends of the receptors. Nerve fibers carry the stimu-

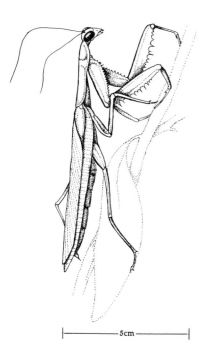

lus from the receptor cells to the brain. The outer surface of the receptor cell is coated with opaque pigment, which prevents light from traveling from one ommatidium to another. Since each ommatidium receives a single pinpoint of light from directly in front of it, the picture formed is a mosaic with very little resolution, like a newspaper picture under high magnification.

PERCEPTION

The compound eye is deficient in acuity, offering less detail than the vertebrate eye. It is better for detecting motion, however, because each ommatidium is stimulated separately and so has a separate visual field. Ability to detect motion can be measured accurately in the laboratory by testing a phenomenon known as *flicker fusion*. In this test, a light is flicked on and off with increasing rapidity until the observer sees the flicker as a continuous beam. The beam is perceived as continuous because stimulation of any retinal cell persists for a brief period even after the stimulus disappears. So, in effect, the flicker-fusion test is a measurement of how quickly the photoreceptor cell recovers from one stimulus and becomes sensitive to another. It is possible to test flicker-fusion rates in animals by training experiments in which the animal learns to associate a flickering light with a re-

5–23 *A cutaway view of the compound eye of the arthropod is shown at (a). The basic structural unit of the eye is the ommatidium (b), which consists of a rhabdom and photoreceptor cells and is covered by a cornea. The rhabdom conducts light to the far ends of the receptor cells, and nerve fibers carry the stimulus to the brain. A cross section of the ommatidium is shown at (c).*

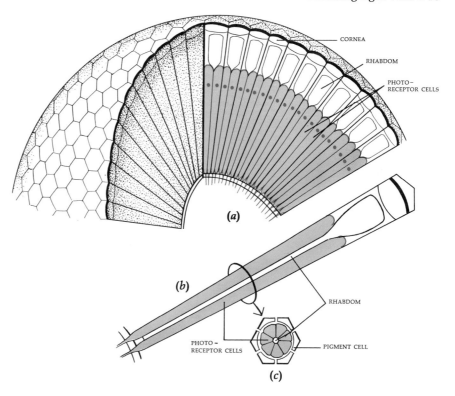

573 *Organization of Arthropod Behavior*

5–24 *The bees in this picture were trained to look for food in a dish placed on a blue card. All the other cards are colored various shades of gray. The bee can distinguish four colors: yellow, blue, blue-green, and ultraviolet. (Dr. Max Renner)*

5–25 *Experiment to prove that ants use the position of the sun to find their way home from feeding places. The ant on the left is headed toward its nest. It is interrupted in its journey and kept in the box for an hour or so. When it is released, it proceeds in a direction which deviates from its original direction by exactly the amount that the sun's position has changed. (The two angles S are equal.) Still orienting itself by the sun, it is now lost.*

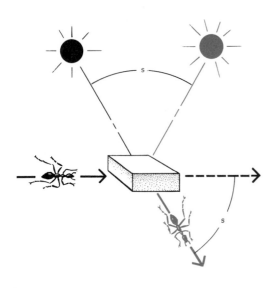

ward (usually food) and a steady beam with no reward, or vice versa. Such tests have proved that the compound eye greatly exceeds the camera eye in this respect. A bee would see in clear outline a moving figure that we would see as blurred; and if the bee went to the movies, the film seen by us as a continuous picture would jerk along from frame to frame in the bee's eye. The ability to perceive motion is extremely important for an insect since it must be able to make out objects when it is flying at high speed (which, as far as the visual apparatus is concerned, presents the same problems as following a moving object).

Some compound eyes also have a wider visual field because of their large, convex surface. A stalked compound eye, such as is found in crustaceans, may cover an arc of 180° or more.

In addition to compound eyes, many of the arthropods possess simple eyes, or ocelli, which seem generally to serve only for light detection. Most insects have two or three ocelli, and spiders, depending on species, may have as many as eight.

COLOR VISION

Some arthropods also possess color vision, as Von Frisch has shown in his ingenious studies of bees. This series of studies, spanning the last half century, provides a model for what can be accomplished by an investigator using little more than intelligence, curiosity, and imagination.

Von Frisch found that if he placed a dish of sugar water on a square of cardboard of a particular color, the bees would learn to come to that color to seek food, picking it out not only from a variety of other colors but also from a number of shades of gray. (A color would look gray to a color-blind insect, as it does to a color-blind person.) The bee, Von Frisch has shown, can distinguish only four different qualities of color: yellow, blue-green, blue, and ultraviolet. Ultraviolet is not visible to us, while red to the bee is indistinguishable from black or dark gray. It is probable that color vision is possessed by all insects that take nectar from flowers and in so doing pollinate them. What is the adaptive advantage in this?

PHOTOORIENTATION

Insects may use their eyes not only for perception but also for photo-orientation. Ants find their way from feeding places to their homes by light. You can prove this to yourself by this experiment, for which you need only an ant that is moving along a straight line in any particular direction and a pocket mirror: Cast a shadow over the ant with your hand and then hold the mirror so that the light of the sun reaches the ant's eyes from the opposite direction. The insect will hesitate for an instant, pivot on its rear legs, and hurry back in the direction from which it has come.

Another experiment that will prove the photoorientation of ants is shown in Figure 5–25. Capture an ant that is headed for its nest and keep it in a dark box for an hour or so. When it is released from the box, it does not continue along its old route but chooses a new one. If you measure the angle between the two directions, you will find that its new route deviates from the old one by the same angle by which the position of the sun has shifted during the insect's imprisonment. Other insects, such as the bee, would still follow the initial course since they possess a time-compensated sun compass.

Touch

MECHANORECEPTORS

The body surface of the arthropods is covered with sensory-receptor units known as *sensilla,* or "little sense organs." Most of the sensilla take the form of fine spines, or *setae,* composed of hollow shafts of chitin. At the bases of these shafts are sensory cells. In their simplest form, the sensilla are mechanoreceptors. In these when the hair is touched or bent the sensory cell responds and initiates a nerve impulse which is transmitted by an afferent fiber. Mechanoreceptors are found, in particular, on the antennae and the legs. In addition to being stimulated by direct contact, they can also be stimulated by vibrations. A spider keeps in touch with what is going on in its web by sensing through its legs vibrations that are transmitted through the threads when the web is touched. Soldier termites of certain species strike the ground or the walls of their nest with their heads when

5–26 *Mechanoreceptor hairs on the legs of a tiger beetle. At the base of the hairs are sensory cells. When a hair is touched or bent, a nerve impulse is fired. (L. West)*

| — 5mm — |

575 *Organization of Arthropod Behavior*

5–27 *Since its eyes do not move, the praying mantis must move its entire head to bring its victim into binocular range. The movement of its head sends impulses through proprioceptive hairs on its head and thorax to its legs. The position of its prey and the movement of its legs are thus automatically coordinated, giving the mantis the ability to strike swiftly at a moving object.*

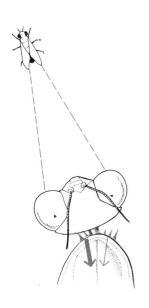

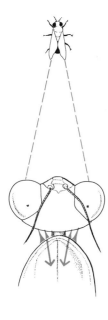

threatened or disturbed; the vibrations they produce warn their colony mates. A fly perceives the air currents from the movement of a hand or fly-swatter and so escapes; a fly in a glass jar is much less likely to be disturbed by such movements.

PROPRIOCEPTORS

Touch receptors can also serve as proprioceptors. The praying mantis, for example, is capable of firing a lightning-swift strike at a moving object. When it sights a potential victim, the insect moves its entire head to bring it into binocular range, since the eyes themselves do not move. (See Figure 5–27.) Movement of the head results in the stimulation of proprioceptive hairs on the head and thorax of the insect. On the basis of the impulses received from these hairs, the position of the prey and the movement of its own legs are automatically coordinated by the mantis. If these hairs are removed, the mantis can strike a moving object only if the object is directly in front of it.

Another type of proprioceptor common in the arthropods is the *campaniform* cell (Figure 5–28). These cells are located in thin, stretchable areas of the cuticle. When these areas are twisted or stretched, the cells signal the central nervous system.

STATOCYSTS

In the Crustacea, groups of sensory hair cells form statocysts, the gravity-sensing organs which were described in Chapter 2–6. The function of the statocyst was first demonstrated in a crustacean, a small decapod shrimp. In the shrimp, the statocyst is located at the base of the antenna and is not entirely enclosed but contains a pore connecting it with the body surface. Its statoliths are grains of sand placed within the statocyst by the crustacean itself, which uses its fine pincerlike claws to insert them through the pore. When the shrimp molts, it loses its sand grains and has to replace them. In 1892, an Austrian zoologist, who had some shrimp in an aquarium, hit upon the ingenious idea of removing all sand from the aquarium and replacing it with iron filings. When the shrimp molted, they replaced the sand grains in their statocysts with iron filings. The investigator then suspended a magnet over the heads of his shrimp. They all promptly turned upside down, and the function of this organ, until that moment a matter of dispute, was conclusively demonstrated.

Except for a few of the crustaceans and aquatic insects, the arthropods do not have statocysts and depend on the proprioceptors to keep them informed of their position in space.

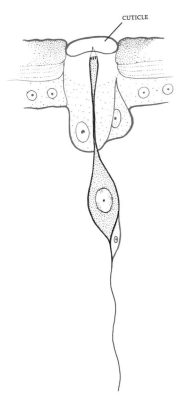

5–28 *Campaniform cell, a type of proprioceptor common in arthropods.*

5–29 *The most elaborate of the insect sound receptors is the tympanic organ. The tympanic air sacs are covered by a membranous drum, and the sensory cells are so arranged in the organ that they are stimulated by movements of the drum or the air-sac walls. Tympanic organs respond to vibrations in the air or in water.*

Hearing

Hearing is a special form of touch reception in which mechanoreceptors are stimulated by vibrations transmitted through air or water. If such vibrations are detected by a receptor organ, they are known as *sound*. The loudness of the sound depends on the force with which the sound waves touch the receptors. The pitch of a sound, that is, whether it is deep or shrill, depends on the frequency of the vibrations; as you probably know, a rapidly vibrating tuning fork produces higher sounds than a slowly vibrating one. Just as photoreceptors receive light of only certain wavelengths, sound receptors receive sounds of only certain frequencies.

The simplest form of sound receptor is a sensillum with a tactile hair which vibrates as a result of being "touched" by sound waves. The antennae of the male mosquito contain thousands of such hairs, which are responsive to the vibrations made by the wings of the female mosquito in flight and so serve to bring the sexes together. When the male mosquito first emerges from its pupal shell, it is sexually immature and also deaf, with its antennal hairs lying flat along the shafts. When the male matures sexually, some 24 hours later, the hairs almost simultaneously become erect.

Other insects have developed special groups of cells for hearing; these are known as *tympanic organs*. (See Figure 5–29.) In these organs, a fine membrane, the *tympanum* (or eardrum), is stretched across an air-filled cavity. The tympanic membrane vibrates in response to sounds of certain frequencies, and this vibration is transmitted to underlying receptor cells.

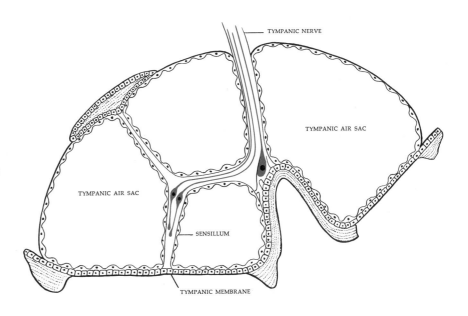

577 *Organization of Arthropod Behavior*

In the grasshopper, the tympanic organ is located on the tibia of the front leg, while in the cricket, locust, and moth, it is found on the side of the posterior thorax or the abdomen.

In general, the animals which make sounds are those which have special sound receptors. An exception is the noctuid moth, which has a tympanic organ that has been specially tuned in the process of evolution to receive the shrill cries of the bat, its natural enemy. The bat's cries, on the other hand (as we shall see in the next chapter), are a special evolutionary adaptation for locating prey, such as noctuid moths.

Smell and Taste

CHEMORECEPTORS

Other setae function as chemoreceptors, serving the senses of smell and taste. In the arthropods, chemoreceptors located on the antennae and the forelegs seem to serve both for smell and for taste, functions which are difficult to distinguish in this class. Taste is generally considered to be the result of the direct contact of chemoreceptor cells with a substance in watery solution, while smell usually refers to the chemoreception of an airborne substance, although it is clear that there is considerable overlap. In special reference to human taste receptors, taste is also sometimes defined as detection of those properties we call sweet, salty, sour, and bitter. The sense of smell, as you know, has a far wider and very subtle range. For example, human beings can distinguish more than 10,000 different odors.

Chemoreceptors concerned with smell are generally located in the antennae of insects and are used by many insects to locate food. Von Frisch, in experiments involving odors similar to the experiments he used for color, showed that the bee can distinguish a wide variety of odors, similar to the spectrum detectable by man.

Other insects are also very discriminating. In many species of wasp, for example, the female deposits her eggs on the larvae of other insects. Each species differs in the type of larva it selects to parasitize and sometimes even in the developmental stage of the host. Certain of these parasitic wasps specialize in parasitizing larvae of the wood wasp, which may be buried several inches deep in the beam of a house or under the bark of a tree. The female of these parasitic species is able to locate the larva by smell receptors on her antennae; she then drills a hole through the wood with her sharp ovipositor and injects the egg into the larva. (See Figure 5–31.)

TASTE RECEPTORS

While smell may perform a variety of functions, taste usually serves as a screening device for substances entering the digestive tract. In insects, as

5–30 *"Ear" (tympanic organ) on the front tibia of a long-horned grasshopper. (Dr. Ross E. Hutchins)*

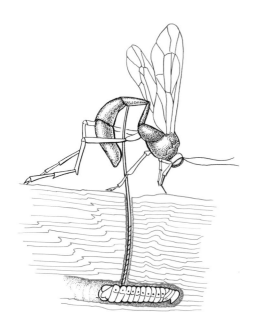

in other animals, taste receptors are often located around the mouth. Certain insects, however, taste with their feet. The next time a housefly visits your kitchen, spread a few drops of sugar water on the table. If one of its front feet touches the sugar water, its spongelike proboscis will be extended and it will stop and eat. This is an absolutely automatic reflex action in the hungry fly.

Some years ago, a transient female blowfly laid eggs in a liverwurst sandwich in the laboratory of Vincent Dethier of the University of Pennsylvania, thus initiating one of the most extensive studies in animal physiology and behavior ever to be carried out on a single species. By observing the reflex extension of the proboscis, Dethier and his collaborators have been able to make an extensive catalog of the tasting ability of this animal. Dethier found that the fly can taste many different types of sugars and that these sugars are just about the same as those that signal "sweet" on our own tongues. But the hungry fly is 10 million times more sensitive to sugar than we are. In other words, if you were to take the most dilute sugar solution in which you could detect any sweetness and dilute it 10 million times more, the fly would still lower its proboscis if it stepped on it. When salty, sour, or bitter substances are added to the sugar water in perceptible quantities, the lowering of the proboscis is inhibited. As a result, it has also been possible to catalog what the blowfly can taste in the way of both acceptable and nonacceptable substances.

The fly also has taste receptors on the tip of its proboscis; these must be appropriately stimulated before the extended proboscis will suck a fluid

5–33 *Apparatus for recording impulses from a single sensillum of the blowfly. A diagram of the sensillum is shown at the top of the figure. When one of the two taste-receptor cells is stimulated, the resulting electrical impulses are recorded on the oscillograph.*

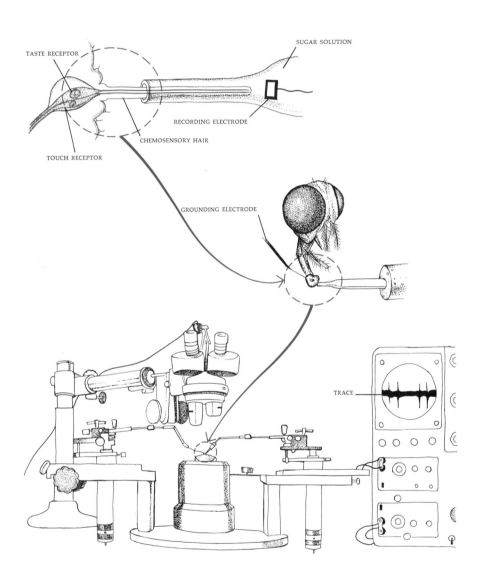

up into the stomach. The receptors on the feet are sunk below the chitin surface, but in those on the tip of the proboscis, a filament from the receptor cells extends out through a chitin shaft. Chemoreceptor cells in general, including those in the vertebrates, are too small to insert an electrode into, and so measurement of the nerve impulse from any single cell has been extremely difficult. Because of the anatomy of the taste cells of the blowfly, and also because the sensory "hairs" are spaced some distance apart, Dethier and his colleagues have been able to record impulses from a single receptor in the blowfly.

Each sensory shaft has three cells at its base. One of these is a touch receptor, and two are taste receptors. All three send impulses directly to the brain. Figure 5–33 diagrams one of these sensilla and shows the apparatus devised by Edward Hodgson of Columbia University for recording impulses from it. Using this apparatus, Hodgson found that one of the taste-receptor cells is sensitive to sugars. When this cell is stimulated, it gives off a characteristic electric impulse, as shown in the diagram. The signal from this receptor (known as the S receptor since it produces the smaller impulse) apparently produces an "on" signal in the brain of the fly, which initiates sucking. The other taste receptor responds only to salty, sour, and bitter substances; when impulses are received through this receptor, the L receptor, the sucking is not initiated even if the S signals are being sent simultaneously.

Communication

COMMUNICATION BY SOUND

The arthropods, and particularly the higher insects, have developed complex forms of sensory communication. They are the first animals to have used airborne sounds as a communicative mechanism. A number of species, such as the locusts, grasshoppers, and crickets, call to one another by sounds made by rubbing their legs or wings together or against their bodies. Five distinct types of calls are known: (1) calling by males and (2) calling by females, both of which are long-range sounds; (3) courtship sounds by males and (4) aggressive sounds by males, both of which are short-range; and (5) alarm sounds, which may be given either by males or by females. Recognition of and response to the sound seem to be based on pattern and on rhythm since insects apparently are not able to distinguish frequencies, or the differences between high and low notes, and so are essentially "tone deaf." The effectiveness of calling songs is often increased by group singing, such as the famous chorus of male seventeen-year cicadas, which can attract females from distances far greater than an individual "voice" would reach. Insects produce songs and respond to appropriate songs without ever having heard a song before.

5–34 *The katydid produces its characteristic loud shrill sounds by rubbing the scraper at the base of its right wing against the file at the base of its left wing. (Dr. Ross E. Hutchins)*

|— 1mm —|

COMMUNICATION BY PHEROMONES

The use of chemicals for communication is common among animals, and the substances employed range from the sex attractants of the little algal cell *Chlamydomonas* to Chanel #5. Many insects communicate by chemicals; such chemicals are known as *pheromones*. Pheromones are chemical messengers. They are usually produced in special glands and are discharged into the environment, where they act on other members of the same species. The chemical structure and biological effects of the pheromones of a number of insects are the subject of studies by several groups of investigators, including E. O. Wilson of Harvard University.

The pheromones are of two general types. One type acts to alter the endocrine and reproductive systems of animals and often even their external forms, as in the termites described in Chapter 2–7. These are characteristically transmitted by mouth. The other type of pheromone, often airborne, causes immediate behavior changes. Some of the most spectacular of these are the mating substances of moths, which are extremely efficient and economical signaling devices.

Moth Pheromones

One female gypsy moth, by the emission of minute amounts of a pheromone commonly known as *gyplure,* can call male moths from several miles away. In fact, a single female contains enough gyplure, somewhere around

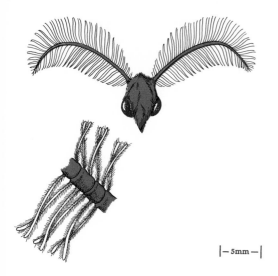

|— 5mm —|

5–35 *The plumed antennae of the male*
cecropia moth are adapted for detecting
the pheromone emitted by the female.

a millionth of a gram, to attract more than a billion males, supposing that it were distributed with the maximum of efficiency. Since the male can detect as little as a few hundred molecules per cubic centimeter of the attractant, gyplure is still potent even when it has become widely diffused.

The male moth characteristically flies upwind, and the pheromone, of course, disperses downwind. Therefore, when a male moth detects the odor of a female of the species, he will fly toward the source even though there is no way to tell which direction it comes from; if he loses the scent, he flies about at random until he either picks it up again or abandons the search. It is not until he is quite close to the female that he can fly "up the gradient" and use the intensity of the odor as a locating device. Figure 5–35 shows the lavishly plumed antennae of the male cecropia moth, which he uses for detection of the female.

Each species appears to detect only the odor of its own species, or at least to be stimulated to sexual activity only by that odor. On any summer night, the air must contain many of these chemical signals. You may be able to find moth cocoons—the cocoon of the cecropia moth is 2 or 3 inches long and very conspicuous—and so procure a new-hatched female. If she is placed in a wire basket or similar container and left in the open air through the night, you will find that her cage is soon surrounded by moths of her own species. You will not be able to detect any of the odor of the sex attractant, however.

Ant Pheromones

Many different types of pheromones are produced by ants. A number of species use chemical messengers as *trail markers*, including the small fire ant, so called because of its stinging ability. If a fire ant finds a food source, it lays down a marking trail as it returns to its nest, as shown in Figure 5–36. The marking substance in this species is produced by a gland

5–36 *One of Dethier's students constructed this experiment as a puzzle for his fellow*
students. He showed them the end result as it is seen in the drawing and asked:
"How were the ants persuaded to follow the instructions on the signs?" They
eventually figured out that he first set a jar of jam where it would be found
by a colony of fire ants. The ants then laid down a marking trail in a straight
line between their nest and the jam, using a pheromone exuded along their stings.
The student then moved the jam jar several times so that the trail to the jar, con-
stantly renewed by the ants, eventually took on the indirect, circular pattern
*shown. To confuse his fellow **students**, he introduced several "Detour" signs.*
(After Dethier, 1963)

583 *Organization of Arthropod Behavior*

(Dufour's gland) in the posterior segment of the animal and is exuded along the animal's extended sting, which is touched to the ground periodically to mark the trail. Other workers follow the chemical trail to the food, and if they find a suitable reward, they will add their marks to the returning trail. As a consequence, a trail to a rich food supply will be constantly renewed and reinforced, attracting more workers. The scent is evanescent, and as soon as the food supply is consumed, the number of workers laying marks diminishes and the trail evaporates. In this way, out-of-date information is quickly eliminated. In general, trails laid by one species of ant are not attractive to other species.

Another type of pheromone common among ants is the *alarm substance*. In the harvester ant (*Pogonomyrmex badius*), the alarm substance (methylheptanone) is produced in the mandibular gland in the animal's head and is released when the animal is injured or disturbed. At low concentrations, the pheromone attracts other ants, drawing them to the point of disturbance and so, if necessary, uniting them against a common enemy. If order is restored, the signal fades out rapidly. If the disturbance spreads, however, involving more and more ants, the pheromone will be produced in increasing concentrations, as each new ant becomes alarmed, until more and more ants and finally, perhaps, the entire colony are excited. Alarm substances are not species-specific, and the warning signal of one species will serve to alert ants of another species to danger. These substances may have a pleasant odor to the human nose; citronellal, producing the familiar "citronella" odor, is an example of an insect alarm pheromone.

The trail and alarm substances are only part of the ant's "chemical vocabulary," as Wilson refers to it. There is evidence for the existence of other secretions that induce gathering and settling of workers, acts of grooming, food exchange, and care of the queen and of the young. For instance, an ant is not pronounced officially dead until its body releases specific decomposition products. A dead ant will be conscientiously groomed by its nestmates for a day or more until it releases the necessary decay signal, at which point it is carried to the funeral heap. Conversely, a healthy ant painted with the "death" substance (one of the fatty acids such as oleic acid) will be repeatedly dragged, struggling, to the refuse pile until the scent wears off.

THE DANCING BEES

Probably the most remarkable example of communication among insects is the "language of the bees" discovered by Von Frisch. The honeybee returning to the hive performs a dance upon the comb which signals quite precisely to her hivemates the location of the food she has found.

When the nectar source is near the home, the bee does a *round dance* to arouse other workers to seek the food source. From the scent on the bee's body, the workers are informed at the same time about the type of flower she has found. When the food source is some distance from the hive (more than 275 feet, in the case of the black Austrian honeybee, *Apis mellifera carnica*, with which Von Frisch did his original studies), the bee does the *wagging dance*, in which she runs a short distance in a straight line, wagging her abdomen from side to side, and returns in a semicircle to the starting point. Then she repeats the straight run and comes back in a semicircle on the opposite side. This cycle, which is shown in Figure 5–37, is repeated many times. The time taken by the straight run indicates the distance of

5–37 *The wagging dance of the black Austrian honeybee communicates to her fellow workers the location of a food source she has found. The bee locates the source with reference to the position of the sun. If she performs her dance outside the hive (a), the straight run of the dance will point directly toward the food source. If she performs her dance inside the hive (b), she orients herself by gravity and the point directly overhead takes the place of the sun. The angle X is the same for both dances. The distance of the food source from the hive is indicated by the rate at which she performs the dance pattern.*

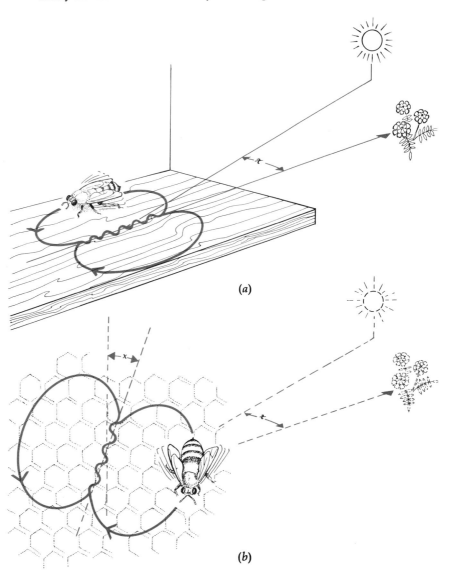

(a)

(b)

the source from the hive. If the source is 1,000 feet away from the hive, the worker bee performs a straight run lasting one-half second; if the source is 2,000 feet away, the straight run takes about twice as long, or one second.

More remarkable, the direction of the straight run of the waggle dance indicates the direction of the food source. The bee locates the food source for herself by reference to the position of the sun, and this is how she finds the food again. Sometimes when she returns, she dances first on a horizontal platform outside the hive. In this case, the straight run of the waggle dance will point directly toward the food source. When she reenters the hive, however, to share and store the nectar, her only dancing spot is on the vertical surface of the comb in the dark interior of the hive. Here she orients herself, not by the sun, but by gravity, and the point directly overhead takes the place of the sun in the bee's map, just as our maps are generally oriented so that the North Pole is on the top. If the food source lies at an angle of 40° to the left of the sun, for example, the wagging run points 40° to the left of the vertical. The bees that follow the dancer translate the information back into a direction for photoorientation and start off toward the food source. A young bee that has been raised away from other bees outside the hive is able to respond to the dance the first time she is exposed to it in the hive.

Von Frisch and his students have found that details of the dance differ from species to species. In one species, *Trigona iridipennis,* the bees have no formal dance at all; a returning worker merely moves excitedly in the hive, stirring up her fellows to go look for themselves for the nectar source. Another species, the dwarf bee *Apis florea,* constructs a very small comb in which there is a horizontal sunlit surface for dancing. The waggle dance of this bee is always oriented directly with reference to the sun.

Von Frisch believes that the behavior of these three species indicates the course of evolution of the dance of the bees: first, a dance with no formal pattern of communication; next, a dance in which the direction of the food source is oriented to the position of the sun; and finally, a dance which communicates in the map language used in the darkened comb.

Built-in Behavior

Even in so brief a survey of arthropod behavior, we are struck first by its complexity and second by how much arthropods "know" without learning. One more example may be useful: The orb webs made by many different types of spiders are probably familiar to you. An orb weaver makes a new web almost every day. A spider does not need to practice web making. Baby spiders make smaller webs, which were thought at one time to prepare them for larger ones, but it has been shown that even a spider that

5–38 *The web of a spider that has lost a leg. Since spiders use their legs to space the turns in their web spirals, this web is somewhat irregular. In addition, the spider has practised an economy of effort by building the web with a shorter thread. (Peter N. Witt, M.D.)*

is confined from egg to adulthood and never permitted to spin a line can make a perfect adult-sized web on its first trial.

Webs vary in size because of variations in the length of spiders' legs; the spider produces each new turn in a web spiral by holding out the new line at leg's length as it crawls along the one just completed. In addition, a spider designs its web on the basis of the protein available for silk and also on the basis of its own weight. If it is short of silk protein, it will reduce the thread length and amount of detail in its web (but not the overall size) so that it does not run out before the web is completed. A heavier spider will build a heavier web. If a tiny piece of lead is stuck onto a spider, it will make a web with a heavier thread and, to compensate, will reduce the number of radii and spiral turns.

Peter N. Witt, who is one of the country's foremost authorities on the web-building spiders, has been using a laser beam to destroy minute areas in the brain of the spider and trying to correlate the effects of such treatment with web-building behavior. In this way, he hopes to correlate some of these intricate functions with specific structures in the arthropod's central nervous system.

Despite increasing knowledge about the sensory receptors of arthropods and detailed accounts of many aspects of arthropod behavior, little is known about the structure and function of the central nervous system, which in some members of the phylum is incredibly small. The bee, for instance, has a brain no larger than a seed of grass. The behavior of the animals in this phylum seems to be based upon the experience of the group as a whole rather than upon the experience of any one individual. Elements of behavior are incorporated slowly into the species, just as are changes in body structure.

SUMMARY

Although the nervous systems of the arthropods are generally similar to those of the annelids, their behavior is vastly more complex. In this chapter, we have examined some of the evolutionary developments which have made these complex activities both possible and necessary.

The *compound eye* of the arthropod gives the animal the ability to perceive motion and to locate itself by photoorientation. Some arthropods also have the ability to distinguish colors.

Arthropods possess *mechanoreceptors* which enable them to "tune in" to very subtle changes in their environment and to make rapid adjustments to these changes. The bodies of all arthropods are covered with *sensilla,* which respond both to direct contact and to vibrations in the air or ground. *Proprioceptors* coordinate the impulses received through the sensory organs with the animal's response movements, thus keeping the

587   *Organization of Arthropod Behavior*

animal informed of its position in space. In the crustaceans and aquatic insects, *statocysts* locate the position of the animal in terms of gravity. Special sound receptors enable some arthropods to communicate by means of sound, to locate prey, or to avoid predators.

By means of extremely sensitive *chemoreceptors*, arthropods make very fine discriminations in taste and smell. Arthropods are able to detect substances in the air or in water at dilutions well outside the range of human powers of discrimination.

These highly developed sense organs are used in various ways by arthropods to communicate with one another. The calling songs of some insects signify courtship, aggression, or alarm. *Pheromones*, transmitted by mouth or airborne, call males to females, signal alarms, and mark trails. The dance of the honeybee, which directs the bee's co-workers to a newly found food source, is based on the ability of the bee to orient herself both by the sun and by gravity.

Bases of Vertebrate Behavior

The French scientist Georges Cuvier (1769–1832), who is generally regarded as the father of paleontology, claimed that from a single bone from the foot of an extinct animal, he could reconstruct the entire skeleton, down to the last tooth. In practice, such feats of reconstruction are not always possible, but Cuvier's principle, the "correlation of parts," now seems to us so obvious as to be hardly worth emphasizing.

Behavior, too, may be considered a "part" of an animal. The behavior of each animal has a "structure" that is as closely related to whether it preys or grazes, flees or hides from its enemies, lives on the plains or in the mountains as the shape of its foot or the physiology of its digestive tract.

Many evolutionary forces have worked together to mold the behavior of the vertebrates. Alfred Romer of Harvard University, who has devoted the largest part of a long and distinguished career to studying the evolution of the vertebrates, believes that the principal evolutionary force has been the pattern of reproduction and, in particular, the care of the young.

In many of our invertebrate, sea-dwelling ancestors, reproductive activities were limited to the shedding of eggs on the quiet ocean floor by the female and their subsequent fertilization by the male. The earliest of the vertebrates are believed to have evolved in fresh water, and in this new habitat, the gametes were likely to be swept away by the currents of the streams or rivulets. Behavior patterns evolved to coordinate the activities of male and female to provide either for internal fertilization or for the construction of shelters or nests.

The next move, the move to land, demanded the "invention" of the amniote egg, which carried within it its own watery environment in which the developing embryo could be bathed. Nesting habits became increasingly complicated to protect these incubating eggs and promote the survival of the young—on which, of course, species survival depends.

589 *Bases of Vertebrate Behavior*

|— 50mm —|

The beginnings of protective care of the eggs and the new-hatched brood are found among the bony fish and the reptiles, but it is in the birds that nesting behavior reaches its pinnacle. Fish can swim and snakes slither from the beginning of their infancy, but flying, which requires unusual strength and coordination, is dependent on physical maturation. Young birds must be fed and protected if they and the species are to survive, and much of the behavior of birds is adapted to the particular exigencies of caring for their young during this period of helplessness.

In the case of the mammals, the nursing habit lengthened still further the period of dependency of the young. And as more care had to be concentrated on the young, the number of offspring had to be reduced. In order to nurture these precious few, families and societies developed, and within this comparatively sheltered environment, the young animal had time to learn. You may owe your college education to some reptilelike mammal suckling her prehistoric brood.

The insects, as we saw, represent the apex of stereotyped behavior, behavior which is based on "averaging out" the experience of the entire species, with the results built into the group as a whole. With the coming of the vertebrates—and, in particular, the higher vertebrates, with their long dependency periods—emphasis shifted to a more flexible kind of behavior, in which each animal had some opportunity to adapt itself as an individual on the basis of its own experience.

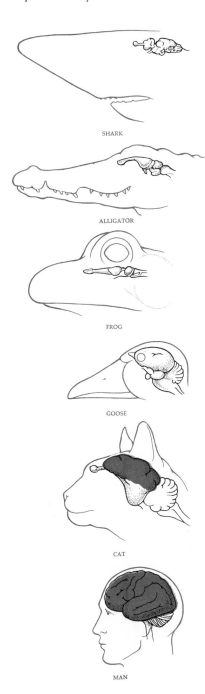

5–40 *The brain in various vertebrates. Note the differences in shapes and relative sizes. The colored areas in the brains of the cat and man indicate the cerebral cortex. How much can you tell about the physical organization and behavior of each of the animals shown from the shape and size of its brain?*

SHARK

ALLIGATOR

FROG

GOOSE

CAT

MAN

THE BRAIN

The nervous systems of the vertebrates and those of the invertebrates differ in several significant ways. Perhaps most important from the point of view of behavior is that the central nervous system of the vertebrates is far larger in proportion to their overall size; this trend increases in the course of vertebrate evolution. Second, and this is closely related to the previous development, a far larger proportion of the brain is devoted to correlation and integration of information, particularly in the higher vertebrates.

In its most primitive form, and also in its embryological development, the vertebrate brain consists of three bulges in the hollow neural tube, each bulge containing a fluid-filled area, or *ventricle*. These three bulges —the hindbrain, the midbrain, and the forebrain—became further differentiated in the course of development, so that in all modern vertebrates, five major structures can be distinguished: (1) the medulla and (2) the cerebellum, both parts of the hindbrain; (3) the midbrain; (4) the thalamus and (5) the cerebrum, both parts of the forebrain.

The Hindbrain

THE MEDULLA

The most anterior part of the hindbrain, the medulla, is a direct extension of the spinal cord. It receives the motor and sensory fibers from the skin and special organs of the neck and head, including the special sense organs, and serves as the channel for the conduction of ascending and descending nerve fibers. It also contains the centers, or groups of neurons, that regulate involuntary functions such as respiration and heartbeat. In some species of fish, the medulla possesses two conspicious lobes, the *vagal lobes*, which are the taste centers. These centers are comparatively much smaller in the other vertebrates, and in man, in whom the sense of taste plays a very limited role, the taste center, or *gustatory nucleus*, is merely a small group of cells within the medulla. In general, however, the medulla, like the spinal cord, has undergone little change in the course of vertebrate evolution.

THE CEREBELLUM

As you can see in Figure 5–40, the brain varies markedly in both size and shape throughout the chordate phylum. The cerebellum lies close to and somewhat above the medulla and is involved in the maintenance of posture and equilibrium. In fish, it is primarily a receiving area for impulses from the sensory organs concerned with balance and hearing (two very closely related functions, as we shall see) and from the proprioceptors. In the higher vertebrates, fibers from all the sensory centers of the brain

591 *Bases of Vertebrate Behavior*

feed into the cerebellum, making possible much finer coordination and integration of movements. The cerebellum reaches its greatest relative size and importance in birds, in which it coordinates the sensory and motor impulses involved in flying.

The Midbrain

The midbrain developed originally as the receiving center for the fibers coming in from the eye, and it was analogous to the great optic lobes of the octopus. In fish and amphibians, the midbrain is still the primary visual center, but it also receives information from all other areas of the brain and serves as the highest level for overall integration of behavior. In reptiles and birds, the visual impulses still travel first to the midbrain, but they are relayed from there to the more forward centers of the brain, where they are coordinated with other incoming information. In mammals, the midbrain is relatively unimportant, serving primarily as a center for relaying messages between the forebrain and the hindbrain and also between the forebrain and the eyes. Thus we see that in the course of evolution, a new center for coordinating information was created in the forebrain.

The Forebrain

THE THALAMUS

This is the terminal for many of the sensory fibers which enter the central nervous system through the spinal cord and the medulla. (See Figure 5–41.) In the lower invertebrates, it is the center for the integration of sensory information. In mammals, with the development of the cerebral cortex, the thalamus established connections with regions of the cortex and began to send information on to them.

THE HYPOTHALAMUS

The area underlying the thalamus, the *hypothalamus*, is the part of the brain involved in the production of emotional behavior. It is concerned with such functions as sleeping, drinking and eating, fighting, and reproductive behavior. Studies have been made in which electric probes have been inserted into the hypothalamus of various animals and the different areas stimulated with a mild electric current. Such stimulation apparently arouses feelings or emotions in the animals. For example, stimulation of a particular area not only can induce an animal to eat but can make it perform elaborate tasks in order to get food, even if it has just eaten.

Many of these studies have been done on cats. J. L. Brown and R. W. Hunsperger of the University of Zurich have found that electrical stimulation of three different areas of the cat brain—the midbrain, the hypothal-

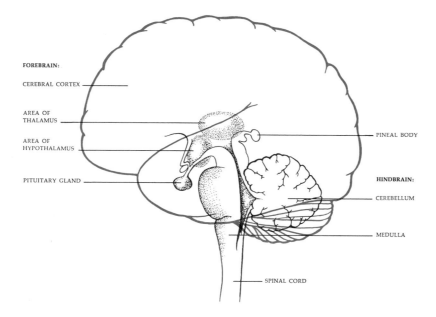

FOREBRAIN:

CEREBRAL CORTEX

AREA OF
THALAMUS

AREA OF
HYPOTHALAMUS

PITUITARY GLAND

PINEAL BODY

HINDBRAIN:

CEREBELLUM

MEDULLA

SPINAL CORD

amus, and the amygdala—will produce *agonistic* (threat) behavior in the cat. Neither the experimenters nor an untreated cat placed in the cage with the stimulated cat were able to detect a difference between such artificially produced rage and normal aggressive behavior. In close anatomical relationship with those areas in the brain in which threat behavior is initiated are areas which, when electrically stimulated, produce reactions of fear and attempts to escape. An especially striking aspect of these studies is that this artificial behavior is entirely unrelated to external circumstances. Regardless of how contented or secure the cat is, when the appropriate areas of the brain are stimulated, the resulting threat or escape behavior will override all other activities or external stimuli. Once stimulation ceases, the cat will return to whatever it was doing before.

In cats in which the hypothalamus has been removed, the animals may hiss or spit or show their claws if they are irritated, but they do not seem to be able to coordinate all these reflex activities into a typical complex expression of rage or fear or attack.

As we noted in Chapter 2–8, the pituitary gland directly underlies the hypothalamus and is connected to it by a stalk. Chemical secretions from the hypothalamus stimulate the pituitary gland, thereby maintaining a close correlation between the brain and the endocrine system.

THE CEREBRUM

The most anterior part of the brain has undergone the most important evolutionary changes in the vertebrates. In fish, amphibians, and reptiles, its most imposing parts are the olfactory bulbs, which directly underlie the special organs for smell and which are attached to the rest of the brain by the olfactory stalks. Behind the olfactory bulbs in these primitive vertebrates are two round swellings that make up the cerebrum. In fish and amphibians, the cerebrum is largely concerned with olfactory sensations, but in the reptiles, we can find the traces of new evolutionary developments which have proved to be of major importance.

A small patch of new nervous tissue began to appear at the forward upper part of the cerebral lobes; this was the beginning of the *cerebral cortex*. Also, the lobes themselves became larger, chiefly as a result of expansion of the bottom layer of the lobes, the *corpus striatum*. The corpus striatum of reptiles receives fibers from other sensory organs besides the olfactory receptors and is an integrating center of the brain, although secondary to the midbrain in dominance. In birds, the corpus striatum reached a relatively huge size in the floor of the cerebrum, becoming the dominant coordinating center of the brain.

Mammals followed a different path; the corpus striatum remained relatively unimportant, but that little patch of gray matter, the cerebral cortex, grew to take over the brain. In the primitive mammals, this area is already greatly expanded and has separated from the rest of the cerebrum. As it grew larger, the cerebral cortex began to fold back over the hemispheres; and in the higher mammals it has become more and more convoluted, thereby greatly increasing its surface area, the area on which its functions seem to depend.

As the cortex increased in size during mammalian evolution, it took over more and more functions from the older, underlying, and more posterior parts of the brain. The original role of the cortex seems to have been that of a sensory receiving system, with fairly well-separated areas for each of the different senses. The mechanisms that control and integrate locomotor patterns apparently were transferred to the cortex in a later stage of evolution. As a result of these progressive changes in which the patterns of control shifted as the brain evolved, many different areas in the brain may now be concerned with the same function, such as vision or hearing; and the higher the mammal is on the evolutionary scale, the more important has become the relative role of the cortex. For instance, if the area of the cortex concerned with vision is removed in the rat, the animal is slightly impaired in its discrimination of patterns. If it is removed in the monkey, the animal can distinguish light from dark, but no patterns. A man whose visual cortex has been damaged is totally blind. Similarly, a dog or a cat whose cerebral cortex has been removed can stand and walk,

5–42 *Functional map of the human cerebral cortex based on experiments involving electrical stimulation. Notice the size of the areas controlling the hands and the mouth compared with the size of those for other parts of the body. As you can see in the insert on the left, a large area of the cortex is devoted to associational fibers, which develop complex interconnections among the motor and sensory activities. (After Penfield, 1959)*

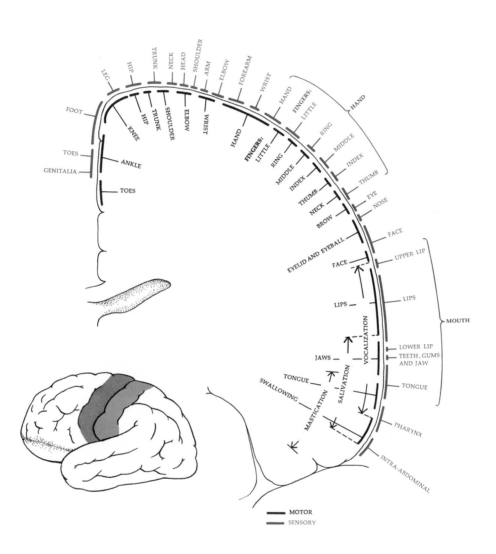

but a monkey or a man cannot. Another important difference between the cortices of the higher and lower mammals is that in the latter almost the whole surface of the cortex is concerned with definite sensory or motor activities, while in man, a large area of this huge ganglion is given over to associational fibers which form complex interconnections between all the impulses received in this area of the brain. (See Figure 5–42.) Nearly all scientists agree that learning ability and intelligence in man and the other primates are generally correlated with the size and degree of development of these large areas of associational cortex, although at present we know very little about the anatomical organization of these abilities.

THE SPECIAL SENSES

We take it for granted that we see with our eyes and hear with our ears and smell with our noses, but actually this is not the case. Seeing, hearing, and smelling all take place within the brain. Furthermore, the brain does not receive a picture or a sound or a smell, but only a series of electrochemical impulses. Instances have been recorded in which a patient undergoing brain surgery saw vivid visual images or heard fragments of tunes when areas of his cortex were stimulated electrically. Perception consists of the organization, analysis, and interpretation of stimuli, rather than their reception. In general, the vertebrates perceive more (that is, they receive more information from their surroundings) than the invertebrates, and the primates more than the fishes, not because the special sensory organs are more acute or more efficient but because of the greater capacity of the larger and more complicated brain to make discriminations and associations on the basis of the signals that it receives.

The Vertebrate Eye

Vision is a dominant factor in the behavior of many vertebrates, including ourselves. A diagram of the vertebrate eye is shown in Figure 5–43; this is a human eye, but a picture of the eye of any other vertebrate species would look much the same. This type of eye is often called a *camera eye,* and camera fans will be quick to recognize that it has a number of features in common with the ordinary camera and also a number of expensive accessories, such as a built-in cleaning and lubricating system, an exposure meter, and an automatic field finder. As indicated in the figure, light from the object being viewed passes through the transparent cornea and lens, which focus an inverted image of the object on the light-sensitive retina in the back of the eyeball. The iris controls the amount of light entering the eye by regulating the size of the pupil.

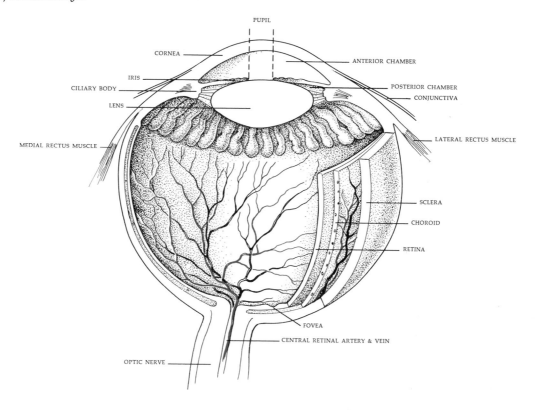

PUPIL

CORNEA

ANTERIOR CHAMBER

IRIS

CILIARY BODY

POSTERIOR CHAMBER

CONJUNCTIVA

LENS

MEDIAL RECTUS MUSCLE

LATERAL RECTUS MUSCLE

SCLERA

CHOROID

RETINA

FOVEA

CENTRAL RETINAL ARTERY & VEIN

OPTIC NERVE

FOCUSING THE EYE

In fish and amphibians, which lack ciliary muscles, the eye is focused in the same way one focuses a camera. Muscles within the eye change the position of the lens, drawing it back toward the retina in order to focus more distant objects. In mammals, the focus is adjusted by contracting or releasing the ciliary muscles and so changing the shape of the lens.

Depth vision, or stereoscopic vision, depends on viewing an object with both eyes simultaneously and seeing one image, not two. When both eyes are trained on an object, the angle at which the two visual axes come together is communicated to the brain by proprioceptors in the ciliary muscles. On the basis of this information, we automatically compute the size and distance of nearby objects. Since our eyes converge only on near objects, we are not able to make such judgments when distances increase. Instead, we estimate these distances on the basis of the known size of the objects or on the basis of other visual clues, such as houses, people, or cars. A young child viewing a distant object, such as an airplane, will think of it as "little" rather than distant.

597 *Bases of Vertebrate Behavior*

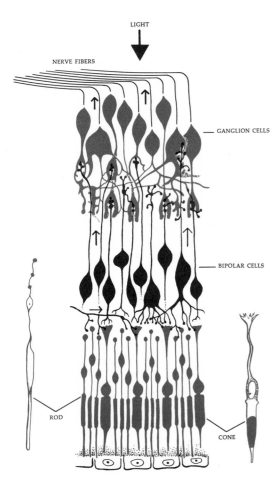

LIGHT

NERVE FIBERS

GANGLION CELLS

BIPOLAR CELLS

ROD

CONE

5–44 *The retina of the vertebrate eye. Light (shown here as entering from the top) must pass through a layer of cells to reach the photoreceptors (the rods and cones) at the back of the eye. Impulses from the photoreceptor cells are transmitted through the bipolar cells to the ganglion cells. As shown by the arrows, the transmission paths are not direct but involve elaborate interconnections.*

In general, hunting animals nearly all have some overlapping of visual fields in the front to provide them with stereoscopic vision for catching prey. Animals which are more likely to be hunted than to hunt tend to have eyes on the side of the head, giving a wider total field. Some birds with large laterally placed eyes—the woodcock, the cuckoo, and certain species of crow—have binocular fields of vision either in front of them or behind them.

THE RETINA

The retina of the vertebrate eye is functionally inside out—that is, the photoreceptors of the eye are pointed toward the back of the eyeball—and light must reach the light-sensitive area by passing through a layer of cell bodies. (See Figure 5–44.) Light that is not captured by the photoreceptors is absorbed by the pigmented chorioid which lines the back of the eyeball.

The photoreceptor cells transmit their impulses to neurons known as *bipolar cells*, which pass the impulses on to the cells the axons of which form the optic nerves. As you can see in the figure, these pathways of transmission are not direct, but varied and elaborate interconnections are made among the cells even before the impulses leave the retina, indicating that some preliminary analysis of visual information takes place in the retina itself. The human retina contains about 125 million photoreceptors and about 1 million optic-nerve fibers.

The retinal nerve fibers are interconnected in a network that fans out over the forward-facing part of the retina. The fibers come together at one point on the retina, and from this point, bundled together like a cable, they pass through the retina and out the back. The point at which the fibers pass out of the eyeball is a blind spot in the eye. We are not generally aware of the existence of the blind spot since we usually see the same object with both eyes and the "missing piece" is always supplied by the other eye. If you are not aware of your own blind spot, you can demonstrate its existence with the help of Figure 5–45.

As shown in Figure 5–43, there is an area just above the blind spot known as the *fovea*. This is the only spot in the eye at which we see a really sharp image. In this area, the photoreceptor cells are packed much more closely together and have a one-to-one connection with the bipolar cells. Birds, which rely on vision above all the other senses, may have two or three foveas. Most vertebrates, however, have no fovea, and their vision is comparable in acuity to what we see out of the corners of our eyes.

RODS AND CONES

The human retina contains two types of photoreceptors. (Figure 5–44). These are known, because of their shapes, as *rods* and *cones*. The cones, of which the human eye contains about 5 million, provide greater resolution

5–45 *With this diagram, you can prove for yourself that you have a blind spot in each eye. Hold the book about 12 inches from your face, cover your left eye, and gaze steadily at the X while slowly moving the book toward your face. Note that at a certain distance, the image of the dot becomes invisible. Then cover your right eye and gaze steadily at the dot while you move the book toward your face. What happens to the X?*

X   ● / /

of vision, giving a "crisper" picture. The photoreceptors in the fovea are all cones. Man has about 160,000 cones per square millimeter of eye. A hawk, with an eye about the same size, has some 1 million cones per square millimeter and has a visual acuity about eight times that of man.

Rods do not provide as great a degree of resolution as cones do, but they are more light-sensitive; in dim light, our vision depends entirely on rods. Some nocturnal animals, such as toads, mice, rats, and bats, have retinas made up entirely of rods, while some diurnal animals, such as reptiles, have only cones.

Cones are responsible for color vision, which is why the world becomes gray to us at twilight. The physiology of color vision is not entirely understood, but it appears that there are three different types of cones, each one of which contains a pigment sensitive to the wavelength of one of three "primary" colors—blue, green, or red. Different shades of color stimulate different combinations of these cells, and these impulses, after being processed in the retina, are analyzed by the brain, which translates them into what we perceive as color. Most species of vertebrates do not have color vision. Among the mammals it is found only in the primates.

VISION AND BEHAVIOR

Vision is a direct stimulus to action in many of the vertebrates. Predatory fish are vision-stimulated, and many such fish literally "cannot help" striking at a moving object of appropriate size. The frog can learn not to strike at a small moving object, but only with difficulty. If it comes to associate an unpleasant experience with a particular shape, it can restrain itself, although apparently with effort, from striking at that shape. On the other hand, it can never learn to take an object that is not moving. Even a frog which has eaten thousands of live flies will starve to death surrounded by motionless ones.

Recently, it has been found that certain nerve fibers leaving the retina of the frog fire impulses only when the frog's eye is stimulated by a small moving object. A large moving object or a small still one provoke no response. These fibers terminate in a special layer of cells in the frog's midbrain, and although no further connections have been traced, it is tempting to speculate that signals are relayed from this part of the midbrain to efferent nerves that control the muscles involved in striking.

In mammals, in general, vision is less important than it is in many of the other vertebrates. Many of the smaller mammals are nocturnal, and most of them live close to the ground in habitats in which their highly developed sense of smell provides the greatest amount of information about their environment. Presumably, it was the tree-dwelling habits of our immediate ancestors that made the sense of smell less useful for the primates. Among the mammals, only the primates have a central fovea for sharp focusing. In man, the highly developed vision is undoubtedly closely correlated with the development of the use of the hands for fine manipulative movements. This reasonable hypothesis is supported by the fact that the human eye is so constructed that the sharpest images—images within the fovea—can be made of objects which are within the reach of the hand.

Among animals which have color vision, colors often play an important role in stimulating behavior. Studies of the three-spined stickleback, a small freshwater fish, have shown that fighting behavior among the males is elicited by the red color of their underbellies, which develops during the mating season. Niko Tinbergen, who kept a laboratory in England full of aquariums containing sticklebacks, found that the male sticklebacks would rush to the sides of their tanks and assume threatening postures every time a red mailtruck passed on the street outside. Similarly, it has been found that fighting behavior among English robins (which are a different species of thrush than our American robins) can be evoked by a small tuft of red feathers. In birds, bright plumage also plays an important part in courtship ceremonies. The mandarin duck, for example, points to a large orange-colored feather on his wing during his courtship ceremony. From studies of related species, ethologists have come to the conclusion, which is the opposite of what one might expect, that the pointing gesture evolved first, as part of the animal's preening ritual, and that the size and bright color of the feather were a secondary development.

Chemoreceptors

If we were to lose our sense of taste or smell, our life would lose many of its pleasures but we would be very little handicapped in our essential activities. Blindness or deafness would be a far more serious threat. For many animals, however, the sense of smell is their window on the world, much as vision is ours. Watch a dog the next time it is let out of the house in the

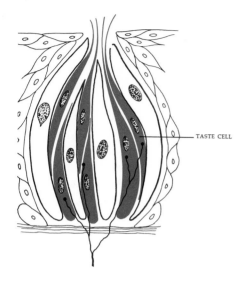

TASTE CELL

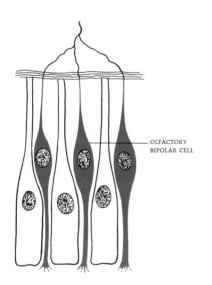

OLFACTORY
BIPOLAR CELL

—46 *Cross sections of a taste receptor and a
smell receptor.*

morning: It does not look around, human fashion; it sniffs the air and then explores the ground with its nose in order to bring itself up to date on the events of the previous night.

Although the organs of chemoreception seem much simpler than those of vision or hearing, we know less about how they work. We do not know (1) how a chemical can trigger a nerve impulse, or (2) how the various different chemicals that we can distinguish by taste or smell manage to identify themselves to the brain.

TASTE

Fish, particularly the bottom feeders, have taste cells scattered over the surfaces of their bodies, and these cells play a major role in determining their behavior. In the carp, for example, the part of the brain which receives information from these taste cells is larger than all the other sensory centers combined. The catfish, also a bottom feeder, has taste cells on its body and, in addition, trails barblets, or "whiskers," along the ground which are richly supplied with gustatory nerve endings. When these are stimulated, the fish turns and snaps at the source of the stimulus.

In the terrestrial animals, taste cells are located inside the mouth, where they act as sentinels, providing a final judgment on what is and what is not to be swallowed. The taste receptors and the supporting cells around them form goblet-shaped clusters known as *taste buds*. (See Figure 5–46.) Man is able to distinguish four primary tastes: sweet, sour, salty, and bitter. While each primary taste appears to stimulate a different type of taste bud, there are indications that a single taste bud may respond to more than one category of substance.

Most animals seem to have the same general range of taste discrimination, although there is some difference in what animals "like" and don't "like." Birds, for example, will readily eat seeds and insects with a bitter taste, whereas for most other vertebrates, bitterness serves as a warning signal. Cats are among the few animals that do not prefer substances that have a sweet taste, and very few fibers that respond to sugar can be found in the cat's tongue. Most animals will work for a sweet reward even though they are not hungry, and the cat's indifference to sweetness is one of the reasons it is difficult to train—although its general social independence is probably a more significant one.

SMELL

In fish, taste and smell are operationally very similar since both involve the detection of substances dissolved in the surrounding water. Taste receptors and smell receptors differ anatomically (see Figure 5–46), however, and the centers of taste and smell within the brain are entirely distinct.

601   *Bases of Vertebrate Behavior*

5–47 *A Smooth snake samples the air with its forked tongue. It will test what it has collected by inserting its tongue into its vomeronasal cavities. (S. C. Bisserôt, F.R.P.S.)*

The smell receptors of fish may be scattered over the body surface, as are the taste receptors, but special groups of smell receptors are also collected in shallow depressions in the forward part of the head. These depressions—as seen in the shark, for example—are merely paired pockets where pools of water can collect and be exposed to the olfactory epithelium. In the course of evolution, these primitive nostrils became deeper and deeper and finally pushed through an opening to the roof of the mouth. In this way, it became possible for the fish to smell substances which were inside its mouth. As you know, most of what we call flavor in food is actually a result of volatile substances reaching the olfactory epithelium.

Amphibians and reptiles have, in addition to nostrils, a special olfactory organ, the *vomeronasal organ,* in the roof of the mouth. Food substances are apparently tested in this organ. When a snake lashes its forked tongue in the air, it is collecting samples for testing in its vomeronasal cavities. (See Figure 5–47.)

In the terrestrial animals, smell and taste have become more clearly separated, with smell being reserved for airborne substances. Even these substances, however, must be dissolved in the watery layer of mucus overlying the olfactory epithelium. In man, this epithelium, which is located high within the nasal passages, is comparatively small, the part within each nostril being only about as large as a postage stamp. Each of these areas contains some 600,000 receptor cells. Even with our relatively insensitive olfactory equipment, we are able to discriminate some 10,000 different odors.

One of the current theories of odor discrimination is that which was developed by John Amoore while he was still an undergraduate at Oxford University in England. According to Amoore's theory, all scents are made up of combinations of seven "primary" odors: camphoric, musky, floral, pepperminty, etherlike, pungent, and putrid. There are also, he hypothesized, seven different types of olfactory receptors, each one of which has its own special shape. Molecules of a certain shape fit into correspondingly shaped receptors, just as a piece of a jigsaw puzzle fits into its own particular space. All substances which have a pungent odor, for example, have the same general shape and fit into the same type of receptor. Some molecules, depending on which way they are oriented, can fit into more than one receptor and so can evoke in the brain two different types of signals. From the signals received from the various different types of cells, the brain constructs a "picture" of an odor.

Odor serves as many functions as vision in the vertebrate world. Most animals hunt by smell; a blindfolded dog can point its nose straight at a rabbit. Odor is also a warning signal to the quarry. Every hunter knows the necessity of staying upwind from almost every animal he stalks. Fish of the minnow family have evolved a mechanism for warning other fish by odor. When a minnow is wounded, a chemical is released from its skin that sets off a fright reaction in other fish. This chemical is an alarm pheromone analogous to the alarm substance released by the harvester ant, which we discussed in Chapter 5–2. In certain minnows, the smell of the predator itself will sometimes cause an avoidance reaction without the minnow alarm substance being present. For example, if the animal that does the wounding is a pike, which is one of the minnow's chief predators, the smell of pike then takes on the function of a warning smell and pike smell alone will cause the fright reaction. On receipt of the warning, the minnows of some species do not flee but stop short and drop like stones to the bottom. This is a singularly useful adaptation since the predatory pike, which is much faster than the minnow, is dominated by vision and not by smell.

Smell, of course, is also the way in which most mammals distinguish friend from enemy, male from female, and infant from adult and in which they identify their mates, their parents, and their offspring. It has been shown in laboratory tests that a white rat can distinguish juvenile and mature male rats, females in heat and females not in heat, and females from which the ovaries have been removed. Brown rats, which travel in large packs, are extremely amiable to other members of the pack, which they identify by smell, but ruthlessly destroy any foreign-smelling stranger.

Recently, it has been discovered that the smell of a strange male mouse may interrupt pregnancy in a female. That overcrowding in a mouse colony considerably diminishes the birthrate has long been known. It now appears that smell may be one important method by which this adaptively useful form of birth control takes place.

Phonoreceptors

HEARING AND BALANCE IN FISH

Hearing and balance in the vertebrates both depend on the movement of tiny hairs which stimulate a response in underlying sensory cells. Figure 5–49 shows such cells as they appear in the *organ of Corti*, the hearing receptor of the mammal, but the sensory cell from any hearing or balancing organ in any of the vertebrates would appear much the same. The hairs on the surface of this cell have the characteristic structure of cilia and are undoubtedly derived from them.

In some fish, hair cells of this sort appear along the surface of the body, but in most species, they are protected beneath the surface in canals that are open to the exterior. The network of canals, known as the *lateral-line system*, runs along the side of the fish, branching out around the head. The movement of the water causes the hairs in the lateral-line canals to bend, and this bending stimulates the dendrites of the underlying neurons. These movements keep the fish informed about other animals in the vicinity—whether prey, predator, or potential mate. They also make it possible for the fish to hear sounds produced by other fish. Fish are able to make a variety of noises, but there is a lack of general agreement on whether such sounds are actually used in communication. Undoubtedly, they serve at the very least to advise fish of the presence of other fish.

Within the head of the fish is another organ, the *labyrinth*, which contains hair cells. The primary function of the labyrinth is balance. It is from this organ that the hearing mechanisms of all the terrestrial vertebrates have evolved. The uppermost part of this structure contains three fluid-filled semicircular canals. These canals are oriented in three directions, representing the three-dimensional space in which we live, and movements of the head cause the fluids within these canals to press upon the hair cells. Impulses from the hair cells report these movements to the brain. Below the semicircular canals and connected with them are three hollow chambers, each containing statocysts which respond to gravity. This part of the

5–48 *The structure of the human ear. Sound enters through the outer ear and vibrates the tympanic membrane. These vibrations are transmitted through the anvil and hammer to the stapes, causing it to tap against a membrane (the oval window) leading to the inner ear. Through the inner ear, the impulse is transmitted to the brain.*

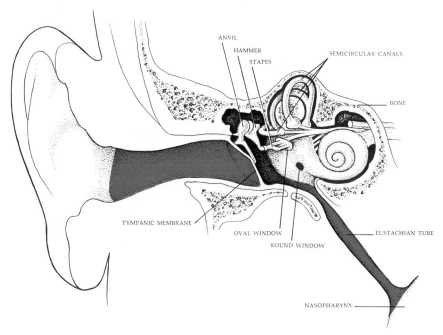

ANVIL
HAMMER
STAPES
SEMICIRCULAR CANALS
BONE
TYMPANIC MEMBRANE
OVAL WINDOW
ROUND WINDOW
EUSTACHIAN TUBE
NASOPHARYNX

labyrinth—the semicircular canals and the chambers containing the stato-cysts—is found in all vertebrates and has changed little in the course of evolution.

In some fish, the lower chambers of the labyrinth are connected either directly or by a small series of bones to the swim bladder, an air-filled pouch which gives the fish buoyancy. Sound waves set up vibrations in the swim bladder, which are transmitted to the labyrinth. The statoliths in one of the three chambers, the *lagena*, respond to these sound vibrations. In fish which do not have a swim bladder, sound impulses are transmitted directly through the head, just as we can feel vibrations through our fingertips.

THE EVOLUTION OF THE EAR

In the course of evolution, the lagena became larger and more elaborate. The outer structures of the ear also underwent changes. In the fish, as we have seen, there is no opening connecting the labyrinth with the outer surface of the animal. In amphibians, there is a tympanic membrane on the surface of the animal's head, and underlying it is a small bone, the *stapes*, which conducts sound from the membrane to the labyrinth. (This bone is "borrowed" from one of the jawbones of the fish.) In reptiles, a ridge or fold of skin may guard the tympanum; and in birds and mammals, the ear-drum is sunk far below the surface, with a deep tube (the outer ear) leading to it. Many mammals have a highly developed external ear, which serves as a scoop for catching sound waves and funneling them into the ear tube. The ear of man no longer serves this function, although some few human beings retain the ability to wiggle their ears, using the same muscles other animals use to cock these special appendages toward the source of a sound.

THE STRUCTURE OF THE HUMAN EAR

Figure 5–48 diagrams the structure of the human ear. Sound travels through the outer ear to the tympanic membrane, in which it sets up a vibration. This vibration is transferred to a series of three very small and delicate bones, which are called, because of their shapes, the *anvil*, the *hammer*, and the *stapes* (or stirrup). Movements in the tympanic membrane cause the stapes to tap gently and rapidly against a membrane leading to the inner ear, and through the inner ear, the impulse is transmitted to the brain.

The *middle ear*, as the area between the eardrum and the inner ear is called, is connected with the nasopharynx by the eustachian tube. This connection makes it possible to equalize the air pressure in the middle ear; it also unfortunately makes the middle ear a fertile breeding ground for in-fectious microorganisms which enter the body through the nose or throat.

The actual organ of hearing is in the fluid-filled *inner ear,* coiled in a bony spiral shell, the *cochlea,* which had its evolutionary origins in the lagena. Figure 5–49 shows a diagram of the cochlea uncoiled. It consists essentially of three canals separated by membranes. The upper and lower canals are connected with one another at the far end of the organ. At the base of each of these two canals is a movable membrane known as a *window.* The little stirrup vibrates against the membrane at the base of the upper canal, known as the *oval window* because of its shape, and the sound waves travel the length of the cochlea, around the apex, and back again to the membrane at the base of the lower canal, the *round window.* As the oval window moves in, the round window moves out, keeping the pressure equalized. You will notice that, although hearing is generally considered to be the detection of airborne sounds, our hearing cells are ultimately stimulated by movements in fluid, just as are the cells in the lateral-line system of the fish.

5–49 *The part of the inner ear concerned with hearing is the cochlea, a coiled tube of 2½ turns—shown here as if it were uncoiled. Vibrations transmitted from the tympanic membrane to the stapes cause the stapes to tap against the oval window, resulting in resonance waves in the fluid which fills the cochlear canals. The pressure wave in the fluid sets up a traveling wave in the basilar membrane, stimulating the sensory endings of the auditory nerve distributed along its length. Sounds at different frequencies (or pitch) have their maximum effect on different areas of the membrane. The round window permits the pressure waves to leave the cochlea.*

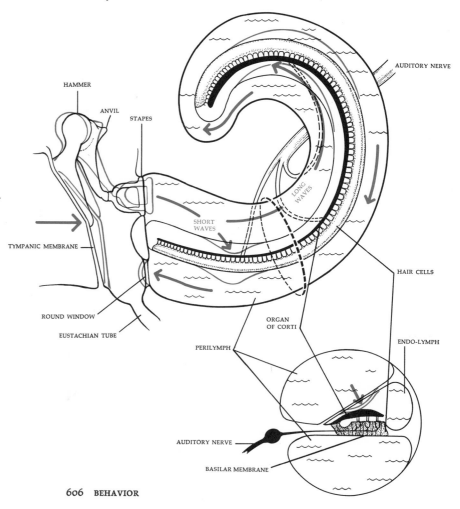

AUDITORY NERVE

HAMMER

ANVIL

STAPES

LONG WAVES

SHORT WAVES

TYMPANIC MEMBRANE

HAIR CELLS

ROUND WINDOW

ORGAN OF CORTI

EUSTACHIAN TUBE

ENDO-LYMPH

PERILYMPH

AUDITORY NERVE

BASILAR MEMBRANE

5–50 *The long ears of the bat are adapted for picking up high-frequency echolocation signals. As the bat flies, it emits shrill squeaks, as many as 30 every second. When it comes closer to some object, it may increase this frequency to about 60 per second. These sounds do not travel far—about 20 feet is the maximum— and they bounce back only about 15 feet. The bat is guided by these echoes in flying and in hunting prey. (S. C. Bisserôt, F.R.P.S.)*

The central canal contains a number of hair cells which rest on the bottom, or *basilar membrane,* of the canal. The movement of the fluid along the outer surface of the central canal sets up motions in the fluid of the central canal, and movements in this fluid stimulate the hair cells, which are the actual phonoreceptors.

The basilar membrane does not vibrate uniformly along its length, but different areas of the membrane respond to different frequencies of sound. In this way, different sensory hairs are stimulated by different frequencies. The fine discriminations of sound of which human beings are capable are made by the brain on the basis of the signals received from the various hair cells.

In general, the human ear can detect sounds ranging from 16 to 20,000 cycles per second, although some children can hear up to 40,000 cycles per second. From middle age onward, there is a progressive loss in ability to hear the higher frequencies, owing to loss in the elasticity of the tympanic membranes.

Our inability to hear very low-pitched sounds (below 16 cycles) is a useful adaptation since if we could, we would be barraged with sounds caused by the movements of our own bodies and conducted through the bones of our own skeletons. We do hear some sounds conducted directly through the skull—for example, the noise we make when we chew celery. We also hear our own voices.

Dogs can hear up to 30,000 cycles a second, and bats up to 100,000. At the highest frequencies, the vibrations of the eardrum are only about one-tenth the diameter of a hydrogen atom.

HEARING AND BEHAVIOR

Hearing is a major behavior determinant throughout the vertebrate world. Consider, for example, the mating calls of frogs, the songs of birds, the chirp of the baby chick, the challenging bellow of the male gorilla. Many of the cries are in ranges we cannot hear. It has been found, for instance, that infant rats and mice are constantly squeaking in frequencies so high that we cannot detect them. It is possible that the world around us is filled with noises of which we are unaware.

One animal in which hearing plays a major and unusual role is the bat. In 1793, Lazzaro Spallanzani, a brilliant Italian scientist, became curious about how animals found their way around in darkness. Owls and other nocturnal creatures, he discovered, relied on their large eyes and became helpless in complete darkness. Bats, however, did not depend on vision at all. Spallanzani, in one of the first biological experiments, captured bats in the bell tower of the Cathedral of Pavia, blinded them, and turned them loose. Several days later, he captured the same bats again; not only had the blind animals found their way back to the bell tower but their stomachs

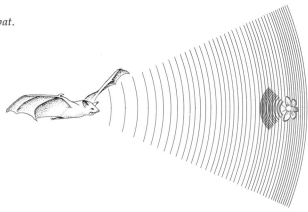

were full of freshly caught moths and the other flying insects which were their normal diet. Guessing that the bats might "hear" their way through the darkness, Spallanzani plugged the ear canals of some captive bats and found that the deafened animals were wholly disoriented and bumped into every obstacle at random.

Little more was known about the navigation of bats until electronic devices were developed which could record the presence of sounds outside the range of human hearing. Donald Griffin, while still a graduate student at Harvard, brought some bats to a laboratory which contained such an apparatus and found that the bats were continuously emitting shrill cries above the frequency range of human hearing. When these sound waves hit a solid object, they echo back to the ears of the bat. On the basis of these echoes, bats can navigate skillfully through a dark room strung with wires little thicker than a human hair or can catch an insect as small as a fly. (See Figure 5–51.)

Man, as you know, applied this same principle in the development of sonar, the use of sound waves to detect underwater objects and to map the ocean bottom. Man's development of listening devices under the sea has revealed that many aquatic animals, including both fish and porpoises, seem to use sonar to find one another, to avoid obstacles, and to hunt prey.

Other Sensory Organs

Many other sensory receptors guide the behavior of animals. Cells in the skin register pain, heat, cold, and in the case of the amphibians, dryness, all of which stimulate action. Some snakes (rattlesnakes, for instance) have areas on each side of the head, between the eye and the nostril, which are sensitive to warmth. These are used to guide the snake to the warm-blooded animals that are its usual prey. One of these pit vipers, as they are known, can detect a mouse up to several feet away. Some fish can precisely detect electric current and can orient themselves by means of electrical fields of their own making.

Many animals also have built-in timepieces. You yourself have probably noticed how often you manage to wake up just before the alarm goes off, and many people are able to "set themselves" to get up at almost any hour, not just their usual arising time. The ability to measure time with great precision is particularly striking in birds. Many types of birds can find their way home after having been transported great distances and released in unknown areas or can perform seasonal migrations that take them literally from pole to pole. Experiments have shown that birds can orient themselves in response to the position of the sun or the stars. For example, in an experiment with European warblers, which are night migrants, the warblers were placed under an artificial sky in a planetarium. In the spring, the warblers tried to migrate "north," as indicated by the star pattern presented to them, and conversely, they headed "south" in

5–52 *During their seasonal migrations, some birds travel halfway around the world. Experiments have indicated that birds are able to find their way over such great distances because they can judge directions at certain times and seasons by the sun or the stars.*

MIGRATION ROUTES OF THE ARCTIC TERN

609 *Bases of Vertebrate Behavior*

the fall. Similarly, birds such as terns, which migrate in the daytime, have been shown to judge direction by the sun.

As all celestial navigators know, in order to steer by the sun or stars, one must have a chronometer. Thus birds must be presumed to have both a much simplified "map" of the sky in their brain and a sense by which they "know" the time and seasons and so can take into account the constantly changing pattern of the heavens. These built-in chronometers of the birds are clearly related to the biological clocks that govern many other physiological activities.

THE ENDOCRINE SYSTEM

Hormones and Behavior

Another major influence on the behavior of the vertebrates is the endocrine system. As you can see in Figure 5–41, the pituitary gland, which is the master controlling gland of the endocrine system, is located under the hypothalamus and is stimulated directly by the brain. The pituitary, as you know from Section 2, releases a number of hormones, including gonadotropic hormones, which act upon the male and female sex glands to induce the release of male and female sex hormones. The hormones induce physiological changes in the reproductive tract and also in secondary sexual organs, such as mammary tissue. These physiological changes in themselves influence behavior; the presence of milk in the breast, for example, stimulates nursing behavior in the mother.

The hormones also apparently act directly on the brain to induce behavior. In female cats, for instance, from which the ovaries (the source of estrogen) have been removed, mating behavior can be brought about by injections of very small amounts of estrogen into certain areas of the hypothalamus; estrogen so administered does not produce any effect at all on the genital tract of the animals.

In male animals, castration of immature animals prevents development both of the male sexual organs and of male sexual behavior. Castration of adult animals similarly brings male sexual behavior to an abrupt halt in most of the vertebrates, including reptiles, amphibians, most birds, and the lower mammals such as the rats. In male cats and dogs and particularly in male primates, however, sexual behavior frequently survives for long periods after castration in adulthood. Apparently, in the higher mammals, the cortex assumes increasing dominance over these activities.

Endocrine Activity and Behavior in Birds

Birds provide particularly interesting examples of the interrelationships between behavior and endocrine activities. Mating and nesting behavior of most birds is timed by external stimuli such as warmer temperature, increased day length, or the beginning of a rainy season. Response to these environmental clues ensures that the eggs will hatch during the period most suitable for care of the young. Seasonal changes are often in themselves not sufficient, however. For example, regardless of the season, the female pigeon will become ready for nesting and mating only in the presence of another pigeon; her own image in the mirror will suffice, however, to bring on reproductive behavior. Other female birds are more demanding. In some species of birds, the males build elaborate and beautiful bridal bowers; some of these may be as much as 6 feet tall and may require several days to complete. Male and female then mate within the bower, after which the female goes off by herself to build a quite ordinary nest, lay her eggs, and raise her brood in solitude. Bower building appears not only to attract the female but also to bring her into reproductive readiness through visual stimulation.

5–53 *A male bowerbird displays to a watching female. The male builds the bower, which is the focus of his territory, and mating almost always takes place in it. The bower may be pulled down and rebuilt several times a year. (Dr. John Warham, F.R.P.S.)*

In some birds, a constant interplay between the endocrine system and the brain is required. Daniel S. Lehrman at Rutgers University has carried out a series of studies of mating behavior in the ringdove, a small relative of the domestic pigeon. It is always springtime in Lehrman's temperature- and light-controlled laboratory, but the solitary male or female dove will show no signs of mating or nesting behavior. If a male and female are placed together, however, they will carry out repeated cycles of reproductive behavior, each lasting six to seven weeks and each accompanied by profound physiological changes.

The first day of the cycle is spent in courtship, with the male bowing, cooing, and strutting. A nest site is selected—an empty bowl provided by the experimenters—and during the following week both birds cooperate in gathering material for the nest. During this period, they mate. Between 7 and 11 days after the beginning of courtship, the female lays the eggs, which the male and female sit on in turn. In about 14 days, the eggs hatch, and the parents begin to feed their young *crop-milk*, a liquid secreted by the lining of the adult's crop, a pouch in the bird's gullet. The young birds are fed for about two weeks, after which the parents lose interest in them. The young birds then develop the ability to peck grain on the floor of the cage. When the young are 15 to 25 days old, the adult male begins once again to bow and coo and the cycle starts over.

During the period from the beginning of courtship to the egg laying, the oviducts of the female bird increase in size some 500 percent, from 800 to 4,000 milligrams. This increase in size can also be seen in a female bird which, although in the same cage as a male bird, is separated from the male by a glass partition. If the male bird is castrated, however, and does not behave like a male, the female's oviducts do not enlarge.

Physiological changes and behavior changes develop in parallel. For instance, if a nest containing eggs is put into the cage at the same time as the male and female are placed in it, the nest is absolutely ignored. When the time comes for the birds to build their nest, they usually build it right on top of the already present eggs. If, however, the birds are allowed to court for seven days, they will sit on a newly introduced nest and eggs quite promptly. Presumably, the courtship prepared them for nesting by stimulating hormone productions. To test this hypothesis, isolated birds were injected with the hormone progesterone for one week. They were then put into cages together and immediately given nests and eggs; the great majority sat promptly on the nest.

During the 14 days when the doves are sitting on their eggs, their crops increase enormously in weight, from 900 to as much as 3,000 milligrams. This increase in crop weight, which contributes to the parents' production of "milk," is stimulated by production of the hormone prolactin. If male birds are removed from the cage during the incubation period, their crops do not increase in weight. If they are merely separated from the female by a glass partition, however, and are permitted to watch her incubate the eggs, the visual stimulus alone is sufficient to induce the secretion of prolactin and the consequent enlargement of the crop. This interplay between hormone action and behavior serves to synchronize the complex activities required for the rearing of the young.

SUMMARY

Modern biology is committed to the proposition that the structures and functions of living organisms can be explained in physicochemical terms. In this chapter, we have attempted to summarize some of the major physicochemical systems that determine behavior in the vertebrates.

As you can see, a summary of the sensory equipment of an animal or of the anatomical divisions of its brain, although these impose certain limits on behavior, does not in any way "explain" it. We may understand the chemical changes which take place in the photoreceptors of an animal, and we may actually trace the optic fibers to their terminus, but this would not allow us to predict what it would do, for instance, if it saw a mouse. Similarly, we know the exact chemical structure of testosterone, but on the basis of neurophysiology alone, we do not know whether an injection of testosterone will cause a given animal to fight, sing, or build a bower.

In the course of evolution, there have been relatively few changes in the structure of the individual nerve cells, the sensory receptors, or the chemicals involved in behavior, but vast changes have occurred in the number and deployment of such cells and in the uses made of them. Although many details are known concerning the "machinery" of behavior and its operation, this is a field in which a wealth of material is still awaiting discovery.

Instinct, Learning, and Memory

INSTINCT

Some of the liveliest research and controversy in the field of behavior center around the word "instinct." If you think of some of the common ways in which this word is used, you will begin to glimpse the problems associated with it. What would you give as examples of instinct? Mother love? Dog-and-cat fights? Fear of snakes? What do you mean when you say "I took an instinctive dislike to that person"?

As used by biologists in the nineteenth century, the word "instinct" meant an inherited pattern of behavior. This is still a useful working definition. On the other hand, we know now that all that can be inherited is that which is contained in the DNA of the egg and the sperm. On the basis of this knowledge, it is possible to describe quite precisely how certain traits, such as sickle-cell anemia, are inherited. The problem of inheritance of other, multifactored characteristics, such as the shape of a jawbone, is far more complicated, as we have seen. And the unknown links between, for example, the three-day ritual of the bower bird adorning his nuptial palace and a particular sequence of purines and pyrimidines are many indeed.

At one time, "instinctive" was synonymous with "unlearned," but the more that is known, the more difficult it is to separate behavior that is learned from that which is genetically determined but does not appear until maturation. We should all agree, for example, that sexual behavior is instinctive, at least in part, and complete patterns of sexual behavior do not appear until an animal is mature. Further, they never appear in an animal that has been castrated before puberty, and they may not appear, as we shall see, in higher animals that have been raised under conditions of social deprivation.

Criteria of Instinctive Behavior

Despite these difficulties of definition, most workers in the field of behavior still find "instinct" a useful term.

It is perhaps simplest to think of instinctive as meaning genetically determined. If you can demonstrate that behavior has a genetic basis, it will be agreed by many, but by no means all, investigators of behavior that the behavior can be called instinctive. Those that disagree argue that the term "instinct" should not be used at all since it is impossible to state on the basis of the knowledge now available just exactly what is being inherited, that is, what is coded in the DNA that results in an animal behaving as it does.

As we come to know more about behavior, it becomes clear that instinct and learning are not opposites but simply matters of gradation. Some behavior patterns are completely programmed, such as the complex sexual response of the male moth to the female pheromone, while others, such as variations in human speech, are composed largely of learned components.

DOES THE BEHAVIOR APPEAR IN ALL MEMBERS OF A SPECIES?

If you have a dog, you may have noticed that he turns around two or three times before lying down, as did his wolf forebears, who made this motion to trample down grass or brush. To prove that this behavior is genetically determined, however, one would have to raise a dog away from all other dogs and see if he still performed these characteristic circling movements. Such experiments have been done with a number of animals. For example, flying squirrels have been raised in bare laboratory cages isolated from other squirrels. The first time such a squirrel is given nuts or nutlike objects, it will "bury" them in the bare floor, making scratching movements as if to dig out the earth, pushing the nuts down into the "hole" with its nose, covering them over with imaginary earth, and stamping on them.

DOES THE BEHAVIOR HAVE A PHYSIOLOGICAL BASIS?

In some cases, what is inherited appears to be physiologically definable. For example, wild rats are much more aggressive in their behavior than tame white rats used in laboratories, and the offspring of wild rats, even though raised in a laboratory, tend similarly to be aggressive. Examination of these animals reveals that they have adrenal glands twice as large as those of their gentle cousins, and it seems reasonable to assume that much of their aggressiveness is based on this fact.

Similarly, as we noted in the last chapter, the fibers from the photoreceptors of the frog that respond to the movement of small objects terminate in a particular locus in the brain, and so presumably the brain of every tadpole is "wired" in this same behavior-determining way. As more is known about neurophysiology, it seems likely that more and more will be explicable on "simple" grounds such as these.

DOES THE BEHAVIOR PERSIST AFTER CROSSBREEDING?

Another approach to the study of transmitted behavior is the crossbreeding of types with different behavior patterns. One species of lovebirds, for instance, cut long strips of paper bark or leaves with which to build their nests. The bird then grasps one end of the strip in its bill, tucks the strip into the feathers of the lower back, and so carries it off to its nest. Another species cut materials in the same way but carry the strips back to the nest in their bills. Hybrids between the two species always try to tuck the nesting material into their feathers but invariably fail to do so. Sometimes the tucking movements are incomplete, or sometimes the bird will hold the strip by the middle or the end, will fail to let go at the right moment, or will tuck it into some inappropriate part of the body. The F_1 hybrids, which were studied over a three-year period, never entirely gave up trying the tucking movements, but by the end of the period, the futile activities related to this method of carrying had decreased considerably.

Studies of this type are interesting and instructive. The chief obstacle to their wider application is that since behavioral differences between types that will interbreed are usually not so clear-cut as in this example, interpretation of the results is difficult.

5–54 *A female lovebird of the Agapornis roseicollis species tucking a strip of nest material in her rump feathers. The bird has torn the strips from the paper on which she is standing. Notice how uniform the three torn strips are in length, width, and straightness. Normally, only the females prepare and carry the nest material. In this particular species, the bird carries two or three strips to the nest at a time. (Dr. W. C. Dilger)*

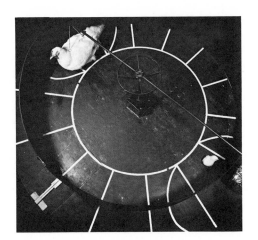

5–55 *A baby chick follows a maternal attraction call instead of a maternal model without call. The sound comes from the box at the right, which the chick cannot see. Both soundbox and stuffed chicken are moving during the test. All chicks tested responded to the sound rather than the sight of the parent. What conclusion would you draw from this? (Dr. Gilbert Gottlieb)*

IS THE BEHAVIOR ADAPTIVE?

Another test for the genetic character of behavior is whether or not the activity is adaptive. This is not always a simple question. For instance, if you saw a female tick drop from a bush onto a warm stone and ram her proboscis into the stone, thereby killing herself, it would not seem she had exhibited adaptive behavior. Perhaps, however, if you found out that the stone had recently been vacated by a hot, perspiring human being, you might piece together the reasons for the tick's "suicide." The female tick, like the mosquito and certain other insects, requires a blood meal before laying her eggs. After mating, she climbs to a branch where she remains for months or even years, until a warm-blooded animal passes by. She senses its presence by one stimulus alone: the smell of butyric acid, a characteristic animal odor. Her biting is determined by a second stimulus: a surface-of-body temperature. These two simple responses have managed to keep the tick population flourishing for eons.

Sometimes behavior can be seen as adaptive only in an historical sense. For example, there is little advantage to the domestic dog in circling the carpet. Some observers report that not all modern dogs show this behavior. Like other genetic characteristics, instinctive behavior does not decline with disuse but may diminish since nothing exists in the environment that makes its continuation selectively advantageous.

Analysis of Instinct

Ethologists approach the study of instinct by the dissection of patterns of behavior. For example, why does the mother hen, long a symbol of maternal concern, behave the way she does, sheltering her brood and literally risking her life to defend it against aggressors? Experiments with the turkey hen have shown that she responds innately to one stimulus only: the peeping of the chick. It is no biological accident that a chick peeps from the moment it is hatched "as if its life depended on it." If a baby chick is placed under a glass jar where the mother can see it frantically struggling to escape, she will not pay any attention to it. On the other hand, if she can hear it peep, she will charge to its rescue, seeking it frantically. Any small object that peeps will be accepted by a hen which is a new mother—for instance, a small stuffed polecat mounted on wheels and equipped with a loudspeaker. Any small object that does not peep will be destroyed if it comes near the nest.

APPETITIVE, RELEASING, AND CONSUMMATORY ACTIVITIES IN STICKLEBACKS

One of the favorite subjects of study of a number of ethologists (Niko Tinbergen, in particular) is the three-spined stickleback, a brightly colored

617   *Instinct, Learning, and Memory*

little freshwater fish which thrives in aquariums and will readily carry out its normal cycles of behavior in captivity. In nature, under the influences of hormonal changes brought on by the increasing daylight of springtime, male sticklebacks isolate themselves from the school in which they ordinarily live, move to shallow water, and select a territory in which to breed. Behavior such as this is known as *appetitive behavior*. When the stickleback arrives in a suitable location, the characteristics of which are largely determined by the presence of certain types of vegetation, he no longer shows this form of appetitive behavior, although presumably the hormonal stimuli which prompted it have remained unchanged. The nesting site, which puts an end to appetitive behavior, is the releasing stimulus, or *releaser,* as it is often called.

If you open the refrigerator door because you feel hungry, this is *appetitive behavior*. The piece of apple pie you find there is the *releasing stimulus,* and the eating of the pie is the *consummatory act.* These terms may seem somewhat ponderous when applied to simple examples of behavior, but they are useful designations to employ in discussions of complex chains of activity. The concept of the releaser has proved to be particularly valuable because, as you will see, it can be tested and analyzed experimentally.

At the time the male begins seeking his breeding site, he changes color —his eyes become a shining blue; his back, instead of dull brownish, becomes greenish; and his underbelly becomes red. Once the site is chosen, the now radiant male begins to build the nest, picking up mouthfuls of sand from the bottom, which he carries and drops some 5 or 6 inches away. When he has made a shallow pit, he gathers nest material, usually threads of algae, and presses it down into the pit. Occasionally, he creeps over the material with slow quivering movements, secreting a sticky substance from the kidney which glues the threads together. In this way, in a matter of a few days, a green mound is completed. The male then bores a tunnel in it by wriggling through.

As nesting activities proceed, the colors of the male become even more intense. The underside becomes a brighter red, and the black color cells on the back contract to minute dots, exposing a deeper layer of shiny whitish blue. In this brilliant nuptial costume, the male parades up and down near his nest. During this period, he is extremely aggressive toward other male sticklebacks, driving them away from the nesting site.

The female sticklebacks, meanwhile, have become swollen with unfertilized eggs. They cruise about in schools, passing through the territories of the males. Each male, if ready to receive a female, reacts to the group by performing a zigzag dance consisting of a series of leaps which take him alternately toward the females and away from them. Most of the females retreat, but one that is ready to lay her eggs turns toward the male, her swollen belly in full view, and begins to follow him as he moves away. (See Figure 5–56.) The male then heads straight for the nest and thrusts his head inside. He lies flat on his side with his colorful flank and bright blue eye on display. The female wriggles past him, enters the nest, and remains in it, her head protruding from one end and her tail from the other. The male now begins to prod the base of her tail with his snout. Quickly, the female spawns. Once her eggs are laid, she slips through the nest and swims away. The male then enters the nest and fertilizes the eggs. He also repairs any damage that has been done to the nest.

5–56 *The mating behavior of the stickleback. A female ready to lay her eggs responds to a displaying male (with red underbelly) by turning her swollen abdomen toward him and then following him to the nest he has built. At the nest, the male lies flat on his side, with his head in the nest, and the female swims past him into the nest. The male then prods the base of the female's tail with his snout, and the female spawns. Finally, the male enters the nest to fertilize the eggs.*

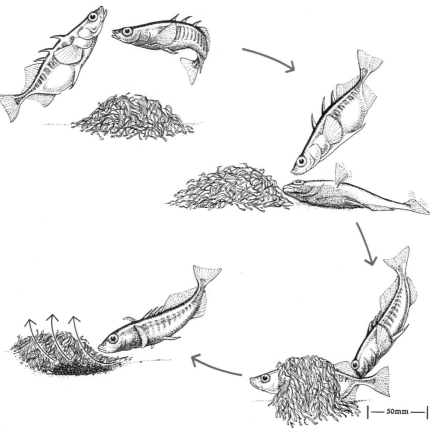

The male may lead as many as three or four females to his nest to deposit eggs, which he fertilizes. Then he ceases to court passing females and devotes himself to parenthood, ventilating the eggs by fanning them and protecting the young once they are hatched. The consummatory act in the chain of mating behavior, it has been shown, is not the fertilization of the eggs by the male but rather the new behavior set in motion by the presence of the eggs.

INNATE RELEASING MECHANISM

To aid in explaining how such behavior can be performed to absolute perfection by a male stickleback raised in complete isolation, Lorenz has proposed the concept of the *innate releasing mechanism* (IRM). He explains instinctive behavior by assuming that within each animal there are a number of inborn movement forms, which he calls *fixed action patterns*. The fixed action patterns of a given species are as specific and constant as its anatomical characteristics. Every specific action pattern remains blocked until the releasing stimulus activates the IRM, which causes the consummatory act to be performed. A given releaser is related to a given IRM, according to this theory, as a key is to a lock. Such a releaser may be a visual cue, a scent, or an activity performed by another animal. For example, to test the IRM which elicits aggressiveness between male fish, Tinbergen constructed a series of models (Figure 5–57) by which he was able to show that a male stickleback reacts much more aggressively to a very crude model of a male with a red underbelly than to an exact replica without the red coloration.

Females similarly are attracted to males because of their red underbellies, and males are attracted to females on the basis of their swollen abdomens. (See Figure 5–58.) A male will court a female stickleback with a swollen abdomen, a crude model of such a female, and also similarly gravid females of other small species; but he will only lead a female to the nest if she responds appropriately to his dance. So, for him, her response is the innate releasing mechanism for the second phase of his courtship, leading her to the nest. It is his prodding that causes her to release the eggs; without such prodding she will not spawn, while gentle prodding with a glass rod by the experimenter can induce egg laying. Finally, if the eggs are removed, the male will continue courting, but if they are present, they release parental behavior.

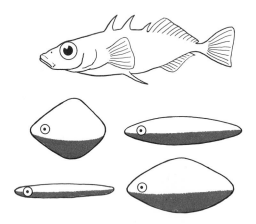

5–57 *Models used by Niko Tinbergen in stickleback experiments. The crude models, colored red, caused much more positive reactions in both male and female sticklebacks (aggressiveness in the males and attraction in the females) than did the exact replica of a male, which was not colored.*

5–58 *The male stickleback is attracted to a female model because of its swollen abdomen.*

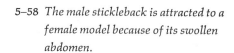

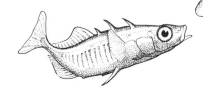

5–59 *Bearded-tit nestlings have very conspicuous mouth markings. The innate
releasing mechanism of the parent is
adapted to these species-specific
markings, and only those young are
fed which have the right markings.
(Eric Hosking, F.R.P.S.)*

5–60 *Response of baby thrush to Tinbergen's
models of parents. Fledglings gape
toward a "head" if it is within certain
size limits, is above them, and shows
movement. To be recognized as a
"head," the protrusion must be about
one-third the size of the "body." On
the left, the young birds are gaping at
the smaller of the two protrusions; on
the right, they have selected the larger
protrusion.*

Thrush

Tinbergen has made similar studies of behavior in birds. Young thrush,
like the young of many other birds, thrust their heads upwards toward
their parents to beg for food, revealing the orange-colored lining of their
mouths. The baby that gapes the most vigorously is fed first; this ensures
that each healthy baby will be fed in turn, since the hungrier the baby is,
the harder it gapes. A weak fledgling, however, will sometimes not be able
to gape vigorously enough to elicit the feeding response in the parents and
so will die. This, too, though seemingly cruel, is adaptive.

When the nestlings first hatch, they are blind, and their gaping response
is released by a light touch on the nest or a puff of air. A heavy touch makes
the baby birds crouch. When they are about one week old, the gaping response is released by visual stimulus, but the birds still gape straight up.
At the age of about 10 days, the gaping is directed toward the head of the
parent. Tinbergen tested various models of parents to see what the fledglings would gape toward. He found that for a "parent" to release the response, it must be within certain limits of size, be above the horizontal
plane of the nestling, and show movement. The response is directed toward the "head," a protrusion on the object's outline; the protrusion is
recognized as a "head" if it is about one-third the size of the "body." (See
Figure 5–60.)

Herring Gulls

The herring gull does not gape to be fed but pecks at the tip of its parent's
bill. The parent then regurgitates the food onto the ground, picks some of
it up in its bill tip, and holds it near the young, which pecks the food from

621 *Instinct, Learning, and Memory*

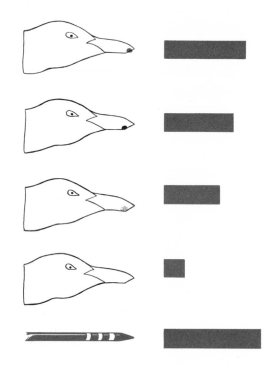

5–61 *Herring-gull models and a knitting needle are used to determine the character of the stimulus which elicits response from the young gulls. The bar graph on the right indicates the relative number of responses obtained from each model. Note that the highest number of responses was obtained from the knitting needle!*

its parent's bill. The herring gull has a yellow bill with a red patch near the end of the lower mandible. The importance of the various stimulus characters of the adult's bill in eliciting pecking has also been studied by a series of models. (See Figure 5–61.) Neither the color of the bill nor the color of the head were found to influence the response. The model obtaining the highest number of responses was long and thin, pointing downward, with a red patch contrasting with the bill near the tip. In fact, the greatest response of all was obtained, not by a three-dimensional model, but by a red knitting needle with three white bands near the tip.

A knitting needle is an example of what is known as a *supernormal stimulus,* of which a number have been found. Tinbergen, using dummy eggs made of wood, showed that the female herring gull, when faced with a choice between an egg the size of her usual eggs and one much larger, will select the larger—even one so large that she cannot sit on it without falling off.

Herring gulls, like some other species of birds, will retrieve eggs that have rolled out of the nest, rolling them back in again with their bills. G. P. Baerends of the University of Groningen in the Netherlands, experimenting with dummy eggs, found that the egg that stimulated this egg-retrieving response the most vigorously was pale green, 1 1/2 times the normal diameter, and covered with a great number of small dark contrasting speckles. (The normal egg is olive brown with both small and large speckles.)

Cuckoos

Responses to supernormal stimuli are not usually harmful under natural conditions; the likelihood of a herring-gull chick encountering a knitting needle is so slight that the fact that it "prefers" it to the bill of its parent places no burden on the species. In some cases, however, such responses are detrimental. One species which gains an advantage from the response to supernormal stimuli is the cuckoo, which lays its eggs in the nests of other birds. The baby cuckoo has a larger head than the young of the songbirds whose nests it usually parasitizes, and since it has a wider gape, it is fed in preference to other fledglings.

The behavior of the cuckoo and its foster parent also emphasizes both the extreme adaptiveness of genetically determined behavior and its limitations. The cuckoo almost immediately upon hatching makes movements that result in the ejection of any other occupants, whether unhatched eggs or fledglings, from the nest. If a baby bird is pushed out of the nest and left clinging to the rim, the parent, which under other circumstances will die to preserve her young, will not push the baby bird back into the nest, nor will it feed it so long as it is outside. But the parent will continue to feed the murderous young cuckoo, now gaping alone.

5–62 *A baby cuckoo ejecting a newly hatched hedge sparrow from its nest. As you can see on the right, another young hedge sparrow and an egg have already been pushed out and are now lodged in the twigs beside the nest. Only the English species of cuckoo lays its eggs in the nests of other birds. In North America similar behavior is seen in the cowbird. (John Markham, F.R.P.S.)*

CRITICISM OF THE IRM THEORY

The theory of the innate releasing mechanism, as you can see, implies that an animal has a genetically determined "picture" of, for example, its rival, its parent's beak, or the behavior of its mate. This theory has been valuable as a working hypothesis, but many behavioral scientists feel that it is not proved, or at least that it is a gross oversimplification. The experiments we just described were designed not so much to test whether or not such a "picture" exists but to discover what the picture looks like. Although certain responses may be innate, the picture is more likely to be built up slowly by experience. The very experiments performed to discover what the picture looks like alter the picture, as do all the various external and internal events which occur to the animal.

At the opposite extreme from Lorenz are psychologists such as T. C. Schneirla at the American Museum of Natural History, who believes that the notion of the IRM and the concept of instinct itself are so ill defined that they serve only to mask ignorance of the underlying mechanisms of behavior. In his view, all behavior is a complex mixture of innate capabilities, normal maturation, and experience. For example, when the chick first emerges from its shell, it almost immediately begins pecking. Some observers would describe this as instinctive behavior, but Schneirla points out that pecking may actually be "learned" by the chick during its embryonic state. While still within the egg, the chick head comes to rest against its thorax and is passively lifted and dropped as the heart beats. Within

623 *Instinct, Learning, and Memory*

a few days, the little embryo is actively nodding its head, and later the beak begins to open and close as the head nods. Shortly before hatching, the head becomes much more mobile and occasionally lifts and thrusts forward, and these thrusts are followed by beak openings and closings. By the time the chick has hatched, it is pecking; but this pecking is not instinctive or innate, it is a result of maturation or development. All "innate" behavior, he suggests, may have a similar origin.

This controversy, which is now dying down (although unresolved), has been an extremely useful one, serving as it did to sharpen thinking in the field, to stimulate new experiments, and most important, to start a search for new experimental approaches to the question of instinct.

LEARNING

Learning is the process which produces adaptive change in individual behavior as a result of experience. Intelligence is usually defined, and therefore tested, as representing the extent to which an animal or a species exhibits learning ability.

Categories of Learning

HABITUATION

One of the simplest forms of learning is *habituation*, which we discussed in our description of the behavior of amoebas in Chapter 5–1. The octopus's loss of fear in the laboratory is another example of habituation. You can probably think of many other examples of ways in which habituation modifies behavior, even your own behavior.

ASSOCIATIVE LEARNING

Another simple and familiar type of learning is known as *associative learning,* in which one object comes to be linked, through experience, with another one. If you keep pets in your home, you will be able to cite many examples of associative learning, such as goldfish coming to the corner of the aquarium to be fed as you walk toward the tank or your dog becoming excited at the sight of a leash.

TRIAL AND ERROR

Other learning is categorized as *trial and error.* An inexperienced frog, as we have seen, will strike at any small moving object, even a tiny jet of water. By trial and error, it learns not to strike at disagreeable or inedible objects. The newly hatched domestic chick will peck at any spots which contrast with the background; as it grows older, it will learn which of these spots represent edible objects. Also, its pecking accuracy will improve.

When young chicks first peck at grain, only about 15 percent of the pecks lead to obtaining a morsel worth swallowing. Accuracy improves with practice and also with maturity. Chicks that have been kept in the dark and fed by hand for a number of days will peck more accurately than younger chicks, but they will not peck as accurately as chicks their own age that have had pecking experience.

DISCRIMINATION

Closely related to these types of learning is the development of *discrimination*. For example, young blackbirds gape in response to auditory stimulation. Initially, a very wide range of noises will elicit gaping, but this range becomes narrower and narrower until eventually, under natural circumstances, the young bird will gape only when it hears the call notes of its own mother. Similarly, in the human baby that has begun to smile, there is a period during which two dots on a white oval background evoke the smile. Later, other features, such as eyebrows and mouth, become necessary. Later still, masks become ineffective and only a human face will elicit smiling. By the middle of the first year, the baby will smile only when he sees the face of his mother and father and perhaps one or two other individuals whom he knows.

IMITATION

Animals learn by *imitation*. Usually this learning is within very narrow limits. For instance, the chaffinch has an elaborate spring song. Chaffinches reared in isolation can sing, but they develop only a very simple type of song without the phrasing and flourishes of the natural song. If chaffinches are hand-reared in isolated groups so that they can hear one another sing, they produce more elaborate songs than those of birds reared individually. The song patterns are usually similar among members of a group but may differ markedly from the songs of other similarly raised groups of the wild birds. Young birds caught in the autumn, which have never sung a spring song but have heard one, produce songs that are close to those of the wild birds. If isolated chaffinches are exposed to recorded artificial songs, they can be made to modify their singing, but only if the artificial song is close in pattern to the normal chaffinch song. Exposure to music totally unlike that of the natural song has no influence on the bird's own singing.

During the past 20 years in England, householders have been the surprised and sometimes angry witnesses of the development by imitation of an entirely new type of behavior in birds. Titmice began opening milk bottles left on doorsteps and drinking off the cream. The tearing of paper and paperlike bark is a common natural trait of this species, so one can guess that the first opened bottle may have been a happy accident. Now, however, at least 11 species of birds have taken up the practice. The milk

5–63 *The great tit attacking a milk bottle. When it has succeeded in tearing through the paper top, it will drink off the cream. (Ronald Thompson, F.R.P.S.)*

bottles are usually attacked within a few minutes after they are left at the door, and there are even reports that troops of birds are now following milk carts down the street.

In some cases, learning by imitation appears to be part of a bird's essential education, as it is in the higher mammals. Many types of birds engage in a practice known as *mobbing,* in which all the members of a flock descend upon a fox or owl or some other natural predator. This often serves to drive the enemy away or, at the very least, to reveal its presence and so interfere with its hunting. In many species, young birds do not recognize their enemies instinctively and only learn to tell them as a result of the mobbing activity of other birds. They themselves then join in the mobbing and become part of the educational system.

In the case of mobbing, there is no intention on the part of the older birds to teach the younger ones. Mobbing takes place even if young birds are not present, just as warning cries are given by birds even if no companions are present for them to warn.

PERCEPTION

The final category of learning is *perception,* or *insight learning*—in other words, "seeing through" a problem. If a puppy sees a dish of food through a screened hole in a short piece of fence, he may scratch helplessly at the screen or sit down and cry. Eventually, by running back and forth, he may find his way around the fence. Some puppies will immediately run around the fence the next time they are confronted with the same problem. If the fence is then made longer, however, some of these puppies will run only as far as the length of the original fence, while others will follow the fence to its end. The latter group has demonstrated insight learning. They understand not just the specific problem but the nature of the problem.

Similarly, if a monkey is taught that he can find a food reward under the lid marked *X* when the other two lids are marked *O,* or under a yellow lid when the other two lids are red, he may then look first under a round lid when the other two are square. This is also an example of insight learning; only a very few species are able to solve the *oddity problem,* as this is called.

Imprinting

Birds, such as swans, chickens, and turkeys, which are physiologically mature enough to leave the nest soon after they are hatched, follow the first moving object that they see. For ducklings, the effective objects can range from a matchbox on a string to a walking man. Once one of these newly hatched birds has become attached to a particular object, it will follow only that object. Under natural circumstances, of course, this object will be a parent, and it is this following response that keeps the young birds close behind and well within the protective range of the mother until the end of their juvenile period, when the response is lost.

The learning pattern which involves this act of recognition is called *imprinting,* and it differs from other types of learning in that the period in which it can occur is very limited. Studies of the newly hatched mallard duckling, using a mechanically operated decoy, showed that imprinting was most effective between 13 and 16 hours after hatching. After 24 hours, 80 percent of the ducklings failed to follow moving objects; and after 30 hours, all the ducklings avoided them. Similarly, chicks will not follow a moving object when they are only a few hours old nor when they are several days old but only during the intervening period. It is believed that the end of the following period is marked by the development of fear responses, which seem to arise in normally reared birds at about the same time that the imprinting period is over.

The more difficult it is for the young bird to follow the moving object, the more firmly it becomes imprinted, according to experiments made with ducklings and a moving decoy. The ducklings which had to waddle rapidly, climb over obstacles, and even endure mild punishment by electric shock in order to follow the decoy were more persistent on subsequent following trials than those which were able to keep up with the decoy more easily.

The gosling is especially susceptible to imprinting. The only way to make an incubator-hatched gosling follow other geese is to bundle it up in a bag and rush it to the barnyard just as it is hatching, thus ensuring that the first object it sees is a goose.

Imprinting also seems to influence mate selection in the adult birds; Lorenz reports many examples of ducks and geese becoming sexually fixated on objects or on members of other species, including Lorenz himself. Controlled experiments in ducklings support these observations. Ducklings raised with females of another species courted females of that species when they reached maturity, while ducklings raised with females of their own species did not.

The term "imprinting" is usually applied only to phenomena associated with the following response in birds, but similar effects are seen in other animals. If a baby lamb is taken from its mother right after birth and bottle-raised, it will not follow other sheep when it is turned back to pasture with the rest of the flock.

First impressions seem to determine the choice of a mate even in birds which do not show the following response. In order to crossbreed two strains of pigeons of different colors, breeders find that the future fathers of the crossbreeds must be raised by foster parents of the opposite spe-

5–64 *A bullfinch male, imprinted to men, courtship-feeding the hand of the human keeper. (Dr. Jürgen Nicolai)*

cies; the male pigeon will not pay court to a female that does not resemble "Mom."

Similar effects occur in parents. The parent jewel fish, a species of cichlid, tend their large brood very solicitously despite the fact that their babies are the same size as the small animals that make up their regular diet. If the first batch of eggs is taken from them and replaced by the eggs of another fish, they will tend these babies equally well, but when they have a second brood of their own, they will eat them. The parents apparently recognize their young by imprinting, in the way that a young bird will become imprinted to the first object or animal presented to it. At any time in the reproductive cycle, substitutes of eggs or of young can be made if the eggs or young are of the same species as the first brood. Analogously, if a female lovebird is given foster fledglings of a different color than her own to raise from eggs, she will subsequently raise only nestlings of the species of her foster young.

Imprinting is in part instinctive and in part the result of a very special, very narrow type of learning.

Learning in the Laboratory

As we mentioned in the introduction to this section, the ethologists were at first primarily concerned with genetically determined behavior, but the principal interest of the psychologists has always been the study of the nature of learning. These studies, all of which are carried out under controlled laboratory conditions, have been criticized because they do not reflect the behavior of the animal in its natural surroundings. The psychologists respond that the goal of their studies is not an understanding of the complete behavior patterns of a particular animal but rather a comprehension of the nature of learning itself.

THE CONDITIONED REFLEX

The best known experiments ever performed in the field of animal behavior were carried out by the Russian physiologist Ivan Pavlov in the late nineteenth century. Pavlov showed that sprinkling meat powder on the tongues of dogs caused the reflex reaction of salivation. He then rang a bell each time he sprinkled the powder, and after a few such trials, he was able to demonstrate that the dogs salivated at the sound of the bell even without the taste stimulus of the meat powder. Such a response is known as a *conditioned reflex*, or conditioned response. As you can see, it is a form of associative learning. It was soon found that conditioned responses could be developed in a great many animals to a large number of different stimuli.

OPERANT CONDITIONING

A second widely used method for studying the learning process is *operant conditioning*, or instrumented conditioning. This differs from the conditioned reflex in that the animal which is the subject of the experiment plays an active rather than a passive role. In its simplest form, the experiment is conducted as follows: An animal, usually a rat or a pigeon, is placed in a box commonly known as the *Skinner box* (after B. F. Skinner of Harvard University, who has been the undisputed leader for 30 years in these studies of behavior). The box, which is completely isolated from the distracting sights and sounds of the outside environment, usually contains a bar or lever which can be pressed by the rat's paw, or a disk that can be easily pecked by a pigeon. In the course of exploring its box, the rat or pigeon will eventually depress the bar or disk, in which case it will be rewarded with a small amount of food.

By a suitable system of rewards, or *reinforcements*, Skinner and his followers have been able to train their experimental subjects to carry out immensely complicated learned patterns of behavior. For example, a rat was taught to pull a chain to obtain a marble from a rack, pick up the marble with its forepaws, carry it to a tube projecting 2 inches above the floor of its cage, lift it to the top of the tube, and drop it inside. Although the complete performance seems highly improbable, each isolated act is closely related to a rat's normal activities—such as pulling nesting material, handling and storing food, and retrieving the young. In the teaching program, the rat was first reinforced, or rewarded, for any movement which caused a marble to roll over any edge of the floor of its cage. Then it was rewarded only when the marble ran over the edge on one side of the cage, then only over a small section of the edge, then only over that sec-

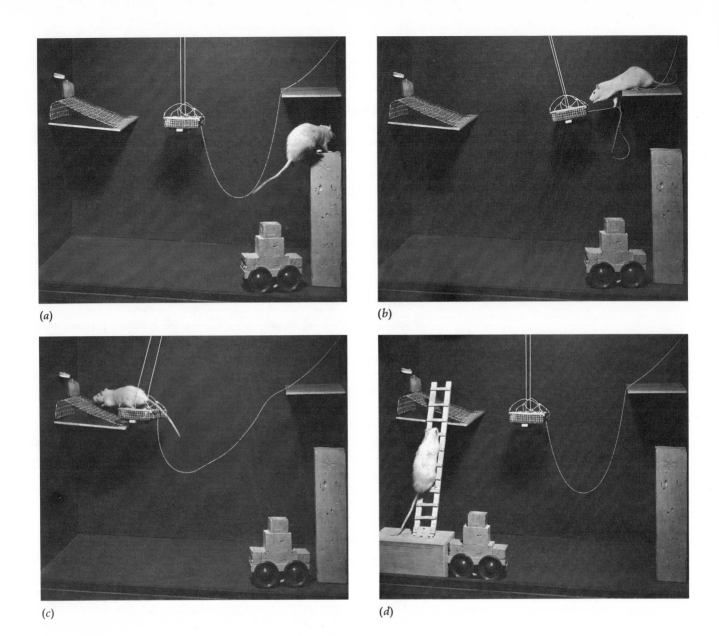

(a)

(b)

(c)

(d)

5–65 *This remarkably well-trained rat finds his way to the food shelf by climbing from the cart to the tower and then to the platform, grasping the chain and pulling the basket in, and swinging in the basket across to the food shelf. When a ladder is introduced, the rat immediately uses this shortcut to the food shelf! (Frank Lotz Miller, Black Star)*

tion slightly raised, and so on. The raised edge became a tube of gradually diminishing diameter and increasing height, and finally the rat received its reward only when it dropped the marble into the tube. Teaching it to pull the chain to get the marble was added last. When the rat accidentally pulled on the chain, it was rewarded with the marble, which it then picked up and put in the tube in order to receive its reward.

Studies such as these by Skinner and his followers reveal various factors which can operate to enhance or disturb the learning process. These forces vary remarkably little from species to species, at least among the vertebrates. In fact, if you have had any experience with learning machines or programmed instructions of learning, you will recognize the resemblances between the way a student is guided toward a correct response and the way the rat was taught this remarkable performance.

MEMORY

The Search for the Engram

More recent studies of learning have had to do with its physical basis. One of the most intriguing questions facing those concerned with the neurophysiology of behavior is the nature of memory, which is, of course, the foundation of all learning. What is memory? And where is it located?

The early Greek philosophers believed that each of us is born with a mind like a blank notebook and that the fingers of experience "write" in the notebook. Remembering then becomes a process of looking up our notes. In the early twentieth century, the idea was advanced that learning produced a definite material change of some kind within an organism's nervous system. (As you can see, this concept, while expressed in more scientifically acceptable terms than that of the Greeks, explains little more.) This permanent physical change, the "scar" of memory, was called the *engram*.

When it was discovered that electrical stimulation of the cortex of a patient during brain surgery could cause a vivid recollection of past events, the theory was advanced, quite naturally, that separate items of memory, the engrams, were filed away in specific places in the brain. The late Karl S. Lashley of Harvard taught rats and other animals to solve various problems and then cut out portions of the animals' brains to see if he could remove a specific engram. However, he was never able to isolate any separate unit so that the animal would remember one thing and forget another. His animals showed only relative forgetting; if he removed 25 percent of the cortex, the animal forgot one-fourth of what it had learned; if he removed 50 percent, it forgot about half. He then speculated that memory might be a system of reverberating impulses, like an electric current going round and round a circuit.

This was an attractive theory because it seemed to offer an explanation of another problem: the difference between short-term memory and long-term memory. We know ourselves, for example, that we sometimes cannot remember the name of the person we were introduced to 20 minutes ago at a party, but we often can recall the name of our teacher in first grade. Following a concussion, recent memories are lost while early ones are unimpaired. Old persons who are forgetful of events that occurred a few hours before may remember experiences of their childhood in great detail. Perhaps older memories etch an actual physical change in the brain, possibly by establishing new synaptic connections between neurons, like the rewiring of an electric circuit.

Lashley found, however, that he could not interfere with the process of memory by making multiple cuts through the cortices of rats, thereby supposedly severing connections between the various areas, and so he felt that his theory must be discarded. In one of his reports on this subject, he concluded wryly: "I sometimes feel, in reviewing the evidence on the localization of the memory trace, that the necessary conclusion is that learning is just not possible."

THE OCTOPUS AGAIN

J. Z. Young and Brian B. Boycott have initiated a series of studies on the nature of memory which appear to offer new support for Lashley's hypothesis. For their experimental subject, they are using the octopus, which not only is easily trained, as we have seen, but is remarkably tolerant of surgical procedures.

The brain of the octopus has three main divisions: the subesophageal ganglia, the supraesophageal ganglia, and the relatively huge optic lobes. (See Figure 5–66.) The lobes of the lower (subesophageal) ganglia are the source of the nerve fibers that stimulate peripheral nerve centers, such as the ganglia in the arms and the mantle. If all the brain except these lower ganglia is removed, an octopus is unable to eat or move about but will nevertheless survive for several weeks. It will be unable to right itself if placed upside down, but it will show a number of reflex activities; for instance, an arm will grasp a small object that touches it and will pass the object toward the mouth.

At the base of the upper (supraesophageal) ganglia are lobes concerned with the integration of motion activities such as walking, swimming, eating, and turning toward and seizing prey.

On top of these ganglia, both literally and figuratively, are the lobes with which Young and Boycott have been particularly concerned. Removal of these lobes does not result in any immediately obvious changes in behavior, but it is apparently in this part of the brain that learning and memory in the octopus leave their traces. If the vertical lobe or the superior

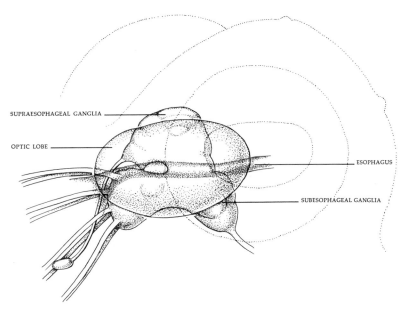

SUPRAESOPHAGEAL GANGLIA

OPTIC LOBE

ESOPHAGUS

SUBESOPHAGEAL GANGLIA

frontal lobe is removed or if the nerve tracts between them are cut, the octopus forgets any visual discriminations that it has learned. Also, as Lashley found in his studies of mammals, there appears to be a definite relationship between the amount of vertical lobe left intact and the accuracy with which a learned response is performed. "Memory is both everywhere and nowhere in particular," as Boycott says.

The vertical lobe is, however, apparently involved only in long-term memory, not in short-term memory. Animals which lack the vertical lobe cannot be taught by the usual training regimen, which involves a training trial every two hours, but they can learn when the training trials are carried out every five minutes. Furthermore, if the vertical lobe is removed, a discrimination learned by one eye of the octopus is not transferred to the other eye; the two sides of the animal have to be taught separately.

On the basis of these observations, Boycott and Young hypothesize that external visual events set up patterns of excitations, somewhat analogous to electric circuits, in the optic lobes. These patterns serve to determine the responses to visual stimuli so long as the patterns endure. If these patterns endure long enough, they activate circuits in the vertical lobe, and the vertical lobe, now activated, seems to reactivate the optic lobe. Continued reexcitation of these circuits, by repeated training trials, results in structural alterations in the connections between the neurons concerned and so establishes the lasting structural changes of long-term memory.

633 *Instinct, Learning, and Memory*

Similar studies have been made on tactile discriminations in the octopus. Here, long-term and short-term memories are readily demonstrable in the intact animal. Wells has found that if he persistently presents an unsuitable object to only one arm of an octopus, he can train that arm to reject the object fairly rapidly. But for half an hour or so, other arms of the octopus will continue to accept the object. Then, apparently, "the news travels," and all the arms will show the effects of the training. If the median inferior frontal lobe of the brain is removed, information received from one arm is never transferred to the other seven. Without the subfrontal lobe, the animals cannot learn to reject objects by touch; if some of the subfrontal lobe is left, however, tactile learning is possible. Apparently, the subfrontal lobe has the same role in tactile learning as the vertical lobe has in visual learning. In other words, it contains the circuits on which persistent memory depends.

The Molecule-code Theory of Memory

MCCONNELL'S EXPERIMENTS WITH PLANARIANS

An entirely different approach to the nature of memory is being followed by James V. McConnell, who began his current studies when he was still a graduate student. As we mentioned in Chapter 5–1, McConnell first became interested in the planarian because of the synaptic arrangement of its nervous system. He set out in 1953 to attempt classical conditioning in this animal.

For these experiments, McConnell used a foot-long semicircular plastic trough filled with pond water. At either end were brass electrodes. When the worm was gliding smoothly in a straight line on the bottom of the trough, the experimenter turned on the light for three seconds. After the light had been on for two of the three seconds, the experimenter added one second of electric shock, which passed through the water and caused the worm to contract. Planarians so treated developed a conditioned response, contracting when exposed to the light alone. (At this point, it should be added that flatworms—which, as you will remember, are photonegative—sometimes contract when exposed to light, even without a conditioning process. This has been one of the sources of criticism of McConnell's work.)

In one series of experiments, when the animals reached the point at which they contracted in response to the light alone 23 out of 25 times, McConnell immediately cut them in half. The head and tail sections were separated and were allowed to regenerate for about four weeks. A control group of animals was not conditioned but was simply cut in half and left for four weeks, and another control group was conditioned and then allowed to rest uncut for a month before being retested. The purpose of this experiment was to find out whether the "learning" of the planarian was retained in the head or the tail. Can you explain why each of the control groups was needed?

The experimenters found to their surprise that the animals that regenerated from the tails remembered just as well as the animals that regenerated from the heads did. In fact, a planarian could be cut in several pieces and all the pieces, once regenerated, would remember equally well. Clearly, the engram was not localized in the planarian's brain.

HYDEN'S RNA THEORY

At about this same time, in the late 1950s, the Swedish biologist Holger Hyden began studying the chemical composition of neurons in the brains of rats. He found that these cells contained large amounts of RNA. RNA, as you will recall, is usually associated with the making of proteins, and the amount of RNA is generally proportionate to protein production. But brain cells do not divide and do not make any known protein for export. Why did these cells contain so much RNA? He trained some of his rats to perform complex tasks and found that the RNA in their neurons increased appreciably during the process. On the basis of this work, Hyden offered the theory that memory is encoded in the RNA molecule.

THE TRANSFER OF MEMORY BY CANNIBALISM

McConnell saw in Hyden's theory an explanation for the behavior of the planarian tails. In order to test his theory, it was necessary to transfer RNA from one group of planarians to another. At that particular time, however, the technical problems associated with removing RNA from large numbers of planarians and injecting it, unaltered, into other planarians seemed insuperable. Then it occurred to him that the planarians could do their own transferring. Hungry planarians are willing cannibals. Trained worms were chopped in small pieces and fed to untrained ones.

Tests were carried out on untrained planarians, on untrained planarians that had eaten other untrained planarians, and on untrained planarians that had cannibalized educated planarians. To ensure against experimental bias, the laboratory workers who tested the flatworms did not know to which of the three groups their experimental subjects belonged. The worms that had eaten the educated worms showed the conditioned response more frequently than the control groups and were trained more rapidly to the criterion (23 out of 25) response. Worms that had eaten untrained planarians showed no effects on their learning ability. As might be expected, McConnell's report on this subject, which he referred to as "the transfer of training by cannibalism," led to a number of jokes about new possibilities for more meaningful student-teacher relationships.

635 *Instinct, Learning, and Memory*

McConnell's results have been confirmed by at least a dozen other investigators, but since they are being disputed by still others, the matter is not resolved. Assuming for the moment that the cannibalism experiments show what they seem to show, what exactly is transferred when an untrained planarian eats a trained one? This is not yet known. The concept that memory is encoded in the nucleic acids is still the most attractive one. Nucleic acids, as we know, encode other kinds of memory, not only the "memory" that makes a child resemble its parents, but also the memory that makes it possible for a new-hatched spider to build a web or a stickleback to woo a mate. Some experimental work seems to confirm the theory. Extracts of RNA from trained planarians have now been shown to improve the learning performance of untrained planarians; and, in some cases, it looks as if a particular memory, an engram, is being transferred. In studies with rats and other vertebrates, however, the results have been inconclusive. When one is dealing with as complex a technical problem as the extraction of RNA and its relocation in specific sites in the brain, negative results do not necessarily prove anything, however, so the question is still an open one.

As an interesting by-product of these studies, RNA extracts or drugs that promote RNA synthesis are being tried in persons with failing memory. A young healthy human being may have upwards of 20 million RNA molecules in each neuron. This total amount increases from infancy to the age of forty, levels off in the forties and fifties, and then diminishes. In some cases, RNA treatments have seemed to have a beneficial effect, which provides supporting evidence of an association between memory and RNA.

On the basis of history, it seems likely that these two apparently opposing theories on the nature of memory and learning—the electric circuit versus the molecule code—will prove to be not so opposite after all. In any case, this is an exciting and very young area of research from which many more results will be forthcoming in the next decade or two.

SUMMARY

One of the fundamental difficulties in behavioral science has been the problem of separating behavior that is instinctive (genetically determined) from that which is learned (not inherited but acquired). We have presented some criteria for determining whether or not a particular activity is instinctive, but the distinction is no longer thought to be so clear-cut as it was once. Many rigid behavior patterns involve a learned component, and most behavior can be altered at least a little by experience.

Ethologists approach the study of instinct by dissecting patterns of behavior. The three-spined stickleback has proved to be an apt subject for this study. In the mating behavior of the stickleback is exemplified the very important concept of *release*, which has provided ethologists with a new understanding of instinctive behavior in invertebrates and the lower vertebrates. To explain how complex patterns of behavior regularly performed by members of a species can be performed in exactly the same way by animals raised in isolation, Lorenz has proposed the *innate releasing mechanism* (IRM). In this theory, the releasing stimulus activates the IRM, which initiates the consummatory act. This concept has been reinforced by Tinbergen's studies of baby thrush, herring gulls, and cuckoos.

The various categories of learning include habituation, associative learning, trial and error, discrimination, imitation, and perception. Imprinting is a special type of learning in that it is a rigid pattern of behavior with a learned component. The study of the nature of learning has been of principal interest to psychologists. Two widely used methods for studying the learning process in the laboratory are the conditioned reflex and operant conditioning.

The physical basis of learning has been the subject of recent studies by neurophysiologists, and there is special interest in the nature of memory, which is the foundation of all learning. Two opposing theories of memory are current: (1) In the electric-circuit theory, external events set up patterns of excitations, like electric circuits, in the brain. Continued reexcitation of these circuits alters the connections between the neurons concerned and so establishes the permanent structural changes of long-term memory. (2) In the molecule-code theory, memory is encoded in the RNA molecule and can be transferred from one animal to another by transferring the RNA. This theory has received support from the results of experiments with planarians, which indicate that memory is transferred from trained planarians to untrained ones by cannibalism.

Chapter 5–5

Social Behavior

Social behavior occurs whenever one animal reacts in any way to the presence of another. This chapter, however, will be limited to interactions among members of the same species. In Section 6, some relationships between the many different species that make up a natural community will be described.

Mating Rituals

The form of social behavior seen most commonly among animals is, of course, sexual. Successful fertilization of the eggs demands at least some degree of synchronization and propinquity of the male and female partners. In some insect species, as we have seen, the two are brought together by a powerful chemical signal, a pheromone, to which the animal responds as unerringly as a growing plant turns toward the light. In other insect species, the exact nature of the attraction is not clear and so must be hidden under the blanketing power of terms like "instinct" or "sexual drive." For instance, except at mating, praying mantises maintain safe distances between themselves and all other members of their species, and with good reason. What is it about the female mantis that causes the male so literally to lose his head? In such instances, we must fall back upon the notion of instinct, at least for the time being.

REPRODUCTIVE DRIVE VS. AVOIDANCE

Although few vertebrates are cannibals, many of them, the fish and birds in particular, have a distinct preference for maintaining discreet distances between themselves and other animals, whether of their own or another species. Such avoidance is adaptive; for many animals, being touched means being captured. Have you ever watched birds lined up on a tele-

5–67 *Fish and birds usually prefer to maintain some space between themselves and others, even when the others are members of their own species. Notice how uniformly these gannetts have spaced themselves out across the ground. (Eric Hosking, F.R.P.S.)*

5–68 *Conflict between hostility and the reproductive drive in the mating behavior of the stickleback. The male "zigs" toward the female (a motion of attack). Instead of fleeing or returning the attack, the female who is ready to lay her eggs turns sideways and then follows the male's "zag."*

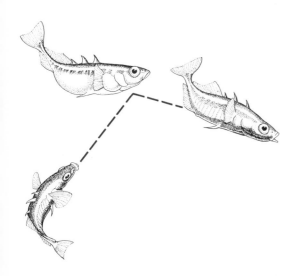

phone wire, for instance? Each will be found almost equidistant from the next, as though measured off by an invisible yardstick. Even those animals that fly in flocks or swim in schools tend not to touch one another.

In the mating ceremonies of these animals, the knowing eye can often discern the conflict between fear and hostility on the one hand and the reproductive drive on the other. In the mating behavior of the stickleback, described in the previous chapter, the male's "zig" toward the female is identical to a motion of attack; and when the male "zags," the motion entices her toward the nest. (See Figure 5–68.) Most females flee the attack motion, but the one whose need to lay her eggs is sufficiently great stands still, turns sideways (an appeasing gesture on her part since an antagonist would zig back), and then follows his zag.

In mating ceremonies between birds, feelings of fear and aggression brought into play by the closeness of another individual may be handled by being redirected at either a real or an imaginary antagonist. Lorenz describes the so-called "triumph ceremony" in the graylag goose, one of his favorite research subjects and companions. As a form of greeting to his partner, the gander proceeds to attack an "enemy." This attack is performed, as is a real attack, with the head and neck pointing obliquely forward and upward and is accompanied by a raucous trumpeting. After the "enemy" is routed or defeated, the gander returns to his partner. On his return, the gander holds his head lowered and pointed forward, but instead of pointing directly at the goose, as he would at an enemy, he points

639 *Social Behavior*

obliquely past her. She comes forward to meet him, her head inverted submissively, and he cackles to her triumphantly.

This ceremony, which probably had a purely sexual origin, now serves to hold entire flocks together, and even small goslings participate in elements of the triumph ceremony. When a young male performs the ceremony with a strange young female, it usually marks the beginning of a mating bond which may last for the entire lifetime of the individuals. The ceremony is typically performed between young geese the year before mating and breeding begin, and it will continue to be performed by the partners throughout their entire lives whenever they encounter one another even after a short separation. By the intensity with which the ceremony is performed, an experienced observer can judge the length and strength of the bond between the partners.

ISOLATING THE SPECIES

Mating rituals have other functions as well. Clearly, one of the most important is the role they serve in isolating a species from other species. In *Drosophila*, for example, males perform elaborate courtship displays which may last as long as many hours. Initially, the male taps the female of his choice, and then he circles her repeatedly, always vibrating the wing on the side closest to her, following her if she moves, and facing her if she stands still—until finally she is persuaded to spread her wings and permit him to copulate. Two species of *Drosophila*, *D. pseudoobscura* and *D. persimilis*, are often found eating and breeding in the same areas, yet only one hybrid between the two has ever been found in nature. If males of one species are raised with females of the other in the laboratory, crossbreeding does take place. When mixtures of males and females of both species are raised together, hybrids occur only very rarely; under these circumstances, courtship ceremonies begin before the flies are physically mature enough to mate and the female thus has time to compare performances and choose. Once a female *D. persimilis* has bred with a male of her own species, she will not accept a male of the other species no matter how urgent and prolonged his courtship. In short, although the mating behavior of the two species looks identical to the observer and the two species are physically able to mate, there is enough difference in their behavior for the experienced female to distinguish between them and so keep the species intact.

REPRODUCTIVE SYNCHRONY

A third important function of mating behavior, which we have mentioned previously, is that it may serve to bring the members of the opposite sexes into reproductive synchrony—as shown, for example, in Lehrman's studies of the ringdoves.

Care of the Young

The bonds that unite parents and their offspring are extremely varied and complex. In all cases, if parental care is to extend over any length of time, there must be reciprocal stimuli. The larvae of social wasps, for example, are fed by the workers, and they drool droplets of liquid which their nurses devour readily in return.

Licking is obviously a "pleasurable" activity for many mammals. Cats and rats repeatedly lick their nipples and genital areas during pregnancy, lick themselves and the young during labor and birth, and lick and so clean and tend their young all during their infancy.

Similarly, nursing is a "pleasurable" sensation to mammals, including the human female, and so provides its own inducement for the mother to suckle her offspring. In many cases, such as the exhausting feeding routines in the rearing of baby birds, the direct rewards to the parent are difficult to identify.

ADULT AGGRESSIONS

What protects young animals from the natural hostility and the predations of the adults of their own species? The young of the cichlid, for example, are just about the size of the small crustaceans and other aquatic life that make up its normal diet. Furthermore, in some species, they are carried about in the mouth of the parent—yet they are not eaten.

A form of imprinting plays an important role in the recognition of the young by parent jewel fish, as we saw in the previous chapter. Some sort of timing mechanism is also involved. Although one batch of eggs or of fry may be substituted for another, free-swimming fry will not be accepted as substitutes for eggs when the parents are in the egg-tending stage and large fry will not be accepted in place of small fry.

Parent jewel fish have been shown to respond to chemical stimuli emitted by the young. If water from an aquarium in which young jewel fish are swimming is piped into an aquarium containing parent fish, the parents will hover around the point of inflow, make fanning motions with their fins (which they do normally to aerate the nest), and show other signs of parental behavior. These patterns of behavior will continue for two to three weeks if the stimulus is continued, until the time that the separation would normally take place. The separation time can be hastened by replacing young fry with older ones and can be postponed by replacing older fry with younger ones. Evidently the chemical stimuli emitted by the young change with age.

Some animals have no inhibitions at all about eating the young. A male guppy will follow the female around as she is giving birth and snap up the fry as soon as they are born; those that do escape make rapidly for sheltering leaves of plants or other cover which offer them their only chance of survival. Some animals are inhibited from cannibalizing their own young but not the young of other animals of their own species. Herring gulls, for example, will often steal one another's eggs and eat them if the parent on duty relaxes its guard for even a second. Herring-gull chicks are frequently killed as a result of running toward a parent not their own.

Most mammals are not aggressive toward the young of their own species. Even the most vicious male dog will not normally attack a puppy, even though the puppy is large enough to be a full-grown dog of some other breed. If the puppy has any reason to believe that its puppyhood has not been recognized, it will roll over on its back and so identify itself as a nonaggressor. If you scold your own dog, particularly if it is one sensitive to rebuke, it may show this same *appeasement gesture*. Other young animals appease their elders by similar movements or postures. In birds, these movements often consist of crouching or begging to be fed, both of which are typical of the young. These same appeasement moves are often made by females during courting ceremonies, and sometimes also by males if they are courting aggressive females.

FAMILY GROUPS

In almost every type of animal family, the younger the brood, the more intensively it is cared for. As the offspring get older, their appearance or behavior or both changes gradually so as to present less attractive stimuli to the parent. At the same time, the young become less needful and more adventurous and tend to move away from the parents, leaving them ready for the next reproductive cycle.

Sometimes the generations remain with their parents, and the family unit enlarges into a herd or flock. Some of the most stable flocks are matriarchies, such as flocks of sheep or of red deer, in which one of the oldest females leads a group consisting of other females and of young. In these cases, the males usually congregate separately—the stag line—except at breeding time.

Other groups are dominated by males. In some of these, such as that headed by the gorilla, only one male of reproductive age is allowed in any one unit, which usually keeps the groups small. The young bachelors live outside the group, waiting for a chance to drive off or destroy the older male, and a male that is not sufficiently strong or aggressive is doomed to a life of celibacy.

In communities such as those of the howler monkeys, pair bonds are not formed and females in heat are unjealously shared by the males of the troop. Care of the young, although devolving primarily on the mother, is shared by the adults of the group.

The reason for this great variation in social organization from one species to another is not yet understood.

Animal Colonies

Many animals form aggregations based primarily on family relationships. Other aggregations, such as those of paramecia described in Chapter 5–1, are based solely on environmental conditions—the availability of food, shelter, or other necessities—and so do not truly represent social behavior; each animal responds singly to environmental stimuli as if it were alone. Animals as diverse as bats, birds, locusts, antelope, bison, fish, and gnats tend to move always in flocks. If you watch birds feeding in a field, for example, they will all move off together when one of them takes off. Even very young minnows less than 10 millimeters in length tend to orient themselves in parallel rows for swimming. Starlings and other birds fly in flocks that may number a thousand or more, swooping and diving together with great precision. The simultaneous, coordinated behavior shown by these animals is sometimes referred to as *infectious behavior,* since it appears as if an individual could not help "catching" the behavior of the group. A common example of infectious behavior in humans is yawning. Don't you feel an irresistible urge to yawn as soon as you see somebody else yawn? In fact, you probably feel an urge to yawn right this minute as you are thinking about it. Besides yawning, alarm, courtship display, and copulative and feeding behavior all tend to spread infectiously in animal societies. Schooling in fishes is an extreme example of social organization based on such imitative behavior.

ADVANTAGES OF GROUP LIFE

Group life affords the individual many advantages. Large groups are unlikely to be attacked by predators; even birds as savage as the hawk nearly always select a solitary flyer or a straggler. Fish that form large schools are less likely to be attacked by larger fish. It is believed that the barracuda, for instance, will mistake a large school of very small fish for one large fish and so leave it alone. Sometimes the sheer numbers of individuals in a large group are confusing to the hunter. *Daphnia,* which are small crustaceans, are common aquarium food, as fish fanciers know. If fish are fed many daphnids all at once, a smaller number are eaten than if a few daphnids are presented at one time; apparently the fish get confused by the conflicting stimuli. In a group, if one member senses danger, its actions warn the rest; in some groups of birds and of mammals, certain individuals appear to act as sentinels.

Small warm-blooded animals, such as mice, provide each other with warmth, and groups of aquatic animals can sometimes survive in a toxic environment more successfully than isolated animals since their combined metabolic processes can serve to detoxify it.

Social animals eat more when kept with members of their group. Even if an isolated hen has been fed to satiety, she will eat half as much again if placed with a flock of hungry chickens. Similarly, fish eat much more if they can see other fish eating; it is very difficult to raise in isolation a fish that usually lives in a school, perhaps because it eats less.

Clearly, group life has many advantages, but little is known of the stimuli which keep congregations of animals together.

Social Dominance

Animal societies can be organized in a variety of ways. Often, as we have mentioned, they will be led or directed by a senior female or a senior male. One type of social dominance that has been studied in some detail is what is called the *pecking order* in chickens. A pecking order is established whenever a flock of hens is kept together over any period of time. In any one flock, one hen usually dominates all the others; she can peck any other hen without being pecked in return. A second hen can peck all hens but the first one; a third, all hens but the first two; and so on through the flock, down to the unfortunate pullet that is pecked by all and can peck none in return. Hens that rank high in pecking order have privileges such as first chance at the food trough, the roost, and the nest boxes. As a consequence, they can usually be recognized at sight by their sleek appearance and confident demeanor. Low-ranking hens tend to look dowdy and unpreened and to hover timidly on the fringes of the group. A hen experimentally moved from flock to flock may have different ranks in each of several different flocks. In a stable flock, the old-timers tend to occupy the top ranks, and any new arrival usually ranks low and has to peck her way up.

During the period when a pecking order is being established, frequent and sometimes bloody battles may ensue, but once rank is fixed in the group, a mere raising or lowering of the head is sufficient to acknowledge the dominance or submission of one hen in relation to another. Life then proceeds in harmony. If a flock is disrupted, the entire pecking order must be reestablished, and the subsequent disorganization results in more fighting, less eating, and less tending to the essential business, from the poultry dealer's point of view, of growth and egg laying.

Cocks do not normally peck hens, but they have their own pecking order. A breeding flock therefore has two hierarchies, one for each sex. The dominant cock is the most successful sexually, while the one lowest in the pecking order is the least successful and indeed may prove to be a psychological castrate. Chickens do not form pair bonds, but jackdaws, which also have pecking orders, do form permanent mating relationships, and in these relationships, the female gives up her previous rank, whether high or low, and takes on the dominance order of her mate.

These studies of social dominance reveal, incidentally, that hens can recognize as individuals astonishingly large numbers of other hens. This memory only lasts about two weeks, however; if a hen is removed from the flock for longer than that time, she has to reestablish her rank in the pecking order.

Territoriality

One of the most efficient ways in which animals organize their societies is through the establishment of territories. Territoriality in some form is seen in animals as widely diverse as crickets, howler monkeys, fur seals, dragonflies, red deer, beaver, prairie dogs, many types of lizards, and a large number of species of birds and fish.

The principle of territory establishment was first recognized by an English amateur naturalist and bird watcher, Eliot Howard, who observed that the spring songs of male birds served not only a courtship function but also to warn other males of the same species away from the terrain that the prospective father had selected for his own. In general, a territory is established by a male and is an area in which he will not permit

5–69 *Three male sage grouse in a territorial dispute. The female will watch the display. Eventually, she will choose among the males and will indicate her choice by entering the selected male's territory. (Dr. Paul A. Johnsgaard)*

645 *Social Behavior*

other males of the same species to intrude. Courtship of the female, nest building, raising of the young, and often feeding are carried out within this territory. Often the female also participates in territory defense. By virtue of territoriality, a mating pair is assured of a monopoly of food and nesting materials in the area and of a safe place to carry on all the activities associated with reproduction and care of the young. Some pairs carry out all their domestic activities within the territory. Others perform the mating and nesting activities in the territories, which are defended vigorously by the males, but do their food gathering on a nearby communal feeding ground, where the birds congregate amicably together. A third type of territory functions only for courtship and mating, as in the bower of the bowerbird, the arena of the prairie chicken, or the stamping ground of the antelope. In these territories, the male prances, struts, and postures—but very rarely fights—while the females look on and eventually indicate their choice of a mate by entering his territory. Males which have not been able to secure a territory for themselves are not able to reproduce; in fact, there is evidence from studies of some territorial animals, such as the Australian magpie, that adults who do not secure territories do not mature sexually.

TYPES OF TERRITORIES

A territory may be an area of plain, a corner of a small wood, or a few feet at the bottom of a pond. Sometimes the territory consists of little more than the nest itself and the immediate area around it. For the male bitterling, a small fish, the territory is an area immediately surrounding a freshwater mussel. The bitterling admits only egg-laden females into his territory, then leads them to the mussel, where they lay their eggs within its gills. (See Figure 5–70.) The male then injects his sperm while swimming over the siphon of the mussel.

Territories vary greatly in size. Among birds, for instance, the golden eagle defends a territory of 93 square kilometers, or about 37 square miles; the European robin, a territory of about 6 square kilometers; and the king penguin, a territory of only 1/2 square meter. Individuals of the same species often have territories of somewhat different sizes, depending partly upon the density of food and shelter in a given area, partly upon population pressure, and partly upon the aggressiveness of the individual.

TERRITORY OWNERS

Even though they may be invisible, the boundaries of almost all territories are clearly defined by the territory owner. With birds, for example, it is not the mere proximity of another bird of the same species that elicits aggression, but his presence within a part of a particular area. The territory owner patrols his territory by flying from tree to tree. He will ignore

5–70 *The territory of the male bitterling is a freshwater mussel. In the figure, a female that he has led to the mussel is laying her eggs in its gills.*

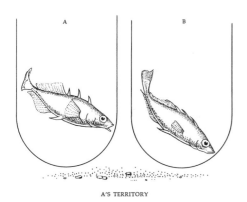

A'S TERRITORY

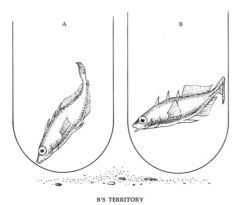

B'S TERRITORY

5-71 *Two male sticklebacks are placed in test tubes and alternately moved into each other's territories. Each fish loses aggressiveness in the other's territory.*

a nearby rival outside his territory, but he will fly off to attack a more distant one that has crossed the border. Animals of other species are generally ignored unless they are prey or predators.

Ordinarily, the territory is established by the male, who waits for the female; but in some cases, such as that of the red-necked phalarope, the female establishes and defends the territory while the drab male defends the nest, incubates the eggs, and takes care of the young. Some birds, such as the American robin and the European swallow, tend to return to the same territory year after year, often with the same mate. Similarly, bull seals year after year occupy the same territory, on which they keep their harems, while immature bulls occupy bachelor areas on the edges of the breeding grounds.

Sometimes territory is the only or the primary bond between partners. Males and females of the South European green lizard, for example, defend their territory against members of the same sex only. Thus the most powerful male and the most powerful female are likely to occupy the most desirable natural dwelling place and so to breed together more frequently than with other partners. Storks and night herons, similarly, are attached to a nesting place rather than to a mate, and if the mate of the previous year does not return the following year, he or she is readily exchanged for a new incumbant.

TERRITORIAL DEFENSE

An animal is virtually undefeatable on his own territory. As shown in Figure 5-71, if a male stickleback is placed in a test tube and moved into the territory of a rival male, he visibly wilts, his posture becoming less and less aggressive the further within the territory he is transported. Similarly, Tinbergen reports that the male cichlid will dart toward a rival male within his territory but that, as he chases the rival back into his own territory, he will begin to swim more and more slowly, his caudal fins seemingly working harder and harder, just as if he were making his way against a current which increases in strength the further he pushes into the other male's home ground. The fish know just where the boundaries are and, after chasing each other back and forth across them, will usually end up each one trembling and victorious on his own side of the truce line.

Fighting among Animals

Although an animal may have to fight to obtain a territory, territoriality, like the pecking order in a hen flock, actually serves to diminish fighting between animals of the same species. Because of the virtual indomitability of the homeowner on his own territory, prancing, posturing, scent marking, and singing and other types of calls usually suffice to make a

| — 30mm — |

5–72 *A fight between two male grunts on their territorial borderline. Each grasps the other by the lips, and the loser is the one who lets go first. Although defeated, the loser is allowed to swim away unharmed. Man is almost the only species which regularly kills members of its own kind. (Hermann Kacher)*

5–73 *Combat dance of Pacific rattlesnakes. (G. E. Kirkpatrick, Frank W. Lane)*

would-be intruder avoid a battle which he is psychologically doomed to lose. There are a variety of other checks on aggression, most of which are also matters of ritualization and all of which serve a useful adaptive function. In fact, man is one of the few species which regularly kills large numbers of his own kind.

Male iguanas of the Galapagos Islands fight by pushing their heads against one another; the one which drops to its belly in submission is no longer attacked. Male cichlid fish of one species first display, presenting themselves head on and then side on, with their dorsal fins erected, and then beat water at each other with their tails. If this does not bring about a decision, each grasps the other by its thick strong lips, and they pull and push with great force until one lets go and, unharmed but defeated, swims away. Rattlesnakes, which could kill each other with a single bite, never bite when they fight but glide along side by side, each pushing its head against the head of the other, trying to push it to the ground in a form of Indian wrestling. (See Figure 5–73.) Stags of the fallow deer, which have long and vicious horns, follow an equally careful ceremony and attack only when they are facing each other, so that their horns are used only for dueling and not for goring. Many other species of antlered animals fight in this way.

648 BEHAVIOR

5–74 *Displacement activity by a female oyster catcher. In* (a), *she is engaged in a fight with her mirror image. In* (b), *she is apparently unable to decide what to do next, so she prepares to go to sleep. (Eric Hosking, F.R.P.S.)*

(a)

(b)

|— 20cm —|

DISPLACEMENT ACTIVITIES

Sometimes, instead of overt fighting, would-be combatants engage in what Tinbergen has called *displacement activities*. A displacement activity, according to Tinbergen's formulation, is an action that occurs when an animal cannot decide between two alternatives and so does something else, often something quite irrelevant. Thus the stickleback, when undecided about whether to flee or to fight, stands on his head; this is a posture used in nest building. The herring gull, when threatening another herring gull, angrily tears out grass by its roots, also a nest-building activity. Some species of ducks may stop and preen their feathers just at the moment when combat seems inevitable. The oyster catcher, when faced with conflict, will tuck its head under its wing and appear to go to sleep.

In the course of evolution, displacement activities are occasionally modified to become signals in their own right. For example, displacement preening in male ducks has become *ritualized* to serve as signals in courtship. That is, certain preening movements have become exaggerated, stereotyped, and hence very distinctive, and these are used exclusively to court females.

Population Control

An important function of territoriality, in addition to providing food and safe dwelling for the young, is population control. Animals that cannot secure their own territories cannot reproduce, and so, since the area to be parceled out—whether a forest, a stretch of veld, a coral reef, or an Antarctic island—is usually limited in extent, the younger must often wait several seasons before breeding. Those sexually mature but too weak to compete successfully for a territory may never breed. This provides a direct and simple method for keeping the population from outgrowing its food supply and for culling out hereditary weaknesses which might otherwise be passed on to another generation. Some biologists believe that these effects are not accidental but actually provide part of the selective force that caused territoriality to evolve in the first place.

For reasons which are not understood, overcrowding often serves to reduce the birthrate among populations as various as *Drosophila*, white mice, and deer. Probably different factors are at work in different species. In mice, for example, there is suggestive evidence of the influence of one or more pheromones. In some species, crowding increases the group's susceptibility to infectious disease. In other species, animals at autopsy have been found to contain greatly enlarged adrenal glands, which is an indication of stress; it is not known whether the stress is in itself fatal or whether it leads to fatal aberrations of behavior, such as destruction of members of one's own species.

Insect Societies

Insect societies rival those of modern man in their complexity of organization; and of all animal organizations, the insect societies are probably the best understood, in terms both of their evolution and of the interplay of forces that keep them together. Like many other animal societies, they are based on the family unit, and the way the mother-egg relationship has gradually developed over the course of millennia into a tightly knit large group is indicated by observations of the behavior of existing species. In fact, the type and degree of care provided to the young insect by the wasp or bee are coming to be used as a taxonomic characteristic for determining relationships between the many species, just as slight differences in the shape of the body or the color of the wing might be used.

SUBSOCIAL BEES

Although we think of all bees as living in communal hives, most of the species are actually solitary, as are most of the wasp species, which are closely related. Among the *solitary species*, the female bee builds a small nest, either burrowing into soil or wood or piling up earth or plant material, lays her eggs in it, stocks it with a mixture of honey and pollen (which is the protein source for the larvae), seals it off, and leaves it.

In *subsocial species,* the mother returns to feed the young larvae; similar behavior is shown by many of the wasps. In one type of subsocial bee (*Allodape pringlei*), the eggs are set in a curved row like a spiral staircase winding up the inside wall of a hollow stem. After hatching, the larvae hold themselves in place by short, plump "arms." The mother drops food into the hollow stem for the larvae, and they hold the food in these special fleshy protuberances and feed themselves.

In another type of subsocial bee (those belonging to the genus *Halictus*), the mother forms a crude comb of 16 to 20 cells underground, packs in food continuously for some time, and finally closes off the chamber. She then guards the entrance so long as she survives, which may be until the young bees emerge. In some of these species, the emergent young extend the old comb and, in turn, remain to watch over their own offspring. This small community is usually destroyed during the winter, and in the spring, each female that has survived founds a new colony.

THE BUMBLEBEE

The bumblebee is a representative of the next stage of socialization. As with the *Halictus* bees, the bumblebees (*Bombidae*) must found their colony anew each spring. Every bumblebee you see in flight in the early spring is a queen and the potential founder of a colony. When she finds a suitable nest site, she constructs two cells from the wax which exudes from the surface of her abdomen. One cell she fills with nectar and pollen from her foraging trips. In the second cell, she lays a group of eggs, usually about eight. She then caps the egg cell with wax and settles down on it like a broody hen. In some three to five days, depending on the species, the eggs hatch; the mother then feeds them on the nectar and pollen. About seven days after hatching, the larvae spin cocoons. The mother continues to guard the cocoons, and she also constructs additional cells, laying eggs in each; in her spare time, she forages for nectar. The larvae within the cocoons pupate for about two weeks, and then, helped by the mother, the damp, soft-bodied, pale-colored young bees crawl out of their cocoons. These workers are all females. In two or three days, the young bees (called *callows*) become hardened, develop the "furry" coat and bright colors of their mother, and go to work, helping to gather nectar and pollen and to care for each successive brood of younger sisters.

With the emergence of the first group of workers, a big step in the socialization process is observed. Now the mother devotes almost all her time to egg laying. The workers do not lay eggs of their own but rather enlarge the nest, which gradually assumes the form of a rough comb, and devote the rest of their time to foraging for the insatiable and ever-growing brood. In other words, the workers care for their sisters (and, eventually, their brothers) rather than try to raise families of their own. As a consequence of this "altruistic" behavior, bumblebees are referred to as truly social rather than merely as subsocial.

The nectar is carried in a special honey stomach of the bee and is regurgitated into a wax container in hives, where it evaporates into honey. The pollen is transported simultaneously in special pollen baskets formed of long stiff hairs on the bees' hind legs. The returning worker scrapes the pollen off her hind legs by means of her middle legs and into one of the pollen bins in the hive.

The colony usually numbers only a few hundred bees, but it may grow as large as a thousand or so. Toward the end of the season, the production of young males and young queens begins, and the young queens mate. The workers, males, and old queens die at the end of the summer, and the young queens scatter and hibernate, emerging in the spring to found a new colony.

THE HONEYBEE

Winter Organization

The honeybee colony, which usually has a population of 30,000 to 40,000 workers, differs from that of the bumblebee and many other social bees or wasps in that it survives the winter. Like other bees, the isolated honeybee cannot fly if the temperature falls below 10°C (50°F) and cannot walk if the temperature is below 7°C (45°F). Within the hive, bees maintain their temperature by clustering together in a dense ball; the lower the temperature, the denser the cluster. The clustered bees produce heat by constant muscular movements of their wings, legs, and abdomens. In very cold weather, the bees inside the cluster keep moving toward the center, while those in the core of the cluster move to the colder outside periphery. The entire cluster moves slowly about on the combs, eating the stored honey from the combs as it moves.

The Life of the Worker

Egg laying begins early in the year, in January or February, with each egg deposited in a separate wax cell. The white, grublike larvae which hatch from the eggs are fed by the nurse workers; each larval bee eats about 1,300 meals a day. After the larva has grown until it fills the cell, a matter of about six days, the nurses cover the cell with a wax lid, sealing it in. It pupates for about 12 days, after which an adult emerges. The adult rests for a day or two and then begins successive phases of employment. She is first a nurse, bringing honey and pollen from storage cells to the queen, drones, and larvae. This occupation usually lasts about a week, but it may

5–75 *A worker bee air-conditions the hive.*
(*Edwin Way Teale*)

be extended or shortened, depending on the conditions of the community. Then she begins to produce wax, which is exuded from the abdomen, passed forward by the hind legs to the front legs, chewed thoroughly, and then used to enlarge the comb. These houseworking bees also remove sick or dead comrades from the hive, clean emptied cells for reuse, and serve as guards at the hive entrance. During this period, they make brief trips outside, seemingly to become familiar with the immediate neighborhood of the hive. In the third and final phase of their existence, the worker bee forages for honey and nectar. The life-span of a worker is usually only about six weeks.

The Queen

Each hive has only one adult queen. The queen caste is genetically the same as the worker caste. All the differences between the two castes depend on the substance fed the queen-to-be in the larval stage and on the hormonal influences she, in turn, exerts upon her subjects. For the first two days of life, all bee larvae are fed "brood food," a white paste produced in the glands of young workers and secreted from the mouth. Worker and drone larvae are then fed honey and pollen, while the larva being made ready for queenhood is fed only the glandular secretions (hence known as *royal jelly*) all during its larval stage. Attempts have been made to identify the substance in royal jelly that confers queenhood, but so far these have not been successful.

Queens are raised in special cells which are larger than the ordinary cells and are oddly shaped, somewhat resembling an empty peanut shell. If a hive loses its queen, workers will notice her absence very quickly, sometimes in only 15 minutes, and will become quite agitated. Very shortly, they begin enlarging worker cells to form emergency queen cells. The larvae in the enlarged cells are then fed exclusively on royal jelly until a queen develops. Any larva so treated will become a queen.

The Queen's Pheromones

The queen exerts influences on her subjects by means of pheromones, of which there appear to be several. As shown by the British entomologist C. G. Butler and his co-workers, the influence of one of the pheromones (9-ketodecenoic acid) inhibits ovarian development in the worker bees and prevents them from becoming queens or producing rival queens. This *queen substance*, as it is sometimes called, passes through the workers of the hive orally. As the workers meet, they often exchange the contents of their stomachs. Studies in which queen substance has been tagged with a radioactive label have shown that as a result of this activity, the pheromone travels through the hive with remarkable rapidity. Within only half an hour after removal of the queen, the shortage of 9-ketodecenoic acid is already noticed, and the hive begins to grow restless. It is difficult to understand how a single queen can produce enough pheromone to influence the entire hive of as many as 40,000 workers or more, as well as tend to her stupendous egg-laying chore, but it has been suggested that after the pheromone is passed among the workers, it is fed back to the queen in a reduced form and she need simply oxidize it to reactivate it.

New Colonies

In the spring, when the nectar supplies are at their peak, so many new broods are raised that the group separates into two colonies. The new colony is always founded by the old queen, who leaves the hive taking about half of the workers with her. This helps to ensure survival of the new colony since this queen is of proven fertility. The group stays together in a swarm for a few days, gathered around the queen, after which the swarm either will settle in some suitable hollow tree or other shelter found by its scouts or will be picked up by a beekeeper and transferred to an empty hive, which it will then furnish with wax.

In the meantime, in the old hive, new queens have begun to develop, often even before the old queen has left, and ovarian development has begun in some of the workers, some of which lay eggs which, since they are unfertilized, develop into males or drones. After the old queen leaves the hive, a new young queen emerges, and any other developing queens are destroyed. The young queen then goes on her nuptial flight, exuding a pheromone (apparently also 9-ketodecenoic acid!) that entices the drones of the colony to follow. She mates only on this one occasion and then returns to the hive to settle down to a life devoted to egg production. During this single mating, she receives enough sperm to last her entire life, which may be some five to seven years. These are stored in her spermatheca and are released, one at a time, to fertilize each egg as it is being laid. The queen usually lays unfertilized eggs only in the spring, at the time males are required to inseminate the new queens, so the release of the spermatozoa from the spermatheca is apparently under the control of her internal or external environment. Participation in the nuptial flight is the only service to the hive performed by the drones. Since they are unable to feed themselves, they become an increasing liability to the hive. As nectar supplies decrease in the fall, they are stung to death or driven out to starve by their sisters.

THE ARMY ANT

All ants are social. Their range of social behavior is so great that it alone is the subject of several books as large as this one.

The dorylines of the world are known also as legionary, army, or driver ants. The two species studied most extensively by Schneirla in Panama

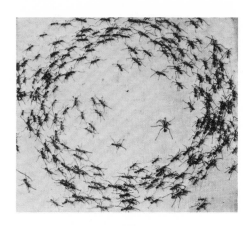

5–76 *Excited army-ant workers in the nomadic phase move in a circular column on a laboratory table. (Dr. T. C. Schneirla)*

|——— 5mm ———|

5–77 *An African driver ant carrying a larva. Like all dorylines, the driver ants are nomadic; they have no permanent nesting places but shift frequently from one nest-site to another on the forest floor. Here a worker is shown carrying one of the young during such an emigration. (Dr. Ross E. Hutchins)*

are the army ants *Eciton hamatum* and *Eciton burchelli*. Like all dorylines, they are raiders, living almost entirely on arthropod prey, and they are nomadic, with no permanent nesting place.

The temporary nest, or *bivouac*, as it is called, of the army ant is not made of wood or dirt, like that of other ants, but is a seething cylindrical cluster of ants hooked one to another. This is made possible by strong hooks which each worker has on the last tarsal segment of each leg. The clusters hang from a natural ceiling, such as the underside of a fallen tree, a branch, or a hollow log. Within the cluster is a labyrinth of corridors and chambers in which the eggs are laid and the queen and brood are sheltered and fed.

Each dawn, the ants awaken and the workers unhook themselves, tumbling into a churning throng on the ground. As more fall, pressure increases until a raiding column literally bursts forth. There is no leader; some of the workers are pushed forward by the surging mass behind, and the others follow the chemical trail they lay down. An "impulse to follow" and tactile stimuli are also important in forming the ant columns, but it is basically the odor trail secreted from the abdomen which is followed. These raiding columns often advance as quickly as 25 meters an hour and may finally extend 250 meters from the nest in an unbroken stream.

The movements of *Eciton* follow a functional cycle with two alternating phases, as do those of all of the army ants. During the *nomadic phase*, the colony carries out vigorous daily raids, which are followed by nightly emigrations of the entire colony to new nesting sites. During the second, or *statary*, phase, the raids are smaller or sometimes absent and emigrations are rare. The length of the cycle is species-specific; in *E. hamatum*, the nomadic phase lasts 16 to 18 days, and in *E. burchelli*, it ranges from 12 to 17 days. The statary phase in both species is 20 or 21 days long. The length of both phases is determined by the developmental stage of the brood.

The nomadic phase begins when the new workers emerge from their cocoons. This stimulates the entire colony. Daily raids increase in size and tempo and are followed by night marches, often lasting five or six hours, to new nesting places. These nightly emigrations are continued throughout the nomadic phase. Midway in the phase, when the excitement generated by the new workers has begun to wear off, the larvae hatch and, in turn, become the motivating force. The workers constantly stroke them with their antennae, lick them with their mouthparts, feed them, and carry them about. When these larvae pupate, the level of excitement in the colony falls sharply and the statary phase begins.

During this phase, the quiescent pupae seem to exert a soothing influence on the workers, which clutch the cocoons in their mandibles. This phase lasts for the 20 to 21 days it takes for the pupae to mature. After the first week, the queen, stimulated by the licking and grooming of the workers, goes into a stupendous eight-to-ten-day labor. In *E. hamatum*, she may lay as many as 80,000 eggs; in *E. burchelli*, 200,000. As the pupae approach maturity and begin to stir and twitch within their cocoons, the workers become excited and start to snatch the cocoons from one another. The level of activity in the colony then builds up, and as new workers emerge from the cocoons, the daily raids become more extensive until one night an exceptionally vigorous daily raid is followed by an emigration. And so another nomadic phase begins.

The queen is the most important factor in clustering and in keeping the colony together. Army ants in the laboratory will cluster wherever the queen has rested long enough to leave a trace of her pheromone. If a colony loses its queen, it can maintain a fairly normal functional cycle so long as the brood she has produced is still developing. After that, the colony enters a statary condition in which it will eventually perish unless fusion occurs with another colony. Normally, workers of different colonies, even though of the same species, will not mix when their raiding columns meet. But if one of the colonies has been without a queen for as little as 12 hours, its workers will mingle readily with those of a colony with a queen.

Affectional Systems

And what of love? What a strange, old-fashioned word that seems in this world where all relationships, in the last analysis, depend on a pheromone, a peep, a flutter of wings, or a flash of red. One scientist, however, still speaks of love; he is Harry F. Harlow, psychologist at the University of Wisconsin, who has been studying social interactions in the rhesus monkey. The monkey, like most other primates, although unlike modern man, lives in a society which is based upon a group or tribe rather than the family. The rhesus is very dependent on the other members of its group. As A. W. Yerkes, one of the early workers in animal behavior, once said, "One chimpanzee is no chimpanzee," and the same is clearly true of the anxious-faced little rhesus. Harlow believes that this monkey society is primarily held together by *affectional systems*, or *categories of love*, each of which probably operates through different neurological and endocrinological mechanisms. He has identified at least five such affectional systems in the rhesus society: mother to child, child to mother, peer to peer (which includes infant to infant, child to child, and adolescent to adolescent), mate to mate, and adult male to members of the group.

Harlow's studies of emotional development in monkeys grew out of an effort to produce and maintain a colony of disease-free young animals for use in various research programs. In order to accomplish this, each infant

5–78 *An Aenictus laeviceps queen distended with eggs.* (*Dr. T. C. Schneirla*)

rhesus was separated from its mother shortly after birth and raised alone in a bare wire cage in a large room with other caged infants which it could see but could not touch. The 56 animals raised in this manner were all germ-free, but all showed abnormalities of behavior that had never been seen in wild monkeys or monkeys raised in groups in zoos or laboratories. They are all adults now, but none has ever mated, and attempts to mate them have often resulted in vicious fights between the two partners. They pay almost no attention to other monkeys, except to show fear or aggression. Among adult males, there is little social grooming, the mutual cleaning and combing rituals commonly seen among normal monkeys. There is also little cooperation; social monkeys loose in a laboratory, for instance, often open cages to free their companions, while these laboratory-born monkeys raised in isolation never do so. They sit staring fixedly into space, circle their cages like automatons, or hold their heads in their hands and rock back and forth for hours at a time. Many of them pinch or tear at their skins or chew on parts of their bodies, sometimes down to the bone. Similar symptoms have been reported in deprived children in orphanages and in withdrawn adolescents and adults in mental hospitals.

What was missing? In order to answer this question, Harlow began a series of studies of social deprivation in which he raised monkeys in various ways to see which interactions in a normal monkey society were the most significant.

MOTHER AND CHILD RELATIONSHIPS

First, he studied the relationships between mother and infant. A mother primate gives her baby intimate bodily contact, food and other physical requirements, and protection. Of these, which would you think would be the most important? And how would you decide? Harlow answered these questions by taking newborns away from their natural mothers and raising them on foster "mothers," a wire model that produced milk and a non-milk-producing terry-cloth model that offered soft body contact to the infant. In all cases, the latter "mother" was preferred. Even when fed by the wire mother, the baby would immediately return to the cosier model. When placed in a strange situation, the infant would run to the terry-cloth mother for reassurance and protection; if "she" was present, the infant would lose signs of fear and begin to explore and play, but if "she" was absent, the infant would often cower in fright. Harlow made some of these "mothers" rejecting and inconsistent in their behavior. One threw her baby off at regular intervals, another released compressed air, a third shook the infant until its teeth chattered. In each case, the baby reacted by clinging more and more tightly. Even after two years of separation, the monkeys still showed a persistent attachment to the effigies.

Despite this devotion to their "mothers," the monkeys raised with the

5–79 *A primate mother with her infant.* (*Courtesy of Wisconsin Regional Primate Research Center*)

models alone are almost indistinguishable in their behavior from those raised in complete isolation. The attachment of an infant monkey to its surrogate mother, although it resembles in many ways the attachment of the infant to a real mother, is usually not sufficient for the development of normal behavior.

Some of the females of this group were impregnated when they became mature in order to observe their behavior toward their own young. Of 20 motherless mothers, 8 were physically abusive to their infants. Four of the eight killed their infants, and a fifth would have if the infant had not been taken from her. Seven of the twenty were indifferent; all these seven showed punishing behavior toward the infants, but it was less violent and less frequent than that of the first group. All the infants in both of these categories required artificial feeding in order to survive. Yet even the infants that suffered violent abuse repeatedly sought bodily contact with their mothers. The five mothers that permitted their infants to nurse were rated as adequate.

RELATIONSHIPS AMONG PEERS

In the experiments just described, the infant monkeys were also denied the association with other young monkeys that they would have experienced in normal monkey society. Harlow and his co-workers did a second series of experiments in which infants with no mothers or with terry-cloth mothers or with abusive mothers were permitted to play with one another from an early age. Every one of these monkeys showed normal social and sexual behavior by the time it was adult, even the infants who were allowed to be in the company of their peers as little as 20 minutes a day. By contrast, infant monkeys isolated with normal mothers for

5–80 *The infant monkey shown here has been taken from his mother and been given, instead, two model "mothers"—a milk-producing wire model and a non-milk-producing terry-cloth model. From this photograph, could you draw any conclusion about the relative importance to the infant of food and bodily contact? (Courtesy of Wisconsin Regional Primate Research Center)*

5–81 *The infant runs to the terry-cloth "mother" for reassurance. (Courtesy of Wisconsin Regional Primate Research Center)*

longer than six months are not capable of forming normal social and sexual relationships. On the basis of these studies, Harlow has concluded that the peer-to-peer affectional system is the most important in normal development.

In observing the play of young monkeys with one another, Harlow has been particularly impressed by the fact that even as infants, male and female monkeys have very different play patterns. The play of infant males includes much more bodily contact and rough and tumble, and as they grow older, the males tend to assume postures of aggression and mock attack. The infant females usually sit on the sidelines and scold and chatter. Males are aggressive toward both males and females, but the females respond by turning their backs, not looking at the males, and walking away —but not too quickly. This is the forerunner of the female sexual response. Female infants occasionally threaten other females, but they never threaten males.

These patterns of behavior are clearly evident by the time the monkeys are 130 days old. Since they appear in infants raised by artificial mothers as clearly as in infants raised by normal mothers, they are obviously innate patterns of behavior rather than the result of maternal or social attitudes of adults of the species. (Besides, all monkeys dress alike, as Harlow says.) Evidence of true aggression does not develop in these monkeys until they are adults. By this time, the affectional system among the peers has been firmly established and appears to act as a check upon the aggression.

An important factor in the normal development of the young monkey is its rejection by the mother. During the first three months of life, in a normal mother-child relationship, much time is spent with the infant clinging to the mother's ventral surface or with the mother cradling the baby against her body. Apparently, this contact clinging binds the mother to the child as well as the child to the mother. Mothers were successfully persuaded to adopt infant monkeys not their own when the infants initiated contact clinging but not when they did not. Toward the end of this three-month period, however, the mother becomes increasingly rejecting, punishing the child often and repelling some of its advances, although she still frequently displays affection. This negative treatment by the mother tends to turn the infant more and more toward the group during this critical period.

No monkeys denied access to their peers beyond the age of six months have developed normally, in Harlow's experience. However, later social relationships do tend to overcome some of the abnormalities of behavior produced by early isolation. Of the five motherless mothers who were rated as adequate, two of them had been placed with other monkeys after they were adults, while only three of the fifteen abusive or indifferent mothers had had any social contact as adults. Three of the mothers that

5–82 *A male bonnet macaque holding a juvenile he has adopted. Older babies are often physically displaced from the mother when a new baby arrives, and during this period, the young monkeys show great separation anxiety. Adult males will then usually adopt these displaced juveniles, holding them in their arms and carrying them on their backs. (Courtesy of Wisconsin Regional Primate Research Center)*

were abusive and three that were indifferent to their firstborn infants were bred again, and of these six, five proved to be adequate mothers to their second infants. Normal females, on the other hand, are usually more indulgent toward their firstborn than toward subsequent offspring.

THE ADULT MALE IN THE GROUP

The affection shown by the monkeys toward one another is shown not only in heterosexual and maternal relationships but also in the play of young monkeys, in mutual grooming, and in cooperative enterprises and mischief in the adults. Normal adult females usually exhibit affection only toward their own offspring and are sometimes suspicious and punitive toward other mothers' children, but an adult male will often "adopt" a young monkey that has been deposed by a new sibling and will take care of it almost as a mother would. Typically, the normally raised adult rhesus male, although sometimes aggressive, shows great affection for all the females and children of the tribe.

SUMMARY

In this chapter, we examined the behavioral interactions of animals of the same species.

The mating rituals of animals perform several useful functions: (1) They help the animals overcome the fear and hostility which are normal components of their reactions to each other, at least long enough to allow the reproductive act to occur. (2) They serve to isolate the species from other species. (3) They bring members of the opposite sex into reproductive synchrony.

An important factor in the relationship between parents and their young is the *reciprocal stimulus*, which offers in the act of caring for the offspring a pleasure component for the parent. In some species, the young must be protected from the aggressiveness or actual cannibalism of the adults of the species. In other species, adults are inhibited from attacking the young, particularly where the young employ appeasement gestures.

Many animals form colonies; some are based on family groups, some are a result of environmental conditions, and some are organized on the basis of imitative behavior. These societies afford their members protection from predators and from toxic elements in the environment. They can be organized in a variety of ways. The pecking order in chickens is a well-known example of one type of social organization; territoriality is another example. Both of these systems tend to diminish fighting between animals of the same species.

Insect societies, which sometimes rival human societies in complexity, are based on the family group. These societies are matriarchies, centering around the care of the queen and the raising of her broods. Two societies were examined in detail: those of the honeybee and the army ant.

The importance of affectional systems in the functioning of the group and the normal development of the individual animal is being investigated in a series of experiments with rhesus monkeys. Five affectional systems have been studied: mother to child, child to mother, peer to peer, mate to mate, and adult male to members of the group. Of these five, peer to peer relationships have proved to be the most significant in this species.

SUGGESTIONS FOR FURTHER READING

CARR, ARCHIE: *Windward Road,* Alfred A. Knopf, Inc., New York, 1955.

————: *So Excellent a Fishe,* The Natural History Press, Garden City, N.Y., 1967.

Two informal narratives, the first now a classic, of the migrations of green turtles and of how scientists have tried to study their astonishing navigations.

DETHIER, VINCENT G.: *To Know a Fly,* Holden-Day, San Francisco, 1963.*

An inside look into the activities, both frivolous and serious, of laboratory life.

EVANS, HOWARD E.: *Wasp Farm,* The Natural History Press, Garden City, N.Y., 1963.

The wasp farm is 8 acres of woods, fields, and brambles occupied by many species of wasps and one observant and devoted entymologist.

FRISCH, KARL VON: *Dancing Bees,* Harcourt, Brace & World, Inc., New York, 1965.*

Karl von Frisch's own account of his studies of the language of the bees.

GRIFFIN, DONALD R.: *Echoes of Bats and Men,* Doubleday and Company, Inc., Garden City, N.Y., 1959.*

An easy-to-read account of Griffin's studies of echolocation, which began when he was a graduate student.

LORENZ, KONRAD Z.: *King Solomon's Ring,* Apollo Editions, Inc., New York, 1961.*

King Solomon's ring imparts to its wearer the magical ability to talk with animals. Much of Lorenz's work was carried out with occupants of his own household—including geese, jackdaws, and cichlids—and Lorenz's highly personalized descriptions of the animals and their behavior make charming and amusing reading.

MCGILL, THOMAS E.: *Readings in Animal Behavior*, Holt, Rinehart, and Winston, Inc., New York, 1965.

A well-chosen, lively selection of papers from the scientific literature, including some of the most important and some of the most controversial subjects in the field.

MARLER, PETER R., AND WILLIAM J. HAMILTON, III: *Mechanisms of Animal Behavior*, John Wiley & Sons, Inc., New York, 1966.

Probably the best up-to-date text.

ROE, ANNE, AND G. G. SIMPSON (EDS.): *Behavior and Evolution*, Yale University Press, New Haven, Conn., 1958.

A number of distinguished biologists, psychologists, neurophysiologists, and ethologists met to consider all aspects of the interrelationship between behavior and evolution. This group of papers is the result of that meeting.

SCHALLER, GEORGE B.: *The Mountain Gorilla: Ecology and Behavior*, The University of Chicago Press, Chicago, 1963.

An interesting and enjoyable field study.

TINBERGEN, NIKO: *Herring Gull's World*, Doubleday & Company, Inc., Garden City, N.Y., 1967.*

Information about the herring gull, an animal which has been the subject of a number of important studies. Also interesting is Tinbergen's account of how he and his students have carried out these studies.

————: *Social Behavior in Animals; With Special Reference to Vertebrates*, 2nd ed., Barnes & Noble, Inc., New York, 1967.*
Observations on social behavior, particularly in birds and other vertebrates.

WELLS, M. J.: *Brain and Behavior in Cephalopods*, Stanford University Press, Stanford, Calif., 1962.

Experimental analyses of behavior in the octopus and squid.

YOUNG, J. Z.: *Doubt and Certainty in Science. A Biologist's Reflections on the Brain*, Oxford University Press, Fair Lawn, N.J., 1960.*

The brain of the octopus is the point of departure for a series of reflections on the nature of science and the scientific method.

* Available in paperback.

POPULATION BIOLOGY AND ECOLOGY

(*Paul A. Moore, Tennessee Conservation Dept.*)

SECTION 6

POPULATION BIOLOGY AND ECOLOGY

Introduction

The next time you walk through the woods, see how many different kinds of living things you can count. The plants will be the most obvious—the larger trees, shrubs, and grasses. The first animals to catch your eye will probably be the birds. Even a few acres of field or woodland can serve as the territory for two and sometimes three nesting pairs and as a transient feeding ground for others; you should be able to spot several different species on a brief walk in the spring or summer. Squirrels and chipmunks are likely to hold their ground as you approach, greeting you with a bright-eyed stare and often, in the case of the squirrels, a scolding chatter. Rabbits, although likely to be present in equal numbers, are more cautious and less curious about human visitors, and deer mice, the most common of all the forest animals, usually remain in hiding during the day, venturing forth only at night.

Lichens will probably be growing on the trees, spread on the bark like a gray-green paste. If the ground is damp and shaded, you will find ferns, mosses, and liverworts. Moving among them will be snails, slugs, and perhaps, if it does not see you first, an occasional frog or toad. Above all, there will be insects, sow bugs, spiders, and other small arthropods; these will far outnumber all other visible species. One small annual plant in flower can be host to several insects simultaneously, and one rotting tree stump can provide ample food and housing for more than a score of different arthropod colonies. No one has ever made a complete census of even one forest community, but from the combination of a number of studies, we know that we can expect to find individuals of the major groups in quite stable proportions. For example, in a typical deciduous forest of the North American temperate zone, the area of land required for one bird will contain about 3 mammals; 13,000 snails and slugs; 20,000 centipedes, millipedes, and sow bugs; 35,000 arachnids; and 225,000 large insects.

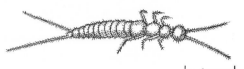

The bristletail feeds on decayed matter.

|—3mm—|

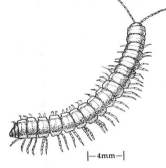

The millipede thrives in damp areas and feeds primarily on decaying vegetable matter.

|—4mm—|

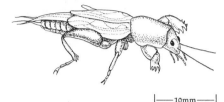

|—10mm—|

The mole cricket, which lives in the tunnels it digs in the soil, feeds on the roots of plants.

*Wood lice are usually found **under** logs, where they feed on the rotting wood. They are also called pill bugs because they curl into a ball when disturbed.*

|—0.3mm—|

Great horned owl. (R. Dale Sanders, U.S. Forest Service)

If we dig into the soil, the number of organisms becomes so large as to be almost inconceivable. A single cubic meter of soil beneath grassland swarms with 165,000 mites. A million flagellates can exist in a teaspoonful of this soil, and bacteria and fungi are present in even greater numbers. In fact, they *are* the soil. If they were removed, the forest humus would be quite different in composition and in its ability to support life. Moving among these microscopic animals are numerous earthworms, comparative giants in this underground world, and other, smaller worms—nematodes (the roundworms) by the thousands. Through this teeming hidden invertebrate world, small mammals such as moles, shrews, and mice build tunnels and runways, which also serve as burrows and hiding places for other animals that feed on the rich litter of the forest floor or on the soil insects.

If we pass this way again next year, all the individual small annual plants we saw and many of the smaller animals will have died. Yet we shall find almost exactly the same kinds of plants and animals in almost equal numbers. In fact, if our grandfathers had walked through this forest, they would in all likelihood have found the same plants and animals that we see today; and if the forest is not destroyed, our great-grandchildren and their children will find the same living things in just about the same propor-

666 BIOLOGY OF POPULATIONS

6–1 *Small mammals such as the eastern mole shown here dig burrows and runways in the forest floor, creating a hive of passageways that assist the soil in retaining water. Moles and shrews move constantly through the soil in search of food; the shrew must eat at least once an hour to survive, and the mole at least once every 12 hours. In its ceaseless search for insects and worms, the mole, which is only about 6½" long, will dig as much as 300 feet of tunnels a day. As you can see, its relatively enormous front paws are specialized for digging. (Leonard Lee Rue III, National Audubon Society)*

tions. But this forest was not here a million years ago, and a million years from now, even if it is not touched by man, it will be different. The changes are going on right now, but they proceed so slowly that only rarely can they be seen in the lifetime of one person or even of several human generations.

The life of a forest—or a prairie or a pond or a strip of seacoast—is the composite of the lives of the organisms that we find within it. Yet a forest is clearly more than a chance collection of trees, mosses, birds, and insects, just as a cell is more than an aggregation of proteins, starches, sugars, and nitrogenous bases and an organism is more than an assembly of cells. Cells, tissues, organs, and plants and animals all represent units of biological organization. Similarly, a natural community represents one of the levels of organization of life, an organization that, like all organizations, operates by a system of laws.

Notice that "law" in the biological sense is different from "law" in the social or legal sense. Man-made laws are imposed from the outside and can be disobeyed; the laws of nature are a part of nature itself. For example, the particular sequence of amino acids in a protein molecule determines how that molecule will fold under certain conditions of temperature and pH. This is a property of the molecule, although we also may refer to it as a law governing its behavior. When a whole group of protein molecules, and other molecules as well, are organized in a certain way, they take on the properties of a cell—another level of organization with its "laws." Similarly, communities of living organisms have their own properties and therefore their own laws.

Population biology is the branch of science concerned with the laws that regulate the ways in which living organisms fill the physical world. These are the laws that determine the kinds and numbers of animals and plants, the ways in which these organisms interact with the physical factors of the environment, and the interactions among the organisms themselves. It is also concerned with the changes that take place in the organisms and in their interactions with one another and with the environment—the evolution of living forms and the evolution of the interactions among living organisms.

The first two chapters of this section concentrate on the forces that have shaped the different kinds of animals and plants into their present forms. Chapter 6–3 examines some of the forces that regulate the number of organisms within a species, the number of different species, and the interplay between birth and death in natural populations. The fourth chapter describes the environments in which plants and animals live and how organisms interact with these environments and with one another to form communities. The last chapter in the section, Chapter 6–5, discusses the evolution of man.

667 *Introduction*

Population Genetics

Modern Evolutionary Theory

In Section 2, we traced some of the phylogeny, the evolutionary history, of the plants and animals. In this final section, we shall concentrate on the processes by which this evolution takes place.

The question of process was, as you will remember, the chief concern of Darwin, and although it is now more than 100 years since the first publication of *The Origin of Species,* Darwin's theory still provides the basic framework for the understanding of organic evolution. In fact, after several decades of dissent and discord, modern students of evolution have come back almost full circle to Darwin's original postulates, and we are today more in agreement with his theory than we have been for half a century. Modern evolutionary theory conceives of evolution as Darwin conceived of it, that is, as involving two factors: (1) variation, which provides the raw material of evolution; and (2) natural selection (or, more precisely, differential reproduction), which shapes and molds the raw material.

MENDELIAN GENETICS VS. DARWINIAN NATURALISM

The weakest point in Darwin's "long argument," as he himself knew, was that he did not understand genetics. Mendelian genetics would have answered for him the crucial question of why rare genetic traits were not "blended out" in a generation or two. On the other hand, the genetics of the early 1900s did more to obscure the process of evolution than to clarify it. After the reports of De Vries, which followed rapidly upon the rediscovery of Mendel, the geneticists seized on mutation as "explaining" all of evolution; in one genetic leap—a *saltation,* as it was called—a new character would assert itself that might endow its possessor with such clear superiority that the mutant form could immediately prosper at the expense of its fellows. Each new form was an incipient species, and the species, therefore, was produced by a single mutation. Saltationism had the great advantage of shortening the time period required for evolution, thus "solving" one of the most vexing problems of the day.

Darwin, despite opposition, had held stubbornly to his tenet that the fabric of evolution was "the full effects of many slight variations, accumulated during an almost infinite number of generations," although he could not explain how these variations were produced, maintained, and passed from generation to generation. This conviction was based on his personal observation of many different kinds of living things. The naturalists that followed him also knew from their own observations that the variations in natural populations were slight and subtle, yet they lacked the background and training to devise laboratory experiments that would convince the geneticists, who were studying pure strains and abrupt phenotypic changes.

THE SYNTHETIC THEORY

The conflict between the geneticists and the naturalists was eventually resolved when the rigorous scientific methods of the geneticists were applied to the study of whole populations. This approach is the basis of the modern theory of evolutionary processes, called the *synthetic theory* because it represents a synthesis of the two opposing views.

For the purposes of population genetics, a population is an interbreeding group of organisms. In this sense, all the fish of one particular species in a pond are a population, and so are all the *Drosophila* in one cage. The population is defined and united by a common gene pool, the sum total of all the genes in the population. Many of these genes will be common to all members of the pool. Some will be present in the genotypes of a sizable part (but not all) of the population. And some will be found in only a few individuals. The genes are no longer seen as acting in isolation but as constantly interacting with one another. This concept opened the way to an understanding (and to mathematical proofs) of what the naturalists had maintained all along, that every population conceals a great wealth of variability and that even a slight advantage of one phenotype over another is sufficient to change the character of the population. *It is the population that evolves, not the individual.*

In this view, the individual is only a temporary vessel, holding a small portion of the gene pool for a short time, testing a particular combination. If the individual has a favorable combination of genes, his genes may be returned to the pool or may be present in an increased proportion in the next generation. If the combination is not favorable, his contribution to the gene pool will be reduced or perhaps eliminated. The "struggle for survival," as Darwin saw but some of his followers overlooked, includes not only differential survival but also relative reproductive capacity. The sole criterion of *fitness* is the relative contribution of individuals to the gene pool of future generations.

THE CHANGING CONCEPT OF THE GENE

For Mendel, the units of inheritance were invisible discrete factors which governed single traits. In the early twentieth century, geneticists described these factors, which came to be called *genes*, in terms of their most obvious phenotypic effects—white-eyed, long-winged, gray, and so forth. This is still the most convenient way to describe genes, and often the only way we have, but it can be very misleading, as Dobzhansky showed in 1927, while he was still working at Columbia University. Dobzhansky arbitrarily selected 12 strains of fruit flies, each with a single different mutation that changed a specific characteristic, such as eye or body color or wing shape, and examined the shape of the spermatheca in the females. Ten out of twelve of the mutant strains showed a variation from normal in the size and shape of this particular organ, although each mutant fly was thought to differ from the norm in only a single obvious characteristic. Thus it was apparent that the genes affected more than one characteristic of the flies.

Sometime later, another investigator, Hans Grüneberg, approaching the problem from the other direction, studied a whole complex of congenital deformities in the rat, including thickened ribs, a narrowing of the tracheal passage, a loss of elasticity of the lungs, hypertrophy of the heart, blocked nostrils, a blunt snout, and needless to say, a greatly increased mortality. All these changes, he was able to demonstrate, were caused by a single mutation, that is, a mutation involving only one gene. This particular gene produces a protein involved in the formation of cartilage, and since cartilage is one of the most common structural substances of the body, the widespread effects of such a gene are not difficult to understand.

More recently, mutation in a single gene has been shown to affect the growth, branching, shape, and size of the leaves and the morphology of the flowers, fruits, and seeds in the coffee plant (*Coffea arabica*). The capacity of a gene to affect a number of different characteristics is known as *pleiotropism*.

After it was found that the actual product of a gene is not a trait but a chemical, i.e., a protein, the pleiotropic effects of genes came to seem logical and consistent, rather than puzzling, as they had at first. The gene complex can now be seen as a highly organized biochemical factory producing, either directly or indirectly, all the substances needed for the structure and function of the organism. And as the population geneticists have demonstrated, it is the entire genotype that must be more fit, not the single gene, since it is the genotype as a whole that determines the fitness of the individual.

BASIC POSTULATES OF THE EVOLUTIONARY THEORY

Within a decade after the publication of *The Origin of Species,* few biologists doubted the fact of evolution. Suppose, however, that we wanted to test Darwin's theory for ourselves. These are the hypotheses involved in the theory of evolution, the foundations on which the theory rests:

1   Like begets like—in other words, there is stability in the process of reproduction.
2   Variations occur in the population, and some of these variations are inheritable.
3   In every species, the number of individuals that survive to reproductive age is very small compared with the number produced.
4   Which individuals will survive and which will perish is determined, in general, not by chance but by their fitness, which in turn determines the contribution that each individual will make to the next generation.

Stability and Variation

THE PRECISION MACHINERY OF INHERITANCE

Darwin based his postulate of the stability of heredity on direct observation. Dogs produce dogs, cats produce cats, children look like parents, one amoeba closely resembles another, and there are no reliable reports of any exceptions to this principle.

We now understand, as Darwin could not in his time, the physical basis for the exact transmission of genetic information. It was first glimpsed in studies of mitosis, the process by which a dividing cell endows each of its daughter cells with an exact copy of its chromosome complement. In asexually reproducing organisms, each new organism, barring accidents, is an exact copy of the parent. In sexually reproducing organisms, the germ cells, like all other cells, are formed from cells that contain exactly the same chromosomal information as is present in the zygote; in the higher animals, as the German zoologist August Weissman pointed out, these cells are "set aside" early in embryonic development.

With the discovery of the role of DNA as the repository of the genetic information, the machinery of inheritance became clear. DNA, by its very structure, makes possible great precision in the copying of the genetic information, a precision that can be demonstrated in the test tube. The biochemical mechanisms by which the genetic information stored in the DNA molecules shapes the development, structure, and functions of an organism can now be seen in broad outline, although the details are just beginning to be understood.

Variations exist among organisms, and these variations often have a genetic basis. Darwin recorded many instances of mutants among animals and plants—*sports*, as they were called—in which the unusual trait was passed on to succeeding generations.

If variations did not exist that could be transmitted by genetic mechanisms, evolution would not be possible.

Origin of Variations: Mutation

Variations originate in mutations, and as we know, they involve changes in the DNA. A mutation may result from a change so small that only a single base pair is affected, and this would be reflected in the substitution of only one amino acid in a polypeptide chain. Such a mutation might have no phenotypic effect whatsoever or perhaps a very subtle one, such as a slight shift in the temperature range in which an enzyme will remain stable. On the other hand, it might have quite dramatic effects.

Almost every textbook in genetics contains a picture of the Ancon ram that was born in the late nineteenth century into the flock of a New England farmer named Seth Wright. This ram had unusually short legs and transmitted them to some of his progeny. By inbreeding the progeny, sheep were developed which were unable to jump over the stone walls that enclose New England pastures. (See Figure 6–2.) The breeding results show that the short legs were the phenotypic result of a single homozygous recessive. The survival of such an animal under natural conditions

6–2 *An example of the sometimes dramatic effects of mutation. The ewe in the middle is an Ancon, an unusually short-legged strain of sheep which originated in New England in the nineteenth century. The strain is the result of inbreeding by sheep raisers, who saw an advantage in legs too short to permit the sheep to jump the stone walls enclosing the New England sheep pastures. (Edmund B. Gerard)*

would be very unlikely, but under conditions of domestication, it was favored. The breed has been permitted to die out in New England, but as the result of a separate mutation, a short-legged breed of sheep has now been established in northern Europe.

Mutations occur constantly. The average spontaneous mutation rate for a given gene locus has been estimated to be 1 or 2 new mutations per 100,000 genes per generation. This means that in every 100,000 sperm cells, 1 or 2 can be expected to carry a new mutation for a particular gene. Suppose there are 10,000 gene loci; this is the estimated number in *Drosophila*. The total mutation rate will be

$$\frac{1}{100,000} \times 10,000, \text{ or } \frac{1}{10}$$

In other words, 1 in every 10 gametes, and, therefore, 1 in 5 diploid organisms, can be expected to carry a new mutation. The mutation is far more likely to be detrimental than useful; yet to remain viable under changing environmental conditions, the population must carry this potentiality for change.

The overall rate of mutation can be increased by ultraviolet light, x-rays, or various chemicals that affect cell division, but these external agents do not influence the type of mutation that is produced. Some gene sites are more mutable than others; such sites are called *hot spots* by bacteriophage workers. Table 6–1 gives examples of the rates of mutation of various characteristics in corn.

Table 6–1 *Mutation in Corn (Zea) (After Savage, 1963)*

Genes	Mutation rate per 1,000,000 gametes
seed color	492.0
seed-color inhibitor	106.0
purple seed color	11.0
sugary seed	2.4
yellow seed	2.2
shrunken seed	1.2
waxy seed	0.0

The Environmental Factor in Variation

One of the problems faced by earlier students of evolution was the fact that many of the significant phenotypic changes, particularly in plants, did not seem to be genetic in origin. A plant grown with minimal light and water will usually be small, straggly, and flowerless, even though its parent plant might have been large and luxuriant. A tree growing within a forest is usually tall and slender, with few branches except at the top, where the cap of foliage reaches into the full sunlight. On the forest's edge, the tree is shorter, and branches and foliage are dense both at the cap and on the side that is exposed to full sunlight.

Plants that grow under rugged environmental conditions often tend to be smaller and stragglier than plants of the same species grown under more favorable conditions. (A striking example of this is shown in Figure 6–3.) This well-known phenomenon was a source of support to scientists who tended to discount the importance of small variations in evolution. But in a now classic study, a team of investigators took samples of a species of yarrow (*Achillea millefolium*) from localities at various altitudes in the Sierra Nevada and grew them at sea level. Although all the plants grew taller at sea level than in their regular environment, they did not all grow to a uniform height; those from the higher localities tended to be shorter

6–3 *A white-barked pine growing near the timberline on a mountain in California. Normally a tall straight tree, the pine shown here has been forced to creep along the rocks by the constant strong winds. (Philip Hyde)*

6–4 *The four regional races, or ecotypes, of Potentilla glandulosa, a relative of the strawberry. The regional differences in the four environments in which this species grows are reflected in the physiological differences among the four ecotypes. When the plants are grown outside their natural environments, these differences persist. What conclusion would you draw from that fact? (After Clausen, Keck and Hiesey, 1958)*

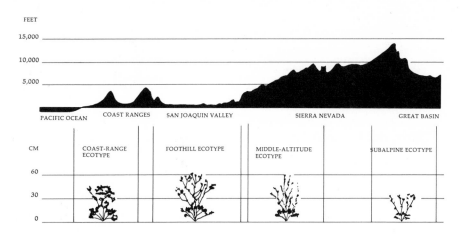

than those collected from the lower, more favorable areas. Therefore, the way in which the plants were affected by the environment was, in part, genetically determined and therefore inheritable.

The low-altitude plants were then divided (thus providing specimens that were all genetically identical), and half the specimens were grown at sea level and half at mid-altitude. The mid-altitude plants, when fully grown, were shorter than their identical twins at sea level. Other important characteristics such as date of flowering, luxuriance, and type of vegetation, which also varied with the genotype, were shown to be affected environmentally.

Latent Variability

Although mutation is the original source of variation, it is only through many sexual recombinations that a mutation establishes itself in the genotype. Most natural populations are believed to contain enough variations so that evolution could proceed for thousands of years without any influx of new mutations.

From your own experience, look at what breeders of domestic animals can find in the way of variation in a genotype. Among dogs, for instance, almost all the extreme forms—long legs, short legs, long pointed noses, pushed-in noses, long coats, hairlessness, smallness, largeness, gentleness, ferocity—have arisen not by new mutations but by selection over and over again of material already present in the original gene pool. Many of these extreme characteristics are caused by homozygous recessives, and they are quickly lost if inbreeding is not maintained. If two purebred dogs of different breeds are crossed, the F_1 puppies will be quite uniform in appearance, but the F_2 generation will be extremely heterogeneous, a fact which you can explain on the basis of Mendelian assortment. By the time

675 *Population Genetics*

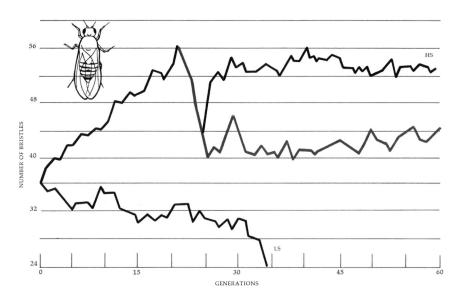

6–5 *The results of an experiment with Drosophila melanogaster, demonstrating the extent of latent variability in a natural population. From a single parental stock one group was selected for an increase in the number of bristles on the ventral surface (HS, high selection line) and one for a decrease in the bristle number (LS, low selection line). As you can see, the HS line rapidly reached a peak of 56, but then the stock began to become sterile. Selection was abandoned at generation 20 and begun again at generation 24. This time the previous high bristle number was regained and there was no apparent loss in reproductive capacity. The LS line died out owing to sterility. (After Mather and Harrison, 1949)*

another generation or two have passed, even an expert would be hard-pressed to trace the original genealogy.

The extent of latent variability in a natural population was demonstrated in the laboratory by experiments in which a population of *Drosophila melanogaster* was selected for a completely arbitrary hereditary characteristic, the number of bristles on the ventral surface of the fourth and fifth abdominal segments. In the starting stock, the average number of bristles was 36. Two selection groups were run, one for increase of bristles and one for decrease. In every generation, individuals with the fewest bristles were selected and crossbred, and so were individuals with the highest number of bristles. Selection for low bristle number resulted in a drop after 30 generations to an average of 25 bristles. In the high-bristle number line, progress was at first rapid and steady. In 20 generations, bristle number rose steadily from 36 to an average of 56. No new genetic material had been introduced. It was apparent that within the single population, a very wide possible range of variation existed, and this had become manifest by selection pressures.

There is a second part to this story. The low-bristle-number line soon died out owing to sterility. (Correlated changes in the factors affecting fertility had also taken place.) When sterility became severe in the high-bristle line, a mass culture was started; members of the high-bristle line were permitted to interbreed without selection. The average number of bristles fell sharply, and in five generations went down to a mere 39. This line fluctuated up and down and finally reached a plateau at 40, which still was higher than the original 36. Then selection was begun again. The previous high bristle number of 56 was regained very rapidly, but this time there was no loss in reproductive capacity. Apparently, the genotype had rearranged and reintegrated itself so that the genes controlling bristle number were present in more favorable combinations.

Mapping studies have shown that bristle number is controlled by a large number of genes, at least one on every chromosome and sometimes several at different loci on the same chromosome. Selection for bristle type, therefore, although the trait itself would appear to be neither useful nor harmful, put a strain on the entire genotype.

Inbreeding and Outbreeding

The effect of sexual recombinations in maintaining variability in a population is considerably reduced if the gene pool is small. In a small gene pool, some of the rarer variants either will not be represented at all or will be lost from the population by chance. If, for example, a particular allele is carried by 5 percent of the population and the population numbers 100,000 individuals, there is little likelihood of those particular 5,000 genes being lost from the gene pool by accident or by unfortunate combination with an unfavorable genotype. If the population numbers 100, however, five genes might well be eliminated at random. This phenomenon, known as *genetic drift*, leads to genes being lost or fixed at random rather than by natural selection.

Small populations may harbor an unusually high proportion of deleterious homozygous recessives. This is because whatever rare recessive genes there are in a small population will come together more often than they would in a large population. An interesting example of such a situation is found in the Old Order Amish of Lancaster, Pennsylvania. Among these people, there is an unprecedented frequency of a gene which, in the homozygous state, causes a combination of dwarfism and polydactylism (extra fingers). Since the group was founded (in the early 1770s), some 50 cases of this rare congenital deformity have been reported, about as many as in all the rest of the world's population. About 13 percent of the persons in the group, which numbers some 17,000, are estimated to carry this rare mutant gene.

The entire colony, which has kept in virtual isolation from the rest of the world, is descended from three couples. By chance, one of the six must have been a carrier of this gene. This is an illustration of the *founder principle* and represents a special case of genetic drift. As we shall see, the founder principle often plays a role in the formation of new species.

Inbreeding does not necessarily produce deformity or disease, as witness Cleopatra and the Ptolemies, but outbreeding is generally known to produce more favorable progeny. We have seen that many plants have evolved elaborate devices to avoid self-pollination.

6–6 *Hybrid corn is derived by first crossing inbred strains A with B and C with D and then crossing the resulting single-cross plants to produce double-cross seed for planting. The increased size and hardiness of the hybrid are probably due to its increased heterozygosity.*

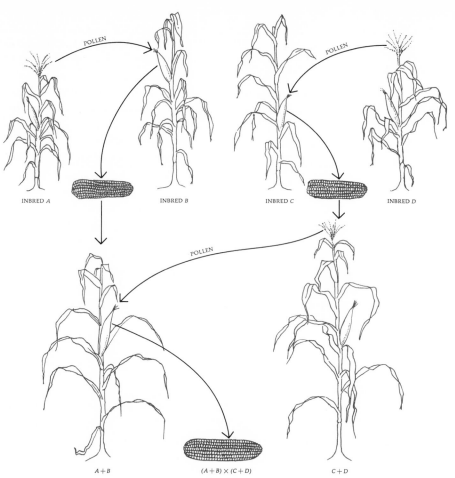

INBRED *A*   INBRED *B*   INBRED *C*   INBRED *D*

A + B   (A + B) × (C + D)   C + D

A striking example of the advantages of outbreeding is found in the development of hybrid corn, which caused a revolutionary improvement in the corn crop of the United States in the 1930s. The increased size and hardiness of the plants, derived by crossing two different varieties to produce the seeds for each planting (Figure 6–6), are generally attributed to the increased heterozygosity of hybrids; hybrids are less likely to be homozygous at any loci for deleterious recessives. Hybrid vigor, also known as *heterosis*, may result from heterozygote superiority, a phenomenon which will be discussed later in this chapter.

Most human cultures encourage outbreeding, at least to some extent. Many primitive societies, for example, demand that a young man choose a wife from another village rather than from his own community, and virtually all cultures have strong prohibitions against incest. Such prohibitions are particularly interesting when you consider that intermarriages between brother and sister or father and daughter would tend to keep property or power within the family and so could be socially and economically advantageous. Followers of Freud would maintain that incest is forbidden by strong psychological taboos, as reflected in the Oedipus myth. More pragmatic biologists hold that the prohibition stems from the observed ill effects of incestuous matings and has been merely reinforced by cultural restraints, which have now become deeply rooted in our subconscious.

Maintaining Variation

The genotype stubbornly resists change. By and large, an organism, the product of tens of thousands of years of evolution, is well in tune with its environment, and unless the environment changes, wide variations in structure or function are almost always doomed to failure. There is a contradiction between the postulated efficiency of natural selection and the continued existence of genetic variation (so essential to evolution) that has worried biologists for more than a hundred years. In this perpetual tug-of-war between stability and variation, how is variety stored in the gene pool and how can it be maintained there? We know some, although not all, of the answers to this question.

LOW-FREQUENCY VARIATIONS

We know from the Hardy-Weinberg principle that a neutral variation will remain in the population in the same ratio over an indefinite period of time provided that the population is sufficiently large and provided also that there is no selection (differential reproduction) of genotypes, no mutation, and no unequal migration into or out of the population.

In the case of a deleterious recessive gene, the lower the frequency of the gene in the population, the less it will be acted upon by natural selection. This is a result of the fact that the proportion of recessive genes in the homozygotes decreases precipitously as the gene frequency decreases. Where q equals the frequency of gene a, the distribution of the recessive will follow the pattern shown below.

q	Genotype frequencies			Percentage of a in heterozygotes
	AA	Aa	aa	
0.9	0.01	0.18	0.81	10
0.1	0.81	0.18	0.01	90
0.01	0.9801	0.0198	0.0001	99

In short, the lower the gene frequency, the smaller the proportion of recessive genes exposed in the homozygotes becomes, and the progress toward removal of the gene from the population slows down accordingly. This result is of particular interest to students of eugenics. If a particular undesirable gene a has a gene frequency q of 0.01 in the human population, so that q^2 individuals made up 0.0001 of the population (1 defect to 9,999 "normals"), it will take 100 generations, roughly 2,500 years, of a program of sterilization of defective homozygote individuals to halve the gene frequency and reduce the number to 1 in 40,000. If a dominant gene becomes lethal, however, it will be removed from a population in one generation.

Certain recessive genes, such as those which cause retinoblastoma in the homozygous recessive, are maintained at a low frequency in the population by spontaneous mutations, which restore the gene to the gene pool as rapidly as it is eliminated.

PROTECTION OF THE RECESSIVE GENE

In Mendel's experiments, genes were unambiguously dominant or recessive; that is, the heterozygote Aa was indistinguishable from the homozygote AA. We now know that this "rule of dominance" is far from being a rule. Rather, most heterozygotes do differ, although sometimes only slightly, from the homozygote. Moreover, a gene may be dominant with respect to one aspect of its phenotypic effect but recessive with respect to another and intermediate with respect to a third.

Dominance is best understood by considering the enzymes, which are the primary products of the genes. Suppose the wild-type gene is producing an enzyme necessary for flower-pigment production. A mutation of this gene may, in the homozygous condition, result in reduced flower color or, perhaps, no color at all. The loss of pigment associated with the mutant gene may result from one of three causes: (1) the mutant gene may produce no functional enzyme at all, (2) the gene may produce an enzyme of reduced efficiency, or (3) the gene may produce an enzyme that actually works to block pigment production. In the first two cases, the gene either will be recessive or will show a very slight effect in heterozygotes. This is because the heterozygote will have one dose of "good" enzyme, which may be quite sufficient to produce all the pigment or, at least, nearly all. In the case of the active, blocking type of mutation, however, the mutant gene will be dominant or will have a strong effect in heterozygotes.

It is sometimes possible to detect the gene product of a recessive gene in heterozygotes, as Pauling showed (Chapter 3–4), and sometimes a recessive gene can be unmasked in the heterozygous condition by special environments. For example, in the case of sickle-cell heterozygotes, the normal allele makes sufficient "good" hemoglobin for the organism to function under conditions of normal oxygen pressure, but at lowered pressure, such as is caused by living at high altitudes, the heterozygote may suffer.

In general, the less effect an allele has on the phenotype, the less exposed to selection it will be and the more slowly it will be eliminated from or built up in the population. Thus, a number of variations exist in the gene pool that are being slowly eliminated or slowly increased when they appear in the homozygous condition. (Remember that some recessive homozygotes may represent an *advantage* over the dominant homozygote or the heterozygote.)

If the homozygous recessive is not highly detrimental, in terms of the entire genotype, the rate of elimination and the rate of restoration of the variant through new mutations may balance out. Such variants, although they may affect the immediate fitness of the organism, may also provide for adaptive change. For example, the recessive allele may produce an enzyme which, in the present environment, does not function as well as that produced by the dominant allele but which, because of a small structural difference, is more heat-resistant. It is presumably the gradual accumulation of such variants that makes it possible for certain types of algae, for instance, to produce strains that can survive in the near-boiling water of hot springs.

Recessive genes, protected from phenotypic selection, are probably the most important source of variation in the gene pool.

CONTINUOUS VARIATIONS

Every population contains a spectrum of continuous visible variations involving traits, such as height and body build, that are under the control of multiple factors. An example of such a variation is given in Figure 6–7, which shows the distribution of height among men in the United States. Fifty years ago, the average height was less but the shape of the curve was the same; in other words, the great majority fell within the middle range and the extremes in height were represented by only a few individuals. Some of these height variations are produced by environmental factors, such as diet, but even if all the men in a population were maintained from birth on the same type of diet, there would still be a continuous variation in height in the population.

This sort of variation occurs in any characteristic that is affected by a number of different genes. It is wrong, for example, to think of the genes that affect height as genes for tallness or shortness. Genes involved in the production of growth hormones, in calcium formation, in the rate of ossification of cartilage, in the secretion of digestive juices—and you can probably think of half a dozen more—could all have slight effects on adult height.

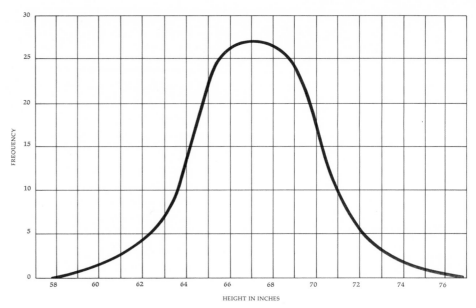

6–7 *Height distribution among U.S. males. Height and weight are examples of continuous variations. These are genetic traits characterized by small gradations of difference. A graph of the distribution of such traits always takes the form of a bell-shaped curve, as shown, with the mean, or average, falling in the center of the curve. (After Merrell, 1964)*

The distribution curve shown in Figure 6–7 applies to any characteristic that is affected by a diversity of genes. We could change the labels and the graph would equally well illustrate the range of seed weight in a particular species of plant or the range of mass in a population of jellyfish or bristle-number distribution in *Drosophila*.

Environmental Correlations

Environmental changes, however, can produce changes in the distribution curve shown in Figure 6–7. Sometimes cataclysmic changes wipe out a large segment of a population, leaving only the individuals on one or the other margin of distribution. Not many years ago, for example, there was an unusually cold winter in certain parts of Europe and the moles were unable to find enough to eat. Almost the only survivors in the mole population were very small animals, whose nutritional requirements were low. The individuals in the European mole population have not yet regained their previous size, although the variations have now distributed themselves again along the same curve.

Sometimes patterns of change can be found to follow a geographic distribution. These patterns are usually related quite directly to temperature, humidity, or other environmental conditions. There are a number of "rules," some predictable and some surprising, which correlate variations with environmental changes. Some species include races which possess small body size in the warmer parts of the species range and races of

(a)

(b)

(c)

6–8 *The ears of foxes help them to get rid of body heat. Of the three foxes shown, the fennec (a) of the North African desert has the largest ears. The red fox (b) of the fields and forests of the eastern United States has ears of intermediate size, and the Arctic fox (c) has the smallest ears. (Credits): (a) (Ron Garrison, San Diego Zoo) (b) (Courtesy of the Pennsylvania Game Commission) (c) (Courtesy of the New York Zoological Park)*

6–9 *What can you conclude about the environment this animal lives in? (Willis Peterson)*

large body size in the cooler parts. Tails, ears, bills, and other extremities of animals are relatively shorter in the cooler part of a species range than in the warmer parts. Arctic foxes have short ears and snouts, whereas tropical foxes have long ones. (See Figure 6–8). This is because the extremities serve to radiate heat. Thus mice with long tails can tolerate higher temperatures than tailless mice.

In the coloration of birds and mammals, black pigments increase in the species in warm and humid habitats, reds and yellow-browns prevail in arid climates, and light colors are general in cold regions.

Fish of cool waters tend to have a larger number of vertebrae than those living in warm waters. In the gypsy moth, a gradual increase in natural incubation time can be found as one moves from south to north, ensuring that the adults do not emerge before cold weather is over. Land snails tend to have smooth, glossy brown shells in cold climates and white or strongly sculptured shells in hot dry climates. In these cases, although the physiological basis is not always clear, the range of natural variation is broadened and maintained by the external environment.

683 *Population Genetics*

6–10 *Polymorphism in land snails. (Dr. P. M. Sheppard)*

6–11 *An "anvil," where song thrushes break land snails open in order to obtain the soft, edible parts. From the evidence left by the empty shells, investigators have been able to show that in areas where the background is fairly uniform, unbanded snails have a survival advantage over the banded type. Conversely, in colonies of snails living on dark, mottled backgrounds (such as woodland floors) banded snails are preyed upon less frequently. (Dr. P. M. Sheppard)*

Polymorphism (from *morphe*, meaning "shape") is the persistence within the population of two or more discontinuously different types of individuals. Human beings, for example, are polymorphic for the blood groups A, B, AB, and O. Apparently, the three alleles associated with these blood types are a part of our ancestral legacy, since the same blood types are also found in other primates. For a number of years after the discovery of blood types, it was assumed that they were all neutral in terms of their selective value and, as a consequence, were all maintained in invariant frequencies in the human population. Now geneticists are becoming more and more reluctant to dismiss any gene as "neutral," and information is accumulating that may be used as evidence against this concept of neutrality. For example, there are irregular geographic distributions of the A, B, AB, and O groups. These differences were at one time thought to represent examples of random genetic drift or of the founder principle, but now geneticists are more inclined to believe they reflect some selective force that may or may not be operating at the present time.

Color and Banding in Snails

An example of balanced polymorphism is found among land snails of the genus *Cepaea*. In the species *Cepaea nemoralis*, the most thoroughly studied of the group, the shell of the snail may be yellow, brown, or any shade from pale fawn through pink and orange to red. The lip of the shell may be black or dark brown (normally) or pink or white (rarely), and up to five black or dark-brown longitudinal bands may decorate it. (See Figure 6–10.) Fossil evidence shows that this polymorphism has existed since before the Neolithic period.

Studies among English colonies of *Cepaea nemoralis* have revealed selective forces at work in some of the colonies. An important enemy of the snail is the song thrush. Song thrushes select snails from the colonies and take them to nearby rocks, where they break them open, eating the soft parts and leaving the shells. (See Figure 6–11.) By comparing the proportions of types of shells around the thrush "anvils" with the proportions in the nearby colony, the investigators have been able to show correlations between the types of snails seized by the thrushes and the habitats of the snails. For instance, of 560 individuals taken from a small bog near Oxford, 296 (52.8 percent) were unbanded, while of 863 broken shells collected from around the rocks, only 377 (43.7 percent) were unbanded. In other words, in bogs, where the background is fairly uniform, unbanded snails are less likely to be preyed upon than banded ones.

Studies of a wide variety of colonies have confirmed these correlations. In uniform environments, a higher proportion of snails are unbanded, while in rough, tangled habitats, such as woodland floors, far more tend to be banded. Similarly, the greenest communities have the highest proportion of yellow shells, while among snails living on dark backgrounds, the yellow shells are much more visible and are clearly disadvantageous, judging from the evidence conveniently assembled by the thrushes.

Many of the snail colonies studied were at distances so great from one another that the possibility of immigration between populations could be entirely ruled out. How then is polymorphism maintained in the face of such strong selection? One would expect populations living on uniform backgrounds to be composed only of unbanded snails and colonies on dark mottled backgrounds to lose all their yellow-shelled individuals. The answer to this problem is not fully worked out, but it seems to involve the fact that there are physiological factors which are correlated with the particular shell patterns and which form a part of the same group of genes that control color and banding. Experiments have shown, for instance, that unbanded snails (especially yellow ones) are more heat-resistant and cold-resistant than banded snails. In other words, linked with color and banding are other strong selection pressures that are also at work, and these may maintain a balanced polymorphism.

Polymorphism in the Primrose

Conspicuous examples of polymorphism are found in many species of the primroses (*Primula*). In these plants, two types of flowers occur in approximately unchanging proportions in every population. In one of these (known as *pin*), the style is long, raising the stigma high in the flower, and the stamens are short, so that the anthers are located low in the body of the flower. In the other form (*thrum*), the stigma is low and the anthers are high. (See Figure 6–12.) A pollinator that moves from primrose to primrose will receive pollen from one type on the part of its body most likely to come into contact with the stigma of the other type. In this way, cross-pollination is ensured.

Genetic analysis has shown that the two different phenotypes act almost as if they were controlled by a single gene locus, with thrum being dominant over pin. Occasionally, however, although very rarely, forms intermediate between pin and thrum are produced, indicating that each of these two characteristics is controlled by a group of genes which are linked so closely to one another that they are generally inherited as a unit.

In addition to the anatomical differences between the two forms, there are other physiological differences that promote cross-pollination between the two types. For instance, the cells of pin stigmas react against pin pollen grains, inhibiting the formation of pollen tubes, but these cells promote the growth of tubes from thrum pollen.

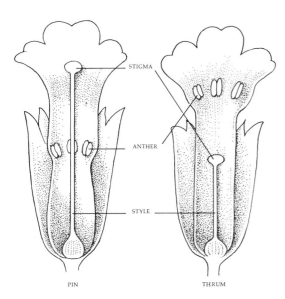

6–12 *Cross sections of a pin type and a thrum type of a species of primrose (Primula officinalis). Notice that the anthers of the pin flower and the stigma of the thrum flower are both situated about halfway up the corolla tube and that the pin stigma is level with the thrum anthers. How does this placement of stigma and anthers in the two types promote the survival of the species?*

6–13 *Seasonal changes in the relative fre-*
quencies of three common gene ar-
rangements in Drosophila. The Stand-
ard inversion is shown by the black
columns, the Arrowhead by the hatched
columns, and the Chiricahua by the
gray columns. The figures indicate per-
centages of the total population studied.
Although chromosomal polymorphism
in Drosophila does not result in any
visible differences among the flies, these
variations do have adaptive significance.
How do the findings shown here dem-
onstrate this fact?

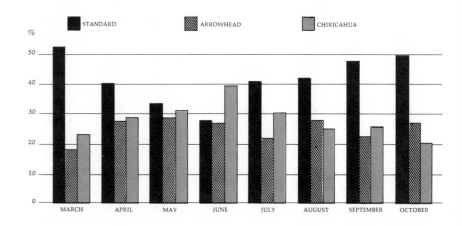

Chromosomal Inversions

From studies of giant chromosomes in *Drosophila*, chromosomal polymorphism due to inversions was found in natural populations of about 30
species. Because the representatives of the various species appeared alike
in visible traits regardless of the gene arrangements, it was believed at first
that the chromosomal polymorphism had no adaptive significance. In all
cases that have been studied intensively, however, the contrary has been
shown to be true.

For example, there are three common gene arrangements, inversions on
the third chromosome, in natural populations of *Drosophila pseudoobscura*; these arrangements are known as *Standard, Arrowhead,* and *Chiricahua*. When samples of the *Drosophila* population were taken repeatedly
from the same localities, it was found that the relative frequencies of the
three chromosomal types changed with the seasons. A summary of observations in a locality on Mount San Jacinto in California is presented in
Figure 6–13. As you can see, the frequency of Standard decreases and that
of Chiricahua increases from March to June, while the opposite change
takes place during the hot season, from June to August.

The adaptive value of the Arrowhead inversion was shown by taking
samples of populations from different elevations in the Sierra Nevada
(Table 6–2). Standard chromosomes are more frequent at low than at high
elevations, and Arrowhead chromosomes increase in frequency as one
ascends. On the other hand, the number of Chiricahua remains relatively
constant. As the weather grows hotter, however, the proportion of Standard increases at the high locations. Thus there are clearly physiological
differences associated with the different chromosomal arrangements and

these differences enable the population as a whole to survive under a variety of environmental pressures. The state of balanced polymorphism is maintained by these changing environmental pressures.

SUPERIORITY OF THE HETEROZYGOTE

As we have seen, variation can be maintained within a population if the different phenotypes produced as a result of genetic variations represent a balance of advantages and disadvantages. Another means of maintaining variation is selection for the heterozygote. If Aa individuals produce more offspring, in relation to their proportion in the population, than either AA or aa individuals, both alleles will tend to remain in the gene pool.

Selection for heterozygosity can be demonstrated easily. As an example, Table 6–3 shows the expected and observed frequencies of three phenotypes in a laboratory population of F_2 generation individuals from a cross between dark (EE) and light (ee) individuals of Drosophila polymorpha. The color itself does not appear to confer any selective value, but it is apparently associated with some other characteristic that does.

One of the most dramatic instances of heterozygote superiority is found in association with sickle-cell anemia. The individual homozygous for sickling almost never lives to maturity. Therefore, almost every time one sickling gene encounters another, two sickling genes are removed from the

Table 6–2 *Incidence of Different Gene Arrangements in Populations of Drosophila pseudoobscura Living at Different Elevations in the Sierra Nevada (After Dobzhansky, 1951)*

| | Gene arrangement (⁰/₀) | | | |
Elevation (ft)	Standard	Arrowhead	Chiricahua	Other
850	46	25	16	13
3,000	41	35	14	10
4,600	32	37	19	12
6,200	26	44	16	14
8,000	14	45	27	14
8,600	11	55	22	12
10,000	10	50	20	20

687 *Population Genetics*

Table 6–3 *Frequency of Three Phenotypes in a Laboratory Population of F₂ Generation Raised from a Cross between Dark (EE) and Light (ee) Individuals of Drosophila polymorpha (Data from Da Cunha, 1949)*

	Dark (*EE*)	Intermediate (*Ee*)	Light (*ee*)
Observed	1605	3767	1310
Expected	1670.5	3341	1670.5
Deviation	— 65.5	+ 426	— 359.5
Relative adaptive values	0.85	1.00	0.695

population. At one time, it was thought that the sickling gene was maintained in the population by a steady influx of new mutations. Yet in some African tribes, heterozygotes for sickling number as high as 40 percent and to replace the loss of sickle genes by mutations alone would require a rate of about 1 mutant per 100 genes. This is about 5,000 times greater than any other known mutation rate in man!

More recently, it has been discovered that the heterozygote is maintained because it confers a selective advantage. In many African tribes, malaria is one of the leading causes of illness and death, especially among young children. Studies of the incidence of malaria among young children show that susceptibility to malaria caused by *Plasmodium falciparum* is significantly lower in individuals heterozygous for sickling. Among Negroes in the United States, only about 9 percent are heterozygous for the sickling gene. Since no more than half of this sickle-gene loss can be explained by the Negro-white admixture in America, the conclusion is that once selection pressure for the heterozygote is relaxed, the mutant will tend to be eliminated slowly from the population. Other genes that are deleterious in the homozygous state appear to be maintained in the population by heterozygote superiority. For example, for reasons that are not known, women who are carriers of hemophilia (heterozygotes) have a fertility rate about 20 percent higher than that of the rest of the female human population.

HOW MUCH HETEROZYGOSITY?

Population geneticists have long debated how much genetic variation a population can hold. On the one hand, variability is absolutely essential if the population is to be able to respond adaptively to environmental change. On the other hand, too much variation can result in a population that is inferior in the single place and time in which it finds itself.

How would you measure the genetic variation in a population? One way would be to do breeding experiments such as Mendel did with plants and Morgan and his group did with *Drosophila*, performing backcrosses to make recessive mutants reveal themselves. The disadvantage of this method, however, is that it only reveals variants that result in obvious phenotypic changes, so it in no way represents a true sample. The ideal method, of course, would be to take samples of DNA from gene loci on one chromosome and compare them, nucleotide by nucleotide, with the corresponding segment of DNA on the homologous chromosome. But this is not technically possible, although it may someday be. We can do something very like this, however. Each of these segments, as we know, makes an enzyme or some other protein; if the segments of DNA at the corresponding loci are identical, the proteins will be identical. If they are different, the proteins will be different. By this method, it is not necessary to know the identity of actual alleles; the proteins themselves can tell the story.

Working on this basis, Richard Lewontin and J. L. Hubby of the University of Chicago set about grinding up fruit flies, both adults and larvae, and extracting proteins from them. Samples were taken from five different populations of *Drosophila pseudoobscura*, and each was analyzed for the presence of 18 functionally different proteins. The proteins were analyzed by electrophoresis, the method that was used, you may remember, by Linus Pauling for demonstrating slight differences in the amino acid composition of normal and sickle-cell hemoglobin.

Of the 18 loci thus analyzed, 9 produced identical proteins in the population samples studied and 9 produced variants. Seven loci (39 percent of the genes tested) produced relatively common variants, often several different ones. One gene locus produced as many as six slightly different proteins; in other words, six alleles for that gene were shown to exist in the species as a whole. Variants at two other loci were discovered that seemed to represent rare alleles existing only in a small local population. Each population of the five sampled was heterozygous at slightly less than a third of the loci tested. On the basis of the total proportions of the variant enzymes produced, it was estimated that each single individual in the population was probably heterozygous at about 12 percent of the loci. These figures are minimal since some changes can occur in a protein that will not affect its electric charge and so all the variants could not be detected by electrophoresis.

SUMMARY

Population biology is concerned with (1) how interbreeding communities of organisms (populations) develop, (2) how they function as populations, (3) how populations interact with one another and with their environment, and (4) how both populations and the interactions of populations continue to evolve. In this chapter, we have examined the forces that mold populations and that change the frequency and kinds of inherited variations in populations.

Modern biologists accept evolution as a fact. The modern theory of evolutionary processes is called the *synthetic theory* because it resolves the conflict which existed in the early part of this century between the Darwinian naturalists and the early Mendelian geneticists. In this theory, Mendelian principles of inheritance are applied to populations and are used to explain genetic variability in nature. Evolution is now conceived of as involving two factors: (1) variation, which provides the raw material, and (2) differential reproduction, which shapes and molds the raw material.

Great precision in the storing, copying and transmitting of genetic information is made possible by the structure of DNA and by the distribution of chromosomes at mitosis.

Variations originate in mutations and are introduced into populations by sexual recombination. Since most natural populations contain a large amount of *latent variability*, most changes arise in populations by selection, through genetic recombination, of mutations already present in the gene pool. The existence of this hidden variability has been demonstrated both by inbreeding and by selection experiments such as those performed with bristle characteristics of *Drosophila*.

Variations are maintained in populations in several ways: (1) By the Hardy-Weinberg principle, neutral variations will tend to remain indefinitely in the population in the same ratio. (2) The lower the frequency of a gene in the population, the less it will be exposed to selection and the more slowly it will be removed from the population. (3) Recessive genes, an important source of variation, are protected when they confer some special adaptive advantage on the heterozygote. (4) Continuous variations occur in any characteristic that is affected by a number of genes. (5) Two very different alleles or groups of genes can be held in a population in a balanced state; this is known as *balanced polymorphism*.

Chapter 6–2

The Processes of Evolution

The Ratio of Increase

"Suppose," said Darwin, in his original paper on evolution, "in a certain spot there are eight pairs of birds and that only four pairs of them annually rear only four young, and that these go on rearing their young at the same rate, then at the end of seven years (a short life, excluding violent deaths, for any bird) there will be 2,048 birds instead of the original sixteen."

In the laboratory, such population explosions can actually be observed. A commercial breeder of laboratory mice can count on each female to produce 60 young in her lifetime, an average of two babies a week. Estrus first occurs on the fifty-eighth day of the mouse's life. From that time on, she will raise a litter of 8 to 10 young every two to three months, 6 to 10 litters per lifetime. Moreover, by the time her second litter is born, her daughters will be launched on their own careers.

Nor is the sanctuary of a laboratory necessary. When a species is first introduced into a new and favorable habitat, its numbers may increase phenomenally. In 1859, an English gentleman named Austin, residing in Australia, imported a dozen rabbits from Europe to grace his estate. Six years later, Austin had killed a total of 20,000 rabbits on his own property and estimated that he still had 10,000 remaining. They soon spread over the continent. In 1887, in New South Wales alone, Australians killed 20 million rabbits, and the war still continues.

In 1890, a group of bird lovers who planned to introduce into the United States all the birds mentioned by Shakespeare released 60 European starlings in New York City. Forty more were released the following year. By 1915, starlings were established residents of Halifax, Nova Scotia. Two years later, one was seen in Savannah, Georgia, and within the next decade, starlings, by then the most abundant of all birds in New York City, were populating most of the country east of the Mississippi.

691   *The Processes of Evolution*

6–14 *A rabbit horde descends on a water hole in Australia. Rabbits rarely drink water since they normally get most of the moisture they need from vegetation; these rabbits, however, have cropped clean the surrounding vegetation. Introduced into Australia in the eighteenth century, the rabbits quickly spread across the continent, destroying pastureland and depleting water supplies. In an effort to exterminate them, the disease myxomatosis was introduced into the population in 1950. At first, the results were spectacular and the rabbit population steadily declined. Now, however, owing to changes in both host and virus, about 95 percent of the rabbits survive the disease. (Courtesy of Australian News and Information Bureau)*

In 1879 and 1881, 435 striped bass from the Atlantic Ocean were planted in San Francisco Bay. In 1899, the commercial net catch alone was 1,234,000 pounds.

Why are we not overrun by all kinds of animals? The answer lies in a broad but useful term, *environmental resistance*. The population of a species is limited in size not by the reproductive capacity of its members but by external forces—the carrying capacity of its natural community. The key to the process of evolution, as Darwin saw clearly, is this excess of individuals, of which only a small proportion restore their genes to the gene pool.

Evolution in a Man-made Environment

We have shown that natural populations contain a large fund of genetic variations and that there is a correlation between these genetic variations and the adaptation of the population to the environment in which it lives. We also know that many more individuals are produced than survive to produce young of their own. Can we show, however, that these forces in combination produce permanent changes in the course of time?

Darwin based most of his argument on the powers of natural selection by drawing analogies with the selective processes employed by breeders of livestock or pets, and for a number of years evolutionists were inclined to agree with Darwin that such a necessarily slow process as evolutionary change could not be observable within a single lifetime. Within recent years, however, investigators have uncovered a number of examples of the evolutionary process taking place around us.

ADAPTATION OF *Biston betularia* TO INDUSTRIALIZATION

One of the most striking examples of an evolutionary process taking place in today's world had begun, in fact, before Darwin died in 1882. Moths of certain species fly at night and spend their days at rest. One such insect, the peppered moth (*Biston betularia*), well known to naturalist-collectors of the nineteenth century, was usually found on lichen-covered trees and rocks. Against this background, their light coloring made them practically invisible. Up until 1845, all reported specimens of *Biston betularia* had been light-colored, but in that year one black moth of this species was captured at the growing industrial center of Manchester.

With the increasing industrialization of England, smoke particles began to pollute the foliage in the vicinity of industrial towns, killing the lichens and leaving the tree trunks bare. In heavily polluted districts, the trunks and even the rocks and the ground became black. During this same period, more and more black *Biston betularia* were found. This mutant form, known as *carbonaria*, spread through the population until black moths

6–15 *Biston betularia, the peppered moth, and its melanic form, carbonaria, at rest on a lichen-covered tree trunk in unpolluted countryside (shown on the right) and on a soot-covered tree trunk near Birmingham, England (on the left). A striking example of an evolutionary change resulting from a drastic environmental change, the black form of the moth began to appear in the latter part of the nineteenth century as the English countryside became increasingly polluted by industrial smoke. (Dr. H. B. D. Kettlewell)*

made up 99 percent of the Manchester population. Where did the black moths come from? Eventually, it was demonstrated that the black color was the result of a rare recurring mutation.

Why were they increasing so rapidly? H. B. D. Kettlewell was among those who hypothesized that the color of the moths protected them from predators, notably birds. In the face of a number of strongly opposed entomologists—all of whom claimed they had never seen a bird eat a *Biston betularia* of any color—he set out to prove his hypothesis. He marked a sample of moths of both colors, carefully putting a spot on the underside of the wings where it could not be seen by a predator. Then he released known numbers of marked individuals into a bird reserve near Birmingham, an industrial area where 90 percent of the local population consisted of black moths, and another sample into an unpolluted Dorset countryside where no black moths ordinarily occurred. He returned at night with light traps to recapture his marked moths. From the area around Birmingham, he recovered 40 percent of the black moths but only 19 percent of the light ones. From the area around Dorset, 6 percent of the black moths and 12.5 percent of the light moths were retaken. (See Table 6–4.)

To clinch the argument, Kettlewell placed moths on tree trunks in both locations, focused hidden movie cameras on them, and was able to record birds actually selecting and eating the moths, which they do with such rapidity that it is not surprising that it was not previously observed. Near Birmingham, when equal numbers of dark and light moths were available, the birds seized 43 light-colored moths and only 15 *carbonaria;* while near Dorset, they took 164 *carbonaria* but only 26 light-colored forms.

At present, only a few of the light-colored populations persist, and these are far from industrial centers. As would be expected, more and more

Table 6–4 *Results of Kettlewell's Studies of Biston betularia*

Moths	Dark wood near Birmingham			Light wood in Dorset		
	Dark	Light	Total	Dark	Light	Total
Not recaptured	72	48	120	443	434	877
Recaptured	82	16	98	30	62	92
Total released	154	64	218	473	496	969

of the moths are black. The change, which is called *industrial melanism,* has been very rapid. Because of the prevailing westerly wind in England, the moths to the east of industrial towns tend to be *carbonaria,* right up to the east coast of England, and the few light-colored populations are concentrated in the west, where lichens still grow. Similar trends have now been found among some 70 other moth species in England and some 100 species of moths in the Pittsburgh area of Pennsylvania.

BACTERIAL RESISTANCE

A familiar example of evolutionary change resulting from man-made selective pressures was first seen in the 1940s following the rapid progress in the development of antibiotic drugs, which selectively destroy many types of bacteria. It was not long before bacteriologists and physicians began to notice that bacterial cells "developed resistance to these drugs."

This was a serious medical problem—which it still remains—and also, for a time, a problem to molecular biologists. As you will recall, much of the work in molecular biology has been carried out with bacteria and other microorganisms. For the purposes of these studies, scientists assumed that bacteria were representative biological systems, a supposition that was already under some attack since bacteria, as you know, are not eucaryotic.

When patients develop resistance to a drug such as a pain-killer, for instance, it means that the drug has produced physiological changes that alter the drug's effect. Many medical investigators, accustomed to thinking in these terms, tended to view the development of resistance in bacterial cells as an analogous process. But the resistant bacterial cells transmitted resistance as an hereditary characteristic!

This dilemma was resolved by a beautifully simple experiment performed by Joshua and Esther Lederberg. (See Figure 6–16.) Bacterial cells grown in a broth were spread thinly on a dish containing agar, a type of jelly which provides a firm medium for bacterial growth. Once visible colonies began to appear—a matter of about 24 hours—the cells were transferred to different dishes containing different kinds of media, including, for example, doses of penicillin and streptomycin.

The method the Lederbergs developed for transferring the cells was ingenious. As you can see in Figure 6–16, a piece of velvet was held on a cylindrical block in the same way that a piece of material is held on an embroidery hoop. The block was marked by an arrow, and so were all the culture dishes. The velvet was pressed gently against the original culture dish and then onto the new medium, with the arrows in careful alignment each time. As a consequence, it was possible to relate each colony that grew on the new culture to a colony in the original "mother culture."

695 *The Processes of Evolution*

6–16 *The Lederbergs' replica-plating method for detecting and isolating drug-resistant bacteria. (a) The bacteria are cultured in a diverse collection of organic molecules referred to as a "broth." (b) A sample of the cell suspension is spread over the surface of a plate containing broth solidified with agar. (c) The plate is incubated until colonies appear. A piece of velveteen held by a ring that fits snugly around a cylindrical block is used to transfer a sample of each colony to a replicate plate (d). (After Stahl, 1964)*

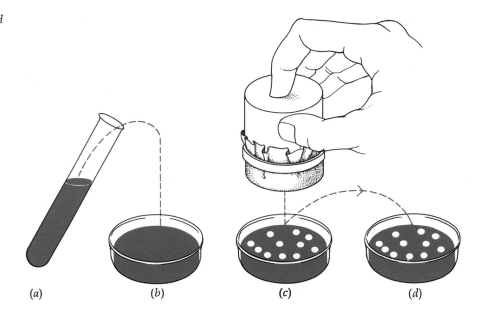

(a)   *(b)*   *(c)*   *(d)*

After transfer of cells to a penicillin-treated agar, a small colony usually arose. But how did it arise? Were the cells random mutants, or did some cells "adapt themselves" to the new environment? To answer this question, the Lederbergs took more cells from the spot on the original colony corresponding to the spot from which the penicillin-resistant cells arose and transplanted them to a new agar dish which contained no penicillin. Free from the competition of other bacterial cells, these cells grew and covered the entire dish. When members of the colony were tested, it was found that they were all penicillin-resistant—yet they had never been exposed to penicillin. The mutation had occurred independent of the exposure. Penicillin-resistant cells had arisen spontaneously in the original bacterial colony, and when placed in an environment for which they were particularly well suited, they flourished and multiplied. They were, therefore, genetic mutants and not produced by the direct action of the environment.

INSECTICIDE RESISTANCE

The development of resistance to insecticides by flies, cockroaches, and similar unwelcome visitors is a phenomenon only too familiar to the general public. Insecticide resistance in a population develops gradually over a number of generations, but from man's point of view, this development is remarkably rapid. For instance, during World War II, DDT was highly effective in controlling body lice, but by the time of the Korean War, it was virtually useless. In fact, within two years after DDT was first

6–17 *The common form of the roadside weed* Camelina sativa *is a branched, bushy annual* (a) *with small seeds and seed capsules* (b). *In regions of eastern and northern Europe where flax is commonly grown,* Camelina *has evolved races specially adapted to infesting flax fields. To compete with the flax plants, which grow tall, straight, and very close together, the flax mimic is tall, straight, and unbranched. Furthermore, the size and weight of its seeds have been adjusted by natural selection to resemble those of flax, which are larger and flatter than the common* Camelina *seeds. In this way, the flax-mimic seeds are not sifted out during winnowing but remain with the flax seeds which the farmer sows back into the field each year. Two enlarged seed capsules, different solutions to this problem of adaptation,* **are shown in** (c) *and* (d).

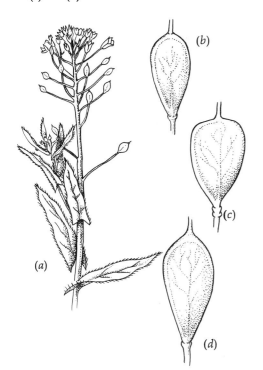

(a)

(b)

(c)

(d)

used, resistant strains of many types of insects had developed independently in different parts of the world.

That DDT resistance has a genetic basis can be demonstrated easily by laboratory experiments. For example, under repeated exposure to the insecticide, two substrains of a population of houseflies (originally obtained from a Long Island supermarket) became DDT resistant within 60 generations of selection. The gene changes that conferred resistance were different in the two strains; when the strains were crossbred, the F_1 generation was less resistant than either parent. Studies of various strains of DDT-resistant flies have shown that they differ in a large number of minor characteristics from nonresistant flies and from strains in which the resistance has arisen by a different genetic route. These variations are probably due not to direct effects of the mutations involved in drug resistance but to the reconstruction of the genotype to accommodate the accumulated mutations.

Another striking example of insecticide resistance has been found in the scale insects (*Coccidae*) that attack citrus trees in California. In the early 1900s, a concentration of hydrocyanic gas sufficient to kill nearly 100 percent of the insects was applied to orange groves at regular intervals with great success. By 1914, orange growers near Corona began to notice that the standard dose of the fumigant was no longer sufficient to destroy one type of scale insect, the red scale. A concentration of the gas that had left less than 1 in 100 survivors in the nonresistant strain left 22 survivors out of 100 in the resistant strain. By crossing resistant and nonresistant strains, it was possible to show that the two differed in a single gene. The mechanism for this resistance is not known, but one group of experiments suggests that the chief point of difference is that the resistant individual can keep its spiracles closed for 30 minutes under unfavorable conditions, while the nonresistant insect can do so for only 60 seconds.

FLAX MIMICS

Another evolutionary change resulting from man-made selection pressures can be found in a weed of the mustard family. This weed (*Camelina sativa*) has developed races capable of growing in the flax fields of northern Europe, where flax is still an important commercial crop.

The parental form of the weed is a branched bushy annual with small white flowers, small seed pods, and rather small rounded seeds; this type is commonly found on roadsides and in open fields. Even if it encroaches on the flax fields, it does not survive there for more than a generation because its seeds are so different in size and shape from the large flat seeds of flax that they are automatically discarded with the chaff when the flax seeds are purified by winnowing and so are not replanted.

However, in areas where flax is commonly grown, new forms of *Came-*

lina have evolved. The plants are tall and unbranched and thus able to compete for sunlight with the tall, unbranched, closely growing flax plants. More important, they have much larger seeds than the races of mustard weed found along the roadside. These seeds, although they are not of the same shape as flax seeds, are not separated by the winnowing machines and so are resown each year by the flax growers. This new race, the *flax mimic,* produces fewer seeds in each seed capsule than wild strains, and since the plant is unbranched, there are fewer seed capsules. On the other hand, the seeds enjoy the uncommon luxury of being sown in a carefully prepared field.

SPECIATION

So far, we have discussed only the changes that take place in a single population under the pressure of natural selection and that bring about relatively minor adjustments of the organism in relation to its environment. These processes are important to study because they are based on hypotheses that are susceptible to experimental verification. In the actual history of evolution, however, *phylogenetic change*—the gradual change in a population in the course of time—is of no more consequence than *speciation,* the breaking up of a single population into separate groups. Speciation, which often involves a far more drastic overhaul of the gene pool, is a perilous undertaking and, like mutation, is usually doomed to failure. It may, however, result in spectacular evolutionary successes.

How does a new species originate? It is only within the last decade or so that there has been any general unanimity of opinion among students of evolutionary theory about the origin of species. A variety of factors is generally involved; two which are crucial are (1) the genetic isolation of a population and (2) time.

Evidence about the length of time required for a new species to develop is based largely on what is known about the ages of various islands. The British Isles, for instance, have been separated from the continent of Europe only since the last glaciers retreated, about 10,000 years ago. During this time Britain has not developed any distinctly new species, so that a period of 10,000 years or so seems inadequate. On the other hand, islands whose age is probably a few million years seem to have many unique species. Hence, between 10,000 and 1 million years seems necessary.

How do we decide when a new species has evolved? The moment at which one species splits to become two contemporary species is certainly not definable. There is no doubt, however, that one species has become two when the two populations can coexist in the same natural environment without interbreeding, and for the purposes of this discussion, this will be the working definition of a species.

Geographic Isolation

No speciation can occur without sexual isolation; this is a commonsense notion. If there is mating among members of two populations, two separate gene pools cannot develop. For decades, evolutionists debated about whether or not the isolation had to be geographic, that is, established by actual physical barriers. Now it is generally agreed that this must be the case except in very special instances, such as speciation by abrupt chromosomal changes in plants, a subject that will be discussed later in this chapter.

DARWIN'S FINCHES

How does a population become isolated from its parent group? Some of the most spectacular examples of isolation are found on islands. Darwin's finches of the Galapagos Islands still provide one of the best examples of what isolation can produce. All the finches are believed to have arisen from one common ancestral group—perhaps a single pair—transported from the South American mainland, some 600 miles away. How they got there is, of course, not known, but it is probable that they were the survivors of some particularly severe storm. (Every year, for instance, some American birds and insects appear on the coasts of Ireland and England after having been blown across the North Atlantic.)

6–18 *The Galapagos Islands, some 600 miles west of the coast of Ecuador, have been called "a living laboratory of evolution." Species and sub-species of plants and animals inhabit these islands that have been found nowhere else in the world. "One is astonished," wrote Charles Darwin in 1837, "at the amount of creative force . . . displayed on these small, barren, and rocky islands. . . ."*

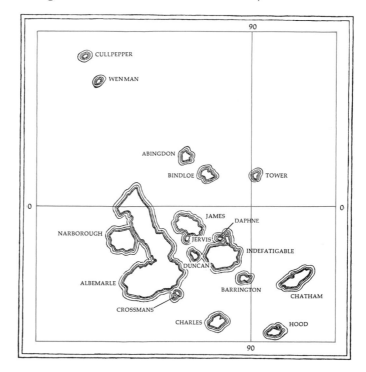

699   *The Processes of Evolution*

We do have an idea of what greeted these unwilling adventurers. The Galapagos archipelago consists of 13 main volcanic islands, with many smaller islets and rocks. On some of the islands, craters rise to heights of three or four thousand feet. The islands were pushed up from the sea more than a million years ago, and most of them are still covered with black basaltic lava.

The major vegetation is a dreary grayish-brown thornbush, making up miles and miles of thick leafless thicket, and a few tall tree cactuses—"what we might imagine the cultivated parts of the Infernal regions to be," young Charles Darwin wrote in his diary. Inland and high up on the larger islands, the land is more humid, and there one can find rich black soil and tall trees covered with ferns, orchids, lichens, and mosses, kept damp by a mist that gathers around the volcanic peaks. During the rainy season, the area is dotted by sparkling shallow crater lakes. The vegetation may have differed when the finches first arrived, but clearly plants preceded the birds or the birds would have been unable to survive.

6–19 *Three of the 13 different species of Darwin's finches. There are six species of ground finch (of which three are shown here), six species of tree finch, and one warblerlike species—all derived from a single ancestral species. Except for the warbler finch, which resembles a warbler more than a finch, the species look very much alike; the birds are all small and dusky-brown or blackish, with stubby tails. The differences between them lie mainly in their bills, which vary from small, thin beaks to huge, thick ones. The small ground finch (Geospiza fuliginosa) shown at the left and the medium ground finch (Geospiza fortis) center are both seed eaters. G. fortis, with a somewhat larger beak than G. fuliginosa, is able to crack larger seeds. On the right is shown the cactus ground finch (Geospiza scandens), which lives on cactus blooms and fruit. Notice that its beak is much larger and more pointed than those of the other two ground-finch species. (Dr. I. Eibl-Eibesfeldt)*

Thirteen different species of finches live on the archipelago, and an additional species lives on Cocos Island, several hundred miles to the north. The ancestral type is believed to have been a ground finch, and six of the Galapagos finches are ground finches. Four species of ground finches live together on most of the islands. Three of them eat seeds and differ from one another mainly in the size of their beaks, which in turn, of course, influences the size of seeds that they eat. The fourth lives largely on the prickly pear and has a much longer and more pointed beak. (See Figure 6–19.) The two other species of ground finch are usually found only on outlying islands, where some supplement their diet with cactus.

There are also six species of tree finches, differing from one another mainly in beak size and shape. One has a parrotlike beak, suited to its diet of buds and fruit. Four have insect-eating beaks, each adapted to a different size range of insects. The sixth and most remarkable of the insect eaters is the woodpecker finch, which has a beak like a woodpecker's but lacks the woodpecker's long prying tongue and so carries about a twig or cactus spine to dislodge insects from crevices in the bark. (See Figure 6–20.)

6–20 *The woodpecker finch (Camarhynchus pallidus) is a rare phenomenon in the bird world because it is a tool user. Like the true woodpecker, it feeds on grubs, which it digs out of trees; but lacking the woodpecker's chisel beak and long barbed tongue, it resorts to an artificial probe, a twig or cactus spine, to dislodge the grub. The woodpecker finch shown has selected a cactus spine (a), which it inserts into the grub hole (b). In (c), the bird has succeeded in prying out the grub, which it then eats (d). If the pick selected turns out to be an efficient tool, the bird will carry it from tree to tree in its search for grubs. (Dr. I. Eibl-Eibesfeldt)*

(a)

(b)

(c)

(d)

The thirteenth species of finch is hardly a finch at all. Classical taxonomists, using all ordinary standards of external appearance and behavior, would classify it as a warbler, but its internal anatomy and other characteristics clearly place it among the finches, and there is general agreement that it, too, is a descendant of the common ancestors.

As students of the Galapagos finches reconstruct the story, the original founding party from the mainland probably made its landfall on one of the larger islands, gained a foothold, and hung on. From time to time, members of the group were carried to other islands. Each founder group that survived must have remained isolated long enough to reconstruct a new population genotype. As we have said, this might be a matter of at least 10,000 years for each of the species, although since there are 13 main islands, several species were probably evolving at the same time.

Finches are not particularly good fliers; if they had been, they might not have speciated. Shore plants, for example, even when found on widely separated islands, are likely to be of the same species since most of these plants are well able to survive long ocean voyages. To speciate, a population must remain isolated; otherwise, it will be swallowed back up into the original gene pool. Once speciation has occurred, however, the different species can live together and maintain their genetic identities. As many as 10 species of finch are found together on some of the larger islands.

OTHER ISLAND SPECIES

The tortoises of the Galapagos, for which the archipelago is named, are different from mainland tortoises and seem to offer an example of speciation in process. The races or subspecies of Galapagos tortoises are so different from each other that, as Darwin observed, the sailors who frequent the Galapagos can tell by the appearance of a tortoise which of the islands it came from. Perhaps in another several thousand years, they will evolve into distinct species. Unfortunately, this experiment will probably never take place; the huge, lumbering tortoises are virtually defenseless, and their numbers have been seriously reduced. For years, sailors stopped regularly at the Galapagos to provision their ships, carrying away two or three hundred tortoises each time. The tortoises, known to be able to live for as long as a year without food or water, were stacked in the hold as a welcome source of fresh meat. In recent years, the tortoises have been protected against man, but they are still threatened by introduced mammals which have gone wild. Donkeys and goats compete with them for food, and wild pigs, dogs, and rats prey upon the eggs and the young.

Most island animals, including the tortoises, have no fear of man. Many island visitors have reported their feelings of delight at having wild birds alight casually on their shoulders or at being able to reach out and stroke a sunning sea lion or walk unnoticed through a crêche of nesting penguins.

6–21 *Two subspecies which have formed on either side of a natural geographic barrier. In this case, the barrier is the Grand Canyon; the Abert squirrel (a) lives only on the south side of the Canyon, and the Kaibab squirrel (b) lives only on the north side. The two subspecies are very similar, the main differences lying in the color of tail and belly. (Willis Peterson)*

(a) |——10cm——|

(b) |——10cm——|

Nature moves slowly, and by the time mechanisms of fear of man and defense against his predations have evolved, hunters will have reaped a rich harvest of meat, fur, and feathers and many island animals will have gone forever. One species of Darwin's finches has already disappeared.

Hundreds of examples of speciation have now been studied, particularly on the Pacific islands. Here one can sometimes trace the repeated ocean voyages of a genus of land snails, for example, from New Guinea, Australia, or the Philippines eastward to New Caledonia, the Samoas, Tahiti, the Marquesas, the Hawaiian Islands, or the Galapagos or westward from the coast of South America across the same island chain. Some of these organisms show only the beginnings of species formation, like the Galapagos tortoises, while some are so changed that their genealogy has become almost impossible to trace.

OTHER TYPES OF GEOGRAPHIC BARRIERS

What is an island? For a plant, it may be a mist-veiled mountain top, and for a fish, a freshwater lake. A forest grove may be an island for a small mammal. A few meters of dry ground can isolate two populations of snails. Islands of this sort usually form by the creation of barriers between formerly contiguous geographic zones. The Isthmus of Panama, for instance, has repeatedly submerged and reemerged in the course of geological time. With each new emergence, the Atlantic and Pacific Oceans became "islands," populations of marine organisms were isolated, and some new species formed. Then, when the oceans joined again (with the submergence of the Isthmus), the continents separated and became, in turn, the "islands."

There are a number of natural geographic barriers in the United States. The Grand Canyon and Upper Colorado River, for example, while not barriers for birds, are very effective at separating populations of small land animals. Several kinds of pocket gophers, wood mice, pocket mice, and field voles reach their northern limits at the south rim of the Canyon; there are related but different species that inhabit the plateau of the other rim. Two such subspecies of squirrel can easily be told apart. (See Figure 6–21.) The Abert squirrel, which lives south of the Grand Canyon, has a grayish tail, a white belly, and great tufted ears. The Kaibab squirrel, found only on the north rim, has a black belly and a pure-white tail. These squirrels are very much the same; both kinds obviously had a common ancestor in the distant past, before the Canyon formed and became a barrier.

Similarly, San Francisco Bay forms an important barrier for mammals. Of 24 species of small mammals studied in the area, 11 occur both north and south of the bay, while 8 are found only in the north and 5 only in the south. What constitutes a barrier for some kinds of animals is not a barrier for others.

703   *The Processes of Evolution*

6–22 *A well-known example of subspeciation is offered by the leopard frog (Rana pipiens). The frogs are found as far north as Quebec and as far south as Mexico; the subspecies shown are from Quebec (a), western Texas (b), Louisiana (c), and southern Florida (d). Which do you think would be likely to produce the greatest number of viable offspring if crossbred? (Dr. John A. Moore)*

(a)

(b)

(c)

(d)

Another example of the effects of geographic barriers is provided by the *Oeneis* butterfly, which is found only on the tops of the Rocky Mountains in Colorado, the White Mountains of New England, and the cool coast of Labrador.

GEOGRAPHIC RACES

Every widespread species that has been carefully studied has been found to contain geographically representative populations that differ from each other to a greater or lesser extent. A species composed of subspecies of this sort is obviously particularly susceptible to speciation if geographic barriers arise.

Because of the work of John Moore of Columbia University, the leopard frog (*Rana pipiens*) has become one of the best known examples of subspeciation. Leopard frogs are found in North America as far north as Quebec and as far south as Mexico. Moore has studied and compared a large number of characteristics in 29 separate populations of this species. He has found that there are marked variations, as might be expected, from population to population and that these changes do not always follow a cline. (A *cline* is a graded series of variations in a species that follow a line of geographic transition.) Crossbreeding of individuals from different populations produces normal offspring when the parents are drawn from populations that are geographically adjacent, such as central and southern Florida, or that lie at roughly the same latitude, such as Texas and central Florida. However, the greater the north-south gap separating the home populations of the parents, the greater also is the proportion of defective, often inviable offspring. In Texas-Vermont hybrids, for example, mortality among the developing embryos may reach as high as 100 percent. Yet because there is a gene flow among adjacent populations, *Rana pipiens* is still one species. One can see, however, that if the intermediate, bridging populations were eliminated, two species would evolve quite quickly—within a few thousand years or so, that is.

Other Factors in Speciation

Speciation, in essence, is the production of two distinct gene complexes from a single parental one. In order for this to occur, the two populations must be prevented from exchanging genes with one another. Suppose two genetically identical populations become separated by a geographic barrier, and suppose, further, that the two geographic locations in which they find themselves are ecologically identical. Will the two populations diverge genetically? We know that different mutations will arise in the different groups and that new recombinants will be formed. Therefore, new gene complexes could eventually emerge.

In studies of the New Guinea kingfisher, no significant variation has been found in the population of kingfishers over the whole of New Guinea, which is a relatively large island and contains dramatic climatic contrasts. But each of the smaller adjacent islands has a race of kingfishers markedly different from the parent population, even though these islands are in the same climatic zone as the neighboring mainland. While small islands are different from large ones by reason of size alone—because of more seacoast, fewer habitats, etc.—the primary factor in this differentiation is genetic isolation.

The two principal components in determining how rapidly genetic differentiation will take place are (1) the size of the founding population and (2) the stability of the environmental conditions.

SIZE OF FOUNDING POPULATION

If a colony is founded by only a few members of the parent population, there is little chance that it will be representative of the parent gene pool. Certainly it will not contain all the variants present in the original gene pool, and the effects of those that it does contain will be greatly distorted, as in the many-fingered Amish of Lancaster.

To test this concept experimentally, Dobzhansky set up 20 isolated colonies of *Drosophila*, all selected at random from a single interbreeding population and raised under the same environmental conditions. Ten colonies were established with 20 founders each, and ten were established with 4,000 founders each. After 17 months, it was found that the 10 originally small colonies differed from each other far more than the 10 which had the larger number of founders.

STABILITY OF ENVIRONMENTAL CONDITIONS

When the environmental conditions change, the chances of genetic change are greatly increased since the selection pressures are altered. Islands again offer the most dramatic examples. The rapid differentiation of the Galapagos finches was undoubtedly due in large part to the marked differences between the relatively deserted little volcanic archipelago and the richly populated mainland.

Some islands have also favored the development of flightless birds, the most improbable of which, perhaps, is the kiwi (Figure 6–23), found in the forests of New Zealand. The kiwi forages at night on the damp forest floors and spends its days sleeping in burrows or hollow logs, with its bill tucked to the side of the body where a wing would be if it had one.

Similarly, there has been a strong tendency among island plants to develop large heavy seeds which will not be blown out to sea and washed away. Such plants and birds have, of course, burned their bridges behind them since they can no longer be dispersed by the mechanisms that

|—10cm—|

6–23 *This curious-looking creature is the kiwi, a flightless bird which inhabits the forests of New Zealand. (Courtesy of National Publicity Studios, New Zealand)*

brought them to the island in the first place. Some, however, like the coconut, have developed a fruit well suited to island voyages, which is why almost every island of the Pacific has at least one coconut palm.

As you can see, speciation is a risky undertaking at best, and the factors that favor rapid speciation—a small founding population subjected to new environmental conditions—are much more likely to result in failure than in success. But given hundreds of millions of years, even a very small proportion of successes may leave their traces, as indeed they have.

How Species Are Maintained

Many species remain geographically isolated, but often species which are members of the same genus and which are obviously closely related will be found living in the same forest or on the same island. How do they maintain their genetic identities?

Genetic isolating mechanisms, as they are called, are divided into two categories: (1) physiological isolating mechanisms, and (2) behavioral isolating mechanisms.

PHYSIOLOGICAL ISOLATING MECHANISMS

These barriers arise because of physiological incompatibilities between two genotypes, which may take any of the following forms:

1 Differences in the shape of the genitalia may prevent insemination.
2 The sperm may not be able to survive in the reproductive tract of the female.
3 The pollen tube (in the case of plants) may not be able to form.
4 The sperm cell may not fuse with the ovum.
5 The ovum, once fertilized, may not be able to develop. Anomalies in development, as we saw, were the chief difficulties encountered in crossbreeding experiments among the races of the leopard frog.
6 The young, or some of the young, may survive but may not become reproductively mature.
7 The offspring may be hardy—the mule, for instance—but sterile. Sterility in such cases is apparently often caused by the fact that the dissimilar chromosomes cannot pair on the spindle for distribution at meiosis.

BEHAVIORAL ISOLATING MECHANISMS

One of the most significant things about the physiological mechanisms is that, in nature, they are rarely tested. In animals, physiologically incompatible genotypes are usually prevented from mating by behavioral isolating mechanisms. These mechanisms can take many forms.

Some involve elaborate courtship behavior. The stickleback may make advances toward a female of another species, but if she does not give the appropriate social response, the affair is at an end.

Visual recognition is important, particularly among birds, which are visually oriented in all their behavior. According to observers, the Galapagos finches clearly recognize each other by their beaks. A male finch may mistakenly pursue a finch of another species—the finches often look very much alike from the rear—only to lose interest as soon as he sees the beak. He will not court a female of another species. The beak is a conspicuous feature in courtship, during which food is passed from the beak of the male to that of the female.

Among many invertebrates, pheromones are the chief isolating mechanisms, serving as signals, as in the case of the cecropia moth, to attract the male or, as with the oyster, to trigger the release of gametes by the female.

Bird songs, frog calls, the strident love notes of cicadas and crickets serve to identify members of species to one another.

The flashings of fireflies (which are actually beetles) are sexual signals. Each species of firefly has its own particular flashing pattern, which is different both in duration of flashes and in intervals between flashes from that of other species. (See Figure 6–24.) For example, one common flash pattern consists of two short pulses of light separated by about two seconds, with the phrase repeated every four to seven seconds. The lights also vary among the species in intensity and color. The male flashes first, and the female answers, returning the species-specific signal. If you watch the firefly signals, you can learn to distinguish different species, and by

6–24 *Flashing patterns of various species of fireflies found in Delaware. Each division on the horizontal lines represents one second, and the height of each curve represents the brilliance of the flash. The black curves are male flashes, and the colored ones are the female responses. Firefly flashes differ not only in duration, intensity, and timing, but also in color. (After Wallace and Srb, 1961)*

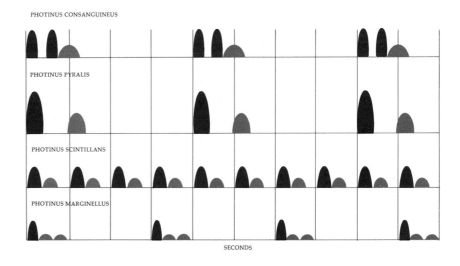

PHOTINUS CONSANGUINEUS

PHOTINUS PYRALIS

PHOTINUS SCINTILLANS

PHOTINUS MARGINELLUS

SECONDS

707   *The Processes of Evolution*

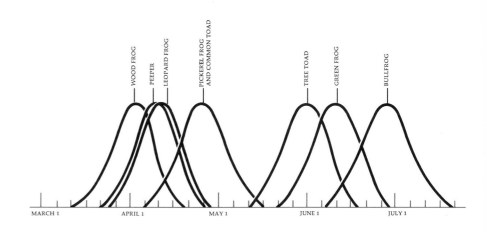

6–25 *Mating timetable for various frogs and toads that live near Ithaca, N.Y., illustrating the operation of a temporal isolating mechanism to prevent the crossbreeding of species. In the two cases where two different species appear to have mating seasons that coincide (peeper and leopard frog, pickerel frog and common toad), the animals involved are so distantly related that they even have different generic names. Further, the breeding sites differ. Peepers prefer woodland ponds and shallow water; leopard frogs breed in swamps; pickerel frogs mate in upland streams and ponds; and common toads use any ditch or puddle. (After Wallace and Srb, 1961)*

mimicking signals with a flashlight, you can attract the males of a given species.

Among mammals, smell is probably the most important single factor. In addition to their normal distinctive odors, mammals also probably produce sexual pheromones that may serve as attractants and isolating mechanisms.

Animal behavior serves as a genetic isolating mechanism for those plants that have evolved species-specific relationships with pollinators.

Temporal mechanisms also play an important role in sexual isolation. Species differences in flowering times are important isolating mechanisms in plants. Most mammals—man is a notable exception—have seasons for mating, often controlled by temperature or by day length. Figure 6–25 shows the mating calendar of species of frogs near Ithaca, New York. The spawning of freshwater fishes is often regulated by water temperatures. Members of the species *Drosophila pseudoobscura* and *Drosophila persimilis*, which often are found in the same areas, congregate and mate almost every day but differ in their mating hour.

A moment's reflection will make clear why the fact that hybrid progeny are often less viable serves to reinforce behavioral isolation. A female cricket that answers to the wrong song or a frog whose personal calendar is not synchronized with that of the rest of the species will contribute less to the gene pool. As a consequence, there will be a steady selection for behavioral isolating mechanisms.

Hybrids

Hybrids sometimes occur in natural populations, particularly among plants. As in the case of hybrid corn, which is, of course, a hybrid between strains of a single species, they may have the advantage of heterosis. When hybrids occur in an area that is the natural boundary between two species, the hybrid will sometimes have advantages in that particular locality. Hybrids often do not mate, however, as we have mentioned before, and when they do, they will often mate with a member of one of the parent species. Such backcrossing may be an important source of genetic variation in some populations.

Speciation by Chromosomal Changes

POLYPLOIDY

A haploid cell has one set of chromosomes ($1n$). Some organisms (e.g., *Escherichia coli*, *Chlamydomonas*, *Neurospora*) are naturally haploid, as are most gametes. A diploid cell has two sets of chromosomes ($2n$); the zygote receives one set from each parent, and the somatic cells of higher animals almost always have the diploid number. A cell that has more than two sets of chromosomes or an individual made up of such cells is known as a *polyploid*.

Polyploidy originates when the chromosomes replicate but the cell does not. A cell may have $3n$, $4n$, or $5n$ chromosomes, or even more in some instances. Polyploidy occurs rarely in animals, except in some types of somatic cells such as those of the liver, but is very frequent in plants. Thus among the largest group of plants, the angiosperms, about half of the approximately 300,000 species known are polyploids. Polyploidy is even more common in ferns, and it occurs in other groups as well. Among animals, it occurs commonly only in those types, such as rotifers and certain crustaceans, that can reproduce parthenogenetically. Why polyploidy is so rare in animals is not known, but it may be related to the fact that polyploidy compromises the usual sex-determining mechanisms in animals. Polyploidy is of special interest as one of the few known means for producing a new species in a single step without geographic isolation.

Polyploids originate when a cell wall does not form following division of the chromosomes. If this occurs, the cell in question, and its daughter cells, will be polyploid, and if these cells give rise to a new individual, either by vegetative reproduction or sexually, this individual will be a polyploid. Such mitotic misadventures can be promoted and increased in frequency by treating a shoot tip or a germinating seed with a chemical known as colchicine. When a polyploid plant is produced, it may have, for example, $4n$ chromosomes, in which case it is called a *tetraploid*. The tetraploid will produce gametes with $2n$ chromosomes and can usually

6–26 *The flower shown at the top is an ordinary (diploid) Easter lily. The Easter lily on the bottom is a tetraploid. The tetraploids are more vigorous than the diploids and have larger flowers and heavier petals. (Courtesy of the U.S. Department of Agriculture)*

only be crossed successfully with another tetraploid plant or, of course, with itself. If it is crossed back to a diploid plant, the resulting hybrid will have $3n$ chromosomes; regular meiosis and the production of fertile gametes cannot occur in such a plant because the homologous chromosomes are in threes, rather than pairs, and cannot be distributed normally. Therefore, the tetraploid plant is unable to cross with its parent and is, in effect, a new species in one step.

There are two types of polyploids, autopolyploids and allopolyploids. In *autopolyploids,* each set of chromosomes present is the same, duplicated four or more times. In *allopolyploids,* on the other hand, the chromosomes of two or more diploid species are combined, and important genetic innovations can be produced by this means. Autopolyploids arise from a single parental species, while allopolyploids must arise from diploid hybrid individuals or by crossing two autopolyploids.

Most of the more important domestic plants are allopolyploids, including cotton, wheat, potatoes, tobacco, oats, bananas, many apples, and some cherries, as well as such garden plants as irises, chrysanthemums, and tulips. As an example of an allopolyploid, consider the man-made hybrid *Raphanobrassica,* formed from the radish and the cabbage, which are members not only of different species but of different genera. Some years ago, an enterprising plant geneticist was struck by the commercial possibilities of such a hybrid since, in the one plant, the roots are edible and, in the other, the leaves. In each plant, the haploid ($1n$) number is 9. A cross between the two produced a plant with nine radish chromosomes and nine cabbage chromosomes, which was, like the mule, a sturdy hybrid but infertile. But since the chromosomes could not pair at meiosis, an artificial tetraploid was developed in which the somatic cells had 18 radish chromosomes and 18 cabbage chromosomes, making it possible for the gamete to receive a full complement (9) of each. As their originator had hopefully anticipated, the hybrids were both sturdy and fertile. Their only drawback: they had a root like a cabbage and a head like a radish!

The reasons for the great success of allopolyploids in nature are related to their occurrence in regions where different races or closely related species come together. In these intermediate regions, the allopolyploids may be better adapted to the particular conditions than either of the parental types.

TRANSLOCATIONS AND INVERSIONS

Translocations and inversions may also lead to rapid speciation in plants. Harlan Lewis and Peter Raven have made a series of studies of several species of *Clarkia,* a genus of wildflowers that grow along the Pacific Coast. *Clarkia biloba* and *Clarkia lingulata* differ in appearance mainly in the presence or absence of a notch at the end of their petals. (See Figure

CLARKIA BILOBA

CLARKIA LINGULATA

6–27 *Clarkia biloba and Clarkia lingulata differ in appearance mainly in the shape of their petals, but their respective chromosome complements are 16 and 18. Apparently, the extra chromosome pair in C. lingulata contains translocated parts of two pairs in C. biloba, the parent species. (After Lewis, 1951)*

6–27.) But *C. biloba* has 16 chromosomes, and *C. lingulata*, 18. Hybrids between the two species, as you would imagine, are sterile. From the behavior of the chromosomes during meiosis, the investigators deduced that the extra chromosome pair of *C. lingulata* is composed of translocated parts of two chromosome pairs from *C. biloba*, the parent species, as shown in Figure 6–27. The new species, which has appeared at the southern end of the species range, appears to be replacing its parent wherever they come into contact.

Differences between Plants and Animals

Adaptive evolution proceeds in plants and animals by mechanisms which, although fundamentally the same, contain some differences: (1) Many new species of plants are produced by polyploidy and other drastic chromosomal changes, while this is rarely the case among animals. (2) Although some plants, such as those that bloom in the desert, are ephemeral, the higher plants, in general, live much longer than animals, and many of them are able to reproduce vegetatively almost indefinitely. (3) Plants can produce thousands of seeds in one lifetime. (4) Once they outgrow the supply of food in the seed, plants must be able to produce food where they grow since they cannot move to a more favorable locality.

For a plant, a seed is a pioneer sent out to explore a new territory. The plant has little control over where the seed will land; the seed must germinate or perish wherever it does land. Therefore, in plants, one strong evolutionary tendency has been toward greater and greater variability, so that the plant has a better chance of adapting to the environment in which it finds itself.

The higher animals must produce viable offspring during their relatively short lifetimes if the species is to survive. The sugar maple has a maximum of 350 years of reproductive life in which to make one additional maple tree, while the pair of mice that live among its roots has at best a year or two to replace itself. The mouse cannot experiment as freely as the maple tree. But the mouse has a big advantage; its offspring are mobile, while plants are not. An animal can search for a suitable habitat, seeking warmth, shelter, food, and water, while a plant seedling has to survive wherever it germinates.

As a result, sexual reproduction has somewhat different functions in plants than it has in animals. In the higher animals, the general evolutionary trend has been toward the production of organisms with increasing freedom from their environment and a high survival rate among their offspring. Further, in animals, evolution has produced homeostatic mechanisms which buffer the internal organization of the individual against the environment. In plants, an evolutionary premium is placed upon genetic

6-28 *A good example of the reproductive versatility of plants is provided by the violet (Viola). Individual Viola plants reproduce in three ways:* (1) *The typical violet flowers are pollinated by insects.* (2) *The smaller flowers, close to the ground, are self-pollinating, producing seeds closely resembling the parental type.* (3) *Creeping underground stems eventually produce a new series of rosettes which become separated from the parent plant (vegetative reproduction).*

and phenotypic heterogeneity: Seeds are scattered over a wide variety of terrains, and the more different kinds of seeds a species can produce and the more phenotypically plastic it is, the greater are its chances of gaining a foothold in some new territory. Lacking the behavioral plasticity of animals, plants must compensate with phenotypic plasticity and genotypic variability.

Viola (Figure 6–28) provides a good example of the reproductive versatility of plants. The larger flowers are pollinated by insects and produce heterozygous seeds, which are sown by the wind. The smaller flowers are close to the ground, never open, and are self-pollinated within the bud. Seeds from these flowers drop close to the parent plant and produce plants that are genetically similar to the parent and so, presumably, apt to grow successfully near the parent. Vegetative reproduction takes place at the same time, producing plants genetically identical and right next to the parent.

Macroevolution

Can the same processes that slowly shape the seed of mustard weed or change the color of the peppered moth create the differences between elephants and daisies or between butterflies and redwood trees? Darwin believed so—all he felt that was needed was time, millions of years of slow change. Today, almost all evolutionists are, in principle, in general agreement with Darwin's conclusions, although with a slight modification. Darwin believed that changes took place at a steady rate. More recent studies of the paleontological record indicate that the great evolutionary changes probably took place fairly rapidly.

The first terrestrial plants and animals suddenly emerged some 425 million years ago. A large number of different populations apparently began the same move at about the same time. Most undoubtedly perished, but a few survived and then differentiated into the many different types of terrestrial plants and animals existing today. A similar, even more rapid burst of evolution gave rise to the birds. Apparently, according to the fossil record, a number of populations of reptiles must have taken to climbing and gliding at about the same time. The shift was made very rapidly from the land to the air, and although these were intermediate populations, gliding cold-blooded reptiles undoubtedly existed at one time. Then they disappeared rapidly and permanently.

What is necessary for these great evolutionary moves to take place? First, there must be an ample store of genetic variation in the gene pool. Second, a genetic upheaval must occur. A population that is well in tune with its environment will probably not undergo the sudden changes that lead to evolutionary breakthroughs. As we have seen in tracing the phylogeny of the plant and animal groups, the ancestral form of a new phylum is never the ultimate form of some previously existent group but is always relatively unspecialized and, therefore, still plastic. A drastic genetic change is most likely to occur in a small population under environmental stress.

Evolution must proceed by certain "logical" steps. Water, which is 800 times heavier than air, can support an animal like a jellyfish and can provide sufficient resistance for ciliary motion, but a jellyfish could never become terrestrial. Animals needed to develop strong supporting skeletons and strong muscles before they could invade the land. A third necessary condition for evolution is, therefore, the existence of previous structures that can be modified to other uses.

For example, the lungs and lobes of the lungfish made it possible for animals to begin the invasion of land once the plants had prepared the way for them. These structures did not develop in the lungfish as an adaptation to terrestrial life but as an adaptation to conditions of drought. The lungs and lobes had been in existence for millions of years. Similarly, although birds and reptiles are very different in their modes of life, very little modification of the basic plan of the reptile skeleton was necessary to produce the skeleton of the bird; for the bird, feathers were the big evolutionary breakthrough. The famous fossil *Archaeopteryx* is essentially a reptile with feathers. In the case of the insects, the rapid development of a great multitude of species depended upon the existence of appendages that could be modified into a large number of specialized structures.

The fourth condition necessary for an evolutionary breakthrough to occur is that a new *adaptive zone* must be available. The land was once such an adaptive zone, and the air another. Once an adaptive zone becomes available, divergent lines of ancestral stock try to cross the barrier until one of them makes it into the new zone. The shift either is rapid or fails completely. Once the shift is made, radiation takes place until the zone is filled. For instance, on a small scale, the Galapagos represented a new adaptive zone for birds, and so the finch evolved not only into more specialized finchlike animals but also into "warblers" and "woodpeckers." If a real woodpecker had existed on the Galapagos, the woodpecker finch, even with its hopefully carried twig, would have been at such a complete disadvantage that it would have been eliminated from the competition. (For a further discussion of this question of interspecies competition and ecological niches, see Chapter 6–3.)

A striking example of adaptive radiation in the absence of competition is found in Australia. Because placental mammals never developed there, marsupials took over the areas which, on other continents, are occupied by placentals—giving rise to a marsupial "rat," a marsupial "woodchuck," a marsupial "bear," and a marsupial "dog." (See Figure 6–29.) One wonders

"RAT" Kangaroo Rat

"DOG" Tasmanian Wolf

"WOODCHUCK" Wombat

"BEAR" Koala Bear

6–29 *An example of adaptive radiation is seen in the marsupials of Australia, which developed there without competition from placental mammals. The fact that the marsupials in the Australian environment took over areas corresponding to those occupied by placentals on other continents is emphasized in the illustration by labeling the marsupials with the common names of their placental counterparts.* ("RAT," "DOG," "BEAR" *Courtesy of Australian News and Information Bureau*) ("WOODCHUCK" *Courtesy of the San Diego Zoo*)

if, given enough time, a marsupial primate might have eventually appeared and perhaps even a marsupial man. Now that placental man has introduced other placental animals into Australia, however, the placentals are crowding out the marsupials, which may eventually become extinct.

Extinction

Little is known about the process of extinction, which is also one of the essential features of evolution since the removal of old species makes way for new ones. Man has rendered some populations extinct either by predation or by so disrupting their natural environment that they could no longer survive. Predators and environmental changes also probably played important roles in the extinction of past populations. However, the major force that drives a population to extinction is probably the same as the driving force of evolution itself, which is adaptation. In the course of time, a population may become increasingly adapted to its environment (like the nematode that is purported to survive only in German beer coasters), and eventually it may become so highly specialized that it cannot meet a new challenge. For example, birds in England are getting better and better at removing tops from milk bottles; if the milk bottle were a living organism, it would have to evolve a better top or perish.

The processes of extinction may prove the most difficult of all to study because the relationships between the forces at work and the fitness of the organism may be very hard to trace. There is a series of mutations widespread in populations of the house mouse (*Mus musculus*) which are known as the *t* mutations because they affect tail length. Male mice homozygous for *t* are sterile. Yet, for reasons which are not understood, heterozygous (*Tt*) male mice pass *t* along to more than 95 percent of their offspring. Thus the *t* gene is driven to high frequencies, and in a small population, all males may become homozygous *tt*, resulting in the extinction of that population. It is very unlikely that this mechanism alone could lead to worldwide extinction of *Mus musculus*, but by causing local populations to become extinct, it does have an influence on geographic distribution, especially on small islands. Moreover, by reducing the reproductive potential of the species, it will contribute (together with other causes) to the eventual extinction of the species.

SUMMARY

Evolution by natural selection proceeds from a combination of three conditions: (1) Natural populations contain a large fund of genetic variations. (2) These variations are correlated with the adaptation of the population to its environment. (3) Many more individuals are produced than survive to produce young of their own.

The action of natural selection can be followed most easily in the rapidly changing man-made environments of today. Some examples of evolutionary changes resulting from man-made selective pressures are the changing color of the peppered moth (*Biston betularia*) to adapt to industrialized surroundings, the evolution of bacteria resistant to drugs and of insects resistant to insecticides, and the development of the flax mimic.

The two types of evolutionary change are (1) *phylogenetic change,* which is the gradual change in a population, and (2) *speciation,* which is the breaking up of a single population into separate, non-interbreeding groups. Essential to the origin of a new species is sexual isolation, and this generally requires that a population be isolated by actual physical barriers. The most famous example of speciation resulting from such geographic isolation is provided by Darwin's finches on the Galapagos Islands, where 13 different species of finches have developed from one ancestral species (perhaps even one pair). Besides islands, other natural barriers such as rivers, canyons, and mountains can isolate populations so that different species and subspecies result. Two principal components of genetic differentiation in populations are (1) a small founding population and (2) a change in environmental conditions.

Speciation can also occur as a result of abrupt chromosomal changes. *Polyploidy,* a condition in which a cell has more than two sets of chromosomes, is one of the few known means for producing a new species in a single step without genetic isolation. This condition rarely occurs in animals, but it is frequently found in plants. *Autopolyploids,* in which each set of chromosomes present is the same, arise from a single parent; while in *allopolyploids,* the chromosomes of two or more diploid species are combined. Translocations and inversions may also lead to rapid speciation in plants.

Closely related species living in the same natural environment maintain their separate identities by means of *genetic isolating mechanisms.* These are behavioral isolating mechanisms, which operate to prevent mating, and physiological isolating mechanisms, which prevent either the fusion of egg and sperm or the development of offspring that might result from mating.

Recent studies indicate that the great evolutionary changes of the past probably took place fairly rapidly. For such evolutionary breakthroughs to occur, four conditions are required: (1) there must be an ample store of genetic variation in the gene pool; (2) a drastic genetic change must occur; (3) structures must exist that can be modified to other uses; and (4) a new adaptive zone must be available.

The Numbers of Plants and Animals

Communities tend to become stabilized not only in the kinds of organisms that live there but in their numbers. In the two preceding chapters, we were concerned with the different *kinds* of plants and animals, that is, with how organisms are shaped and molded by their environment. In this chapter, our chief concern will be with the forces that regulate the *numbers* of plants and animals.

For the number of organisms in a particular population to remain stable (without emigration or immigration), the rate of reproduction and the mortality rate, although they may fluctuate from season to season or from year to year, must remain in equilibrium. The fact that one species may differ widely from another within the same community in numbers of individuals, in birthrate, or in lifespan indicates the tremendous variety of forces that are at work in this system of checks and balances. Although these various factors can only be examined one at a time, it is important to remember that in any one instance, many of them are at work simultaneously.

REPRODUCTION AND MORTALITY

Factors Controlling Individual Reproductive Rates

The sole criterion of fitness, as we stated in Chapter 6–1, is the contribution of an individual to the ancestry of future generations. In other words, the most fit individuals are those that produce the largest number of young—with the provision, of course, that these young live to maturity and also reproduce.

The number of young produced at one time is partly an hereditary characteristic. In some animals, particularly mammals, the size of the body cavity or of the uterus seems to impose the chief limitation. In the human

(a)

|—2mm—|

(b)

|—25mm—|

6–30 *Two ways of providing for the survival of the young:* (a) *The female wolf spider carries her young about with her. If you look closely, you can see that what appears to be the female's very hairy body is actually a mass of tiny spiders clinging to one another and to their mother underneath.* (b) *The female giant water beetle (below) has captured a male (above) and laid her eggs on his back.* (Dr. Ross E. Hutchins)

female, a single infant is slightly more likely to be born alive and healthy than twins, and as we know, the survival of even one of a set of quadruplets or quintuplets is often problematic. Other mammals have a larger capacity; a cat, dog, or mouse can produce and rear as many as a dozen offspring, although they are likely to be smaller and weaker than the members of a smaller litter.

Among egg-laying animals, the relative advantages of large numbers versus large size have also been weighed species by species in the evolutionary balance. Is it better to lay 2,000 small eggs or 1,000 larger ones? Do sheer numbers alone favor greater survival, or will it be more advantageous for each egg to have a larger built-in food supply? Will three small larvae have a better chance of escaping from a predator than one large larva? A large Chinook salmon lays 5,000 eggs in her single spawning, 4,000 of which become fertilized. An oyster lays more than a million eggs a season; a carp, 2 to 4 million; a tapeworm, 120,000 a day. The sea catfish, on the other hand, lays only about 30 eggs, but these are sheltered in the mouth of the male until they hatch, so a much higher proportion survives to maturity. For each of these species, evolution has provided a different answer.

PARENTAL CARE

In animals such as the catfish, in which parental care is important, the number of young that can be cared for is a principal limiting factor in determining how many are born. From the work of the British ornithologist David Lack, we have many examples of this principle. Each species of bird lays a characteristic number of eggs: the petrel, one; the pigeon, two; the gull, three; the plover, four; on up to the partridge, which is likely to lay as many as twenty. The number of eggs laid during one nesting period is called a *clutch*.

Does the clutch size simply represent the maximum number of eggs the female can produce? We know from our own experience that this is not true. A female chicken, for example, can lay an egg a day if the eggs are removed. Similarly, among some wild birds, if a newly laid egg is removed from the nest or destroyed, the female will usually lay another one. The restriction of clutch size is a positive act; when the nest contains the requisite number, the eggs already formed in the oviduct will be resorbed.

Studies have shown that the clutch size, the number of eggs the female "wants," is genetically controlled and, like other genetic variations, is acted upon by natural selection. The adaptive force is the maximum number of young that the parent can provide for.

Table 6–5 *Survival in Relation to Number of Young in Swiss Starlings (After Lack, 1954)*

Number of young in brood	Number of young marked	Number of individuals recaptured after 3 months, per 100 birds ringed
1	65	—
2	328	1.85
3	1,278	2.03
4	3,956	2.075
5	6,175	2.08
6	1,156	1.68
7	651	1.46
8	120	1.28
9, 10	28	—

6–31 *The characteristic clutch of the Arctic tern is three eggs, which she lays in a nest she has hollowed out in the ground. The world's champion traveler, the Arctic tern is on the wing seven months of the year, flying the 8,000 to 10,000 miles from the Arctic to the Antarctic each autumn and returning each spring. Her young will have less than three months in which to learn to fly well enough to follow her on this long migration. (Eric Hosking, F.R.P.S.)*

As you can see in Table 6–5, there is a disadvantage, in terms of surviving young, for the Swiss starling to have a clutch size of more or less than five. The female whose genotype dictates this particular clutch size will leave more young than other members of her species.

One English bird species studied by Lack, the common swift (*Apus apus*), was found to lay either two or three eggs per clutch, two more often than three. The parent swifts feed their young on airborne insects. In continued bad weather, such insects virtually disappear and the young swifts often starve to death. An analysis of mortality among nestling swifts in four colonies in southern England between 1946 and 1950 showed that in broods of two young, 82 percent left the nest, whereas in broods of three young, with the food being shared among three mouths instead of two, only 45 percent left the nest. As a result, broods of two gave rise to an average of 1.6 survivors per brood, and broods of three resulted in only 1.4 survivors. In the summer of 1949, the weather was warm and unusually sunny and the average number of young raised per brood was higher from the broods of three than from the broods of two. The swift is polymorphic for two eggs or three, and the polymorphism appears to be maintained by environmental fluctuations.

In some birds, clutch sizes can be modified to suit environmental conditions. In Sweden, the thick-billed nutcracker feeds its young primarily on hazelnuts. The bird gathers the nuts in the autumn and stores them until spring, so that the quantity of food available for its young is determined before it lays its eggs. The size of the nut crop varies from year to year. The usual clutch is three, and in years in which the nut crop was average or below average, no larger clutches were found. But in a year following a particularly bountiful hazelnut harvest, 11 of the 13 clutches studied contained four eggs and one even contained five. The investigator experimented with supplying nuts for some of the wild nutcrackers and found that by so doing, he could increase clutch size. In a below-average year, when other wild birds were laying no more than three eggs per clutch, his nutcrackers laid an average of four. He never found clutches of less than three or more than five, however, no matter how many hazelnuts were available.

Close parallels occur in mammals, which, like birds, have a definite family and feed their young. Most domestic animals, such as domestic pigs and domestic rabbits, have larger litters than their wild counterparts, indicating that large litter size is selected against in wild populations. Apparently, litter size is determined by the number of young the mothers can actually nourish.

Besides birds and mammals, the only species which regularly feed their young are social insects, and in these animals, the number of eggs laid is closely linked with the amount of food available. Thus the queen termite lays only 15 to 50 eggs during her first season, when there are at first no workers and later only a few to help her feed the larvae. Once she has a sufficient work force established, however, she may lay as many as 7,000 eggs a day.

Reproductive Success

In terms of *fitness*—the number of genes returned to the gene pool relative to other genotypes—survival is of no consequence unless the surviving individual reproduces. Phrases such as "the struggle for survival" tend to obscure the fact that, in biological terms, the race is not always to the swift nor the battle to the strong. For example, even though a male white-eyed *Drosophila* may be as strong and as fertile as the wild type, wild-type females will mate with him only if wild-type males are not available. Thus this genetic variant will be quickly eliminated from the natural population, even though the ill-favored male may live out an entirely normal, though celibate, life-span. As far as the gene pool is concerned, he might as well never have been born.

Mortality Rates

In a natural population, the mortality rate may be extremely high. Here again, birds offer some of the best examples since they can be banded and recaptured more easily than many other animals. In a study made of the saltmarsh song sparrows of San Francisco Bay, it was estimated that of every 100 eggs laid, 26 are lost before hatching. Of the 74 live nestlings, only 52 leave the nest, and of these 52, 80 percent die the first year. The remaining 10 breed the following season, but during the next year, 43 percent of these die, leaving only 6 out of the original 100. Each subsequent year, mortality among the survivors amounts to 43 percent.

Once a bird survives its first risk-laden year, the mortality rate for the years before old age remains more or less constant. In nearly all species, the probability of survival for one more year or one more period of time seems to be highest during the middle of life and lowest for both very young and very old individuals. Patterns of mortality differ from species to species, however. Figure 6–32 shows the basic types of survivorship curves. In the oyster, for example, mortality is extremely high during the free-swimming larval stage, but once the individual attaches itself to a favorable substrate, life expectancy levels off. Among hydras, the mortality rate is the same at all ages. If all individuals lived out the average life-span of their species, their curve would resemble the hypothetical curve shown at the top of the graph. The mortality curve for man, as you can see, approaches this curve, indicating that the human population as a whole is reaching a uniform age of mortality.

Among plants and animals, only man lives for a significant period (one-third of the life-span) past reproductive maturity. Except for the members of the worker caste in social-insect organizations, man is the only animal that can make a significant contribution to the population other than his contribution to the gene pool. Traditionally, postreproductive human beings have played important roles both in raising their young through their ever-lengthening period of immaturity and in the cultural evolution of the human race—which, in man's recent history, has been of far greater significance than physical changes.

ENVIRONMENTAL RESISTANCE

Environmental resistance is a term used to designate any external factors that limit the life-span and therefore the reproductive capacity of an organism.

The elements of environmental resistance vary from species to species and community to community. For the plants and animals that eke out a living in an extreme environment—such as the Arctic or the desert—the

6–32 *Representative survivorship curves, plotted from life-table data on the basis of survivors per 1,000 log scale (vertical coordinate) and age in relative units of mean life-span (horizontal coordinate). As you can see, the oyster's chances of survival greatly improve with age, while mortality among hydras remains constant throughout the life-span. The curve at the top of the graph is for a hypothetical population in which all individuals live out the average life-span of the species—a population, in other words, in which all individuals die at about the same age. The fact that man's curve approaches this hypothetical curve indicates that the human population as a whole is reaching a uniform age of mortality.*

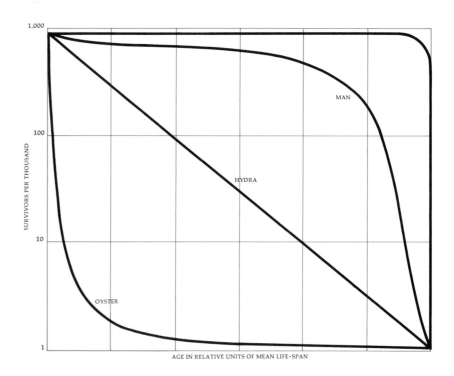

physical environment is usually the chief factor in limiting life-span. The special problems of existence under such conditions will be discussed in Chapter 6–4. In most communities, however, environmental resistance consists largely of food shortage, predators, and disease.

Food Supply

Food supply is a primary force in controlling population size. The number of animals in a population tends to increase and decrease in direct proportion to its food supply. For example, since the advent of the automobile, the sparrows in city streets have declined markedly; cars and trucks, although perhaps more efficient than horses, do not produce manure.

At any given time, the amount of food available to the individual from the supply depends directly on the number of individuals in the population. If there are too many individuals for the food supply to support, some will starve and the population will decrease until an equilibrium is reached. If the supply then increases, the population will increase proportionately; but until the supply increases, the population cannot increase.

Regulating the food supply is one of the methods that man uses to control the size of animal populations. This procedure was applied, with remarkable success, to the tsetse fly, which carries the protozoan that causes sleeping sickness. The tsetse fly lives chiefly on the blood of ungulates, large hoofed herbivorous animals. It needs to feed frequently, especially during hot weather, but because it does not stay on or near its host after taking a meal, each meal must be preceded by an independent search for a host.

Following an epidemic of sleeping sickness in northwest Tanganyika, wildlife experts suggested that the flies could be controlled if the number of animals on which they fed was reduced. Hunters were hired to shoot large mammals within an area of about 10 square miles around the community in which the disease had been most severe. About 9,000 were shot, greatly reducing the numbers, and the flies were wiped out.

There was still plenty of food in the absolute sense; a single antelope could support a large number of flies, but the chance of a single fly finding food every time it needed it was sufficiently reduced to exterminate the fly population and eradicate the disease.

Predation

LABORATORY STUDIES OF PREDATION

Predator-prey relationships are often difficult to demonstrate in the laboratory. Many years ago, some now classic experiments were performed with *Paramecium* and the barrel-shaped carnivorous ciliate, *Didinium*, which lives almost exclusively on *Paramecium*. *Didinium* lacks certain necessary digestive enzymes. These the paramecium supplies, and the enzymes are used by *Didinium* for its own digestion.

A didinium needs to have a fresh paramecium every three hours. It does not actively hunt but swims about rapidly, fastening onto any object it encounters by means of a knotlike holding organ located in the center of the "barrel lid." If the object turns out to be a paramecium, it holds on and sucks it in.

No matter what the initial proportion of didinia to paramecia, didinia always eventually consumed all the paramecia and then perished. If the culture was supplied with oatmeal (to feed the bacteria to feed the paramecia) from which the sediment had not been washed away, the paramecia tended to congregate in the sediment, probably because of the presence of the bacteria there. The sediment formed a barrier against the didinia, and so, under these conditions, the latter perished. Only when the experimenter introduced a regular supply of immigrants—for example,

6–33 *A laboratory example* (a) *of a predator-prey relationship. The graph shows the population densities of two species of mites over a period of two months. As you can see, after the predator found and exterminated the prey, it, too, died out.* (b) *The relationship between the same predator and prey in a much more complicated environment. Here the investigator assisted the prey movements and set up partial barriers to the predator movements, with the result that the two species persisted, with periodic oscillations as shown.*

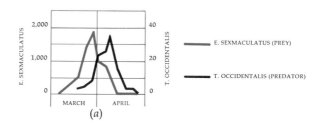

(a)

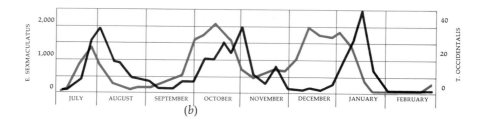

(b)

6–34 As heavily armored as its placental counterpart, the echidna, or spiny ant-eater, is the "porcupine" of Australia and New Guinea. It is the only other member, besides the duckbill platypus, of the primitive order of monotremes. It lays eggs, suckles its young, and develops a pouch only when breeding. (Courtesy of the San Diego Zoo)

6–35 A pair of ants struggling to get at a pill bug. Curled up in a tight armor-plated ball, the pill bug is literally invulnerable. (Dr. Thomas Eisner)

one paramecium and one didinium every third day—could he achieve a regularly oscillating population.

Since the predator rarely eliminates the prey in a natural environment and one or the other will almost always be eliminated in the laboratory, it is clear that the natural environment is a complicated one.

C. B. Huffaker produced a laboratory example of the effect of complicating an environment and thereby reducing predator efficiency. He used two mite species, one which fed on oranges and one which fed on the other mites. When the laboratory environment allowed the predator to move easily from orange to orange, the predator found and exterminated most of the prey and then itself died (Figure 6–33a).

The prey (but not the predator) could move by floating from high points on strands of silk. When Huffaker slowed the predator movements with partial barriers and speeded up the prey movements by putting in "launching posts," the prey persisted in the face of predation. Under these circumstances, the prey was able to build up local colonies from which individuals could disperse. Predators would eventually find the local concentration and exterminate it, but in the meantime a new prey population was increasing somewhere else. As a result, the two species persisted, with periodic oscillations as shown in Figure 6–33b.

NATURAL DEFENSES IN ANIMALS

Few organisms are as unresisting to predation as *Paramecium*, whose only real defense seems to be its ability to multiply with great rapidity. Some animals are formidably armored, such as the armadillo, the porcupine, and the sea urchin. Some have ingenious behavioral devices. The armadillo and the pill bug roll themselves up in a tight armor-plated ball. Cephalopods vanish, jet-propelled, leaving behind only an ink cloud. Many lizards have brightly colored tails that break off when they are attacked and, bright-colored and wriggling, divert the predator from the prey—which is escaping, tailless but with all its vital organs intact. (See Figures 6–36.) Hermit crabs often carry sea anemones as passengers on their shells. The anemone protects the crab from predators while enjoying the benefits of mobility (and perhaps some stray morsels of food). When the crab changes shells, it often coaxes its sea anemone from its old home to the new one.

Grazing animals feed in herds, and birds, when threatened, tend to tighten their flock. It is almost impossible for a hawk to catch a bird that is within the flock since the hawk will be subjected to a constant bombardment of other bird bodies moving at higher speed.

The periodical cicadas protect one another in a quite different way. In the first place, by emerging from their well-hidden pupal casings only after a long interval, they are assured that no natural predator dependent on the cicada will be present; the predator simply could not wait that

725   *The Numbers of Plants and Animals*

long. The 17-year species of periodical cicadas of the genus *Magicicada* usually emerge simultaneously. Similarly, three southern periodical cicadas of the same genus, with a 13-year life cycle, also are in synchrony. Thus, although the same numbers of insects may be lost to predators, the proportion lost of any given species is substantially reduced.

Some birds emit alarm cries to warn the flock of an approaching predator. This seeming altruism has been interpreted by some scientists as running counter to theories of natural selection within species since the bird that calls attention to itself in this way is more likely to be lost—and its genes with it—to the predator than the bird that is not so altruistic. Other scientists point out, however, that since the bird is nearly always closely related genetically to the other members of its own flock, the genotype it saves, while perhaps not its own, is very similar. Therefore, genotypes dictating warning behavior would be more likely to be returned to the gene pool than those that do not. A somewhat similar but simpler situation is seen in the worker bee that dies on stinging an intruder; in so doing, she saves her hive of sisters.

6–36 *The black lizard (*Lacerta ilfordi*) shares with many other lizards a peculiar method of defense. When it is attacked, its tail breaks off, distracting the predator long enough for the lizard to escape. After a time, the tail will grow back again. (Walter Jarchow, Frank W. Lane)*

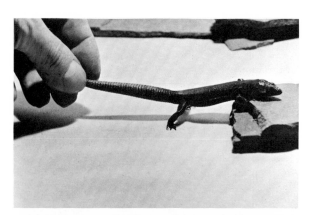

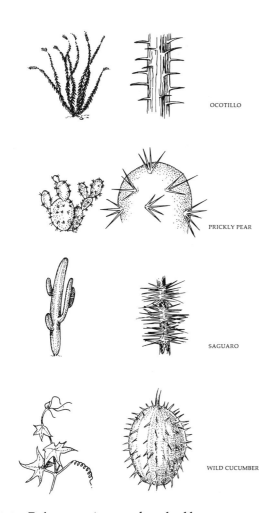

Birds also take risks to save their young. "Injury feigning" is a common device among many types of ground-nesting birds. The parent bird flutters on the ground as though crippled, uttering piteous cries but always managing to stay just beyond reach of the intruder. Some scientists prefer to call this behavior *distraction display* to emphasize that the bird does not know what it is doing, although this latter term implies that the bird is being distracting, which it is equally unlikely to know. Regardless of the bird's intention, anyone who has seen this display cannot fail to marvel at the perfection of the performance, shaped as stringently and delicately by the unarguable forces of evolution as a bone is shaped, or a beak, or a feather.

NATURAL DEFENSES IN PLANTS

Plants also have defenses. Some are physical, such as the sharp-toothed edges of the holly leaf, the thorn of the rosebush, the spine of the cactus, and the sting of the nettle. Plants also produce a number of chemical substances for which the plant itself has no physiological use and which appear to function as defenses against leaf-eating insects and other predators. These chemicals include many substances presently useful to man, among them digitalis, quinine, castor oil, peppercorns and other spices; some of more questionable value, such as nicotine, caffeine, and morphine; and others, such as the active principles in marijuana, mescaline, and peyote, whose desirability for the animal world is a matter of debate at many institutions of higher learning. Plants appear to have been waging psychological warfare long before the coming of man, and it is possible that some small leafhopper was the first of all animals to have its mind expanded in a psychedelic experiment.

CONCEALMENT AND CAMOUFLAGE

Hiding is one of the chief means of escape from predators. The young of many birds and of some other vertebrates respond to the warning cries of their parents by "freezing" or by running to cover. Small mammals often have nests or burrows or makeshift residences in hollow logs or beneath tree roots in which they conceal themselves from their enemies.

Protective coloration is common. Mice, lizards, and arthropods that live on the sand are often light-colored, and such light-colored species, if removed from their home territories, will immediately try to return to them. Snails that live on mottled backgrounds are often banded, as we have seen. Grass snakes are grass-colored, as are many of the insects that live among the grasses.

Some animals are countershaded for camouflage. Next time you pass a fish market, look at the specimens laid out on view. Fish are nearly always darker on the top than on the bottom. Countershading reduces the con-

6–37 *Defenses against attack evolved by some desert plants. The barbs of the ocotillo are actually the stem and midrib of modified leaves. The spines of the prickly pear and the saguaro grow directly from the plants' outer skins. Cactus spines are often so sharp that they can pierce a bicycle tire. The spikes of the wild cucumber protect the fruit of the plant.*

OCOTILLO

PRICKLY PEAR

SAGUARO

WILD CUCUMBER

727 *The Numbers of Plants and Animals*

(a)　　|——50mm——|

(b)

6–38　(a) *The polyphemus moth* (Telea polyphemus) *at rest.* (b) *Disturbed by
prodding, the moth "flashes" its eyespots.* (Dr. Thomas Eisner)

6–39　*The mock eye on the tail of the butterfly fish deflects attack. A predator striking at this "eye" meets empty water
as the fish darts away.* (*Courtesy of
Marineland of Florida*)

|——10cm——|

trast between the shaded and unshaded areas of the body when the sun is shining on the organism from overhead. A fish was once found—the Nile catfish—that was reverse-countershaded; that is, its dorsal surface was light and its ventral surface dark. The selective theory of camouflage was momentarily threatened, but scientific order was restored when it was discovered that the Nile catfish characteristically swims upside down.

Other organisms hide by looking like something else. One type of insect, the treehopper, looks like a thorn; another, the walkingstick, like a twig. Young larvae of swallowtail butterflies look like bird droppings. In order for such disguises to work, animals must behave appropriately. *Biston betularia* lies very flat and motionless. Some moths that sit exposed on the bark of trees even habitually orient themselves so that the dark markings on their wings lie parallel to the dark cracks in the bark. Some desert succulent plants look like smooth stones, revealing their vegetable nature only once a year when they flower.

Some insects manage through warning coloration to frighten off their would-be predators. Large spots that look like eyes are commonly found on the backs of butterflies or the bodies of caterpillars, where they will suddenly appear when the insect spreads its wings or arches its body. Small birds that have been reported to flee at the sight are probably birds that themselves are likely to be the prey of larger, large-eyed birds, such as owls or hawks. Smaller eyespots, while probably not frightening, seem to have the effect of deflecting the point of attack away from the head. Examination of wounded butterflies has shown that if a part of the wings bears beak marks or is missing, it is most often the part that contains the eyespots. One investigator has tested and confirmed this conclusion by painting eyespots on the wings of living insects, releasing them, and later recapturing them for examination.

ON BEING OBNOXIOUS

Some animals defend themselves, or their species at least, by having a disagreeable taste, odor, or spray, often derived from distasteful chemicals in the plants they eat. Such animals are, generally, carefully avoided. The monarch butterfly, for instance, tastes bad to birds; it flies very slowly in order to prevent flicker-fusion of its wing pattern and to afford the predator time to recognize its highly characteristic colors. Louis Leakey, the well-known anthropologist, has hypothesized that primitive man may have survived, like the monarch butterfly, by not tasting very good to other animals. This hypothesis is supported by the fact that man, who is relatively defenseless compared with other vertebrates his size, apparently shared the water holes and other habitats of large carnivores.

Obviously, tasting bad, while useful, is not an ideal defense from the point of view of the individual, since making this fact known may demand a certain amount of personal sacrifice. (Actually, birds drop the monarch butterfly after the first bite, but they often inflict fatal injury in the process.) Obnoxious sprays and odors have the advantage of warding off predators before they harm the prey. To man, the most familiar of such animals is the skunk, which advertises its malodorous threat by its distinctive coloration. Many insects and other arthropods have developed defense secretions. In some millipedes, for example, the secretion oozes out of the glands onto the surface of the animals' bodies. Other arthropods are able to spray their secretion over a distance, in some instances even aiming it precisely at their attacker. The caterpillar *Schizura concinna*, whose single spray gland opens ventrally just behind its head, directs the spray simply by aiming its front end in the appropriate direction. In the beetle *Eleodes longicollis*, the spray glands are in the rear, and the beetle, when disturbed, does a quick headstand and spreads a secretion from its abdominal tip (Figure 6–40). The soldiers of certain termite species possess a pointed cephalic nozzle from which their defensive spray is ejected. This spray not only can incapacitate a small predator but also acts as a pheromone to summon more troops. In the whip scorpion, two glands open at the tip of a short knob that moves like a gun turret. Many arthropods possess a number of glands but discharge only from those closest to the point of attack, thus saving ammunition and gaining efficiency. The secretions usually act as topical irritants, especially to the mouth, nose, and eyes of the predator. Because of their relatively permeable skin, frogs and toads, common predators of arthropods, are sensitive to these irritants over their entire bodies.

6–40 *The beetle Eleodes longicollis, on the left, has defensive glands in its abdomen, and when disturbed, it does a headstand so that it can secrete a malodorous golden-brown liquid from its abdominal tip. The beetle on the right is its mimic, Megasida obliterata, which also stands on its head when annoyed but lacking the necessary glands, is quite incapable of producing any such secretion. (Dr. Thomas Eisner)*

|—10mm—|

729   *The Numbers of Plants and Animals*

6–41 *A toad being repelled by a bombardier beetle. The toad considers the beetle (a), strikes at it with its sticky tongue (b), and rejects it (c). (Dr. Thomas Eisner)*

(a)

(b)

(c)

Vertebrates learn quickly to recognize an obnoxious prey. Blue jays, for instance, having once been sprayed by a walkingstick, will remain aloof from it even when the insect is presented two or three weeks later. Predators also may learn to counter these defenses. Grasshopper mice feed on beetles like *Eleodes longicollis* by jamming them butt end into the earth, so that their chemical arsenal is harmlessly expended in the soil, and then eating them head first. (See Figure 6–42.)

MÜLLERIAN MIMICRY: ADVERTISING

For animals that have a highly effective protective device, such as a sting, a revolting smell, or a poisonous or bad-tasting secretion, it is advantageous to advertise. The more inconspicuous or rare such an animal is, the larger the proportion of individuals that must be sacrificed before the bird or other predator learns to avoid it. *Müllerian mimics*, named after F. Müller, who first described the phenomenon, are groups of insects that, although not closely related phylogenetically, all have effective obnoxious defenses and all resemble one another. Bees, wasps, and hornets probably offer the most familiar example; even if we cannot tell which is which, we recognize them immediately as stinging insects by their striking black and yellow banding and keep a respectful distance. Similarly, large numbers of bad-tasting butterflies are look-alikes. Müllerian mimicry is adaptive for all species involved because each prospers from a predator's experience with another.

BATESIAN MIMICRY: DECEPTION

Batesian mimicry, first described by the British naturalist H. W. Bates in 1862, is deceptive mimicry. In Batesian mimicry, the mimic fools its predator by resembling a stinging or bad-tasting "model" which the predator has learned to avoid, although the mimic itself is innocuous. Some species of harmless flies resemble bees or hornets, and many species of butterflies resemble monarchs or other unpalatable butterflies or moths.

Laboratory experiments have clearly demonstrated Batesian mimicry in operation. Jane Brower, working at Oxford, made artificial models using mealworms dipped in a solution of quinine and marked with a band of green cellulose paint. Other mealworms, which had first been dipped in distilled water, were painted green like the models, so as to produce mimics, and still others were painted orange to indicate another species. These colors were chosen deliberately; orange is usually a warning color, since it is clearly distinguishable, while green is usually found in species that are not repellent and therefore do not wish to advertise.

The painted mealworms were fed to caged starlings, which ordinarily eat mealworms voraciously. Each of the nine birds tested received models and mimics in varying proportions. After initial tasting and violent rejec-

6–42 *A grasshopper mouse feeding on the beetle Eleodes longicollis. The mouse holds the beetle with its abdominal tip pushed into the earth, so that its secretion is harmlessly expended in the soil, and eats its head first. (Dr. Thomas Eisner)*

tion, the models were generally recognized by their appearance and avoided. In consequence, their mimics were protected also. Even when mimics made up as much as 60 percent of the green-banded worms, 80 percent of the mimics escaped the predators. In fact, two starlings which were given 10 percent models and 90 percent mimics left 17 percent of the mimics untouched.

Batesian mimicry obviously works to the advantage only of the mimic. The model, on the other hand, suffers from attacks not only from inexperienced predators but from predators who have had their first experience with mimic rather than with model. The mimetic pattern will be at its greatest advantage if the mimic is rare, that is, less likely to be encountered than the model, and also if the mimic makes its seasonal appearance after the model, thus reducing its chances of being encountered first. (However, if the model is sufficiently distasteful—like a quinine-soaked mealworm—it may protect mimics even if the latter are very common, as Brower found in her experiments.) It is also advantageous to the mimic for it to be slightly smaller than the model. Studies with birds have shown that a bird will select the larger of two insects 99 times out of 100, even if the bird is so small and the insect so large that eating it presents a serious problem.

In some species of butterflies, various females of a single palatable species mimic a number of different species of distasteful butterflies. Only the females are polymorphic, however, perhaps because they would refuse males that they could not identify.

Müllerian mimicry and Batesian mimicry are not always diametrically opposed, since "edible" and "inedible" are subjective and relative terms. For example, cases might be found in which the supposed mimic was distasteful to a particular predator and so protected the model. One in-

6–43 *An example of Batesian mimicry. On the right is the unpalatable monarch butterfly, and on the left is a palatable mimic, the viceroy butterfly. (Dr. Ross E. Hutchins)*

6–44 *Foster-mother feeding young cuckoo.*
(*Eric Hosking, F.R.P.S.*)

vestigator, E. B. Ford, ate a monarch butterfly and reported that it was quite palatable. Presumably, he will now also readily eat monarch mimics, while had he but begun with a distasteful mimic, both models and mimics might have been protected from this new form of predation.

AGGRESSIVE MIMICRY

Sometimes the predator rather than the prey is the mimic. One species of desert lizard tempts insects to their death because the corner of its mouth when opened resembles a small red desert flower. In the angler fish, an extension of the spinal column dangles in front of it like a worm to lure other fishes within reach of its gaping mouth. One species of Australian orchid depends upon a particular species of wasp for its cross-pollination. The flower not only emits an alluring scent but also closely resembles the female of the insect in appearance. It thus attracts the males, which copulate repeatedly with the flowers, carrying pollen from orchid to orchid. Perhaps the cruelest of the aggressive mimics, from the anthropocentric point of view, are female fireflies of the genus *Photuris*, which are carnivorous. These fireflies mimic the flashes of females of other species and, upon the arrival of the suitor, eat him.

Another type of aggressive mimicry is exhibited by birds, such as the cuckoo in Europe and the cowbird in the United States, that lay their eggs in the nests of other birds. The unwary foster parents then incubate and feed the young cuckoo, which proceeds to push out of the nest all the legitimate members of the brood. Many birds will destroy an unfamiliar-looking egg or will perhaps even abandon completely a nest occupied by a stranger. Therefore, the closer the egg resembles those of the "host" species, the more chance it has to survive. In some areas of Europe, female cuckoos lay several very distinct types of eggs, always leaving the "right" egg in the "right" nest. Studies have shown that each individual female lays only one kind of egg, and since male cuckoos are highly promiscuous, it is presumed that the egg type is determined by genes on the Y chromosome. (In birds, as you may remember, the females are XY, while the males are XX.) Some investigators have suggested that the selection of the "right" nest by the female cuckoo may be determined by imprinting of the female at birth. How could this hypothesis be tested? These birds have not yet been successfully raised in captivity.

VALUE OF PREDATION

Predation is not necessarily bad for the population as a whole. Wolves, for instance, have great difficulty overtaking healthy adult caribou or even healthy calves. Over 50 percent of the kills that wolves make are crippled or sick caribou, although the incidence of such individuals in the population is less than 2 percent.

733 *The Numbers of Plants and Animals*

Destruction by crows of the eggs and young of ducks sometimes keeps a whole generation from being wiped out. If many of the first, early-spring nestlings are destroyed, the ducks then lay replacement clutches and so stagger their nestings through a longer period of time. These later-born birds are less likely to meet widespread disaster in the form of a late freeze or a flooding or similar catastrophe.

Early in the 1900s, animal lovers undertook to protect a population of mule deer on the Kaibab plateau in Arizona. There were about 4,000 deer living there at that time in a healthy, stable population, but it appeared that there was ample food for more (actually, the carrying capacity of the plateau at that time had been estimated at about 30,000 deer). Why not protect these gentle deer by exterminating the bloodthirsty animals that preyed upon them, it was argued. Hunters were encouraged to kill hundreds of natural predators—mountain lions, coyotes, and wolves. By 1918, the deer population had increased to 40,000, and the food plants were beginning to show damage. By 1920, some fawns were starving. In 1923, the deer population was up to 100,000 and the forage on the range was so damaged that 60,000 deer died of starvation during the next two winters. The population then dropped to about 10,000, where it has remained stabilized.

Disease

PARASITE-HOST RELATIONSHIPS

Nearly all diseases in organisms (except those diseases in man, such as arthritis, heart disease, and most forms of cancer, which are linked to his prolonged life-span) are caused by parasites, including microorganisms. Such diseases are special cases of predator-prey relationships. In these instances, the predator is considerably smaller than the prey, and the prey is known as the *host*, which implies a gracious acceptance and is therefore somewhat misleading. Large vertebrates may sometimes be parasites. The hagfish (Figure 2–118), which sucks out the flesh of other fish, might be classified either as a predator or as a parasite. The tapeworm, often yards long, is indisputably a parasite. Usually the term "parasite" is not applied to infectious microorganisms such as fungi, bacteria, and viruses, but the principle is the same; only the relative sizes are different.

The average host, whether plant or animal, supports hundreds of parasites of many species—in fact, perhaps, millions, if one were to count the viruses. Most parasites do not kill their host, and parasites almost never wipe out entire populations. We know this from our own experience. Bacterial disease is fatal only when the bacteria find themselves a particularly favorable place to multiply, such as in the blind pouch of an infected appendix or in an open wound. Most bacteria are harmless, like

Escherichia coli, and some are helpful, such as those in the stomachs of the herbivores and those in our own intestinal tracts. Modern antibiotics often cause nausea and diarrhea because they destroy the useful and protective bacteria of the intestinal tract. Of all the viral diseases of man, only one, rabies, is regularly fatal if unchecked.

In animal and plant communities, diseases are most likely to wipe out the very young, the very old, and the disabled, either directly or, often, indirectly by making them more susceptible to predators or to the effects of climate. Most infectious diseases tend to spread more rapidly when populations are crowded and to subside as the population thins out. In this way, they serve as a check on population density, in much the same way that food shortage does.

It is logical that a parasite-caused disease should not be too virulent or too efficient. If a parasite were to kill all the hosts for which it is adapted, it, too, would perish.

This principle is particularly well illustrated by the changes that have taken place in the myxoma virus of rabbits in Australia. The myxoma virus causes only a mild disease in the South American rabbit, its normal host, but a rapidly serious one, laboratory studies have shown, in the European rabbit, which has had no previous evolutionary experience with this disease. To end the scourge of introduced rabbits in Australia, myxoma-infected rabbits were set free on the continent. At first the effects were spectacular, and the rabbit population steadily declined, yielding a share of pastureland once more to the sheep herds on which much of the economy of the country depends. But then occasional rabbits began to survive, and their litters also were resistant. Now some 95 percent of the rabbits survive an attack of myxoma virus. A double process of selection took place. The virus, as originally introduced, was so rapidly fatal that often a rabbit died before it could be bitten by a mosquito and thereby infect another rabbit, and the virus strain then died with the rabbit. Strains less drastic in their effects, on the other hand, had a better chance of survival since they had a greater opportunity to spread to a new host. (After the initial infection, the rabbit is immune to the virus, just as human beings usually become immune to mumps or measles after one infection.) So, first, selection began to work in favor of a less virulent strain, as proved by tests of the Australian virus on European rabbits in the laboratory. Almost simultaneously, the rabbits began to develop resistance, as proved by tests of the South American virus on Australian rabbits. Now the two are reaching a peaceful equilibrium, like most hosts and parasites.

Some parasitologists maintain that parasites that harm their hosts are probably the result of recent evolutionary relationships—the two simply have not yet "learned" to get along well together. Parasites that alternate between two different types of hosts usually are harmful only to the more recent arrival on the evolutionary scene. Many parasites are more virulent to man, for example, than to the alternate vertebrate host. Another example is found in the parasites that travel from vertebrate to vertebrate by way of insects. Multiplying in both hosts, these parasites often harm the vertebrates but apparently never the insects.

It is equally logical to argue that most parasites first made their way into the host, evolutionarily speaking, quite by accident. This view is supported by the fact that, except for the skin, the intestinal tract is the most common habitat of parasites and that many parasites residing in the intestinal tract are closely related to free-living forms. The invasion of the central nervous system by the tsetse-borne flagellate that causes African sleeping sickness or of the red blood cells by the malaria plasmodium must represent the end product of millennia of increasing encroachment.

UPSETTING THE BALANCE

Epidemics of disease in which large populations are destroyed are usually the result of some sudden shift in relationship between parasite and host. Smallpox and venereal diseases began their spread through Europe with the age of exploration. Measles, considered a relatively mild disease, has been known to be widely fatal in populations never previously exposed to it. For example, within three months after the first case of measles was introduced on the island of Fiji in 1875, one-fourth of the population had died. The chestnut blight, a fungus which was introduced into the United States with Chinese chestnut trees about 1900, spread from New York through the Blue Ridge Mountains and the Piedmont Plateau and de-

6–45 *The prickly pear threatened to overrun Australia, spreading at the rate of about a million acres a year, until a moth was introduced whose caterpillars attack and kill the plant. Today, both the moth and the prickly pear are scarce. This photograph was taken in 1928, before the introduction of the moth. (Courtesy of the Biological Section Laboratory, Australian Department of Lands)*

stroyed the great bulk of American chestnut trees by 1935. The speed of intercontinental travel has served to transport various strains of influenza around and around the world much more rapidly than the population can become immune to them.

The prickly-pear cactus was brought to Australia from South America. It soon escaped from the garden of the gentleman who had imported it and spread into fields and pastureland until there were more than 30 million acres so densely covered with prickly pears that they were valueless. The cactus then began to take over the rest of Australia at the rate of about a million acres a year. A moth (*Cactoblastis cactorum*), the caterpillars of which live exclusively on prickly pear, was introduced from South America, and during the next five years, 3 billion of them were set loose. They multiplied and spread, completely destroying the cactus wherever they found it. Now both are relatively scarce, but both are kept from complete extinction by the occasional cactus seeds left to sprout and the occasional moths that find them.

Notice that, depending on your viewpoint, the relationship between the prickly-pear cactus and the moth might be considered as food–consumer, as prey–predator, or as host–parasite.

Self-regulation of Animal Populations

Although the human population may multiply beyond its resources, as Malthus warned in 1798, few animal populations do so. Some limiting factors, as we have seen, are food supply, predation, and disease. In addition, an outside force, such as climate or rainfall, may act as a limiting factor to keep populations in check. In some cases, however, limiting factors are not so obvious.

In one experiment, for example, a census of a particular species of butterfly was taken each year for eight years. Each fall, there were from 8,000 to 14,000 larvae of the species in a field in New England. In most years, about 30 larvae survived until spring; and most summers, there were about 20 butterflies. In the autumn of the sixth year, the field was stocked with 20,000 additional larvae. Eighty spring larvae were present the following year, but by summer, there were only 22 butterflies in the field, about the usual number. That fall, only 400 autumn larvae could be found. Examination of the surrounding areas revealed that many more eggs than usual had been laid outside the field. In response to the overstocking of the field, the butterflies had emigrated, despite the fact that ample food was left for the larvae and ample space remained for the deposit of eggs.

In another experiment, 50 guppies of various sizes, both male and female, were placed in one tank, and one pregnant female guppy was placed in another tank of the same size. Food was not a limiting factor. After six months, both tanks had attained the same stable complement of nine guppies each.

In such cases, regulation of animal numbers appears to depend on factors within the population rather than outside of it. Two of the most important of these self-regulatory factors are territoriality and dominance.

TERRITORIES

As we mentioned in Chapter 5–5, animals that do not gain possession of territories or that are excluded from the "home range" or breeding area do not produce young. As older animals die, younger ones will contend for their places, keeping the breeding population stabilized. Under particularly favorable conditions, or if the range is enlarged, more animals can gain access to the breeding community.

The muskrat has been the subject of a number of studies, in part because of the economic value of muskrat pelts. Muskrats make their burrows along the edges of streams or around any other body of shallow water close to a supply of grass or grains. All breeding takes place within the burrows, from which nonbreeding populations are excluded. If the population increases, more animals are driven out. On the other hand, if freezing, drought, or trapping reduces the population, outsiders are allowed in and breeding increases. Limited hunting or trapping of the animals does not decrease the population; similarly, control of other predators does not increase the population. The only way to increase the muskrat population is to increase the food, cover, and space—the *carrying capacity*, as it is called—of the breeding area. This was clearly demonstrated when the construction of dams, dikes, and canals in the Saskatchewan River diverted water into marshes suitable for muskrat habitation. In four years, the number of muskrats in the area increased from 1,000 to 200,000.

Laboratory studies have confirmed the tendency of some populations to regulate their own numbers. In one group of studies, investigators confined populations of the house mouse (*Mus musculus*) in pens 6 feet wide and 25 feet long. In the first phase of the study, a fixed amount of food was supplied each day, regardless of the size of the population. The population increased to a density at which all the food was eaten within two hours of being presented. Then two striking things occurred: (1) There was a sharp rise in the mortality of infant mice in the pens—up to 85 percent died. (2) Breeding stopped. There was no rise in mortality among adults and no obvious malnutrition; all individuals maintained their weight, and there was no fighting. Any animals that were removed from the restricted environment regained their reproductive capacities immediately.

In the second phase of the study, food was always supplied in abundance to each pen no matter how numerous the mice became. In the majority of the groups, the population increased rapidly to a maximum and then declined slowly or remained fairly steady despite an excess of food. In this situation also, there was a high death rate among young mice; almost 100 percent died before they were weaned. Then there was a marked decrease in the reproductive rate.

The density at which the different groups felt crowded differed markedly from pen to pen. In one pen, for instance, crowding occurred when there were 15 mice per 150 square feet; but in another, the mice did not show signs of being crowded until there were 130 mice per 150 square feet. One might postulate that the degree of stress caused by crowding is determined by genetic factors and that the differences among the populations reflect chance variations in the founder groups.

DOMINANCE HIERARCHIES

Dominance hierarchies—"pecking orders"—also reduce the breeding population. Both male and female rats of a lower dominance order, for example, are "socially castrated" in a crowded population, while those of higher rank may keep on breeding freely. The inferior rats simply show no normal sexual interest. If they are removed from the restrictive environment, however, they will, like the mice, mate promptly and reproduce normally.

Dominance hierarchies and territories not only limit reproduction but also ensure that the individuals eliminated by food shortage or predators are more likely to be those already deemed surplus, reproductively speaking. Animals within the breeding ground are more protected than those outside it. The muskrat in its burrow, for instance, is relatively invulnerable. Studies of muskrat carcasses found in the stomachs of minks, the chief predator of the muskrat, showed that 60 to 75 percent of those that had been eaten were demonstrably diseased or otherwise disabled. Animals lower in the dominance order will starve, while those of higher rank will eat normally. Nor is any energy expended by either the weaker or the stronger in the "struggle for survival"; that is, social competition rarely leads to killing or even overt fighting once territories or ranks are established.

Studies of food deprivation among nestling birds reveal that, for many, a similar weeding out of the less fit takes place. One chief effect of food shortage is a decrease in weight, not of most members of the brood but only of one or two, which were probably smaller and weaker at birth. Once a nestling has begun to drop in weight below its fellows, it rapidly loses more since it cannot compete successfully with its nestmates for food, and so it quickly dies. If the food shortage continues, another nestling may then grow feebler and die, but the rest of the brood will still be healthy and heavy. Evolution is an unsentimental process.

The previous part of this chapter was concerned with the factors that regulate the number of organisms within a species. In this final part of the chapter, we shall examine some of the factors that regulate the number of species within a community. Actually, in principle, the conditions which we examine should be the same in both cases.

The number of animals within a species is controlled, directly or indirectly, by environmental factors. Under conditions of competition, the organisms that survive are those that are best adapted to their environment, and in general, those that are least adapted perish. The same principle governs the number of species within a community. If two species are in direct competition for space, food, light, hiding places, nesting materials, or any other life-sustaining factor, the species that is best able to procure or make use of the limited supply available will eradicate the other species, just as a more fit genotype will replace one that is less fit within a species.

The rate at which this takes place depends on the degree of competition and the degree of difference between the two species; therefore, two species in direct competition might coexist temporarily, as do two genotypes in transient polymorphism. This situation is now apparently occurring in Australia, where placental animals, recently introduced, are tending to supplant their marsupial counterparts.

Other factors may intervene to reduce the competition and slow down the rate of replacement. For example, spells of extreme heat or extreme cold might keep both species at such a low level that little effective competition would exist between the two.

Ecological Niches

The position of a species in the environment is related to what it eats and what it does, how it defends itself from enemies, and where it lives. The combination of these factors is referred to as the *ecological niche*.

GAUSE'S PRINCIPLE

The principle that similar species have difficulty coexisting in the same locality if they have the same ecological requirements was formulated by the Russian biologist G. F. Gause and is generally known as *Gause's principle*. Gause demonstrated this by a number of laboratory experiments. His simplest, now classic experiment involved laboratory cultures of two species of paramecia, *Paramecium aurelia* and *Paramecium caudatum*. When the two species were grown under identical conditions in separate containers, *P. aurelia* grew much more rapidly than *P. caudatum*, indicating that the former used the available food supply much more efficiently than the latter. When the two were grown together, the former rapidly outmultiplied the latter, which soon was wiped out. (See Figure 6–46.)

OTHER ENVIRONMENTAL FACTORS: THE *Tribolium* CASE

As is the case in predator-prey relationships, results of studies of interspecific competition for a niche become less clear-cut when other factors in the environment are brought under consideration. When equal numbers of two species of flour beetle, *Tribolium castaneum* and *Tribolium confusum*, were introduced into the same flour container at a temperature of 34°C and a relative humidity of 70 percent, *T. castaneum* exterminated *T. confusum*. When the conditions of temperature and humidity were varied, investigators found surprising variations in the results of the interspecific competition between the two beetles. These results are given in Table 6–6.

The protozoan *Adelina*, which parasitizes both beetles, was introduced into the isolated cultures. It decreased the *T. castaneum* population by two-thirds, but it did not affect *T. confusum* nearly so drastically. When the parasite was absent, *T. castaneum* usually won out; when *Adelina* was present, *T. confusum* usually dominated.

6–46 *Results of Gause's experiment with two species of Paramecium demonstrate Gause's principle that similar species have difficulty occupying the same ecological niche. Paramecium caudatum and Paramecium aurelia were first grown separately under controlled conditions and with constant food supply. As you can see, P. aurelia grew much more rapidly than P. caudatum, indicating that it uses available food supplies more efficiently. When the two protozoans were grown together, P. aurelia rapidly outmultiplied P. caudatum, and the latter was eliminated.*

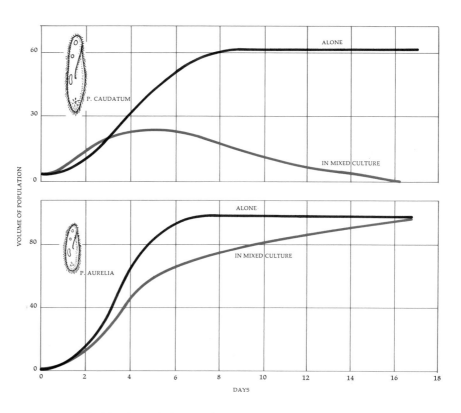

Table 6–6 *Results of Interspecific Competition between Populations of Two Species of Flour Beetles* (*Tribolium*)

Climate	Temperature (°C)	Relative humidity (%)	*Tribolium castaneum* wins (% cases)	*Tribolium confusum* wins (% cases)
Hot-wet	34	70	100	0
Hot-dry	34	30	10	90
Warm-wet	29	70	86	14
Warm-dry	29	30	13	87
Cool-wet	24	70	31	69
Cool-dry	24	30	0	100

In another series of experiments, *T. confusum* was shown to eliminate regularly the smaller flour beetle *Oryzaephilus surinamensis* in a laboratory culture. But when the experimenter placed in the medium small pieces of glass tubing in which the smaller beetles could hide and pupate and into which the larger ones could not enter, both species survived.

COMPETITION FOR THE NICHE IN A NATURAL ENVIRONMENT

Examples of direct competition in natural populations are more difficult to obtain since one is more likely to encounter only the direct result. One clear-cut instance that has been studied extensively is competition among barnacles. Before barnacles can change from their immature larval forms, in which they resemble tiny shrimp, into their adult, feeding forms, they must cement themselves to a rock and secrete a shell. In Scotland, one species of barnacle, *Chthamalus stellatus* occurs in the high part of the intertidal seashore, whereas another barnacle, *Balanus balanoides*, occurs lower down. Although young *Chthamalus* often attach to the rock in the lower, *Balanus*, zone after their short stay as drifters in the plankton, no adults are ever found there.

The history of a population of barnacles can be recorded very accurately by holding a pane of glass over a patch of barnacles and noting with glass-marking ink each spot where a barnacle is. Once attached, barnacles are fixed, so that by returning later, one can check exactly which barnacles have died and which new ones have arrived.

By doing this, the investigator was able to show that in the lower zone, *Balanus*, which grows faster, ousts *Chthamalus* by crowding it off the rocks or growing over it. When *Chthamalus* was isolated from contact with *Balanus*, it lived with no difficulty in the lower zone, showing that the reason for the restriction of *Chthamalus* to the high shore levels was interspecific competition with *Balanus*.

MODIFYING FACTORS IN THE CONCEPT OF THE NICHE

From these examples, you can see that the concept of ecological niche is not an absolute one. Two species, as in the large and small flour beetles, may live in one niche but breed in another. This often also occurs among birds in natural communities. Two species may nest in the same woods, but one species will feed in the territory around its nest while another feeds in a communal feeding area. Since, by definition, no two species are exactly alike, no two will inhabit exactly the same ecological niche. Therefore the question is actually one of how much overlap can be tolerated. This can probably be answered only in terms of particular species under particular environmental conditions.

6–47 *Interspecies competition in Balanus and Chthamalus barnacles. The larvae of both species settle over a wide range, but the adults live in quite precisely restricted areas. The upward limits of the Balanus area are determined by physical factors such as desiccation. The Chthamalus barnacles, however, are prevented from living in the Balanus area not by physical factors—they would probably thrive there since the area is less physically limiting—but by the Balanus barnacles. The Balanus grows faster, and whenever it comes upon Chthamalus in the Balanus area, it either pries it off the rocks or grows right over it. (After Connell, 1961)*

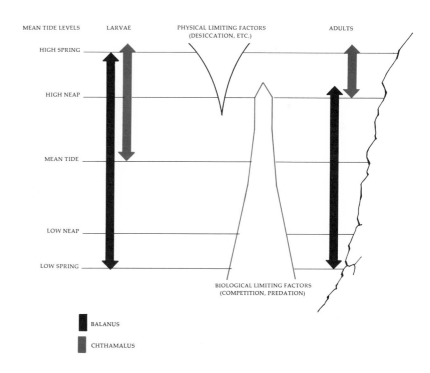

Also, it is very hard to prove that a niche exists unless it is filled. Once the prickly pear overran Australia, it was clear that an unoccupied environmental niche had been awaiting this particular plant, but this fact was not predicted beforehand. Similarly, when the Suez Canal was opened in 1869, 15 Red Sea species of fish colonized the Mediterranean, and some have become quite abundant. It is probable that these species filled vacant niches, because there was no apparent decrease in the frequency of any of the Mediterranean species. No Mediterranean fish succeeded in entering the Red Sea, however, so one presumes that there were no vacant niches available there, or at least no niches which could be filled by Mediterranean fish.

If each of two species in competition is favored when rare and is placed at a disadvantage when common, neither will be eliminated. Rareness may be an advantage for a variety of reasons. For example, if each species of tree required a different nutrient, such as a trace element, the growth of each species' offspring directly beneath it might be inhibited. The roots of the adult tree would be able to remove all the essential nutrient from the upper soil; other species, which did not require this nutrient, would be able to grow in the space.

Or, if a species becomes rare, predation may decrease. One investigator studied the predation by tits of insect larvae which spend the winter concealed beneath the cuticle of ripening pinecones. The birds locate their prey by tapping the cone, and then they excavate the larvae. He found that predation was very light at low prey densities, increasing abruptly as the density increased. This suggested the operation of something like a "specific search image." If a predator specifically searched for high-density prey, this would promote the recovery of species that had become rare.

The Niche and Interspecies Competition

DARWIN'S FINCHES

Lack's studies of Darwin's finches provide a good example of the effects of interspecies competition. The large ground finch (*Geospiza magnirostris*), the medium ground finch (*Geospiza fortis*), and the small ground finch (*Geospiza fuliginosa*) differ from each other principally in overall size and in size of beak. Because of the differences in beak size, these ground finches eat seeds of different sizes and therefore do not compete.

On the northern islands of the Galapagos (Abingdon, Bindloe, James and Jervis), there is a distinct separation between the three species. On Albemarle and Indefatigable, *G. fuliginosa* and *G. fortis* are clearly separated; here, however, the separation between *G. magnirostris* and *G. fortis* is not so clear. A possible explanation for this can be found in the fact that on Albemarle and Indefatigable, only 9 percent of the specimens collected were *G. magnirostris,* as compared with 55 percent on the northern islands.

On Charles and Chatham, *G. magnirostris* no longer exists at all, and *G. fortis,* as you can see, shows some overlap in beak size with the *G. magnirostris* of the other islands. On Daphne, which is only half a mile in diameter, only one species exists. This species is *G. fortis,* but having no other species to compete with, it has a beak size intermediate between those of the small and medium ground finches found on islands where the two coexist. The Crossmans are even smaller than Daphne. Since these islands are too small to support populations of both species, the species that has managed to persist there might be expected to evolve a beak of intermediate size since it then could use food normally available for both species.

NORTH AMERICAN WARBLERS

In a test of Gause's principle, Robert MacArthur undertook a study of five warblers, all members of the same genus (*Dendroica*), that live in the spruce forests of Maine. Unlike Darwin's finches, these birds do not have any obvious physical differences among them. But when MacArthur observed them carefully, he found that each species tends to live and feed

6–48 *Beak sizes in three Geospiza species of Darwin's finches. Beak measurements, in millimeters, are plotted horizontally, and the percentage of specimens of each size is shown vertically. On Daphne and the Crossmans, which are very small islands, only one species exists and this species has a beak size halfway between that of the small and medium-sized finches on the larger islands. Can you explain why? (After Lack, 1961)*

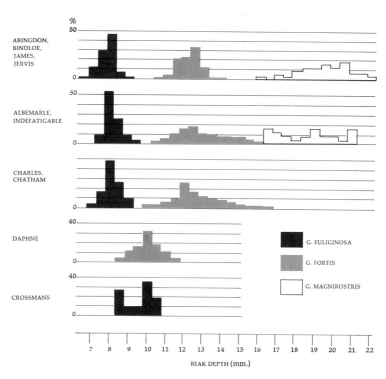

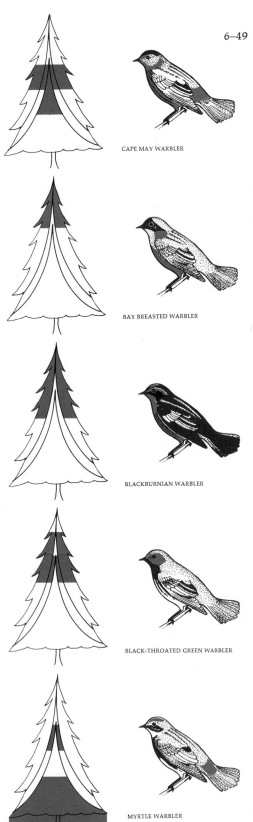

CAPE MAY WARBLER

BAY BREASTED WARBLER

BLACKBURNIAN WARBLER

BLACK-THROATED GREEN WARBLER

MYRTLE WARBLER

6–49 *A classic demonstration of Gause's principle: the feeding zones in a spruce tree of five species of North American warblers. The colored areas in the tree indicate where each species spends at least half its feeding time. With this arrangement, all five species can feed in the same tree without competing. (After MacArthur, 1958)*

in a particular zone in and below the spruce trees and to prey on different types of insects. (See Figure 6–49.) In the case of the finches, the species are structurally specialized to use different resources, while in the case of the warblers, the species appear to be behaviorally specialized (although this specialization is quite probably the result of inconspicuous structural differences). In both cases, the end result is the same.

HAWAIIAN SNAILS

Studies of species of one genus of snails (*Conus*) found on the wave-cut beaches of Hawaii have shown that each of the species occupies a different zone along the seashore and has distinctly different food preferences. One of the factors confining each to its zone is probably the capacity to withstand exposure to air at low tide.

Why Are There So Many Species?
THE ADAPTIVE VALUE OF COMPLEXITY

Communities in which there are large numbers of different species tend to be much more stable in their composition than communities in which there are only a few species. For example, the few mammalian species present in Arctic regions fluctuate wildly in numbers. At one place near Point Barrow in northern Alaska, Siberian lemmings were scarce from 1949 to 1951, increased in 1952, and reached a peak in 1953. Associated with this rise in lemming population was a marked increase in the number of predators. Snowy owls, for instance, which did not breed at all in 1951, began breeding in 1952. Weasels and Arctic foxes, which hardly had been observed, became common. Then, because of heavy predation, the lemming population was reduced by mid-July of 1953 to one-tenth of what it had been early in June; the predators then also declined precipitously in number. Similarly, a study of the fur catch of the Hudson Bay Company shows radical oscillations among such animals as lynx and rabbits. Such fluctuations are also seen on sparsely populated islands.

The noted ecologist G. E. Hutchinson of Yale speculates that evolution may favor the development of many different kinds of plants and ani-

6–50 *The number of lynx and snowshoe hare pelts received yearly by the Hudson Bay Company over a period of almost 100 years, indicating a pattern of 10-year oscillations in population density. The lynx reaches a population peak every 9 or 10 years, and these peaks are followed in each case by several years of sharp decline. The snowshoe hare follows the same cycle, with a peak abundance generally preceding that of the lynx by a year or more. On the basis of these cyclic patterns, can any statement be made about the probable relationship of these two species? (After Odum, 1959)*

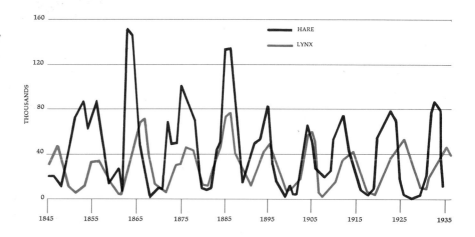

mals since the community which contains many different species is more stable and therefore more likely to survive—and its plants and animals with it—than the community with only a few members. Most very old communities, such as the tropical rain forest and the coral reef, abound in a great variety of different species.

IS THERE AN ADVANTAGE IN SPECIATION?

One certainly could not settle the question of the advantages of speciation by looking at man and the insects, the two kinds of animals that dominate the modern world. The insects have followed the evolutionary course of ever-increasing speciation, the constant subdividing of the ecological niche. For example, three different kinds of mites occupy three different body areas of one honeybee. Several different species of insects may exist in different parts of the same host plant—in the flower buds, the upper stem, the lower stem, and the root stalk. Several different species of ant may build nests in different areas of decayed tree stumps.

Man is at the other extreme. He lives in every environment from the poles to the equator; he can eat a pure meat diet, as does the Eskimo, or a purely vegetable diet; and he can get his food in a number of different ways. Man seemingly has left room for no other species of the genus *Homo*, for there is no ecological niche available for another species to occupy.

SUMMARY

In this chapter, we have examined some of the forces that regulate the numbers of plants and animals, both in populations and within commu-

747   *The Numbers of Plants and Animals*

nities. These forces operate in a system of checks and balances, in which reproductive rates and mortality rates are controlled by various factors in the environment and in the physical structures of the organisms themselves.

Individual reproductive rates are limited by the physical capacity of the organism—that is, the size of the body cavity in the female—and, in animals in which parental care is important, by the number of young that the parent can provide for (which, in turn, is often determined by specific environmental conditions).

The external factors that limit the life-span of an organism and therefore its reproductive capacity are called the *environmental resistance*. The principal limiting factors that comprise environmental resistance are (1) food shortage, (2) predators, and (3) disease.

Plants and animals have developed many kinds of natural defenses against predators. These include (1) armor in animals and thorns, spines, and sharp-edged leaves in plants; (2) warning behavior; (3) concealment by hiding and by camouflage; (4) imitative markings, such as eyespots, which either threaten would-be predators or deflect attack; (5) chemical protective devices which impart to the animal or plant a disagreeable taste or odor or which take the form of an offensive secretion; (6) *Batesian mimicry*, in which an animal resembles a stinging or bad-tasting "model." Mimicry is also used by some predators to attract prey.

Nearly all diseases in organisms are caused by parasites. Most parasites do not kill their host, and they almost never wipe out entire populations. The resistance developed by the rabbits in Australia to the myxoma virus is an example of the way in which host and parasite may reach an equilibrium. A sudden shift in the relationship of parasite and host may cause this balance to be upset, with a resultant epidemic of disease.

Population densities are controlled not only by external limiting factors but also by self-regulation. Two important internal limiting factors are territoriality and dominance.

The position of a species in the environment—what it eats and does, how it defends itself, and where it lives—is its *ecological niche*. According to *Gause's principle,* similar species have difficulty coexisting in the same locality if they have the same ecological requirements. The number of species within a community is therefore controlled by interspecific competition. One species may eliminate a similar species in competition for the same ecological niche, or the structural differences among several similar species may allow them to coexist in the same area, but in clearly separated zones.

Communities which contain many different species tend to be more stable, with fewer population fluctuations, and therefore more likely to survive than communities in which there are only a few species.

Chapter 6—4

The Plants and Animals at Home

The name given to the subdivision of biology that deals with the organization and functioning of populations and communities in their environments is *ecology*, a word which comes from the Greek *oikos*, meaning "household." Thus, literally, ecology is the study of "houses," or to put it more precisely, "environments." But modern ecology is concerned with more than just environments; its field of study is the whole living world —the lands, the oceans, and the fresh waters, the groups of organisms that inhabit these areas, and the interrelationships that develop among the groups and between the organisms and the places where they live.

In the preceding chapters of this section, we have been concerned with the interactions of populations and communities in specific environments. In this chapter, we shall add another dimension by considering how these many different, specific environments interlock with one another to form the world around us.

The Biosphere

The part of the planet in which organisms live is known as the *biosphere*. This word was coined by Lamarck in 1809 to denote the whole zone at the surface of the earth occupied by living things. As we mentioned in Chapter 1–1, there are probably many more biospheres than our own, but these are at the present time beyond our knowledge.

The biosphere of the earth, in proportion to the planet as a whole, is only a thin film which covers part of the earth's surface, extending just above and below it. This film is the only part of the planet on which both liquid (water) and an energy source (the sun's radiation) can be found. The biosphere is subdivided into various seascapes and landscapes, each of which possesses a particular kind of climate and a characteristic group of plants and animals. These regions are often referred to as *biomes*. A forest is a biome, as is the desert, the ocean, the seashore, or the grasslands.

Biomes, in turn, are made up of ecological systems, communities of species known as *ecosystems*. An ecosystem can be a whole forest, a lake within that forest, a temporary pond, or even an aquarium. It need only be large enough and have existed long enough to have achieved a reasonable stability. The ecosystem comprises both the community, which is an aggregation of living organisms, and the nonliving environment.

Ecosystems are subdivided into *habitats*, the places where the organisms live. A fish, for example, may live in an entire pond, so in this case, "ecosystem" and "habitat" would be equivalent terms. On the other hand, a protozoan or a small crustacean would probably inhabit only a specific area of even a very small pond, and this specific area would be its habitat. The term "habitat" is therefore not synonymous with "ecological niche" for a given habitat may offer a number of niches to the various species within it.

SEASCAPES AND LANDSCAPES: THE BIOMES

The Sea

The oceans cover almost three-fourths of the earth's surface and reach down to an average depth of 3 miles. If the earth's surface were smooth, it would be entirely covered by water.

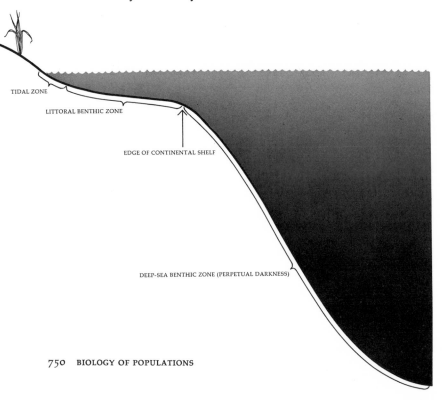

6–51 *There are two principal divisions of the sea: the benthic (bottom) zone and the pelagic (swimming) zone. The benthic zone is subdivided into the tidal, littoral and profundal (deep-sea) zones, as indicated in the drawing. In the pelagic zone of the open sea, light penetrates about 600 feet (200 meters) below the surface. (After Buchsbaum, 1957)*

TIDAL ZONE

LITTORAL BENTHIC ZONE

EDGE OF CONTINENTAL SHELF

DEEP-SEA BENTHIC ZONE (PERPETUAL DARKNESS)

Life first evolved in the sea, and today representatives of all the major groups, or phyla, into which animal life has been divided can be found there—in other words, every phylum on land is also in the sea. In the tidal zone, where land and sea meet, and in the shallow seas around the continents, the vast majority of all the ocean's life occurs. Marine life is also present in the open sea—on the surface of the ocean and in the zone of light below the surface, which extends down about 600 feet. And only recently, scientists have begun to explore a third domain of ocean life, the zone of perpetual darkness in the ocean depths.

CURRENTS

The trade winds, created by temperature differences between the poles and the equator and by the earth's rotation, cause the ocean to move in great currents. These turn like giant pinwheels, spinning clockwise in the northern hemisphere and counterclockwise in the southern hemisphere. As a result of this motion, warm currents flow north and south from the equator; the Gulf Stream, which bathes Bermuda, skirts the coast of Massachusetts, and reaches as far as Northern Europe, is one such current.

Some currents cause *upwellings*, which bring to the surface cold water from the bottom of the sea. This water is rich in the nutrients that accumulate in the depths. Rising to the surface, these nutrients become the food source for the plants that form the primary nourishment—the base of the food pyramid—for marine life. Upwellings are found off the coasts of California, Portugal, and Peru, and these areas, abounding with fish, form the great fisheries of the world, frequented by both marine birds and commercial trawlers.

THE PYRAMID OF LIFE AT SEA

All life in the ocean depends for its existence on the phytoplankton, the meadow of the sea. The phytoplankton, which floats on or near the surface, is composed mainly of diatoms and dinoflagellates (Figure 6–52). One cubic foot of seawater may contain as many as 12 1/2 million of these chlorophyll-bearing cells. Sunlight sufficient for photosynthesis only reaches to a depth of about 600 feet in the ocean, and so the phytoplankton is confined to this zone.

The zooplankton, or animal plankton, includes representatives from virtually every group of marine animals (Figure 6–53); tiny shrimp and other small crustaceans are the dominant forms, and intermingled with them are the immature forms of many of the larger animals—the eggs and larvae of fish, the planula larvae of coelenterates, the medusa stage of sessile hydroids, the tadpole larvae of tunicates, the pluteus larvae of starfish. Most of the zooplankton is transparent; when caught in the fine silk mesh of a plankton net, zooplankton looks like a solid gelatinous mass.

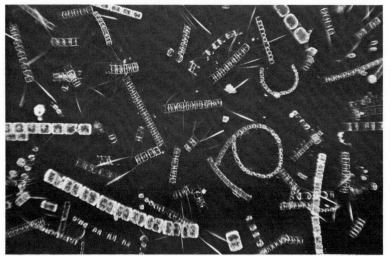

|— 200μ —|

6–52 *Living phytoplankton, consisting mainly of chains of one-celled algae known as diatoms. Each diatom is enclosed in a transparent silicon case, manufactured by the cell from the minerals of the sea around it. The odd shapes and projections help keep the organisms afloat in water. (Dr. Douglas P. Wilson, F.R.P.S.)*

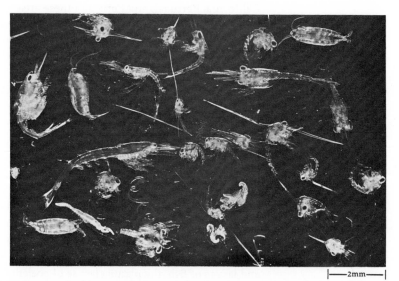

|—2mm—|

6–53 *Living zooplankton, consisting mainly of various* crustacean *larvae, adult copepods, worm and mollusk larvae, and young pilchards. (Dr. Douglas P. Wilson, F.R.P.S.)*

6–54 *The food pyramid in the sea. At the base of the pyramid and making up by far the largest group of organisms are the planktons—phytoplankton and zooplankton. These support a smaller number of larger forms which feed on them, and the larger forms, in turn, are eaten by a still smaller number of still larger creatures. Finally, at the top of the pyramid, are a few very large fish and other large sea creatures, which could not exist without the vast numbers of organisms comprising the pyramid below them. For example, every few hours, a single humpback whale needs about a ton of herring. Each herring may have six or seven thousand small crustaceans in its stomach, and each crustacean may contain as many as 130,000 diatoms.*

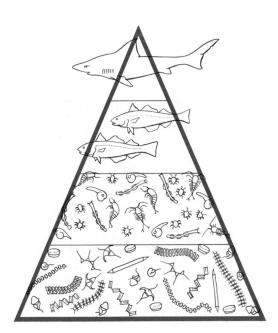

Phytoplankton usually "blooms" twice a year. During the winter, nitrogen- and phosphorus-bearing ions increase in the sea because of the decomposition of organisms that have died. In the spring, with rising temperatures and increasing light, the phytoplankton increases to its maximum for the year, utilizing the accumulated nutrients. Zooplankton, which feeds off the phytoplankton, also increases, reaching its maximum in midsummer. By midsummer, the nitrogen and phosphorus reserves become depleted, the phytoplankton declines, and following it, the zooplankton. The decomposition of the zooplankton returns nitrogen and phosphorus to the surface waters, and a second bloom may occur in the fall. Large populations of zooplankton and phytoplankton do not occur in the same place at the same time, perhaps because the zooplankton eats the one-celled plants so rapidly or perhaps because the plants secrete some sort of antibiotic that limits the animal growth.

The larger animals of the sea are either plankton eaters or carnivores; the sea has no large herbivorous animals such as the cattle, horses, zebras, and antelopes of the land. The largest of the sea animals, in fact the largest of all the animals that have ever lived, is the blue whale. One blue whale, 89 feet long, was found to weigh 120 tons. These huge mammals live entirely on zooplankton. Toothed whales, such as the sperm whale, live mainly on squid, as judged by the contents of their stomachs. The largest fish are the sharks; the basking shark and the whale shark both reach a maximum length of about 45 feet. The basking shark feeds on plankton, like the blue whale, while the whale shark feeds on small fish, such as sardines, and on squid. The bony fish are infinitely more numerous and varied than the cartilaginous types. The biggest are the tunas, the broadbill swordfish, and the marlin, all of which are consumers of smaller fish. Most numerous are members of the herring family, eaters of small crustaceans; these are the main source of revenue for commercial fishers. Some birds, such as albatrosses, shearwaters, and petrels, must be considered as sea animals since they spend most of their lives traveling and feeding over the oceans, gathering on land only to breed.

THE OCEAN DEPTHS

It was once calculated that the maximum depth in which organisms could live would be about 300 fathoms (1,800 feet) because of the great pressures below that point. Then, in 1858, one of the submarine cables that had been recently laid in the Mediterranean broke and was hauled up for repair. It had been lying at a depth of about a thousand fathoms, yet it was found to be encrusted with a variety of bottom-living animals. Actually, studies have now shown that animals can live at any depth as long as the fluids inside and outside the body are at exactly the same pressure.

(a)

6–55 *Some representative deep-water fishes. Notice how large the teeth and jaws of these fish are in relation to their sizes. Can you account for this in terms of the environment? The oceanic angler fish (a) is a female, and the structure above her eye is a parasitic male. This arrangement presumably solves the problem of finding partners in the dark. The beard of the other oceanic angler fish (b) is probably luminescent. Many of these fish are surprisingly small. For example, the fierce-looking Chanliochus slossi (c) could be held in the palm of your hand. (Courtesy of the American Museum of Natural History)*

Explorers in bathyspheres (vessels designed for deep-water exploration) have found animals at the greatest depths of the ocean, some 7 miles down.

At the ocean bottom, the world is calm and unchanging. The temperature is remarkably uniform over wide areas, usually less than 3°C. The lowest depths at which light detectable to the eyes of man can be found is about 2,000 feet. It is a pale blue light; the longer wavelengths, the reds and the oranges, are filtered out near the surface. All color values change as one goes deeper in the ocean. Many of the deep-dwelling invertebrates are reddish-colored in normal "white" light, but they appear dark and shadowy in this light from which all red has been removed.

The bottom surface is an ooze made up of the shells of diatoms and foraminifers, which have been raining steadily on the ocean bottom from the surface for millions of years. Some animals live beneath this ooze; explorers have reported seeing holes and furrows and mounds in the mud, but no one has seen the animals that left them there. The animals that live on the bottom have a variety of spikes and spines and strange appendages to keep them from sinking into the ooze. The fish that live at these great depths have jaws and teeth that are huge in proportion to their size, and some have expandable stomachs so that they are able to swallow animals larger than themselves. Food is scarce on the ocean bottom, and its inhabitants must be able to seize every opportunity. Fragile glass sponges and long-legged crabs can exist here because of the complete stillness of the water. Many of the fish are bioluminescent. The adaptive significance of these underwater lights is not known; they may serve for species and sex recognition, as they do among the fireflies. Many of the fish have very

(b)

(c)

large eyes, like owls, to permit vision at this low light intensity. Those that have small eyes have a compensating development of the olfactory organs. There are no plants, except for a few species of fungi. The ocean bottom is the exclusive realm of animals.

THE SEASHORE

The edges of the continents extend out into the sea from 10 to 150 miles. Along these edges, the *continental shelves*, life is much denser than in the open seas. Sessile animals, such as sponges, corals, and coelenterates, although they are found all over the ocean bottom, only occur in abundance close to the shores and especially in the warmer waters. Predators, such as mollusks, crustaceans, and many kinds of fish, roam over the bottoms of the continental shelves. Eel grasses and turtle grasses, which are angiosperms, and seaweeds provide shelter for myriad animals and increase the supply of oxygen. Few of the animals actually eat the grasses or seaweeds, but microscopic algae and small animals fasten themselves to them. Snails, slugs, and worms crawl over their surfaces, eating off the encrusted growth, and fish nibble the smaller animals that cling to them.

Seacoasts are of three general types: rocky, sandy, and muddy. Rocky coasts are the most stratified in their plant and animal life. Every rocky coast has a periwinkle zone, a barnacle zone, and a seaweed zone. The sandy bottom has fewer bottom dwellers because in these areas the sand is constantly shifting. Some animals, such as the crabs, can run in and out with the tides, but mollusks and the smaller arthropods must be able to withstand the alternate submergence in water and exposure to air as well

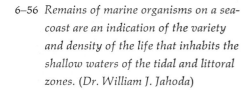

6–56 *Remains of marine organisms on a seacoast are an indication of the variety and density of the life that inhabits the shallow waters of the tidal and littoral zones. (Dr. William J. Jahoda)*

as the battering of the waves. The shell of a *Mytilus* mussel exposed to heavy surf may weigh as much as 58 grams, while the shell of an animal of the same species found in calm water will weigh only half that. Organisms avoid drying out by crawling under stones or thick algal growths, by closing their shells, by retreating into crevices, or by sealing themselves in with a plug of mucus. Among those that cannot burrow or hide, a number of different holdfast and anchoring devices have been developed. The starfish of the rocky coasts lies spread-eagled on the rocks, clinging with its suction cups. The abalone holds tight with its well-developed muscular foot. Mussels, scallops, and oysters anchor themselves to the bottom or to rocky surfaces with coarse ropelike strands which they secrete.

The mud flat, while not so rich or diverse in species as the rocky coast, is the most suitable of all three types of seacoast for animal growth. It is a constant bustle of changing activities. At low tide on the mud flats, the bottom forms retreat into their burrows and the motile forms scurry seaward. The snails continue to browse on the algae, and insects and birds come into the exposed area for prey and debris. As the tide comes in, insects and birds retreat toward the land, but the clams extend their siphons once more, the annelids rise from their burrows, and shrimps, crabs, and fish move about over the surface again. A mud flat can support tens of thousands of individuals per square meter.

THE CORAL REEF

The coral reef is the most diverse of all marine communities. The coelenterates that form the reef can grow only in warm, well-lighted surface water, where the temperature seldom falls below 21°C (70°F). The oceans are rising slowly, 4 to 6 inches every 100 years as the glaciers melt, but the upward growth of the coral keeps the reef tops in the well-lighted zone. The longest reef in the world is the Great Barrier Reef of Australia, which extends some 1,200 miles. Other reefs are found throughout the tropical waters and as far north as Bermuda, which is warmed by the Gulf Stream. The upper Keys of Florida, which begin just south of Miami, were built by coral animals during a warm period before the last glaciation. When the glacial ice built up in the north, the water level fell, exposing the upper surface of the Keys and killing the coral coelenterates.

Each polyp in the colony secretes its own calcium-containing skeleton, and when it dies, the next generation builds on top of it. The reef is not the work of the animals alone, however; symbiotic algae occur on and in the inorganic skeleton, as well as inside the bodies of the polyps. In fact, the entire colony contains about three times as much plant as animal tissue. Laboratory studies have shown that while the coral animals can live independent of the algae, algae are necessary for the rate of reef formation seen under natural conditions. The algae photosynthesize by day, contributing oxygen and organic compounds to the coral animals, and at night the carnivorous polyps extend their tentacles and capture zooplankton from the surrounding waters.

The reef furnishes both food and shelter for other sea animals. Small fish with spectacular colors and patterns graze on the coral. Among freshwater fish, color is usually seen only in males and, as in the stickleback, is associated with periods of mating and courtship. But many of the coral fish, including the females and even the babies, flaunt their bright colors constantly. According to Lorenz, these colors are the signals by which they advertise their fiercely guarded territories. In the coral bed, with its many hiding places, a higher value is placed on conspicuously advertising the limits of one's property than on concealment from predators. Nonterritorial fish that school in the waters around the coral beds are not brightly arrayed.

6–57 *The coral reef abounds in brilliantly colored fish. Apparently, the bright colors and striking patterns serve to advertise the limits of each fiercely guarded territory within the reef. (Courtesy of the American Museum of Natural History)*

The Land

The biomes of the land are usually identified in terms of the plants that grow on them. The growth of plants is regulated by a number of physical factors—the temperature, the length of the day and of the growing season, the amount of rain and when it falls, and the soil. The last, which seems so important to the home gardener, is actually the least important, since over a long period of time plants can make their own soil. The map of the vegetation of North America (Figure 6–58) illustrates how these factors work together to produce the terrestrial biomes.

First, there are definite north-south zones of vegetation: the Arctic tundra; the coniferous forests, forming a belt just south of the tundra; the deciduous forests of the temperate regions; and the tropical forests, including broad-leaved evergreen rain forests and tropical deciduous forests that lose their leaves during the dry season. All four vegetation zones occur in bands around the world. These zones are dependent largely on temperature, but as you can see by the map, they are interrupted and irregular.

6–58 *Climate, rainfall, and soil together form the patterns of vegetation around the world. In this vegetation map of North America, you can see how the major north-south zones have been modified and interrupted by conditions of soil and rainfall, particularly across the western half of the United States and Mexico. (After Wilson and Loomis, 1958)*

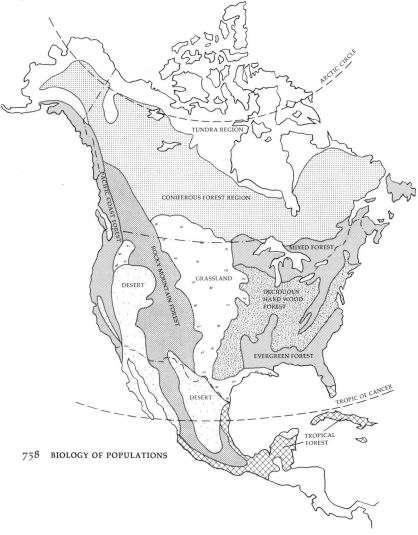

6–59 *Traveling eastward from the Pacific Ocean, moisture-laden winds encounter the high barrier of the coastal mountain ranges and are forced to rise abruptly. As they rise, they become cooled and their moisture condenses into rain or snow. Most of this moisture is deposited on the westward slopes, with a resultant dry area, a "rain shadow," being produced on the eastward slopes, where as a consequence, the desert begins.*

6–60 *Diagram showing the mean annual rainfall (vertical columns) in relation to altitude at a series of stations from Palo Alto on the Pacific coast across the Coast Range and the Sierra Nevada. Notice the rain shadows on the landward side of the two mountain ranges.*

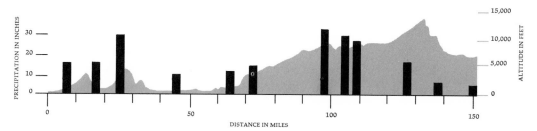

The second major pattern, superimposed upon the first, is caused by rainfall. The western half of the United States offers one of the simplest models of how the vegetation is regulated by rainfall. (See Figures 6–59 and 6–60.) When the moisture-laden winds moving in from the Pacific reach the coastal ranges, they rise, cool, and spill out a deluge of rain on the westward slopes. As much as 12 feet of rain a year fall on the Olympic rain forest in the Olympic Peninsula in Washington. In this dank, dripping, dark-green world, the trees grow to truly olympian heights and moss lies inches thick on the ground, hangs from the trees and shrubs, and climbs the tree trunks. The prevailing winds, traveling eastward, also hit the Cascade–Sierra Nevada system (the "Snowy Range"), dropping

759 *The Plants and Animals at Home*

6–61 *The Olympic rain forest, a result of the heavy rainfall precipitated from the moisture-laden winds off the Pacific. As much as 12 feet of rain a year fall on this forest. In the water-soaked soil, the roots of even the biggest trees are shallow, going down into the ground only about 3 feet. For this reason, uprooting is common, and rotting logs are everywhere. These logs usually provide the nourishment for new tree growth since the tree seedlings cannot compete with ground plants for nourishment from the earth. The young trees on the right have had their beginnings in rotten logs. (Dr. Virgil Argo)*

another cargo of rain. On the westward slopes of these mountains, giant sequoias and other huge forest trees loom, but on the eastward slopes, in the *rain shadow*, the plains and the desert begin. The winds, now dry, sweep over the great central basin of the United States; most of the moisture they collect is carried with them until they reach the western slopes of the Appalachians. On the eastern coast, the pattern is not so simple, since air above the land receives moisture not only from the Atlantic Ocean but also from the Gulf of Mexico, the Mississippi River, and the Great Lakes and thus is not so dependent upon the ocean winds. Furthermore, other factors, chiefly man and fire, have greatly changed the patterns of vegetation.

The third major pattern is the result of glaciers. Four times in the Cenozoic period, much of the land was scraped clear of life by these ice sheets, and four times, in the wake of the retreating glaciers, the bare land was reclaimed by forests. Technically, we are still living in an ice age since there are great continental glaciers covering much of Antarctica and Greenland.

THE TUNDRA

The Arctic tundra extends from the line of perpetual ice and snow, at the southern edge of the northern glacier, to the tree line, forming a continuous belt around North America and Eurasia. It is a vast expanse of treeless vegetation. Even if trees could withstand the cold air, they could not grow on the tundra because the ground is permanently frozen a few

6–62 *A tenth of the earth's land surface, 5 million square miles, is Arctic tundra. Extending from the northern tree line to the shores of the Arctic Ocean, the tundra forms a belt of treeless vegetation around the North Pole. This picture shows the tundra during the brief Arctic summer, a scant eight weeks of above-freezing temperatures. (Urban C. Nelson, U.S. Fish and Wildlife Service)*

6–63 *One of the few birds that never leaves the tundra, the ptarmigan is white in winter but changes to brown for the summer and gray for autumn. (Courtesy of the Canadian Government Travel Bureau)*

inches below the surface. During the summer, the ground commonly thaws to a depth of a few inches and becomes wet and soggy; in winter, it freezes again to the top. The growing season is so short that many of the plants only set seed occasionally, and much of the reproduction is vegetative. All the plants—lichens, grasses, sedges, and dwarf willows—are small, stunted, and compact, resistant to the wind and snow.

The alpine tundra, the region above the tree line on mountains, is much the same as the Arctic tundra, confirming the conclusion that the character of the vegetation is determined by such environmental conditions as low temperatures, constant wind, unstable soil, and too much or too little water—conditions that all tundras have in common.

The largest animals of the Arctic tundra are the caribou of North America and the reindeer of the Old World. Lemmings, small furry rodents with short tails, and ptarmigans, which are pigeon-sized grouse, feed off the tundra. The ptarmigan is one of the few birds that lives year around on the tundra. It is also notable because it has not just two, but three changes of wardrobe to suit the season—drab brown for summer, gray for autumn, and white for winter (Figure 6–63). The white fox and the snowy owl of the Arctic live largely on the lemmings.

During the brief Arctic summer, insects emerge in great numbers; the most numerous, or at least the most memorable from the point of view of human visitors, are the devastating hordes of mosquitoes, blackflies, and deerflies. Migratory birds visit in the summer to take advantage of

761 *The Plants and Animals at Home*

the insect hordes and the long periods of daylight. With the approach of winter, however, the land becomes almost deserted again. The insects become dormant, mainly in immature stages. The voles and other small mammals retreat to nests or runways, the ptarmigans tunnel into the snowbanks, and the caribou move slowly southward to the edges of the coniferous forest.

THE CONIFEROUS FOREST

Below the tundra, the northern coniferous forest, the *taiga*, stretches across both North America and Eurasia. This forest is composed of needle-leafed coniferous evergreens—pine, spruce, and hemlock. A thick layer of needles and dead twigs, matted together by fungus mycelium, covers the ground. Along the stream banks grow tamarack, willow, birch, alder, and poplar.

The principal large animals of the coniferous forest are moose and muledeer. Among the smaller animals are porcupines, red-backed mice, snowshoe hares, shrews, wolverines, lynxes, warblers, and grouse. The small animals use the dense growths of the evergreens for breeding and for shelter. Wolves feed upon these smaller mammals, rarely attacking the larger ones such as caribou and deer, and then usually only those that are sick or wounded. The black bear and grizzly bear eat everything—leaves, buds, fruits, nuts, berries, fish, the supplies of campers, and occasionally the flesh of other mammals. Porcupines are bark eaters, and many seriously damage trees by girdling them. Other herbivorous animals of the forest, of

6–64 *Interior of a virgin coniferous forest of Engelmann spruce in Colorado. (Courtesy of the U.S. Forest Service)*

which the moose is the most conspicuous, are largely browsers. Insects feed on the conifers. Spruce budworms and needle-eating caterpillars are found everywhere.

The coniferous forest on its southern border blends into the deciduous hardwood forest, which is slowly moving northward as the temperature rises.

THE DECIDUOUS FOREST

Deciduous forests occupy areas of abundant rainfall and moderate temperatures which change with the seasons. These forests once covered most of eastern North America, as well as most of Europe, part of Japan and Australia, and the tip of South America. In the United States, only scattered patches of the original forest still remain.

About 90 percent of the forest ground is shaded by the canopy of the taller trees. There is usually an understory of smaller trees and shrubs, also deciduous. These increase at the forest edge, where they can get more sunlight. The flowers of the forest, which may carpet the floor in the spring, are early bloomers, catching the sun before it is obscured by the new leaves of the canopy.

The forest floor is covered with a dense layer of leaves in various stages of decay. Beneath these leaves is the soil of the forest, a rich humus, or topsoil. Such soil is composed largely of organic material—the decomposing parts of plants, and insects and other animals—and the bacteria, protozoans, fungi, worms, and arthropods that live on this organic mat-

6–65 *Interior of a temperate-zone deciduous forest of sugar maple, basswood, and American elm in Wisconsin. (Courtesy of the U.S. Forest Service)*

763   *The Plants and Animals at Home*

ter. The roots of plants penetrate the earth to depths measurable in feet and add organic matter to the soil when they die. Carnivorous arthropods carry fragments of their prey to considerable depths in the soil. The myriad passageways left by the dead roots and by the earthworms and other small animals that inhabit the forest make the soil into a sponge that holds the water and minerals.

The dominant trees of the deciduous forests vary from region to region, depending largely on the local rainfall. In the northern and upland regions, oak, birch, beech, and maple are the most prominent trees. Before the chestnut blight struck North America, an oak-chestnut forest ran from Cape Ann, Massachusetts, and the Mohawk River Valley of New York to the southern end of the Appalachian highland. The Great Smoky Mountains of North Carolina and Tennessee (named for the wisps of fog and haze that hover over them constantly) are the home of 130 species of trees. Each time the glacier moved down the face of the continent, trees were forced southwards, adding new species to the ancient forest of the Great Smokies, which the glaciers did not reach. Maple and basswood predominate in Wisconsin and Minnesota, and maple and beech in Southern Michigan, becoming mixed with hemlock and white pine as the forest moves southward. The southern and lowland regions have forests of oak and hickory.

The rich harvest of the fruits, nuts, leaves, bark, stems, seeds, and seedlings supports an abundance of animal life, far more species and in-

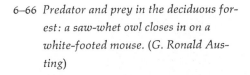

6–66 *Predator and prey in the deciduous forest: a saw-whet owl closes in on a white-footed mouse.* (G. Ronald Austing)

dividuals than can be found among the conifers to the north. There are many more mammals. The smaller mammals, such as the chipmunk, vole, squirrel, racoon, oppossum, shrew, and white-footed mouse, live mainly on the nuts and fruits of the forest. The wolves, bobcats, gray foxes, and mountain lions, in the areas where they have not been driven out by the encroachments of civilization, feed on these smaller mammals. Deer live mainly on the forest borders, where shrubs and seedlings grow.

Except in the winter, the forest is a noisy place. Here vision is often less important than hearing since visibility is limited. In the spring, birds proclaim their territories, chipmunks and squirrels chatter and call. Frogs and insects chorus through the summer nights. When autumn comes, a hush begins to fall over the forest. Often, more than three-quarters of the birds leave for the winter. Those that remain abandon their territories and gather in flocks, seeking shelter on the lee side of the forest or in the river valleys. The mammals den up in hollow logs or trees during the coldest periods. Woodchucks and bats hibernate in the true sense, with their body temperatures dropping almost to freezing and all their metabolic processes slowing down. Bears, larded with fat, maintain their body temperature but stay in a state of winter torpor, during which their cubs are born. Chipmunks nap and doze, waking up from time to time to eat their stores of nuts. Most insects and other invertebrates move out of the trees and shrubs and migrate down into the forest floor; many species survive only in the egg or other immature stages. The deer move into the forest from its borders to seek shelter, grazing on the buds and bark of forest trees and on cedar foliage and twigs. Each hair in a deer's winter coat is hollow and filled with air, acting as a thermal blanket to hold in the warmth of its body.

SOUTHERN FORESTS

South of the oak-hickory deciduous forests grow the pine forests of the southern states, beginning in New Jersey and spreading south and west until they merge with the grasslands beyond the Mississippi Delta. In moist locations, southern hardwoods, which are evergreen trees—tupelo, live oak, magnolia, bay, holly, and cypress—grow through the pinewoods. The magnolia forest extends along the Gulf and Atlantic Coasts from east Texas to central South Carolina, including most of the Florida peninsula. Wolves no longer inhabit the forest, but bears and mountain lions are found there occasionally, and deer still abound. As one travels southward, chameleons and spadefoot toads are encountered. Along the coasts, the forest merges with the salt and brackish water marshes and, in the lower Mississippi Valley and near other sluggish or still fresh water, with the cypress swamps (Figure 6–67).

6–67 *Standing in water, cypress trees anchor themselves in the spongy soil with buttressed trunks and long thick roots. The trees are large—some as tall as 120 feet. (Courtesy of the U.S. Department of Agriculture)*

6–68 *Heavy stand of Douglas fir on the west side of the Cascade Mountains in Pierce County, Washington. The small trees are hemlocks. (A. Gaskil, U.S. Forest Service)*

THE PACIFIC COAST

The Pacific Coast, like the Great Smokies, escaped the glaciers, and the northern Pacific forest is a very ancient one. In Alaska, it is composed largely of hemlock and Sitka spruce. Between British Columbia and Oregon, the Douglas fir is the dominant tree (Figure 6–68). In southern Oregon and northern California are found the coastal redwoods. *Sequoia sempervirens*, the "always green" redwood, has a life-span of more than 2,000 years (Figure 6–69). Nearly all these redwoods grow within 20 miles of the ocean. The trees of the Pacific forests are all very tall, taller than those of the deciduous forests. The tallest living specimen of redwood measures 359 feet, 4 inches! Douglas firs range up to 260 feet tall and 50 feet in circumference.

Giant Sequoias

The giant sequoia, *Sequoiadendron giganteum*, occurs only on the western slopes of the Sierra Nevada. (See Figure 6–70.) Some of these trees are known to be more than 2,000 years old. At one time, they were thought to be a climax species, but recent studies have shown that these forests, too, may owe their existence to fires that cleared the ground of the seedlings of other trees while leaving the thick-barked sequoias virtually unharmed. Most of the ancient trees have extensive fire scars. In one of the groves that was studied in detail, 18 large fires, started either by lightning or by man, occurred between 1760 and 1889. Borings into the trees, which reveal

6–69 *Old-growth coastal redwoods (Sequoia sempervirens) in Del Norte County, California. The undergrowth of dense ferns and scattered evergreen huckleberry is typical of these forests. Some of these trees may be as much as 2,000 years old. (Dan Todd, U.S. Forest Service)*

6–70 *Giant sequoia (Sequoiadendron giganteum) in the Sierra Nevada in California. Known as the Frank Boole tree, it is the lone surviving big tree in an area logged in the 1860s. Its circumference is 112 feet, and its height is 269 feet. (Norman L. Norris, U.S. Forest Service)*

the annual rings, show that each of the fires was followed by a growth spurt. The forest has been fire-free since that time, and now trees such as the fir are moving in, making the shade so dense that the young sequoias cannot grow. For, despite the enormous size of the parent tree, sequoia seeds are small, and small seeds have only a slight chance of getting started in dense shade since the amount of stored food material in them permits only a short growth of seed roots.

Chaparral

Some of the mountain slopes in central and southern California and adjacent states are occupied by the vegetation type known as *chaparral*. Part of the land along the slopes is used for orchards, but where native vegetation exists, it consists of thickets of dry, leathery-leaved evergreen shrubs. Similar communities, with similar conditions of winter rainfall and hot dry summers, are found along the shores of the Mediterranean and along the southern coast of Australia. Mule deer live in the chaparral during the spring growing season, moving out to cooler regions during the summer. The resident vertebrates—brush rabbits, wood rats, lizards, and brown towhees—are generally small and dull-colored, matching the finely branched, dull-colored vegetation. As the vegetation dries in the late summer, fires may sweep the slopes. Following a fire, many chaparral shrubs sprout vigorously, while others seed abundantly on the burned ground.

767   *The Plants and Animals at Home*

Much of the center of the country, where the rainfall is lower than in the forest areas, is covered with grasslands. These fertile lands have played an important part in the evolution of man, and many anthropologists believe that modern man could not have existed had the grasslands not come first. All our principal food plants have evolved by natural or artificial selection from grasses. The grasslands also are the chief support for other terrestrial life. Most of the vegetation of the forest remains as vegetation year after year, but the grasses of the open plains are used to a large extent as animal fodder, supporting the buffalo of early America, the gazelles and zebras of the African veld, the wild horses of the Asiatic steppes, and now the domestic herbivores raised by man. These large grass-eating mammals, in turn, support the carnivores, such as the lions, tigers, and wolves, as well as omnivorous man.

The large animals graze in herds to afford some protection on the open plains, while the smaller mammals, such as the ground squirrels, prairie dogs, and gophers, burrow underground. The herds of grazing animals serve, as do the ground fires, to maintain the nature of the landscape. Shrubs and trees that venture into the prairies are eaten as seedlings. In nature, the land is usually protected by the carnivores from overgrazing, but man has sometimes permitted sheep and cattle to destroy the roots and trample the ground to the point where the grasses can no longer recover.

6–71 *A food chain on the African veld. The grasses of the open plains support the large grass-eating mammals, such as the zebras shown here, and these, in turn, support the carnivores, represented by the two lions in the foreground. (R. D. Estes)*

6–72 *A group of giant saguaro cacti. The largest of the desert plants, saguaros may grow as tall as 50 feet and weigh as much as 10 tons, four-fifths of it water. The saguaro's roots are wide and shallow, enabling it to soak up moisture from a wide area after a downpour. The thick, cylindrical form exposes a minimum of evaporating surface to air and light, and the spiny surface discourages thirsty animals. Fluted like an accordion, the stem can expand quickly when the plant takes up water and contract as it uses up the stored water. (Courtesy of the U.S. Department of Agriculture)*

THE DESERT

The life of the desert depends on occasional rainbursts. The giant saguaro cacti of the American desert, for example, may grow as tall as 50 feet and weigh as much as 10 tons. These cacti have no tap roots but spread out thin disklike networks reaching for yards around them just below the ground. When a rain falls, they can quickly take up water from a wide area, swelling visibly and sometimes absorbing as much as a ton of water from one rainfall, after which they may live as long as a year before the next rain. The mesquite bushes, on the other hand, have very deep root systems, penetrating 30 to 100 feet into the ground to the underlying water. These larger desert plants are characteristically spaced out, as in an orchard; if they were closer together, all might die from lack of water. Some studies have indicated that antibiotics produced by the roots inhibit the roots of other species and thus may play a part in the spacing of the desert plants. Some desert plants pass through an entire annual cycle within a few weeks after a single rainfall, producing seeds that may not germinate for several years, that is, until enough rain falls again.

The animals that live in the desert have special adaptations to this way of life. Reptiles and insects, for example, have waterproof outer coverings and dry excretions. The few mammals of the desert are small and nocturnal and get what little water they require from the plants they eat. One of the most remarkable adaptations is seen in the desert species of the spadefoot toad. Most amphibians require two or three months for their metamorphosis, but the desert spadefoot must complete transformation from egg to young toad before its birthplace, a rain puddle, becomes a mudhole in the searing sun. The tiny spadefoot has been observed to progress from egg to tadpole to small hopping toadlet in only 9 1/2 days.

THE RAIN FOREST

The richest and most diverse of all terrestrial biomes is the tropical rain forest. The naturalist Marston Bates describes it as a great green cathedral of towering evergreens, strangely silent. Little light touches the floor of the rain forest. There is no accumulation of pine needles, as in the coniferous forest, or of fallen, rotting leaves and humus, as in the deciduous forest. Decomposition is too rapid; everything that touches the ground disappears —carried off, consumed, or decomposed. In many places, the ground is actually bare. Areas of tropical rain forest have sometimes been cut down in the belief that the ground would support rich gardens, but always the ground has proved barren and infertile, unlike the ground of the desert, for example, which may be rich in long-accumulated minerals and need only water to bring it to life. The taller trees reach an average height of about 150 feet (higher than in the deciduous forest, where trees average

6–73 *The edge of a tropical rain forest in Puerto Rico. (Bluford W. Muir, U.S. Forest Service)*

only about 100 feet, but not so tall as in the forests of the Pacific Northwest).

The rain forest is far richer in species than most other forests. No plant or tree is likely to be the same as its neighbors. In North Queensland, Australia, 141 different species were found among the 1,261 trees counted on 1 1/4 acres. (The count for a similar area in the temperate zone would be 10 to 15 species.) Bates tells of finding 18 different species of swallowtail butterflies within a 10-minute walk from his home in tropical South America; in all the United States, there are only 20 species of swallowtails, and some of these are sporadic migrants. Food is plentiful, termites and fruits providing the richest diet. Insects abound, eating the plants and one another and providing food for birds, amphibians, reptiles, and small mammals. In a 6-square-mile area in the Panama Canal Zone, some 20,000 different species of insects were catalogued.

Many animals whose temperate-zone relatives live on the ground are tree dwellers in these tropics. Plants live on other plants. Snails climb to the topmost branches. The large leathery leaves of pineapplelike plants growing high in the branches form cups in which pools of water accumulate, and in these pools can be found protozoans, rotifers, aquatic arthropods, and small amphibians completing their metamorphoses. Some frogs are entirely arboreal, gluing their eggs to leaves or carrying them on their backs. In these frogs, the tadpole stage is passed before the eggs hatch. Such birds as parrots, toucans, and trogons nest in holes.

Insects that complete only one generation a year in the temperate zone rush through their life cycles in a month in the tropics. Cold-blooded animals reach their largest sizes here. In the Amazon forest, there are spiders large enough to feed on the small birds that get caught in their webs. Some moths have a wingspread of almost a foot. Millipedes may be some 10 inches long, and slugs almost that large.

In past geologic ages, before the glaciers came, the tropical rain forests may have extended over great areas of the world, and it is believed that they may represent the point of origin for many groups of plants and animals.

The Inland Waters

The freshwater habitat is nearly as old as the planet itself, but each existing lake, pond, river, and stream is comparatively young. One of the oldest lakes in the world, Lake Baikal in eastern Siberia, was formed in the Meso-

---

THE WORLD'S OLDEST LAKE

Lake Baikal in Siberia holds one-fifth of the world's lake water, and because it is the oldest body of fresh water in the world (about 25 million years old), it is a veritable museum of unique species. More than a thousand varieties of plants and animals are found only at Baikal. Over the millions of years, they have found special ways to thrive in its cold mineral-free water.

Some of the most peculiar habits of Baikal's fish derive from the vast quantities of crustaceans in the lake. To protect their eggs from these predators, some fish, such as the omul, breed in tributary rivers. Others, like the Baikal perch and pike, lay eggs that are poisonous or evil-smelling to the crustaceans. A fish called the golomyanka, which lives hundreds of feet below the surface, gives birth to living young—about 2,000 of them at a time! Another species, Cottus inermis, places its eggs under stones for protection; the male has evolved enormous side fins that he spreads over the stones.

Specialists in limnology (the study of freshwater lakes) have been disturbed about the possibility of the waters of Lake Baikal becoming polluted by the discharge of waste materials from an enormous pulp factory recently erected on the lakeshore. It is feared that any change in the chemistry of the water will render many of the lake's unique species extinct. Further, if the temperature is raised by factory discharge, predators now kept out of the lake by its frigidity will invade and annihilate many of the hundreds of crustacean varieties peculiar to the lake.

---

771   *The Plants and Animals at Home*

zoic era, the age of reptiles. It is more than a mile deep at its deepest point. In Lake Baikal, 98 percent of the 384 species of arthropods are found nowhere else, and 81 percent of the 36 species of fish are also endemic. Because of its high proportion of unique species, this lake is often called "the Australia of fresh water."

LAKES AND PONDS

If you look at a map of North America, you will see that nearly all the lakes are in the northern part of the United States and in Canada. These lakes are traces of the last glaciation, formed in the scratches and recesses scraped on the face of the continent by the glaciers. In a geologic sense, therefore, they are relatively young. Ponds range in life-span from a few weeks or months, in the case of small, seasonal ponds, to several hundred years.

Like the oceans, lakes and large ponds contain three distinct environments, or zones: (1) the *littoral zone* along the shore, in which rooted vegetation lives; (2) the *limnetic zone* of open water, dominated by plankton; and (3) the deep-water *profundal zone*. (See Figure 6–74.)

Lakes in temperate regions tend to become thermally stratified in the summer and again in winter as the upper layer of water is alternately heated and cooled. Water increases in density as its temperature drops until just above freezing (4°C). Therefore, in the summer, the upper part of the lake will consist of a layer of water which has been heated by the sun, and the denser, cold water will form a bottom layer. In winter, the coldest water (below 4°C) will remain on top, and the slightly warmer water will sink to the bottom. This stratification effectively seals off the depths from any contact with air. Further, the nutrients derived from the organic debris that collects on the lake bottom cannot rise to the surface. Consequently, during the summer and winter, the supply of oxygen in the profundal zone and of nutrients in the limnetic zone may run short, imposing special stresses on the inhabitants of these zones. In the spring and fall, when the entire body of water approaches the same temperature, mixing again occurs, often resulting in "blooms" of phytoplankton.

Fresh water is variable in its dissolved chemicals. If an organism is moved from one lake to another, it may pass from almost pure water to water more saline than that of the sea or to water with completely different proportions of ions. For example, the calcium content varies greatly from lake to lake, and the animal life of "soft-water" lakes is often very different from that of lakes with a high content of calcium. Mollusks are almost nonexistent in Michigan lakes because the amount of available calcium in the water is so low that there is not enough for them to build their shells with. There is also great variation in the size and degree of isolation of lakes. Small lakes, ponds, and streams, which are more

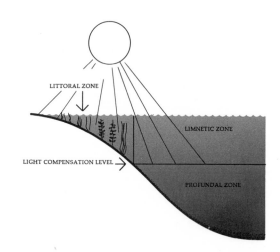

6–74 *The three major zones of a lake.*

LITTORAL ZONE

LIMNETIC ZONE

LIGHT COMPENSATION LEVEL

PROFUNDAL ZONE

likely to dry up than larger ones, present the organisms with a choice of hibernation or emigration. Some freshwater organisms, such as algae, bacteria, fungi, and most of the invertebrates, probably evolved from sea plants and animals. However, one large group of animals—the insects—invaded from land. Their wax coatings, which keep moisture in on land, serve equally well to keep salts in or water out, and thus they do not expend much energy maintaining an osmotic balance. Insects that can fly are able to emigrate if the water dries up.

Many insects have special adaptations for the aquatic life. For example, the whirligig beetle, which skims along the surface, has eyes that are divided into two parts like bifocal eyeglasses, one-half for seeing above the water and one-half for seeing below. Some insects dive beneath the surface to feed and periodically surface for air. Air-breathing insects are so buoyant that they must cling to vegetation or some other object to remain submerged. They carry a bubble of air with them so that they can stay below longer, surfacing only every two or three minutes to renew their supply of air.

In large lakes, phytoplankton is usually the only plant life found in the limnetic zones. The zooplankton that feeds upon it is made up of small crustaceans, which also form part of the zooplankton of the ocean. In these small animals, as in the algae, rapid proliferation is the key to survival, and mating has been largely eliminated as an unadaptive waste of time. Cladocera, such as *Daphnia*, may produce either sexually or parthenogenetically. So long as the temperature is favorable, the eggs all develop without fertilization and they all become females. Only when there is a drastic change in the environment, such as drop in temperature, a change in the oxygen content of the water, or a decrease in the food supply, will any of the eggs become males. The females then mate and after mating produce winter eggs, which have a resistant shell and are capable of surviving in a dry pond. Copepods do not reproduce parthenogenetically, but the female is able to store enough sperm at one copulation to last for many batches of eggs. In both cases, the females are able to act as very productive and almost completely independent egg factories.

The water of lakes is less clear than that of the ocean, so the depth at which phytoplankton can grow is even more limited. As a result of this lack of plant productivity and also because of the oxygen deprivation discussed earlier, there is little animal life at the bottom of large lakes.

The edge of the lake is its most productive zone. Here the most abundant and conspicuous plants are seed plants, which are rooted to the bottom, such as cattails and rushes. Water lilies grow farther out from shore; their roots are fastened to the bottom, but their leaves spread out on the surface, shading the water. The duckweeds, also seed plants, are not rooted and float on the top, but other pond weeds grow entirely beneath

6–75 *The water beetle feeds beneath the surface but must rise periodically for air. In order to prolong its stay underwater, it carries a bubble of air down with it. (Dr. Ross E. Hutchins)*

|———— 10mm ————|

6–76 *A giant water bug feeds on a water snake which it has just killed. The snake is 8 inches long! (Dr. Ross E. Hutchins)*

the water. In many lakes, one can almost see the land taking over the water as the plants creep inward.

At the edges of ponds and lakes, snails, small arthropods, and mosquito larvae feed upon the plants. Other insects, such as the larvae of the dragonfly and damselfly, and the water scorpion are carnivorous. Clams, worms, snails, and still other insect larvae burrow in the mud. Frogs, salamanders, water turtles, and water snakes are found almost exclusively in these littoral zones, where they feed largely upon the insects and other small animals. Fish, too, are more abundant along the lake margins. Ducks, geese, and herons feed on the plants, the insects, the mollusks, the fish, and the amphibians; and otters, muskrats, and beavers live in the water and along the marshy edges.

There is no clear-cut line of demarcation between lake and pond. Ponds are smaller and, as a consequence, are likely to resemble the edge of the lake in their composition rather than the far less fertile central area. However, they are even more subject to the hazards of drying up, and organisms in such environments must be able either to move out of the water or to survive in a dormant stage during the dry periods. Because of their productivity, their relatively small size, and their accessibility, ponds are among the most popular of the ecosystems analyzed by ecologists.

STREAMS AND RIVERS

In flowing-water ecosystems, there are two major zones: (1) *rapids zones*, where the current keeps the bottom clear of silt and other loose materials and where the bottom, therefore, is generally firm; and (2) *pool zones*, where the bottom is soft because comparatively still water allows silt and other loose materials to settle on it.

The conditions of existence in these two zones are very different, and therefore the communities that inhabit them are different. In pool zones, the communities are similar to those found in ponds. The species of fish and aquatic insects are much the same as those that occupy ponds and lakes, and also, as in the limnetic zones of ponds and lakes, a considerable development of phytoplankton may occur. The life in the hard-bottom rapid zones, on the other hand, is composed of more unique and specialized forms—such as the net-spinning caddis (the larva of the caddis fly), which constructs a fine silk net to catch food particles in the flowing waters.

BIOLOGICAL REGULATION OF THE COMMUNITY

Ecological Succession

Ecological succession is the process by which a community goes through a number of temporary developmental stages before arriving at a final, sta-

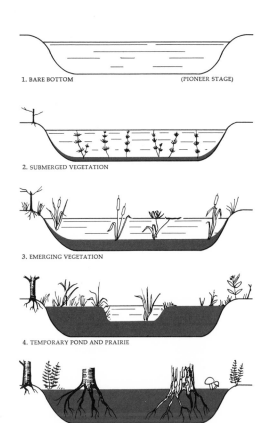

1. BARE BOTTOM (PIONEER STAGE)

2. SUBMERGED VEGETATION

3. EMERGING VEGETATION

4. TEMPORARY POND AND PRAIRIE

5. BEECH AND MAPLE FOREST (CLIMAX STAGE)

6–77 *An example of primary succession: a pond at the south end of Lake Michigan gradually becomes a forest. (After Buchsbaum, 1957)*

ble condition. The successive stages may be entirely different in structure and function from the community that eventually develops on the site, just as many organisms go through different stages before reaching adulthood.

The pattern of succession is determined by the physical environment but is not caused by it. Ecological succession is *community-controlled*; that is, each temporary community changes the local conditions of temperature, light, etc., and thereby sets up favorable conditions for the next temporary community. When the site has been modified as much as possible by biological processes, a steady state develops—at least in theory.

These stages of succession are known as the *seral stages*, or *sere*, and the final, stable state is the *climax*. When succession begins on a sterile area or on one not previously occupied by a similar community, it is called *primary succession*. For example, primary succession occurs when a pond slowly fills up to become a bog or a meadow (Figure 6–77). *Secondary succession* takes place on a site which once housed a similar community or where conditions of existence are already favorable, such as abandoned croplands or cutover forests.

In regions where the climate or some other physical factor is particularly severe, such as the desert or the tundra, the seral stages are short since the community cannot modify the harsh physical environment to any great extent. Climatic cycles, storms, etc., are likely to interfere sooner or later, and often the climax stage is never reached. In the Arctic, for example, succession goes on all the time on a seral basis; the changing of the seasons prevents a stable condition from ever developing.

PRIMARY SUCCESSION: LAKE SHORE

An example of primary succession is given in Table 6–7, which shows the various developmental stages between initial growth and climax forest in a community on the Lake Michigan shore. Lake Michigan was once much larger; in retreating, it left successively younger and younger sand dunes. One can see the pioneer stages at the lake shore and the increasingly older stages as one proceeds away from the shore. The climax community is the stable final community, self-perpetuating and in equilibrium with its physical environment.

SECONDARY SUCCCESSION: FOREST

If a farmer abandons a plowed field, numerous plants attempt to invade it, bombarding it with their seeds, and it is captured by those which can germinate most quickly. In an open field, these are the plants that can survive the sunlight and drying winds—weeds and grasses and such trees as cedars, white pines, poplars, and birch. For a while, these plants rule the forest, but eventually they eliminate themselves since their seedlings can-

775 *The Plants and Animals at Home*

Table 6–7 *Ecological Succession of Plants and Invertebrates on the Lake Michigan Dunes (After Shelford, 1913)*

Invertebrates of ground strata	Seral Stages				
	Cottonwood—beach grass	Jack-pine forest	Black-oak dry forest	Oak and oak-hickory moist forest	Climax beech-maple forest
White tiger beetle (*Cicindela lepida*)	• •				
Sand spider (*Trochosa cinerea*)	• •				
White grasshopper (*Trimerotropis maritima*)	• •				
Long-horn grasshopper (*Psinidia fenestralis*)	• •	• •			
Burrowing spider (*Geolycosa pikei*)	• •	• •			
Digger wasps (*Bembex* and *Microbembex*)	• •	• •			
Bronze tiger beetle (*Cicindela*)		• •			
Ant (*Lasius niger*)		• •			
Migratory locust (*Melanoplus*)		• •			
Sand locusts (*Ageneotettix* and *Spharagemon*)		• •			
Digger wasp (*Sphex*)		• •	• •		
Ant-lion (*Cryptoleon*)			• •		
Flatbug (*Neuroctenus*)			• •		
Grasshoppers (six species not listed above)			• •		
Wireworms (Elateridae)			• •		
Snail (*Mesodon thyroides*)			• •		
Green tiger beetle (*C. sexguttata*)				• •	• •
Millipedes (*Fontaria* and *Spirobolus*)				• •	• •
Centipedes (*Lithobius, Geophilus, Lysiopetalum*)				• •	• •
Camel cricket (*Ceuthophilus*)				• •	• •
Ants (*Camponotus, Lasius umbratus*)				• •	• •
Betsy beetle (*Passalus*)				• •	• •
Sowbugs (*Porcellio*)				• •	• •
Earthworms (Lumbricidae)				• •	• •
Woodroaches (Blattidae)				• •	• •
Grouse locust (Tettigidae)				• •	• •
Cranefly larvae (Tipulidae)				• •	• •
Wood snails (seven species not found in previous stages)					• •

not compete in the shade cast by the parent trees. Some seedlings can thrive in partial shade, however—for instance, oaks, red maples, white ash, and tulip trees. As the forest matures, these trees grow tall, and finally they shut out so much light that even their own seedlings cannot grow. Eventually, the only young trees that can grow in the forest are those that can survive in the dimmest light, such as the hemlock, beech, and sugar maple, and these ultimately take over the forest. Nothing else can compete with them in the conditions that have been established. This is the *climax forest*. Forests in all stages of succession can be found throughout the United States.

Fire

In some areas of the country, fire plays an important part in determining the climax stage in forest succession. Young seedlings of deciduous trees are very susceptible to fire, while pines are resistant to it. Jack pines, in fact, open their cones and release their seeds only after they have been heated, so they tend to spread most readily after a fire. In the woods of the south and in the northern lake area, recurrent ground fires maintain the pinewoods, keeping the forest perpetually young. It is important, however, to distinguish between the light ground fires, characteristic of the fire-type ecosystem, and the uncontrolled crown fires of northern forests, which spread through the tree tops, destroying entire communities of plants and animals and leaving the ground barren.

6–78 *This aspen forest in New Mexico offers an example of a seral stage in forest succession. Can you explain what is happening here? (Rex King, U.S. Forest Service)*

777   *The Plants and Animals at Home*

6–79 *In the nitrogen cycle, the overall amount of nitrogen remains the same even though the materials circulate over and over again in the ecosystem. The circulation of nitrogen between organisms and environment is shown in* (a). *In* (b), *the same basic steps are arranged in an ascending-descending series to distinguish steps which require energy from those which release energy.* (After Odum, 1959)

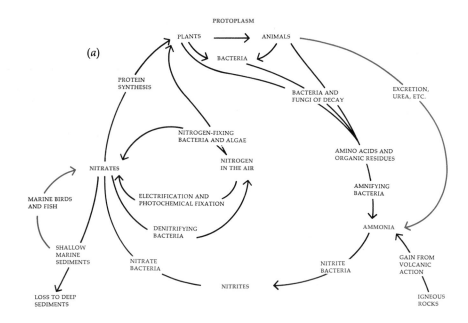

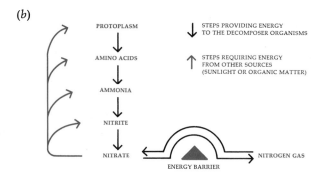

Energy Flow in Ecosystems

ENERGY AND MATERIALS

Ecological systems are generally recognized as having four constituents: (1) nonliving compounds, both organic and inorganic; (2) "producers," or plants; (3) consumers, largely animals that digest producers or other consumers; and (4) decomposers, chiefly bacteria and fungi that break down the complex organic substances of dead organisms and release them back into the environment, where they can be used by the consumers. (See Figure 6–79.)

Each of the four components may affect all the others. For instance, soils differ in the minerals they contain, and this difference in mineral content, in turn, affects not only the plants but the animals. Studies were made, for example, of the comparative weights of thousands of rabbits caught by farm boys in various areas of Missouri. Rabbits from the more fertile northwest weighed one-third more than those from the south. Furthermore, the large leg bones of the northern rabbits had a breaking strength 37 percent greater than those of the animals from the poorer land.

The materials of which living organisms are composed—nitrogen, carbon, water, etc.—may circulate many times between living and nonliving entities and may be used over and over again. Energy, on the other hand, flows through a community, just as it flows through an organism, only once. The *one-way flow of energy* and the *circulation of materials* are fundamental principles of the physical universe (the "laws" of entropy and of conservation of matter) and apply to all organisms in all environments.

FOOD CHAINS

Most of the energy coming in from the sun is degraded into heat energy, but in areas of land and water where plants occur, a small portion of it is turned into food energy—plant protoplasm, starch, sugar, and cellulose. This food energy is transferred from organism to organism in a series of repeated stages of eating and being eaten that is known as the *food chain*. In the food chain, there are three, and sometimes four, *trophic levels*. Green plants (the producers) occupy the first trophic level; plant eaters (primary consumers), the second level; carnivores that eat the herbivores (secondary consumers), the third level; and carnivores that eat the secondary consumers, the fourth level.

In Figure 6–80, you can see the flow of energy through the food chain. Only about half of the average sunlight that reaches the green plants is

6–80 *The flow of energy through the food chain. The boxes represent the standing crop of organisms in the community, and the pipes indicate the energy flow. Only about half of the sunlight reaching green plants is absorbed by their photosynthetic machinery, and only a small portion of the absorbed energy (about 1º/o) is converted into food energy. Only about 10º/o of the food energy in the plant (or 0.05º/o of the total light energy) is passed on to the herbivore.*

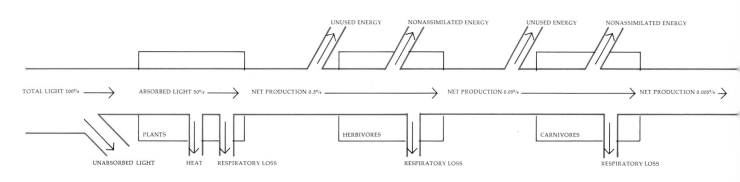

779   The Plants and Animals at Home

6–81 *Ecological pyramids of numbers, show-*
ing the quantitative relationships of
producers and consumers in the three
major types of food webs found in
nature. In (a), the primary producers
are small, and so a large quantity of
them is required to support the
herbivores that feed on them. In (b),
the primary producers are large (for
instance, trees) and an individual can
support many herbivores. An inverted
pyramid with plants as the primary pro-
ducers and small hyperparasites (para-
sites of other parasites) as the secondary
consumers is shown in (c).

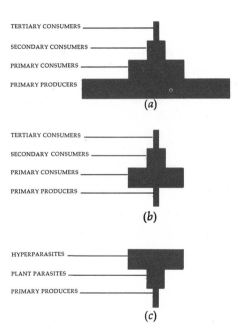

TERTIARY CONSUMERS

SECONDARY CONSUMERS

PRIMARY CONSUMERS

PRIMARY PRODUCERS

(a)

TERTIARY CONSUMERS

SECONDARY CONSUMERS

PRIMARY CONSUMERS

PRIMARY PRODUCERS

(b)

HYPERPARASITES

PLANT PARASITES

PRIMARY PRODUCERS

(c)

absorbed by their photosynthetic machinery. Some of this energy is lost by the plant in transpiration and respiration, and some is used in the processes of living, but a portion (1 to 5 percent) is transformed into organic compounds to form more plant substances. If the plant is consumed by an animal, this animal also derives some of this energy that was originally the sun's, and if another animal consumes the first, a portion of energy will again be passed along. Since energy is lost at every trophic level, diagrams of the flow of energy nearly always form pyramids. These can be a pyramid of numbers, in which the numbers of individual organisms are depicted; a pyramid of biomass, based on total dry weight of the organism or of calories; or a pyramid of energy, in which the productivity of the different trophic levels is depicted. (See Figures 6–81 to 6–83.)

Productivity and biomass, although related, are not the same. In the ocean, for example, the biomass of phytoplankton, as measured by the "standing crop" at any particular moment, may be greater than the biomass of animals that will feed upon it, but phytoplankton can double itself in a very short time, while the growth rate of the animals is much smaller. A small biomass of phytoplankton can supply food for a larger biomass of zooplankton because of the greater productivity of the former. In general, the more stable an ecosystem is, the greater the proportion of biomass to productivity, since less energy is lost. Also, productivity and yield to man are not the same thing; a coral reef is highly productive in terms of the life of the reef, but man profits little from its products.

In general, the total amount of energy transferred from plant to herbivore to carnivore is only about 10 percent at each step, whether the plant is *Chlamydomonas* and the consumer *Daphnia* or the plant grass and the consumer a cow. About 90 percent of the total calories is lost in heat at each transfer, and only about 10 percent is stored in the form of protoplasm. If you burn any animal completely (including its gametes), you will get only 10 percent as much energy as if you burn all the food the animal has eaten in its lifetime. In other words, each stage can expect to take in energy at about one-tenth of the rate of the previous stage (see Table 6–8); hence the tertiary carnivores, the carnivores which eat the carnivores which eat the herbivores, are reduced to roughly $1/10 \times 1/10 \times 1/10 = 1/1,000$ of the energy taken in by the plants. Supercarnivores, which eat these, would be reduced to one-tenth of this, or 1/10,000 of what the plants received, and so on. Among farm animals, the pig is generally considered to be the most efficient converter. Under good management, a maximum of about 20 percent of what is fed to a pig is converted into products edible by man. Individuals, like man, at the top of the ecological pyramid may have to be quite large, as individuals, in order to capture and eat other animals, but they must always be smaller in total number, total biomass, or total captured energy than the animals at lower trophic levels.

Table 6–8 Energy Transfer at Various Trophic Levels in Three Aquatic Ecosystems

Trophic level	Energy intake efficiency (%)		
	Cedar Bog Lake, Minnesota	Lake Mendota, Wisconsin	Silver Springs, Florida
Photosynthetic plants (producers)	0.10	0.40	1.2
Herbivores (primary consumers)	13.3	8.7	16.0
Small carnivores (secondary consumers)	22.3	5.5	11.0
Large carnivores (tertiary consumers)	Not present	13.0	6.0

6–82 *Ecological pyramids of biomass, showing the relationship of producers and consumers in terms of dry weight. Inverted pyramids occur only when the producers and primary consumers are very small. Like pyramids of numbers, pyramids of biomass indicate only the quantity of organic material present at any one time; they do not give the total amount of material produced or the rate at which it is produced. In view of this, can you explain how a smaller weight of phytoplankton can be shown to produce a greater weight of zooplankton in such a pyramid?*

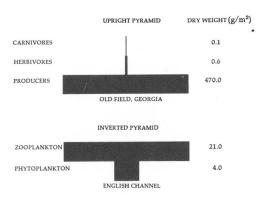

UPRIGHT PYRAMID   DRY WEIGHT (g/m²)

CARNIVORES   0.1
HERBIVORES   0.6
PRODUCERS   470.0

OLD FIELD, GEORGIA

INVERTED PYRAMID

ZOOPLANKTON   21.0
PHYTOPLANKTON   4.0

ENGLISH CHANNEL

These facts have economic significance. The shorter the food chain leading from producer to ultimate consumer, the less energy is lost. A starving population will be better off, at least from the point of view of total calories, eating wheat or other plant products than feeding the plants to herbivores and eating the herbivores. In lakes and ponds which are fertilized to give the maximum yield of fish (by increasing the plants and thereby increasing energy as surplus), many more pounds of herbivorous fish can be harvested per unit of fertilizer than of carnivorous fish. Recently, an ecologist suggested that an efficient method of food production would be to capture plankton-eating whales and raise them for meat like sheep or cattle.

6–83 *Ecological pyramid of energy. Each bar represents the total amount of energy used by the different feeding types in a square meter over a period of one year.*

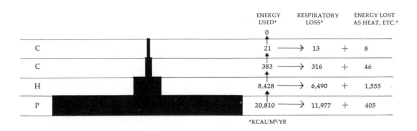

		ENERGY USED*		RESPIRATORY LOSS*		ENERGY LOST AS HEAT, ETC.*
		0				
C		21	→	13	+	8
C		383	→	316	+	46
H		8,428	→	6,490	+	1,555
P		20,810	→	11,977	+	405

*KCAL/M²/YR

781   *The Plants and Animals at Home*

DDT

CARNIVORE 2

CARNIVORE 1

HERBIVORE

PLANTS

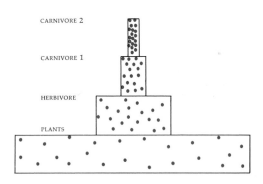

6–84 *Concentration of DDT residues being passed along a simple food chain. As the biomass, or living material, is transferred from one link to the next in the chain, about half of it is usually consumed in respiration or is excreted; the remainder forms new biomass. The losses of DDT residue, however, are small in proportion to the respiration and excretion losses. Consequently, the concentration of DDT increases as the material passes along the chain, and high concentrations occur in the carnivores. (After Woodwell, 1967)*

CONTAMINATION OF THE FOOD CHAIN

Unfortunately, not only energy but also man-made pollutants may pass through a food chain. One of the most serious of these has been strontium-90, a by-product of the testing of atomic weapons. Strontium-90 is a close relative of calcium and can substitute for it in the food chain. It also has a relatively long half-life (28 years). The strontium-90 released into the air is collected in the rain. Like calcium, it is taken in by plants directly through the foliage and also through the soil. In the dairylands, these grasses are eaten by cows, which concentrate the strontium-90 into milk, and the milk is consumed largely by infants and children because of their special needs for calcium for bone growth. By 1959, the bones of children in North America and Europe averaged an estimated 2.6 micromicrocuries of strontium-90 per gram of bone calcium, compared with 0.4 micromicrocuries per gram of calcium in the bones of adults. This small amount of radioactivity has not been proved to be dangerous, but since radiation is known to cause leukemia, bone cancer, and genetic abnormalities, it has been a matter of widespread concern.

The channeling of strontium-90 along the calcium food chain might have been anticipated. Other results were less predictable. For example, in the Arctic, only slight radiation exposure from the atomic tests was expected because the amount of fallout that reaches the ground at the poles is much less than it is in the temperate parts of the United States. However, Eskimos in the Arctic were discovered to have amounts of radioactivity in their bodies which were much higher than those found in the inhabitants of temperate regions. The link in this chain was the lichens. Since they have no real roots, lichens absorb their minerals directly from the air, and so they absorbed a large amount of direct fallout, little of which had had time to decay and none of which was dissipated by absorption into the soil. In the winter, caribou live almost exclusively on lichens, and at the top of the food chain, Eskimos live largely on caribou. As shown in Figure 6–84, DDT also may accumulate as it is passed from plant to herbivore to carnivore.

Another unexpected instance of pollution occurred when the establishment of large duck farms along the southern shore of Long Island led to extensive fertilization of the Great South Bay with duck manure. There are few outlets from bay to ocean, and as a result, the nutrients accumulated, causing a great increase in phytoplankton productivity—but phytoplankton which turned out to be of the wrong kind. Two genera of small green flagellates thrived because they were able to short-circuit the nitrogen cycle and grow well on nitrogen in the form of urea, uric acid, and ammonia, while the ordinary phytoplankton of the area needed inorganic nitrogen. The crowding out of the normal phytoplankton proved disastrous to the thriving bluepoint-oyster industry. The oysters were unable

6–85 *As man's knowledge of the interde-pendence of all living systems increases, ignorance no longer can serve as an excuse. (Courtesy of the U.S. Department of Agriculture)*

to use the new green flagellates for food, and now only a few remain, starving to death full of undigested green flagellates.

Most of the harmful effects produced by man in the economy of nature have been the result of ignorance. As our knowledge increases of the interdependence of all the components of living systems, ignorance no longer can serve as an excuse. Man's power to influence the biosphere is unique, and with this power comes special responsibilities. All of us, citizens and scientists alike, must learn to use our influence with wisdom—not for sentimental reasons but to ensure our own welfare, which is inextricable from the welfare of the rest of the world of living things.

SUMMARY

Ecology is the subdivision of biology that deals with the interactions of populations and communities with each other and with their environments. The part of the planet in which organisms live, known as the *biosphere,* is subdivided into regions called *biomes.* Each biome possesses a particular kind of climate, temperature, and soil and is inhabited by a characteristic group of plants and animals.

Biomes, in turn, are made up of *ecosystems,* which comprise both the community and the environment in which that community lives. The particular places occupied by organisms are their *habitats.* The habitat of an individual may be the same area as the ecosystem of which it is a part, or it may be a small portion of the ecosystem.

The principal ecological divisions of the biosphere are the sea, the land, and the fresh waters. The greatest diversity of species is found in the sea, where life first evolved. There are three main zones of life in the sea: (1)

783 *The Plants and Animals at Home*

the shallow waters of the continental shelves; (2) the open sea, both the surface and the zone of light, which extends about 600 feet below the surface; and (3) the ocean depths, the zone of perpetual darkness.

The biomes of the land are usually identified in terms of their plant life, on which the animal life depends. Patterns of vegetation are basically determined by three elements: (1) north-south zones, (2) rainfall, and (3) glaciers. The principal terrestrial biomes follow the north-south patterns of vegetation. The northernmost biome is the Arctic tundra, and below that are the coniferous forests. Deciduous forests occupy the temperate zones, and in the tropics are rain forests and tropical deciduous forests, which shed their leaves during the dry seasons.

The forests of the Pacific Coast offer an excellent example of how rainfall can affect the vegetative character of an area. When the moisture-laden winds from the ocean reach the coastal ranges and the Sierra Nevada, rain is precipitated on the westward slopes of these mountains, resulting in abundant vegetation. On the eastward slopes, which are in the *rain shadow*, the desert begins.

Two other important terrestrial biomes are the grasslands and the desert.

Although freshwater habitats are nearly as old as the planet itself, most existing lakes and ponds are relatively young. In North America, the great majority of the lakes were formed by retreating glaciers during the last glaciation. Like the oceans, lakes and large ponds are divided into three principal zones: (1) the *littoral zone* along the shore, (2) the *limnetic zone* of open water, and (3) the *profundal zone*. Most of the life in lakes and ponds occurs in the littoral zones. The two major zones of flowing-water ecosystems (streams and rivers) are (1) rapids zones and (2) pool zones.

Ecological succession can be defined as follows: (1) It is the orderly process of community changes; these are directional and, therefore, predictable. (2) It results from the modification of the physical environment by the community. (3) It culminates in the establishment of as stable an ecosystem as is biologically possible on the site in question. The developmental stages of succession are known as *sere,* and the final, stable state is the *climax.*

Non-energy-yielding materials such as nitrogen, carbon, and water circulate within an ecosystem and are used over and over again. Energy, which is derived from the sun, flows through a system only once. Only about half of the sun's radiation reaching green plants is absorbed by them and used for photosynthesis. Of this half, between 1 and 5 percent is converted into a food source for the herbivores that feed on the plants. At each stage (*trophic level*) of the food chain, only about 10 percent of the energy is converted from consumed to consumer, the rest being lost in heat.

Chapter 6—5

The Evolution of Man

Our knowledge of the evolution of man is constructed from three different kinds of data. First, we have a *general knowledge of the processes of evolution*. When we reviewed this knowledge at the beginning of the section, we saw that genetic variations occur entirely at random with respect to the needs of the organism or the forces of the environment and that the direction of evolution is a product of natural selection acting upon these random variations. This point is worth repeating here because, as the history of the last hundred years has shown, it is sometimes very difficult even for the trained scientist not to feel that the course of evolution has somehow been directed first toward the appearance of man and then toward ensuring his progressive improvement. Evolution is basically biological history, as Simpson has aptly pointed out, and does not include such concepts as progress or purpose.

The second kind of data on which we base our knowledge of human evolution is the *fossil record*. Pertinent fossils are comparatively rare for several reasons: (1) Populations of apes and prehumans were always small, not at all comparable to the great herds of grazing animals, for example, of which we have a rich fossil record. (2) Crucial stages in primate evolution apparently occurred in the tropics, where both preservation and discovery of fossils are difficult and where exploration has generally lagged. (3) Primates tended to live in forests and to avoid falling into swamps and lakes where their remains, being concealed from scavengers, would become fossilized and thus preserved. Owing to the assiduous work of paleontologists and anthropologists, the number of new finds—both in the field and among unpublished museum collections—has increased rapidly in the last decade or so, however, and the scientific value of these discoveries has been greatly enhanced by the new dating methods, such as those described in Chapter 1—1.

6–86 *Man and his relatives, the other primates. A striking feature of the Primate order is that its existing members can be arranged in a graded series that approximately parallels what we know of the actual evolutionary developments in the order. As shown here, the lowest branch of the family tree is occupied by the primitive tree shrew and at the top is Homo sapiens. This does not mean, of course, that man is derived from the ape as it exists today or that the ape is a descendant of the modern monkey; each of the various primates stands at the end of a separate evolutionary path.*

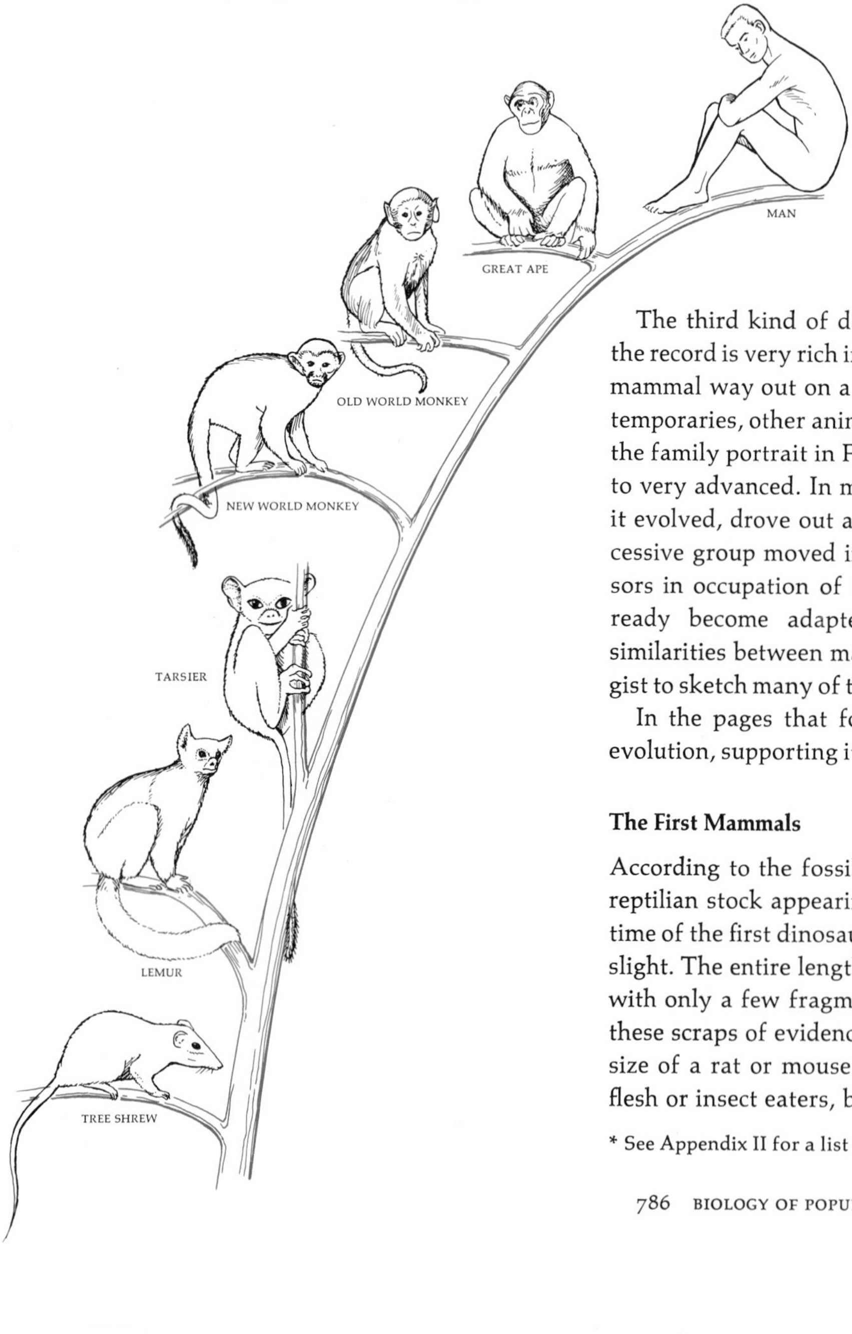

MAN

GREAT APE

OLD WORLD MONKEY

NEW WORLD MONKEY

TARSIER

LEMUR

TREE SHREW

The third kind of data comes from studies *of existing primates*. Here the record is very rich indeed. Unlike the duckbill platypus, that egg-laying mammal way out on a limb of the evolutionary tree, man has living contemporaries, other animals that closely resemble him. As you can see from the family portrait in Figure 6–86, the primates range from very primitive to very advanced. In most other mammalian orders, each new species, as it evolved, drove out and replaced the old, but in the primates, each successive group moved into a new ecological domain, leaving its predecessors in occupation of the particular environment to which they had already become adapted. Therefore, examination of differences and similarities between man and his fellow primates permits the anthropologist to sketch many of the major evolutionary developments.

In the pages that follow, we shall trace briefly the history of man's evolution, supporting it with some of the data from these three sources.

The First Mammals

According to the fossil record, the first mammals arose from a primitive reptilian stock appearing in the middle of the Mesozoic era, at about the time of the first dinosaurs.* Our information about these mammals is very slight. The entire length of the Jurassic and Cretaceous periods has left us with only a few fragments of skulls and some rare teeth and jaws. From these scraps of evidence, we know that the first mammals were about the size of a rat or mouse. They had sharp teeth, indicating that they were flesh or insect eaters, but since they were too small to attack other verte-

* See Appendix II for a list of geological periods.

brates, they are assumed to have lived mostly on insects and worms, supplementing their diet with tender buds, fruit, perhaps eggs, and probably whatever else they could find. Although they were puny and unimpressive compared with the reptiles that were their contemporaries, they had several great advantages over them. The most crucial perhaps is that they were warm-blooded. We know this because they had a bony palate separating the nasal cavity from the mouth. This is an adaptation of animals that breathe continuously and regularly, even when eating, which most warm-blooded animals do and reptiles do not. Being warm-blooded meant that these early mammals had a higher rate of metabolic activity than their reptile contemporaries and could supply their bodies with oxygen and energy more efficiently. Also, the chief characteristic of warm-bloodedness, a high and constant body temperature, would have enabled them to be active at twilight and throughout the night, as they most likely were, when the reptiles were rendered inactive by the cold.

The presence of a bony palate is one of the criteria by which paleontologists classify a transitional animal as a mammal. Other criteria are whether the jaw is a single bone and whether the two bones which form the joint between the skull and jaw in reptiles have moved to join the stapes and so form the delicate, three-bone mechanism of the mammalian middle ear.

For about 80 million years, these small animals led their secretive, probably nocturnal existences in a land dominated by carnivorous reptiles. Then suddenly, as geologic time is measured, the dinosaurs disappeared. Their disappearance occurred at a time when, geologists believe, there was a drop in the average temperature. Perhaps the plant life changed, reducing the number of large herbivores and, consequently, the carnivores that preyed upon them. Some have suggested that mountain building resulted in the drainage of the warm marshes in which the dinosaurs lived and fed and that the large animals could not support their great bulk on dry land. It is possible the mammals ate the reptile eggs. In any case, by the end of the Cretaceous period, the very large reptiles had disappeared forever, and about 75 million years ago, an explosive radiation of the mammals began.

The early mammals immediately diverged into the two dozen or so different lines that included the *monotremes*, or egg-laying mammals, of which the duckbill platypus is one of the few remaining examples; the *marsupials*, such as the kangaroos, wallabies, opossums, koala bears, and others whose young are born in embryonic form and continue their development in pouches; and the *placentals*. Among the placentals are the carnivores, ranging in size from the saber-toothed tiger down to small, weasel-like creatures; the herbivores, or ungulates, which include not only the many wild grazing animals but also most of our domesticated farm

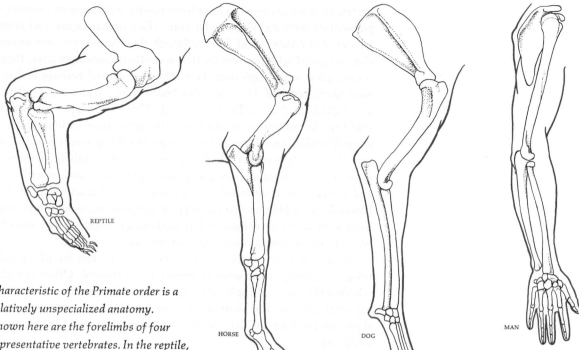

REPTILE

HORSE

DOG

MAN

6–87 *Characteristic of the Primate order is a relatively unspecialized anatomy. Shown here are the forelimbs of four representative vertebrates. In the reptile, we see the proto-mammalian pattern; the earliest four-legged mammals had this arrangement of the five separate digits on each hand and foot, with each digit capable of independent movement. Various modifications of the pattern have evolved in most mammals to adapt them to particular specialized functions. The horse, for example, developed a forelimb specialized for running; the lower part of the limb lengthened, the separate forearm bones were lost, and the number of digits narrowed down to one. Similarly, the dog, in adapting to the particular needs of its existence, exchanged the flexible digits for the more specialized paw. Man and the other primates have generally retained the basic pattern.*

animals; the omnipresent rodents, so called because of their gnawing ability; and such odd groups as the whales and dolphins, the bats, and the modern insectivores, which include the moles and the hedgehogs.

The Early Primates

The most important event in the history of the primates occurred when a mouse-sized primitive mammal took to the trees. This move was a fateful one in terms of the future development of the primates. Life in the trees placed a high premium on visual acuity among mammals, just as flying did with the birds, which also were evolving rapidly at this time. At about the same time, the expansion of the brain began. Also, and perhaps more important in early primates, this form of life fostered a relatively unspecialized anatomy.

HANDS AND FEET

The first four-legged mammals all had five separate digits on each hand and foot, and each digit except the thumb and the first toe had three separate segments that made it flexible and capable of independent movement. In the course of evolution, most mammals developed hooves and paws more suited for running, springing, seizing prey, tearing, and digging; the primates retained and elaborated on the primitive pattern.

Similarly, in the basic quadrupedal structure, the forelimb is supported by two bones (the radius and the ulna), a pattern that provides for flexibility, but among mammals, it is the primates that have retained the ability to twist the radius, the bone on the thumb side, over the ulna so that the hand can be rotated through a full semicircle without moving the elbow or the upper arm. Try it. You do it all the time but perhaps without appreciating how important it is for the efficient use of your hands.

Most other mammals (bats are a notable exception) have also lost the ability to move the upper arm freely in the shoulder socket. A dog or horse, for instance, usually moves its legs in only one plane, forward and backward; the apes and man are the only higher mammals that can rotate the arm widely in the socket.

DENTITION

Another factor of great importance in characterizing the primate order is dentition. Teeth may seem a rather dull subject to the amateur, but for the anthropologist they are highly prized structures that support most of our current theories, both of primate relationships and of the development of early man. Figure 6–88 shows a reconstruction of early mammalian dentition and the dental pattern of several different mammals. In dentition, as well as in other anatomical characteristics, the primates have remained relatively unspecialized. Their teeth reflect the omnivorous diet

6–88 *Dentition patterns in mammals. All mammals have four different types of teeth: chisel-like incisors in the front, for nipping and cutting; dagger-like canines at the front corners, for slashing and piercing; premolars and the heavier molars at the back, for grinding. In carnivores, such as the dog, the cusps on the molars are arranged to form a jagged line for tearing flesh and cracking up bones, and the canines are prominent. The horse, on the other hand, has developed broad and symmetrically ridged molars for grinding up tough vegetable matter; its canines are small, and its front teeth are adapted for cropping. The large incisor teeth of the gorilla are geared to its coarse vegetable and fruit diet, and its strong canines are used for piercing shells and rinds. Omnivorous man, as you can see, has remained relatively unspecialized.*

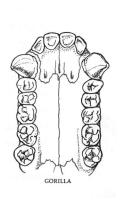
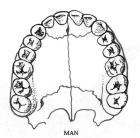

DOG   HORSE   GORILLA   MAN

789   *The Evolution of Man*

6-89 *A male olive baboon displays its impressive canines in a typical threat posture. (Dr. Irven DeVore)*

6-90 *At the bottom of the Primate ladder is the tree shrew, which the earliest prosimians, and indeed the earliest mammals, probably resembled. Notice the five-digited paws. Although clawed, they can be spread out and used in the beginning of a grasp. (Courtesy of the San Diego Zoo)*

of the early primates, a diet probably related to the lack of competition in those early days of treetop existence. An exception is the lemur, whose lower front teeth (both the canines and incisors) have been turned, quite literally, into a comb that it uses to groom its hair.

The original number of teeth in placental mammals is believed to have been 44. The front teeth were the incisors, fine-pointed today in the lower primates and flat and blade-edged in the higher primates. These are the teeth we use for biting an apple or a sandwich and that herbivores use for shearing grass. Behind the incisors, one in each quadrant of the mouth, were the canines—the fighting, seizing teeth prominent in the wolf and the great cats and the saber tooth of the saber-toothed tiger. Behind the canines were the less specialized premolars, and in the very back of the jaw were the molars, the large, heavy grinding teeth of horses and elephants. In almost all mammals, with the exception of certain whales and their relatives, the characteristic number of 44 has been reduced in the course of evolution. In all the Anthropoidea, the group of primates that includes the monkeys, the great apes, and man, the number of teeth is 32. In each half of each jaw, from front to back, are two incisors, one canine, two premolars, and three molars. As you can see, the basic primate pattern is close to the original mammalian dental structure. The extreme regularity in the arrangement of human teeth, one of the chief characteristics of men and premen, has been a later development.

The Prosimians

In the early Paleocene epoch, about 70 million years ago, the primates were already splitting into the various prosimian lines shown in Figure 6-86. All the earliest primate fossils belong to this group. During the Eocene epoch, temperatures became warmer, the tropical forests extended much further to the north and south of the equator than they do today, and prosimians flourished throughout most of the world, especially in North America. The oldest collections of prosimian fossils have been found in the Rocky Mountain region. Then quite suddenly, toward the end of the Eocene epoch, they vanished almost completely and are almost unknown as fossils during the rest of the Tertiary period. William Howells has postulated that the prosimians sowed the seeds of their own decline by giving rise to the higher primates—the monkeys and hominoids. These new animals were probably living in the same forest environment and eating the same foods as their prosimian contemporaries and so might have provided sufficiently vigorous competition to explain the apparently sudden disappearance of this large group.

Modern prosimians, relatively few in both numbers and species, live in tropical Asia and Africa. The only colony flourishing today is a highly

A ring-tailed lemur. Lemurs have flattened nails on all digits of the hands and feet except, as you can perhaps see, the second digit of each foot which has a "grooming claw." (Courtesy of the New York Zoological Park)

diversified group of lemurs on the island of Madagascar, whose ancestors made their way to the island early in their evolutionary history. There are no other primates on Madagascar except man, who is a very recent arrival.

The early prosimians, and indeed the earliest mammals, probably looked somewhat like the modern tree shrew, which is a shy, nervous, incessantly active, always hungry animal about the size of a small rat. The tree shrew has claws on the end of each digit, which it uses to scramble up and down the tree trunks like a squirrel, but its digits do possess some mobility. Lemurs are somewhat larger—many of them are about the size of a kitten and some are as large as a good-sized dog—and more monkeylike than the tree shrews. Notice in particular the hands and feet of the lemur. It has a claw only on the second digit of each hind foot, which it uses for scratching and grooming; the rest of the claws have been modified into flattened nails similar to the nails of all the primates higher on the phylogenetic scale.

The tarsier, although certainly not a direct ancestor of the more advanced primates, closely resembles them in a number of ways. One of its most striking features is the fact that its upper lip is free from the gum like that of the higher primates but not of the lemurs. This permits the tarsier to have a wide range of facial expressions. Another way in which the tarsier resembles the higher primates is that it does not have the naked and moist skin of the muzzle at the point of attachment of the cleft upper lip. This feature, common among mammals (including the fox-faced lemur), is absent in most of the primates; its loss is correlated with a diminishing sense of smell. A decreasing reliance on smell and a greater dependence on vision are typical of tree-dwelling animals. The enormous eyes of the tarsier are a special adaptation for night vision, like the eyes of the owl. The tarsier has stereoscopic vision; in other words, both eyes cover most of the same visual field and permit a composite picture of the field in the brain. This is important for judging short-range distances, an essential ability for an active treetop dweller. The tarsier also, like all the other higher primates, has a fovea, a special area in the retina of the eye capable of particularly acute vision. According to W. E. Le Gros Clark, the British anatomist, the little saucer-eyed tarsier has existed relatively unchanged for some 50 million years.

6–92 *A native of Indonesia, the little tarsier (about the size of a small kitten) is the most "advanced" of the prosimians. Its upper lip, like ours, is free from the gum below it, giving it the ability (as you can see) to make faces. Its senses are well developed, and it has a larger brain than the lemur's. Living entirely in trees, it has hands and feet with enlarged skin pads for grasping branches, and its hind limbs are specialized for hopping—rather like a kangaroo's except that the limb ends with a hand. (Douglas Fisher, F.R.P.S., Frank W. Lane)*

The Anthropoidea

MONKEYS

The monkeys arose from prosimian stock during the Eocene epoch. The New World monkeys and the Old World monkeys seem to have evolved separately since both groups appeared at about the same time on different continents. Monkeys are members of the Anthropoidea, a suborder which also includes the apes and man. They bear a distinct resemblance to man, as all of us know who have stood uneasily in front of a cage in a zoo and been inspected through the bars by a bright-eyed curious anthropoid. Perhaps the most striking point of resemblance is the way the head is balanced on the spine. A dog's head, for instance, would be directed toward the ground, not straight ahead, if it had the same relation to the spine that our head has, and this is also true of the primitive mammal. In the course of evolution, man's face has rotated down about 90°. The monkey's face has not moved quite that far, but far enough to look "human" to us. In addition, the eyes are placed so that they face straight ahead, and the snout is greatly diminished. A long nose is an advantage to the animal that explores the world by sniffing and nuzzling; if the snout is long enough, the

6–93 *The long-armed spider monkey inhabits the jungles of Central America and northern South America. A remarkable acrobat, it has a strong prehensile tail equipped with a hairless, "nonskid" area on the underside that helps it grasp branches as it races through the trees. (Courtesy of the San Diego Zoo)*

eyes can see what it is doing and help evaluate what it has found. In an animal that is exploring with its hands and eyes, however, the long snout is of no advantage and may actually interfere with stereoscopic vision. This is why natural selection operated in favor of the flat face characteristic of the anthropoids. The monkeys also have a larger, rounder brain case than the prosimians and a larger and more advanced brain. Their hands and feet are definitely prehensile, although not more so than in some of the prosimians.

The New World monkeys, from South and Central America, are all strictly arboreal in their habits, and many of them use their tails as a fifth, prehensile "limb," which none of the Old World monkeys can do. The New World monkeys include the marmoset, the howler monkey, the spider monkey, and the capuchin—the familiar monkey of the organ-grinder. The Old World monkeys include, among others, the macaque, or rhesus monkey, and the green monkey. They are distinguished by hard, calloused skin areas that form sitting pads on their buttocks. Their tails are used as balancing rather than prehensile organs. The Old World monkeys spend more time on the ground than the New World monkeys, but they are all four-footed, and most walk flat on palms and soles. The largest of the Old World monkeys are the baboons, drills, and mandrills, which have reverted entirely to a four-footed walking existence. They have developed, secondarily, doglike faces with long snouts and, in the males, ferocious canines.

THE GREAT APES

The hominoids (which include the apes and man) arose also in the Old World from a prosimian stock, evolving separately from the monkeys. The hominoid line probably dates back to the late Eocene epoch, about 40 million years ago or more, when the early prosimians were vanishing and the Old World monkeys were making their first appearance. The hominoids differ from the monkeys in that most of them are larger, with a generally larger brain case, and all of them are tailless.

The tree-dwelling apes move from branch to branch not by leaping and scrambling, as do the monkeys, but by *brachiating*, swinging from one arm and then the other with their bodies erect. Man's immediate primate ancestors were also brachiators, and this type of locomotion plays an important part in the transition from the body structures associated with crouching, characteristic of the lower primates, to the body structure that makes possible the erect posture of man. The first well-defined apes are found in the Oligocene epoch in Africa. The modern apes are few in number, belonging to just four genera: the gibbon (*Hylobates*), the orangutan (*Pongo*), the chimpanzee (*Pan*), and the gorilla, whose genus name (*Gorilla*) is the same as its common one.

793 *The Evolution of Man*

6–94 *The nearly tailless mandrill from West Africa differs from other baboons in its large size and colorful muzzle. Adult males stand over 3 feet high and weigh more than 100 pounds. On each side of the male's large snout is a grooved area of blue and purple; the center section is a bright scarlet decorated with yellow whiskers. Additional color is contributed by its hairless seat pads, which are violet and red. Its grasping ability is demonstrated by the mandrill shown here, which is holding a single hair in its left hand. (Courtesy of the New York Zoological Park)*

6–95 *The basic habit of the apes is an upright, suspended body. Instead of jumping and scrambling through the trees as the monkeys do, apes brachiate, that is, swing hand over hand, and related to this brachiation is a complex of structural features that distinguishes them from the monkeys. Compare this chimpanzee with the spider monkey in Figure 6–93. The chimpanzee's shoulders are broader, facing outward, and the chest is broad and flat instead of deep and pointed. There are also basic differences in the spine and pelvis. (Ron Garrison, San Diego Zoo)*

6–96 *Gibbons are the smallest and, apparently, the least intelligent of the apes. In addition, they are probably the greatest acrobats of all existing animals. They spend most of their time high in the trees. When they do descend to the ground or when they are walking along large limbs, they have the most erect carriage of any of the apes. (Ron Garrison, San Diego Zoo)*

Gibbons

The gibbon, limited today to southeast Asia, is much the smallest of the apes—averaging about 3 feet tall—and the lightest in build, with a slim body and long spidery arms. The gibbon is the only one of the apes to be completely covered by dense hair; the other apes have sparse body hair. It forms permanent pairs, each couple living by itself with its younger offspring. The gibbon can stand erect and walk, using its arms for balancing as though it were on a tightrope.

Dryopithecus

Contemporary with the gibbon in the late Miocene epoch was an apparently large and widespread group of apes which have been given the generic name *Dryopithecus*. This group consists of seven recognized species, ranging in size from a large baboon to a gorilla. Based on an abundance of fossil fragments, mostly jaws and teeth, *Dryopithecus* is known to have ranged through much of Africa, Asia, and Europe. The best known and most complete specimens of *Dryopithecus* have been collected by the British anthropologists Louis and Mary Leakey in an area near Lake Victoria in East Africa. One of the first to be described was given the name of *Proconsul*, as an affectionate tribute to a favorite performing chimpanzee named Consul. The modern descendants of *Dryopithecus* include the orangutan, the chimpanzee, and the gorilla.

Orangutans

The orangutan, the redheaded, orange-bearded "man of the woods," as its name means in Malayan, is shy and solitary, and although large—averaging about 5 feet tall—it is strictly arboreal. The orangutan is long-armed like the gibbon. When it stands erect, its fingertips reach its ankles. Its foot is prehensile, as are those of the other apes, and quite "handlike," with a very small heel and a widely divergent big toe, which is also greatly reduced in size. It moves on the ground only when forced to, and then it must walk on the curled edges of its feet rather than flat on the soles, and on its fists. The modern orangutan is found in Sumatra and Borneo.

Gorillas and Chimpanzees

The gorillas and the chimpanzees are more closely related to one another than to the orangutan and are the closest of all the other anthropoids to man. Recent studies of blood proteins and of chromosomes confirm these relationships. The chimpanzee is a tree dweller and a brachiator, feeding and sleeping in the trees. However, it spends a large part of its time on the ground and, being well adapted to quadrupedal walking, is very much at home there. The gorilla has almost completely abandoned the trees, with

795   *The Evolution of Man*

6-97 *An adult male lowland gorilla. Gorillas spend most of their time on the ground. Usually, they walk on all fours, as shown in (a), carrying their weight on the second joints of their fingers and on the soles of their feet. When they walk upright (b), they step on the flat of the foot. (Courtesy of the New York Zoological Park)*

(a)

(b)

the exception of some of the smaller animals that sleep in nests in the lower branches. The larger gorillas sleep on the ground, and all feed on ground plants. Both chimpanzees and gorillas have powerful canines and strong incisors for ripping the tough rinds of fruits and other vegetable products that are their staple diet. Because of these large canines, the apes are limited in their side-to-side or rotary chewing movements. Both have relatively long arms and short legs. As a result, even when they are on all fours, their bodies are partially erect. Their feet are excellent grasping structures.

The gorilla is the closest to man in body skeleton. Its chest is broad in contrast with the thin deep chest of the monkey. It is about as tall as a man but weighs several times more. Its legs are much shorter in proportion to its body than are man's, while its arms are much longer and extremely powerful. The gorilla has an arm span of about 9 feet, much longer than man's, who usually has an arm span about equal to his height. The gorilla's hind feet are flat-footed on the ground, and it ordinarily moves by walking quadrupedally on the knuckles of its hands. It can stand erect, as it does when challenging an enemy, and it can also walk erect, although not nearly as well and as easily as it can on all fours. It has a beetling brow; a strong, heavy jaw; and, on the top of the skull of adult males, a bony crest to which the strong jaw muscles are attached. These are homologous to the jaw muscles you can feel moving in your own temples when you chew or grind your teeth.

The gorilla's foot lacks the arch and the long great toe which adapt our own feet so well for walking, but unlike the other apes, it has a pronounced heel. The pelvic bone is the most divergent skeletal structure of all between apes and man. The long, relatively narrow pelvis of the ape throws his spine forward, whereas man's hipbones are bent backward and downward, carrying the sacrum and spine into an erect position over his straight, columnar legs. Two-leggedness, or bipedalism, is the essential difference between man and ape—representing the evolutionary fork at which the two diverged.

The Road to Modern Man

Before we talk about man, we should define perhaps the particular features by which the anthropologists distinguish him. In biological terms, man is a primate that evolved from the less specialized apelike creatures from which the chimpanzee, the orangutan, and the gorilla also probably evolved. He is distinguished from the apes by his upright posture, his ability to walk continuously and for long distances on two legs, his teeth, his brain, which is proportionately larger and has a more complex cerebrum than any other animal of equivalent size, and his skull, which is

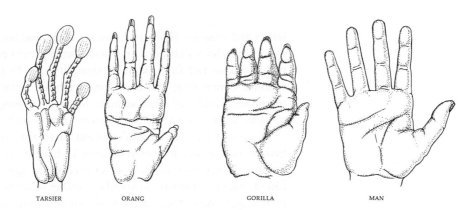

TARSIER ORANG GORILLA MAN

6–98 *Some primate hands. One of the distinguishing features of the primate is its ability to grasp, but except in man, all primate hands are specialized in some degree for a particular function. The hand of the tarsier has enlarged skin pads for grasping branches. In the orangutan, the fingers are lengthened and the thumb reduced for more efficient brachiating. The gorilla's hand, which is used in walking as well as handling, has shortened fingers. The human hand is the least specialized and the most generally skillful. The opposition of thumb and fingers, on which the handling ability depends, is greatest in man.*

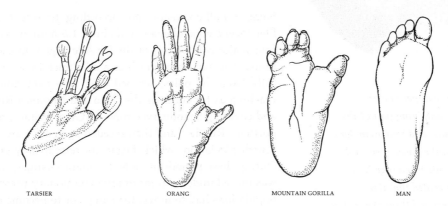

TARSIER ORANG MOUNTAIN GORILLA MAN

6–99 *While man's hand follows the basic primate pattern, his foot is very different from those of other primates. All primates except man have handlike feet with opposable first toes—in fact, the feet of many primates (for example, the tarsier) are better graspers than the hands. In man, as you can see, the first toe has lost its opposability and the other toes are very short, bringing all the joints at the base of the toes in line and making a ball to the foot. It is this ball that is the secret of man's ability to walk erect; it allows him to shift his weight from heel to ball and so stride forward. No other primate can do this, not even the gorilla, which has a larger heel and shorter side toes than those of the other apes.*

797   The Evolution of Man

larger and rounder. His lateral toes are short, and his big toe is in line with the others. His vertebral column makes an S curve balanced over his broad pelvis and his two fully extended straight legs. His jaws are short, with a rounded dental arch, and his canine teeth are usually no larger than his premolars. Unlike all other animals, he has a language capable of communicating abstract ideas. He both uses and makes tools.

Traces of what may be man's earliest ancestor were found in 1934 in the Siwalik Hills of northwestern India by G. E. Lewis of Yale, who gave it the name of *Ramapithecus*. Only small parts of an upper and lower jaw were found, but these indicate a curved arc, rather than the U-shaped jaw typical of the apes. Also it had a relatively small canine tooth. (Figure 6–100). Lewis suggested that it was more manlike than apelike, and this opinion gained support when Leakey found other jaw pieces (belonging to *Kenyapithecus*) almost identical in form, in Kenya. Both of these have been dated as being about 14 million years old—a time near the boundary between the Miocene and Pliocene epochs. The other characteristics of *Ramapithecus* are not known, but on the basis of this evidence, it would seem that manlike creatures began a course of evolution extending over at least two continents not long after the first appearance of the other anthropoids.

THE PLEISTOCENE EPOCH

Some 3 million years ago, according to recent geologic evidence, the Pleistocene epoch began, and about 1.5 million years ago, the first of the four major cold phases of the Ice Age began. In each of these four glaciations, sheets of ice as much as a mile thick in some regions spread out locally from the poles, scraped their way over much of the continents—reaching as far south as the Ohio and Missouri Rivers in North America and covering Scandinavia, most of Great Britain, northern Germany, and northern Russia—and then receded again. We are living at the end of the fourth glaciation, which began its retreat only some 20,000 years ago. During these periods of violent climatic changes, the life of the continents was placed under extraordinary evolutionary pressures. Plant and animal populations had to move, to change, or to become extinct. In the interglacial periods, during which the average temperatures were warmer than those of today, the tropical forests and their inhabitants spread up through today's temperate zones. During the periods of glaciation, only animals of the northern tundra could survive in these same locations. Rhinoceroses, great herds of horses, large bears, and lions roamed Europe in the inter-glacial periods, and in North America, as the fossil record shows, there were camels and horses, lions, saber-toothed cats, and great ground sloths, one species as large as an elephant. In the colder periods, reindeer ranged as far south as southern France, while during the warmer periods, the hippopotamus reached England.

6–100 *A fragment of the upper jaw of Ramapithecus, containing part of the palate, two molars, and two premolars (on the left). On the basis of several such jaw fragments fitted together, scientists have decided that this primate, which ranged throughout Asia and Africa some 14 million years ago, was more manlike than apelike. With no other evidence available, how was this decision made? (Courtesy of the American Museum of Natural History)*

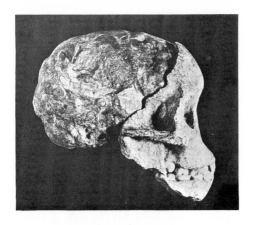

6–101 *The skull of a child, found in a lime-stone quarry in Taung, Africa, in 1924, was the first specimen discovered of the earliest known homonid, Australopithecus africanus. Shown here are the skull and a reconstruction drawing of the head of the child, which was about five or six years old when it died. An erect-walking creature with a brain larger than the gorilla's and with non-simian teeth, Australopithecus lived on the ground, probably ate meat, and used tools of his own making. (Courtesy of the American Museum of Natural History)*

In 1925, the anatomist Raymond A. Dart published a description of a new kind of higher primate recovered from a limestone fissure in South Africa. Dart named his specimen *Australopithecus africanus*, the "southern ape" of Africa. Recognizing that it was not simply an ape but showed some general tendencies in the human direction, he suggested that it be classified as a new family. Since that time, eight different sites in East and South Africa have yielded fossils of australopithecines. Well over 300 different individuals now recognized as related to the earliest known hominid have been discovered. Some of these are represented by only a tooth or two, but for others, we have almost complete skulls and a number of limb bones. Perhaps the most publicized of these is *Zinjanthropus*, the so-called "nut-cracker man," discovered by the Leakeys in 1959 in the Olduvai Gorge in Tanzania, East Africa. The find included an incomplete but well-preserved skull and all 16 upper teeth. The oldest fossil presently classified as belonging to the australopithecines is a portion of an upper arm bone discovered in Kenya in 1965 by Bryan Patterson of Harvard. This specimen has recently been dated as having lived about 2 1/2 million years ago.

Australopithecines had cranial capacities ranging from about 450 cubic centimeters to 600 or more, compared with 350 to 750 for male gorillas and 1,000 to 2,000 for modern men. Their hands were slightly more humanlike than those of a chimpanzee, having a broad flat thumb and the beginnings of a human-style grip. The bone structure of the skull reveals that the head was held erect. The teeth were not apelike but were very much like our own. The molars were very large, however, larger than in modern man, and often the specimens are heavily worn down on the flat, even surfaces, indicating that unlike the apes, he was capable of the side-to-side chewing which results in such wear. It seems that australopithecines were eaters of meat, like man, as well as fruit eaters like the apes. The camp sites of *Zinjanthropus* contain the bones of small animals—birds, frogs, fish, lizards, rats, and mice—and the young of larger animals, such as antelopes.

The australopithecine walked upright but not with our heel-and-toe striding gait. From the shape of the pelvic skeleton, which is long rather than short as in man, we know that he could not extend his legs as efficiently as modern man does. He probably covered the ground with quick, short steps, knees slightly bent in somewhat of a jog trot. Physiologically, this is a relatively inefficient type of motion. Obviously, man did not first learn to walk efficiently and then begin to pick up sticks and stones. Bipedalism would have been comparatively inefficient for millions of years; it must have been accompanied by a very powerful secondary advantage. This advantage was clearly the freeing of the hands for other purposes—in particular, the use of tools. Changes in dentition are also indicative of an increased use of the hands. Gorillas use their teeth for food-gathering—their incisors for nibbling and their large canines for stripping bark from trees—and they use their mobile projecting lips for investigation, as do the chimpanzees. The australopithecine, with his short teeth and erect posture, probably relied much more heavily on his hands. We used to think that man first became intelligent and then began to use tools. Actually, it seems to have been the other way around. The reliance on tools and the dexterity needed to use them gave intelligence a tremendous selective advantage. The brain increased in size and complexity, and the cranium of the tool-using ape-man expanded to accommodate the brain. But we are getting ahead of our story.

Australopithecines existed for about 2 million years and were spread over East and South Africa and possibly southern Asia as well. A number of differences among the specimens have been discovered. Some feel that these differences are not more significant than those that an anthropologist of 2 million years from now might note among the skeletal and cultural remains of, for example, an Eskimo, a European, and an Australian aborigine, all of whom we classify as *Homo sapiens*. Others believe that *Australopithecus africanus* should be subdivided into two distinct groups, which coexisted for about a million and a half years. One of these groups is believed to have been more primitive and finally to have become extinct, and the other is believed to have evolved into *Homo*. One of the chief controversies centers around specimens found in different strata of excavations at Olduvai in 1960 by Leakey and given the name of *Homo habilis*. Fragments of seven specimens of *Homo habilis* have been found. He was only about 3 1/2 to 4 1/2 feet tall and had a cranium with a capacity some 80 cubic centimeters larger than the average australopithecine. His teeth were generally smaller and more humanlike, and he had a number of manlike features in his foot and limb bone. He seems to have differed from previously discovered specimens of which he is a contemporary, not only in these physical characteristics, but also, as some anthropologists interpret the evidence, by having been a toolmaker as well as a tool user. Leaky believes, as the name implies, that *Homo habilis* belongs to the genus *Homo* rather than to the genus *Australopithecus* and that it is *H. habilis* and not *Australopithecus* that is the ancestor of man. Other anthropologists are more inclined to consider *H. habilis* as a transitional species or subspecies of *Australopithecus africanus*.

Homo erectus

Homo erectus, the probable progenitor of *Homo sapiens*, made his first appearance some 700,000 years ago, during the late Pleistocene epoch. The first fossil specimen of *H. erectus* was discovered in 1891 by a young Dutch army surgeon, Eugene Dubois. While still in his early twenties,

6–102 *A great deal of skill was required for the manufacture of this hand ax. After rough shaping with a hammerstone, the ax was chipped around the edge, using a piece of wood or bone, to form a sharp straight cutting edge. Homo erectus probably used this tool for skinning and cutting up game. (Courtesy of the American Museum of Natural History and the Rockefeller University Press)*

Dubois became fascinated with the idea of finding an apelike fossil of man. Because of the presence of living orangutans in the Indo-Malayan region, he reasoned that there was the place to search for man's early ancestors. When the Netherlands government refused to launch an expedition under his command, he secured a post as an army surgeon in the Netherlands Indies, set to digging on the banks of the Solo River in Central Java, and before long, by a remarkable combination of confidence and luck, discovered what came to be known as the Java man. Since Dubois' discovery, fossils similar to Java man have been found not only along the Solo, which yielded a number of other specimens, but in China (Pekin man), where more than three dozen have been found, in East Africa (at Olduvai), in North Africa (Algeria, Ternifine), and in South Africa. This group lived during a period of about 500,000 years, from the end of the first Pleistocene interglacial period to the end of the second glacial period. Some of its members were also known as *Pithecanthropus*, but all have recently been unified under the name of *Homo erectus*.

H. erectus had a body skeleton much like our own and was about the same size as modern man. The bones of his leg are indistinguishable from those of a modern man, and it is clear that he had a stride similar to our own. He had stone tools which he made himself and which could be used to cut through animal skins and to butcher meat. And the group that lived in China clearly knew the use of fire.

Hearths are abundant in the caves where Pekin man lived and are strewn with the bones of large animals, which he obviously hunted and killed. At these sites, there are far more *H. erectus* skulls than bones of the body skeleton, and many of the skulls are broken open neatly at the base, suggesting the possibility that the brains were used for food. The first member of the genus *Homo* may have been a cannibal.

The skull capacity of this early man species averaged between 900 and 1,250 cubic centimeters or somewhat higher, overlapping the capacity of modern man. His face was still essentially chinless and primitive, with a large bony shelf above the eyes, a very low retreating forehead, and a skull that was long and narrow posteriorly. His teeth were smaller than those of most of the australopithecines, as one would imagine in an evolving group of individuals who had not only tools but fire. *Australopithecus* was perhaps more of a vegetarian than a meat eater, although the use of crude tools probably enabled him to obtain a slightly varied diet, and a tough vegetable diet requires larger, stronger teeth than a meat diet does. *H. erectus*, because of his superior skill as a hunter and his possession of fire, ate a diet rich in protein and clearly nutritious, although we may not want to contemplate the details of his menu.

The rate of evolution of man during the Pleistocene epoch, as measured by changes in cranial capacity, was extraordinarily rapid, more rapid than

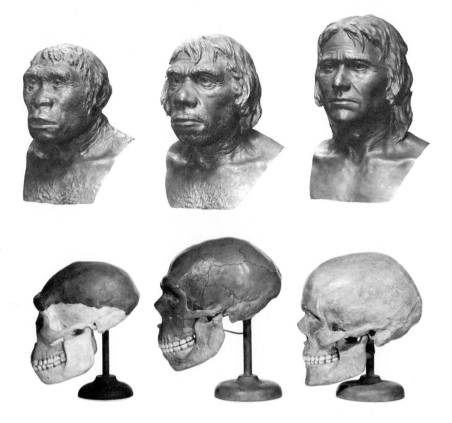

6–103 *Skulls and head reconstructions of (from left to right) Pithecanthropus erectus, Neanderthal man, and Cro-Magnon man. (Courtesy of the American Museum of Natural History)*

that known for any other species during any other period of time. Apparently, individuals with large skulls tended to have many more surviving offspring than individuals whose cranial capacities were smaller. Some authorities correlate the selective value of the large skull with man's increasing dexterity and skill in tool using and toolmaking. Others, pointing out that tools had been in use for many millions of years, believe that it was associated with the development of the essentially human ability to speak.

NEANDERTHAL MAN

Neanderthal man has been a problem since he was first discovered, but he is now accepted as a member of the genus *Homo*. The first Neanderthal fossil to attract widespread interest was found in the Neander Valley near

Düsseldorf in 1856. Some experts identified it as an early manlike creature swept by the Flood of the Biblical story into the cave in which it was found. One German pathologist said it was not ancient at all, merely a modern victim of disease. The poor man must have had rickets, he explained, pointing out the bowed limb bones characteristic of this group of Neanderthals. This caused him so much pain that his brows were furrowed in constant anguish; in response to this muscular contraction, the massive bony ridges grew out. So, he concluded, the man from the Neander Valley was most probably a Cossack from the Russian forces pursuing Napoleon west in 1814, who had been overcome by his illness and crawled into the cave to die.

Fossil specimens have been found in abundance all over Europe, including Spain, Italy, Germany, France, and Greece, and in the Near East, Iran, and Central Asia. It is now generally recognized that these specimens date from the fourth glacial period, roughly 100,000 years ago.

Neanderthal men were short in stature—the males were just over 5 feet tall—but ruggedly constructed and probably heavily muscular. Their brows were low, but they had a backward projection of the skull that gave them a cranial capacity equal to and often larger than that of modern man. They hunted a wide range of game, including animals such as the mammoth and the woolly rhinoceros. They had no domesticated animals—not even the dog had yet become man's companion—no agriculture, and, apparently, no permanent homes. One of the clearest glimpses we have of Neanderthal man, one that suddenly reveals to us his essential humanness, is the fact that he sometimes buried his dead, often with gifts of food and other sacrifices. We do not know when man first began to speak—some anthropologists believe that speech evolved among the australopithecines —but apparently Neanderthal man was capable not only of simple speech but of speech that conveyed complex abstract ideas, such as the concept of a life after death. We also know from these burial sites that Neanderthal man, like ourselves, feared, hoped, dreamed, and wondered.

Most anthropologists classify Neanderthal man as a subspecies of *Homo sapiens*. Later Neanderthal man, such as the type found in the Neander Valley, was clearly not our immediate ancestor. In fact, older specimens, such as those found recently at Swanscombe and Steinheim, which have been dated as belonging to the second interglacial period, are more like modern *sapiens* than are the later Neanderthals of the fourth glacial period. It seems most reasonable to believe that the late Neanderthal man and modern man had some common ancestor, but that Neanderthal man, for reasons that we do not understand yet, took a divergent evolutionary course. In any case, Neanderthal man quite suddenly vanished from the fossil record, either just before, just after, or (more likely) at the time of the appearance of modern man.

6–104 *Some Stone Age tools. Two examples of the earliest recognizable man-made tools are shown at the top. Known as choppers, they are naturally rounded stones which were turned into tools by knocking a few chips off one side to make a rough cutting edge. The two flake tools and the hand ax in the center are Neanderthal. Notice that the edges have been finished. On the bottom are a ground stone ax of the New Stone Age (left) and a Cro-Magnon blade tool (right). To make the blade tool, a core was first prepared by breaking a large piece of flint in two and then knocking off thin flakes from the outside rim, producing a tapered fluted shape. From this, many finished blades could be struck. (Courtesy of the American Museum of Natural History)*

CRO-MAGNON MAN

About 35000 B.C., during a time when the fourth glaciation had ameliorated somewhat and the forest had grown northward once more, Neanderthal man gave away in Europe to an entirely new type of *Homo sapiens*. He was physically quite different from Neanderthal, being about 5 feet 6 inches tall, with a skull very much like our own and with a fully domed head, having a high forehead, vertical sides, and a rounded back. His facial bones were much more delicate and lighter than those of his predecessors, his skull was thin-walled, and his brows were no heavier than our own. You would not look twice at a suitably attired Cro-Magnon if you passed him on the street. His culture was also conspicuously different from that of Neanderthal man. For one thing, Neanderthal man made flake tools; he took a piece of flint and chipped off flakes from it, which he then employed as cutters and scrapers. Cro-Magnon made blade tools; from a carefully prepared core of flint, he struck off long, narrow, straight blades which could be converted into a large number of specialized tools. These two different types of tools are found over and over again in association with the two different types of fossils, and there is no doubt that they represent entirely separate cultures. Cro-Magnon also made clothing in a fairly sophisticated way. Many bone needles and awls have been found at his campsites.

The clearest picture that we have of Cro-Magnon culture is afforded not by his bones or by his tools but by the graceful imaginative cave drawings that have now been found in many sites throughout Europe. Drawn in black outline and filled in with earth colors, the drawings are almost always of animals or of hunts, and the animals are those that Cro-Magnon man hunted. Man is seldom represented, and when he is, it is as a simple stick figure such as children draw, although the drawings of the animals are remarkably accurate representations. The drawings that have survived are almost always found deep within hidden subterranean corridors. They seem to have played a part in mystical or religious ceremonies associated with the hunt.

DEVELOPMENT OF AGRICULTURE

Early Cro-Magnon man, like all the men who came before him, was a seasonal hunter. It was not until fairly recent times, about 9,000 years ago, that man first began to cultivate the land, to raise domestic animals, and to live in permanent homes and communities. Agriculture appeared about 7000 B.C. in the Middle East, around the fertile crescent of southwestern Asia, and in the Mexican states of Puebla and Tamaulipas. In the Middle East, there are fossil imprints of cultivated wheat and barley, remains of domesticated goats and dogs, pottery vessels, and stone bowls and mortars. The farmers of Mexico grew pumpkins, squash, gourds, and cotton.

From these centers, the arts of agriculture spread, and the social and cultural patterns developed that dominate modern life.

Present Courses of Evolution

The course of man's evolution has been dominated by culture, that is, by learned skills and knowledge passed from one generation to another and leading to an ever-increasing control over the natural environment. In the past, the selective pressures of cultural evolution operated with great rapidity, bringing about relatively large physical changes in the size of the brain, the shape of the hand, the dentition, and the bones and muscles involved in bipedal locomotion in a very short period of time. This sort of change stopped some 35,000 years ago; we have no reason to believe that modern man is more intelligent, more dexterous, swifter of movement, or even better looking than Cro-Magnon man.

The selective pressures have greatly changed in modern times. The little patches of cultivated land in Asia and in Mexico have extended over larger and larger proportions of the fertile areas of the world. With a more assured food supply and with the greater physical safety of community living, man was able to increase his numbers—a hundredfold in the course of 8,000 years. As man came to live more and more of a community existence, the survival of his offspring came to be related less and less to his individual abilities than to his place in the society and to the fate of the society as a whole. New selection pressures began to operate in the form of plagues, famines, crusades, and military invasions in which large numbers of the population were destroyed. These pressures were as rigorous in their own way as those to which early man had been subjected. Judging from the fossils, Neanderthal man, once he reached adulthood, might be expected to live to be about 35 years old. A man reaching adulthood in fourteenth century England had about the same life expectancy. These pressures undoubtedly also had biological consequences, such as the selection of individuals with increased resistance to disease, although we do not have ways to measure this retrospectively.

In more recent times, there has once again been a series of radical changes which affect evolutionary history. First of all, through his increase both in sheer numbers and in technological skills, man's influence dominates the landscape. Through agriculture, the breeding of domestic animals, the destruction of natural resources, and the provision of favorable habitats for insects and other sharers of human dwelling places, man now determines to a large extent which plants and animals will survive, which will change, and which will become extinct. Man has even altered local weather; as a result, agriculture, rainfall, and the climate have been changed in many parts of the world. The activities of man, both deliberate and unwitting, are a major force in evolution today.

One of the ways in which man is influencing his own evolution has been through the conquest of many types of disease, partly as a result of modern medical progress but more as a consequence of public health measures, such as clean water supplies and sanitary means for sewage and garbage disposal. An infant born 300 years ago had little better than a fifty-fifty chance of surviving its first year, while in many countries today, infant mortality is only about 2 or 3 percent of live births. (Incidentally, it may surprise you to learn that the United States ranks comparatively low, about thirteenth or fourteenth among modern nations, in its control of infant mortality.) In the United States, the average life expectancy has increased 13 years since 1900, now having reached about 67 years for men and about 74 for women.

These changes, all desirable in themselves, have brought with them a number of undesirable consequences. Individuals with heredity-linked diseases, such as infantile diabetes, who would not have survived childhood even a few decades ago, are now living and raising children, keeping the genes in circulation. The possibility exists that the incidence of various constitutional defects will rapidly increase with the decline in natural selective pressures.

This problem has led some geneticists to propose the establishment of sperm banks and other means by which the genetic constitution of the next generation can be directed. Such a proposal is unlikely to be accepted. Not only would it interfere with personal liberty to a probably intolerable extent, the opponents point out, but we really do not know which are the qualities that we want to preserve or improve, much less how to go about getting them. One is reminded of the lady who proposed marriage to George Bernard Shaw. "You have the greatest brain in the world," she pointed out, "and I have the most beautiful body; so we ought to produce the most perfect child." Shaw unhesitatingly refused, replying that he was entirely unwilling to run the parallel risk of having children with *his* looks and *her* intelligence.

The gravest consequence of these rapid cultural changes, and one with which every thinking person, scientist or not, must be concerned, is the rapid increase in the population. In absolute number, the population has increased fivefold in the last 300 years and threatens to double once again by the year 2000. Even if we can manage to feed these greatly increased numbers of people adequately, which we are not doing at the present time, we can only wonder about the quality of life in a world where there is "standing room only."

Darwin concluded his *Descent of Man* with these words:

Man may be excused for feeling some pride at having risen, though not through his own exertions, to the very summit of the organic scale; and the fact of his having thus risen, instead of having been aboriginally placed there, may give him hope for a still higher destiny in the distant future. But we are not here concerned with hopes or fears, only with the truth as far as our reason permits us to discover it; and I have given the evidence to the best of my ability. We must, however, acknowledge, as it seems to me, that man, with all his noble qualities, with sympathy which feels for the most debased, with benevolence which extends not only to other men but to the humblest living creature, with his godlike intellect which has penetrated into the movements and constitution of the solar system—with all these exalted powers—man still bears in his bodily frame the indelible stamp of his lowly origin.

Physiologically, man is very similar to other organisms. He must eat, excrete, and respire. His essential nutritional requirements are similar to those of a protozoan. His genetic material is strikingly close in its basic chemical constitution to that of a bacterium. Gorilla and man share some of the same blood groups. We know that man differs from the animals and all other organisms, however, in his powers to reason and plan, to invent and manipulate, to exercise foresight, and to communicate his ideas and beliefs to his fellow man. These are the powers which have catapulted him to his present position of evolutionary dominance. He also differs from other animals, we hope, in qualities of judgment, restraint, wisdom, tolerance, compassion, and ethical commitment, and also in his sense of wonder and beauty. It is these qualities, also the product of his cultural evolution, on which the resolution of present dilemmas may depend.

SUMMARY

Our study of the evolution of man is based upon three different kinds of data: (1) our knowledge of the processes of evolution, (2) the fossil record, and (3) the comparative study of man and contemporary primates.

The first mammals—warm-blooded, rodent-sized, and probably nocturnal—developed from reptilian stock in the late Mesozoic era and radiated explosively. Eventually, some took up life in the trees and developed into the early primates, with hands and feet adapted to grasping and climbing.

Dentition is of great importance in characterizing the primate orders since differences of size, shape, and number of teeth are distinctive. The Old World monkeys, the apes, and man have 32 teeth, which are relatively unspecialized.

Early in the Paleocene epoch, the small tree dwellers split into various prosimian lines, which are represented today only by the lemurs, the tree shrews, and the tarsiers.

The monkeys, members of the Anthropoidea group, which also includes the apes and man, evolved independently in the New World and the Old World. The change from prosimian to monkey involved chiefly a reduction in the primitive sense of smell, the development of binocular, stereoscopic color vision (with a concomitant switch to diurnal life), and an increase of four or five times in brain size. Monkeys also lost the long snout of the prosimians.

The apes also developed from the prosimians but evolved a different mode of locomotion. While the monkeys are quadrupedal, the apes *brachiate*, that is, swing from one arm and then the other through the trees. This means of locomotion involved a rearrangement of body structure. *Dryopithecus* is the generic name of a large group of apes of Africa, Asia, and Europe which were contemporary with the gibbon in the late Miocene epoch. The modern descendents of *Dryopithecus* are the orangutan of southeast Asia and the gorilla and chimpanzee of Africa. The latter are chiefly ground dwellers and are more closely related to each other and to man than to the orangutan.

Man evolved from less specialized apelike creatures and is distinguished from other primates by his upright posture, his ability to walk continuously on two legs, his brain, his ability to make and use tools, and his language and culture.

Ramapithecus, who lived about 14 million years ago in India, is the oldest specimen yet found of what might be an ancestor of man. About 2 1/2 million years ago, australopithecines became established in East and South Africa. The australopithecine had a cranial capacity of 450 to 600 cubic centimeters, walked erect though with bent knees and hips, ate meat as well as vegetables, and used tools. He may also have made tools, but this is not agreed upon.

Homo erectus lived in Asia, Africa, and Europe from about 700,000 to about 200,000 years ago. His body skeleton was much like modern man's, and his cranial capacity averaged between 900 and 1,250 cubic centimeters, overlapping that of modern man. He knew the use of fire, ate meat, and made tools.

Neanderthal man ranged throughout Europe, Africa, the Near East, and Central Asia 100,000 to 35,000 years ago. His cranial capacity was equal to or larger than modern man's. He was a hunter, made flake tools, had language, and buried his dead.

Cro-Magnon man appeared about 35000 B.C. and was physically almost indistinguishable from modern man. He fashioned blade tools and made clothing. He is perhaps known best for his cave paintings.

Agriculture began about 7000 B.C. in two areas—Mexico and the fertile crescent around the eastern Mediterranean.

From very early, man's evolution has been dominated by his culture. Evolutionary changes brought about cultural advances, and these, in turn, caused selective pressures which led to further evolutionary changes. The rapid physical changes which resulted from this cultural evolution stopped about 35000 B.C., the time of Cro-Magnon man. Since then, man has probably altered very little, but selective pressures have changed as man has gained greater and greater control over his environment. This control places on man a very great responsibility; today his activities are a major force not only in his own evolution but in the evolution of all the living things around him.

SUGGESTIONS FOR FURTHER READING

ALLEN, DURWARD L.: *Our Wildlife Legacy*, rev. ed., Funk & Wagnalls Company, New York, 1962.

A description of wildlife conservation in the United States, written for a general audience.

BATES, MARSTON: *Animal Worlds*, Random House, Inc., New York, 1963.

A spectacularly illustrated account of animal habitats and ecology throughout the world.

——: *The Forest and the Sea*, Vintage Books, Random House, Inc., New York, 1965.*

A compelling and wide-ranging study of the economy of nature and the ecology of man, beautifully written.

CARLQUIST, SHERWIN: *Island Life: A Natural History of the Islands of the World*, The Natural History Press, Garden City, N.Y., 1965.

An exploration of the nature of island life and of the intricate and unexpected evolutionary patterns followed by island plants and animals.

CARSON, RACHEL L.: *The Sea around Us*, New American Library of World Literature, Inc., New York, 1954.*

Miss Carson was a rare combination of scientist and poet. This deservedly popular book traces the history of the formation of the oceans, describes their role in the origin of life and in its evolution, and discusses their present-day importance to human life.

DOBZHANSKY, THEODOSIUS: *Genetics and the Origin of Species*, 3rd ed., Columbia University Press, New York, 1951.*

A presentation of the basic themes of population genetics by one of the foremost leaders in studies of Drosophila.

FARB, PETER: *Face of North America*, Harper & Row, Publishers, Inc., New York, 1963.

An interesting and comprehensive account for a general audience of the natural history of the continent—the interplay of geologic change, climate, and plant and animal life.

FISHER, RONALD A.: *The Genetical Theory of Natural Selection*, 2nd ed., Dover Publications, Inc., New York, 1958.

First published in 1929, this is one of the crucial books in the new synthetic theory of evolution and remains one of the best expositions of the subject for the interested student.

HOWELLS, W. W.: *Mankind in the Making*, rev. ed., Doubleday & Company, Inc., Garden City, N.Y., 1967.

A clear and lively treatment of the story of human evolution, with a conjectural glimpse into the future.

HUTCHINSON, G. EVELYN: *The Ecological Theater and the Evolutionary Play*, Yale University Press, New Haven, Conn., 1965.

By one of the great modern experts on freshwater ecology, this a charming and sophisticated collection of essays on the influence of environment in evolution —and also on an astonishing variety of other subjects.

KRUTCH, J. W.: *Desert Year*, The Viking Press, Inc., New York, 1960.*

A description by one of the best contemporary American nature writers of the animal and plant life of the American desert.

LACK, DAVID L.: *Darwin's Finches*, Harper Torchbooks, Harper & Row, Publishers, Inc., New York, 1961.*

An ornithologist's study of the finches of the Galapagos proves, once again, that these drab little birds offer one of the most provocative demonstrations of Darwinian evolution.

LE GROS CLARK, W. E.: *Antecedents of Man: An Introduction to the Evolution of the Primates*, Harper and Row, Publishers, Inc., New York, 1963.*

In the hands of Le Gros Clark, an expert in primate anatomy, details of dental and bone structure become fascinating clues in the great detective story of evolution. This book is primarily suited for the student with a special interest in the evolution of man.

MACARTHUR, ROBERT, AND JOSEPH CONNELL: *The Biology of Populations*, John Wiley & Sons, Inc., New York, 1966.

A tough, basic treatment, dealing with the development of populations, their genetic composition, and their functioning and interactions.

MAYR, E.: *Animal Species and Evolution*, Harvard University Press, Cambridge, Mass., 1963.

A masterly, substantial, and illuminating statement of contemporary thinking about species—how they arise and their roles as units of evolution.

MEDAWAR, PETER B.: *The Future of Man*, Mentor Books, New American Library of World Literature, Inc., New York, 1961.*

An urbane and fascinating collection of essays on man and his prospects.

ODUM, EUGENE P., AND HOWARD T. ODUM: *Fundamentals of Ecology*, 2nd ed., W. B. Saunders Company, Philadelphia, 1959.

A sturdy and reliable general textbook of ecology.

SIMPSON, GEORGE GAYLORD: *The Meaning of Evolution*, rev. ed., Yale University Press, New Haven, Conn., 1967.*

In this lucid, nontechnical exposition, Professor Simpson, a leading paleontologist, explores three questions: what has happened in the course of evolution, how did it come about, and what does it mean in terms of the nature of man and his future. For the thoughtful reader.

*Available in paperback.

APPENDIX 1

CLASSIFICATION OF ORGANISMS

There are several alternate ways to classify the organisms. The one presented here follows the overall scheme described at the end of Section 2–1, in which organisms are divided into three major groups, or Kingdoms: Monera, Plantae, and Animalia.

All of the phyla of which there are living representatives are included. The chief taxonomic divisions are: Kingdom, Phylum (for animals) or Division (for plants), Class, Order, Family, Genus, Species. This classification often includes the classes and sometimes also the orders. The phyla within each kingdom and the classes within each phylum are arranged, as much as possible, in order of increasing complexity. The number of species given for each phylum is the approximate number of living species described and named.* In many, probably most, phyla there are undoubtedly many more species still undescribed.

This list is not intended as a complete catalog of all organisms, but as a guide to the important groupings of plants and animals.

* The sources followed for the number of species are—for plants, *An Evolutionary Survey of the Plant Kingdom* by R. F. Scagel and others (1965) and, for animals, *A Classification of Living Animals* by Lord Rothschild (1961).

KINGDOM MONERA

PHYLA

PHYLUM SCHIZOMYCOPHYTA: the bacteria. Unicellular; procaryotic (lacking a nuclear membrane); reproduction usually asexual by cell division (fission); nutrition usually heterotrophic. About 3,000 species.

PHYLUM CYANOPHYTA: blue-green algae. Unicellular or colonial; procaryotic; chlorophyll, but no chloroplasts; nutrition usually autotrophic; reproduction by fission. Common on damp soil and rocks and in fresh and salt water. About 7,500 species.

KINGDOM PLANTAE

Organisms usually have rigid cell walls; nutrition is autotrophic, saprophytic, or parasitic; usually possess chlorophyll and are photosynthetic; cells are eucaryotic.

Subkingdom

Thallophyta (Thallus Plants)

Primitive, mainly aquatic plants with no highly differentiated tissues (such as root, stem or leaf) and no vascular tissues (xylem and phloem). Zygote does not develop into an embryo while enclosed within the female sex organ on the plant.

Thallophytes with Chlorophyll (The Algae)

DIVISION EUGLENOPHYTA: the euglenoids, including *Euglena* and *Peranema*. Microscopic; unicellular; green or colorless, with usually one or two flagella; true cell walls absent; reproduction usually asexual, by cell division; nuclei and chloroplasts well defined. About 1450 species.

DIVISION CHLOROPHYTA: green algae, the desmids, *Chlamydomonas, Volvox,** *Ulva, Spirogyra* and others. Unicellular, colonial or multicellular; food stored as true starch; reproduction usually asexual, but also sexual; alternation of generations in *Spirogyra*; definite nuclei and chloroplasts; cellulose cell wall. Majority found in fresh water, but some marine. About 7,000 species.

DIVISION CHRYSOPHYTA: yellow-green and golden-brown algae, chiefly diatoms. A varied phylum including motile and immotile unicellular species and filamentous and nonfilamentous colonial forms; have chlorophylls a and c; outer shells of silicon; food stored as oil. Common on soil and in fresh and salt water. About 9,200 species.

DIVISION PYRROPHYTA: chiefly single-celled algae, such as the dinoflagellates. Microscopic; unicellular; usually with a heavy cell wall (divided into plates) and 2 flagella; most photosynthetic; sexual reproduction uncommon or totally absent. About 1,000 species.

DIVISION PHAEOPHYTA: brown algae, including the large kelps, *Fucus* and *Laminaria*. Multicellular, often with large and complex bodies as in the large seaweeds; reproduction usually sexual; alternation of generations; have chlorophylls a and c; food stored as sugar or oil but never as starch. Chiefly marine. About 1,500 species.

DIVISION RHODOPHYTA: red algae. Multicellular, nonmotile. Sexual reproduction by nonmotile gametes. Most common in warm waters; chiefly marine. About 4,000 species.

Thallophytes without Chlorophyll (The Fungi)

DIVISION MYXOMYCETES: the "true" or acellular slime molds. Plant body plasmodium (mass of protoplasm with many nuclei); not sharply divided into cells; spores usually formed in sporangia, but do not form hyphae upon germination; movement amoeboid. Nutrition phagocytic. About 450 species.

DIVISION EUMYCOTA: the true fungi. Thallus a fine mat (mycelium) composed of many interconnecting branches (hyphae). Principally decomposers; definite cell walls; sexual or asexual reproduction by means of spores; immotile; no chlorophyll. About 100,000 species.

* You will note that *Volvox* and *Chlamydomonas* are also listed under Class Mastigophora of Phylum Protozoa.

CLASSES	*Class Phycomycetes:* the algal fungi. Bread molds, such as *Rhizopus,* and leaf molds. Most have hyphae and many nuclei but no cross walls or fruiting structures. Many aquatic.
	Class Ascomycetes: the sac fungi, including the single-celled yeasts, the mildews, truffles, morels, cheese molds, blue and green molds such as *Penicillium,* and red bread molds such as *Neurospora.* Source of most antibiotics; cross walls divide hyphae; have fruiting structures; spores develop within a closed ascus.
	Class Basidiomycetes: club fungi, mushrooms, toadstools, rusts, and smuts. Hyphae divided by cross walls; spores develop externally in a club-shaped hyphae (basidium).
	Class Deuteromycetes: Fungi Imperfecti. A heterogeneous collection of fungi in which complete sexual reproductive cycle is unknown and which are not easily assigned to one of the other classes. Most are parasitic.
	Class Lichenes: Plants made up of an alga and a fungus in a symbiotic association. Reproduction usually vegetative. More than 17,000 species.

Subkingdom	**Embryophyta** Plants with an embryo stage with the zygote developing into a multicellular embryo while still encased in the female sex organ (archegonium) or within an embryo sac. Generally less primitive than the thallophytes with more specialization of tissues and more adapted to the conditions of life on land. Alternation of generations occurs in all embryophytes.

DIVISION	DIVISION BRYOPHYTA: multicellular, usually terrestrial, with sexual reproduction by alternation of generations; the plant body is the gametophyte generation and the sporophyte is attached to and dependent on the gametophyte; no true vascular tissue or roots; no stiff, supporting structures; multicellular sex organ (archegonium in the female and antheridium in the male). Free water necessary for reproduction. Damp environments; mostly tropical. About 23,600 species.
CLASSES	*Class Hepaticae:* liverworts. Usually simple, prostrate plants without stem or leaves. Sporophyte ephemeral. About 9,000 species.
	Class Musci: mosses. Leafy, radially symmetrical; erect or prostrate; gametophyte long lived; sporophyte not ephemeral. About 14,000 species.
	Class Anthocerotae: the hornworts. Gametophyte small, lobed, approximately circular in outline. About 100 species.

DIVISION		DIVISION TRACHEOPHYTA: true vascular plants with specialized vascular (xylem and phloem) and supporting tissues; archegonia usually present, except in the flowering plants (angiosperms); plant body represents the sporophyte generation. About 321,468 species.

SUBDIVISIONS

SUBDIVISION PSILOPSIDA: leafy plants with rhizoids but no true roots; simple vascular bundles. Mostly tropical. Represented chiefly by fossil forms. 3 living species, including whisk fern.

SUBDIVISION LYCOPSIDA: simple conducting tissues; undeveloped roots; very small green leaves. Represented by the modern club mosses. About 11,000 species.

SUBDIVISION SPHENOPSIDA: horsetails. Jointed stems; small true leaves and roots; simple vascular tissues; silicon in epidermis. Known mostly as fossils. About 25 living species.

SUBDIVISION PTEROPSIDA: by far the largest group of living plants; well-adapted to terrestrial conditions; complex vascular systems, an excellent root system and large conspicuous leaves. About 310,450 species.

CLASSES

Class Filicineae: the ferns and related forms. Fertilization by swimming sperms; sporangia numerous and usually on the lower sides of leaves. About 10,000 species.

Class Gymnospermae: the naked seed plants, including seed ferns, ginkos, conifers, cycads and others. Seeds usually borne in cones; pollen usually wind-borne to the ovules; lack ovule case, true flowers or fruits. About 450 species.

Class Angiospermae: the flowering plants. Ovules completely enclosed in an ovule case; seeds enclosed in a fruit. About 300,000 species.

SUBCLASSES

Subclass Monocotyledons: embryo has one cotyledon; vascular tissue scattered throughout stem; cambium usually absent; flower parts in groups of three or six; leaves with parallel veins. Represented by grasses, lilies, orchids, palms and others. About 50,000 species.

Subclass Dicotyledons: embryo has two cotyledons; vascular tissue bunched in a ring in the stem; possess cambium; flower parts in groups of four or five; net-like leaf venation. Represented by herbs and woody plants, such as ragweeds, mustards, peas, cacti, maples, elms, oaks, and others. About 250,000 species.

KINGDOM **ANIMALIA**

Organisms usually multicellular, motile, without rigid cell walls or chlorophyll; nutrition commonly heterotrophic.

PHYLUM

PHYLUM PROTOZOA: microscopic, unicellular or simple colonial animals; usually with distinct nucleus and cytoplasm; reproduction usually asexual by mitotic division; classified by type of locomotion. About 30,000 species.

815   *Classification of Organisms*

CLASSES		*Class Mastigophora:* the flagellates, including *Euglena, Volvox, Chlamydomonas.** Also parasitic species, such as *Trypanosome.* Some possess chlorophyll.
		Class Sarcodina: protozoans with pseudopodia, including *Amoeba, Arcella* and the *Foraminifera.* No stiffening pellicle outside cell walls.
		Class Ciliophora: protozoans with cilia, including *Paramecium, Stentor, Euplotes.*
		Class Sporozoa: parasitic protozoans; usually without locomotive organs during a major part of their life cycle.

Subkingdom **Parazoa**

Includes the sponges, the only major group of multicelled animals with no digestive cavity.

PHYLUM   PHYLUM PORIFERA: the sponges. Simple multicellular animals; largely marine; with a stiff supporting skeleton and a body perforated by many pores that admit water containing food particles. About 4,200 species.

Subkingdom **Metazoa**

Animals whose bodies consist of many cells, as distinct from the unicellular Protozoa.

PHYLUM   PHYLUM COELENTERATA: the coelenterates. Radially symmetrical, "two-layered"; possess nematocysts; of a jellylike consistency; reproduction asexual or sexual. Aquatic, mostly marine. About 9,600 species.

CLASSES   *Class Hydrozoa: Hydra, Obelia* and other hydra-like animals. Often colonial, and often having a regular alternation of asexual and sexual generations. Polyp form dominant.

Class Scyphozoa: the marine jellyfishes or "cup animals," including *Aurelia.* Medusa form dominant; true muscle cells.

Class Anthozoa: sea anemones ("flower animals") and colonial corals. No medusa stage.

PHYLA   PHYLUM CTENOPHORA: the comb jellies and sea walnuts. Free-swimming, often almost spherical animals; translucent, gelatinous, delicately colored; often bioluminescent; possess eight bands of cilia, for locomotion. About 80 species.

* You will note that *Volvox* and *Chlamydomonas* are also listed under Division Chlorophyta.

PHYLUM PLATYHELMINTHES: the flatworms. Bilaterally symmetrical; three tissue layers; gut, when present, has only one opening; no coelom or circulatory system; complex hermaphroditic reproductive system; excretion by means of flame cells. About 15,000 species.

CLASSES

Class Turbellaria: the planaria and other non-parasitic flatworms. Ciliated; carnivorous; have ocelli.

Class Trematoda: the flukes. Parasitic flatworms with a digestive tract.

Class Cestoidea: the tapeworms. Parasitic flatworms with no digestive tract; absorb nourishment through body surface.

PHYLA

PHYLUM NEMERTEA: the proboscis or ribbon worms. Nonparasitic; usually marine; have a tube-like gut with mouth and anus, and a protrusible proboscis armed with a hook for capturing prey; simple circulatory and reproductive systems. About 550 species.

PHYLUM NEMATODA: the roundworms and nematodes. Includes minute free-living forms, such as vinegar eels, and plant and animal parasites, such as hookworms. A fairly large phylum; characterized by elongated, cylindrical, bilaterally symmetrical bodies. About 10,000 species.

PHYLUM ACANTHOCEPHALA: the spiny-headed worms. Parasitic worms with no digestive tract and a head armed with many recurved spines. About 300 species.

PHYLUM CHAETOGNATHA: arrow worms. Free-swimming planktonic marine worms; have a coelom, a complete digestive tract and a mouth with strong sickle-shaped hooks on each side. About 50 species.

PHYLUM NEMATOMORPHA: the horsehair worms. Extremely slender, brown or black worms up to 3 feet long; adults are free-living, but the larvae are parasitic in insects. About 250 species.

PHYLUM ROTIFERA: microscopic, wormlike or spherical animals, commonly called "wheel animalcules." Have complete digestive tract, flame cells, and a circle of cilia on the head, the beating of which suggests a wheel; males minute and either degenerate or unknown in many species. About 1,500 species.

PHYLUM GASTROTRICHA: microscopic, wormlike animals moving by longitudinal bands of cilia. About 140 species.

PHYLUM BRYOZOA: "moss" animals. Microscopic aquatic organisms; characterized by a U-shaped row of ciliated tentacles, with which they feed; usually fixed and in branching colonies; superficially resemble hydroid coelenterates but are much more complex; have anus and coelom; retain larva in special brood pouch. About 4,000 species.

PHYLUM BRACHIOPODA: the lamp shells. Marine animals with two hard shells (one dorsal and one ventral), superficially like a clam; obtain food by means of ciliated tentacles; fixed by a stalk or one shell in adult life. About 260 living species; 3,000 extinct.

817   *Classification of Organisms*

PHYLUM PHORONIDEA: sedentary, elongated, wormlike animals that secrete and live in a leathery tube; U-shaped digestive tract and a ring of ciliated tentacles with which they feed. Marine. About 15 species.

PHYLUM ANNELIDA: ringed or segmented worms, usually with well-developed coelom (fluid-filled cavity within mesoderm), one-way digestive tract, head, and circulatory system; appendages nonjointed, when present; have nephridia, well-defined nervous system. About 7,000 species.

CLASSES

Class Archiannelida: small simple, probably primitive, marine worms. About 35 species.

Class Polychaeta: mainly marine worms, such as *Nereis.* Have a distinct head with palps and tentacles and many bristled lobose appendages; parapodia often brightly colored. About 4,000 species.

Class Oligochaeta: soil, fresh water and marine annelids, including the earthworm (*Lumbricus*). Scanty bristles and usually a poorly differentiated head. About 2,500 species.

Class Hirudinea: leeches. Posterior sucker and usually an anterior sucker surrounding the mouth; fresh water, marine and terrestrial; either free-living or parasitic. About 300 species.

PHYLUM

PHYLUM MOLLUSCA: unsegmented animals, with a head, a mantle and a muscular foot, variously modified; mostly aquatic; soft-bodied, often with one or more hard shells; all but *Pelecypoda* have a radula (rasplike organ used for scraping or marine drilling); three-chambered heart. About 100,000 species.

CLASSES

Class Amphineura: the chitons. Simplest type of mollusks; elongated body covered with mantle in which are imbedded eight dorsal shell plates. About 700 species.

Class Pelecypoda: two-shelled, bivalve mollusks, including clams, oysters, mussels, scallops. Usually have a hatchet-shaped foot and no distinct head. Generally sessile. About 15,000 species.

Class Scaphopoda: the tooth or tusk shells; includes *Dentalium.* Marine mollusks with a conical tubular shell. About 350 species.

Class Gastropoda: asymmetrical mollusks including snails, whelks, slugs. Usually with a spiral shell and a head with one or two pairs of tentacles. About 80,000 species.

Class Cephalopoda: octopus, squid, *Nautilus.* "Headfoot" with eight or ten arms or many tentacles; mouth with two horny jaws; well-developed eyes and nervous system; shell external (*Nautilus*), internal (squid) or absent (octopus); all except *Nautilus* have ink gland. About 400 species.

PHYLUM		PHYLUM ARTHROPODA: the largest phylum in the animal kingdom. Segmented animals; paired jointed appendages, hard jointed exoskeleton; growth involves molting; complete digestive tract; coelom reduced; no nephridia; brain dorsal; nerve cord ventral; paired ganglia in each segment. About 765,257 species.
	CLASSES	*Class Merostomata:* horseshoe crabs. Aquatic; book gills; "living fossils." 5 species.
		Class Crustacea: lobsters, crabs, crayfishes, shrimps. Mostly aquatic; two pairs of antennae; one pair of mandibles, and typically two pairs of maxillae; thoracic segment with appendages; abdominal segments with or without appendages. About 25,000 species.
		Class Arachnida: spiders, mites, scorpions. Most members terrestrial, air-breathing; usually 4 or 5 pairs of legs; first pair of appendages used for grasping; have chelicerae (pincers or fangs) instead of jaws or antennae. About 30,000 species.
		Class Onychophora: simple, terrestrial arthropods. All belong to one genus, *Peripatus*; have many short unjointed pairs of legs. About 73 species.
		Class Insecta: insects. Most are terrestrial; most breathe air by means of trachea; one pair of antennae, three pairs of legs; three distinct parts of the body (head, thorax and abdomen); most have 2 pairs of wings. Include bees, ants, beetles, butterflies, fleas, lice, bugs, flies, etc. About 700,000 species.
		Class Chilopoda: the centipedes. 15 to 173 trunk segments, each with one pair of jointed appendages. About 2,000 species.
		Class Diplopoda: the millipedes. Abdomen with 20 to 100 segments, each with two pairs of appendages. About 7,000 species.
PHYLUM		PHYLUM ECHINODERMATA: radially symmetrical in adult stage; well-developed coelom formed from enteric pouches; endoskeleton of calcareous ossicles and spines; unique water vascular system; tube feet; marine. About 5,700 species.
	CLASSES	*Class Crinoidea:* sea lilies and feather stars. Sessile animals, often having a jointed stalk for attachment; ten arms bearing many slender lateral branches. Most species are fossils.
		Class Asteroidea: starfishes. Have five to fifty arms; oral surface directed downward. Two to four tube feet.
		Class Ophiuroidea: brittle stars, serpent stars. Greatly elongated, highly flexible slender arms; rapid horizontal locomotion.
		Class Echinoidea: sea urchins, sand dollars. Skeletal plates form rigid test which bears many movable spines.
		Class Holothuroidea: sea cucumbers. Sausage-shaped or worm-like elongated body.

| PHYLUM | | PHYLUM CHORDATA: animals having at some stage a notochord, pharyngeal gill slits, and a hollow nerve cord on the dorsal side. About 44,794 species. |

PHYLUM CHORDATA: animals having at some stage a notochord, pharyngeal gill slits, and a hollow nerve cord on the dorsal side. About 44,794 species.

SUBPHYLA

Subphylum Hemichordata: small group of marine animals, including the acorn, or proboscis worms. Wormlike animals with a notochordlike structure in the head end; gill slits; solid nerve cord. About 91 species.

Subphylum Tunicata: tunicates or ascidians. Saclike; adults usually sessile, often forming branching colonies; marine; feed by ciliary currents; have gill slits, reduced nervous system, no notochord. Larva active with well developed nervous system and notochord. About 1,600 species.

Subphylum Cephalochordata: lancelets. Small subphylum containing only *Amphioxus* and related forms. Somewhat fishlike marine animals with a permanent notochord the whole length of the body; nerve cord; pharynx with gill slits; no cartilage or bone. About 13 species.

Subphylum Vertebrata: the vertebrates. Most important subphylum of Chordata. Notochord replaced by cartilage or bone, forming the segmented vertebral column or backbone; skull surrounding a well-developed brain; usually a tail. About 43,090 species.

CLASSES

Class Agnatha: lampreys and hagfishes. Eel-like aquatic vertebrates without limbs; jawless sucking mouth; single nostril; no bone, scales or fins.*

Class Chondrichthyes: sharks, rays, skates, and other cartilaginous fish. Without air bladders; have complicated copulatory organs, scales. Almost exclusively marine.*

Class Osteichthyes: the bony fish, including nearly all modern freshwater fish, such as sturgeon, trout, perch, anglerfish, lungfish and some almost extinct groups. Usually with an air bladder or (rarely) a lung.*

Class Amphibia: salamanders, frogs, and toads. Usually breathing by gills in the larval stage and by lungs in the adult stage; incomplete double circulation; skin usually naked; the limbs are legs. The first vertebrates to inhabit the land, and ancestors of the reptiles; eggs unprotected by a shell and embryonic membranes. About 2,000 species.

Class Reptilia: turtles, lizards, snakes, crocodiles; includes extinct species such as the dinosaurs. Breathe by lungs; incomplete double circulation; skin usually covered with scales; the four limbs are legs (absent in snakes); cold-blooded; mostly live and reproduce on land though some are aquatic; embryo enclosed in an egg shell and has a protective amnion and an allantois. About 5,000 species.

Class Aves: the birds. Warm-blooded animals with complete double circulation; skin covered with feathers; the forelimbs are wings. Includes the extinct *Archeopteryx.* About 8,590 species.

* According to Rothschild, the total number of species of fishes is about 23,000.

| | | *Class Mammalia:* the mammals. Warm-blooded animals with complete double circulation. Distinguished by skin usually covered with hair; young nourished with milk secreted by the mother; four limbs, usually legs (forelimbs sometimes arms, wings, or fins); diaphragm used in respiration; lower jaw made up of a single pair of bones; three bones in each middle ear connecting ear drum and inner ear; 7 vertebrae in neck. About 4,500 species. |

SUBCLASSES

Subclass Prototheria: the monotremes. Oviparous (egg-laying) mammals with imperfect temperature regulation. Only two living species are the duckbill platypus and spiny anteater of Australia and New Guinea.

Subclass Metatheria: the marsupials, including kangaroos, opossums, and others. Viviparous mammals without a placenta (or with a poorly developed one); the young are born in an undeveloped state and are carried in an external pouch of the mother for some time after birth. Found chiefly in Australia.

Subclass Eutheria: mammals with a well-developed placenta. Comprises the great majority of living mammals. The principal *orders* of Eutheria are the following:

ORDERS

Insectivora: shrews, moles, hedgehogs, etc.
Edentata: toothless mammals—anteaters, sloths, armadillos, etc.
Rodentia: the rodents—rats, mice, squirrels, etc.
Artiodactyla: even-toed ungulates—cattle, deer, camels, hippopotamuses, etc.
Perissodactyla: odd-toed, hoofed mammals—horses, zebras, rhinoceroses, etc.
Proboscidea: elephants
Lagomorpha: rabbits and hares
Sirenia: the manatee, dugong, and sea cows. Large aquatic mammals with the forelimbs finlike, the hind limbs absent.
Carnivora: carnivorous animals—cats, dogs, bears, weasels, seals, etc.
Cetacea: the whales, dolphins, and porpoises. Aquatic mammals with the forelimbs fins, the hind limbs absent.
Chiroptera: the bats. Aerial mammals with the forelimbs wings.
Primates: the lemurs, monkeys, apes, and man.

GEOLOGIC ERAS

ERAS	PERIODS	EPOCHS	BIOLOGICAL EVENTS	GEOLOGICAL EVENTS
CENOZOIC	QUATERNARY	Recent		
		Pleistocene	Early man	Glacial conditions
	TERTIARY	Pliocene	Large carnivores	Warm climates, gradually cooling; continental areas mainly free of seas; continued growth of mountains, including Alps and Himalayas
		Miocene	First abundant grazing mammals	
		Oligocene	Large running mammals	
		Eocene	Many modern types of mammals appear	
		Paleocene	Expansion of mammals	
MESOZOIC	CRETACEOUS		First primates (?) First placental mammals First flowering plants; extinction of dinosaurs	At first great swamp deposits; followed by birth of Rocky Mountains and Andes, and cooling of climates
	JURASSIC		First mammals and birds; dinosaurs abundant	Much of continental lowlands near sea-level
	TRIASSIC		First dinosaurs; abundant conifers	Widespread desert conditions
PALEOZOIC	PERMIAN		Extinction of many kinds of marine animals; great expansion of primitive reptiles	Continued mountain-building, and variable climates including aridity and perhaps glaciation
	CARBONIFEROUS *Pennsylvanian*		Great coal forests; first conifers; reptiles appear	Lands low and warm with seas over much of continents at the beginning; coal swamps, from which come the greatest coal deposits; mountain-building toward the end
	Mississipian		Sharks and amphibians abundant; large and numerous scale trees and ferns	
	DEVONIAN		First amphibians; fishes abundant	Still considerable portions of land under water; evidences of aridity and of continental areas
	SILURIAN		First land plants	Much of land below the sea at first, followed by mountain-building at the end
	ORDOVICIAN		Earliest known fishes; invertebrates dominate	Great submergence of land
	CAMBRIAN		Appearance of abundant marine invertebrates; trilobites dominate	Lowlands and mild climates; first abundant fossil-bearing rocks
			Earliest known fossils	

Millions of Years Ago
1½–2 —
7 —
26 —
38 —
53–54 —
65
136 —
195 —
225
280 —
310 —
345 —
395 —
440 —
500 —
570–600

(After Simpson, Simons, and Hanson)

GLOSSARY

This list does not include names of taxonomic groups or of geological eras, which can be found in Appendixes 1 and 2, or terms that are used only once in the text and defined there.

A- (Gr. *an*-, not): Prefix, negates the succeeding part of the word.

A: Abbreviation of angstrom unit.

AB- (L., away, off): Prefix, meaning "away from" or "off."

ABDOMEN: In vertebrates, that portion of the trunk containing visceral organs except for heart and lungs; in arthropods, the posterior portion of the body composed of a group of similar segments and containing the reproductive organs and posterior portion of the digestive tract.

ABORAL: Opposite to or away from the mouth.

ABSCISSION ZONE: A layer of thin-walled cells extending across the stem of a leaf or fruit, the breaking of which causes the organ to separate from the plant.

ABSORPTION: The passage of water and dissolved substances into the cell or organism.

ACID (L. *acidus*, sour): A substance that dissociates, releasing hydrogen (H^+) ions but not hydroxyl (OH^-) ions; whose aqueous solution has a pH less than 7.

ACRO- (Gr. *akros*, highest, outermost): Prefix, meaning "pertaining to the tip."

ACROSOME: The structure at the tip of an animal sperm that fuses with the egg during fertilization.

ACTIVE TRANSPORT: The energy-expending process by which a cell moves a substance across the cell membrane, often from a point of lower concentration to a point of higher concentration, against the diffusion gradient.

AD- (L., toward, to): Prefix, meaning "toward" or "to."

ADAPTATION: (L. *adaptare*, to fit): 1) The acquiring of characteristics by an organism (or group of organisms) which make it better suited to live and reproduce in its environment. 2) A peculiarity of structure, physiology, or behavior of an organism which especially aids in fitting the organism to its particular environment.

ADAPTIVE RADIATION: The evolution from a relatively primitive and unspecialized type of organism to several divergent forms specialized to fit numerous distinct and diverse ways of life, as occurred in Darwin's finches or the marsupials of Australia.

ADENOSINE TRIPHOSPHATE (ATP): The major source of usable energy in cell metabolism; composed of adenine, ribose, and three phosphate groups. On hydrolysis, ATP loses one phosphate and one hydrogen to become adenosine diphosphate (ADP) and releases energy in the process.

ADRENAL GLAND: A vertebrate endocrine gland. The cortex (outer surface) is the source of cortisol, aldosterone, and other steroid hormones; the medulla (inner core) secretes adrenaline.

AEROBIC (Gr. *aēr, aeros*, air + *bios*, life): Requiring free oxygen for respiration.

AFFERENT NERVE FIBER: A fiber carrying impulses from a receptor toward the central nervous system or central ganglion; a sensory nerve fiber.

AGAR: A gelatinous substance derived from certain red algae which is used as a solidifying agent in the preparation of nutrient media for growing microorganisms.

ALGA: A photosynthetic organism lacking multicellular sex organs.

ALKALINE: Pertaining to substances which release hydroxyl (OH^-) ions in water; having a pH greater than 7.

ALLANTOIS (Gr. *allantoeides*, sausage-shaped): A saclike outgrowth from the ventral surface of the posterior part of the embryonic gut and membrane in reptiles, birds, and mammals that functions as an embryonic urinary bladder or as a respiratory extension of the hindgut, carrying blood vessels to and from the placenta.

ALLELE (ALLELOMORPH) (Gr. *allēlōn*, of one another + *-morphē*, form): One of the alternate forms of the same functional gene. Alleles occupy the same position (locus) on homologous chromosomes, and so are separated from each other at meiosis.

ALLOPOLYPLOID: A polyploid in which the different sets of chromosomes come from different species or widely different strains.

ALTERNATION OF GENERATIONS: In plants, a reproductive cycle in which a usually haploid (1*n*) organism or tissue, the gametophyte, gives rise to gametes which, after fusion to form a zygote, develop into a usually diploid (2*n*) organism, the sporophyte. Spores produced by meiotic division from the sporophyte give rise to new gametophytes, completing the cycle.

AMINO ACIDS: Organic acids containing an amino (NH_2) group; the subunits of protein molecules. There are 20 common amino acids.

AMNION (Gr. dim. of *amnos*, lamb): Inner, fluid-filled sac composed of a thin double membrane that surrounds the embryo in reptiles, birds, and mammals.

AMOEBOID (Gr. *amoibē*, change): Moving or eating by means of pseudopodia (temporary cytoplasmic protrusions from the cell body).

AMPHI- (Gr., on both sides): Prefix, meaning "on both sides," "both," "of both kinds."

AMPHIBIAN (Gr. *amphibios*, living a double life): A class of vertebrates intermediate in many characteristics between fish and reptiles, which live part of the time in water and part on land.

AMPHIBIOUS: Pertaining to any organism capable of living both in water and on land.

AN- (Gr., not): Prefix, equivalent to "a-", meaning "not"; used before a vowel or "h."

ANAEROBIC: Applied to cells (largely bacterial) that can live without oxygen; strict anaerobes cannot live in the presence of oxygen.

ANALOGOUS (Gr. *analogos*, proportionate): Applied to structures similar in function but different in evolutionary origin, such as claw and hand.

ANDRO- (Gr. *anēr*, *andros*, man): Prefix, meaning "man" or "male."

ANDROGEN: Male sex hormone.

ANGIOSPERM (Gr. *angeion*, a vessel + -*sperma*, seed): A flowering plant. Seeds are enclosed by a matured ovary (fruit).

ANGSTROM: Unit of measurement equal to 1/100,000,000 centimeter or 1/10,000 micron.

ANIMAL HEMISPHERE: That half of the egg or zygote in which there is less yolky material, which contains the nucleus, and which is most active in cell cleavage. Contrasts with vegetal hemisphere.

ANIMAL POLE: Imaginary point on the surface of the egg or zygote which lies in the center of the animal hemisphere, opposite to the vegetal pole.

ANNUAL: A plant which completes its life cycle from seed germination to seed production, followed by death, in a single growing season.

ANTERIOR (L. *ante*, before, toward, in front of): The front end of an organism; in human anatomy, the ventral surface.

ANTHER: In plants, the pollen-bearing portion of a stamen.

ANTHERIDIUM: In plants, the sperm-producing cell or organ.

ANTHOCYANIN (Gr. *anthos*, flower + *kyanos*, blue): A water-soluble pigment in plants. It occurs in solution in the cell sap and is responsible for red, blue, and violet colors.

ANTHROPO- (Gr. *anthropos*, man, human): Prefix, meaning "man" or "human."

ANTHROPOMORPHISM: Assignment of human characteristics, abilities, or feelings to nonhuman organisms.

ANTIBODY: A globular protein that is produced in the body fluids, chiefly of birds and mammals, in response to a foreign substance, generally a protein or polysaccharide (antigen) and reacts specifically with it.

ANTIGEN: A foreign substance, usually a protein or polysaccharide, which stimulates the formation of specific antibodies.

APICAL DOMINANCE: In plants, the influence of a terminal bud in suppressing the growth of lateral buds through the release of the growth-regulating hormone, auxin.

APICAL MERISTEM: The growing point, composed of meristematic tissue, at the tip of the root or stem in vascular plants.

ARBOREAL: Tree-dwelling.

ARCH-, ARCHEO- (Gr. *archē*, *archos*, beginning): Prefix, meaning "first," "main," "earliest."

ARCHEGONIUM, pl. ARCHEGONIA (Gr. *archegeonos*, first of a race): In plants, the multicellular egg-producing organ of most embryophytes.

ARCHENTERON: The principal cavity within the early embryo (gastrula) of many animals. Lined with endoderm, it opens to the outside by means of the blastopore and ultimately becomes the digestive tract.

ARTHROPOD (Gr. *arthron*, joint + *pous*, *podos*, foot): An invertebrate animal with jointed appendages; a member of the phylum Arthropoda.

ASEXUAL REPRODUCTION: Any reproductive process, such as fission or budding, that does not involve the union of gametes.

ATOM (Gr. *atomos*, indivisible): The smallest unit into which a chemical element can be divided and still retain its characteristic properties.

ATOMIC NUCLEUS: The central core of an atom, containing protons and neutrons, around which electrons orbit.

ATOMIC NUMBER: The number of protons in the nucleus of an atom.

ATOMIC WEIGHT: The weight of a representative atom of an element relative to the weight of an atom of carbon (C^{12}), which is assigned the integral value of 12.

ATP: Abbreviation of adenosine triphosphate.

ATRIUM (L., yard, court, hall): Entrance or exit cavity. The term usually refers to the heart chamber, but it is also applied to other organs.

AUTO- (Gr. *autos*, same self): Prefix, meaning "same" or "same self."

AUTONOMIC (Gr. *nomos*, law): Self-controlling, independent of outside influences.

AUTONOMIC NERVOUS SYSTEM: A special system of motor nerves and ganglia in vertebrates which is not under voluntary control and which innervates the heart, glands, visceral organs, and smooth muscle. It is subdivided into the sympathetic and the parasympathetic nervous systems.

AUTOPOLYPLOID: A polyploid in which the chromosomes all come from the same source.

AUTOSOME: Any chromosome other than the sex chromosomes. Man has 22 pairs of autosomes and 1 pair of sex chromosomes.

AUTOTROPH (Gr. *trophos*, feeder): An organism that is able to synthesize all the nutritive substances it requires from inorganic substances, in contrast to heterotroph. Most green plants and some bacteria and fungi are autotrophs.

AUXIN (Gr. *auxein*, to increase): A growth-regulating hormone produced in the shoot tips of plants which stimulates cell enlargement and inhibits growth of lateral buds, producing apical dominance.

AXIS: An imaginary line passing through a body or organ around which parts are symmetrically aligned.

AXON: The part of a neuron which carries impulses away from the cell body.

BACKCROSS: The crossing of a hybrid with one of its parents or with an organism genetically equivalent to a parent. A cross between an individual which is heterozygous for a pair of alleles and one that is homozygous for all recessive genes involved in the experiment. A mating in which one member is homozygous for one or more genes if the homozygous genes are recessive is called a test cross.

BACTERIOPHAGE (L. *bacterium* + Gr. *phagein*, to eat): A virus that parasitizes a bacterial cell.

BACTERIUM (Gr. dim. of *baktron*, staff): A small, unicellular organism characterized by the absence of a formed nucleus; the genetic material may be dispersed throughout the cytoplasm.

BALANCED POLYMORPHISM: The continued presence in a population of more than one allele of a gene as a result of natural selection.

BARK: All plant tissues outside of the cambium in a woody stem.

BASE: A substance that, on dissociation, releases hydroxyl (OH^-) ions, but not hydrogen (H^+) ions; having a pH of more than 7; the opposite of an acid.

BASE-PAIRING RULE: The requirement that adenine must always pair with thymine (or uracil) and guanine with cytosine in a nucleic acid double helix.

BEHAVIORAL ISOLATING MECHANISMS: Modes of behavior, such as display rituals or courtship patterns, which serve to prevent mating between species.

BI- (L. *bis*, twice, double, two): Prefix, meaning "two," "twice," "having two points."

BIENNIAL (L. *annus*, year): Occurring once in 2 years; a plant which requires 2 years to complete its reproductive cycle, with vegetative growth occurring in the first year and flowering, seed production and death in the second.

BILATERAL SYMMETRY: An arrangement in which the right and left halves of an organism are mirror images of each other.

BINOMIAL SYSTEM: A system in which the name of an organism consists of two parts, the first designating the genus and the second designating the species.

BIO- (Gr. *bios*, life): Prefix, meaning "pertaining to life."

BIOLOGICAL CLOCK: An unidentified internal factor or factors in plants and animals which govern the innate biological rhythms (growth and activity patterns) of the organism.

BIOMASS: Total weight of all organisms in a particular habitat or area.

BIOMES: A world-wide complex of communities, characterized by distinctive vegetation and climate; for example the grassland areas collectively form the grassland biome, the tropical rain forests form the tropical rain forest biome, etc.

BIOSPHERE: The whole zone of air, land, and water at the surface of the earth occupied by living things.

BIOSYNTHESIS: Formation of organic compounds from simple compounds by living organisms.

BLADDER: A membraneous sac which serves as the receptacle of some fluid or gas; for example, gall bladder, swim bladder, urinary bladder.

-BLAST, BLAST-, BLASTO- (Gr. *blastos*, sprout): Suffix or prefix, meaning "pertaining to an embryo"; for example, osteoblast, an embryonic bone cell or a bone-forming cell.

BLASTODISK: Disklike area on the surface of a large yolky egg that undergoes cleavage and gives rise to the embryo.

BLASTOMERE (Gr. *meros*, part): One of the cells into which the egg divides during the cleavage phase of development.

BLASTOPORE: The opening connecting the archenteron of the gastrula stage of an embryo with the outside; represents the future mouth in some animals (Protostomes), the future anus in others (Deuterostomes).

BLASTULA: An animal embryo after cleavage and before gastrulation; usually consists of a hollow sphere surrounded by a single layer of cells.

BUD: 1) In plants, the end of a stem or branch enclosed by young leaves. 2) In animals, such as *Hydra*, an asexually produced protuberance which develops into a new individual.

BUFFER: A substance that prevents appreciable changes of pH in solutions to which small amounts of acids or bases are added.

BULB: A modified bud with thickened leaves adapted for underground food storage.

CALORIE (L. *calor*, heat): The amount of energy in the form of heat required to raise the temperature of one gram of water one degree centigrade; in making metabolic measurements the kilocalorie

(Calorie) is generally used. A Calorie is the amount of heat required to raise the temperature of one kilogram of water one degree centigrade.

CAMBIUM (L., exchange): In plants, a cylindrical sheath of embryonic (meristematic) cells, the division of which produces secondary phloem outwardly and secondary xylem inwardly.

CAMERA EYE: An eye containing a lens system which concentrates light and focuses a precise image on a light-sensitive retina.

CAMOUFLAGE: Disguise resulting from color, pattern, or shape or a combination of these that tends to blend an organism with its surroundings and make it less visible to predator or prey.

CAPILLARY (L. *capillaris*, relating to hair): A small, thin-walled blood vessel connecting arteries and veins, through which diffusion and filtration into the tissues can occur.

CARBOHYDRATE: An organic compound consisting of a chain of carbon atoms to which hydrogen and oxygen are attached in a 2:1 ratio; includes sugars, starch, glycogen, cellulose, etc.

CARBON CYCLE: World-wide circulation and utilization of carbon atoms chiefly due to metabolic processes.

CARNIVOROUS: Flesh-eating.

CAROTENE: (L. *carota*, carrot): A yellow or orange pigment found in plants, converted into vitamin A in the vertebrate liver.

CAROTENOIDS: A class of pigments that includes the carotenes (yellows and oranges) and the xanthophylls (yellow).

CARPEL: The floral structure enclosing the ovule of the angiosperm; a flower may have one or more carpels, either single or fused.

CARTILAGE: The skeletal connective tissue of vertebrates; forms much of the skeleton of adult lower vertebrates and immature higher vertebrates.

CATALYST: A substance that accelerates the rate of a chemical reaction but which is not used up in the reaction; enzymes are catalysts.

CELL: The structural unit of protoplasm, composed of cytoplasm and one or more nuclei and surrounded by a plasma membrane. In plants there is a cell wall outside of the membrane.

CELL MEMBRANE: The outermost membrane of most animal cells; plasma membrane.

CELL WALL: The rigid outermost layer of plant cells, formed by the protoplasm and composed chiefly of cellulose.

CELLULOSE: The chief constituent of the cell wall in all green plants and some fungi; an insoluble complex carbohydrate formed of microfibrils of glucose molecules.

CENTRAL NERVOUS SYSTEM: In vertebrates, the brain and spinal cord; in invertebrates it usually consists of one or more solid cords of nervous tissue plus their associated ganglia.

CENTRIOLE: A cytoplasmic organelle generally found in animal cells, usually outside of the nuclear membrane, which doubles before mitosis; the two centrioles then move apart to form the spindle poles.

CENTROMERE: A region on the chromosome to which the spindle fiber attaches during mitosis and meiosis.

CEPHALO- (Gr. *kephalē*, head): Prefix, meaning "head."

CEREBELLUM: (L. dim. of *cerebrum*, brain): An enlarged part of the dorsal side of the vertebrate brain near its rear end; chief muscle coordinating center.

CEREBRAL CORTEX: A layer of gray matter on the upper surface of the cerebrum, well developed only in mammals; the seat of conscious senses.

CEREBRUM (L., brain): An enlarged part of the dorsal and lateral sides of the brain at its front end; controls many voluntary functions and is the source of conscious sensations, learning and memory.

CHEMICAL REACTION: A change of one or more substances into different substances by recombination of their constituent atoms into different kinds of molecules.

CHEMORECEPTOR: A receptor which detects substances according to their chemical structure; includes smell and taste receptors.

CHEMOTROPISM: The behavioral response of an organism to chemical stimulation; the turning to or away from a chemical stimulus.

CHIASMA (Gr. *chiasma*, two lines placed in a cross): The x-shaped figure formed by the breakage and reunion of two non-sister chromatids of homologous chromosomes; presumably the result of crossing over.

CHITIN: A tough, resistant polysaccharide present in the exoskeleton of arthropods, the epidermal cuticle or other surface structures of many other invertebrates, and the cell walls of certain fungi.

CHLORO- (Gr. *chlōros*, green): Prefix, meaning "green."

CHLOROPLAST: A membrane-bounded organelle in green plant cells in which the chlorophyll is contained; site of photosynthesis.

CHLOROPHYLL: The green pigments of plant cells, necessary for photosynthesis.

-CHORD, CHORDA- (L. *chorda*, cord, string): Suffix or prefix, meaning "cord."

CHORDATE: Member of the animal phylum (Chordata) in which all members possess a notochord, dorsal nerve cord, and pharyngeal gill slits, at least at some stage of the life cycle.

CHORION: The outermost embryonic membrane of reptiles, birds and mammals; in placental mammals it contributes to the structure of the placenta.

CHROM- (Gr. *chrōma*, color): Prefix, meaning "color."

CHROMATID: One of the two daughter strands of a duplicated chromosome which are joined by a single centromere.

CHROMATIN: The deeply staining nucleoprotein complex of the chromosomes.

CHROMOSOME (Gr. *soma*, body): One of the bodies in the cell nucleus containing genes in a linear order; visualized as threads or rods of chromatin which appear in a contracted form during mitosis and meiosis.

CHROMOSOME MAP: A plan showing the relative position of the genes on the chromosome, determined chiefly by analysis of the relative frequency of crossing over between any two genes.

CILIUM, pl. CILIA (L., eyelash): A short hairlike structure, present on the surface of many types of cells, that beats in a regular fashion to move the cell or the organism or to move food particles over the surface; has a highly characteristic internal structure of two inner fibrils surrounded by nine pairs of outer fibrils; usually numerous and arranged in rows.

CIRCADIAN RHYTHMS (L. *circa*, about + *dies*, day): Regular rhythms of growth and activity found throughout the plant and animal kingdoms; usually on a close-to-24-hour basis.

CIRCULATION: The movement of nutritive fluids, such as sap or blood, in living organisms.

CISTRON: A unit of a chromosome that specifies one polypeptide chain.

CLEAVAGE: The successive cell divisions of the fertilized egg to form the multicellular blastula.

CLIMAX COMMUNITY: Final or stable community in a successional series (sere) which is more or less stable in equilibrium with existing environmental conditions and composed of a definite group of plant and animal species.

CLOACA (L., sewer): The exit chamber from the digestive system; also may serve as exit for the reproductive system and urinary system.

CLONE: A population descended by mitotic division from a single ancestor.

CNIDOBLAST (Gr. *knidē*, nettle): A stinging cell containing a nematocyst; characteristic of coelenterates.

COCHLEA (Gr. *kochlias*, snail): Part of the inner ear of mammals, concerned with hearing.

CODON: Sequence of three adjacent nucleotides that code a single amino acid.

-COEL, COELA-, COELO- (Gr. from *koilos*, hollow): Suffix or prefix, meaning "cavity."

COELENTERATE (Gr. *enteron*, an intestine): An invertebrate animal possessing a single alimentary opening and tentacles with sting cells, for example, jellyfish, corals, sea anemones, hydroids. Member of the phylum Coelenterata.

COELENTERON: The single cavity within the body of a coelenterate.

COELOM (Gr. from *koilōma*, a hollow): A body cavity formed between layers of mesoderm and lined entirely by mesoderm.

COENZYME: An organic molecule which plays an accessory role in enzyme-catalyzed processes, often by acting as a donor or acceptor of a substance involved in the reaction; ATP and NAD are common coenzymes.

COLINEARITY: The correspondence between the linear sequence of DNA nucleotides and the linear sequence of amino acids in a polypeptide.

COLLAGEN (Gr. *kolla*, glue): A fibrous protein material in bones, tendons and other connective tissues.

COLLOID: A permanent suspension of fine particles; many types of protoplasm appear to be colloidal systems.

COLON: The large intestine of vertebrates leading to the rectum or cloaca.

COLONY: A group of unicellular or multicellular organisms living together in close association.

COMMENSALISM (L. *com*, together + *mensa*, table): The living together of two species in which one lives on or with the other without conferring either benefit or harm.

COMMUNICATION: The process by which information is imparted between organisms by means of odor, sound, touch, or movement.

COMMUNITY: The organisms inhabiting a common environment and interacting with one another.

COMPOUND (L. *componere*, to put together): A combination of atoms in definite ratios, held together by chemical bonds; a substance containing only one kind of molecule, each molecule composed of two or more kinds of atoms.

COMPOUND EYE: A complex eye composed of a number of separate elements (ommatidia), each with light sensitive cells and a refractory system which can form an image; common in arthropods and crustaceans.

CONDITIONAL LETHAL MUTATION: A mutation that causes a loss of functions that would be fatal in some environments but not in others (such as the ability to function at one temperature but not at another). Used in genetic analyses.

CONDITIONED REFLEX: A habitual response to a particular stimulus determined by the previous experience of the organism.

CONE: 1) In plants, the reproductive part of a conifer. 2) In animals, a type of light-sensitive nerve cell in the vertebrate retina, concerned in the perception of color and in the most acute discrimination of detail.

CONJUGATION: The process in bacteria, protozoans, and certain algae and fungi by which two individuals transfer nuclear material.

CONNECTIVE TISSUE: A type of tissue which lies between groups of nerves, glands, and muscle cells and beneath epithelial cells in which the cells are irregularly distributed through a relatively large amount of intercellular material; includes bone, cartilage, blood and lymph tissue.

CONVERGENCE (L. *convergere*, to turn together): The evolution of similar characteristics in organisms of widely different ancestry. Often found in organisms living in similar environments, such as the porpoise and the shark.

COORDINATION: The process of maintaining harmonious interactions between the various parts and processes of an organism.

CORNEA (L. *corneus*, horny): The transparent epidermis and connective tissue covering the outer surface of the vertebrate eye, overlying the iris and pupil.

CORPUS ALLATUM, pl. CORPORA ALLATA (L. added body): An endocrine gland in the insect head, behind the brain, secreting the hormone inducing larval molt.

CORTEX (L. *cortex*, bark): The outer surface.

COTYLEDON (Gr. *kotylēdōn*, a cupshaped hollow): In plants, a leaflike structure produced by the embryo of a seed plant and concerned with digestion and storage of food.

COVALENT BOND: A chemical bond formed between atoms as a result of the sharing of a pair of electrons.

CROSS-FERTILIZATION: The mutual exchange of sperm between two hermaphroditic individuals and subsequent union of eggs and sperm, as in snails, earthworms.

CROSSING OVER: The exchange of genetic material of different parental origins. In higher organisms, it refers to genetic exchange between homologous chromosomes during meiosis.

-CYTE, CYTO- (Gr. *kytos*, vessel, container): Suffix or prefix, meaning "pertaining to cell."

CYTOPLASM: The living matter of a cell between cell membrane and nucleus; the protoplasm of a cell excluding the nucleus.

CYTOSTOME: In protozoa, the "mouth" opening.

-DACTYL, DACTYLO- (Gr. *daktylos*, finger): Suffix or prefix, meaning "finger" or "toe."

DAUGHTER CELLS: The two cells that have been formed by the mitotic division of one cell.

DE- (L., away from, down, off): Prefix, meaning "down," "away from" or "off"; for example, dehydration, "removal of water."

DECIDUOUS (L. *decidere*, to fall off): In plants, shedding leaves at a certain season.

DECOMPOSERS: Organisms (bacteria, fungi) in an ecosystem that convert dead organic material into plant nutrients.

DEDIFFERENTIATION: The change toward a more primitive, embryonic, or earlier state; for example, a process changing a highly specialized cell to a less specialized cell.

DELETION: A mutation which results in the loss of an extended region of a chromosome or gene.

DENDRITE (Gr. from *dendron*, akin to *drys*, tree): The area of a neuron that transmits impulses toward a nerve cell body.

DEOXYRIBONUCLEIC ACID (DNA): Carrier of genetic information in cells; composed of chains of phosphate, sugar molecules (deoxyribose) and purines and pyrimidines; capable of self-replication as well as of determining RNA synthesis.

DERMIS (Gr. *derma*, skin): The inner layer of the skin beneath the epidermis.

DEVELOPMENT: The progressive production of the phenotypic characteristics of an organism.

DI- (Gr. *dis*, twice, double, two): Prefix, meaning "twice," "double"; like L. "bi-"; for example disect, "to cut in two."

DIAPHRAGM (Gr. from *diaphrassein*, to barricade): A sheet-like muscle forming the partition between the abdominal and thoracic cavities.

DICOTYLEDON (Gr. *kotylēdōn*, a cupshaped hollow):- A subclass of angiosperms having two seed leaves or cotyledons; often abbreviated as dicot.

DIFFERENTIATION: The developmental process by which a relatively unspecialized cell or tissue undergoes a progressive change to become a more specialized cell or tissue.

DIFFUSION (L. *diffundere*, to pour out): The random movement of suspended or dissolved particles from a more concentrated to a less concentrated region as a result of molecular activity; the process tends to distribute them uniformly throughout a medium.

DIGESTION: The process by which foods are chemically simplified and made soluble so that they can be used by cells.

DIPLOID: The chromosome state in which each type of chromosome except for the sex chromosomes is represented twice ($2n$), in contrast to haploid ($1n$).

DISTAL: Situated away from or far from point of reference (usually the main part of body); opposite to proximal.

DNA: Abbreviation of deoxyribonucleic acid.

DOMINANT: Applied to a gene that exerts its full phenotypic effect regardless of the presence of a particular allele; a gene that masks the effect of any allele. Generally, a dominant allele is dominant with respect to most, if not all, other alleles. Occasionally, however, a given allele may be dominant in relation to a second allele but recessive in relationship to a third allele.

-DONT (Gr. *odontos*, tooth): Suffix, meaning "tooth."

DORMANCY: In plants and animals, a period during which growth ceases and is resumed only if certain requirements, as of temperature or day length, have been fulfilled.

DORSAL (L. *dorsum*, back): In a direction toward the backbone; opposite of ventral.

DRONE: A male honeybee; has no sting and gathers no honey; its only function is to fertilize the queen.

ECO- (Gr. *oikos*, house, home): Prefix, meaning "house" or "home."

ECOLOGICAL NICHE: The place occupied by a species in the community structure of which it is a part.

ECOLOGICAL SUCCESSION: The process by which a community goes through a number of temporary developmental stages each characterized by a different species composition, before reaching a final stable condition, known as a climax community.

ECOLOGY (Gr. *oikos*, house, home + *logos*, a discourse): The study of relationships of organisms to one another and to their environment.

ECOSYSTEM: All organisms in a community plus the associated environmental factors with which they interact.

ECTO- (Gr. *ektos*, outside): Prefix, meaning "outside," "outer."

ECTODERM (Gr. *derma*, skin): The outermost of the three embryonic tissue layers in the gastrula; gives rise to skin, nervous system, sense organs, etc.

EFFECTOR: Cell, tissue, or organ (such as muscle or gland) capable of reacting to stimuli.

EFFERENT NERVE (L. *ex*, out, away + *ferre*, to carry): A nerve which carries impulses from the central nervous system or central ganglion to an effector; motor nerve.

EGG: A female gamete, or germ cell, which usually contains abundant cytoplasm and yolk; usually immotile, often larger than a male gamete.

ELECTROLYTE (Gr. *elektron*, amber + *lysis*, a loosening): A substance which dissociates into ions in an aqueous solution and so makes possible the conduction of an electric current through the solution.

ELECTRON: A subatomic particle with a negative electric charge; orbits around the atomic nucleus.

ELEMENT: A substance composed of only one kind of atom; one of about 100 distinct natural or man-made types of matter which, singly or in combination, compose all materials of the universe.

EMBRYO (Gr. *en*, in + *bryein*, to swell): The early developmental stage of an organism produced from a fertilized egg; a young organism before it emerges from the seed, egg, or the body of its mother.

ENDERGONIC: Energy-requiring, as in a chemical reaction; applied to an "uphill" process.

ENDO- (Gr. *endon*, within): Prefix, meaning "within."

ENDOCRINE GLAND (Gr. *krinein*, to separate): Ductless gland whose secretions (hormones) are released into the circulatory system; in vertebrates includes pituitary, sex glands, adrenal, thymus, and others.

ENDODERM (Gr. *derma*, skin): The innermost of the three embryonic tissue layers in the gastrula; forms the primitive gut.

ENDOPLASMIC RETICULUM (L. *reticulum*, network): An extensive system of double membranes in most cells, dividing the cytoplasm into compartments and channels, often coated with ribosomes.

ENDOSPERM (Gr. *sperma*, seed): In plants, a tissue containing stored food that develops from the union of a male nucleus and the polar bodies of the egg; found only in angiosperms.

ENERGY: The capacity to do work, such as producing movement.

ENTOMOLOGY (Gr. *entomon*, insect + *logos*, a discourse): The study of insects.

ENTROPY: The degree of randomness or disorder of a system.

ENVIRONMENT: The sum of all physical, chemical and biological factors to which an organism is subjected.

ENVIRONMENTAL RESISTANCE: The limitation of the numbers of a population by external forces or the carrying capacity of its natural community.

ENZYME: (Gr. *enzymos*, leavened): A protein molecule that speeds the rate of (catalyzes) a chemical reaction.

EPI- (Gr., upon): Prefix, meaning "on" or "up."

EPIDERMIS: (Gr. *derma*, skin): In plants and animals, the outermost layer of cells; one cell-layer thick in plants; several cell-layers thick in vertebrates.

EPITHELIAL TISSUE (Gr. *thēlē*, nipple): A type of tissue that covers a body or structure or lines a cavity; epithelial cells form one or more regular layers with little intercellular material.

ESTRUS (Gr. *oistros*, frenzy): The mating period in female mammals, characterized by intensified sexual urge.

ETHOLOGY (Gr. *ēthos*, custom, character + *logos*, a discourse): The study of the whole range of animal behavior (usually under natural conditions).

EUCARYOTIC (Gr., from *eu*, good + *karyon*, nut, kernel): Applied to organisms having membrane-bound nuclei, Golgi apparatus and mitochondria; contrasts with procaryotic.

EVOLUTION (L. *e-*, out + *volvere*, to roll): The process of descent with modification as the result of which present-day species have risen from those of the past.

EXERGONIC: Energy-producing, as in a chemical reaction; applied to a "downhill" process.

EXOSKELETON: In invertebrates, a skeleton covering the outside of the body; common in arthropods.

EXTERNAL FERTILIZATION: Union of egg and sperm cells outside of parental body.

EXTERNAL RESPIRATION: Exchange of oxygen and carbon dioxide at general external respiratory surfaces, such as lungs and gills; contrasts with internal, or cellular, respiration.

EXTRAEMBRYONIC MEMBRANES: Membranes formed of embryonic tissues that lie outside the embryo and are concerned with its protection and metabolism; include amnion, chorion, allantois, and yolk sac.

F_1 (FIRST FILIAL GENERATION): The offspring resulting from the crossing of plants or animals of the parental generation.

F_2 (SECOND FILIAL GENERATION): The offspring resulting from crossing members of the F_1 generation among themselves.

FERTILIZATION: The fusion of two gametes, and so of their nuclei, to form a diploid or polyploid zygote.

FETUS (L., offspring): Late stage of embryological development of vertebrates; in man refers to the embryo between the end of the third month of development and birth.

FIBRIL: Any minute threadlike organelle within a cell.

FILAMENT: In plants: 1) a chain of cells; 2) the stalk of a stamen.

FISSION (L. fissus, split): Asexual reproduction in organisms by division of the body into two or more equal, or nearly equal, parts; common among protozoa.

FITNESS: The relative ability to leave offspring.

FLAGELLUM, pl. FLAGELLA (L. whip): A fine, long thread, composed of protoplasm, protruding from a cell body; longer than a cilium; capable of a vibratory motion; used in locomotion and feeding; common in protozoa, sponges, motile gametes.

FLOWER: The reproductive structure of angiosperms; a complete flower includes calyx, petals, stamens (male sex organs) and carpels (female sex organs), but some of these are absent in flowers of many species.

FOOD: Any material that the organism obtains from its environment that can yield energy for the activities of the organism or material for its growth.

FOOD CHAIN, FOOD WEB: A chain of organisms existing in any natural community such that each link in the chain feeds on the one below and is eaten by the one above; there are seldom more than six links in a chain, with plants, bacteria and other scavenging forms on the bottom and the largest carnivores at the top.

FOREBRAIN: Most anterior of the three primary divisions of the vertebrate brain; includes the cerebral hemispheres, hypothalamus, optic lobes, etc.

FOSSIL (L. fossilis, dug up): The remains of an organism, or direct evidence of its presence (such as tracks). May be an unaltered hard part (tooth or bone); a mold in a rock; petrifaction (wood or bone); unaltered or partially altered soft parts (a frozen mammoth).

FRUIT (L. fructus, fruit): In plants, a matured, ripened ovary and associated structures; formed from the ovule case of an angiosperm; contains the seeds.

FUNCTION: Characteristic role or action of any structure or process in the maintenance of normal metabolism or behavior of an animal.

GAMETE (Gr., wife): The mature functional haploid reproductive cell whose nucleus fuses with that of another gamete of an opposite sex (fertilization), with the resulting cell (zygote) developing into a new individual.

GAMETOPHYTE: In plants having alternation of generations, the haploid ($1n$) gamete-producing generation.

GASTRULA (Gr. gastēr, stomach): An embryo in the process of gastrulation, the stage of development during which the blastula with its single layer of cells turns into a three-layered embryo, made up of ectoderm, mesoderm and endoderm, often enclosing an archenteron.

GEL: A mixture of semi-solid or solid constituency containing a large proportion of liquid trapped in its solid component.

GENE (Gr. genos, race, stock, descent): A unit of heredity which is a small section of the chromosome, defined by the functions it controls. The function is generally the specification of a protein and is recognized by its control of the development of a trait as determined by the interaction of the gene product with the internal and external environment of the organism. Capable of self replication and transmission as a part of the chromosome.

GENE FREQUENCY: The incidence (relative occurrence) of a particular allele in a population.

GENE POOL: All of the alleles of all of the genes in a population.

GENETIC CODE: The three-symboled system of base-pair sequences in DNA; referred to as a code because it determines the amino acid sequence in the enzymes and other protein components synthesized by the organism.

GENETIC DRIFT: Change in the average genetic composition of a population due to random sampling; deviations which are accentuated in a very small population.

GENOTYPE: The genetic constitution of an organism, regardless of its appearance.

GEOLOGY (Gr. gaia, gē, the earth): The study of the history and structure of the earth.

GERM CELLS: Gametes or the direct antecedent cells of gametes.

GERM LAYER: One of the three primary embryonic main layers or groups of cells; ectoderm, mesoderm, or endoderm.

GERMINATION: The resumption of growth by a spore or seed.

GILL: The respiratory organ of aquatic animals, usually a thin walled projection from some part of the external body surface or, in vertebrates, from some part of digestive tract.

GLAND: A cell or organ producing one or more secretions which are discharged to the outside of the gland.

GLUCOSE: A six-carbon sugar ($C_6H_{12}O_6$); the chief fuel substance of most organisms; the most common monosaccharide.

GLYCOGEN: A complex carbohydrate (polysaccharide); one of the main stored food substances of most animals and fungi; it is converted into glucose by hydrolysis.

GONAD (Gr. *gonē*, seed): Gamete-producing organ of multicellular animals; ovary or testes.

GRAY CRESCENT: A crescent shaped area on the surface of the fertilized egg between the animal and vegetal hemispheres caused by a shift of the surface pigments.

GYMNOSPERM (Gr. *gymnos*, naked + *-sperma*, seed): A seed plant with seeds not enclosed in an ovary, such as the conifers.

HABIT: 1) In animals, a usually invariable response determined by the previous experience of an individual. 2) In plants, the general form of the plant body.

HABITAT: The specific place where a particular organism lives.

HABITUATION: The process by which an organism becomes accustomed to and ceases to respond to a stimulus.

HAPLOID (Gr. *haplos*, single): The chromosome state in which each type of chromosome is represented only once ($1n$); in contrast to diploid ($2n$) or polyploid.

HARDY-WEINBERG LAW: The mathematical expression of the relationship between the relative frequencies in successive generations of two alleles in a population; demonstrates that the frequencies of both dominant and recessive genes tend to remain constant in a random mating population in the absence of mutation and selection.

HEMO-, HEMATO- (Gr. *haima*, blood): Prefix, meaning "blood".

HEMOGLOBIN: The iron-containing protein in the blood capable of carrying oxygen.

HEMOPHILIA: A hereditary disease in man characterized by failure of the blood to clot and excessive bleeding from even minor wounds.

HERBIVOROUS: Plant-eating.

HEREDITY: The transfer of characteristics from parent to offspring, usually by the transmission of genes from ancestor to descendent through the germ cells, although not always, as in the case of social characteristics.

HERMAPHRODITE (Gr. *Hermes* and *Aphrodite*): An organism possessing both male and female reproductive organs.

HETERO- (Gr. *heteros*, other, different): Prefix, meaning "other" or "different."

HETEROSIS: Hybrid vigor, the superiority of the hybrid over either parent in any measurable character.

HETEROTROPH (Gr. *trophos*, feeder): An organism which cannot manufacture organic compounds and so must feed on complex organic food materials that have originated in other plants and animals; in contrast to autotroph.

HETEROZYGOTE SUPERIORITY: The greater fitness of a heterozygote as compared with the two homozygotes.

HETEROZYGOUS: Having two different alleles at the same locus on homologous chromosomes.

HINDBRAIN: Posterior of the three primary divisions of the vertebrate brain, includes medulla and cerebellum.

HOMEO, HOMO-, HOMOLO- (Gr. *homos*, same, similar): Prefix, meaning "similar" or "same."

HOMEOSTASIS (Gr. *stasis*, standing): The maintaining of a relatively stable internal physiological environment.

HOMOLOGOUS CHROMOSOMES: The two chromosomes, one from each parent, that generally have the same set of gene loci; homologous chromosomes normally pair and then separate during meiosis.

HOMOLOGY (Gr. *homologia*, agreement): Similarity in structure resulting from a common ancestry, regardless of function.

HOMOZYGOUS: Having identical alleles at the same locus on homologous chromosomes.

HORMONE (Gr. *hormaein*, to excite): A chemical substance secreted, usually in minute amounts, in one part of an organism which has a specific effect on another part of that organism to which it is transported.

HOST: An organism on or in which a parasite lives.

HYALINE (Gr. *hyalos*, glass): Glassy, translucent.

HYBRID: Offspring of two parents that differ in one or more heritable characters; offspring of two different varieties or of two different species.

HYDROLYSIS (Gr. *hydōr*, water + *lysis*, loosening): Splitting of one molecule into two by addition of H^+ and OH^- ions of water.

HYPER- (Gr., above, over): Prefix, meaning "above" or "over."

HYPEROSMOTIC: Having a concentration of solutes high enough to gain water across a membrane from another solution.

HYPHA (Gr. *hyphē*, web): A single tubular filament of a fungus; the hyphae together comprise the mycelium.

HYPO- (Gr., less than): Prefix, meaning "under" or "less."

HYPOOSMOTIC: Having a concentration low enough to lose water across a membrane to another solution.

HYPOTHALAMUS (Gr. *thalamos*, inner room): The floor and sides of the vertebrate brain just below the cerebral hemispheres; contains centers of coordination and body temperature control.

HYPOTHESIS (Gr. *hypo-*, under + *tithenai*, to put): A temporary working explanation or supposition based on accumulated facts and suggesting some general principle or relation of cause and effect; a postulated solution to a scientific problem which must be tested by experimentation and, if not validated, discarded.

IMPRINTING: A rapid and extremely narrow form of learning which occurs during a very short period in the early life of an organism, such as the following response in certain birds.

IMPULSE: A physiochemical excitation ("message") carried along a nerve fiber.

INBREEDING: The mating of related individuals.

INDEPENDENT ASSORTMENT: The independent distribution of genes of different allelic pairs located on different pairs of homologous chromosomes; occurs during meiosis. Two genes of different allelic pairs on different chromosomes will be distributed into gametes independently of one another.

INDEPENDENT EFFECTORS: Cells that both receive and respond to stimuli; include cnidoblasts and epitheliomuscular cells.

INDUCTION (L. *inducere*, to induce): The process in an animal embryo in which one tissue or body part causes the differentiation of another tissue or body part.

INGESTION: The process of taking solid food into the body.

INSIGHT: The ability to perceive relations between simple data.

INSIGHT LEARNING (PERCEPTION): The production of a new response as a result of the evaluation of previous experience.

INSTINCT: A genetically determined pattern of behavior or response not based on the previous experience of the individual.

INTELLIGENCE: The capacity to profit by experience, based on analysis and association of ideas; mental capacity characteristic, in varying degrees, of the higher vertebrates and marked by an ability to associate facts, truth and meaning, and a capacity for adaptive behavior and understanding.

INTER- (L., between): Prefix, meaning "between"; for example, intercellular, "between cells."

INTRA: (L., within): Prefix, meaning "within"; for example, intracellular, "within cells."

INVAGINATION (L. *in*, in + *vagina*, sheath): The local infolding of a layer of tissue, especially in animal embryos, so as to form a depression or pocket opening to the outside.

INVERSION: The reversal of a segment of a chomosome so that the linear arrangement of certain genes is in reverse order.

INVERTEBRATE: An animal without a backbone.

ION: An electrically charged atom or group of atoms.

IONIZATION: The addition to or removal of electrons from atoms.

IRRITABILITY: The ability to respond to stimuli or changes in environment; a general property of all living organisms.

ISO (Gr. *isos*, equal): Prefix, meaning "equal"; like "homo-."

ISOLATING MECHANISMS: Mechanisms that prevent gene exchange between different species; may be morphological, behavioral, or physiological.

ISOMER (Gr. *meros*, part): One of a group of compounds identical in atomic composition but differing in structural arrangement.

ISOSMOTIC: Having the same osmotic concentration.

ISOTOPE (Gr. *topos*, place): One of several possible forms of a chemical element, differing from other forms in the number of neutrons in the atomic nucleus, but not in chemical properties.

KARYOTYPE: The general appearance of the chromosomes with regard to number, size and shape.

KERATIN (Gr. *keras*, horn): One of a group of tough fibrous proteins; a horny tissue formed by certain epidermal tissues, especially abundant in skin, claws, hair, feathers, hooves.

LARVA (L., ghost): An immature animal such as a caterpillar or tadpole that is morphologically very different from the adult.

LEARNING: The process that produces adaptive change in individual behavior as the result of experience.

LETHAL GENE: A gene that stops development at some point and causes death.

LEUCOCYTE (Gr. *leukos*, white + *kytos*, vessel): White blood cell.

LEUCOPLAST (Gr. *plastēs*, molder): In plants, a colorless cell organelle that serves as a starch repository; usually found in cells not exposed to light, such as roots and internal stem tissue.

LICHEN: A symbiotic association of an alga and a fungus.

LIFE CYCLE: The entire sequence of phases in the growth and development of any organism from time of zygote formation until death.

LINKAGE: The tendency in heredity for certain genes to be inherited together owing to the fact that they are located on the same chromosome.

LIPID (Gr. *lipos*, fat): One of a large variety of organic fat or fat-like compounds; includes beside fats, steroids, phospholipids, and carotenes.

LOCUS, pl. LOCI (L., place): The position of a gene on a chromosome.

LYMPH: Colorless fluid occurring in intercellular space cavities and special lymph ducts, derived from blood by filtration through capillary walls.

-LYSIS, -LYTIC, -LYTE (Gr. *lysis*, a loosening): Suffix, meaning "pertaining to dissolving."

μ: Abbreviation for micron.

MACRO- (Gr. *makros*, large, long): Prefix, meaning "large" or "long"; opposite of "micro-."

MACROMOLECULE: A molecule of very high molecular weight; refers specifically to proteins, nucleic acids, polysaccharides, and complexes of these.

MANTLE: In mollusks, the outermost layer of the body wall or a soft extension of it, usually secretes a shell.

MARINE (L. from *mare*, the sea): Living in salt water.

MARSUPIAL (Gr. *marsypos*, pouch, little bag): A nonplacental mammal in which the female has a ventral pouch or folds surrounding the nipples; the premature young leave the uterus and crawl into the pouch where each one attaches itself by the mouth to a nipple until development is completed.

MECHANORECEPTOR: Any sense cell or organ that receives mechanical stimuli such as those involved in touch, pressure, hearing, and balance.

MEDULLA (L., the marrow): 1) The most posterior region of the vertebrate brain. 2) The inner as opposed to the outer part of an organ, as in the adrenal gland.

MEDUSA: The free-swimming bell- or umbrella-shaped stage in the life cycle of many coelenterates; a jellyfish.

MEGA- (Gr. *megas*, great, large): Prefix, meaning "large."

MEGASPORE: In plants, a haploid ($1n$) spore that develops into a female gametophyte.

MEIOSIS (Gr. *meioun*, to make smaller): The two successive nuclear divisions that lead to the formation of gametes in animals and of spores in plants, in which the chromosome number is reduced from diploid ($2n$) to haploid ($1n$), and segregation of the genes occurs.

MENDEL'S FIRST LAW: The factors for a pair of alternate characters are separate and only one may be carried in a particular gamete (genetic segregation).

MENDEL'S SECOND LAW: The inheritance of one pair of characteristics is independent of the simultaneous inheritance of other traits, such characters "assorting independently" as though there were no other characters present (later modified by the discovery of linkage which restricts its application to genes on different chromosomes).

MERI-, MERO-, MERE-, -MER: Prefix or suffix, meaning "part" or "portion."

MERISTEM: The undifferentiated plant tissue from which new cells arise.

MESENCHYME (Gr. *mesos*, middle + *enchyma*, infusion): An embryonic or unspecialized connective tissue, derived from mesoderm in vertebrates.

MESODERM (Gr. *derma*, skin): The middle of the three embryonic tissue layers, between the ectoderm and the endoderm; gives rise to skeleton, circulatory system, musculature, excretory system and most of the reproductive system.

MESSENGER RNA (mRNA): The RNA that carries genetic information from the gene to the ribosome where it serves as a template for protein synthesis.

METABOLISM: (Gr. *metabolē*, change): The sum of all chemical reactions occurring within a living unit.

METAMORPHOSIS (Gr. *metamorphoun*, to transform): Abrupt transition from larval to adult form, such as the transition from tadpole to adult frog.

MICRO- (Gr. *mikros*, small): Prefix, meaning "small."

MICROBE (Gr. *bios*, life): A microscopic organism.

MICROGAMETE: In organisms with gametes of two sizes, the smaller, usually male, gamete.

MICRON: A unit of microscopic measurement convenient for describing cellular dimensions; 1/1,000 of a millimeter, or 1/25,000 inch, abbreviated μ.

MICROSCOPIC: Invisible with the naked eye, but visible with the microscope.

MICROSPORE: A spore which develops into a male gametophyte; in seed plants, it becomes a pollen grain.

MIMICRY (Gr. *mimos*, mime): The superficial resemblance in form, color, or behavior of certain organisms (mimics) to other more powerful or more protected ones (models), resulting in protection or concealment or some other advantage for the mimic.

MITOCHONDRION, pl. MITOCHONDRIA: An organelle bound by a double membrane in which energy is captured in the form of ATP in the course of cellular respiration.

MITOSIS (Gr. *mitos*, thread): Nuclear division characterized by exact chromosome duplication and the formation of two identical daughter cells; the means by which somatic cells divide.

MOLECULE (L. *moles*, mass): Smallest possible unit of a compound substance, consisting of two or more atoms.

MOLECULAR WEIGHT: The sum of the atomic weights of the constituent atoms in a molecule.

MOLT: Shedding of all or part of outer covering; in arthropods, periodic shedding of the exoskeleton to permit an increase in size.

MONO- (Gr. *monos*, single): Prefix, meaning "one," "single."

MONOCOTYLEDON (Gr. *kotylēdōn*, a cupshaped hollow): A subclass of angiosperms, characterized by a variety of features among which is the presence of a single seed leaf (cotyledon); abbreviated as monocot.

MONOSACCHARIDE (Gr. *sakcharon*, sugar): A simple sugar, such as 5- and 6-carbon sugars.

-MORPH, MORPHO- (Gr. *morphē*, form): Suffix or prefix, meaning "form."

MORPHOGENESIS: The development of size, form, and other structural features of organisms.

MORPHOLOGY: The study of form and structure, at any level of organization.

MUTAGEN: An agent which increases the mutation rate.

MUTANT: A mutated gene or an organism carrying a gene that has undergone a mutation.

MUTATION (L. from *mutare*, change): An inheritable change in the chromosomes; usually a change of a gene from one allelic form to another.

MYC-, MYCO- (Gr. *mykes*, fungus): Prefix, meaning "pertaining to fungi."

MYCELIUM: The vegetative portion of a fungus; the mass of hyphae which forms the body of a fungus.

MYELIN: A fatty material surrounding the axons of nerve cells in the central nervous system of vertebrates.

MYO- (Gr. *mys*, muscle): Prefix, meaning "muscle."

MYONEME: A contractile filament within a cell; common in coelenterates.

MYX-, MYXO- (Gr. *myxa*, slime): Prefix, meaning "slime."

NAD: Abbreviation of nicotinamide-adenine-dinucleotide, a coenzyme which functions as a hydrogen acceptor.

NATURAL SELECTION: Differential reproduction of genotypes in a natural population where the observed differences are too great to be attributed to chance alone.

NEMATOCYST (Gr. *nēma, nematos*, thread + *kyst*, bladder): A thread-like stinger, containing a poisonous or paralyzing substance, found in a cnidoblast of a coelenterate.

NEPHRIDIUM: A type of excretory organ found in many invertebrates.

NEPHRON (Gr. *nephros*, kidney): A unit of the kidney structure in reptiles, birds, and mammals; a human kidney is composed of about a million nephrons.

NERVE: A group or bundle of nerve fibers with accompanying connective tissue.

NERVE FIBER: A filamentous process of a nerve cell or neuron; either dendrite or axon.

NERVE IMPULSE: A physiochemical excitation (excitement) transmitted along a nerve fiber from one part of an animal to another.

NERVE NET: A diffuse network of simple branching nerve cells with no differentiation between dendrites and axons.

NERVOUS SYSTEM: All of the nerve cells of an animal; the receptor-conductor-effector system; in man, the nervous system consists of brain, spinal cord and all nerves.

NEUR-, NEURO- (Gr. *neuron*, nerve): Prefix, meaning "nerve."

NEURAL GROOVE: Dorsal longitudinal groove which forms in a vertebrate embryo; bordered by two neural folds; preceded by neural plate stage and followed by neural tube stage.

NEURAL PLATE: Thickened strip of ectoderm in early vertebrate embryos; forms along the dorsal side of the body and gives rise to the central nervous system.

NEURAL TUBE: Primitive hollow dorsal nervous system of the early vertebrate embryo formed by fusion of neural folds around neural groove.

NEURON: A nerve cell, including the cell body, dendrites, and axons.

NEUROSECRETORY CELL: A neuron which produces one or more hormones.

NITRIFY: To convert organic nitrogen compounds into ammonium compounds, nitrates and nitrites, as by nitrifying bacteria and fungi.

NITROGEN BASE: A nitrogen-containing molecule having basic properties (tendency to acquire an H atom); a purine or pyrimidine.

NITROGEN CYCLE: World-wide circulation and revitalization of nitrogen atoms, chiefly due to metabolic processes of plants and animals; plants take up inorganic nitrogen, convert it into organic compounds (chiefly proteins) which are assimilated into bodies of one or more animals; excretion, burning and bacterial and fungal action on dead organisms return nitrogen atoms to inorganic state.

NITROGEN FIXATION: Conversion of atmospheric nitrogen into organic nitrogen compounds available to green plants; a process that can be carried out only by certain soil bacteria.

NODE (L. *nodus*, knot): In plants, a joint of a stem; the place where branches and leaves are joined to stem.

NONDISJUNCTION: The failure of homologous chromosomes to separate during meiosis, resulting in one or more extra chromosomes in the cells of some offspring.

NOTOCHORD: A longitudinal, solid, elastic, rod-like structure serving as the internal skeleton in the embryos of all chordates; in most adult chordates the notochord is replaced by a vertebral column which forms around (but not from) the notochord.

NUCLEAR ENVELOPE: The double membrane surrounding the nucleus within a cell.

NUCLEIC ACID: An organic acid consisting of joined nucleotide complexes; the principal types are deoxyribonucleic acid (DNA) and ribonucleic acid (RNA).

NUCLEOLUS: An RNA-containing spherical body within the nucleus of most cells, produced by the chromosomes, probably the site of ribosomal RNA synthesis.

NUCLEOTIDE: A single unit of nucleic acid composed of phosphate, 5-carbon sugar (either ribose or deoxyribose), and a purine or a pyrimidine.

NUCLEUS (L., a kernel): 1) A body present in most cell types containing chromosomes and nucleoli enclosed in an external nuclear membrane. 2) The central body of an atom.

OCELLUS, pl. OCELLI (L. dim. of *oculus*, eye): A simple light-receptor common among invertebrates.

OLFACTORY (L. *olfacere*, to smell): Pertaining to smell.

OLIGO- (Gr. *oligos*, few, small): Prefix, meaning "few," "small"; for example, oligochaete, "having few bristles."

OMMATIDIUM, pl. OMMATIDIA (Gr. *ommos*, eye): The single visual unit in the compound eye of arthropods, containing light-sensitive cells and a refractory system able to form an image.

OMNI- (L. *omnis*, all): Prefix, meaning "all."

OMNIVOROUS: Eating "everything," i.e. using both plants and animals as food.

ONTOGENY (Gr. *on*, being + *genesis*, origin): The developmental history of an individual organism from zygote to maturity.

OO- (Gr. *ōion*, egg): Prefix, meaning "egg."

OOGAMY: Sexual union of a large non-motile egg and a small motile sperm.

OPERATOR GENE: The gene responsible for regulating the function of a group of genes closely linked to it.

OPERON: A group of adjacent genes that are under the control of a single operator gene.

OPPOSABLE THUMB: Thumb that rotates at the joint so that the tip of the thumb can be placed opposite the tip of any one of the four fingers.

ORGAN: A structure composed of different tissues cooperating functionally to perform a composite task.

ORGANELLE: A formed body in the cytoplasm of a cell; a cytoplasmic structure.

ORGANIC: Pertaining to organisms or living things generally, to compounds formed by living organisms, and to the chemistry of compounds containing carbon.

ORGANISM: Any individual living creature, either unicellular or multicellular.

ORGANIZER: Part of an embryo capable of inducing undifferentiated cells to follow a specific course of development; in particular, the dorsal lip of the blastopore in the amphibian.

OSMOSIS (Gr. *osmos*, impulse, thrust): The movement of water between two solutions separated by a semipermeable membrane; the water moves from the side containing a lesser concentration of solute (and therefore a greater concentration of water molecules) to the side containing a greater concentration of solute; migration continues until the particles are concentrated equally on both sides.

OSTEOBLAST (Gr. *osteon*, bone + *blast*, germ): Bone-forming cell.

OV-, OVI- (L. *ovum*, egg): Prefix, meaning "egg."

OVARY: The egg-producing organ of animals; the ovule-containing organ of flowering plants.

OVIDUCT (L. *ductus*, duct): The tube serving to transport the eggs to the uterus or to the outside.

OVULATION: Release of an animal egg from the ovary.

OVULE: In seed plants, the megasporangium, a structure composed of protective outer coat, a tissue specialized for food storage and a female gametophyte with egg cell; becomes a seed after fertilization.

OVUM: The egg cell; female gamete.

OXIDATION: Loss of an electron by an atom. Oxidation (loss of an electron by an atom) and reduction (gain of an electron) take place simultaneously since an electron that is lost by one atom is accepted by another. Oxidation-reduction reactions are an important means of energy transfer within living systems.

PAEDOMORPHOSIS (Gr. *pais*, child + *morphē*, form): The evolution of a new group of animals from an earlier developmental stage of an ancestral form.

PAIRING OF CHROMOSOMES: Side-by-side association of homologous chromosomes.

PALEO- (Gr. *palaios*, old): Prefix, meaning "old."

PALEONTOLOGY: The study of the life of past geologic times, principally by means of fossils.

PARA- (Gr., from *para*, beside, akin to): Prefix, meaning "akin to," "at the side of," or "beside."

PARASITE (Gr. *sitos*, food): An organism that lives on or in an organism of a different species and derives nutrients from it.

PARASYMPATHETIC NERVOUS SYSTEM: A subdivision of the autonomic nervous system of vertebrates; centers are located in brain and most anterior part and most posterior parts of spinal cord; stimulates digestion and has a general inhibitory effect on other functions.

PARENCHYMA: A plant tissue composed of living, thin walled, randomly arranged cells with large vacuoles; usually photosynthetic or storage tissue.

PARTHENOGENESIS (Gr. *parthenos*, virgin): The development of an egg without fertilization.

-PED, -PEDIA, PEDI- (L. *pes, pedis,* foot): Suffix or prefix, meaning "foot"; like Gr. "*-pod*"; for example, bipedal, "two-footed."

PELLICLE (L. dim. of *pellis,* skin): A thin translucent envelope located outside of the plasma membrane in many protozoa.

PENT-, PENTA- (Gr. *pente,* five): Prefix, meaning "five"; for example, pentose, "five-carbon sugar."

PEPTIDE: Two or more amino acids linked together; molecules made up of a relatively small number of amino acids (2 to about 100) are called peptides while those formed of a larger number of amino acids are called polypeptides or proteins.

PEPTIDE BOND: The type of bond formed when two amino acid units are joined end to end; the acidic group (COOH) of one amino acid is attached to the basic group (NH_2) of the next and a molecule of water (H_2O) is lost.

PERENNIAL (L. *per,* through + *annus,* a year): A plant which persists in whole or in part from year to year and flowers in more than one year.

PERI- (Gr., around): Prefix, meaning "around"; for example, peristomial, "around the mouth"; peristalsis, "wavelike compression around a tubular organ," such as the gut.

PERITONEUM (Gr. *peritonos,* stretched over): A mesodermal epithelial membrane lining the body cavity and forming the external covering of the visceral organs.

PERMEABLE (L. *permeare,* to pass through): Penetrable, usually applied to membranes which let given substances pass through.

PH: A symbol denoting the relative concentration of hydrogen ions in a solution; in biological systems pH values normally run from 0 to 14, and the lower the value the more acid a solution, that is, the more hydrogen ions it contains; pH 7 is neutral, less than 7 acid, more than 7 alkaline.

PHAGO-, -PHAGE (Gr. *phagein,* to eat): Prefix or suffix, meaning "eating."

PHAGOCYTE: Any cell that engulfs foreign particles.

PHAGOCYTOSIS: Cell "eating"; the intake of solid particles by a cell, by flowing over and engulfing them; characteristic of amoebas, digestive cells of some invertebrates and vertebrate white blood cells.

PHENOTYPE (Gr. *phainein,* to show): The physical appearance of an organism resulting from interaction between its genetic constitution (genotype), and the environment.

PHEROMONE: Substance secreted by an animal that influences the behavior or morphological development or both of other animals of the same species, such as sex attractants of moths, odor trail of ants.

PHLOEM (Gr. *phloos,* bark): Vascular tissue composed of living cells (sieve cells) that conducts sugars and proteins from the leaves to other parts of the plant.

PHORO-, -PHORE (Gr. *-phoros,* bearing, carrying): Prefix or suffix, meaning "bearing."

PHOTO- (Gr. *photos,* light): Prefix, meaning "light."

PHOTOPERIODISM: The response in plant growth and development to differing lengths of exposure to light.

PHOTORECEPTOR: A cell or organ capable of detecting light.

PHOTOSYNTHESIS: The process by which simple carbohydrates are manufactured from carbon dioxide (CO_2) and water by chlorophyll-containing cells, using light as an energy-source and releasing oxygen as a side product.

PHOTOTAXIS: Movement of an organism towards or away from a light source.

PHOTOTROPISM (Gr. *trope,* turning): Movement in which the direction of the light is the determining factor, as the growth of a plant towards a light source; turning or bending response to light.

PHYCO- (Gr. *phykos,* seaweed): Prefix, referring to aquatic plants; for example, phycomycete, primitive (often aquatic) fungus.

PHYLLO-, PHYLL- (Gr. *phyllon,* leaf): Prefix, meaning "leaf."

PHYLOGENY (Gr. *phylon,* race, tribe): Evolutionary relationships among organisms; developmental history of a group of organisms.

PHYLOGENETIC CHANGE: The gradual change in a population in the course of time.

PHYSIOLOGY (Gr. *physis,* nature + *logos,* a discourse): The study of function in cells, organs, or entire organisms.

PHYTO-, -PHYTE (Gr. *phyton,* plant): Prefix or suffix, meaning "plant."

PHYTOCHROME: Pigment found in cytoplasm of green plants that is associated with the absorption of light; changes in response to either light or dark and is involved with a number of timing processes, such as flowering, dormancy, leaf formation, and seed germination.

PHYTOFLAGELLATE: A cell, such as *Chlamydomonas,* containing chlorophyll and one or more flagella.

PHYTOPLANKTON (Gr. *planktos,* wandering): Aquatic free-floating microscopic plant life.

PINOCYTOSIS (Gr. *pinein,* to drink): Cell "drinking"; the intake of fluid droplets by a cell.

PITUITARY (L. *pituita,* phlegm): Endocrine gland in vertebrates; composed of anterior, intermediate, and posterior lobes, each representing a functionally separate gland; stimulated by neurosecretory cells in the brain.

PLACENTA (Gr. *plax,* a flat object): A structure formed in part from the inner lining of the uterus and in part from the tissues of the embryo; develops in most species of mammals and serves as the connection between the mother and the embryo during pregnancy through which exchanges occur between the blood of mother and of embryo.

PLANKTON (Gr. *planktos*, wandering): Free-floating, mostly microscopic, aquatic organisms, both plant and animal.

PLANULA (L. dim. of *planus*, flat): The ciliated, free-swimming larval type occurring in many coelenterates.

PLAQUE: Clear, round area in a sheet of cells resulting from the killing or lysis of contiguous cells, usually by virus growth.

PLASMA-, PLASMO-, -PLAST (Gr. *plasma*, form, mold): Prefix or suffix, meaning "formed" or "molded"; for example, protoplasm, "first-molded" (living matter); chloroplast, "green-formed" (body).

PLASMA MEMBRANE: The extremely thin membrane covering the surfaces of all cells of plants; composed of lipid and protein; responsible for the selective permeability of cells.

PLASMODIUM: Stage in life cycle of myxomycetes; a multinucleate mass of protoplasm surrounded by a plasma membrane.

PLASTID: A cytoplasmic, often pigmented organelle in plant cells; (three types are leucoplasts, chromoplasts, and chloroplasts).

PLEIOTROPISM: The capacity of a gene to affect a number of different characteristics.

PLUTEUS (Gr. *plein*, to sail, float, flow): The small, free-swimming, tent-shaped larva of the sea urchin and other echinoderms.

POLAR BODY: Minute, non-functioning cell produced during meiotic divisions in organisms, contains nucleus but very little cytoplasm; so-called because it usually appears at the animal pole of the egg.

POLARITY: A characteristic resulting from differentiation between two ends of a living system.

POLLEN (L., fine dust): In plants, male gametophytes at the stage in which they are shed from the anthers.

POLLEN TUBE: A tubular protuberance of the male gametophyte of seed plants which transports the male gametes to the ovule.

POLLINATION: The transfer of pollen from where it was formed (the anther) to a receptive surface (the stigma, in angiosperms) associated with an ovule of a flower.

POLY- (Gr. *polys*, many): Prefix, meaning "many."

POLYMER: A large molecule composed of many like molecular subunits.

POLYMORPHISM: Occurrence together of two or more morphologically distinct forms of a species.

POLYP (Gr. *poly-*, many + *pous*, foot): The sessile stage in the life cycle of coelenterates; a single attached individual of any colonial or solitary coelenterate.

POLYPEPTIDE: Numerous amino acids linked together by peptide bonds.

POLYPLOID: Possessing one or more extra sets of chromosomes; having a chromosome complement in which the number of chromosomes in the body cells is a multiple of the haploid ($1n$) number greater than 2.

POLYSACCHARIDE: A carbohydrate composed of many joined monosaccharide units in a long chain; for example, glycogen, starch, cellulose.

POPULATION: Any group of one species of individuals.

POST-, POSTERO- (L., behind, after): Prefix, meaning "at," "near," or "toward the hind part"; opposite of "pre-," and "antero-."

POSTERIOR: Of or pertaining to the rear end; in man, the back of the body is said to be posterior.

PRE- (L., before, in front of): Prefix, meaning "before," or "in front of"; opposite of "post-."

PRIMARY GROWTH: In plants, growth originating in the apical meristem of the shoots and roots, as contrasted with secondary growth.

PRIMATE: Order of mammals to which man belongs.

PRIMITIVE (L. from *primus*, first): Not specialized; at an early stage of development.

PRIMITIVE STREAK: The thickened dorsal longitudinal strip of ectoderm and mesoderm in early bird and mammal embryos; equivalent to blastopore in other forms.

PROCAMBIUM (L. *cambium*, change, exchange): One of the three primary meristematic tissues; gives rise to vascular tissues of primary plant body.

PROCARYOTIC (L. *pro*, before + Gr. *karyon*, nut, kernel): Lacking a membrane-bound nuclei, plastids, and Golgi apparatus, as in bacteria and blue-green algae.

PROGESTERONE: Steroid hormone produced by corpus luteum that helps prepare the uterus for reception of the ovum.

PROPRIOCEPTOR (L. *proprius*, one's own): Internal sensory receptors which give information to the brain regarding movements, position of body, and muscle stretch.

PROTEIN (Gr. *proteios*, primary): A complex organic compound composed of one or more polypeptide chains, each made up of many (about 100 or more) amino acids joined by peptide bonds.

PROTO- (Gr. *protos*, first): Prefix, meaning "first"; for example, Protozoa, "first animals."

PROTON: A subatomic, or elementary, particle, representing a unit of positive electric charge with a mass of 1; a component of an atomic nucleus.

PROTOPLASM (Gr. *plasma*, anything molded): The living substance of all cells.

PROXIMAL (L. *proximus*, near): Situated near the point of reference (usually the main part of body or the point of attachment); opposite of distal.

PSEUDO- (Gr. *pseudes*, false): Prefix, meaning "false."

PSEUDOPLASMODIUM: A multicellular mass of individual amoeboid cells, representing the aggregate phase in the cellular slime molds.

PSEUDOPODIUM, pl. PSEUDOPODIA (Gr. *pod-*, *pous*, foot); A temporary cytoplasmic protrusion from an amoeboid cell which functions in locomotion or in feeding by phagocytosis.

PUPA (L. girl, doll): A developmental stage, non-feeding, immotile, and sometimes encapsulated or in a cocoon, between the larval and adult phases in insects.

PUNNETT SQUARE: The checkerboard diagram used for analysis of gene segregation.

PURINE: A nitrogenous base such as adenine or guanine; one of the components of nucleic acids.

PYRAMID OF ENERGY: Energy relationships between various feeding levels involved in a particular food chain; plants (at the base of the pyramid) represent the greatest amount of energy utilization, herbivores next, then primary carnivores, secondary carnivores, etc.

PYRIMIDINE: A nitrogenous base such as cytosine, thymine, or uracil; one of the components of nucleic acids.

QUEEN: The fertile, or fully developed, female of social bees, ants, and termites whose function is to lay eggs.

RADIAL SYMMETRY: The regular arrangement of parts around one longitudinal axis; any line drawn through this oral-aboral axis will divide similar halves; seen in coelenterates and adult echinoderms.

RADIATION (L., a spoke of a wheel, hence, a ray): The movement of energy from one place to another.

RADIOACTIVE ISOTOPE: An isotope with an unstable nucleus that stabilizes itself by emitting radiation.

RECEPTOR: Any cell, tissue or organ that detects internal or external stimuli.

RECESSIVE (L. *recedere*, to recede): Applied to a gene whose phenotypic expression is masked by a dominant allele and so is manifest only in the homozygous condition.

REDUCTION (L. *reducere*, to lead back): Gain of an electron by a compound; takes place simultaneously with oxidation (loss of an electron by an atom) since an electron that is lost by one atom is accepted by another.

REDUCTION DIVISION: The reduction of chromosomes during meiosis from the diploid ($2n$) to the haploid ($1n$) number; meiosis.

REFLEX (L. *reflectere*, to bend back): Unit of action of the nervous system involving a sensory neuron, an association neuron or neurons, and one or more motor neurons.

REGENERATION: The replacement of lost or injured parts.

REGULATOR GENE: A gene that influences whether or not a product, such as a polypeptide, is produced by another gene.

REGULATORY SYSTEMS: Systems concerned with the organization of the internal activities of complex organisms and their integration with the environment; the chief such system is the endocrine system.

RENAL (L. *renes*, kidneys): Pertaining to the kidney.

REPRESSOR: The substance produced by a regulator gene that represses protein formation.

RESOLVING POWER: Ability of a lens to distinguish two lines as separate.

RESPIRATION (L. *respirare*, to breathe): The intake of oxygen and the liberation of carbon dioxide; the oxidative breakdown and release of energy from fuel molecules by reaction with oxygen.

RETICULUM (L. *reticulum*, network): Any network or weblike structure, as in endoplasmic reticulum.

RETINA (L. *rete*, a net): The innermost nervous tissue layer of the eyeball; contains several layers of neurons and light receptor cells (rods and cones); receives the image formed by the lens and is connected to the brain by the optic nerve.

RHIZOID (Gr. *rhiza*, root): Rootlike, anchoring structure in nonvascular plants.

RHIZOME (Gr. *rhizoma*, mass of roots): In plants, a horizontal underground stem, often enlarged for storage.

RIBONUCLEIC ACID (RNA): Type of nucleic acid involved in protein synthesis; composed of chains of phosphate, sugar molecules (ribose) and purines and pyrimidines; genetic material of many viruses.

RIBOSOME: A small subcellular particle composed of protein and ribonucleic acid; the site of protein synthesis.

RITUALIZATION: A stereotyped response which has become specialized in the course of evolution of the species.

ROD: Light-sensitive nerve cell found in the vertebrate retina; sensitive to very dim light, responsible for "night vision."

ROOT: That part of a vascular plant that usually grows down into the soil, anchoring the plant and absorbing water and nutrients.

SAPROPHYTE (Gr. *sapros*, rotten + *phyton*, plant): An organism that secures its food directly from nonliving organic matter.

SECONDARY GROWTH: In plants, growth derived from secondary or lateral meristem, such as cambium; secondary growth results in an increase in the width of the stem and roots and in the production of woody tissue.

SECONDARY SEX CHARACTERS: External characters that distinguish between the two sexes but which have no direct role in reproduction, such as the rooster's comb.

SECRETION: Product of any cell, gland or tissue which is released through the cell membrane.

SEED: The characteristic reproductive structure of seed plants, derived from the ovule and consisting of an embryo sporophyte surrounded by the remains of the mother gametophyte (in gymnosperms) or the endosperm (in angiosperms) and enclosed in a protective outer coating.

SEGREGATION: The separation of two alleles into different gametes during meiosis. See Mendel's First Law.

SELF-FERTILIZATION: The union of egg and sperm produced by a single hermaphroditic organism.

SELF-POLLINATION: The transfer of pollen from anther to stigma in the same flower or to another flower of the same plant, leading to self-fertilization.

SEMEN (L., seed): Product of male reproductive system; includes sperm and the sperm-carrying fluid.

SEMIPERMEABLE MEMBRANE: A membrane that can be penetrated by different substances to different degrees.

SENSE ORGAN: A multicellular receptor including sensory cells and associated structures.

SENSILLUM, pl. SENSILLA: Sensory-receptor unit on body surface of arthropods; responsive to touch, smell, taste, and vibration (sound).

SENSORY NERVE: Any nerve that carries impulses only toward the central nervous system or central ganglion and away from the receptor.

SENSORY NEURON: A neuron that carries impulses from a receptor to the central nervous system or central ganglion.

SERE (L. from series, series): A series of plant and animal communities that follow one another in a gradual but definite sequence ending in a climax typical of a particular climate and part of the world.

SESSILE (L. from sedere, to sit): Attached, not free to move about.

SEX CHROMOSOMES: Special sex-determining chromosomes, not occurring in identical numbers or shapes in both sexes.

SEX-LINKED: Applied to genetic characteristics determined by genes located on the X or Y chromosome, such as color blindness.

SEXUAL REPRODUCTION: Reproduction involving the union of a female gamete (egg) with a male gamete (sperm).

SMOOTH MUSCLE: Muscle that is under involuntary control; lines the walls of the intestine, stomach and arteries.

SOLUTION: A mixture (usually liquid) in which one or more substances are dispersed in the form of separate molecules or ions throughout the entire substance.

SOMATIC CELLS: The differentiated, usually diploid ($2n$) cells composing body tissues of multicellular plants and animals; all body cells except the germ cells.

SOMATO- (Gr. soma, body): Prefix, meaning "body," or "of the body."

SOMATOPLEURE (Gr. pleura, side): In vertebrate embryos, a tissue composed of mesoderm and adjacent ectoderm that gives rise to much of the body wall and to the amnion and chorion.

SOMITE: One of the segments into which the body of many animals is divided, especially an incompletely developed embryonic segment.

SPECIAL CREATION: The creation of life by some supernatural power, either once or at successive intervals; in contrast to evolution.

SPECIALIZED: 1) Of organisms, having special adaptations to a particular habitat or mode of life. 2) Of cells, having particular functions.

SPECIES, pl. SPECIES (L., kind, sort): A group of animals or plants that actually (or potentially) interbreed and are reproductively isolated from all other such groups.

SPECIES-SPECIFIC: Characteristic of (and limited to) a species.

SPECIFICITY: Uniqueness, as in proteins in a given organism and of enzymes in given reactions.

-SPERM, SPERME-, SPERMA-, SPERMATO- (Gr. sperma, seed): Suffix or prefix, meaning "seed."

SPERM: A mature male sex cell or gamete, usually motile and smaller than the female gamete; contains little cytoplasm and no yolk.

SPERMATHECA: Receptacle for sperm storage, found in many types of female invertebrates.

SPERMATID: Each of four haploid cells resulting from the meiotic divisions of a spermatocyte, which become differentiated into a sperm cell.

SPERMATOCYTES: The diploid cells formed by the enlargement of the spermatogonia; give rise by meiotic division to the spermatids.

SPERMATOGENESIS (Gr. genesis, origin): The process by which spermatogonia develop into sperm.

SPERMATOGONIA: The unspecialized diploid ($2n$) germ cells on the walls of the testes which by meiotic division become spermatocytes, then spermatids, then spermatozoons or sperm.

SPERMATOZOON, pl. SPERMATOZOA: A sperm cell.

SPINAL CORD: The part of the vertebrate central nervous system which consists of a thick longitudinal bundle of nerve fibers extending from the brain posteriorly along the dorsal side.

SPIRACLE (L. spirare, to breathe): One of the external openings of the respiratory system in terrestrial arthropods.

SPLANCHNOPLEURE (Gr. splanchnon, entrails + pleura, side): In vertebrate embryos, layer of mesoderm and adjacent endoderm which encloses the gut and gives rise to the yolk sac and allantois.

SPONTANEOUS GENERATION: The origin of organisms from non-living things; not possible under present conditions on earth.

SPORA-, SPORO- (Gr. *spora*, seed): Prefix, meaning "seed."

SPORANGIUM, pl. SPORANGIA: A hollow unicellular or multicellular structure in which spores are produced.

SPORE: An asexual reproductive cell, usually unicellular, capable of developing into an adult without fusion with another cell; in contrast to a gamete.

SPOROPHYTE: In plants, a spore-producing organism; in plants having alternation of generations, the diploid (2n) generation produced by the fusion of gametes.

STAMEN (L., a thread): The male organ of a flower which produces microspores or pollen; consists of a stalk bearing an anther at its apex.

STARCH: A complex carbohydrate (polysaccharide); the chief stored food of most green plants.

STATO- (Gr. *statos*, standing stationary, positioned): Prefix, meaning "stationary."

STATOCYST (Gr. *kystis*, sac): An organ of balance, consisting of a vesicle containing granules of sand (statoliths) or some other material which stimulates sensory cells when the animal moves.

STEM: The part of the axis of vascular plants that is above ground.

STEREOSCOPIC VISION (Gr. *stereos*, solid + *optikos*, pertaining to the eye): Solid or three-dimensional viewing of an object.

STEREOTYPED BEHAVIOR: Behavior based on "averaging out" the experience of the entire species, with the results incorporated into the genotype of the group as a whole; the insects are conspicuous examples of such behavior.

STIGMA: 1) The red eyespot of algae. 2) The region of a carpel serving as a receptive surface for pollen grains and on which they germinate.

STIMULUS (L., goad, incentive): Any internal or external change which influences the activity of an organism or of part of an organism.

-STOME, -STOMA, -STOMATA (Gr. *stoma*, mouth): Suffix meaning "mouth"; for example, cytostome, "cell mouth."

STRIATED MUSCLE (L. from *striare*, to groove): Skeletal, voluntary muscle.

SUB-, SUS- (L., under, below): Prefix meaning "under" or "below"; for example, subepidermal, "underneath the epidermis."

SUBSTANCE: Any material composed of only one kind of molecule.

SUBSTRATE (L. *substratus*, strewn under): 1) The foundation to which an organism is attached. 2) A substance acted on by an enzyme.

SUCCESSION: In ecology, the slow, orderly progression of changes in species composition of a community during development of vegetation in any area.

SUCROSE: A common sugar; a disaccharide found in many plants.

SUGAR: Any monosaccharide or disaccharide.

SYM- (Gr. *syn*, together, with): Prefix, meaning "together," like "syn-."

SYMBIOSIS (Gr. *bioun*, to live): A close association between two or more organisms of different species in which each is benefited.

SYMPATHETIC NERVOUS SYSTEM: A subdivision of the autonomic nervous system; centers are located in the mid-portion of the spinal cord; slows digestion, has a general excitatory effect on other functions.

SYN- (Gr. *syn*, together): Prefix, meaning "together"; like "sym-."

SYNAPSE (Gr. *synapsis*, a union): The region of nerve impulse transfer between two neurons.

SYNAPSIS: The pairing of homologous chromosomes that occurs prior to the first meiotic division; crossing over occurs as a result of synapsis.

SYNTHESIS: The formation of a more complex substance from simpler ones.

SYSTEMATICS: Scientific study of the kinds and diversity of organisms and of the relationships between them.

TAXIS (Gr. *taxis*, arrangement): A movement toward or away from a stimulus.

TAXONOMY (Gr. *nomos*, law): The science of the classification of organisms.

TEMPLATE: A pattern or mold guiding the formation of a negative (antitemplate) which then can serve as a mold for a duplicate of the original template; a term applied especially to DNA duplication, which is explained in terms of a template hypothesis.

TENTACLES (L. *tentare*, to touch): Long, flexible protrusions located about the mouth in many invertebrates; usually prehensile or tactile.

TERRITORY: An area or space occupied by an individual or a group, trespassers into which are attacked (and usually defeated). Common among vertebrates; may be the site of breeding, nesting, and food-gathering or any combination thereof.

TEST CROSS: A genetic mating of an organism with a parent or parent stock; mating between a homozygous recessive individual and a dominant phenotype in order to determine genetic constitution of the latter.

TESTIS pl. TESTES (L., witness): The male gamete-producing organ, which is also the source of male sex hormone.

TETRAD (Gr. *tetras*, four): In plants, a group of 4 spores formed by meiosis within a mother cell.

THALAMUS (Gr. *thalamos*, chamber): A part of the vertebrate forebrain just posterior to the cerebrum; an important intermediary between all other parts of the nervous system and the cerebrum.

THALLUS: A simple plant body without true roots, leaves, or stems.

THERMODYNAMICS (Gr. *therme*, heat + *dynamis*, power): The study of energy, using heat as the most convenient form of measurement of energy. The First Law of Thermodynamics states that in all processes, the total energy of the universe remains constant. The Second Law states that the entropy or degree of randomness tends to increase.

THEORY (Gr. *theorein*, to look at): A generalization which is based on observation and experiments which were conducted to test the validity of a hypothesis and found to support the hypothesis.

THORAX: In vertebrates, that portion of the trunk containing the heart and lungs; in insects, the three leg-bearing segments between head and abdomen.

THYROID GLAND: An endocrine gland of vertebrates, located in the neck region, that secretes an iodine-containing hormone (thyroxine) which increases the rate of oxidative processes (metabolic rate).

TISSUE (L. *texere*, to weave): A group of similar cells organized into a structural and functional unit.

TISSUE CULTURE: A technique for maintaining fragments of plant or animal tissue or somatic cells alive after removal from the organism.

TRACER ELEMENT: A radioactive isotope which can be followed in a particular substance by means of a counter.

TRACHEA (Gr. *trachys*, rough): An air-conducting tube, such as the windpipe of mammals and the breathing system of insects.

TRACHEOPHYTE (Gr. *phyte*, plant): A vascular plant; that is, one possessing xylem and phloem.

TRANSDUCTION: The transfer of genetic information from one bacterium to another by a bacterial virus carrying bacterial DNA.

TRANSFER RNA (tRNA): Low molecular weight RNA that attaches to an amino acid and guides it to the correct position for protein synthesis; known also as soluble RNA (sRNA); there is one tRNA molecule for each amino acid.

TRANSFORMATION: A genetic change produced by the incorporation into a cell of DNA from another cell.

TRANSLOCATION: 1) In plants, the transport of dissolved foods. 2) In genetics, the interchange of chromosome segments between nonhomologous chromosomes.

TRANSPIRATION (L. *spirare*, to breathe): The evaporation of water from leaves or other exposed surfaces.

-TRICH, TRICHO- (Gr. *trichos*, hair): Suffix or prefix meaning "hair"; for example, heterotrich, "possessing different types of hairs."

TROCHOPHORE (Gr. *trochos*, wheel): The ciliated, free-swimming larva characteristic of some annelids and mollusks.

-TROPH, TROPHO- (Gr. *trophos*, feeder): Suffix or prefix meaning "feeder," "feeding"; for example, autotrophic, "self-nourishing."

TROPIC (Gr. *trope*, a turning): Pertaining to behavior or action brought about by specific stimuli, for example, phototropic (light-oriented) motion, gonadotropic (stimulating the gonads) hormone.

TROPISM: The involuntary response or movement of an organism, the direction of which is determined by the source of the stimulus.

TURGOR (L. *turgere*, to swell): The rigid distention of a plant cell by its fluid contents.

UREA (Gr. *ouron*, urine): An organic compound formed in the vertebrate liver from ammonia and carbon dioxide and excreted by the kidneys; the principal form of ammonia disposal in mammals and some other animal groups.

URETER (Gr. from *ourein*, to urinate): The tube carrying urine from the kidney to the cloaca (in reptiles and birds) or the bladder (in amphibians and mammals).

URETHRA: The tube carrying urine from the bladder to the exterior in mammals.

URINE: The liquid waste filtered from the blood by the kidney and excreted by the bladder.

UTERUS (L., womb): The muscular, expanded portion of the female reproductive tract modified for the storage of eggs or for housing and nourishing the developing embryo.

VACUOLE (L. *vacuus*, empty): A space within a cell, bounded by a membrane and filled with water and solid materials in solution.

VALENCE (L. *valere*, to have power): A measure of the bonding capacity of an atom; an atom may be monovalent, divalent, trivalent, etc., indicating the number of other atoms it may bond with; bonds may be electrovalent (formed through electron transfer) or covalent (formed through electron sharing).

VASCULAR: Containing or concerning vessels which conduct fluid.

VASCULAR BUNDLE: In plants, a group of longitudinal supporting and conducting tissues (xylem and phloem).

VASCULAR PLANTS: Plants having vascular systems.

VEGETAL HEMISPHERE (L. *vegetare*, to animate): That half of the egg or zygote that contains the most yolk; contrasts with animal hemisphere.

VEGETAL POLE: An imaginary point on the surface of the egg or zygote in the center of the vegetal hemisphere; lies opposite the animal pole.

VENTRAL (L. *venter*, belly): Pertaining to the undersurface of an animal that moves on all fours; to the front surface of an animal that holds its body erect.

VENTRICLE (L. *ventriculus*, the stomach): A chamber of the heart which receives blood from an atrium and pumps out blood from the heart.

VERTEBRA (L., joint): A segment of the spinal column.

VESICLE (L. *vesicula*, a little bladder): Any small sac.

VESSEL: A series of conducting cells or xylem elements whose function is to conduct water and minerals from the ground up the plant.

VIABILITY: Ability to live.

VIRUS (L., slimy liquid, poison): A submicroscopic, noncellular particle, composed of a nucleic acid core and a protein shell; parasitic; reproduces only within a host cell.

VISCERA: The collective term for the internal organs of an animal.

VITAMIN (L. *vita*, life): Any of a number of unrelated organic substances that cannot be synthesized by a particular organism and are essential in minute quantities for normal growth and function.

WILD-TYPE: In genetics, the phenotype which is characteristic of the vast majority of individuals of a species in a natural environment.

WORKER: An infertile female, as in bees or termites.

XANTHOPHYLL (Gr. *xanthos*, yellow): In a leaf, one of a group of yellow pigments; a member of the carotenoid group.

XYLEM (Gr. *xylon*, wood): A complex vascular tissue through which most of the water and minerals of a plant are conducted; consists of tracheids or vessel elements and other cell types; constitutes the main portion of wood.

YOLK: The stored food material in egg cells.

ZOOLOGY (Gr. from *zōē*, life + *logos*, a discourse): The study of animals.

ZOOPLANKTON: A collective term for the nonphotosynthetic animal organisms present in plankton.

ZYGO- (Gr. *zygon*, yolk, pair): Prefix, meaning "yolk" or "pair."

ZYGOTE (Gr. *zygotos*, paired together): The cell resulting from the fusion of male and female gametes, usually diploid (2*n*); in higher organisms, the fertilized egg.

INDEX

Page numbers in italics indicate references to illustrations or tables.

abscission layer, 236
Acetabularia, 58, 59, 65
Acetyl group, *104*
acetylcholine, 334
acetyl-Co A, 144, 145, 146, 147
Achillea, 674–675
acids, 111–115
acrasin, 467
acromegaly, 332
acrosome, 512, 513
ACTH (adrenocorticotropic hormone), *329*, *330*, 331, 339
actin, *81*, 82
Actinosphaerium, 248
active transport, 43, 55, 99, 141, 148, 149, 156
actomyosin, 123, 125, 148
adaptive radiation, 713, *714*
Addison's disease, 332
adenine, 132–136, 411, 417, 420–426
adenosine diphosphate (ADP), 134–135, 142–155
adenosine triphosphate (ATP), 134–*135*, 137, 142–156, 431
adrenal glands, *329*–332, 615, 650
adrenal hormones, 122, 136, *329*, 331, *332*
adrenaline, *329*, 332
adrenocorticotropic hormone (ACTH), *329*, *330*, 331, 339
afferent nerves, 336, 337
African sleeping sickness, 248, 723, 736
agar, 188
aggressions, controls over, *639–649*
Agnatha, 297, 298
agriculture, development of, 804, 809
albumen, egg, 129, *325*
alcohol, *142*, 143
aldosterone, 331, *332*
algae, *24*, 174–188, 195–197, 199 (see also specific types)
allantois, 527, *528*, *529*
alleles, 356–359, 363, 399, 677, 680, 681
allelomorphs, 358
alpha helix, *129*
alternation of generations, 182, *183*, *184*, 187, 198, 200, 201, 202, 204
amino group (NH₂), *104*, 113, 125, 129, 418
amino acids, 22, 123–129, 137, 228, 406, 407, 412, 418, 428–437
Amish, 677
ammonia, 21, 101, *103*, 314, 315, 782
amnion, 300, 527, *528*, *529*, 536
amniote egg, 299–300, *325*, 524, 589
Amoeba, 30, *31*–*32*, 33, 36, 57, 248, 250, 464–465, 479
  behavior in, 552, *553*
amoebocytes, 251, 310
amoeboid movement, *31*, 84, 197–198
Amoore, John, 602
amphibians, *294*, 299, 303, 306
  development in, *482*, 483, 484, 507–509, 519–524, 769
  sex determination in, *543*, 545
amphioxus, *291*–292, 296, 303, 516–519
analogy, *160*
Ancon ram, 672
anemia, sickle-cell, 375, 380, *406*, *407*, 437, 687
angiosperms, 200, 208, 212–218, 219
angler fish, 733
animals, classification of, 247–303
animalcules, 349, 352
animalculists, 351
anions, 315
annelids, 262–268, 277, *294*–296, 305, 310, 316, 756 (see also earthworm)
anteater, spiny, 725
ants, *20*, 571, *574*, 575, 583–584, 654–656, 725
anther, 213, 685
antheridium, 201, 202
anthocyanins, 236
Anthozoa, 258–259
Anthropoidea, 792–796, 808
antibiotics, 190–191, 695, 769
antibodies, 84, 376–379, 380
antidiuretic hormone, 320
apes, *786*, 793–797
aphids, *229*
apical dominance, 232, 244

apical meristem, *222*, 223
arachnids, 282–283
Arcella, 248
Archaeopteryx, *301*, 713
archegonium, 200, 201, 202, 209, 218
archenteron, *489*, 492, *517*
archeocytes, 251, 252, 276
arctic, 758, 760–762, 784
arctic tern, *720*
Aristotle, 1, 160–161, 285, 349, 350, 481
army ants, *654–656*
arthropods, 278–291, *294*, 302, 310, 570–588, 665, 764, 772 (see also specific organisms)
ascidians, 297, 303, *485–486*
Ascomycetes, *193*–194, 199
ascus, 191, 199
association neuron, 333, *560*
atomic number, 18, 94–95
atomic weight, 18, 106
atoms, structure of, 17–*18*, *19*, 94–98, 115
ATP (adenosine triphosphate), 134–*135*, 137, 142–156, 431
atrioventrical node, 313
atrium, of heart, 268, *269*, 271, 310, 311, *312*, *313*, 341
Aurelia, 256, *257*
Australia, 691–*692*, 713–*714*, *736*, 737, 740, *770*
australopithecines, 799, 800, 801, 808
autonomic nervous system, 337–338, 343
autopolyploids, 710, 716
autosomes, 381, 382, 396, 398
autotrophs, 23–24, 26, 29
auxins, 230–234, 244
Avery, O. T., 409, 411
Avogadro number, 106
axon, 86, 92, 99, 100, 334

baboons, 790, 793
bacillus, 170, *171*
backcross, 357, 709
bacteria, 49, 169–*172*, 173, 175, 176, 439, 666, 696, 734, 735

genetic studies in, 409, 413–417, 439–442, 457
bacterial resistance, 695–696
bacteriophages, *173*, 413–417, 431, 446, 459
Baerends, G. P., 622
Baikal, Lake, 771, 772
balance, *576*, 603–605
bark, 225
barnacles, 281, 742, *743*, 755
bases, 111–115, 116
Basidiomycetes, 191, 194–195, 199
Bates, H. W., 731
Bates, Marston, 769, 770
bats, 215, 578, *607–608*
Beadle, George, 402–406, 412, 438
Beagle, H. M. S., 1, 6, 7
bees, *215*, 288, 322, 394–395, *574–575*, 584–586, 588, 650–654, 747
beetles, *164–165*, 575, *729*, *730*, *731*, 742, 743, 773
Benzer, Seymour, 444–447, 450, 471
Bernard, Claude, 246
Berrill, N. J., 297
Berthold, A. A., 326
biennial plants, 235, 244
bilateral symmetry, 259, *260*, 277, 558, 569
bile, 309–310, 341
binomial system, 162–163, 167
biological clocks, 241–243, 340–341, 343, *609–610*
biomass, *780*, *781*
biomes, 750–774
biosphere, 150, 749, 750, 783
birds, *294*, 301, 303, 306, 311, 315, 319, 327–328, 340 (see also specific organisms) behavior, 610–612, 621–622, 626, 645–647
Biston betularia, 693, *694*, 716
bitterling, *646*
bivalents, 66–68
blastema, 507
blastocoel, *488*, 491, 492, *520*, 521
blastodisk, 524–527, 530
blastomere, 482
blastopore, 295, 491, 492, 516, *517*, 520, 521, 522, 527
blastula, 479, 487, 516, 519, *520*
blending inheritance, 352, 359
blood
  circulation of, 310–314, 341–342
  composition of, 84–85, 92, 314
  pH of, 113–115, 116, 506
blood pressure, 311
blood types, 375–*378*, 380, 684

blowfly, 579, *580*, 581
blue-green algae, *24*, 169, *174–176*, *268*
Bohr, Niels, 94, 95
bombardier beetle, *730*
bonds, chemical, 100–108, 115–116, 120, 134
bone, *79*, 80, *292*
Bonner, James, 239
Botticelli, 162
bowerbird, *611*
Boycott, Brian, 632, 633
brachiation, 793, *794*, 795, *797*, 808
brachydactylism, *370*, 374, 380
brain
  in invertebrates, 286, 565, *566*, *567*, 570, 591
  in vertebrates, 292, *532*, 591–596, 788, 805
brain hormone, 286–288, 302, 303
Bridges, Calvin, 392
Brien, P., 474
Briggs, R., 483
Brower, Jane, 731
Brown, J. L., 592–593
Bryophyta, 200, 201–202, 218
Buchner, Eduard, 10
budding, 232, 321, 478, 480
buffer systems, 113–115, 116
Buffon, George-Louis Leclerc de, 2
bulbs, *217*, 218
bullfinch, *628*
bumblebees (*Bombidae*), 651, 652
Burnett, A. L., 476
Butler, C. G., 653
butterflies, 279, 704, 728, 731, 732, 733, 737, 770
butterfly fish, *728*

cactus, *727*, *736*, *737*, 744, *769*
calcium (Ca), *79*, 95, 99, *228*, 235, 772, 782
calorimeter, 110
calling songs, 581, 588
cambium, 223–225
camera eye, *565*, 596
camouflage, 727–728, 748
campaniform cell, *576*, 577
cancer, 52, 374–375, 380, 508–509, 782
capillaries, *83*, 311, 341
carbohydrates, 117–120, 136
carbon (C), *18–20*, 94, 95, *104*–106, 116, *124*
carbon dating, 20

carbon dioxide, 21, 105
  in photosynthesis, 24, 29, 141, 153, 226, 243
  in respiration, 115, 140, *141*, *148*, 266, 304–307, 314, 341
carbon cycle, *779*, 784
carboxyl group, *104*, 112, 120, *121*, *125*, 129
cardiac muscle, 80, 82, *83*, 92, 312
caribou, 761, 762, 782
carotene, 122, *123*, 137, 151, 174
carotenoids, 30, 121, *123*, 136
carpel, 213
cartilage, *78*, 79, 123, *292*, 670
catalysts, 129–131
catastrophism, 4
caterpillars, 285, *286*, 287, 729
cecropia moth, *286–287*, 583, 707
cell division, 59–69
cell membrane, 38, 41, 46, 47, 49, 55, 169, 228
cell theory, 42, 352
cell wall, *39*, 40, 45–*46*, 60–61, 169, 228
cells, 15–155
  anatomy of, 43–54
  differentiation of, 502–503, 505, 506
  origin of, 15–26
cellular slime molds, 465–472, 479
cellulose, 45, *46*, 64, 120, 178, 180, 191, 197
centrioles, *54*, 55, 63
centromere, 60–*63*, 66–*67*, 69
Cephalochordata, 291–292
cephalopods, 269, 271–272, *273*, 277, 563, (see also specific organisms)
cerebellum, 591–592, *593*
cerebral cortex, 591, 594–596
cerebrum, 594–596
chaffinches, *625*
chaparral, 767
Chaplin, Charlie, 377
Chargaff, Erwin, 417, 420
Chase, Martha, 416
chelicerates, 282–283, *294*, 302
chemical bonds, 100–108, 115–116, 134, 421, 426
chemical equilibrium, 110–*111*, 116
chemical reactions, 106, 108–115, 116
chemoreceptors, 559, 578–581, 588, 600–603
chestnut blight, 190, 736, 764
chiasma, 387
chick
  behavior in, 617, 623–624, 627
  development in 503, *504*, *505*, 523–528, 537, 538, 539

chimpanzee, 656, 794, 795, 800
chitin, 279, 283, 570
chitons, 268–269
Chlamydomonas, 29, 36, 37, 38, 47, 49,
  51, 178–180, 321, 582, 709
chloragen cells, 264
chlorine (Cl), 95, 98, 99, 101, 102, 106,
  227, 228
chlorocruorin, 307
chlorophyll, 24, 29, 36, 50, 51, 55,
  132, 137, 151, 152, 153, 174, 178, 185,
  186, 228, 236
chlorophytes, 178–184, 198
chloroplasts, 29, 38, 39, 49–51, 55, 65,
  69, 140–141, 151, 155
choanocytes, 251, 252, 276
cholesterol, 122, 136
cholinesterase, 334
Chondrichthyes, 298
chondrocyte, 78, 79
chordamesoderm, 521, 523, 533
chordates, 278, 291–292, 296–303
chorioallantoic membrane, 527, 528
chorion, 527, 528, 529, 536
chromatids, 60–61, 62, 66–67, 68, 69
chromatin, 56–57, 62, 68, 69
chromosomes
  abnormalities in, 393, 396–397
  discovery of, 361, 379
  in *Drosophila*, 382–384, 386–396,
    398, 686–687
  giant, 391–392
  human, 366, 394–398, 399
  inversion in, 392, 686–687, 710–711
  mapping, 381–399
  in meiosis, 65–69, 361, 362, 387, 399
  in mitosis, 59–63, 69, 361, 362
  polyploidy in, 709–710
  sex, 381–384, 392–396
  translocations in, 710–711
Chrysophyta, 185
chymotrypsin, 131
cicadas, 707, 725, 726
cichlid fish, 647, 648
cilia, 33, 35, 36, 43–45, 54–55, 75–77, 90,
  91
ciliates, 34, 247, 249–250, 276
circadian rhythms, 240–244, 339–341,
  343
circulatory systems, 265–266, 280, 310–
  314, 341–342
cirrus, 34, 35, 36
cis-trans test, 447–448
cistron, 448, 450, 459
clams, 43, 268, 269–270, 277, 561, 756
Clarkia, 710, 711

cleavage, 487, 524, 531, 537
Cleopatra, 677
climax, ecological, 775, 776, 777, 784
cline, 704
cloaca, 309, 322
clone, 439, 470
club mosses, 204, 218
clutch size, 719, 720
cnidoblasts, 254, 255, 259, 474, 477
coacervates, 22
cocci, 170, 171
cochlea, 606
cocklebur, 238–239
cocoon, cecropia, 287
Cocos Island, 701
codons, 432, 433, 435, 436, 437, 438
coelenterates, 253–258, 276–277, 294,
  310, 557, 569
coelenteron, 253, 277, 473
coelom, 262–263, 264, 274, 277, 295, 302
  development of, 518, 521, 529, 530,
    535
coelomates, 294, 295
coenzymes, 135, 137, 142, 145, 146
cohesion-tension theory, 226, 243
colchicine, 709
coleoptile, 230, 231
colinearity, 456–459
collagen, 78, 123, 129
colloid, 47
color blindness, 384, 386
color vision, 574–575, 599, 600
columnar cells, 75, 77, 92, 502
companion cells, 73, 74
complementation, 450
conditional lethal mutations, 403, 444,
  452
conditioned reflex, 629, 637
conditioning, operant, 629, 630, 637
cones, of retina, 87, 89, 598, 599
cones, pine, 208, 209–210, 218–219
conidia, 194
conifers, 209–211, 219, 224
coniferous forests, 758, 762–763, 769,
  784
conjugation
  in bacteria, 440–443
  in protozoa, 250
  in *Spirogyra*, 182
connective tissue, 78–79, 92
consummatory act, 618, 620
continental shelf, 750, 755, 784
contractile vacuoles, 29, 42
corals, 65, 258
coral fish, 757
coral reef, 65, 756–757, 780

corn, 225, 231, 673, 678
cornea, 572
corpora allata, 286, 302
corpus luteum, 329
corpus striatum, 594
cortical granules, 490, 491
cortisol, 329, 330, 331, 332
cortisone, 331, 332
cotyledons, 210, 217
courtship behavior, 324, 707
covalent bonds, 101, 103, 116
cowbird, 623, 733
crabs, 279, 281, 282, 725, 755
crayfish, 280
Cretaceous period, 212, 300, 786, 787
cretinism, 330
Crick, Francis, 419, 420, 422, 424, 425,
  426
crickets, 645, 666
Cro-Magnon man, 804, 805, 809
crop-milk, 612, 613
crossovers, gene, 386–390, 398, 449, 450
crustaceans, 279, 280–282, 294, 302, 752,
  753
cuckoos, 622, 623, 637, 733
cuttlefish, 271, 272
Cuvier, Georges, 4, 589
cyclic photophosphorylation, 153
cyclostomes, 297–298
cypress swamps, 765, 766
cytochromes, 132, 147, 151, 155
cytoplasm, 31–32, 34, 46, 47, 52, 53, 57,
  69, 80, 87, 169
cytoplasmic determinants, 483–486,
  493–494
cytosine, 132–134, 417, 421, 422, 424
cytostome, 32, 33, 34, 554

daisy, 213
Daphnia, 281, 643, 773, 780
Dart, Raymond A., 799
Darwin, Charles, 1–9, 17, 352, 358, 368,
  668, 669, 671, 672, 691, 807
Darwin's finches, 6, 82, 83, 699–702, 703,
  705, 707, 716, 744–745
Darwin, Erasmus, 2
DDT, 696, 697, 782
deciduous forests, 665, 763–765
decomposers, 189, 198, 778, 779
dedifferentiation, 507–508
deer, 303, 648, 734, 762, 765, 767
Delbrück, Max, 413, 414
deluvianists, 4
dendrites, 86, 92, 100, 334, 500
Dentalium, 485

dentition, *789, 790, 798*, 800, 805, 808
deoxyribonucleic acid (DNA)
  evidence for genetic function, 408–410, 413–417
  in bacteria, 169, 408–409, 439–442
  in organelles, 65
  in protein biosynthesis, 426–438, 451–458
  in viruses, 172, 413–416, 443–454
  replication, 419–422, 424–425
  structure, 132–134, 137, 409–411, 417–424
dermis, 498–509
Descartes, René, 10
desert, 318, 769
desmids, *178*
desmosomes, 502
Dethier, Vincent, 579
deuterostomes, 295, 303
Devonian period, 205, 298, 299
De Vries, Hugo, 368, 379, 668
diabetes, 332, 806
diaphragm, 302
diatoms, 185, 751, *752, 753*
dicotyledons, 217–218, 219
Dictyosteleum discoideum, 465–472
differentiation, 466, 468–472, 475–477, 502–504
diffusion, 41
digestion, 282, 284, 308–310, 341
digestive tract, 263, 264, *265*, 269, 277, 281, 284, 308–310, 341
dinoflagellates, 185–186, 240–241, 751
dinosaurs, 300
diplococcus, 170, *171*
diploidy, 56, 65, 363, 399, 709
disaccharides, *119*–120, 136
distraction display, 727
disks, imaginal, 285
division plate, 64
DNA (see deoxyribonucleic acid)
Dobzhansky, T., 670, 705
dogs, 325, 615, 626, 642, 675
dominance
  genetic, 355, 356, 357, 358, 359, 368, 369–375
  social, 644–645, 660, 739, 748
dormancy, 235–238, 244
dorsal lip, 520–523, 537
Down's syndrome, *395, 396*, 397
dragonfly, *285*
Driesch, Hans, 482
Drosophila
  behavior of, 640, 708, 721
  chromosomes of, *381–384, 386–396, 398*, 686–688

population studies of, 676–677, 686–688, 689, 721
Dryopithecus, 795, 808
Dubois, Eugene, 800
ducks, 627, 649, 782
Dufour's gland, 584
Duve, Christian de, 54

ear, *604–607* (see also hearing)
Earth, 5–6, 16–17, 21, 26
earthworm, *263–267*, 277, 316, 322, 335, *559–561*
Easter lily, *710*
E. coli (see *Escherichia coli*)
ecdysone, 286, 302
Echidna, 725
echinoderms, 273–276, 277, *294* (see also specific organisms)
echolocation, *608*
ecological niche, 740–746, 748, 750
ecological succession, 774–777, 784
ecosystem, 750, 774, 778–783
ecotypes, 674–675
ectoderm, 259, 260, *261*, 517, 518, 521
  development of, 527–533
Edgar, Robert S., 452
effector, independent, 254–255, 333, 557
efferent nerves, 336–337
egg
  amniote, 299–300, 523–524
  cleavage of, *524*
  formation of, 65, 69, 77, 321, 513–514, 538–545
  of amphibian, 299, 322, 325, 482–484, 519–524
  of amphioxus, 516–519
  of ascidian, *485–486*
  of chick, 524–528
  of *Dentalium*, 485
  of human, 28, *463*
  of *Hydra*, 478–479
  of mouse, 513–515
  of sea urchin, 360, *488–491*
electrolytes, 98, *99, 100*, 115
electron transport chain, 147–148, 150, 151, 155
electrons, 28, 94–108, 115
electrophoresis, *406, 407*, 689
elements, 94, *95*
Eleodes longicollis, *729, 731*
embryo
  of amphibian, 483–484, 519–523, 539–545
  of amphioxus, 516–518
  of chick, 524–528, *538, 539*

of elk, *292*
of human, 378, *536, 541*, 544
of mouse, 513, *514*, 515–516, 528–532
of mule deer, *303*
of plant, 210, 216
Embryophyta, 200, 201–202, 218
endergonic reactions, 110, 116
endocrine system, 326–332, 342, 593, 610–613
endoderm, 259, 260, 261, 517, 518, 521, 527–531, 535–536
endoplasmic reticulum, 51–52, 53, 54, 55
endosperm, 216
energy, in biological systems, 15, 29, 51, 109, 110, 138–156, 778–781
engram, 631–634
entropy, 139, 140, 141, 155
environment, internal, 246–247, 315, 342
environmental resistance, 692, 722–739, 748
enzymes, 10, 52, 53, 54, 77, 129–132, 137, 141, 143–147, 400–406, 424, 431, 453, 454, 455, 456, 457, 458, 680
Eocene epoch, 790, 792, 793
epidermal cells, 71, 72, 91
epidermis, 474, *498–509*
epigenesis, 481
episomes, 441–443
epithelial cells, *75, 77*, 92
epitheliomuscular cells, 251, 256, 276
equation, chemical, 108, 109
equilibrium, chemical, 110–111, 116
Equisetum, 205
ergot, 190
erythrocytes, 42, 47, 84–85, 92
Escherichia coli, 171–172, 413, *414–417*, 425, 431, 439–459, 463, *464*
estrogen, *329, 330*, 331, *332*
estrus, 324–325, 515, 691
ethology, 550–551
eucaryotes, *167*, 169, 176
Euglena, 29–*31*, 36, 185, 250
euglenoids, *184–185*
Euplotes, *34–36*, 248
evolutionary theory
  and embryology, 516, 518
  and taxonomy, 166
  development of, 1–11
  new synthetic theory, 669–671, 690
excretion, 261–262, 266, 284, 314–317, 319, 320, 341–342
excretory system, *263, 266, 271, 281*, 284, 342
exergonic reactions, 110, 116

exoskeleton, 279, 302
extraembryonic membranes, 527–528
eye
  compound, 570, *572–575*, 587
  of mollusk, *91, 272, 562, 564, 565,* 633
  of vertebrate, 89–91, 532–533, 596–600
eyespots, *286, 728,* 748

F (fertility) factor, 441–443
FAD, 135, 137, 145, 146
fallopian tubes, 45, 322
fallout, radioactive, 782
fat cells, 80, 146
fats, 120, *121,* 146
feather stars, 276
fermentation, 143
ferns, 205, 208, 218
ferredoxin, 153
fertility (F) factor, 441–443
fertilization, 209, 273, 276, 281, 321–325,
  326, *491,* 514–515, 537 (see also
  mating pollination, reproduction)
fertilization cone, 491
fertilization membrane, *490,* 491
fetus, *292, 303,* 378 (see also embryo)
Feulgen, Robert, 411
Feulgen staining, 411
fibrinogen, 314
fibrocytes, 78
fiddleheads, 205, *206*
finches, Darwin's, *6,* 82–83, 699–702,
  703, 705, 707, 716, 744–745
fire ant, *583*
fireflies, 707, 733
fish, *294,* 297–298, *303,* 317, 318, 319,
  326, 601–602, *603–605,* 643, *728, 753,*
  754 (see also particular species)
fitness, biological, 670, 717, 721
flagellates, 29–*30,* 43–45, 54, 55, 247–
  248, 276, 512, 736, 783
flame cells, 261, *262*
flatworms, 43, 259–262, 277, *294,* 321
  (see also planarians)
flax mimics, *697–698,* 716
Fleming, Alexander, 190–191
flicker fusion, 573–574
flour beetle, 741–742
flowers, *212–214, 215,* 219, *353*
flukes, 262
food chain, 779, 781, 782
food supply, 723, 748
foot, primate, *791, 792, 793, 795,* **796,**
  797

Foraminifera, 248, *249,* 754
Ford, E. B., 733
forest, 758, 762–765, 769–771, 777, 784,
  790
fossils, 20, 176, 293, *301,* 785, 786, 808
founding populations, 677, 705
fovea, 598, 599, 600, 791
foxes, *683*
freemartins, 542
Frisch, Karl von, 574, 575, 578, 584–586
frog, 299, 311, *704,* 794
  behavior of, 592, 599, *708*
  development of, *483, 484,* 519–*524,*
    704
  sex determination in, 542–544
fructose, *118, 119,* 120, *130*
fruit, 212, 214, 216–217, 219
fruit flies (see *Drosophila*)
Fucus, 187
fungi, 189–195, 199, 234, 666, 755, 762

Galapagos Islands, *6,* 648, *699*–703, 713,
  716, 744–745
gall bladder, 309
Galston, Arthur, 233
gametes, 179–180, 182, 184, 187, 206,
  273, 321–322, 342, 352, 356, 399
  (see also egg, sperm cell)
  formation of, 65–69, 362–366, 478–
    479, 510–514, 537
gametophyte, *183, 184,* 198, 202, 206,
  209, 210, 216, 218
ganglia, 267, 277, *335, 561, 562,* 569, 570
Garrod, Sir Archibald, 400, 401
gastrodermis, 255, 276, 474, 475
gastropods, 270–*271,* 273, *562*
gastrula, 487, 488–489, *520*
gastrulation
  in amphioxus, 516–518
  in frog, 520–521
  in sea urchin, 488–489, 492–493
Gause, F. G., 740
Gause's principle, 740–746, 748
gemmules, 252, 473
Genera Plantarum, 163
gene pool, 669, 675, 712, 722
genes
  and enzymes, 400–408
  biochemistry of, 408–426
  chromosomal location of, 360–364,
    381–393, 399, 440–444, 451–453
  dominant, *354, 355, 356, 371, 373,* 380,
    680–681

in population, 369–374
  independent assortment of, 357–358,
    359
  Mendelian concept of, 355, 358, 359,
    399
  operator, 455, 456
  recessive, *371, 373,* 374, 380, 669, 675,
    677, 678, 679, 680, 681
  recombination within, 444–450, 458
  regulatory, 454, *456,* 459
genetic code, 134, 427, 428, 434–437, **438**
genetic drift, 677
genetic isolation, 698–704, 706–708, 716
genetic variation, 671–689, 712, 715
  716, 785
genotype, 356, 359, 679
geographic barriers, *703*
geology, 3–5
germ cells, 539–545, 671
germ layers, 517
giantism, 332
gibberellins, *234,* 244
gibbon, 793, *795*
gill slits, *291, 303, 535*
gills, 268–*269,* 270, 271, 274, 277, 278,
  281, 305, 341
glaciers, 756, 760, 772, 784
glands, endocrine, *329, 330,* 542, 545
  (see also specific glands)
glass sponges, *251,* 754
glomerulus, 316, 342
glow worm, *165*
glucagon, 309, 329
glucose, 24, 25, 29, 45, 46, 51, 109, *118,*
  119–120, *130,* 136, 140, *141, 142, 143,*
  144, 145, 146–150, 155, 170, 332
glyceraldehyde, *118,* 119
glycerol, 120, *121*
glycogen, *119,* 120, 310
glycolysis, 142–145, 149, 153, 154, 155
Golgi, Camillo, 53
Golgi complex, 40, 46, 53–54, 55, 87,
  512
gonads, 322, 539–545
gonadotropic hormones, *330*
Gonium, 180
Gonyaulax, 186, 240–242, 244
goose, 627, 639, 640
gorilla, 642, *789,* 793, 795–797, **799**
Graaf, Regnier de, 351
gram atoms, 106
gram molecule, 106
grana, *39,* 51, 152, 153
Grand Canyon, 703
grasshopper, 279, 283–285, 302, 362,
  363, 578

grasslands, 768
gray crescent, *483*, 484
Great Barrier Reef, 756
Griffin, Donald, *608*
Griffith, Frederick, 408, 409
growth, in plants, 74, 75, 220–225, 229–235, 243–244
growth hormone, *329*, 331, 332
Gruneberg, Hans, 670
guanine, 132–134, *417*, 421, 422, 424
Gulf Stream, 751, 756
guppy, 641, 642
gymnosperms, 208–211, 219
gyplure, 582

habitats, 750
habituation, 552, 553, 624
Haeckel, E. H., 516
hagfish, 297, *298*, 734
hair, growth of, 499–501, 509
Halicystis, 184
Hammer, K. C., 239
hand, primate, *788*, 789, *790*, 792, *794*, 797, 799
hand ax, 801
Hapsburg lip, 347, *348*
Hardy, G. H., 370
Hardy-Weinberg Law, 369–374, 380, 679, 690
Harlow, Harry E., 656, *657*, 658, *659*, 660
Hastings, J. Woodland, 240
hearing, 577–578, 603–608
heart, 80, 82, *83*, 92, *265*, 266, 268, *269*, *270*, 271, 280, 310–314, 341–342
heartbeat, 312–314, 341
heat energy, 21, 110, 779
height distribution, *682*
Heisenberg Uncertainty Principle, 96
helium, *18*
helix
    DNA, 420, *421–426*
    protein, *128*, 129
Helmont, Jean-Baptiste van, 349
hemocyanin, 307
hemoglobin, 53, 85, 92, 132, 137, 307, 406–408, 412
    sickle-cell anemia, 375, *406*, 407, 412, 437, 545, 680
hemophilia, *385*, 386, 688
Henle, loop of, 317, 319–320, 342
hens, 617, 644–645
herbals, *161*
d'Herelle, Felix, 413, 414

hermaphrodites, *543*
hermit crabs, 725
herring gulls, 621–*622*, 637, 649
Hershey, Alfred D., 416
heterosis, 678, 709
heterotroph, 23, 26, 75, 245
heterozygotes, 356, 369–378, 680, 681, 687–689
Hertwig, Oscar, 360
His, bundle of, 313
Hodgson, Edward, 581
Homer, 349
homeostasis, 315, 342
hominoids, 790, 793
Homo erectus, 800–802, 809
Homo habilis, 800
Homo neanderthalensis, 802–803, 806, 809
Homo sapiens, 165, *786*, 802–809
homologues, *66–67*, 68, 363
homology, *160*
homozygotes, 356–359, 679, 681
homunculus, *351*, 481
honeybees, 215, 322, 584–586, 588, 652–654, 747
Hooke, Robert, 42, 46
hormones (see also specific hormones)
    insect, 285–288
    plant, 229–235, 244
    vertebrate, 77, 303, 326, 328, *332*, 501, 610–613
horseshoe crab, 282–283
horsetails, 205, 218
housefly, *579*
Howard, Eliot, 645
Howells, William, 790
Hudson Bay Company, 746
Hubby, J. L., 689
Huffaker, C. B., 725
humus, 189, 198, 666, 763
Hunsperger, R. W., 592
Hutchinson, G. E., 746
Hutton, James, 3
hybrid vigor, *678*
hybrids, 357, 678, 709
Hyden, Holger, (RNA), 635
hydra, *254, 256*, 277, 295, 321
    behavior of, 557–558, 569
    development of, 473–480
hydrocarbons, 104
hydrochloric acid, 109, 112, 149, 308
hydrogen, *17–18*, 21, *94*, *95*, 103, 105, 107
hydrogen bomb, 18
hydrogen bond, 105–*107*, *128*, 420, *421*, *423*, 424, 426
hyrolysis, 119, 120, *130*, 134, 136

hydrophobic interaction, 105, 107, 108, 116, 120–121
hydroxyl group, *104*, 112, 418
Hydrozoa, 254–256
hypothalamus, *329*, 332, 592–593

IAA (indoleacetic acid), *230*, 233, 235
iguanas, 648
imaginal disks, 285
imitation, learning by, 625–626
immunological reactions, 376–379, 380
imprinting, 626, *628*
inbreeding, 675, 677–679
independent assortment, 357–*358*, 359, 363–364
independent effectors, 254, 333, 557
indoleacetic acid (IAA), *230*, 233, 235
induction, 503–505, 509
infant mortality rate, 806
influenza virus, 173
injury feigning, 727
innate releasing mechanism (IRM), 620, 623, 624, 637
insects, 283–291, *294*
    and plants, 214, *215*, 216
    behavior of, 570–588
    metamorphosis in, 285–288, 302, 303
    social, *20*, 288–291, 650–656
insecticides, 288, 334, 696, 697, 716
insight learning, 626
instar, 285, 286, 302
instinct, 551, 614–624
insulin, 126, *127*, 329, 332
intestine, small, 77, 308, *309*, 341
inversions, chromosomal, *392*, 686, 687, 710
iodine, 330, 331
ions, 98, *99*, 101, *102*, 115, 315, 753
ionic bonds, 101, 115
IRM (innate releasing mechanism), 620, 623, 624, 637
irritability, 552–553
iron (Fe), 95, *132*, 147, 228, *331*
isogametes, 197, 198
isotopes, 17, 18

Jacob, François, 432, 440–442, 455
Janssens, F. A., 387
Java man, 801
jellyfish, *256–258*, 277
jewel fish, *628*, 641
Jurassic period, 300, 786
juvenile hormone, 303

Kaibab plateau, 734
kangaroo, 302
kangaroo rat, 318
karyotype, *394, 395, 397*
katydid, *582*
kelps, 186
Kenyapithecus, 798
keratin, 123, 499, 500, 502, 503, 504
Kettlewell, H. B. D., *694*
Khorana, H. G., 436, 438
kidney, 316–317, 342, *535, 536*
kinins, 234–235, 244
kinetic energy, 138, 139, 148, 155, 156
King, T. J., 483
kiwi, *705*
Kornberg, Arthur, 424
Krakatoa Island, 175
Krebs, Sir Hans, 144
Krebs cycle, 144–147, 155

LSD, 190
labyrinth organ, 604, 605
Lack, David, 719, 720
lactic acid, *143*, 144
ladder of life, 1, 2
lakes, 772–774, *775, 776*
Lake Baikal, 771, 772
Lamarck, Jean Baptiste, 4–5, 352, 749
Laminaria, 187, 188
lamprey, 297, 298
Landsteiner, Karl, 375
larvae
    amphibian, 54, 299
    ascidian, *297*
    insect, 285, *286*, 302, 737, 744
    planula, 293–295, 303, 479
    pluteus, 487, *489*, 492–493
    trochophore, *295, 296*, 303
Lashley, Karl, 631, 632, 633
lateral-line system, 603, 604, 606
Le Gros Clark, W.E., 791
lead (Pb), 19
leaf, *71*, 91, 223, 225–226
Leakey, Louis, 728, 795, 798, 799
Leakey, Mary, 795, 799
learning, 549, 551, 552, 556, 557, 624–
    631, 637
Lederberg, Esther, 695, *696*
Lederberg, Joshua, 440, 443, 695, *696*
Leeuwenhoek, Anthony van, 27, 37,
    349, 351, 352
leguminous plants, 172
Lehrman, Daniel, 612
lemurs, *786, 790, 791*, 808

leucoplast, 51, 71
Levene, P. A., 411
Lewis, G. E., 798
Lewis, Harlan, 710
Lewontin, Richard, 689
lichens, *195–197*, 199, 665, 693, **782**
light
    in microscopy, 28
    in photoorientation, 30, *31*, 121, 181,
        230, *231*, 244, *468*, *550*, *574*, *575*
    in photoperiodism, 238–240, 244
    in photosynthesis, 24, 25, 51, *72*, *141*,
        150, 153, 154
    ultraviolet, 22, 25, 26, 64, 369, 471
lilac (*Syringa vulgaris*), 222
Linnaeus, Carolus, 2, 162–163, *164*
lipids, 46, 117, *120–122*, 136
liver, 309–310, 315, 341
liverworts, 201–202, 218
lizards, *300, 327, 725, 726*
lobster, 279, 280–282, 302
Loeb, Jacques, 549, 551
loop of Henle, 317, 319–*320*, 342
Lorenz, Konrad, *550*, 620, 627, 637,
    639, 757
lovebird, *616*
Lucretius, 349
luminescence, 186, 242
lungs, 305–*307*, 341
lungfish, 298–299, 306, 713
Luria, Salvadore, 413, 414, 444
lutenizing hormone, *329*, 514
Lycopsida, 204
Lyell, Charles, 5–6
lymphatic system, 314
lymphocytes, 379
lynx, *747*
lysogenic viruses, 443–444
lysosomes, *40*, 54, 55
Lysenko, Trofim, 5

McConnell, James V., 559, 634, 635, 636
MacArthur, Robert H., 745
macroevolution, 712–715
macromolecules, informational, 117,
    123–135, 136
macronucleus, 34
magnesium (Mg), *95, 98*, 132, 228
Mairan, Jean Jacques de, 240
malaria, 250, 375, 688, 736
Malpighi, Marcello, 225
Malthus, Thomas, 7, 737
maltose, *119*, 120
mammals, 294, 301–302, 307, 308, 309,

311, 314, 318, 319, 324, 326, 327–328,
    341, 500, 590, 600, 786–788, 790, **808**
man, evolution of, 785–809
mandrill, 793, 794
Mangold, Hilde, 522
mantis, praying, 571, *572, 573, 576*
mantle cavity, 268–273, 562
maple tree, *164*
mapping
    chromosome, 381–399
    gene, 446–460
marijuana, 727
Mars, 16, 21, 26, 347
marsupials, 301, *302*, 713–714, 740, 787
mating, 261, 267, 322–325, 638–640, **641**,
    660 (see also fertilization)
Matthaei, Heinrich, 434, 435
Mayr, Ernst, 8
mealworms, 731
measles, 736
mechanoreceptors, 559, 575, 577, 587
medusa, 256–258, 277
megaspores, 204, 218
meiosis, 65–69, 321, 342, 363–367, 379,
    380, 382, 405, 514, 706
melanocytes, 499, 500
membranelles, 34, 36
membranes
    auditory, *606*
    cell, 38, 41, 46, 47, 49, 55, 169, 228
    egg, 49, 491, 526, 528
    unit, 47, 48, 51, *122*
memory, theories of, 631–636
Mendel, Gregor, 353–359, 368, 370, 668,
    670, 689
Mendelian principles of inheritance,
    353–359, 363, 364, 368, 369, 370,
    379, 675
menstruation, *324*
Mercury, 16, 21
meristem, 74–75, 92, 220, 221, 222, 223,
    243
mescaline, 727
mesenchyme, 492, 507, 533
mesoderm, 259, 260, *261*, 517–518, 521,
    533–535
mesoglea, *253, 255*, 256, 277
Mesozoic era, 206, 771, 786, 808
messenger RNA (mRNA), 429, 431–438
metabolism, 117, 330
    inborn errors of, 400–401
metamorphosis, *285–288*, 299
micelles, 107, 108
micronucleus, 34
microspores, 204, 206
microvilli, 77

Miescher, Friedrich, 411
Miller, Stanley, 22
millipede, *335, 666*
mimicry, 731–733, 748
minerals, in plant nutrition, 227, 228, 243
Miocene epoch, 798, 808
Mirsky, Alfred, 417
mites, 282, 725
mitochondria, *38, 40,* 47, 49, 55, 65, 69, 82, *83,* 85, 140, *141, 148,* 149, *150,* 512
mitosis, 59–65, 69, 74–75, 342, 362–363, 671
mobbing behavior, 626
mole, forest, *667*
mole (unit of measurement), 106
molecular bonds, 100–108
molecular weight, 106
molecules, 100, *106,* 115, 117–137, 418
mollusks, 268–273, 290, *294,* 295, 310, 561–569 (see also specific organisms)
molting, 279, 302
monarch butterfly, 728, 732, 733
Monera, 166, 167, 169–176
mongoloidism (Down's syndrome), *395,* 396, *397*
monkeys, 642, *786,* 790, 792–793, 808 behavior in, 626, 656–661
monocotyledons, 217, 218, 219
Monod, Jacques, 432, 434, 455
monosaccharides, 117, *118, 119,* 136
monotremes, 725, 787
Montagna, William, 495
Moore, John, 704
morels, *193*
Morgan, Thomas Hunt, 382, 383, 386, 387, 392, 689
morphine, 727
morphogenesis, 466, 499–501
mortality rates, 721–*723,* 806
mosquitos, 250, *279*
mosses, 201–202, 218
moths, *287, 288,* 578, 582–*583,* 683, 693, *694,* 728, 737
motor nerves, 86, *88,* 336, *337,* 343
Mount Jacinto, 686
mouse, *513, 514,* 515–516, 528–532, 603, 715, 738, 739, *764*
mud flat, 756
mud puppy, 299
mule deer, *303,* 734, 762, 767
Muller, H. J., 369
Müller, F., 731
Mus musculus, 715, 738
muscle, *80*–84, 92, 145, 150
mushrooms, 191, 194–195, 199

muskrat, 738, 739
mussels, *646,* 756
mutagens, 369
mutation, *368,* 369, 379, 380, 385, 386, 401, 403, 404, 405, 439–442, 444–459, 672–673, 680, 715
myelin, 87, *89,* 92
myofibrils, 81, 82
myonemes, 249, 474, 475, 557
myosin, *81, 82*
myotomes, 292, 533, 535
myxomatosis, 735, 748
myxomycetes, 197–198, 199

NAD (nicotinamide adenine dinucleotide), 135, *136,* 137, 142–147
NADP, 135, 137, 151, 153
Nautilus, 271
Neanderthal man, *802*–803, 804, 806, 809
nectar, 214, *215*
nematocysts, *254*
nematodes, 666
Neolithic period, 684
Neopilina, 296
nephridia, 263–264, 266, *269,* 281, 316
nephron, 316–317, 319–320, 342
Nereis, 267, 268
nerve cells (see neurons)
nervous system,
  in arthropods, 570–588
  in lower vertebrates, 557–569
  in vertebrates, 86–91, 92, 332–340, 342–343, *521, 532,* 591–610
nesting behavior, 610, 611, 612
neural crest, *521, 532*
neural groove, *521,* 526–527, 530
neural plate, 517, *521, 523*
neural tube, *518, 521,* 532
neurons, 86–91, 99, 100, 256, 261, 266, 333–334, 336, 343, *560*
Neurospora crassa, 401–405, 412, 709
neutron, 18, 94
nicotinamide adenine dinucleotide, (NAD), 135, 136, 137, 142–147
Nirenberg, Marshall, 434–436, 438
nitrogen (N), 18, 21, 26, *95, 103,* 107, 172, *227, 228,* 243, 314, 425, 753
nitrogen bases, 132, *133,* 417, 421, 667
nitrogen cycle, *778*
Noah, 349
notochord, 291, 303, 517, 518, 521, 522, 527, *531*

nuclear envelope, 56, *57, 60,* 62, 64, 69
nucleic acids, 117, 132–134, 137, 172, 173, 635, 636 (see also deoxyribonucleic and ribonucleic acids)
nucleolus, 56, *57,* 69, 540, 541
nucleotides, 132, *133,* 137, 228, 411, *422,* 435, 436, 437
nucleus, atomic, 17–18, 94, 95, 115
nucleus, cell, 29, 56–69, 85, 116

ocelli, 256, 258, 259, 277, 558, 574
Ochoa, Severo, 435
octopus, 271–272, 273, *563–568,* 569, 632–634
oddity problem, 626
odor discrimination, 578, 601–603
Oligocene epoch, 793
oligochaetes, 263–267
Olympic rain forest, 759
ommatidium, 572, *573*
oocyte (see egg cell)
oogenesis, *367,* 513–514 (see also egg cell)
Oparin, A. I., 21
operant conditioning, 629, 630, 637
operon, 455
orangutans, 793, 795, 797
organ of Corti, 603, *606*
organelles, cellular, 30, 31, 47–54, 65, 69
organic compounds, definition, *104,* 105, 117–137
organizer (in embryology), 522–523
organogenesis, *531–537*
Origin of Species, 8, 166, 352, 668, 671
osmosis, *41–43,* 55, 226, 243, 315
Osteichthyes, 298
osteocytes, 79, 80
ostia, 280, 310
ostrich egg, 28
outbreeding, 677–679
ova, (see egg cells)
ovary, 212, 213, 322, *329,* 330, 366, 513, *543*
oviducts, 261, 322, 515, 612
ovists, 351, 352
ovulation, 324, 514
ovule, 206, 208, *209,* 212
owls, *666,* 746, *764*
oxidation-reduction, 25, 96–97, 98, 115, 148
oxidative phosphorylation, 146, 147, 148, 149

oxygen (O), 21, 24–26
  in chemical reactions, 97, *98*, *103*, *105*, *106*, *107*, 108
  in photosynthesis, 24–26, 150, 151
  in respiration, 24–26, 84–85, 142, 144–148, 304–307, 341
  structure of, *18*, *94*, *95*
oyster, 269, 273, 561, 756
oyster catcher, *649*

pacemaker, 312–313, 342
Pacific coast, 766–767
paedomorphosis, 295
Palade, George, 52
Paleocene epoch, 790, 808
Paleozoic era, 200, 206
palisade cells, *71*, 225
pancreas, 309, 329, 341
Pandorina, 180–181
paramecia, *32–34*, 37, 65, 246, 248, 315, 321, 553, *554*, *555*, *557*, 723–725, 740
paramylum, 184
parasites, 65, 262, 734–736, 748
parasympathetic nervous system, 337–339, 343
Parazoa, 251–253, 276
parenchyma cells, *71*, *72*, *74*, 91
parental care, 326, 589–590, 641–642, 657–658, *718–721*, 748
Pasteur, Louis, 143, 350
Patterson, Bryan, 799
Pauling, Linus, 406, 407, 412, 418, 420, 680, 689
Pavlov, Ivan, 629
pea plant, *353*, 354, 355, *356*, *357*, *358*
pecking orders, 644–645, 647, 660
Pekin man, 801
Pelecypoda, 270, 277
penicillin, 191, 695
pepsin, 308
peptide bond, *125*, 126
Peranema, 184–185
Permian epoch, 206, 212
petiole, 230
peyote, 727
pH, 113, *114*, 116, 667
phagocytes, 54, 376, 506
phagocytosis, 32, 45, 54, 55, 57, 84
pharynx, 260–261, 265, 292, 297, 303
phenotype, 356, 359
phenylketonuria (PKU), 400, *401*
pheromones, 288–291, 303, 582–584, 588, 653–654, 707, 708
phloem, 72, 73, 92, 202–203, 210, 222,

223, 224, 227, 229
phosphate, *104*, 228
phospholipids, 120–122, 136
phosphorous (P), *95*, 104, 228, 753
photoelectron transport, 150–155
photon, 90, 151, *154*
photoorientation, 30, 181, 230, 244, *550*, *574*, *575*, 584–586
photoperiodism, 238–240, 244
photoreceptors, 30, 36, 87–91, 178, *598*, *599* (see also eye)
photosynthesis, 23–26, 29, 51, 55, 65, 72, 91, 150–155, 170, 751
phycobilins, 174, 176
phycomycetes, 193
phytochrome, 240, 244
pigeons, 627–628, *629*
pill bug, 549, *550*, 666, *725*
pine cone, *208*, *209–210*
pine needle, *211*
pine seed, *209–210*
pine tree, 209–210, *674*
pinocytosis, 32, 55, 77
pin and thrum, *685*
pistil, 213
pith, 223, 224
Pithecanthropus erectus, 801, *802*
pituitary gland, *329*, *330*, 332, *593*, 610
pit vipers, 608
PKU (phenylketonuria), 400, *401*
placenta, 378, *529*, 530
placentals, 301, *303*, 530, 787
placoderms, *298*
planarians, 259–262, 316, 558–*559*, 569, 634–636, *637*
plankton, 742, 751, 752, 753, 772, 773, 782
plants, 177–244, 711–712 (see also specific types)
planula larvae, *257*, 293–295, 303, 479
plasma, blood, 84, 314
plasma membrane, (see cell membrane)
plasmodesmata, 73
Plasmodium, 250, 688
plastids, 51
platypus, 301, 786, 787
Platyhelminthes, 259–261, 262
pleiotropism, 670
Pleistocene epoch, 798, 801
Pleodorina, 181
Plutarch, 349
pluteus larva, 487, *489*, 492–493
Pluto, 16, 21
pneumococci, 170, 409
polar bodies, 321, *367*, *513*, *514*
polarity, *105*, 107, **181**, 467, 477

pollen, *208*, 209, 214–216, 219
pollen tube, *209*, 214–216, 685, 706
pollination, *208*, 209–210, 214, *215*, 216, 218–219, 685
polychaetes, 267–268
polydactylism, 677
polymorphism, *684–687*, 690, 720, 740
polyp, 253, 257, 258, 277, 756
polypeptide chains, 125–131, 137, 432, 435, 672
polyphemus moth, 288, *728*
polyploidy, 540, 709–*710*, 711, 716
polysaccharides, *119–120*, 136, 169
poly-U, 435
ponds, 772–774
population genetics, 369–374; 668–690
porphyrins, *132*, 137
porpoise, *326*
Portuguese man-of-war, 256
potassium (K), 20, *95*, 98, 99, 100, 228
potato blight, 190
Potentilla glandulosa, *675*
pox virus, 172, 414
praying mantis, 571, *572*, *573*, 576
predation, 723–734
preformation theory, 481
prenatal care, 325–326
prickly pear, 701, 727, 736, 737, 744
primates, 656–661, 785–809
primitive streak, 525, *526*, *527*, *529*, 530
primrose, 368, 379, 685
procambium, 223, 243
procaryotes, 167, 169–175, 176, 463–464
Proconsul, 795
progesterone, *329*, *330*, 332
prolactin, 612
proprioceptors, 568, *576*, 577, 587
prosimians, 790, 808
proteins
  and genes, 117, 400–408, 412, 453–454, 689
  biosynthesis of, 228, 427–438, 449
  structure of, 123–132, 137, 406–407, 412
protons, 17, *18*, *94*, 112, 116
protostomes, 295, 303
Protozoa, 42, 47, 54, 247–250, 276, *294*, 552–557, 750
Psilopsida, 203–204, 218
ptarmigan, 761–762
Pteropsida, 205–218, 219
Punnett, L. C., 356
Punnett squares, *356*, *357*, *358*, 370, *371*
pupa, 285, 287, 288, 302

purines, 132, *133*, 417, 422, 426
pyramids, ecological, 751, *753*, *780–782*
pyrenoid body, 29, 36, 51, 179
pyrimidines, 132, *133*, 417, 422, 426, 429
Pyrrophyta, 185–186
pyruvic acid, 141, 142, 143, 144, 146, 147, 149
pythons, *590*

queen substance, 288, 653
Queen Victoria, *385*

rII mutants, 440–450, 458
rabbits, *683*, 691, 692, 735, 746
rabies, 735
radioactive dating, 17–20, 26
radioactive fallout, 782
radula, *269*, *271*
ragweed, 238
rain forest, 759, 760, 769–771
rainfall, *758*, *759–760*, 769, 784
Ramapithecus, 798, 808
Rana pipiens, 321, 543, 544, *704*
Raphanobrassica, 710
rats, 615, 629, *630*, 692
rattlesnakes, *648*
Raven, Peter, 710
Rawles, Mary, 505
Ray, John, 159–162
recessiveness, genetic, 368–369, 375, 380, 675, 677, 678, 679, 680, 681
recombination, genetic, 440–450
red blood cells, 41, 47, 84–85, 92, 307
Redi, Francesco, 350
reduction (see oxidation-reduction)
reduction division (see meiosis)
reductive synthesis, 151
reductionism, 10
redwoods, 209, 766, *767*
reflex action, 335–336, 637
reflex arc, 336, *337*
reflex, conditioned, 629
regeneration, 281, 477, 480, 497, *506–508*
regulator genes, 455, *456*, 459
reinforcement, 629
reproduction,
  differential, 668, 679, 690
  in animals, 74, 261, 267, 273, 276, 321–326, 342, 347, 362, 589, 638–640, 711–712, 717
  in plants, 712

in single celled organisms, 175, 179–180, 250–251, 367, 464
  rates of, 691–692, 717–721
reptiles, 225, 294, 299–300, 303, 306, 311, 327, *788*
resistance, drug, 695–697
resistance, environmental, 692, 722–739
respiration
  cellular, 144–148
  external, 266, 277, 304–307, 340–341
respiratory pigments, 307
respiratory tract, 284–285, 305–307, 535–536
retina, *90*, 533, *598*, 599
retinene, 90, 122, *123*
retinoblastoma, 374, 375, 380, 680
Rh factor, 378
rhesus monkey, 656–661
Rhizobium, 172
rhizoids, 193, 203
rhizomes, 201, 218
Rhizopus, *192–193*
Rhodnius prolixus, 285–286
rhodophytes, 187–188
ribonucleic acid (RNA)
  and memory, 635–636, 637
  in protein biosynthesis, 427–438
  structure, 132, *133*, 134, 137, 429, *430*
ribose, *118*, 132, *133*
ribosomes, 52–53, 55, 169, 429, 431, 432, *433*, 434, 438
ribulose diphosphate, *149*, *150*, *152*, 153
ringdove, 612–613
RNA (see ribonucleic acid)
rockweed (*Fucus*), *186*, 187
rod cells, 87, 89, 90, 221, *598*, 599
Romer, Alfred, 589
root, 220–222, 226, 231, 232, 243
roquefort cheese, 190
Roux, Wilhelm, 482
royal jelly, 653
rust disease, *190*

sage grouse, *645*
saguaro cactus, *727*, 769
Saint Anthony's fire, 190
salamanders, *299*, 323, *326*, 482, 507–*508*, 522
Salmonella, 443
salt glands, 319
saltation, 668, 669
San Francisco Bay, 692, 703, 721
Sanger, Frederick, 126

saprophytes, 32, 172
sarcodines, 248
sarcomere, *81*, *82*, 148
sarcoplasmic reticulum, *81*, 82
Sargasso sea, 186
Scala Naturae, 1, 5
scale insects, 697
scallops, 89, *91*, *270*, 272, 277, 561, *562*, 756
Schneirla, T. C., 623, 654
Schwann cell, 87, *89*, 92, 122, 334
Schwann, Theodore, 42
scorpions, 282, *323*, 729
Scyphozoa, 256
sea, 750–757, 783
sea anemones, 258, 259, *270*, 725
sea lettuce, 182–*183*
sea lilies, 275
sea slug, *270*
sea squirt (see ascidian)
sea urchin, 275, 277, 360, *361*, 486–494
seashore, 755–756
seaweeds, *186–188*, 755
seed, 206–208, 209–*210*, 216–217, 218, 219, 237
Selaginella, 204, 206
seminiferous tubules, 322, *511*, *543*
sensilla, 575, *576*, 580, 581, 587
sensory nerves, 86, 255–256, 335, 336, *337*, 559–560 (see also special senses)
sepals, 213
sequoias, 766, *767*
sere, 774–777, 784
sex chromosomes, 381–384, 392–396, 398–399, 542, 543
sex determination, 381, *382*, 392–396, 398–399, 542–545
sex glands, 330, 342, 542–544
sex hormones, 122, 136, *329*, 331, 501, 544
sharks, 298, *753*
Shaw, George Bernard, 807
shoot tip, 222–223
shrimp, 281, 576
Siamese cats, 132
sickle-cell anemia, *375*, 380, *406*, *407*, 437, 545, 687
sieve cells, 73, 202, 211, 227–229, 244
silicon (Si), 73, *95*, 105, 185, 228
Simpson, George Gaylord, 785
skin, 495–509
Skinner, B. F., 549, 629
slime molds
  cellular, 198, 465–472, 479
  plasmodial, 197–198, *199*
slugs, *270*, 271, 562

smallpox, 736
smell receptors, 578, 579, 601–603
Smith, William, 3
snails, *268, 270–271, 277,* 562, 683, 684–685, 746, 756
snakes, 300, *602, 608, 648*
snapdragon, *368, 369*
sodium atom (Na), *95, 98, 99,* 100, 101, *102,* 106, 228
sodium chloride (NaCl), *99,* 101, 102, 106, 109, 113
sodium hydroxide (NaOH), 109, 112, 113
sodium stearate, 108
somatopleure, 518, 522, 527, *528*
somatotropin, *329,* 332
somites, 517, 522, *526, 527, 528, 530, 531,* 533, 535
song thrush, 684
Sörensen, Sören, 113
sound receptors, 577–578, 581 (see also ears, hearing)
spadefoot toad, 769
Spallanzani, Lazzaro, 607, 608
speciation, 698–715, 716, 746
species (definition of), 159, 160, 162–163
Species Plantarum, 162
Spemann, Hans, 483, 484, 522
sperm cells, 54, *351, 359,* 361, 362 formation of, 65, 68, 321, 362–363, *366, 382,* 511–513, 515
spermatheca, 108, 322, 323, 654, 670
spermatophore, 323
spermists, 351
sphagnum, 201
Sphinx moth, *215*
Sphenopsida, 205, 218
spiny anteater, *725*
spider monkey, *793*
spiders, 282–283, 302, 575, *586–587*
spinal cord, *88,* 292, 303, *336, 337*
spindle, *60–64, 66–67, 68,* 69
spiracles, *284,* 285
spirilli, 170, *171*
Spirogyra, 179, 182
splanchnopleure, 518, 522
sponges, *251–253,* 276, *294,* 321, 472–473, 480, 754
spontaneous generation, 349, 350
sporangia, 191, 199, 202, *205–207*
spores, *66–67,* 170, 175, 183, 191–192, 198, 199, *207,* 403
sporophyte, *183, 184,* 198, *199,* 202, 208, 209, 210, 218
Sporozoa, 250, 276

squamous cells, 75, 92, 502
squid, *268,* 271–272, 277
squirrels, 615, *703*
stamens, *212,* 213, 214
Stanley, Wendell, 430
staphylococcus, 170
starch, 71, 120
starfish, 273, *274–275,* 756
starlings, *719*
statocysts, 256, 258, 272, *294,* 562, 576, *588*
stem rust, *190*
Stentor, 249, 556, 557, 569
stereoscopic vision, 701, 793, 808
steroid hormones, 122, 136, 329–332
sticklebacks, 600, 617–620, 636–637, *639, 647,* 649, 707, 757
stigma, *212,* 213
stinkhorn fungus, *194*
stirrup, *605,* 606
stomata, *71, 72,* 92, 226, 243
stratum corneum, 499, 502
streptococcus, 170
stroboli, *204, 205*
strontium, 20, 782
Sturtevant, A. H., 388, 391
succession, ecological, 655, 774–777, 784
sucrose, *119, 130,* 229
sugars, 117–120, 132–134, 310, 332, 341
sulfur (S), 95, 228
sun, energy of, 15–17, 18, 26, *141,* 142, 154, 779
supernormal stimulus, *622*
Sutton, Walter S., *362,* 363, 364, 368, 379, 381, 398
Sussman, Maurice, 471–472
swift, *720*
swim bladder, 605
symbiosis, 65, 171–172, 196–197, 199, 756
sympathetic nervous system, 337–339, 343
synapse, 68, 86–87, *88,* 92, 261, 334, 337, 338, 343
Systema Naturae, 2, 163
Szent-Györgyi, Albert, 93, 138

taiga, 762
tapeworms, 262, *263,* 734
tarsier, *786,* 791, *792,* 808
taste, 578–581, *601,* 602
Tatum, Edward L., 402–406, 412, 438, 440

teeth, primate, *789–790, 798,* 800, 805, 808
temperature regulation, 327–328
template, 427, 428
termites, 288–291, 575–576, 720–721
territoriality, 645–648, 738, 748
Tertiary period, 790
testcross, *357*
testes, 322, *329, 330,* 366, 478, 511, *543*
testosterone, *329, 330, 332,* 544
tetanus, 144
thalamus, 592, *593*
thallophytes, 177–199
thallus, 177, 182
Theophrastus, 348
thermodynamics, laws of, 139–140, 155
thermonuclear reaction, 15
thrushes, *621, 637,* 684
thymine, 132, *133, 134,* 417, 421, 422, 424
thyroid gland, *329, 330*
thyroxine, *329–331*
ticks, 282, 617
tidal zone, 751
tiger beetle, *575*
tits, 621, *625–626*
Tinbergen, Niko, 550, 621, 622, 637
toads, 299, 544, *708, 730*
toadstools, 194, 199
tobacco mosaic virus (TMV), *173,* 430, *431,* 433
tongue, 308
tongue rolling, *374,* 380
tools, Stone Age, *804*
tortoises, Galapagos, 6, 702, *703*
touch, 559, 566, *567,* 568, 575–576
trachea, 75–77, 306
tracheids, 73, 210, 224
Tracheophyta, 200, 202–218
transduction, 443–444
transfer RNA, 429, 430–431, *433,* 436, 483
transforming factor, *408,* 409, 410
translocation, chromosomal, 227–229, 243, 397, 710, *711*
translocation, in plants, 227–229, 243
transpiration, 225–226, 243
tree shrew, 301, *786,* 790
trematodes, 262
Trembley, Abraham, 477
Tribolium, 741, 742
trilobites, 278, 293
triumph ceremony, 639, 640
trochophore, *295, 296,* 303
tropical rain forest, *770*
tryptophan synthetase, 457–458

tsetse fly, 248, 723, 736
tubifex worm, 305
tuna, 753
tundra, 758, 760–762, 784
tunicates, *186, 297,* 303, *485–486*
turgor pressure, 43, 72
twins, 366–367
tympanic organ, *577, 578*

ultraviolet light, 22, 25, 26, 64, 369, 471
Ulva, 179, 182, *183*
ungulates, 723, 787
uniformitarianism, 3
unit membrane, 47, *48,* 51, *121, 122*
uracil, 132–134, *429*
uranium (U), 18, 19, 97
urea, 315
ureter, 317, 535
urine, formation of, 319, *320*
uterus, 515

vaccinia virus, *173*
vacuoles
    contractile, *29, 30, 38,* 42
    digestive, *32, 33,* 34
    in plant cells, *39, 43,* 71
valence, 97–98, 115
van der Waals bond, 105, 108, 116
veins, 311, *312, 313,* 341
vena cava, 311, *313*
venereal disease, 736
Venus, 16, 21, 26, 347
vertebrates, *292–293, 294,* 303, 308, 311–
    312, 335–336, 341–343, 499, 589–613,
    788
Vesalius, 162
vessel elements, *73*
Victoria, Queen, 385
villi, 309

da Vinci, Leonardo, *162*
Viola, 712
Virchow, Rudolf, 42
viruses, *172–174,* 176, 735, 748
    in genetic studies, 413–417, 443–453
vision
    in arthropods, *572–575*
    in mollusks, *564, 565–566*
    in vertebrates, 599–600
vitalism, 10
vitamin A, 122, *123*
vitelline membrane, 491, 513
volvocines, 180–182
Volvox, 181–182, 293–294
vomeronasal organ, *602*

wak-wak tree, *349*
warblers, *745–746*
wasps, 578, *579*
water
    in biological systems, 21, 29, 200, 201,
        225–226, 243, 261, 274, 275, 277,
        309, 314–315, 317–320, 342
    properties of, *103, 105, 107,* 112, 226,
        342
water beetle, *773*
water bug, *774*
Watson, James D., 419–426
Watson-Crick DNA model, 419–426
Weinberg, G., 370
Weismann, August, 482, 538–541, 671
Weiss, Paul, 507
Wells, Martin, *564, 566–568,* 634
Went, Frits, 230
Wessels, N. K., 504
whales, 753
whelks, 271, 562
whisk fern, *203, 204*
white blood cell, 84, 92, 314, 376, 379,
    380, 506
Wigglesworth, Sir Vincent B., 285–286

Wilkins, Maurice, 420
Williams, Carroll, 287–288
Wilson, E. B., 384
Wilson, E. O., 582, 584
Witschi, Emil, 543, 544
Witt, Peter N., 587
Wöhler, Friedrich, 10, 315
Wollman, Elie, 440–442
wolves, 733
wood louse (pill bug), 549, *550,* 666, **725**
wound healing, *506*
Wright, Seth, 672

x-ray diffraction, 418, *419*
x-rays and mutation, 369, 379
xanthophyll, 174, 186
Xenopus, 540–544
xylem, 72, *73,* 92, *202–203,* 210, 222,
    223, 224

Yanofsky, Charles, 457
yarrow, 674
yeasts, 143, 144, 190
Yerkes, A. W., 656
yolk sac, 527, *528, 536*
Young, J. Z., *632–633*

Zamecnik, Paul, 430
Zea (corn), *673*
Zinder, Norton, 443
Zinjanthropus, 799
zona pellucida, *463, 513,* 514
Zoothamnium, 250
zygospore, *182, 192*
zygotes, *179, 182, 183, 184, 187,* 208,
    257, 321, 322, 362, 363, 367, 382, 393,
    394, 396, 399, 671